BUY YOUR ART
& ANTIQUES
FROM THE
<u>REAL</u> EXPERTS

LOOK FOR THIS SIGN

MEMBERS OF THE BRITISH
ANTIQUE DEALERS' ASSOCIATION

For a full list of members ring 020-7589 4128
or write to 20 Rutland Gate, London SW7 1BD
www.bada.org or info@bada.org

4

guide to the
ANTIQUE
SHOPS
of BRITAIN 2004

compiled by
Carol Adams

© Copyright 2003 Antique Collectors' Club Ltd.
World Copyright reserved ISBN 1 85149 433 2

British Library CIP Data.
A catalogue record for this book is available from the British Library.

While every reasonable care has been exercised in compilation of information contained in this Guide, neither the editors nor The Antique Collectors' Club Ltd., or any servants of the company accept any liability for loss, damage or expense incurred by reliance placed on the book or through omissions or incorrect entries howsoever incurred.

Origination by Antique Collectors' Club Ltd., England. Printed and bound in the Czech Republic.

U.K. OFFICE	U.S. OFFICE
Sandy Lane, Old Martlesham, Woodbridge, Suffolk, IP12 4SD.	Market Street Industrial Park, Wappingers' Falls, NY 12590.
Tel: 01394 389950 Fax: 01394 389999	Tel: (845) 297 0003 Fax: (845) 297 0068
Email: carol.adams@antique-acc.com	Email: info@antiquecc.com
Website: www.antique-acc.com	Website: www.antiquecc.com

FRONT COVER: (From left to right) Brass fire dogs c.1830; Oyster veneer side table c.1800; Globe on walnut frame stand 1827; One of a pair of walnut gothic chairs with original tapestry c.1840; Walnut turned leg stool, original tapestry c.1830; Painted terracota dog c.1850; Brass candle sticks with pushers c.1800; Gentlemans mahogany toilet mirror c.1800.

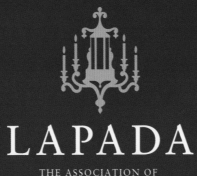

Thousands of collectors use our services to locate the objects they need to build their collections

Here are just 6 of them

Invaluable, providing collectors with
the world's most effective auction search services.

What can we find for you?

Call us on **0800 376 8590** to try our service completely **free**
and see why thousands of collectors already use us to locate
the objects they need to build their collections.

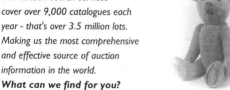

*Our auction search services
cover over 9,000 catalogues each
year - that's over 3.5 million lots.
Making us the most comprehensive
and effective source of auction
information in the world.*
What can we find for you?

Invaluable

Catherine House
76 Gloucester Place
London W1U 6HJ
International +44 1983 826000

www.**invaluable**.com

PROVIDING THE WORLD'S MOST EFFECTIVE SEARCH SERVICES

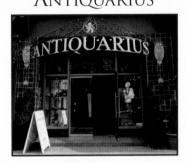

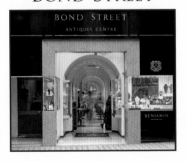

International Fine Art Packers & Shippers

Founded in London in 1933, Gander & White has established a reputation as one of the world's leading packers and shippers of antiques and works of art. A family owned business with staff of over 100, we pride ourselves on our skills at combining the traditional standards of service with the modern skills and expertise needed to meet the requirements of museums, dealers and individuals for the packing, shipping and storage of antiques and fine art.

London   –   21 Lillie Road, London SW6 1UE
Tel: (020) 7381 0571 Fax: (020) 7381 5428

Sussex   –   Newpound, Wisborough Green, Nr. Billingshurst
West Sussex, RH14 0AZ
Tel: (01403) 700044 Fax: (01403) 700814

Paris   –   2 Boulevard de la Liberation
93200 Saint Denis, Paris
Tel: 01 55 87 67 10 Fax: 01 48 09 15 48

New York   –   21-44 44th Road, Long Island City, New York 11101
Tel: (718) 784 8444 Fax: (718) 784 9337

Palm Beach   –   Units 30-31, 1300 North Florida Mango Road,
West Palm Beach, Florida 33409
Tel: (561) 687 5665 Fax: (561) 687 5383

THE ENGLISH Home

The international magazine of English style

Subscribe now! Save 25% plus ~ FREE BOOK worth £12.99

The English Home is the leading international magazine for everyone who loves beautiful homes. Each issue is packed with wonderful interiors to delight and inspire you ...

... Expert advice from top British designers ... Timeless ideas for an elegant English lifestyle ... Stylish interiors ... Luxurious furnishings ... Practical decorating solutions

YOURS FREE ~ When you subscribe

Collecting Antique Furniture worth £12.99

Published by the *Antique Collectors Club*, '**Antique Furniture**' is an inspirational book full of advice and ideas for every discerning home-owner. With **192 pages** and **over 200 illustrations** this beautiful book charts the history and development of furniture from medieval times up to the start of the 20th Century.

WORTH £12.99

	UK		Overseas	
❑ 6 issues (1 year)	£22.50 £16.75	OAL	£29.50 £24.50	OVS

❑ Free gift 'Collecting Antique Furniture' (Gift applies UK ony)

MY DETAILS

Mr/Mrs/Ms _____

Address _____

_____

_____ Postcode _____

Email _____ Telephone Number _____

PAYMENT DETAILS   In case we have a query about your order.

❑ I enclose my cheque for £ _____ payable to **The English Home**

OR   Issue no _____

❑ Charge my MasterCard/Visa/Switch (Switch only)

the sum of £ _____

Card Number _____ Expiry date _____

Signature _____ Date _____

By Post: The English Home, FREEPOST RG2509, Wokingham, Berkshire RG40 1BR (No stamp required if posting in the UK)
By Phone: 01858 438 889   ACC2
Online: www.subscription.co.uk/englishhome/ACC2

❑ Please tick if you do NOT wish to receive information about products which we feel may interest you.

PATRICK MOORHEAD ANTIQUES

THE SOUTH OF ENGLAND'S LARGEST
QUALITY ANTIQUE WAREHOUSE 30,000 SQ FT

50 Minutes mainline from London Victoria Station
2 minutes from Brighton Station
20 Minutes London Gatwick Airport
(collection service available)

Extensive stock of quality 18th,
19th & 20th Century English and
Continental Antiques

Open Monday to Friday
9.30 to 5.30 or by appointment

76 Church Street,
corner of Spring Gardens Brighton
BN1 1RL

Tel: 01273 779696
E.Mail:
patrick.moorhead@virgin.net

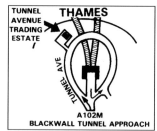

POT-LIDS
AND OTHER COLOURED PRINTED STAFFORDSHIRE WARES

REFERENCE AND PRICE GUIDE

K.V. Mortimer

Foreword by Geoffrey A. Godden

- *Profusely illustrated with over 500 colour illustrations*

- *Features all new photographs*

- *The most comprehensive and up-to-date reference and price guide available*

- *Extensive coverage of the variations which occur on lids and their values*

- *Coverage of all lids which have been reproduced and exist as late issues*

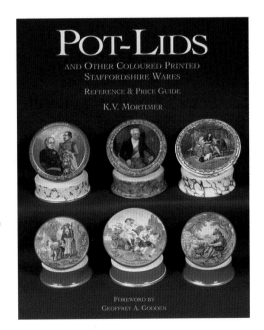

This comprehensive book is the most up-to-date volume on the subject – the existing literature is over twenty years old. Mistakes in identifying and recording lids have led to errors being perpetuated through successive publications. *Pot-Lids and other Coloured Printed Staffordshire Ware* corrects the errors and omissions which have occured in the past.

Contents include: Pot-lids and why they were produced; Dating pot-lids; Valuing lids; Pictures on lids; Prattware, and Jars.

This fascinating book also includes special features on the USA and other overseas lids.

Available from all good booksellers and direct from the publisher:
ANTIQUE COLLECTORS' CLUB
Sandy Lane, Old Martlesham, Woodbridge, Suffolk, IP12 4SD.
Tel: 01394 389950 Fax: 01394 389999
Email: sales@antique-acc.com
Website: www.antique-acc.com

11 x 8½in./279 x 216mm.
248pp.,
500+ col.
1 85149 438 3
£35.00

CONTENTS

INTRODUCTION

This is the 32nd edition of the **Guide to the Antique Shops of Britain** which is now universally accepted as *the* guide for anybody who wishes to buy antiques in Britain.

Nearly 6,000 establishments are listed in this latest edition and, as usual, every one has been confirmed before reprinting. We appreciate, however, that quantity without quality is meaningless and therefore the range of information we provide is more detailed and up-to-date than in any other publication. We state the obvious facts - name of proprietor, address, telephone number, opening hours and stock and also size of showroom and price range (where supplied). Additional information gives details of major trade association members, the date the business was established, the location and also the parking situation. Whilst none of these points are decisive in themselves, we feel they build up to a useful picture of the sort of establishment likely to be found and may well influence a prospective buyer's decision whether or not to visit a particular shop.

We start preparing the next edition in early 2004. Please let us know of any changes in your area - openings and closures. We do not print information about other dealers without first contacting them, but obviously the more shops in a particular town or village, the more attractive it is to prospective buyers on trips around the country. We would also be grateful for your comments on the Guide and, if you find any information given in the Guide to be incorrect, please let us know. We have occasionally had prospective customers telephoning to say that the stock listed is not what they found when visiting a particular establishment but then refuse to tell us the name of the shop - which means we can do nothing about the complaint. Constructive criticism is welcomed and we look forward to your comments.

ACKNOWLEDGEMENTS

Our main sources of information are still the trade magazines but we would like to thank those dealers who provide information about new shops and closures in their area. Without their assistance our job would be far more difficult.

We would also like to thank those dealers who supported us with advertising - without this revenue each copy would cost £30, instead of £14.95. Each year we include a form at the end of the Guide which dealers can use to up-date details about their own business. In anticipation of next year's Guide, we are grateful to those dealers who make use of this form.

Editorial **Carol Adams and Diana Dutson**
Advertising Sales **Jean Johnson and Alison Hart**

HOW TO USE THIS GUIDE

The Guide is set out under six main headings; London, Counties, Channel Islands, Northern Ireland, Scotland and Wales. Counties are listed alphabetically, within counties the towns are listed alphabetically and within towns the shops are listed, again alphabetically. London is divided into postal districts.

To make route planning easier there is a map at the beginning of each county, and a list showing the number of shops in any one town or village. The roads indicated on the map are only a broad intimation of the routes available and it is advisable to use an up-to-date map showing the latest improvements in the road system.

Apart from the six main headings above, there are further helpful lists - an alphabetical list of towns, showing the counties in which they will be found for those not familiar with the location of towns within counties, e.g. Woodbridge is shown in the county of Suffolk. One therefore turns to the Suffolk section to look up Woodbridge. This listing is a valuable aid to the overseas visitor. The second is particularly important to British dealers and collectors - giving an alphabetical list of the name of every shop, proprietor and company director known to be connected with a shop or gallery. Thus, if A. Bloggs and B. Brown own an antique shop called Castle Antiques, there will be entries under Bloggs, A., Brown, B., and Castle Antiques. Listings of specialist dealers, auctioneers, shippers and packers, services and fairs organisers are also included.

We strongly suggest making a prior telephone call to confirm opening hours before setting off on a long journey. In the main, dealers are factual and accurate in describing their stock to us but there are probably a few who list what they would like to stock rather than as it is! We would appreciate you letting us know of any such anomalies. Please telephone (01394) 389968 or drop us a postcard and help us to ensure that the Guide remains Britain's premier listing of antique shops and galleries.

ABBREVIATIONS IN ENTRIES

BADA:	British Antique Dealers Association
LAPADA:	The Association of Art and Antique Dealers
BABAADA:	Bath and Bradford on Avon Antique Dealers Association
EADA:	Essex Antique Dealers Association
HADA:	Highlands Antique Dealers Association
TADA:	Tetbury Antique Dealers Association
TVADA:	Thames Valley Antique Dealers Association
CADA:	Cotswold Antique Dealers Association
CL:	When the business is normally closed in addition to Sunday
SIZE:	Showroom size. Small - under 60 sq. metres; medium - between 60 and 150 sq. metres; large over 150 sq. metres
LOC:	Location of shop
SER:	Additional services which the dealer offers

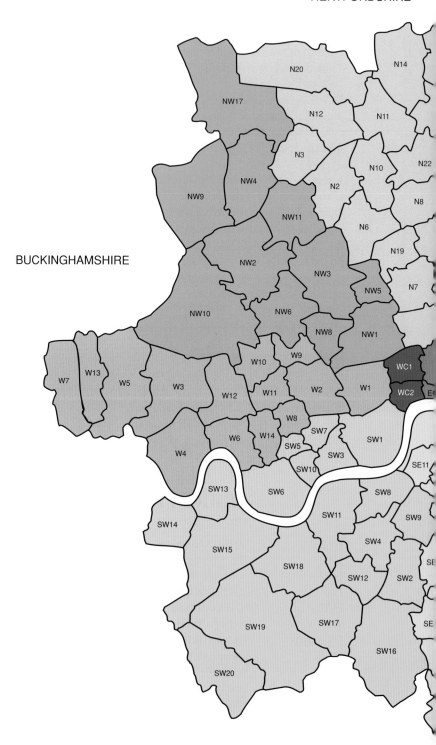

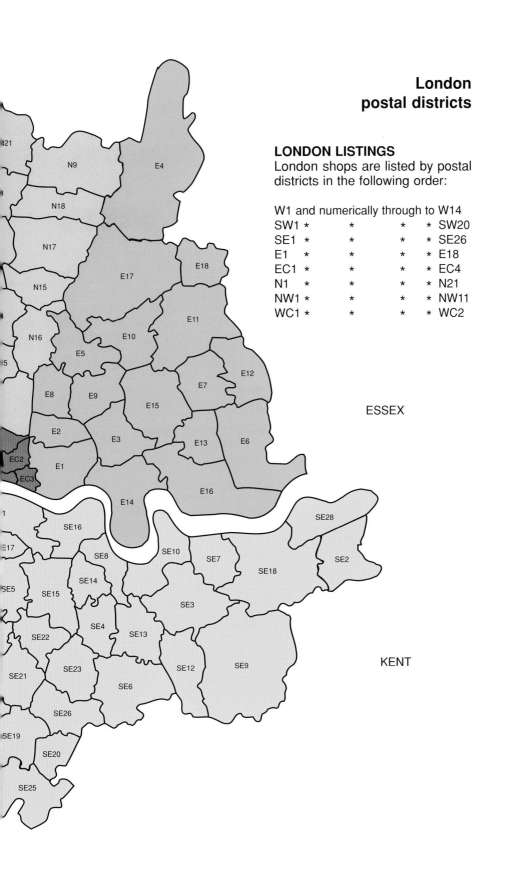

London
postal districts

LONDON LISTINGS
London shops are listed by postal
districts in the following order:

W1 and numerically through to W14
SW1 ★   ★   ★   ★ SW20
SE1 ★   ★   ★   ★ SE26
E1   ★   ★   ★   ★ E18
EC1 ★   ★   ★   ★ EC4
N1   ★   ★   ★   ★ N21
NW1 ★   ★   ★   ★ NW11
WC1 ★   ★   ★   ★ WC2

ESSEX

KENT

W1

David Aaron Ancient Arts & Rare Carpets `LAPADA`
22 Berkeley Sq., Mayfair. W1D 6EH. Est. 1910. Open 9-6, Sat. by appointment. SIZE: Large. *STOCK: Islamic and ancient art; antique carpets.* PARK: Easy. TEL: 020 7491 9588; fax - 020 7491 9522; e-mail - david_aaron@hotmail.com. SER: Valuations; restorations. VAT: Stan/Spec.

Aaron Gallery
125 Mount St. W1K 3NS. Est. 1910. Open 10-6, Sat. by appointment. *STOCK: Ancient art; Greek, Roman, Egyptian, Near Eastern and Islamic antiquities.* TEL: 020 7499 9434; fax - 020 7499 0072; website - www.aarongallery.com; e-mail - simon@aarongallery.com.

Agnew's `BADA`
43 Old Bond St. W1S 4BA. SLAD. Est. 1817. Open 9.30-5.30, Sat.11-4. SIZE: Large. *STOCK: Paintings, drawings, watercolours, engravings of all schools; contemporary art.* TEL: 020 7290 9250; fax - 020 7629 4359; e-mail - agnews@agnewsgallery.co.uk; website - www.agnewsgallery.co.uk. VAT: Spec.

Adrian Alan Ltd `BADA` `LAPADA`
66/67 South Audley St. W1K 2QX. Est. 1963. Open 10-6. CL: Sat. SIZE: Large. *STOCK: English and Continental furniture, especially fine 19th C; sculpture and works of art.* TEL: 020 7495 2324; fax - 020 7495 0204; e-mail - enquiries@adrianalan.com; website - www. adrianalan.com. SER: Restorations; transport, storage and shipping; insurance and finance. FAIRS: Palm Beach. VAT: Stan/Spec.

Altea Maps & Books
Third Floor, 91 Regent St. W1B 4EL. (Massimo De Martini). PBFA. ABA. ILAB. IMCOS. Est. 1993. Open Mon.-Fri. 10-6 or by appointment. SIZE: Medium. *STOCK: Antiquarian maps, 15th-19th C, £50-£5,000; travel books, atlases, 16th-19th C, £200-£20,000; globes, 17th-20th C, £200-£20,000.* LOC: 150 yards from Piccadilly Circus. PARK: NCP nearby. TEL: 020 7494 9060; fax - 020 7287 7938; e-mail - info@alteamaps.com; website - www.alteamaps.com. SER: Valuations; restorations (paper, cleaning, colouring and book binding); buys at auction (maps, books and globes). FAIRS: IMCOS (June); ABA Chelsea (Nov); ABA Olympia (June). VAT: Stan.

Ancient Art & Coins
at Fortnum & Mason, 4th floor, Piccadilly. W1A 1ER. Open 10-6. *STOCK: General antiques, artefacts and coins.* TEL: 020 7734 8040 ext. 2309.

Argyll Etkin Gallery
Ramillies Buildings, 1-9 Hills Place, Oxford Circus. W1R 1AG. (Argyll Etkin Ltd). Est. 1954. Open 9-5.30. CL: Sat. SIZE: Medium. *STOCK: Classic postage stamps, postal history and covers, Royal autographs, signed photographs, historical documents and antique letters, 1400-1950, £50-£25,000; stamp boxes and associated writing equipment, 1700-1930, £50-£500.* TEL: 020 7437 7800 (6 lines); fax - 020 7434 1060. SER: Valuations; collections purchased. FAIRS: Major stamp exhibitions worldwide. VAT: Stan.

Armour-Winston Ltd
43 Burlington Arcade. W1J 0QQ. Est. 1952. Open 9-5. Sat. 9.30-2. SIZE: Small. *STOCK: Jewellery, especially Victorian; gentlemen's cufflinks, classic watches.* LOC: Off Piccadilly. Between Green Park and Piccadilly underground stations. PARK: Savile Row. TEL: 020 7493 8937; website - www.armourwinston.co.uk. SER: Valuations; restorations. VAT: Stan/Spec.

Victor Arwas Gallery - Editions Graphiques Gallery Ltd
3 Clifford St. W1. (V. Arwas). Est. 1966. Open 10-6, Sat. 10-2. SIZE: Large. *STOCK: Art Nouveau and Art Deco, glass, ceramics, bronzes, sculpture, furniture, jewellery, silver, pewter, books and posters 1880-1940, £25-£50,000; paintings, watercolours and drawings, 1880 to date, £100-£20,000; original graphics, lithographs, etchings, woodcuts, 1890 to date, £5-£10,000.* LOC: Between New Bond St. and Savile Row. PARK: 50yds. TEL: 020 7734 3944; fax - 020 7437 1859. SER: Valuations; buys at auction. VAT: Stan/Spec.

J. & A. Beare Ltd `BADA`
30 Queen Anne St. W1G 8HX. (J. and A. Beare Ltd). Est. 1892. Open 10-12.30 and 1.30-5. *STOCK: Violins, violas, cellos and bows.* TEL: 020 7307 9666; fax - 020 7307 9651; e-mail - violins@beares.com; website - www.beares. com. SER: Valuations. VAT: Stan/Spec.

Paul Bennett `LAPADA`
48A George St. W1U 7DY. (M.J. Dubiner). Est. 1970. Open 10-6. CL: Sat. SIZE: Large. STOCK: Silver, 17th-20th C, £10-£10,000; Sheffield plate. PARK: Meters. TEL: 020 7935 1555/7486 8836; e-mail - paulbennett@ukgateway.net; website - www.paulbennett.ukgateway.net. FAIRS: Olympia; Claridges. VAT: Stan/Spec.

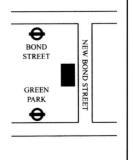

Bentley & Skinner Ltd BADA LAPADA
8 New Bond St. W1S 3SL. (Mark Evans). LAPADA. Open 10-5.30. *STOCK: Jewellery, Fabergé, objets d'art, silver.* PARK: Meters. TEL: 020 7629 0651. SER: Valuations; repairs; tiara and jewellery hire. VAT: Stan/Spec.

Daniel Bexfield Antiques BADA LAPADA
26 Burlington Arcade, Mayfair. W1J 0PU. CINOA. Open 9-6. SIZE: Large. *STOCK: Silver and objects of vertu, 17th-20th C, £200-£25,000.* PARK: Nearby. TEL: 020 7491 1720; fax - 020 7491 1730; e-mail - antiques@ bexfield.co.uk; website - www.bexfield.co.uk. SER: Valuations; restorations (repairs and repolishing silver, blue glass liners). FAIRS: BADA. VAT: Spec.

Peter Biddulph
34 St George St., Hanover Sq. W1R 0ND. Open 10-6. CL: Sat. *STOCK: Violins, violas, cellos and bows.* TEL: 020 7491 8621; fax - 020 7495 1428; website - www.peterbiddulph.co.uk.

H. Blairman and Sons Ltd. BADA
119 Mount St. W1K 3NL. (M.P., P.A. and W.Y. Levy and P.A. Hannen). Est. 1884. Open daily. CL: Sat. SIZE: Medium. *STOCK: English and Continental furniture and works of art, 1800-1900.* TEL: 020 7493 0444; fax - 020 7495 0766; e-mail - blairman@atlas.co.uk; website - www.blairman.co.uk. FAIRS: Grosvenor House; Fine Art & Antique Dealers, New York. VAT: Spec.

Blunderbuss Antiques
29 Thayer St. W1U 2QW. (C. and P. Greenaway). Open 9.30-4.30. *STOCK: Arms and armour, militaria.* TEL: 020 7486 2444; fax - 020 7935 1645; e-mail - mail@blunderbuss-antiques.co.uk; website - www.blunderbuss-antiques.co.uk.

Bond Street Antiques Centre
124 New Bond St. W1. (Atlantic Antiques Centres Ltd). Est. 1970. Open 10-5.30, Sat. 11-5.30. SIZE: Large - 27 dealers. *STOCK: Wide range of general antiques especially jewellery.* LOC: Bond St., Oxford St. or Green Park underground stations. TEL: Enquiries - 020 7351 5353; fax - 020 7969 1639; e-mail - antique@dial.pipex.com. Below are listed some of the dealers at this market.

Philip Cyrlin
Stand 17. *Watches.* TEL: 020 7629 0133.

Adele de Havilland
Stand 18. *Oriental porcelain, netsuke, jade.* TEL: 020 7499 7127.

David Duggan LAPADA
Stands 1A, 1B, 22. *Vintage watches.* TEL: 020 7491 1362; fax - 020 7408 1727.

Elisabeth's Antiques LAPADA
Stand 7. (Mrs. E. Hage)*Jewellery.* TEL: 020 7491 1723.

Matthew Foster
Stand 5. *Jewellery.* TEL: 020 7629 4977.

Saul Greenstein
Stand 13. *Jewellery.* TEL: Mobile - 07900 067548

Jan Havlik
Stand 21. *Jewellery.* TEL: Mobile - 07775 708198.

Kemal Ibrahim
Stand 34. *Watches.* TEL: Mobile - 07802 299001.

Janis Collection
Stand 1D. *Jewellery.* TEL: 020 7629 0277.

Katta
Stand 12. *Mosaic jewellery and silver.* TEL: 020 7493 1854.

Massada Antiques LAPADA
Stand 2. (Mr. and Mrs. Yacobi). Est. 1970. Open Mon.-Fri. 10-5.30. *Jewellery and silver.* TEL: 020 7493 4792.

Nonsuch Antiques LAPADA
Stand 3. (E. Michelson). *Jewellery and objects.* TEL: 020 7629 6783.

John Silverman
Stand 4. *Jewellery.* TEL: 020 7499 3256.

Sergio Tencati
Stand 16. *Jewellery and silver.* TEL: 020 7493 6272.

Trianon Antiques LAPADA
Stands 1C, 10/11. (Mrs. L. Horton). *Jewellery.* TEL: 020 7629 6678.

Mrs. Matsuko Yamamoto
Stands 14/15. *Jewellery and porcelain.* TEL: 020 7491 0983.

Bond Street Silver Galleries
111-112 New Bond St. W1Y 0BQ. Open 9-5.30. CL: Sat. PARK: Meters. TEL: 020 7493 6180; fax - 020 7495 3493. Below are listed the dealers at these galleries.

Barnes Jewellers
Fine jewellery. TEL: 020 7495 7554; fax - 020 7495 7556.

Brian Beet
Silver and works of art. TEL: 020 7437 4975; fax - 020 7495 8635.

A. and B. Bloomstein Ltd BADA
Silver, Sheffield plate. TEL: 020 7493 6180; fax - 020 7495 3493. SER: Valuations; restorations.

Bruford and Heming LAPADA
NAG. *Domestic silver especially flatware, jewellery.* TEL: 020 7499 7644/629 4289; fax - 020 7493 5879. SER: Valuations; restorations. VAT: Stan/Spec.

R. Close Jewellery Restoration
TEL: 020 7495 0287.

O. Frydman
Silver, Sheffield and Victorian plate. TEL: 020 7493 4895. VAT: Stan/Spec.

Michael Gardner Antiques
Jewellery and object d'arts. TEL: 020 7495 7592; mobile - 07831 863852.

Graus Antiques
Objets d'art, jewellery and silver. TEL: 020 7629 6680/6651; fax - 020 7629 3361.

R.S. & S. Necus
Silver and plate. TEL: 020 7499 0770; fax - same.

Rare Jewellery Collections Limited
(Elizabeth Powell). *Fine and collectable jewellery.* TEL: 020 7499 5414; fax - 020 7499 6906; mobile - 07771 788189; e-mail - info@rarejewel collections.com.

Damian Scott
Fine jewellery. TEL: 020 7495 4975; fax - same.

M. Sedler
Silver and plate. TEL: 020 7839 3131.

Selco Crystal Ltd.
Crystal and glass. TEL: 0870 230 7215; fax - 0870 330 1003; e-mail - info@selcocrystal.com.

Guy Steel
Fine jewels. TEL: 020 7495 7554/7594; fax - 020 7495 7556.

D. P. Stern Jewellery and Silver Restoration
TEL: 020 7629 6292; fax - 020 7355 1427.

E. Swonnell (Silverware) Ltd
Silver, Sheffield plate. TEL: 020 7629 9649; fax - same. VAT: Stan/Spec.

Zebrak - London
Fine jewels. TEL: 020 7495 7554/7594; fax - 020 7495 7556.

Brandt Oriental Art BADA
First Floor, 29 New Bond St. W1Y 9HD. (R. Brandt). Est. 1981. Open by appointment. *STOCK: Oriental works of art, £500-£10,000.* TEL: 020 7499 8835; mobile - 07774 989661. VAT: Spec.

Browse and Darby Ltd
19 Cork St. W1S 3LP. SLAD. Est. 1977. *STOCK: French and British paintings, drawings and sculpture, contemporary British artists, 19th-20th C.* TEL: 020 7734 7984; website - www.browseanddarby.co.uk. VAT: Spec.

John Bull (Antiques) Ltd JB Silverware LAPADA
139A New Bond St. W1S 2TN. Open 9-5. CL: Sat. *STOCK: Antique silver and reproduction giftware, photo frames, cutlery.* TEL: 020 7629 1251; fax - 020 7495 3001; e-mail - sales@jbsilverware.co.uk; websites - www. jbsilverware.co.uk; www.antique-silver.co.uk. SER: Valuations; repairs. FAIRS: Antiques For Everyone, NEC. VAT: Global/Margin.

Burlington Paintings Ltd `BADA`
10 and 12 Burlington Gardens. W1S 3EY. (A. Lloyd, M. Day, J. Lloyd and A. Hardy). Est. 1981. Open 9.30-5.30, Sat. 10-5. SIZE: Medium. *STOCK: British and European oil paintings, 19th-20th C, from £1,000.* LOC: Between Old Bond St. and Regent St., facing Savile Row. PARK: APCOA, Old Burlington St. TEL: 020 7734 9984; fax - 020 7494 3770; e-mail - pictures@burlington.co.uk; website - www.burlington.co.uk. SER: Valuations; restorations (lining, cleaning, reframing oils and watercolours); buys at auction (pictures). VAT: Stan/Spec.

C. & L. Burman `BADA`
5 Vigo St. W1S 3HF. (Charles Truman and Lucy Burniston). Open by appointment. *STOCK: 18th-19th works of art including silver, glass, furniture, ceramics and sculpture.* TEL: 020 7439 6604; fax - 020 7439 6605. SER: Valuations; restorations; buys at auction. FAIRS: New York Ceramics (Jan); Grosvenor House (June); Harrogate (Sept/Oct); Olympia (Nov). VAT: Spec.

The Button Queen Ltd.
19 Marylebone Lane. W1U 2NF. (I. and M. Frith). Est. 1953. Open 10-5, Thurs. and Fri. 10-6, Sat. 10-4. SIZE: Large. *STOCK: Antique, old and modern buttons.* LOC: Off Wigmore St. TEL: 020 7935 1505. VAT: Stan.

Carrington and Co. Ltd
170 Regent St. W1R 6BQ. Open 10-6. *STOCK: Regimental jewellery and silver, trophies, watches, clocks.* TEL: 020 7734 3727.

Paul Champkins `BADA`
41 Dover St. W1S 4NS. Est. 1995. Open by appointment. SIZE: Small. *STOCK: Chinese, Korean and Japanese art, £1,000-£100,000.* LOC: Off Piccadilly. TEL: 020 7495 4600; fax - 01235 751658. SER: Valuations; restorations. FAIRS: Grosvenor House; BADA (March). VAT: Spec.

Antoine Cheneviere Fine Arts `BADA`
27 Bruton St. W1J 6QN. Open 9.30-6. CL: Sat. *STOCK: 18th-19th C furniture and paintings, objets d'art from Russia, Italy, Austria, Sweden and Germany.* TEL: 020 7491 1007.

Andrew Clayton-Payne Ltd
2nd Floor, 14 Old Bond St. W1S 4PP. Open by appointment. SIZE: Small. *STOCK: British paintings and watercolours, 1700-1850, £2,000-£500,000.* PARK: Easy. TEL: 020 7493 6980; fax

- 020 7629 9151. SER: Valuations; buys at auction (pictures). VAT: Spec.

Sibyl Colefax & John Fowler
39 Brook St. W1K 4JE. Est. 1933. Open 9.30-5.30. CL: Sat. SIZE: Large. *STOCK: Decorative furniture, pictures, lamps and carpets, 18th-19th C.* PARK: Meters. TEL: 020 7493 2231/7355 4037; e-mail - antiques@sibylcolefax.com; website - www.colefaxantiques.com. FAIRS: Olympia (June). VAT: Spec.

P. and D. Colnaghi & Co Ltd `BADA`
15 Old Bond St. W1S 4AX. SLAD. Est. 1760. Open Mon.-Fri. 10-6. SIZE: Large. *STOCK: Old Master paintings and drawings, 14th-19th C.* TEL: 020 7491 7408; fax - 020 7491 8851; e-mail - contact@colnaghi.co.uk. SER: Experts and appraisers. FAIRS: Maastricht (TEFAF); IFAAD New York; Grosvenor House, London; Biennale, Paris; Biennale Haus Der Kunst, Munchen. VAT: Spec.

Connaught Brown plc
2 Albemarle St. W1X 3HF. (A. Brown). SLAD. Est. 1985. Open 10-6, Sat. 10-12.30. SIZE: Medium. *STOCK: Post Impressionist, Scandinavian and modern works, from £5,000+; contemporary, from £500+.* LOC: Off Piccadilly and parallel to Bond St. PARK: Berkeley Sq. TEL: 020 7408 0362. SER: Valuations; restorations (paintings, drawings, watercolours and sculpture). FAIRS: Olympia. VAT: Stan/Spec.

Sandra Cronan Ltd `BADA`
18 Burlington Arcade. W1J 0PN. Est. 1975. Open 10-5. *STOCK: Fine and unusual jewels, 18th to early 20th C, £500-£150,000.* TEL: 020 7491 4851; fax - 020 7493 2758. SER: Valuations; design commissions. FAIRS: Fine Art & Antiques; BADA (March): 20th Century, New York (Nov): Grosvenor House (June). VAT: Stan/Spec.

Barry Davies Oriental Art `BADA`
1 Davies St. W1K 3DB. Open 10-6. CL: Sat. *STOCK: Japanese works of art, netsuke, lacquer and bronzes.* TEL: 020 7408 0207; fax - 020 7493 3422; e-mail - bdoa@btinternet.com; website - www.barrydavies.com.

A. B. Davis Ltd
18 Brook St., (Corner of New Bond St). W1S 1BF. NAG. Est. 1920. Open 10-5. CL: Sat. *STOCK: Antique and secondhand jewellery, small silver items, objets d'art and gold coins.* TEL: 020 7629 1053; 020 7242 7357

(ansaphone).; fax and ansaphone - 020 7499 6454. SER: Valuations; repairs (jewellery and silver). VAT: Stan/Spec.

Richard Day Ltd

173 New Bond St. W1Y 9PB. Open 10-5. CL: Sat. *STOCK: Old Master drawings.* TEL: 020 7629 2991; fax - 020 7493 7569. VAT: Stan.

Dover Street Gallery

13 Dover St. W1S 4LN. (Edmondo di Robilant and Richard Nagy). SLAD. CINOA. Est. 1978. Open Mon.-Fri. 10-6 by appointment. SIZE: Large. *STOCK: Austrian and German Expressionists, including Gustav Klimt, Egon Schiele, 1910-30, from £20,000; Italian and French Old Master paintings, 15th-19th C.* LOC: Parallel to Albemarle St., opposite The Ritz. TEL: 020 7409 1540; fax - 020 7409 1565; e-mail - info@doverstreetgallery.com; website - www. artnet.com/dover.html. SER: Valuations; buys at auction. FAIRS: New York Fine Art; Maastricht (TEFAF); Milan; Florence; Rome. VAT: Spec.

Charles Ede Ltd `BADA`

20 Brook St. W1K 5DE. Est. 1970. Open 12.30-4.30 or by appointment. CL: Mon and Sat. *STOCK: Greek, Roman and Egyptian antiquities, £50-£50,000.* PARK: Meters. TEL: 020 7493 4944; fax - 020 7491 2548; e-mail - charlesede@attglobal.net; website - www. charlesede.com. SER: Valuations; buys at auction. VAT: Spec.

Andrew Edmunds

44 Lexington St. W1F 0LW. Open Mon.-Fri. 10-6 appointment advisable. SIZE: Small. *STOCK: 18th to early 19th C caricature and decorative prints and drawings.* TEL: 020 7437 8594; fax - 020 7439 2551; e-mail - prints@andrewedmunds. com. FAIRS: London Original Print; Grosvenor House. VAT: Stan/Spec.

Elwes and Hanham Ltd

14 Old Bond St. W1S 4PP. (Ben Elwes and William Hanham). Est. 1993. SIZE: Medium. *STOCK: Old Master and British paintings, 1500-1830.* LOC: 150 yards from Piccadilly. TEL: 020 7491 4966; fax - 020 7491 4976; e-mail - info@eandh.co.uk; website - www.eandh.co.uk. SER: Valuations. FAIRS: Olympia. VAT: Stan/Spec.

Emanouel Corporation (UK) Ltd

`LAPADA`

64 & 64a South Audley St. W1K 2QT. (E. Naghi). Est. 1974. Open 10-6, Sat. by appointment. *STOCK: Important antiques and*

fine works of art, 18th-19th C; Islamic works of art. TEL: 020 7493 4350/7499 0996; fax - 020 7629 3125; mobile - 07831 241899; e-mail - emanouelnaghi@aol.com; website - www. emanouel.net. VAT: Stan/Spec.

John Eskenazi Ltd `BADA`

15 Old Bond St. W1S 4AX. Open 9-6, Sat. by appointment. SIZE: Medium. *STOCK: Oriental art, rugs and textiles; Indian, Himalayan and South East Asian art.* PARK: Meters. TEL: 020 7409 3001; fax - 020 7629 2146; e-mail - john.eskenazi@john-eskenazi. com. FAIRS: Asian Art, New York (March); Asian Art, London (Nov). VAT: Spec.

Eskenazi Ltd `BADA`

10 Clifford St. W1S 2LJ. (J.E. Eskenazi, P.S. Constantinidi and D.M. Eskenazi). Est. 1960. Open 9.30-6, Sat. by appointment. SIZE: Large. *STOCK: Early Chinese ceramics; bronzes, sculpture, works of art; Japanese porcelain and screens.* TEL: 020 7493 5464; fax - 020 7499 3136; e-mail - gallery@eskenazi. co.uk; website - www.eskenazi.co.uk. VAT: Spec.

Essie Carpets

62 Piccadilly. W1V 9HL. (E. Sakhai). Est. 1766. Open 9.30-6.30, Sun. 10.30-6.30. CL: Sat. SIZE: Large. *STOCK: Persian and Oriental carpets and rugs.* LOC: Opposite St. James St. and Ritz Hotel. PARK: Easy. TEL: 020 7493 7766; mobile - 07710 120000. SER: Valuations; restorations; commissions undertaken; exchange. VAT: Stan/Spec.

The Fine Art Society plc

148 New Bond St. W1S 2JT. SLAD. Est. 1876. Open 9.30-5.30, Sat. 10-1. SIZE: Large. *STOCK: British fine and decorative arts, 19th-20th C.* LOC: Bond St. or Green Park underground stations. PARK: 300yds. TEL: 020 7629 5116/7491 9454; e-mail - art@faslondon.com; website - www.faslondon.com. SER: Buys at auction. FAIRS: London Original Print; New York. VAT: Stan/Spec.

Sam Fogg `BADA`

15d Clifford St. W1S 4JZ. ABA. Est. 1971. Open Mon.-Fri. 9.30-5.30 or by appointment. *STOCK: Manuscripts - Western medieval, Islamic and Oriental and works of art; Indian paintings.* LOC: Off New Bond St. PARK: NCP Burlington Gardens. TEL: 020 7534 2100; fax - 020 7534 2122; e-mail - info@ samfogg.com; website - www.samfogg.com. SER: Valuations; buys at auction. FAIRS:

Asian Art, New York; Biennale, Paris. VAT: Margin.

H. Fritz-Denneville Fine Arts Ltd
31 New Bond St. W1S 2RW. SLAD. *STOCK: Paintings, drawings and prints, especially German Romantics, Nazarenes and Expressionists.* TEL: 020 7629 2466; fax - 020 7408 0604. SER: Valuations; restorations; buys at auction.

Deborah Gage (Works of Art) Ltd
38 Old Bond St. W1S 4QW. Est. 1982. Open 9.30-5.30. CL: Sat. *STOCK: European decorative arts, British and European paintings, Renaissance to 1940, from £5,000.* TEL: 020 7493 3249; fax - 020 7495 1352; e-mail - art@deborahgage.com. SER: Valuations; cataloguing; buys at auction. VAT: Stan/Spec.

Thomas Goode and Co (London) Ltd
19 South Audley St. W1K 2BN. Est. 1827. Open 10-6. SIZE: Large. *STOCK: China, glass, silver, tableware, ornamental, lamps, mirrors and furniture.* TEL: 020 7499 2823; fax - 020 7629 4230. SER: Restorations. VAT: Spec.

The Graham Gallery
LAPADA
60 South Audley St., Mayfair. W1K 2QW. Est. 1973. Open 10.30-6. SIZE: Large. *STOCK: Library furniture, works of art, oil and sculptures.* PARK: Easy. TEL: 020 7495 3151. VAT: Stan.

Grays Antique Markets
58 Davies St. and 1-7 Davies Mews. W1K 5LP. Est. 1970. Open 10-6. CL: Sat. TEL: 020 7629 7034; fax - 020 7629 3279. SER: Engraving and jewellery repair. Below are listed the dealers at this market.

A & T
Stand G104. *Jewellery.* TEL: 020 7495 7068.

Abacus
Stand G313-315. *Jewellery.* TEL: 020 7629 9681.

Emmy Abe
Stand G131-132. *Jewellery.* TEL: 020 7629 1826,

Maria Alcazar
Stand G323. *Jewellery.* TEL: 020 7629 7034.

Anastasya Jewellery
Stand G141/142. *Jewellery.* TEL: Mobile - 07092 001355.

Anthea Antiques
LAPADA
Stand G154-5. (Anthea Geshua). *Jewellery.* TEL: 020 7493 7564.

Arca
Stand G351-353. (R. & E. Innocentini). *Objets d'art and miniatures.* TEL: 020 7629 2729.

Armoury of St. James
Stand MB16. *Militaria.* TEL: 020 7403 5082.

M. Artab
Stand MA22. *Islamic.* TEL: 020 7629 8033.

Artonotria
Stand MK32. *Small antiques.* TEL: 020 7493 0900.

Elias Assad
Stand MJ28-L13. *Islamic and antiquities.* TEL: 020 7499 4778.

Aurum Antiques
Stand G310-11. *Jewellery.* TEL: 020 7409 0215.

Automotormania
Stand MM13. *Toys.* TEL: 020 7495 5259.

Osman Aytac
Stand G331-2. *Watches and clocks.* TEL: 020 7629 7380.

B & T Engraving
Stand G109. TEL: 020 7408 1880.

Colin Baddiel
Stand MB25-C12. *Toys.* TEL: 020 7408 1239.

David Baker
Stand MM10/11. *Asian.* TEL: 07973 625 229.

Charlotte Barnes
Stand M FS003. *Ceramics.* TEL: 020 7629 7034.

Don Bayney
Stand MC22/23. *Militaria.* TEL: 020 7491 7200.

Linda Bee
Stand ML18-21. *Jewellery.* TEL: 020 7629 5921.

Barbara Berg
Stand G333/4. *Jewellery.* TEL: 020 7499 0560.

Beverley R
Stand G343/4. *Jewellery.* TEL: 020 7408 1129.

Biblion
Books. TEL: 020 7629 1374.

Bjs.Online.com
Stand G384. *Glass and perfume bottles.* TEL: 020 7495 6914.

Britannia
Stand G101/2. *Ceramics.* TEL: 020 7629 6772.

S. Brown
Stand MM12. *Jewellery.* TEL: 020 7491 4287.

Christopher Cavey
Stand G178. *Gems and minerals.* TEL: 020 7495 1743.

Cekay
Stand G172. *Small antiques.* TEL: 020 7629 7034.

Jocelyn Chatterton
Stand G126. *Asian.* TEL: 020 7629 1971.

Collection Antiques
Stand G329/30. *Jewellery.* TEL: 020 7493 2654.

Olivia Howard Collins
Stand G103. *Jewellery.* TEL: 01428 645 435.

Ann Corday
Stand MV001. *Vintage fashion.* TEL: 020 7629 7034.

Sharon Dale
Stand MV0014. *Jewellery.* TEL: 020 7629 7034.

Donnelly Antiques
Stand G124. *Objets d'art.* TEL: 020 7495 4898.

Douch & Nicolov
Stand G10/11. *Jewellery.* TEL: 020 7493 9413.

Sally Eade
Stand MD13/14. *Vintage and fashion.* TEL: 020 7409 0400.

Rosemary Erbrich
Stand GC26. *Small antiques.* TEL: 020 7629 7034.

Evonne Antiques
Stand G301. *Silver.* TEL: 020 7491 0143.

Finishing Touch
Stand G176. *Jewellery.* TEL: 020 7495 0592.

Forever Young
Stand G371. *Jewellery.* TEL: 07970 832026.

Gallery Diem
Stand G171. *Jewellery.* TEL: 020 7493 0224.

Peter Gaunt
Stand G120. *Silver.* TEL: 020 7629 1072.

Gilded Lily `LAPADA`
Stand G145/6. (Korin Harvey). *Jewellery.* TEL: 020 7499 6260.

Gordon Medals
Stand MG14/15. *Coins and medals.* TEL: 020 7436 0900.

R.G. Grahame
Stand G129/30. *Prints and paintings.* TEL: 020 7629 7034.

David Gray
Stand MC10/11. *Prints and paintings.* TEL: 020 7629 7034.

Solveig & Anita Gray `LAPADA`
Stand G307-309. *Asian.* TEL: 020 7408 1638.

Sarah Groombridge `LAPADA`
Stand G335-7. *Jewellery.* TEL: 020 7629 0225.

Guest & Gray
Stand MH25-28. *Asian.* TEL: 020 7408 1252.

Alice Guillesarian
Stand MK33. *Jewellery.* TEL: 020 7629 7034.

Linda Gumb
Stand G123. *Textiles.* TEL: 020 7629 2544.

Abdul Hadi
Stand MA12/13. *Islamic and antiquities.* TEL: 020 7629 2813.

Hallmark Antiques
Stand G319. *Jewellery.* TEL: 020 7629 8757.

Diane Harby
Stand G148. *Textiles.* TEL: 020 7629 5130.

Satoe Hatrell
Stand G156/166. *Jewellery and jet.* TEL: 020 7629 4296.

Lynn and Brian Holmes `LAPADA`
Stand G304-6. *Jewellery.* TEL: 020 7629 7327.

J.L.A.
Stand G364-6. (Alan Jacobs and Stephen Lack). *Jewellery.* TEL: 020 7499 1681.

Linda Jackson
Stand MFS004. *Jewellery.* TEL: 020 7629 7034.

Baba Jethwa
Stand G136. *Clocks and watches.* TEL: 020 7495 7327.

John Joseph `LAPADA`
Stand G345-7. *Jewellery.* TEL: 020 7629 1140.

Judson
Stand G321. *Jewellery.* TEL: 020 7499 4001.

JUS Watches
Stand G108. *Clocks and watches.* TEL: 020 7495 7404.

K & M Antiques
Stand G369/70. (Martin Harris). *Ceramics.* TEL: 020 7491 4310.

K. & Y. Oriental Antiques
Stand MK24/5. *Asian.* TEL: 020 7491 0264.

Minoo & Andre Kaae   LAPADA
Stand MG22/23. *Jewellery.* TEL: 020 7629 1200.

Kikuchi Trading Co Ltd   LAPADA
Stand G357-359. *Jewellery and watches.* TEL: 020 7629 6808.

Barbara Lankester
Stand G339-350. *Jewellery.* TEL: 020 7483 0123.

Lazarolia
Stand G325/326. *Objets d'art.* TEL: 020 7408 0154.

Lennox Gallery
Stand MK10-12. *Coins and medals, Islamic.* TEL: 020 7491 0091.

Licht & Morrison
Stand G158. *Jewellery.* TEL: 020 7493 7497.

Monty Lo
Stand G269/70. *Ceramics.* TEL: 020 7493 7457.

Michael Longmore
Stand G378/379. *Jewellery.* TEL: 020 7491 2764.

Maureen Lusted
Stand MB5. *Dolls and teddy bears.* TEL: 020 7629 7034.

Marko Pollo Antiques
Stand MC21. *Islamic.* TEL: 020 7629 3788.

Michael Marks
Stand G324. *Jewellery.* TEL: 020 7491 0332.

Alison Massey
Stand MB32. *Jewellery.* TEL: 020 7629 7034.

Mazar Antiques
Stand MA28/29. *Islamic.* TEL: 020 7491 3001.

Michael's Boxes
Stand ML14/15. *Objets d'art and miniatures.* TEL: 020 7629 5716.

Margaret Millard
Stand G322. *Glass and perfume bottles.* TEL: 020 7491 1718.

A. Atighi Moghadam
Stand ME14/15. *Islamic and antiquities.* TEL: 020 7629 7272.

Brian Moore
Stand MB25-C12. *Ceramics.* TEL: 020 7491 7208.

Stephen Naegel
Stand MB23. *Toys.* TEL: 020 7491 3066.

Morris Namdar
Stand MB18-C15. *Islamic and antiquities, Asian.* TEL: 020 7629 1183.

Neville & Carpenter
Stand G127. *Prints and paintings, objets d'art.* TEL: 020 7491 7623.

Glenda O'Connor
Stand MA18/19. *Dolls and teddy bears.* TEL: 020 88367 2441.

Pavlou Pavlos
Stand ML17. *Coins and medals.* TEL: 020 7629 9449.

The Pearl Gallery
Stand G328. *Jewellery.* TEL: 020 7409 2743.

Persepolis Gallery
Stand ME18-20. *Islamic.* TEL: 020 7629 7388.

Pieces of Time   BADA
Stand MM17-19. (Johnny Wachsman). *Watches and clocks.* TEL: 020 7629 3272.

Jack Podlewski
Stand 302. *Silver.* TEL: 020 7409 1468.

Lanca Poynder
Stand GB093/4. *Glass and perfume bottles.* TEL: 020 7491 7623.

Lucinda Prince
Stand MM9024. *Dolls and teddy bears.* TEL: 020 7629 7034.

Prushkin Antiques
Stand G312. *Jewellery.* TEL: 07900 000562.

Rasoul Gallery
Stand MK34/35. *Islamic and antiquities.* TEL: 020 7495 7422.

RBR Group
Stand G175. (Olivia Gerrish). *Jewellery.* TEL: 020 7629 4769.

Regal Watches
Stand G128-140. *Clocks and watches.* TEL: 020 7491 7722.

Ian Roper
Stand ML12/13. *Coins and medals.* TEL: 020 7491 0091.

Sabor Safi
Stand MC27. *Islamic, jewellery.* TEL: 020 7434 0575.

Samiramis   `LAPADA`
Stand MM14-16. (Hamid Ismail). *Islamic and antiquities.* TEL: 020 7629 1161.

Satrapel
Stand MM20/21. *Coins and medals.* TEL: Mobile - 07955 597075.

Charlotte Sayers
Stand G360/1. *Jewellery.* TEL: 020 7499 5478.

Second Time Around Ltd/Jadefare
Stand G316-318. *Clocks and watches.* TEL: 020 7499 7442.

Chris Seidler
Stand MG12/13. *Militaria.* TEL: 020 7629 2815.

Sarah Sellers
Stand MA25. *Dolls and teddy bears.* TEL: 020 7629 7034.

Shadad Antiques   `LAPADA`
Stand MA16/17. (Farah Hakemi). *Islamic and antiquities.* TEL: 020 7499 0572.

Shapiro & Co
Stand G380. *Jewellery.* TEL: 020 7491 2720.

Mousa Shavolian
Stand MB20. *Glass and perfume bottles.* TEL: 020 7499 8273.

Shiraz Antiques
Stand MH10/11. (R.P. Kiadah). *Islamic and antiquities.* TEL: 020 7495 0635.

Peter Sloane
Stand ME12/13. *Asian.* TEL: 020 7408 1043.

Solemani Gallery
Stand ME16/17. (Helen Zokee). *Islamic and antiquities.* TEL: 020 7491 2562.

Boris Sosna
Stand G374/5. *Jewellery.* TEL: 020 7629 2371.

Spectrum
Stand G372/3. (Sylvia Bedwell). *Jewellery.* TEL: 020 7629 3501.

Jane Stewart
Stand ML25-27. *Pewter, early 17th C-19th C, £50-£1,000; oak, £500-£1,000; writing slopes, 19th C, £80-£150; medieval.* TEL: 020 7355 3333. SER: Valuations; restorations (pewter, oak). VAT: Spec.

Sultani Antiques
Stand MK28-30. *Islamic and antiquities.* TEL: 020 7629 7034.

Tagore Ltd
Stand G302/3. (Ronald Falloon). *Gentlemen's gifts, drinking and smoking paraphernalia.* TEL: 020 7499 0158.

Timespec
Stand G366. *Watches and clocks.* TEL: 020 7499 9814.

Trianon Ltd.
Stand G378/9. *Objets d'art.* TEL: 020 7491 2764.

Trio
Stand ML24. (Teresa Clayton). *Glass and perfume bottles.* TEL: 020 7492 2736.

Michael Ventura-Pauly
Stand G354-357. *Jewellery.* TEL: 020 7495 6868.

June Victor
Stand MC10/11. *Vintage fashion.* TEL: 020 7723 6105.

Mary Wellard
Stand G165. *Small antiques.* TEL: 020 7629 7034.

Westleigh Antiques
Stand G341. (Pat Sneath). *Jewellery.* TEL: 020 7493 0123.

Westminster Group   `LAPADA`
Stand G138-150. (Paulette Bates and Richard Harrison). *Jewellery.* TEL: 020 7493 8672.

David Wheatley   `LAPADA`
Stand G106. *Asian.* TEL: 020 7629 1352.

Wheels of Steel
Stand MB10-12. (Jeff Williams). *Toys.* TEL: 020 7629 2813.

Margaret Williamson
Stand MD12. *Vintage fashion.* TEL: 020 7702 8180.

Wimpole Antiques   `LAPADA`
Stand G338-349. *Jewellery.* TEL: 020 7499 2889.

ZMS Antiques
Stand G125. *Silver.* TEL: 020 7491 1144.

Richard Green   `BADA`
147 New Bond St., 33 New Bond St. and 39 Dover St. W1S 2TS. SLAD. Open 9.30-6, Sat. by appointment. *STOCK: Paintings - Old Master and British; French impressionist and*

modern British; Victorian sporting and British marine. PARK: Meters. TEL: 020 7493 3939; fax - 020 7629 2609; e-mail - paintings@richard-green.com; website - www.richard-green.com. VAT: Stan/Spec.

Simon Griffin Antiques Ltd
3 Royal Arcade, 28 Old Bond St. W1. (S.J. Griffin). Est. 1979. Open 10-5, Sat. 10-5.30. *STOCK: Silver, old Sheffield plate.* TEL: 020 7491 7367; fax - same. VAT: Stan/Spec.

Hadji Baba Ancient Art
34a Davies St. W1K 4NE. (Hadji Soleimani). Est. 1939. Open 9.30-6, Sat. and Sun. by appointment. SIZE: Medium. *STOCK: Antiquities and Islamic art.* LOC: Mayfair, near Claridges. PARK: Meters. TEL: 020 7499 9363/9384; fax - 020 7493 5504. SER: Valuations.

Halcyon Days   `BADA`
14 Brook St. W1S 1BD. (Peter Norman). Est. 1950. Open 9.30-6. *STOCK: 18th to early 19th C enamels, fans, treen, papier mâché, tôle, objects of vertu, Georgian and Victorian scent bottles.* LOC: Hanover Sq. end of Brook St. PARK: Meters and Hanover Sq. TEL: 020 7629 8811; fax - 020 7409 0280; e-mail - info@halcyondays.co.uk; website - www.halcyondays.co.uk. VAT: Stan/Spec.

Robert Hall   `BADA`
15c Clifford St. W1X 1RF. Est. 1976. SIZE: Large. *STOCK: Chinese snuff bottles, Ching dynasty; Oriental works of art, 17th-19th C; all £300-£20,000; contemporary Chinese paintings.* LOC: Mayfair. PARK: Meters. TEL: 020 7734 4008; fax - 020 7734 4408; e-mail - roberthall@snuffbottle.com; website - www.snuffbottle.com. SER: Buys at auction. FAIRS: Maastricht (TEFAF); Asian Art, New York. VAT: Stan/Spec.

Hancocks and Co   `BADA`
52 & 53 Burlington Arcade. W1J 0HH. Est. 1849. Open 9.30-5.30. CL: Sat. SIZE: Medium. *STOCK: Fine estate jewellery and silver.* TEL: 020 7493 8904; fax - 020 7493 8905; e-mail - info@hancocks-london.com; website - www.hancocks-london.com. SER: Valuations; re-modelling. FAIRS: Grosvenor House; Miami Beach; Palm Beach; Maastricht (TEFAF); IFAAD. VAT: Stan/Spec.

Harcourt Antiques
5 Harcourt St. W1 1DS. (J. Christophe). Est. 1961. Open by appointment. SIZE: Medium. *STOCK: English, Continental and Oriental porcelain, pre-1830.* PARK: Easy. TEL: 020 7727 6936. VAT: Stan. *Trade Only.*

Brian Haughton Antiques
3B Burlington Gardens, Old Bond St. W1S 3EP. Est. 1965. Open 10-5.30. SIZE: Large. *STOCK: British and European ceramics, porcelain and pottery, 18th-19th C, £100-£50,000.* PARK: Nearby, Savile Row NCP. TEL: 020 7734 5491; fax - 020 7494 4604; e-mail - info@haughton.com; website - www.haughton.com. SER: Buys at auction (porcelain and pottery). FAIRS: Organiser - International Ceramics Fair & Seminar, Park Lane Hotel; IFAAD; International Fine Art and International Asian Art; International Art & Design; New York. VAT: Spec.

Gerard Hawthorn Ltd   `BADA`
104 Mount St., Mayfair. W1K 2TL. Open 10-6, Sat. by appointment. STOCK: Oriental art - Chinese ceramics, porcelain and pottery; cloisonné and painted enamels, jade, hardstones, lacquer, bronzes, metalwork, paintings, textiles, ivory, works of art including Korean, Tibetan and Japanese, 2000BC to 1960. LOC: Opposite Connaught Hotel. PARK: Easy. TEL: 020 7409 2888; fax - 020 7409 2777. SER: Valuations; restorations; buys at auction; exhibitions twice yearly (illustrated catalogues). FAIRS: New York; Olympia (June).

G. Heywood Hill Ltd
10 Curzon St. W1J 5HH. Open 9-5.30, Sat. 9-12.30. *STOCK: Books, new and old, architecture, literature, children's, natural history and illustrated.* TEL: 020 7629 0647; fax - 020 7408 0286; e-mail - books@gheywoodhill.com; website - www.gheywoodhill.com.

Holland & Holland
31 and 33 Bruton St. W1X 8JS. Est. 1835. Open 9.30-5.30, Sat. 10-4. SIZE: Medium. *STOCK: Modern and antique guns, rifles, associated items; sporting prints, pictures and antiquarian books; antique sporting objects.* PARK: Meters. TEL: 020 7499 4411; fax - 020 7499 4544.

Holmes Ltd   `BADA`
24 Burlington Arcade. W1V 9AD. (A.N., B.J. and I.J. Neale). Open 9.30-5. *STOCK: Jewels and silver.* TEL: 020 7629 8380. SER: Valuations; restorations. VAT: Stan.

Howard Antiques
8 Davies St., Berkeley Sq. W1K 3DW. Est. 1955. Open 10-6, Sat. by appointment. SIZE: Medium.

STOCK: English and Continental furniture, objects. LOC: Mayfair. PARK: NCP nearby. TEL: 020 7629 2628. SER: Valuations; advice; commissions.

C. John (Rare Rugs) Ltd   BADA
70 South Audley St., Mayfair. W1K 2RA. Est. 1947. Open 9-5. CL: Sat. STOCK: Rugs, carpets, tapestries, textiles and embroideries, 16th - 19th C. TEL: 020 7493 5288; fax - 020 7409 7030; e-mail - cjohn@dircon.co.uk. SER: Restorations, cleaning. FAIRS: Grosvenor House. VAT: Stan/Spec.

Johnson Walker & Tolhurst Ltd   BADA
64 Burlington Arcade. W1J 0QT. (Miss R. Gill). Est. 1849. Open 9.30-5.30. STOCK: Antique and secondhand jewellery, objets d'art, silver. TEL: 020 7629 2615. SER: Restorations (jewellery, pearl-stringing). VAT: Stan/Spec.

Daniel Katz Ltd
13 Old Bond St. W1S 4SX. (Daniel Katz and Stuart Lochhead). SLAD. Est. 1970. Open 9-6. CL: Sat. SIZE: Large. *STOCK: European sculpture, early medieval to 19th C, from £5,000.* LOC: Near Green Park underground station. TEL: 020 7493 0688; fax - 020 7499 7493. VAT: Spec.

Roger Keverne   BADA
2nd Floor, 16 Clifford St. W1S 3RG. Est. 1996. Open Mon.-Fri. 9.30-5.30. SIZE: Large. STOCK: Oriental art - Chinese jade, lacquer, pottery and porcelain, bronzes, ivories and enamels; all Chinese art from 2500 BC to 1916. PARK: Meters. TEL: 020 7434 9100; fax - 020 7434 9101; e-mail - enquiries@keverne.co.uk; website - www.keverne.co.uk. SER: Valuations; restorations; buys at auction; two exhibitions a year; catalogues available. FAIRS: New York (Winter and March Oriental). VAT: Stan/Spec.

D.S. Lavender (Antiques) Ltd   BADA
26 Conduit St. W1R 9TA. Est. 1945. Open 9.30-5. CL: Sat. STOCK: Jewels, miniatures, works of art. PARK: Meters. TEL: 020 7629 1782; fax - 020 7629 3106. SER: Valuations. VAT: Stan/Spec.

Liberty
Regent St. W1R 6AH. Est. 1875. Open 10-6.30, Thurs. 10-8, Fri. and Sat. 10-7. SIZE: Large. *STOCK: British furniture, ceramics, glass and metalware, 1860-1930, Gothic Revival, Aesthetic Movement and Arts & Crafts.* LOC: Regent St. joins Piccadilly and Oxford Circus. PARK: Meters and underground station in Cavendish Sq. TEL: 020 7734 1234. VAT: Stan.

Maas Gallery
15a Clifford St. W1S 4JZ. (R.N. Maas). SLAD. Est. 1960. Open Mon.-Fri. 10-5.30. SIZE: Medium. *STOCK: Victorian and Pre-Raphaelite paintings, drawings, watercolours and illustrations.* LOC: Between New Bond St. and Cork St. PARK: Easy. TEL: 020 7734 2302; fax - 020 7287 4836; e-mail - mail@maas gallery.co.uk; website - www.maasgallery.com. SER: Valuations; buys at auction. VAT: Spec.

Maggs Bros Ltd   BADA
50 Berkeley Sq. W1J 5BA. (J.F., B.D. and E.F. Maggs, P. Harcourt, R. Harding, H. Bett and J. Collins). ABA. Est. 1853. Open 9.30-5. CL: Sat. SIZE: Large. STOCK: Rare books, manuscripts, autograph letters and medieval miniatures. PARK: Meters. TEL: 020 7493 7160 (6 lines); fax - 020 7499 2007; e-mail - ed@maggs.com; website - www.maggs.com. VAT: Stan/Spec.

Mahboubian Gallery
65 Grosvenor St. W1X 9DB. (H. Mahboubian). Open 10-6. CL: Sat. TEL: 020 7493 9112; e-mail - kmahboubian@aol.com.

Mallett and Son (Antiques) Ltd   BADA
141 New Bond St. W1S 2BS. Est. 1865. Open 9.15-6, Sat. 10-4. SIZE: Large. STOCK: English furniture, 1690-1835; clocks, 17th-18th C; china, needlework, paintings and watercolours, objects and glass. PARK: Meters in Berkeley Sq. TEL: 020 7499 7411; fax - 020 7495 3179; e-mail - antiques@mallett.co.uk. FAIRS: Grosvenor House; Maastricht; IFAAD New York; Winter Show, New York; Palm Beach; San Francisco (Fall).

Mallett at Bourdon House Ltd
2 Davies St., Berkeley Sq. W1K 3DJ. Est. 1962. Open 9-6. SIZE: Large. *STOCK: 18th C Continental furniture, clocks, objets d'art; garden statuary and ornaments.* PARK: Meters in Berkeley Sq. TEL: 020 7629 2444; fax - 020 7499 2670; e-mail - antiques@mallett.co.uk; website - www.mallettantiques.com. FAIRS: Winter Antiques; Palm Beach; Maastricht; Grosvenor House; IFAAD. VAT: Stan/Spec.

Mallett Gallery   BADA
141 New Bond St. W1S 2BS. SLAD. Open 9.30-6, Sat. 11-4. STOCK: 18th to early 20th C paintings, watercolours and drawings. TEL: 020 7499 7411; fax - 020 7495 3179. FAIRS:

Olympia; Grosvenor House; IFAAD, New York; Maastricht; Palm Beach. VAT: Spec.

Mansour Gallery `BADA`
46-48 Davies St. W1K 5JB. (M. Mokhtarzadeh). Open 9.30-5.30, Sat. by appointment. *STOCK: Islamic works of art, miniatures; ancient glass and glazed wares; Greek, Roman and Egyptian antiquities.* TEL: 020 7491 7444/7499 0510. VAT: Stan.

Map World `LAPADA`
25 Burlington Arcade, Piccadilly. W1J 0PT. (J. T. Sharpe). IMCOS. Est. 1980. Open 10-5.30. SIZE: Small. *STOCK: Maps, worldwide, 1500-1850, £50-£85,000.* TEL: 020 7495 5377; fax - same; e-mail - info@map-world.com; website - www.map-world.com. SER: Valuations; buys at auction.

Marks Antiques `BADA` `LAPADA`
49 Curzon St. W1J 7UN. (Anthony Marks). Est. 1935. Open 9.30-6, Sat. 9.30-5. SIZE: Large. *STOCK: Fine 17th-19th C silver and Fabergé.* LOC: Green Park underground station, opposite Washington Hotel. PARK: Meters. TEL: 020 7499 1788; fax - 020 7409 3183. SER: Valuations; buys at auction. FAIRS: Grosvenor House; BADA; Olympia; Hong Kong; Palm Beach; Dallas. VAT: Stan/Spec.

Marlborough Fine Art (London) Ltd
6 Albemarle St. W1S 4BY. SLAD. Est. 1946. Open 10-5.30, Sat. 10-12.30. *STOCK: Graphic works; exhibitions by leading contemporary artists and sculptors.* PARK: Meters or near Cork St. TEL: 020 7629 5161; fax - 020 7629 6338; e-mail - mfa@marlboroughfineart.com; website - www.marlboroughfineart.com. FAIRS: Madrid; Maastricht; Geneva; Basel; Paris; Cologne.

Marlborough Rare Books Ltd
144-146 New Bond St. W1S 2TR. (Jonathan Gestetner). ABA. Est. 1946. Open 9.30-5.30. CL: Sat. SIZE: Medium. *STOCK: Illustrated books of all periods; rare books on fine and applied arts and architecture; English literature.* PARK: Meters. TEL: 020 7493 6993; e-mail - sales@mrb-books.co.uk. SER: Buys at auction; valuations; catalogues available. FAIRS: Olympia; Chelsea; Los Angeles; New York.

Mayfair Carpet Gallery Ltd
10a Berkeley St. W1X 5AD. *STOCK: Persian, Oriental rugs and carpets.* TEL: 020 7493 0126.

Mayfair Gallery Ltd
39 South Audley St. W1K 2PP. (M. Sinai). Open 9.30-6, Sat. by appointment. *STOCK: 19th C antiques and decorative Continental furniture, clocks, chandeliers, Meissen, ivories and objets d'art.* TEL: 020 7491 3435/3436; fax - 020 7491 3437; e-mail - mayfairgallery@mayfairgallery.net; website - www.artnet.com/mayfairgallery.html. SER: Valuations; restorations; shipping. FAIRS: Miami Beach; Olympia (June).

Melton's
27 Bruton Place. W1J 6NQ. (Cecilia Neal). IDDA. BIDA. Est. 1990. Open Mon.-Fri. 9.30-5.30. *STOCK: Small antiques and decorative accessories: lamps, prints, porcelain, textiles, English and Continental.* LOC: Mayfair, near Bond St. PARK: Meters Berkeley Sq. TEL: 020 7629 3612; fax - 020 7495 3196; e-mail - meltons.uk@virgin.net; website - www.meltons.co.uk. SER: Interior design and decoration.

Messums (Contemporary) `BADA` `LAPADA`
8 Cork St. W1S 3LJ. SLAD. Open 10-6, Sat. 11-5, other times by appointment. *STOCK: British Impressionist and contemporary paintings and sculpture.* TEL: 020 7437 5545; fax - 020 7734 7018. SER: Valuations; restorations; framing. VAT: Stan/Spec.

John Mitchell and Son `BADA`
1st Floor, 160 New Bond St. W1S 2UE. SLAD. Est. 1931. Open 9.30-5, Sat. by appointment. SIZE: Medium. *STOCK: Old Master paintings, drawings and watercolours, especially flower paintings, 17th C Dutch, 18th C English and 19th C French.* LOC: Nearest underground station Green Park. PARK: Meters. TEL: 020 7493 7567. SER: Valuations; restorations (pictures); buys at auction. FAIRS: TEFAF; Palm Beach; IFAAD New York.

Paul Mitchell Ltd `BADA`
99 New Bond St. W1Y 9LF. Open 9.30-5.30. CL: Sat. SIZE: Large. *STOCK: Picture frames.* PARK: Meters. TEL: 020 7493 8732/0860. VAT: Stan.

Moira
11 New Bond St. W1. Open 9-6. *STOCK: Fine antique and Art Deco jewellery.* TEL: 020 7629 0160. SER: Valuations; repairs.

Sydney L. Moss Ltd `BADA`
51 Brook St. W1K 4HP. (P.G. Moss). Est. 1910. Open Mon.-Fri. 10-5.30. SIZE: Large. *STOCK: Chinese and Japanese paintings and works of art; Japanese netsuke and lacquer, 17th-20th C; reference books (as stock).* LOC:

From Grosvenor Sq., up Brook St. to Claridges. PARK: Meters. TEL: 020 7629 4670/7493 7374; fax - 020 7491 9278; e-mail - mail@slmoss.com; website - www.slmoss.com. SER: Valuations and advice; buys at auction. FAIRS: Asian Art, New York (March). VAT: Spec.

Richard Ogden Ltd   BADA
28 and 29 Burlington Arcade, Piccadilly. W1J 0NX. Est. 1948. Open 9.30-5.15, Sat. 9.30-5. SIZE: Medium. *STOCK: Antique jewellery.* PARK: Meters and NCP. TEL: 020 7493 9136; e-mail - admin@richardogden.com. SER: Valuations; repairs. VAT: Spec.

Paralos Ltd
4th Floor, 23/24 Margaret St. W1W 8RU. (Panagiotis Chantziaras, Louise Bryan and Tim Bryars). ABA. ILAB. PBFA. IMCOS. Est. 1997. Open by appointment. SIZE: Large. *STOCK: Antiquarian books, prints (including decorative and natural history), maps and atlases, printed before 1800; early printing, classics, plate books, voyages and travels, £10-£20,000.* LOC: From Oxford Circus, north up Regent St., second road on right. PARK: Cavendish Sq. TEL: 020 7637 0796; fax - 020 7637 0819; e-mail - paralos@

paralos.co.uk; website - www.paralos.co.uk. FAIRS: Map & Print (2nd Sun. monthly), Bonnington Hotel. VAT: Stan. *Trade Only.*

Partridge Fine Arts plc   BADA
144-146 New Bond St. W1S 2PF. (John, Frank and Rosemary Partridge, Michael Pick, Lucy Morton and Anthony Smith). SLAD. CINOA. Est. 1905. Open 9-5.30, Sat. 10-1 (Oct-July - check beforehand), other times by appointment. SIZE: Very large - 4 floors. *STOCK: 18th-19th C French and English furniture and works of art; paintings, silver, clocks and chandeliers, tapestries, lamps, needlework, carpets, sculpture.* LOC: North of Bruton St.-Conduit St. crossing. PARK: Meters and NCP nearby. TEL: 020 7629 0834; fax - 020 7495 6266; e-mail - enquiries@partridgeplc.com; website - www.partridgeplc.com. SER: Valuations; buys at auction; upholstery; restorations; carving and gilding; annual exhibitions. FAIRS: Biennale, Paris. VAT: Spec.

A. Pash & Sons
37 South Audley St. W1K 2PN. (Arnold and Robert Pash). Est. 1940. Open 9-5. SIZE: Medium. *STOCK: Silver.* PARK: NCP nearby. TEL: 020 7493 5176; fax - 020 7355 3676; e-mail - david.pash@idnet.co.uk; website - www.pashantiques.com.

W.H. Patterson Fine Arts Ltd   BADA
19 Albemarle St. W1S 4BB. (Mrs. P.M. Patterson and James Kayll). SLAD. Open 9.30-6. SIZE: Large. *STOCK: 19th C and regular exhibitions for contemporary artists, the New English Art Club, Paul Brown, Peter Brown, Willem Dolphyn, Susan Ryder and Donald Hamilton Fraser.* LOC: Near Green Park underground station. PARK: Meters. TEL: 020 7629 4119; fax - 020 7499 0119; e-mail - info@whpatterson.com; website - www.whpatterson.com. SER: Valuations; restorations. VAT: Spec.

Pelham Galleries Ltd   BADA
24/25 Mount St., Mayfair. W1K 2RR. (A. and L.J. Rubin). Est. 1928. *STOCK: Furniture, English and Continental; tapestries, decorative works of art and musical instruments.* TEL: 020 7629 0905; fax - 020 7495 4511. FAIRS: Palm Beach; Maastricht; Grosvenor House; Biennale Paris. VAT: Spec.

Pendulum of Mayfair Ltd
King House, 51 Maddox St. W1. (K. R. Clements and Dr H. Specht). Open 10-6, Sat. 10-5. *STOCK:*

Clocks, mainly longcase, also bracket, mantel and wall; Georgian mahogany furniture. TEL: 020 7629 6606; fax - 020 7629 6616; e-mail - pendulumclocks@aol.com; website - www.pendulumofmayfair.co.uk. SER: Valuations. FAIRS: Buxton. VAT: Spec.

Ronald Phillips Ltd `BADA`
26 Bruton St. W1J 6LQ. (Simon Phillips). Est. 1952. STOCK: English 18th C furniture, objets d'art, glass, clocks and barometers. LOC: Mayfair. TEL: 020 7493 2341; fax - 020 7495 0843. FAIRS: Grosvenor House. VAT: Mainly Spec.

S.J. Phillips Ltd `BADA`
139 New Bond St. W1A 3DL. (M.S., N.E.L., J.P. and F.E. Norton). Est. 1869. Open 10-5. CL: Sat. SIZE: Large. STOCK: Silver, jewellery, gold boxes, miniatures. LOC: Near Bond St. underground station. PARK: Meters. TEL: 020 7629 6261; fax - 020 7495 6180; website - www.sjphillips.com. SER: Restorations; buys at auction. FAIRS: Grosvenor House; Maastricht. VAT: Stan/Spec.

Piccadilly Gallery
43 Dover St. W1S 4NU. (R.G. and E.E. Pilkington). SLAD. Est. 1953. Open 10-5.30. *STOCK: Symbolist and Art Nouveau works, 20th C; drawings and watercolours.* PARK: Meters. TEL: 020 7629 2875; fax - 020 7499 0431; e-mail - art@piccadillygall.demon.co.uk; website - www.piccadillygall.demon.co.uk. VAT: Spec.

Pickering and Chatto
1st Floor, 36 St George St. W1R 9FA. Est. 1820. Open Mon.-Fri. 9.30-5.30 or by appointment. SIZE: Medium. *STOCK: Literature, economics, politics, philosophy, science, medicine, general antiquarian.* PARK: Meters. TEL: 020 7491 2656; fax - 020 7491 9161; e-mail - rarebooks@pickering-chatto.com.

Nicholas S. Pitcher Oriental Art
1st Floor, 29 New Bond St. W1Y 9HD. Est. 1990. Open 10.30-5 by appointment. CL: Sat. except by appointment. SIZE: Medium. *STOCK: Chinese ceramics and works of art, early pottery, to 18th C, £200-£10,000.* LOC: Four doors from Sotheby's, above Gordon Scott shoe shop. PARK: Nearby. TEL: 020 7499 6621; home - 020 7731 5672; mobile - 07831 391574; e-mail - nickpitcher@aol.com. SER: Valuations; buys at auction. FAIRS: Arts of Pacific Asia New York and Santa Monica. VAT: Spec.

Portal Gallery
43 Dover St. W1S 4NU. (Lionel Levy and Jess Wilder). Est. 1959. Open 10-5.30, Sat. 10-4. SIZE: Medium. *STOCK: Curios, bygones, artefacts, country pieces and objects of virtue, 19th C, £50-£500; contemporary British idiosyncratic paintings, including Beryl Cook.* TEL: 020 7493 0706; fax - 020 7629 3506.

Jonathan Potter Ltd `BADA` `LAPADA`
125 New Bond St. W1S 1DY. ABA. Est. 1975. Open 10-6, Sat. by appointment. STOCK: British and world maps, atlases and travel books, 16th-19th C, £50-£10,000. PARK: Meters nearby. TEL: 020 7491 3520; fax - 020 7491 9754; e-mail - jpmaps@attglobal.net; website - www.jpmaps.co.uk. SER: Valuations; restorations; colouring; framing; buys at auction (maps and prints); catalogue available. VAT: Stan.

Pyms Gallery `BADA`
9 Mount St., Mayfair. W1K 3NG. (A. and M. Hobart). SLAD. Est. 1975. Open 9.30-6. CL: Sat. SIZE: Large. STOCK: British, Irish and French paintings, 18th-20th C. TEL: 020 7629 2020; fax - 020 7629 2060; e-mail - paintings@pymsgallery.com; website - www.pymsgallery.com. SER: Valuations; restorations; buys at auction. FAIRS: Grosvenor House. VAT: Spec.

Bernard Quaritch Ltd (Booksellers)
`BADA`
5-8 Lower John St., Golden Sq. W1F 9AU. (Lord Parmoor). ABA. Est. 1847. Open 9-6. CL: Sat. SIZE: Large. STOCK: Rare books and manuscripts. LOC: Piccadilly Circus. PARK: Meters, 50yds. TEL: 020 7734 2983; fax - 020 7437 0967; e-mail - rarebooks@quaritch.com; website - www.quaritch.com. SER: Buys at auction. FAIRS: Various International. VAT: Stan.

Rabi Gallery Ltd
82P Portland Place. W1N 3DH. (R. Soleymani). Est. 1878. Open 10-6. CL: Sat. *STOCK: Ancient art, antique carpets and works of art.* TEL: 020 7580 9064; fax - 020 7436 0772.

Gordon Reece Gallery
16 Clifford St., Mayfair. W1X 1RG. Open 11-5.30. CL: Mon. SIZE: Large. *STOCK: Flat woven rugs and nomadic carpets, tribal sculpture, jewellery, Chinese, Japanese and Indian furniture, decorative and non-European folk art, ethnic and Oriental ceramics.* TEL: 020 7439

0007; fax - 020 7437 5715; website - www. gordon.reece.galleries.com. SER: Restorations.

David Richards and Sons
10 New Cavendish St. W1G 8UL. (M. and E. Richards). Open 9.30-5.30. CL: Sat. SIZE: Large. *STOCK: Silver and plate.* LOC: Off Harley St., at corner of Marylebone High St. PARK: Nearby. TEL: 020 7935 3206/0322; fax - 020 7224 4423. SER: Valuations; restorations. VAT: Stan/Spec.

Crispian Riley-Smith
at John Mitchell & Son, 160 New Bond St. W1S 2UE. Est. 1997. Open 10-5. SIZE: Medium. *STOCK: Old Master drawings, 1500-1900, £500-£100,000.* TEL: 020 7491 0820; fax - 020 7493 7567; mobile - 07771 552509; e-mail - crispian@riley-smith.com; website - www.riley. smith.com. SER: Valuations. FAIRS: IFAAD, New York; Master Drawings in London.

Michael Rose - Source of the Unusual
3, 15, 44 Burlington Arcade, Piccadilly and 10 New Bond St. W1J 0QY. *STOCK: Victorian, antique and period diamonds, jewellery and watches.* TEL: 020 7493 0714; 020 7493 0590; website - www.rosejewels.co.uk.

Rossi & Rossi Ltd
13 Old Bond St. W1S 4SX. (Anna Maria and Fabio Rossi). Est. 1984. Open 10-5, Sat. and Sun. by appointment. SIZE: Medium. *STOCK: Himalayan art, 12th-17th C, to £10,000+; Indian art, 1st-13th C, to £10,000+.* LOC: Off Piccadilly. PARK: Meters. TEL: 020 7355 1804; fax - 020 7355 1806. SER: Valuations; buys at auction. VAT: Spec.

The Royal Arcade Watch Shop
4 Royal Arcade - at 28 Old Bond St. W1S 4SD. Open 10-5.30. SIZE: Small. *STOCK: Modern and vintage Rolex, Cartier, Patek Phillipe.* PARK: Easy. TEL: 020 7495 4882.

Royal Exchange Art Gallery at Cork St.
24 Cork St. W1S 3NJ. Est. 1974. Open 10-6. *STOCK: Fine marine oils, watercolours and etchings.* TEL: 020 7439 6655; fax - 020 7439 6622; e-mail - enquiries@marinepictures.com; website - www.marinepictures.com.

Frank T. Sabin Ltd `BADA`
46 Albemarle St. W1X 3FE. (John Sabin). Open 9.30-5.30, Sat. by appointment. STOCK: English sporting and decorative prints; English 18th-19th C paintings. TEL: 020 7493 3288; fax - 020 7499 3593.

Alistair Sampson Antiques Ltd `BADA`
120 Mount St., Mayfair. (Formerly of 156 Brompton Rd). W1K 3NN. Open 9.30-5.30. SIZE: Large. STOCK: English pottery, oak and country furniture, metalwork, needlework, primitive pictures, decorative and interesting items, 17th-18th C. PARK: Meters. TEL: 020 7409 1799; fax - 020 7409 7717; e-mail - info@alistairsampson.com; website - www. alistairsampson.com. FAIRS: BADA; Grosvenor House; Ceramics, New York; IFAAD; International Ceramics. VAT: Spec.

Robert G. Sawers
PO Box 4QA. W1A 4QA. Open by appointment. *STOCK: Books on the Orient, Japanese prints, screens, paintings.* TEL: 020 7794 9618; fax - 020 7794 9571; website - www.bobsawers.com.

Scarisbrick and Bate Ltd
111 Mount St. W1Y 5HE. (R.A.J. Cotgrove). Est. 1958. Open 9.30-5.30. CL: Sat. SIZE: Medium. *STOCK: Furniture, decorative items, mid-18th C to early 19th C.* Not Stocked: Glass and china. LOC: By Connaught Hotel (off Park Lane). PARK: Meters. TEL: 020 7499 2043/4/5; fax - 020 7499 2897. SER: Restorations (furniture); buys at auction. VAT: Stan.

Seaby Antiquities
14 Old Bond St. W1X 3DB. Est. 1980. Open 10-5. CL: Sat. SIZE: Medium. *STOCK: Antiquities.* LOC: Just off Piccadilly, nearest underground station Green Park. TEL: 020 7495 2590; fax - 020 7491 1595.

Jeremy Seale Antiques/Interiors
15 St. Andrews Mansions, Dorset St. W1U 4EQ. Est. 1988. Open by appointment. SIZE: Small. *STOCK: Furniture, 18th-19th C, £300-£6,000; decorative items, 19th C; pictures and prints, 18th-19th C; both £50-£500.* TEL: 020 7935 5131; mobile - 07956 457795. SER: Finder; valuations; interior design consultant; homefinder. VAT: Stan/Spec.

Shapero Gallery
24 Bruton St. W1J 6QQ. (Bernard J. Shapero). ABA. Est. 1980. Open 9.30-6.30, Sat. 11-5. SIZE: Large. *STOCK: Antique and rare prints, maps, watercolours especially natural history, travel and general decorative, 16th-20th C; 19th C photographs; all £50-£50,000.* PARK: Easy. TEL: 020 7491 0330; fax - 020 7629 5324; e-mail - gallery@shapero.com; website - www.shapero. com. SER: Valuations; restorations; framing. FAIRS: Palm Beach International; Maastricht TEFAF; Grosvenor House; ABA Olympia.

Bernard J. Shapero Rare Books
32 St George St. W1S 2EA. Est. 1979. Open 9.30-6.30, Sat. 11-5. SIZE: Large. *STOCK: Antiquarian books - travel, natural history, modern first edition, colour plate.* LOC: Near Hanover Sq. and Bond St. TEL: 020 7493 0876; fax - 020 7229 7860; e-mail - rarebooks@shapero.com; website - www. shapero.com. SER: Valuations; restorations (antiquarian books); buys at auction. FAIRS: Book - London, Paris, New York, San Francisco.

W. Sitch and Co. Ltd.
48 Berwick St. W1F 8JD. (R. Sitch). Est. 1776. Open 8-5. SIZE: Large. *STOCK: Edwardian and Victorian lighting fixtures and floor standards.* LOC: Off Oxford St. TEL: 020 7437 3776; fax - 020 7437 5707. SER: Valuations; restorations; repairs. VAT: Stan.

The Sladmore Gallery of Sculpture
32 Bruton Place, Berkeley Sq. W1J 6NW. (E.F. Horswell and G. Farrell). SLAD. Open 10-6. CL: Sat. SIZE: Large. *STOCK: Bronze sculptures, 19th C - Mene, Barye, Fremiet, Bonheur; Impressionist, Bugatti, Troubetzkoy, Pompon; contemporary, Geoffrey Dashwood birds, Mark Coreth African wildlife, Nic Fiddian-Green horse heads.* TEL: 020 7499 0365; fax - 020 7409 1381; e-mail - sculpture@sladmore.com; website - www. sladmore.com. SER: Valuations; restorations. FAIRS: Grosvenor House. VAT: Stan/Spec.

Stephen Somerville (W. A.) Ltd
14 Old Bond St. W1S 4PP. SLAD. Est. 1987. Open by appointment. SIZE: Small. *STOCK: Old Master prints and drawings; English paintings, watercolours, prints and drawings, 17th-20th C, £50-£50,000.* LOC: Piccadilly end of Old Bond St. TEL: 020 7493 8363. SER: Buys at auction (as stock). VAT: Spec.

Henry Sotheran Ltd
2/5 Sackville St., Piccadilly. W1S 3DP. ABA. PBFA. ILAB. Est. 1761. Open 9.30-6, Sat. 10-4. *STOCK: Antiquarian books and prints.* TEL: 020 7439 6151; fax - 020 7434 2019; e-mail - sotherans@sotherans.co.uk; website - www. sotherans.co.uk. SER: Restorations and binding (books, prints); buys at auction. VAT: Stan.

A. & J. Speelman Ltd
129 Mount St. W1K 3NX. Est. 1931. Open 9.30-6. SIZE: Large. *STOCK: Rare Chinese, Japanese and Himalayan works of art including Tang pottery and Chinese export ceramics, Buddhist images and ritual objects.* LOC: Mayfair. TEL: 020 7499 5126; fax - 020 7355 3391; e-mail - enquiries@ajspeelman.com; website - www.ajspeelman.com. SER: Valuations. FAIRS: Asian Art, New York. VAT: Spec.

Pip Todd Warmoth, 'Harvesting, Early Evening, Tibet', oil on board, 35in. x 59in., priced at £7,000 at the Kings Road Gallery.

From an article entitled "Contemporary British Artists" by Anthony J. Lester which appeared in the March 2003 issue of ***Antique Collecting***. For more details and to subscribe see page 21.

Stair and Company Ltd   BADA
14 Mount St. W1K 2RF. CINOA. Est. 1911.
Open 9.30-5.30, Sat. by appointment. SIZE:
Large. *STOCK: 18th-19th C English furniture,
works of art, mirrors, chandeliers, barometers,
needlework, lamps, clocks, prints.* LOC: Past
Connaught Hotel, towards South Audley St.
PARK: Meters and Adam's Row. TEL: 020 7499
1784; fax - 020 7629 1050; e-mail - stair
andcompany@talk21.com; website - www.stair
andcompany.com. SER: Restorations. FAIRS:
Grosvenor House; BADA. VAT: Spec.

Jacob Stodel   BADA
Flat 53 Macready House, 75 Crawford St.
W1H 5LP. Est. 1949. Open by appointment.
*STOCK: Continental furniture, objets d'art,
ceramics, English furniture.* TEL: 020 7723
3732; fax - 020 7723 9813; e-mail -
jacobstodel@aol.com. FAIRS: Maastricht
(TEFAF). VAT: Margin/Spec.

**June and Tony Stone Fine Antique
Boxes**   LAPADA
5 Burlington Arcade. W1J 0PD. Est. 1990. Open
9-6. SIZE: 2 floors. *STOCK: Fine boxes
especially tea caddies, 18th-19th C, £200-
£30,000.* TEL: 020 7493 9495; fax - 020 7493
9496; sales - 07092 106600; fax - 07092 106611;

e-mail - jts@boxes.co.uk; website - www.boxes.
co.uk. FAIRS: Olympia (June, Nov. and Feb);
LAPADA (Oct); Claridges (April); Harrogate
(April, Sept). VAT: Stan/Spec.

Stoppenbach & Delestre Ltd
25 Cork St. W1S 3NB. SLAD. Open 10-5.30, Sat.
10-1. *STOCK: French paintings, drawings and
sculpture, 19th-20th C.* TEL: 020 7734 3534; e-
mail - contact@artfrancais.com; website -
www.artfrancais.com.

Tessiers Ltd   BADA
1st Floor Gallery, 12 St. George St. W1S 2FB.
Open 10-5. *STOCK: Jewellery, silver, objets
d'art.* TEL: 020 7629 0458; fax - 020 7629 1857.
SER: Valuations; restorations. VAT: Spec.

William Thuillier
14 Old Bond St. W1S 4PP. Open by appointment.
STOCK: Old Master paintings and drawings.
TEL: 020 7499 0106; website - www.thuillart.
com; e-mail - thuillart@aol.com. SER:
Valuations; research. FAIRS: Olympia (Feb.,
June and Nov).

Toynbee-Clarke Interiors Ltd
95 Mount St. W1Y 5HG. (G. and D. Toynbee-
Clarke). Est. 1953. Open 11-5.30. CL: Sat. SIZE:

Medium. *STOCK: Decorative English and Continental furniture and objects, 17th-18th C; Chinese hand painted wallpapers, 18th C; French scenic wallpapers, early 19th C; Chinese and Japanese paintings and screens, 17th-19th C.* LOC: Between north-west corner of Berkeley Sq. and Park Lane. PARK: Meters. TEL: 020 7499 4472; fax - 020 7495 1204. SER: Buys at auction. VAT: Stan/Spec.

M. Turpin Ltd `LAPADA`
27 Bruton St. W1J 6QN. CINOA. Est. 1948. Open Mon-Fri. 10-6 or by appointment. SIZE: Large. *STOCK: English and Continental furniture, mirrors, chandeliers, objets d' art, 17th to early 19th C.* LOC: Between Berkeley Sq. and Bond St. PARK: Meters. TEL: 020 7493 3275; fax - 020 7408 1869; mobile - 07799 664322; e-mail - mturpin@mturpin.co.uk; website - www.mturpin.co.uk. SER: Restorations (upholstery); buys at auction. VAT: Spec.

Jan van Beers Oriental Art `BADA`
34 Davies St. W1Y 1LG. Est. 1978. Open 10-6. CL: Sat. SIZE: Medium. *STOCK: Chinese and Japanese ceramics and works of art, 200BC to 1800AD.* LOC: Between Berkeley Sq. and Oxford St. PARK: Easy. TEL: 020 7408 0434; website - www.janvanbeers.com. SER: Valuations. VAT: Spec.

Vigo Carpet Gallery `LAPADA`
6a Vigo St. W1S 3HF. Open 10-6, Sat. 11-5. *STOCK: Oriental antique carpets and rugs; recreations of hand-made carpets and rugs in vegetable dyes and hand-spun wool.* TEL: 020 7439 6971; fax - 020 7439 2353; e-mail - vigo@btinternet.com. SER: Valuations; restorations.

Rupert Wace Ancient Art Ltd `BADA`
14 Old Bond St. W1S 4PP. IADAA. ADA. Est. 1984. Open Mon.-Fri. 10-5 or by appointment. *STOCK: Ancient Egyptian, Classical, near Eastern and Celtic antiquities.* LOC: West End. TEL: 020 7495 1623; fax - 020 7495 8495; e-mail - rupert.wace@btinternet.com; website - www.rupertwace.co.uk. SER: Valuations. FAIRS: Grosvenor House; Basel; Winter Show, New York.

Walpole Gallery
38 Dover St. W1S 4NL. SLAD. Open 9.30-5.30. CL: Sat. except when exhibitions held. *STOCK: Italian Old Master paintings.* TEL: 020 7499 6626.

Wartski Ltd `BADA`
14 Grafton St. W1S 4DE. Est. 1865. Open 9.30-

5. CL: Sat. SIZE: Medium. *STOCK: Jewellery, 18th C gold boxes, Fabergé, Russian works of art, silver.* PARK: Meters. TEL: 020 7493 1141. SER: Restorations. FAIRS: IFAAD, New York; European Fine Art; Maastricht (TEFAF); IAA, Palm Beach. VAT: Stan/Spec.

Waterhouse and Dodd `BADA`
26 Cork St. W1S 3MQ. (R. Waterhouse and J. Dodd). Est. 1987. Open 9.30-6, Sat. by appointment. SIZE: Medium. *STOCK: British and European oil paintings, watercolours and drawings, 1850-1950, £2,000-£50,000.* TEL: 020 7734 7800. SER: Valuations; restorations; buys at auction (paintings). FAIRS: Antiques & Fine Art; Olympia. VAT: Spec.

The Weiss Gallery
1B Albemarle St. W1. Open 10-6. CL: Sat. *STOCK: Elizabethan, Jacobean and early European portraits.* TEL: 020 7409 0035. SER: Valuations; restorations.

William Weston Gallery
7 Royal Arcade, Albemarle St. W1S 4SG. SLAD. IFPDA. Est. 1964. Open 9.30-5.30, Sat. 11-4. SIZE: Small. *STOCK: Lithographs and etchings, 1850-1990.* LOC: Off Piccadilly. TEL: 020 7493 0722; fax - 020 7491 9240; e-mail - www@williamweston.co.uk; website - www. williamweston.co.uk. FAIRS: Grosvenor House; 20th/21st C British Art; Royal Academy Print: New York. VAT: Spec.

Rollo Whately Ltd
1st Floor, 9 Old Bond St. W1X 3TA. Est. 1995. Open 9-6. CL: Sat. SIZE: Small. *STOCK: Picture frames, 16th-19th C, £500-£2,000.* LOC: Piccadilly end of Old Bond St. TEL: 020 7629 7861; e-mail - frames@rollowhately.demon. co.uk. SER: Valuations; restorations (frames); search; buys at auction. VAT: Stan.

Wilkins and Wilkins
1 Barrett St., St Christophers Pl. W1M 6DN. (M. Wilkins). Est. 1981. Open 10-5. CL: Sat. SIZE: Small. *STOCK: English 17th-18th C portraits and decorative paintings, £700-£20,000.* LOC: Near Selfridges. TEL: 020 7935 9613; fax - 020 7935 4696; e-mail - info@wilkinsandwilkins. com. VAT: Stan/Spec.

Wilkinson plc
1 Grafton St. W1S 4EA. Est. 1947. Open 9.30-5. CL: Sat. *STOCK: Glass, especially chandeliers, 18th C and reproduction; art metal work.* LOC: Nearest underground station - Green Park. TEL: 020 7495 2477; fax - 020 7491 1737; e-mail -

enquiries@wilkinson-plc.com; website - www. wilkinson-plc.com. SER: Restorations and repairs (glass and metalwork).

Williams and Son
2 Grafton St. W1X 3LB. (J.R. Williams). Est. 1931. Open 9.30-6. CL: Sat. SIZE: Large. *STOCK: British and European paintings, 19th C.* LOC: Between Bond St. and Berkeley Sq. TEL: 020 7493 4985/5751; fax - 020 7409 7363; e-mail - art@williamsandson.com; website - www. williamsandson.com. VAT: Stan/Spec.

Thomas Williams (Fine Art) Ltd
22 Old Bond St. W1S 4PY. Open 9-6. CL: Sat. *STOCK: Old Master drawings, £300-£1,000,000.* TEL: 020 7491 1485; fax - 020 7408 0197. SER: Valuations; buys at auction (paintings and drawings).

Windsor House Antiques Ltd `LAPADA`
28-29 Dover St. and 23 Grafton St., Mayfair. W1S 4NA. (D.K. Smith). Est. 1959. Open 10-6, Sat. 10-1. SIZE: Large plus Georgian town house. *STOCK: English furniture, 18th-19th C; paintings and objects.* TEL: 020 7659 0340; fax - 020 7499 6728; e-mail - sales@windsor houseantiques.co.uk; website - www.windsor houseantiques.co.uk. SER: Shipping arranged. VAT: Stan/Spec.

Linda Wrigglesworth Ltd `LAPADA`
34 Brook St. W1K 5DN. Est. 1978. Open Sat. 11-7 by appointment. *STOCK: Chinese, Korean and Tibetan costume and textiles, 14th-19th C.* LOC: Corner of South Molton Lane, Brook St. end. PARK: Grosvenor Square. TEL: 020 7408 0177/7491 9812; e-mail - info@linda wrigglesworth.com; website - www.linda wrigglesworth.com. SER: Valuations; restorations; mounting, framing; buys on commission (Oriental). FAIRS: Maastricht; Asian Art, London and New York; San Francisco.

A. Zadah
130 Mount St. W1K 3UY. Est. 1976. Open 9.30-6. *STOCK: Oriental and European carpets, rugs, tapestries and textiles.* TEL: 020 7493 2622/2673.

W2

Sean Arnold Sporting Antiques
21-22 Chepstow Corner, off Westbourne Grove. W2 4XE. Est. 1980. Open 10-6. SIZE: Large. *STOCK: Sporting antiques and decorative items; golf clubs, 1840-1915, £30-£6,000; tennis racquets, £10-£3,000; football memorabilia,* *globes and pond yachts; vintage luggage.* LOC: Notting Hill Gate. PARK: Meters. TEL: 020 7221 2267; fax - 020 7221 5464. SER: Mail order. VAT: Stan.

David Black Carpets
27 Chepstow Corner, Chepstow Place. W2 4XE. (David Black and Richard Morant). Est. 1966. Open 10-6. SIZE: Large. *STOCK: Antique, custom made and outsize carpets, rugs, kilims, dhurries and silk embroideries, £500-£25,000.* TEL: 020 7727 2566; fax - 020 7229 4599; e-mail - richardmorant@david-black.com; website - www.david-black.com. SER: Valuations; restorations; cleaning underfelt. VAT: Spec.

Connaught Galleries
44 Connaught St. W2 2AA. (M. Hollamby). Est. 1966. Open 10-6, Sat. 10-1. SIZE: Medium. *STOCK: Antique and reproduction sporting, historical, geographical and decorative prints.* LOC: Near Marble Arch. PARK: Meters. TEL: 020 7723 1660. SER: Picture framing. VAT: Spec.

Craven Gallery
30 Craven Terrace. W2. (A. Quaradeghini). Est. 1974. Open 11-6, Sat. 3-7, other times by appointment. SIZE: Large and warehouse. *STOCK: Silver and plate, 19th-20th C; Victorian furniture, china and glass.* LOC: Off Bayswater Rd. PARK: Easy. TEL: 020 7402 2802; home - 020 8998 0769. VAT: Stan. *Trade Only.*

Manya Igel Fine Arts Ltd `LAPADA`
21/22 Peters Court, Porchester Rd. W2 5DR. (M. Igel and B.S. Prydal). Est. 1977. Open Mon.-Fri.10-5 by appointment only. SIZE: Large. *STOCK: Traditional Modern British Art, £250-£25,000.* LOC: Off Queensway. PARK: Nearby. TEL: 020 7229 1669/8429; fax - 020 7229 6770; e-mail - paintings@manyaigel.com; website - www.manyaigel.com. FAIRS: 20th/21st C British Art; Olympia (Spring); Chelsea (Spring); Claridges; VAT: Spec.

Ian Lieber
The Shop, 29 Craven Terrace, Lancaster Gate. W2 3EL. Est. 1965. Open by appointment. SIZE: Medium. *STOCK: Furniture, early 19th C and decorative; porcelain, objets d'art, paintings, costume jewellery.* LOC: Near Bayswater Rd. TEL: 020 7262 5505; fax - 020 7402 4445. SER: Buys at auction. FAIRS: Olympia. VAT: Stan/Spec.

The Mark Gallery `BADA`
9 Porchester Place, Marble Arch. W2 2BS. (H. Mark). CINOA. Est. 1969. Open 10-1 and 2-6,

Sat. 11-1. SIZE: Medium. *STOCK: Russian icons, 16th-19th C; modern graphics - French school.* LOC: Near Marble Arch. TEL: 020 7262 4906; fax - 020 7224 9416. SER: Valuations; restorations; buys at auction. VAT: Spec.

W4

The Chiswick Fireplace Co.
68 Southfield Rd., Chiswick. W4 1BD. (Mrs R. O'Grady). Open 9.30-5. SIZE: Medium. *STOCK: Original cast iron fireplaces, late Victorian to early 1900's, £200-£1,000; marble, wood and limestone surrounds.* LOC: 8 mins. walk from Turnham Green underground station. PARK: Easy. TEL: 020 8995 4011; fax - 020 8995 4012. SER: Restorations; installation. VAT: Stan.

David Edmonds
1-4 Prince of Wales Terrace, Chiswick. W4 2EY. Est. 1985. Open 10.30-6, Sun. 12-4. SIZE: Large. *STOCK: Fine antiques from India and subcontinent, £10-£10,000.* LOC: Off Chiswick High St. PARK: Easy. TEL: 020 8742 1920; fax - 020 8742 3030; mobile - 07831 666436; e-mail - daveindia@aol.com. SER: Valuations; restorations; buys at auction (as stock). VAT: Stan.

Marshall Phillips
38 Chiswick Lane, Chiswick. W4 2JQ. Est. 1985. Open 10-6, Sat. 10-5. SIZE: Medium. *STOCK: Decorative and unusual objects, furniture, bronzes and chandeliers, £100-£50,000; garden statuary and furniture, to £30,000.* LOC: Off A4/M4 at the Hogarth roundabout or Chiswick High Rd. PARK: Easy. TEL: 020 8742 8089; fax - same. SER: Valuations; restorations (oil and water gilding; metal patination and non-ferrous casting). VAT: Spec.

The Old Cinema Antique Department Store
160 Chiswick High Rd. W4 1PR. Est. 1977. Open 10-6, Sun. 12-5. SIZE: Large. *STOCK: General antiques including furniture, gardenalia, decorative and architectural items, 1660-1960, £100-£6,000.* PARK: Easy. TEL: 020 8995 4166; fax - 020 8995 4167; e-mail - theoldcinema@antiques-uk.co.uk; website - www.antiques-uk.co.uk. SER: Restorations; delivery. VAT: Stan/Spec.

Oriental Furniture and Arts
11a Devonshire Rd., Chiswick. W4 2EU. (Steven Glynn-Williams). Est. 1993. Open 10-5. SIZE: Medium. *STOCK: Oriental furniture, 18th-19th C, to £3,500; Oriental decorative objects, 19th C and modern, £40-£350; tomb figures and neolithic potteries.* LOC: Off Chiswick High Rd. PARK: Easy. TEL: 020 8987 8571.

Strand Antiques
46 Devonshire Rd., Chiswick. W4 2HD. Est. 1977. Open 10.30-5.30. SIZE: Medium. *STOCK: English and French brocante, furniture, glass, lighting, jewellery and silver, garden and kitchenware, books and prints, textiles and collectables, £1-£500.* LOC: Off Chiswick High Rd. 5 mins Turnham Green underground station. PARK: Meters. TEL: 020 8994 1912.

W5

Aberdeen House Antiques LAPADA
75 St. Mary's Rd. W5 5RH. (N. Schwartz). LAPADA. CINOA. Est. 1972. Open 10-5.30. SIZE: Medium. *STOCK: Furniture and pictures, £150-£4,000; decorative items and textiles, £25-£2,000; china, glass and silver, £25-£1,000; all 18th-20th C.* LOC: On B455 1 mile north of A4. PARK: Easy and at rear. TEL: 020 8567 5194/1223. SER: Valuations. VAT: Stan.

Ealing Gallery
78 St. Mary's Rd., Ealing. W5 5EX. (Mrs N. Lane). Est. 1984. Open 10.30-6. CL: Mon. and Wed. *STOCK: Oil paintings, £250-£10,000; watercolours, £100-£5,000; both 18th-20th C; contemporary paintings, £150-£4,000.* LOC: Piccadilly Line underground, South Ealing. PARK: Nearby. TEL: 020 8840 7883; fax - same; e-mail - info@ealinggallery.com; website - www.ealinggallery.com. SER: Valuations; restorations (oils and watercolours); framing. VAT: Spec.

Terrace Antiques
10-12 South Ealing Rd. W5 4QA. (N. Schwartz). Est. 1972. Open 10-5.30. SIZE: Medium. *STOCK: Georgian, Victorian and Edwardian furniture, 1780-1920, £50-£1,000; china, glass and pictures, silver and plate, 1850-1950, £10-£600.* LOC: 1 mile north of A4 on B455. PARK: Easy and opposite. TEL: 020 8567 5194/1223. SER: Valuations. VAT: Stan.

W6

Architectural Antiques
351 King St. W6 9NH. (G.P.A. Duc). Est. 1985. Open Mon.-Fri. 8.30-4.30. SIZE: Medium. *STOCK: Marble/stone chimney pieces, 18th-19th C, £500-£8,000; gilt/painted overmantels, 19th C, £300-£1,500; antique French doors, £200-*

£1,000; bathroom fixtures, basins, £200-£800.
PARK: Easy and Black Lion Lane. TEL: 020
8741 7883; fax - 020 8741 1109; mobile - 07831
127541; website - www.AA-fireplaces.co.uk.
SER: Valuations. VAT: Stan. *Trade Only.*

Paravent
Flat 10, Ranelagh Gardens, Stamford Brook Ave.
W6 0YE. (M. Aldbrook). Est. 1989. Open by
appointment. *STOCK: Screens, 17th-20th C,
£500-£10,000.* TEL: 020 8748 6323; fax - 020
8563 2912; e-mail - aldbrook@paravent.
freeserve.co.uk. SER: Restorations; finder
(screens); lectures worldwide. VAT: Stan/Spec.

Richard Philp `BADA`
7 Ravenscourt Sq. W6 0TW. Est. 1961. Open
by appointment. *STOCK: Old Master drawings,
16th-17th C English portraiture and Old Master
paintings, medieval sculpture, early furniture
and 20th C drawings, £50-£40,000.* PARK:
Easy. TEL: 020 8748 5678; website - www.
richardphilp.com. FAIRS: Grosvenor House.
VAT: Spec.

W8

AntikWest AB
150-152 Kensington Church St. W8 4BN. (Bjorn
Gremner and Jonathan Robinson). KCSADA.
CINOA. Est. 1979. Open 10-6, Sat. 10-4. SIZE:
Small. *STOCK: Chinese pottery and porcelain,
Tang to late 19th C, £200-£35,000; Chinese
furniture, £200-£2,000.* LOC: 100 yards south of
Notting Hill Gate. PARK: Meters. TEL: 020 7229
4115; website - www.antikwest.com. FAIRS:
Olympia (June); Eurantica, Brussels; Stockholm,
Alvsjo; Helsingborg, Sweden; Hong Kong
International. VAT: Spec.

Valerie Arieta
97b Kensington Church St. W8 7LN. Est. 1972.
Open 10.30-5, appointment advisable. *STOCK:
American Indian and Eskimo art; English and
Continental antiques.* TEL: 020 7243 1074/7794
7613.

Garry Atkins
107 Kensington Church St. W8 7LN. (Garry and
Julie Atkins). KCSADA. Est. 1986. Open 10-
5.30, Sat. am. by appointment. SIZE: Small.
*STOCK: English and Continental pottery, to 18th
C, £100-£10,000.* LOC: Between Kensington
High St. and Notting Hill Gate. PARK: Meters.
TEL: 020 7727 8737; fax - 020 7792 9010; e-mail
- garry.atkins@englishpottery.co; website -
www.englishpottery.co. SER: Valuations; buys at
auction (English and Continental pottery); annual

exhibition (March), catalogues available. FAIRS:
New York Ceramic. VAT: Spec.

Gregg Baker Asian Art `BADA` `LAPADA`
132 Kensington Church St. W8 4BH.
KCSADA. Est. 1985. Open 10-6, Sat. 11-4 or
by appointment. SIZE: Small. *STOCK:
Japanese and Chinese works of art and screens,
mainly 18th-19th C, £500-£250,000.* PARK:
Meters. TEL: 020 7221 3533; fax - 020 7221
4410; e-mail - gbakerart@aol.com; website -
www.greggbaker.com. SER: Valuations.
FAIRS: Olympia (June); NY Asian Art
(March). VAT: Stan/Spec.

Eddy Bardawil `BADA`
106 Kensington Church St. W8 4BH. (E.S.
Bardawil). KCSADA. Est. 1979. Open 10-1 and
2-5.30, Sat. 10-1.30. SIZE: Medium. *STOCK:
English furniture - mahogany, satinwood,
walnut; mirrors, brassware, tea-caddies, all pre-
1830, £500-£50,000; prints, 18th C.* LOC:
Corner premises, Berkeley Gardens/Church St.
PARK: Easy. TEL: 020 7221 3967; fax - 020
7221 5124. SER: Valuations; restorations
(furniture); polishing. VAT: Stan/Spec.

Baumkotter Galler `LAPADA`
63a Kensington Church St. W8 4BA. (Mrs L.
Baumkotter). KCSADA. Est. 1968. Open 10-
5.30, Sat. by appointment. SIZE: Large. *STOCK:
17th-19th C oil paintings.* TEL: 020 7937 5171;
fax - 020 7938 2312; e-mail - n.baumkotter
@btclick.com. VAT: Spec.

Berwald Oriental Art `BADA`
101 Kensington Church St. W8 7LN. (John R.
Berwald). KCSADA. Est. 1986. Open Mon.-
Fri. 10-6, other times by appointment. SIZE:
Medium. *STOCK: Chinese porcelain, 16th to
early 18th C; Chinese pottery, 200BC to 15th C;
Oriental works of art; all £1,000-£100,000.*
PARK: Meters and nearby. TEL: 020 7229
0800; fax - 020 7229 1101; e-mail -
info@berwald-oriental.com; website - www.
berwald-oriental.com. SER: Valuations;
restorations; buys at auction (Oriental).
FAIRS: Asian Arts, New York; International
Ceramics, London; IFAAD, New York. VAT:
Spec.

David Brower Antiques
113 Kensington Church St. W8 7LN. KCSADA.
Est. 1970. Open 10.30-5.30. CL: Sat. SIZE:
Large. *STOCK: Specialist in Meissen, KPM,
European and Oriental porcelain, French
bronzes and Japanese works of art.* PARK:
Meters nearby. TEL: 020 7221 4155; fax - 020

7221 6211; e-mail - David@davidbrower-antiques.com; website - www.davidbrower-antiques.com. SER: Buys at auction. FAIRS: Olympia (June). VAT: Stan/Spec.

Butchoff Antiques `LAPADA`
154 Kensington Church St. W8 4BN. (Ian Butchoff). Est. 1964. Open 9.30-6, Sat. 9.30-4. SIZE: Large. *STOCK: Fine 18th-19th C English and Continental furniture, mirrors, lighting, objets d'art and paintings, £500-£50,000.* PARK: Easy. TEL: 020 7221 8174; fax - 020 7792 8923; e-mail - enquiries@butchoff.com; website - www.butchoff.com. SER: Restorations (furniture). FAIRS: Olympia (June).

The Lucy B. Campbell Gallery `BADA`
123 Kensington Church St. W8 7LP. KCSADA. Est. 1983. Open 10-6, Sat. 10-4. SIZE: Medium. *STOCK: Figurative, contemporary, naive and botanical paintings.* PARK: Meters. TEL: 020 7727 2205; fax - 020 7229 4252; e-mail - lucy@lucybcampbell. co.uk; website - www.lucybcampbell.com. SER: Framing. FAIRS: Olympia (Spring). VAT: Stan.

Cohen & Cohen `BADA`
101B Kensington Church St. W8 7LN. (Ewa and Michael Cohen). KCSADA. Est. 1973. Open 10-6, Sat. 11-4. SIZE: Large. *STOCK: Chinese export porcelain and works of art.* TEL: 020 7727 7677; fax - 020 7229 9653; e-mail - cohenandcohen@aol.com. SER: Valuations; buys at auction. FAIRS: Grosvenor House. VAT: Stan/Spec.

Garrick D. Coleman
5 Kensington Court. W8 5DL. (G.D. and G.E. Coleman). Est. 1944. Open by appointment. SIZE: Medium. *STOCK: Chess sets, 1750-1880, £100-£4,000; decorative items, £50-£2,000; glass paperweights, £200-£3,000; conjuring and magic items.* PARK: Easy. TEL: 020 7937 5524; fax - 020 7937 5530; e-mail - coleman-antiques-london@compuserve.com; website - www.antiquechess.co.uk/. VAT: Stan/Spec.

Mrs. M.E. Crick Chandeliers
166 Kensington Church St. W8 4BN. (M.T. Denton). Est. 1897. Open Mon.-Fri. 9.30-5.30. *STOCK: English and Continental crystal, glass and ormulu chandeliers, 18th-19th C.* TEL: 020 7229 1338; fax - 020 7792 1073.

Denton Antiques
156 Kensington Church St. W8 4BN. (M.T. Denton). Open Mon.-Fri. 9.30-5.30. *STOCK:*

Glass, chandeliers, candelabra, 18th-19th C. TEL: 020 7229 5866; fax - 020 7792 1073.

H. and W. Deutsch Antiques `LAPADA`
111 Kensington Church St. W8 7LN. Est. 1897. Open 10-5. CL: Tues., Wed. and Sat. SIZE: Large. *STOCK: 18th-19th C Continental and English porcelain and glassware; silver, plate and enamel ware, miniature portraits; Oriental porcelain, cloisonné, bronzes, £300-£5,000.* TEL: 020 7727 5984. VAT: Stan/Spec.

Peter Farlow
34 Kensington Church St. W8 4HA. Est. 1986. Open 9.30-5, Sat. 11-4. SIZE: Small. *STOCK: Decorative arts, original painted furniture.* PARK: NCP Kensington High St. TEL: 020 7937 3388; fax - 020 7937 5588. VAT: Stan/Spec.

C. Fredericks and Son `BADA`
142 Kensington Church St. W8 4BN. (R.F. Fredericks). KCSADA. Est. 1947. Open 9.30-5.30, Sat. by appointment. SIZE: Large. *STOCK: Furniture, 18th C, £500-£15,000.* LOC: Near Notting Hill Gate underground station. TEL: 020 7727 2240; fax - same; mobile - 07831 336937; e-mail - antiques@ cfredericksandson.freeserve.co.uk. SER: Restorations. FAIRS: BADA; Olympia (Winter). VAT: Stan/Spec.

Michael German Antiques Ltd `BADA` `LAPADA`
38B Kensington Church St. W8 4BX. KCSADA. Est. 1954. Open 10-5, Sat. 10-12.30. *STOCK: European and Oriental arms and armour; walking stick specialist.* TEL: 020 7937 2771; fax - 020 7937 8566; websites - www. antiquecanes.com and www.antiqueweapons. com.

Green's Antique Galleries
117 Kensington Church St. W8 7LN. (S. Green). Open 9-5. SIZE: Medium. *STOCK: Jewellery, 18th C to date; pre-1930 clothes and lace; dolls, china, silver, furniture, paintings, masonic, crocodile and leather items.* PARK: Easy. TEL: 020 7229 9618. VAT: Stan/Spec.

Robert Hales Antiques
131 Kensington Church St. W8 7LP. Est. 1973. Open Tues.-Fri. 9.30-5.30 preferably by appointment. SIZE: Small. *STOCK: Fine Islamic and Oriental arms and armour, 15th-19th C, £300-£50,000+.* TEL: 020 7229 3887; e-mail - RHAntique@aol.com. SER: Valuations; buys at auction. FAIRS: Park Lane Arms (Feb). VAT: Spec.

Adrian Harrington

64A Kensington Church St. W8 4DB. KCSADA. ABA. ILAB. PBFA. Est. 1970. Open 10-6. SIZE: Large. *STOCK: Fine and rare antiquarian books, first editions, literature, children's, fore-edge paintings, library sets, Winston Churchill.* LOC: 5 mins. from Kensington High St. and Notting Hill Gate underground stations. PARK: Meters. TEL: 020 7937 1465; fax - 020 7368 0912; e-mail - rare@harringtonbooks.co.uk; website - www. harringtonbooks.co.uk. SER: Bookbinding; restoration. FAIRS: Olympia Book (June); Chelsea Book (Nov). VAT: Stan.

Haslam and Whiteway

105 Kensington Church St. W8 7LN. (T.M. Whiteway). KCSADA. Est. 1972. Open 10-6, Sat. 10-2. SIZE: Small. *STOCK: British furniture, £300-£50,000; British decorative arts, £200-£50,000; Continental and American decorative arts, £200-£10,000; all 1850-1930.* LOC: From Notting Hill Gate underground station, into Kensington Church St., premises approx. 300yds. on right. PARK: Meters. TEL: 020 7229 1145; fax - 020 7221 7065. SER: Valuations; buys at auction. VAT: Stan.

Jeanette Hayhurst Fine Glass `BADA`

32A Kensington Church St. W8 4BX. KCSADA. Open 10-5, Sat. 12-5. *STOCK: Glass - 18th C English drinking, fine 19th C engraved, table decanters, contemporary art, scent bottles, Roman and Continental.* **TEL: 020 7938 1539.**

D. Holmes

47c Earls Court Rd. (in Abingdon Villas), Kensington. W8 6EE. (Don and Sarah Holmes). Est. 1965. Open Fri. 9-7, Sat. 9-2 or by appointment. *STOCK: Decorative items and furniture, 18th-19th C.* PARK: Meters. TEL: 020 7937 6961 or 01208 880254; mobile - 07790 431895. SER: Restorations (furniture). FAIRS: Olympia (June). VAT: Stan/Spec.

Hope and Glory

(Commemorative Ceramics Specialists) 131a Kensington Church St. W8 7LP. (R.R. Lower). KCSADA. Est. 1982. Open 10-5. *STOCK: Commemorative china.* LOC: Entrance in Peel St. TEL: 020 7727 8424. SER: Mail order (no catalogue).

Jonathan Horne `BADA`

66c Kensington Church St. W8 4BY. CINOA. KCSADA. Est. 1968. Open 9.30-5.30, Sat. and Sun. by appointment. SIZE: Medium. *STOCK: Early English pottery, needlework and works of art.* **TEL: 020 7221 5658; fax - 020 7792 3090;** e-mail - JH@jonathanhorne.co.uk; website - www.jonathanhorne.co.uk. SER: Valuations. FAIRS: BADA; Olympia (June and Nov); International Ceramics; New York Ceramics; Buxton; IFAAD. VAT: Stan/Spec.

Iona Antiques `BADA`

PO Box 285. W8 6HZ. Est. 1974. Open by appointment. SIZE: Large. *STOCK: 19th C animal paintings, £1,000-£30,000.* **LOC: 3 mins. walk from Odeon Cinema, Kensington High St. PARK: Nearby. TEL: 020 7602 1193; fax - 020 7371 2843; e-mail - iona@ ionaantiques.com; website - www.iona antiques.com. FAIRS: Grosvenor House, Olympia.**

J.A.N. Fine Art

134 Kensington Church St. W8. (Mrs F.K. Shimizu). KCSADA. Est. 1976. Open 10-6, Sat. by appointment. SIZE: Medium. *STOCK: Japanese and Chinese porcelain, 1st to 20th C, from £150; Japanese bronzes and works of art, 15th-20th C, from £150; Japanese paintings and screens, 16th-20th C, from £250; Tibetan thankas and ritual objects, 12th-18th C, from £250.* PARK: Meters. TEL: 020 7792 0736; fax - 020 7221 1380. VAT: Spec.

Japanese Gallery

66d Kensington Church St. W8 4BY. (Mr and Mrs C.D. Wertheim). Est. 1977. Open 10-6. *STOCK: Japanese wood-cut prints; books, porcelain, netsuke.* TEL: 020 7229 2934; fax - same; e-mail - sales@japanesegallery.co.uk; website - www.japanesegallery.co.uk. SER: Free authentification; on-the-spot framing for Japanese prints; sales exhibitions.

Roderick Jellicoe `BADA`

3A Campden St., off Kensington Church St. W8 4EP. KCSADA. Est. 1974. Open 10-5.30, Sat. by appointment. SIZE: Medium. *STOCK: English porcelain, 18th-19th C, £50-£20,000.* **PARK: Meters. TEL: 020 7727 1571; mobile - 07775 580051; e-mail - Jellicoe@English Porcelain.com; website - www.English Porcelain.com. SER: Valuations; buys at auction (18th C English porcelain). VAT: Spec.**

John Jesse

160 Kensington Church St. W8 4BN. KCSADA. Est. 1963. Open 10-6, Sat. 11-4. *STOCK: Decorative arts, 1880-1980, especially Art Nouveau and Art Deco silver, glass, bronzes and jewellery.* TEL: 020 7229 0312; fax - 020 7229 4732; e-mail - jj@johnjesse.com; website - www.johnjesse.com.

Howard Jones - The Silver Shop
43 Kensington Church St. W8 4BA. (H. Howard-Jones). Est. 1971. Open 9.30-5.30. SIZE: Small. *STOCK: Silver, antique and modern, £10-£3,000.* PARK: Nearby. TEL: 020 7937 4359; fax - same. VAT: Stan.

Peter Kemp
170 Kensington Church St. W8 4BN. KCSADA. Est. 1975. Open 10-5. CL: Sat. SIZE: Medium. *STOCK: Porcelain - 10th-19th C Chinese, 17th-19th C Japanese, 18th C Continental; Oriental works of art and porcelain, 18th-19th C.* LOC: 200yds. from Notting Hill underground station. PARK: Meters nearby. TEL: 020 7229 2988. SER: Valuations; restorations (porcelain). VAT: Spec.

Kensington Church Street Antiques Centre
58-60 Kensington Church St. W8 4DB. KCSADA. Open 10-6. Below are listed some of the dealers at this Centre. TEL: 020 7376 0425; fax - 020 7937 3400.

Abstract `LAPADA`
20th C decorative and design. TEL: 020 7376 2652; fax - same; website - www.abstract-antiques.com.

Nigel Benson
20th C glass, British 1870-1980 including Powell, Monart/Vasart; post-war Scandanavian and Italian. TEL: 020 7938 1137; home - 020 7729 9875; fax - same.

Nicolaus Boston
Majolica, Palissy, Dresser and Aesthetic movement porcelain. TEL: 020 7937 2237; fax - 020 8944 1280. VAT: Stan/Spec.

Didier Antiques `LAPADA`
Open by appointment only. *Jewellery and silver, objets d'art, 1860-1960.* TEL: 020 7938 2537; fax - same. VAT: Stan/Spec.

F C R Gallery
20th C fine art and design. TEL: 020 7938 5385.

Jag
20th C decorative arts, Liberty pewter and silver, terracotta and watercolours by Archibald Knox. TEL: 020 7938 4404; fax - same.

Colin Monk
Oriental porcelain. TEL: 020 7229 3727; fax - 020 7376 1501.

Robert Peterson Ltd.
19th-20th C decorative arts, all the major movements. TEL: 020 7937 8319; mobile - 07768 951617; e-mail - info@20th.co.uk; website - www.20th.co.uk.

Zeitgeist
Continental Art Nouveau and Art Deco metalware, ceramics and glass. TEL: 020 7938 4817; fax - same; e-mail - zeitgeistantiques@btopenworld. com; website - www.zeitgeistantiques.com. Stan/Spec.

The Lacquer Chest
71 and 75 Kensington Church St. W8 4BG. (G. and V. Andersen). Est. 1959. Open 9.30-5.30, Sat. 10.30-3. SIZE: Large. *STOCK: Furniture - painted, oak, mahogany; blue and white, Staffordshire, lamps, candlesticks, samplers, prints, paintings, brass, mirrors, garden furniture, unusual items.* LOC: Half-way up left-hand side from High St. PARK: Meters. TEL: 020 7937 1306; fax - 020 7376 0223. VAT: Stan/Spec.

Lev (Antiques) Ltd
97A & B Kensington Church St. W8 7LN. (Mrs Lev). Est. 1882. Open 10.30-5.30. SIZE: Medium. *STOCK: Jewellery, silver, plate, curios and pictures.* PARK: Meters. TEL: 020 7727 9248; fax - same. SER: Restorations (pictures).

Lewis and Lloyd `BADA`
65 Kensington Church St. W8 4BA. KCSADA. Est. 1968. Open 10.15-5.00, Sat. 10-2.30. SIZE: Medium. *STOCK: Furniture and works of art, 18th-19th C, £2,000-£100,000.* **PARK: Easy. TEL: 020 7938 3323; fax - 020 7361 0086; e-mail - pclewis2000@aol.com. FAIRS: Olympia (Feb., June and Nov). VAT: Spec.**

Libra Antiques
131d Kensington Church St. W8. KCSADA. *STOCK: Blue and white pottery, lustre ware.* TEL: 020 7727 2990.

London Antique Gallery
66E Kensington Church St. W8 4BY. (Mr and Mrs C.D. Wertheim). Open 10-6. *STOCK: Porcelain including English, Worcester, Meissen, Dresden and Sèvres; French and German bisque dolls.* TEL: 020 7229 2934; fax - same. SER: Restorations (prints, porcelain and dolls).

E. and H. Manners `BADA`
66a Kensington Church St. W8 4BY. (Errol and Henriette Manners). KCSADA. Est. 1986. Open Mon.-Fri. 10-5.30 appointment advisable. *STOCK: European ceramics, pre-19th C, £100-£20,000.* **TEL: 020 7229 5516; fax - same; home - 020 8741 7084; e-mail - manners@europeanporcelain.com; website - www.europeanporcelain.com. FAIRS: International Ceramic. VAT: Spec.**

S. Marchant & Son   BADA
120 Kensington Church St. W8 4BH. (R.P. and S.J. Marchant). KCSADA. Est. 1925. Open 9.30-5.30. CL: Sat. *STOCK: Chinese and Japanese pottery and porcelain, jades, cloisonné, Chinese furniture and paintings.* PARK: Easy. TEL: 020 7229 5319/3770; fax - 020 7792 8979; e-mail - marchant@dircon. co.uk; website - www.marchantasianart.com. SER: Valuations; restorations (porcelain); buys at auction. FAIRS: Grosvenor House; Asian Art New York and Paris; IFAAD, New York. VAT: Stan/Spec.

R. and G. McPherson Antiques   BADA
40 Kensington Church St. W8 4BX. (Roger and Georgina McPherson). KCSADA. Est. 1985. Open 10-5.30, Sat. 10-1. SIZE: Large. *STOCK: Chinese, Japanese and other south-east Asian ceramics, including early monochromes, Chinese export ware, shipwreck ceramics, blue and white and blanc de Chine.* LOC: Kensington High St. underground station. PARK: Meters. TEL: 020 7937 0812; fax - 020 7938 2032; mobile - 07768 432630; e-mail - rmcpherson@orientalceramics.com; website - www.orientalceramics.com. SER: Valuations (verbal); identification. FAIRS: Olympia (June). VAT: Spec.

Michael Coins
6 Hillgate St., (off Notting Hill Gate). W8 7SR. (M. Gouby). Est. 1966. Open 10-5. CL: Mon. and Sat. SIZE: Small. *STOCK: Coins, English and foreign, 1066 A.D. to date; stamps, banknotes and general items.* LOC: From Marble Arch to Notting Hill Gate, turn left at corner of Coronet Cinema. PARK: Easy. TEL: 020 7727 1518; fax - 020 7727 1518; website - www.michael-coins.co.uk. SER: Valuations; buys at auction. VAT: Stan/Spec.

Arthur Millner
2 Campden St. W8 7EP. KCSADA. Est. 1996. Open Tues.-Fri. 12-6, Sat. 10-3. SIZE: Small. *STOCK: Indian objects, 16th-19th C, up to £4,000; Indian paintings, 18th-19th C, £200-£1,500; Islamic art, 16th-18th C, £1,000-£5,000.* LOC: Off Kensington Church St., Notting Hill Gate underground station. PARK: Meters. TEL: 020 7229 3268; fax - same; e-mail - info@arthurmillner.com; website - www. arthurmillner.com. SER: Valuations. FAIRS: Olympia; San Francisco (Fall). VAT: Spec.

New Century
69 Kensington Church St. W8 4BG. (H.S. Lyons). KCSADA. Est. 1988. *STOCK: Arts and Crafts, aesthetic and Art Nouveau furniture,*

metal, glass and ceramics, 1860-1910, £20-£10,000. TEL: 020 7937 2410. SER: Valuations; restorations; buys at auction. VAT: Stan/Spec.

Pawsey and Payne [BADA]
PO Box 11830 W8. (Hon. N.V.B. and L.N.J. Wallop). Est. 1910. Open by appointment. *STOCK: English oils and watercolours, 18th-19th C.* TEL: 020 7930 4221; fax - 020 7937 3440; e-mail - nicholas.wallop@btclick.com. SER: Valuations; restorations. VAT: Stan/Spec.

Pruskin Gallery
73 Kensington Church St. W8 4BG. KCSADA. *STOCK: Fine Art Nouveau and Art Deco glass, bronzes, silver, furniture, ceramics, paintings, posters and prints.* TEL: 020 7937 1994; evenings - 020 7938 2892.

Raffety & Walwyn [BADA] [LAPADA]
79 Kensington Church St. W8 4BG. CINOA. KCSADA. Open 10.00-5.30, Sat. 11-2.30. *STOCK: Fine English longcase and bracket clocks, 17th-18th C; barometers and period furniture.* TEL: 020 7938 1100; fax - 020 7938 2519; e-mail - raffety@globalnet.co.uk; website - www.raffetyantiqueclocks.com. SER: Valuations; buys at auction. FAIRS: BADA, Olympia (June). VAT: Stan/Spec.

Paul Reeves
32B Kensington Church St. W8 4HA. Est. 1976. Open 10-6, Sat. 11-4. *STOCK: Architect designed furniture and artifacts, 1860-1960.* TEL: 020 7937 1594.

Reindeer Antiques Ltd [BADA] [LAPADA]
81 Kensington Church St. W8 4BG. (Adrian Butterworth and Peter Alexander). KCSADA. Open 9.30-6, Sat. 10.30-5.30. *STOCK: Period English and Continental furniture and works of art.* PARK: Meters. TEL: 020 7937 3754; fax - 020 7937 7199; e-mail - pejwal@hotmail.com; website - www.reindeerantiques.co.uk. FAIRS: BADA. VAT: Stan/Spec.

Roderick Antique Clocks [LAPADA]
23 Vicarage Gate, Kensington. W8 4AA. (Roderick Mee). KCSADA. Est. 1975. Open 10-5.15, Sat. 10-4. *STOCK: Clocks - French decorative and carriage, 19th C, £250-£3,500; English longcase and bracket, 18th-19th C, £2,000-£12,000.* LOC: At junction of Kensington Church St. PARK: Easy. TEL: 020 7937 8517; e-mail - rick@roderickantiqueclocks.com; website - www.roderickantiqueclocks.com. SER: Valuations; restorations (English and French movements and cases). VAT: Spec.

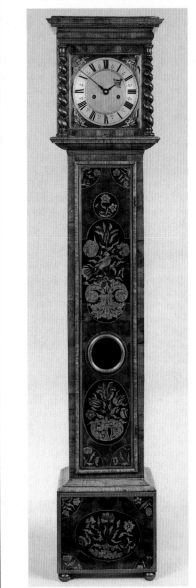

Raffety & Walwyn
79 Kensington Church Street,
London W8 4BG
Tel: 020 7938 1100

JOHN HUNT, LONDON
A fine small late 17th century longcase clock with 10in square dial. The case is veneered with olivewood oysters and panels of flowers and bird marquetry. Circa 1690. Height: 75in (191cm)

John Hunt was a member of the Clockmakers Company and was active in the last quarter of the 17th century

Brian Rolleston Antiques Ltd `BADA`
104A Kensington Church St. W8 4BU.
KCSADA. Est. 1950. Open 10-1 and 2-5.30.
SIZE: Large. *STOCK: English furniture, 18th
C.* TEL: 020 7229 5892; fax - same; e-mail -
antiques@brianrolleston.freeserve.co.uk.
FAIRS: Grosvenor House.

Patrick Sandberg Antiques `BADA`
150-152 Kensington Church St. W8 4BN. (P.C.F.
Sandberg). KCSADA. Est. 1983. Open 10-6, Sat.
10-4. SIZE: Large. *STOCK: 18th to early 19th C
English furniture and accessories - candlesticks,
tea caddies, clocks and prints.* TEL: 020 7229
0373; fax - 020 7792 3467. FAIRS: Olympia
(Feb., June, and Nov). VAT: Spec.

Santos `BADA`
21 Old Court House. W8 4PD. CINOA. Open
by appointment. *STOCK: Chinese export
porcelain, 17th-18th C.* TEL: 020 7937 6000;
fax - 020 7937 3351; e-mail - companhiaindias
@aol.com; website - www.santoslondon.com.
VAT: Spec.

Sinai Antiques Ltd
219-221 Kensington Church St. W8 7LX. (E.
Sinai Ltd). KCSADA. Est. 1973. Open 10-6, Sat.
and Sun. by appointment. *STOCK: Fine 19th C
Continental furniture, clocks, porcelain,
chandeliers and objet d' art; Oriental and Islamic
decorative arts and antiques.* TEL: 020 7229
6190; fax - 020 7221 0543.

Simon Spero
109 Kensington Church St. W8 7LN. Author of
'The Price Guide to 18th C English Porcelain'
and three other standard reference books.
KCSADA. Est. 1964. Open 10-5, Sat. by
appointment. SIZE: Medium. *STOCK: 18th C
English ceramics and enamels.* PARK: Meters.
TEL: 020 7727 7413; fax - 020 7727 7414. SER:
Valuations; buys at auction; lecturer. VAT: Spec.

Stockspring Antiques `BADA` `LAPADA`
114 Kensington Church St. W8 4BH. (Antonia
Agnew and Felicity Marno). KCSADA. Est.
1979. Open 10-5.30, Sat. 10-1. SIZE: 2 floors.
*STOCK: English, European and Oriental pottery
and porcelain.* TEL: 020 7727 7995; fax - same;
e-mail - stockspring@antique-porcelain.co.uk.
SER: Packing and shipping; valuations. FAIRS:
Olympia (June and Nov). VAT: Spec.

Pamela Teignmouth and Son
108 Kensington Church St. W8 4BH. (Pamela
Teignmouth and T. Meyer). Est. 1982. Open 10-6,
including Sat. in winter only. SIZE: Medium.

*STOCK: English and Continental furniture, 18th-
19th C, decorative items, £100-£10,000.* PARK:
Meters. TEL: 020 7229 1602; fax - 020 7792
5042. VAT: Spec.

Through the Looking Glass Ltd
137 Kensington Church St. W8 7LP. (J.J.A. and
D.A. Pulton). KCSADA. Est. 1958. Open 10-
5.30. SIZE: Large. *STOCK: Mirrors, 19th C,
£500-£10,000.* LOC: 200yds. from Notting Hill
Gate. PARK: Side roads. TEL: 020 7221 4026;
fax - 020 7602 3678. VAT: Spec.

Geoffrey Waters Ltd `BADA`
133 Kensington Church St. W8 7LP. Open
10.15-5.30, Sat. 10.30-4.30. SIZE: Medium.
*STOCK: 16th-18th C Chinese porcelain, mainly
export.* TEL: 020 7243 6081; fax - 020 7243
6081.

**Jorge Welsh Oriental Porcelain &
Works of Art** `BADA`
116 Kensington Church St. W8 4BH.
KCSADA. Est. 1987. Open 10-5.30, Sat. 10-2.
SIZE: Medium. *STOCK: Chinese export
porcelain and Oriental works of art.* LOC: Off
Kensington High St. PARK: NCP Bayswater
Rd. TEL: 020 7229 2140; fax - 020 7792 3535;
e-mail - uk@jorgewelsh.com; website - www.
jorgewelsh.com. SER: Valuations;
restorations; buys at auction. FAIRS:
International Ceramic. VAT: Spec.

Neil Wibroe and Natasha MacIlwaine
77 Kensington Church St. W8 4BG. Est. 1984.
Open 9-6. *STOCK: 18th C English furniture and
works of art.* TEL: 020 7937 2461; fax - 020 7938
3286; mobile - 07831 748433. SER: Restorations.

Mary Wise & Grosvenor Antiques
`BADA`
27 Holland St., Kensington. W8 4NA.
(Elisabeth Lorie). Est. 1959. Open Mon.-Fri.
10-5 or by appointment. *STOCK: English
porcelain, works of art, bronzes, Chinese
paintings.* Not Stocked: English pottery,
jewellery. PARK: Meters and nearby. TEL:
020 7937 8649; fax - 020 7937 7179; e-mail -
info@wiseantiques.com; website - www.
wiseantiques.com. SER: Buys at auction
(Chinese and English porcelain). FAIRS:
BADA; Grosvenor House; Olympia (Nov); San
Francisco. VAT: Spec.

W9

Fluss and Charlesworth Ltd `LAPADA`
1 Lauderdale Rd. W9 1LT. (E. Fluss and J.

Charlesworth). Est. 1970. Open by appointment. *STOCK: 18th to early 19th C furniture and works of art.* TEL: 020 7286 8339; mobile - 07831 830323. SER: Interior decor. FAIRS: Olympia; LAPADA.

Beryl Kendall, The English Watercolour Gallery
2 Warwick Place, Little Venice. W9 2PX. Est. 1953. Open 2-6, Sat. 11-3.30. CL: Mon. *STOCK: English watercolours, 19th C.* PARK: Easy. TEL: 020 7286 9902.

Vale Antiques
245 Elgin Ave., Maida Vale. W9 1NJ. (P. Gooley). *STOCK: General antiques.* TEL: 020 7328 4796.

W10

Crawley and Asquith Ltd BADA
133 Oxford Gardens. W10 6NE. Open by appointment. *STOCK: 18th-19th C paintings, watercolours, prints, books.* TEL: 020 8969 6161; fax - 020 8960 6494.

W11

Admiral Vernon Antiques Market
141-149 Portobello Rd. W11 2DY. (Angelo Soteriades). PADA. Est. 1995. Open Sat. 5-5. SIZE: 200+ dealers. *STOCK: Wide range of general antiques and collectables.* TEL: 020 7727 5242; mobile - 07956 277077; e-mail - info@portobello-antiques.com; website - www.portobello-antiques.co.uk. SER: Valuations; repairs (pens, jewellery, watches, and lighter).

Alice's
86 Portobello Rd. W11 2QD. (D. Carter). Est. 1960. Open Tues.-Fri. 9-5, Sat. 7-4. SIZE: Large. *STOCK: General antiques and decorative items.* TEL: 020 7229 8187; fax - 020 7792 2456.

Arbras Gallery
292 Westbourne Grove. W11 2PS. Est. 1972. Open Fri. 10-4, Sat. 7-5. SIZE: 2 floors. *STOCK: General antiques - silver, jewellery, glass, porcelain, clocks, scientific instruments, decorative arts and antiquities.* LOC: 50 yards from Portobello Road. TEL: 020 7229 6772; fax - same. VAT: Stan/Spec.

Axia Art Consultants Ltd
121 Ledbury Rd. W11 2AQ. Est. 1974. Open Mon.-Fri. 10-6. *STOCK: Works of art, icons, textiles, metalwork, woodwork and ceramics, Islamic and Byzantine.* TEL: 020 7727 9724; fax - 020 7229 1272.

B. and T. Antiques LAPADA
79/81 Ledbury Rd. W11 2AG. (Mrs B. Lewis). Open 10-6. *STOCK: Furniture especially mirrored, silver, objets d'art, Art Deco.* PARK: Easy. TEL: 020 7229 7001; fax - 020 7229 2033; e-mail - bt.antiques@virgin.net. VAT: Spec.

Sebastiano Barbagallo
15-17 Pembridge Rd., Notting Hill Gate. W11 3HL. Est. 1975. Open 10.30-6 including Sun., Sat. 9-7. SIZE: Medium. *STOCK: Chinese furniture; antiques and handicrafts from India, Tibet, SE Asia and China.* LOC: Just before Portobello Road. TEL: 020 7792 3320; fax - same. VAT: Stan.

Barham Antiques
83 Portobello Rd. W11. Est. 1954. Open 9.30-5, Sat. 7-5. SIZE: Large. *STOCK: Victorian and Georgian writing boxes, tea caddies, inkwells and inkstands, glass epergnes, silver plate, clocks, paintings, Victorian furniture, tantalus and jewellery boxes.* TEL: 020 7727 3845; fax - same; e-mail - mchlbarham@aol.com; website - www.barhamantiques.co.uk. SER: Valuations; buys at auction.

Elizabeth Bradwin
Stands 1 & 2, 75 Portobello Rd. W11 2QB. PADA. Est. 1989. Open 10.30-4.30, Sat. 7-5. SIZE: Small. *STOCK: Animal subjects including animalier bronzes, 19th-20th C, £100-£4,000; Vienna bronzes, Staffordshire, carved wood, inkwells, tobacco jars.* PARK: Easy. TEL: 020 7221 1121; home and fax - 020 8947 2629; mobile - 07778 731826; e-mail - eliz@elizabethbradwin.com; website - www.elizabethbradwin.com. VAT: Spec.

Caelt Gallery
182 Westbourne Grove. W11 2RH. Est. 1967. Open 9.30-8, Sun. 10.30-6. SIZE: Large. *STOCK: Oil paintings, 17th-20th C, £200-£10,000 but mainly £300-£900.* PARK: Easy. TEL: 020 7229 9309; fax - 020 7727 8746; e-mail - art@caeltgallery.com; website - www.caeltgallery.com. SER: Re-lining; restorations; framing. VAT: Spec.

Jack Casimir Ltd BADA LAPADA
23 Pembridge Rd. W11 3HG. Est. 1933. Open 10-5.30 and by appointment. SIZE: Large. *STOCK: 16th - 19th C British and European brass, copper, pewter, paktong.* Not Stocked: Silver, china, jewellery. LOC: 2 mins. walk from Notting Hill Gate underground station. PARK: 100yds. TEL: 020 7727 8643. SER: Exports. VAT: Stan/Spec.

Central Gallery (Portobello)

125 Portobello Rd. W11 2DY. (C. Hickey). Est. 1996. Open Sat. 6-3. SIZE: 25+ dealers. *STOCK: Jewellery - 18th C to 1960's, including cameos, hardstone, shell, lava, coral, amber, ivory, jet, tortoiseshell, piqué, micro-mosaics, pietra-dura, Art Nouveau, plique é jour, horn pendants, Art Deco, enamels, Austro-Hungarian, cut-steel, Berlin iron, Scottish, Victorian silver and gold, Alberts, Albertines, longuards, curbs, gates, fobs, seals, intaglios, pocket watches, vintage wristwatches, cufflinks, fine diamonds, rare gemstones, signed pieces, pearls, from £50-£5,000+.* LOC: Notting Hill. PARK: Pay and Display. TEL: 020 7243 8027; fax - same. FAIRS: Olympia; Park Lane Hotel (every Sunday); NEC. VAT: Stan/Spec/Global.

Chelsea Clocks & Antiques

73 Portobello Rd., Notting Hill. W11 2QB. (Donald Lynch). PADA. Est. 1978. Open 10-5. SIZE: Small. *STOCK: English, French and German clocks, especially dial, 1800-1930, £150-£10,000; brass, fireplace tools, stationery items, globes, boxes, scales, barometers.* PARK: Easy. TEL: 020 7229 7762; fax - 020 7274 5198; e-mail - info@chelseaclocks.co.uk; website - www.chelseaclocks.co.uk.

The Coach House   `BADA` `LAPADA`

Ledbury Mews North, Notting Hill. W11 2AF. (Jay Arenski and Peter Petrou). Open by appointment. *STOCK: Fine furniture - Regency, Gothic Revival, Arts & Crafts, Aesthetic, Colonial and Campaign, Islamic and Egyptian Revival; oil paintings including maritime, Old Masters and modern, naïve portraits including animal, watercolours and prints; classical and Vienna bronzes, Grand Tour items, ormolu, metalware and treen; decorative glass, silver and plate, pottery including majolica, equestrian objects and tribal art, £200-£200,000.* **Not Stocked: Shipping goods and jewellery. PARK: Easy. TEL: 020 7727 8599/7229 9575; fax - 020 7727 7584; e-mail - arenski@netcomuk.co.uk and peterpetrou@btinternet.com; websites - www. arenski.com and www.peterpetrou.com. SER: Interior decor; shipping arranged. FAIRS: Olympia (June); BADA (May). VAT: Stan/Spec.**

Garrick D. Coleman

75 Portobello Rd. W11 2QB. Est. 1944. Open 10.30-4.30, Sat. 8.30-3.30. *STOCK: Chess sets, 1750-1880, £300-£15,000; works of art £50-£3,000; glass paperweights, £200-£3,000; also conjuring and magic items.* TEL: 020 7937 5524; fax - 020 7937 5530; e-mail - coleman-antiques-london@compuserve.com; website - www. antiquechess.co.uk/. VAT: Stan/Spec.

Sheila Cook

283 Westbourne Grove. W11 2QA. Est. 1970. Open Fri. and Sat. 10-6. SIZE: Medium. *STOCK: Textiles, costume and accessories, 1750-1980, £15-£3,000.* LOC: Corner of Portobello Rd. PARK: Meters. TEL: 020 7792 8001; fax - 020 7229 3855; e-mail - sheilacook@ sheilacook.co.uk; website - www.sheilacook. co.uk. SER: Valuations. VAT: Global/Spec.

The Corner Portobello Antiques Supermarket

282-290 Westbourne Grove. W11. (B. Lipka & Son Ltd). Open Fri. 12-4, Sat. 7-5. SIZE: 150 dealers. *STOCK: General miniature antiques, silver and jewellery.* TEL: 020 7727 2027. SER: Valuations; restorations.

Crown Arcade

119 Portobello Rd. W11. (Angelo Soteriades). PADA. Est. 1986. Open Sat. 5.30-5. SIZE: Medium, 25 stalls. *STOCK: 18th-19th C glass, bronzes, sculpture, silver, jewellery, Arts & Crafts, Art Nouveau, Art Deco, treen, boxes, humidors, tortoishell, ivory, Austrian glass, pewter, decorative prints, Italian glass, decanters, decorative objects.* LOC: Near Westbourne Grove. TEL: 020 7436 9416/7792 3619 (Sat. only); mobile - 07956 277077; e-mail - info@portobello-antiques.com; website - www.portobello-collections.co.uk. SER: Valuations.

Curá Antiques

34 Ledbury Rd. W11 2AB. (G. and M. Antichi). Open 11-6, Sat. 10.30-1. *STOCK: Continental furniture, sculptures, majolica and paintings.* TEL: 020 7229 6880; e-mail - mail@cura-antiques.com; website - www.cura-antiques.com.

Daggett Gallery   `LAPADA`

1st and 2nd Floors, 153 Portobello Rd. W11 2DY. (Caroline Daggett). Est. 1992. Open 10-5 (prior telephone call advisable), Sat. 9-3.30. SIZE: Medium. *STOCK: Frames, 18th-20th C, from £1.* LOC: 200 yards from Westbourne Grove towards Elgin Crescent. PARK: Meters. TEL: 020 7229 2248. SER: Restorations (frames); gilding; picture plaques; framing; special paint effects. VAT: Stan/Spec.

Charles Daggett Gallery   `LAPADA`

1st and 2nd Floors, 153 Portobello Rd. W11 2DY. (Charles and Caroline Daggett). Est. 1977. Open 10-4 (prior telephone call advisable), Sat. 9-3.30. SIZE: Medium. *STOCK: British pictures, 1740-1840.* LOC: 200 yards from Westbourne Grove, towards Elgin Crescent. PARK: Meters. TEL: 020 7229 2248; fax - 020 7229 0193. SER:

An oak gateleg table having two gates supporting each leaf, on baluster turned legs and stretchers, England, c.1700-15. £3,000-£5,000, making generous allowance for faults noted in catalogue description. (Sotheby's)

From an article entitled "Contemporary British Artists" by Anthony J. Lester which appeared in the March 2003 issue of ***Antique Collecting***. For more details and to subscribe see page 21.

Restorations (pictures and frames); framing. VAT: Stan/Spec.

John Dale
87 Portobello Rd. W11 2QB. Est. 1950. Open 11-3, Sat. 7-5. SIZE: Medium. *STOCK: General antiques.* TEL: 020 7727 1304. VAT: Stan.

Michael Davidson
54 Ledbury Rd., Westbourne Grove. W11 2AJ. Est. 1961. Open 9.45-12.45 and 1.15-5, Sat. 1-5. *STOCK: Regency and period furniture, objets d'art.* TEL: 020 7229 6088; fax - 020 7792 0450. SER: Valuations. VAT: Stan/Spec.

Delehar
146 Portobello Rd. W11 2DZ. Est. 1919. Open Sat. 9-4. SIZE: Medium. *STOCK: General antiques, works of art.* Not Stocked: Furniture. TEL: 020 7727 9860. VAT: Spec.

Peter Delehar
146 Portobello Rd. W11 2DZ. Est. 1919. Open Sat. 10-4. SIZE: Medium. *STOCK: Fine and interesting antique works of art, scientific and medical instruments.* TEL: 020 7727 9860 (Sat.) or 020 8423 8600; fax - same; e-mail - peter@peterdelehar.co.uk. FAIRS: International Scientific and Medical Instrument. VAT: Spec.

Demetzy Books
113 Portobello Rd. W11. (P. and M. Hutchinson). ABA. PBFA. Est. 1972. Open Sat. 7.30-3.30. SIZE: Medium. *STOCK: Antiquarian leather bound books, 18th-19th C, £5-£1,000; Dickens' first editions and children's and illustrated books, 18th-20th C, £5-£200.* LOC: 20yds. from junction with Westbourne Grove, opposite Earl of Lonsdale public house. PARK: Meters. TEL: 01993 702209. SER: Valuations; buys at auction (books). FAIRS: ABA Chelsea; PBFA Russell Hotel, London (monthly); Randolph Hotel, Oxford; York.

Gavin Douglas Fine Antiques Ltd LAPADA
75 Portobello Rd. W11 2QB. (G.A. Douglas). PADA. CINOA. Est. 1993. Open 10.30-4.30, Sat. 7.30-5. SIZE: Medium. *STOCK: Neo-classical clocks, 18th-19th C, to £100,000; bronzes, sculpture, porcelain and objects, to £50,000.* PARK: Easy. TEL: 020 7221 1121; 01825 723441; fax - 01825 724418; website - www.antique-clocks.co.uk; e-mail - gavin@antique-clocks.co.uk. SER: Valuations; restorations; buys at auction. FAIRS: Olympia (Summer, Winter and Spring); LAPADA; Harrogate; New York. VAT: Stan/Spec.

The Facade
196 Westbourne Grove. W11 2RH. Est. 1973. Open Tues.-Sat. 10.30-5. *STOCK: French and Italian decorative items and lighting, 1900-1940.* PARK: Easy. TEL: 020 7727 2159. VAT: Stan.

Fleur de Lys Gallery
227a Westbourne Grove. W11 2SE. (H.S. and B.S. Coronel). Est. 1967. Open 10.30-5.30. SIZE: Medium. *STOCK: Oil paintings, 19th C, £2,000-£8,000.* PARK: Easy, but limited. TEL: 020 7727 8595; fax - same; home - 01372 467934; e-mail - fleurdelysgallery@yahoo.com; website - www.fleur-de-lys.com. VAT: Spec.

Judy Fox `LAPADA`
81 Portobello Rd. W11 2QB. Est. 1970. Open 10-5. SIZE: Large. *STOCK: Furniture and decorative items, 18th-20th C; inlaid furniture, mainly 19th C; pottery and porcelain.* TEL: 020 7229 8130; fax - 020 7229 6998.

Graham and Green
4 Elgin Crescent. W11 2JA. (A. Graham and R. Harrison). Est. 1974. Open 10-6, Sun. 11-5. SIZE: Medium. *STOCK: Indian and Vietnamese Colonial furniture, decorative objects and textiles.* LOC: Near Portobello Rd. PARK: Nearby. TEL: 020 7727 4594; fax - 020 7229 9717; e-mail - info@grahamandgreen.co.uk; website - www.grahamandgreen.co.uk. VAT: Stan.

Gavin Graham Gallery
47 Ledbury Rd. W11 2AA. Est. 1973. *STOCK: Oil paintings.* TEL: 020 7229 4848; fax - 020 7792 9697. VAT: Spec.

Henry Gregory
82 Portobello Rd. W11 2QD. (H. and C. Gregory). Est. 1969. Open 10-4, Sat. 8-5. SIZE: Medium. *STOCK: Victorian decorative objects, silver, plate, jewellery, small furniture and sporting items, £2-£2,000.* LOC: Between Westbourne Grove and Chepstow Villas. PARK: Easy. TEL: 020 7792 9221; fax - same. SER: Export packing and shipping. VAT: Stan/Spec.

Hedgehog Antiques
20th C Gallery, 291 Westbourne Grove. W11 2QA. (K. Dahmen and K. Sinclair). PADA. Est. 1990. Open Sat. 7-3. SIZE: Small. *STOCK: Kitchenalia, garden tools, decorative items especially bamboo (including faux), mirrors, small furniture, pond yachts, coat racks, metal work, corkscrews.* PARK: Meters.

Hickmet Fine Arts `LAPADA`
75 Portobello Rd. W11 2QB. (David Hickmet).

CINOA. PADA. Open 10-4, Sat. 8-5. SIZE: Medium. *STOCK: Art Deco sculpture, £500-£5,000; Art Nouveau glass, £200-£2,000; contemporary sculpture, £1,000-£10,000.* PARK: Easy. TEL: Mobile - 07050 123450. SER: Valuations; commission purchases. FAIRS: Olympia; LAPADA; NEC; Harrogate; GMEX; SECC. VAT: Spec.

Hirst Antiques
59 Pembridge Rd. W11 3HG. Est. 1963. Open 10-6. SIZE: Medium. *STOCK: Four poster and half-tester beds; decorative furniture and articles; bronze and marble sculpture.* LOC: End of Portobello Rd., near Notting Hill Gate underground station. TEL: 020 7727 9364. SER: Valuations.

Humbleyard Fine Art
141-149 Portobello Rd. W11 2DY. (James Layte). PADA. Est. 1973. Open Sat. 6-2. SIZE: Small. *STOCK: Scientific, medical and marine items, sailors' woolworks, shell valentines, primitive pictures, needleworks, boxes, pottery and curiosities, 18th-19th C, £50-£5,000.* TEL: 01362 637793; fax - same; mobile - 07836 349416. SER: Valuations. FAIRS: Olympia (June, Nov); Decorative (Jan., Sept); Little Chelsea (April, Oct); Scientific Instrument (April, Oct).

Jones Antique Lighting
194 Westbourne Grove. W11. (Judy Jones). Est. 1978. Open 9.30-6 or by appointment. SIZE: Large. *STOCK: Original decorative lighting, 1860-1960.* TEL: 020 7229 6866; fax - same. SER: Valuations; repairs; prop hire. VAT: Stan.

Kleanthous Antiques `LAPADA`
144 Portobello Rd. W11 2DZ. (Chris and Costas Kleanthous). PADA. Est. 1969. Open Sat. 8-4 and by appointment. SIZE: Large. *STOCK: Vintage wrist watches, clocks, jewellery, silver, objets d'art and furniture.* PARK: Restricted. TEL: 020 7727 3649; fax - 020 7243 2488; mobile - 07850 375501/375502. Below are listed the dealers at this address. FAIRS: Olympia (June and Nov).

James Forbes Fine Art
Est. 1982. *Works of art, silver and jewellery, from 1700, £50-£5,000.* TEL: 01886 821216.

Kleanthous Antiques Ltd `LAPADA`
Est. 1969. Open Sat. 7.30-4 and by appointment. *Specially selected pieces of jewellery - Georgian, Victorian, Art Nouveau, Art Deco, to 1950; vintage pocket and wrist watches by Rolex, Cartier, Patek Phillipe, Vacheron and Constantin, Jaeger le Coultre, Longines, I.W.C., Universal and Omega; English and Continental silver, 18th-20th C;*

boudoir, desk, carriage and mantel clocks; objects of vertu; furniture. Full guarantee with all purchases. TEL: 020 7727 3649; fax - 020 7243 2488; mobile - 07850 375501/375502; e-mail - antiques@kleanthous.com; website - www.kleanthous.com. VAT: Stan/Spec.

S. and G. Antiques

(*G. Sirett*). *Specialist in miniature porcelain cups and saucers, teasets and vases, £25-£500; English and Continental glass, £25-£1,000; Meissen porcelain and objets d'art, £20-£5,000.* TEL: 020 7229 2178 (Sat.); 020 8907 7140; fax - 020 8909 3277; mobile - 07768 366677; e-mail - gary@sandgantiques.co.uk; website - www.sandgantiques.co.uk. VAT: Stan/Spec.

Lacy Gallery

203 Westbourne Grove. W11 2AB. Est. 1960. Open Tues.-Fri.10-5, Sat. 10-4. SIZE: Large. *STOCK: Period frames, 1700-1940; decorative paintings and art, posters.* LOC: Two roads east of Portobello Rd. PARK: Easy. TEL: 020 7229 6340; fax - 020 7229 9105. VAT: Stan/Spec.

M. and D. Lewis

1 Lonsdale Rd., 172 Westbourne Grove, 83-85 Ledbury Rd. W11. Est. 1960. Open 9.30-5.30, Sat. 9.30-4. *STOCK: Continental and Victorian furniture, porcelain, bronzes.* TEL: 020 7727 3908. VAT: Stan.

M.C.N. Antiques

183 Westbourne Grove. W11 2SB. Est. 1971. Open 10-6, Sat. 11-3 or by appointment. *STOCK: Japanese porcelain, cloisonné, Satsuma, bronze, lacquer, ivory.* LOC: Near Portobello Rd. market. PARK: Easy. TEL: 020 7727 3796; fax - 020 7229 8839. VAT: Stan.

Robin Martin Antiques

44 Ledbury Rd. W11 2AB. (Paul Martin). Est. 1972. Open 10-6. SIZE: Medium. *STOCK: English and Continental furniture and works of art, 17th-19th C.* LOC: Westbourne Grove area. TEL: 020 7727 1301; fax - same; mobile - 07831 544055; e-mail - paul.martin11@virgin.net. FAIRS: Olympia (June and Nov). VAT: Spec.

Mayflower Antiques

117 Portobello Rd. W11. (J.W. Odgers). PADA. Est. 1970. Open Sat. 7-5. SIZE: Medium. *STOCK: Clocks, mechanical music, scientific and marine instruments, general antiques.* TEL: 01255 504079; Sat. - 020 7727 0381; mobile - 07860 843569; e-mails - mayflower@johnodgers.com and mail@johnodgers.com; website - www.oldjunk.co.uk. FAIRS: Newark; London Scientific & Medical Instrument. VAT: Stan/Spec.

Mercury Antiques   BADA

1 Ladbroke Rd. W11 3PA. (L. Richards). Est. 1963. Open 10-5.30, Sat. 10-1. SIZE: Medium. *STOCK: English porcelain, 1745-1840; English pottery and Delft, 1700-1850; glass, 1780-1850.* Not Stocked: Jewellery, silver, plate, Art Nouveau. LOC: From Notting Hill Gate underground station, turn into Pembridge Rd. and bear left. TEL: 020 7727 5106; fax - 020 7229 3738. VAT: Spec.

Milne and Moller   LAPADA

W11 2BU. (Mr and Mrs C. Moller). Est. 1976. Open by appointment. SIZE: Small. *STOCK: Watercolours, oils, ceramics and sculpture, 19th C to contemporary.* LOC: Near junction of Westbourne Grove and Ledbury Rd. PARK: Easy. TEL: 020 7727 1679; home - same. SER: Portrait commissioning. FAIRS: Olympia. VAT: Spec.

Mimi Fifi

27 Pembridge Rd., Notting Hill Gate. W11 3HG. (Mrs Rita Delaforge). Est. 1990. Open 11-6.30, Sat. 10-7, Sun. 11-4. SIZE: Medium. *STOCK: Vintage and collectable toys, especially Snoopy, Smurfs, Betty Boop, Simpsons, and memorabilia, 20th C, £5-£500; perfume miniatures and related collectables, 19th-20th C, £5-£1,000.* LOC: 200 yards from Notting Hill underground station. PARK: Nearby. TEL: 020 7243 3154; fax - 020 7938 4222; website - www.mimififi.com.

Myriad Antiques

131 Portland Rd., Holland Park Ave. W11 4LW. (S. Nickerson). Est. 1970. Open Tues.-Sat. 11-6. CL: Aug. SIZE: Medium. *STOCK: Decorative and unusual furniture (including garden) and objects, mainly French, 19th C, £10-£1,500.* LOC: Between Notting Hill Gate and Shepherds Bush roundabout. TEL: 020 7229 1709. VAT: Stan.

The Nanking Porcelain Co. Ltd

Admiral Vernon Arcade, 141-149 Portobello Rd. W11 2DY. (Maurice Hyams and Elizabeth Porter). Open Sat. 8.30-3.30. SIZE: Large. *STOCK: Chinese export porcelain, Oriental ivories.* TEL: 020 7924 2349; fax - 020 7924 2352; mobile - 07836 594885; e-mail - nankingporcelain@aol.com. SER: Valuations. FAIRS: Olympia (June).

Old Father Time Clock Centre

Portobello Studios, 1st Floor, 101 Portobello Rd. W11 2QB. (John Denvir). Open Fri. 10-1, Sat. 8-2, other times by appointment. *STOCK: Clocks - all types, especially electric (eg. Eureka), mystery, Atmos, novelty, skeleton, carriage, dial, bracket; barometers.* TEL: 020 8546 6299; fax - same; 020 7727 3394; mobile - 07836 712088; website - www.oldfathertime.net; e-mail - clocks@oldfathertime.net.

Phillips   **LAPADA**
99 Portobello Rd. W11 2QB. Est. 1962. Open 10-5. *STOCK: Ecclesiastical antiques and stained glass.* TEL: 020 7229 2113; fax - 020 7229 1963.

Piano Nobile Fine Paintings
129 Portland Rd., Holland Park. W11 4LW. (Dr Robert A. Travers). SLAD. Est. 1986. Open Tues.-Sat. 10.30-5.30. SIZE: Medium. *STOCK: Fine 19th C Impressionist and 20th C Post-Impressionist and Modernist British and Continental oil paintings and sculpture, Les Petit Maitres of the Paris Schools and leading contemporary figurative painters & sculptors, £500-£100,000.* PARK: Easy. TEL: 020 7229 1099; fax - same; e-mail - art@piano-nobile.com; website - www.piano-nobile.com. SER: Valuations; restorations (paintings and sculptures); framing; buys at auction (19th-20th C oil paintings). FAIRS: Grosvenor; 20th C British Art; Olympia; BADA; Art London.

Portobello Antique Co
133 Portobello Rd. W11 2DY. (L. Meltzer). PADA. Est. 1950. Open Fri. 11-4.30, Sat. 8-4.30, other times by appointment. SIZE: Small. *STOCK: Porcelain, small furniture, reproduction silver plate and cutlery.* LOC: Off Westbourne Grove. PARK: Easy. TEL: 020 7221 0344; home - 020 8959 8886; fax - 020 8801 1780. SER: Packing and shipping. VAT: Stan/Spec.

Portobello Antique Store
79 Portobello Rd. W11 2QB. (J.F. Ewing). Est. 1971. Open Tues.-Fri. 10-4, Sat. 8.15-4. SIZE: Large. *STOCK: Silver and plate, £2-£3,000.* LOC: Notting Hill end of Portobello Rd. PARK: Easy weekdays. TEL: 020 7221 1994. SER: Export. VAT: Stan.

Quadrille
146 Portobello Rd. W11 2DZ. (Valerie Jackson-Harris). Open Sat. 9-4. *STOCK: Ephemera.* TEL: 01923 829079; fax - 01923 825079.

The Red Lion Antiques Arcade
165/169 Portobello Rd. W11. (Angelo Soteriades). PADA. Est. 1951. Open Sat. 5.30-5.30. SIZE: 80 dealers. *STOCK: General antiques including ethnic antiquities, bronzes, ivory statues, jade, precious metals, dolls, silver and plate, drinking vessels, costumes, Oriental and Western porcelain, furniture, collectables,* *prints, lace, linen, books, manuscripts, stamps, coins, banknotes, paintings, etchings, sporting memorabilia, Tibetan, East and South East Asian antiquities, decorative arts and designer objects, jewellery - gold, silver, pearls, semi-precious stones.* TEL: 020 7436 9416; mobile - 07956 277077; e-mail - info@portobello-antiques.com; website - www.portobello-collections.co.uk. SER: Valuations; shipping.

Rezai Persian Carpets
123 Portobello Rd. W11 2DY. (A. Rezai). Est. 1966. Open 9-5. *STOCK: Oriental carpets, kilims, tribal rugs and silk embroideries.* TEL: 020 7221 5012.

Roger's Antiques Gallery
65 Portobello Rd. W11. (Bath Antiques Market Ltd). Open Sat. 7-4.30. SIZE: 65 dealers. *STOCK: Wide range of general antiques and collectables with specialist dealers in most fields, especially jewellery.* TEL: Enquiries - 020 7351 5353; fax - 020 7351 5350. SER: Valuations.

Schredds of Portobello   **LAPADA**
107 Portobello Rd. W11 2QB. (H.J. and G.R. Schrager). PADA. Est. 1969. Open Sat. 7.30-3. SIZE: Small. *STOCK: Silver, 17th-19th C, £10-£5,000; Wedgwood, 18th-19th C.* TEL: 020 8348 3314; home - same; fax - 020 8341 5971; website - www.schredds.com/. SER: Valuations; buys at auction. FAIRS: Kensington (Jan. and Aug). VAT: Stan/Spec.

The Silver Fox Gallery (Portobello)
121 Portobello Rd. W11 2DY. (C. Hickey). Est. 1993. Open Sat. 6-3. SIZE: 25+ dealers. *STOCK: Jewellery - 18th C to 1960's including Victorian, Art Nouveau, Arts & Crafts, Art Deco, rings (diamond and gemset), earrings, brooches, pendants, gold and silver, Alberts, Albertines, chains longuards, bracelets, curbs, gates, fobs, seals, intaglios, pocket watches, vintage wristwatches, cufflinks, fine diamonds, rare gemstones, cameos, coral, amber, ivory, jet tortoiseshell, piqué, micro-mosaics, pietra-dura, lava, horn pendants, enamels, pearls, Austro-Hungarian cut steel, Berlin iron, Scottish, niello, £50-£5,000+.* LOC: Notting Hill. PARK: Pay and Display. TEL: 020 7243 8027; fax - same. FAIRS: Olympia; Park Lane Hotel (every Sunday); NEC. VAT: Stan/Spec/Global.

Justin F. Skrebowski Prints
Ground Floor, 177 Portobello Rd. W11 2DY. Est. 1985. Open Sat. 9-4, other times by appointment. SIZE: Small. *STOCK: Prints, engravings and lithographs, 1700-1850, £50-£500; oil paintings,*

Justin F. Skrebowski Ground Floor, 177 Portobello Road, London, W11 2DY, UK
Tel/Fax/Answerphone: 020 7792 9742 Mobile: 07774 612474
e-mail: justin@skreb.co.uk website: www.skreb.co.uk

- Folio Stands/Browsers
- Display Easels
- Desk Top Stands
- Solid Mahogany

- Beautiful Antique Finish
- Exported Worldwide
- Used by Galleries & Museums
- Ideal for Studies & Homes

1700-1900, £200-£1,500; watercolours, drawings including Old Masters, 1600-1900, £50-£1,000; modern mahogany folio stands and easels; frames - gilt, rosewood, maple, carved, 18th-19th C. PARK: Meters. TEL: 020 7792 9742; mobile - 07774 612474; e-mail - justin@skreb.co.uk; website - www.skreb.co.uk. SER: Valuations. FAIRS: PBFA; Hotel Russell (Monthly). VAT: Stan/Spec.

Colin Smith and Gerald Robinson Antiques

105 Portobello Rd. W11 2QB. Est. 1979. Open Sat., Fri. by appointment. SIZE: Large. *STOCK: Tortoiseshell, £100-£2,000; silver, ivory and crocodile items.* TEL: 020 8994 3783/020 7225 1163. FAIRS: Olympia. VAT: Stan.

Staffordshire Pride

Lipka Arcade, 290 Westbourne Grove. W11. (Sharon Racklyeft). Est. 1976. Open Sat. 8.30-2.30. SIZE: Medium. *STOCK: Staffordshire figures, 1800-1870, £50-£300; blue and white china, £10-£50.* LOC: Corner of Portobello Rd. TEL: Mobile - 07958 453295; home - 020 8883 6180. SER: Valuations.

Stern Pissarro Gallery   `LAPADA`

46 Ledbury Rd. W11 2AB. (David Stern). Est. 1963. Open 10-6. SIZE: Medium. *STOCK: English and European oil paintings, 19th-20th C, especially the Pissarro family.* LOC: Off Westbourne Grove near Portobello. PARK: Easy. TEL: 020 7229 6187; fax - 020 7229 7016; e-mail - stern@pissarro.com; website - www.stern-art.com. SER: Valuations; restorations. VAT: Stan.

Temple Gallery

6 Clarendon Cross. W11 4AP. (R.C.C. Temple). Est. 1959. Open 10-6, weekends and evenings by appointment. SIZE: Large. *STOCK: Icons, Russian and Greek, 12th-16th C, £1,000-£50,000.* PARK: Easy. TEL: 020 7727 3809; fax - 020 7727 1546; e-mail - info@templegallery.com;

website - www.templegallery.com. SER: Valuations; restorations; buys at auction (icons); illustrated catalogues published. VAT: Spec.

Themes and Variations

231 Westbourne Grove. W11 2SE. (L. Fawcett). Open 10-1 and 2-6, Sat 10-6. *STOCK: Post war and contemporary decorative arts, furniture, glass, ceramics, carpets, lamps, jewellery.* TEL: 020 7727 5531; fax - 020 7221 6378; website - www.themesandvariations.co.uk.

Christina Truscott

Geoffrey Van Arcade, 105-107 Portobello Rd. W11 2QB. PADA. Est. 1967. Open Sat. 6.45-3.30. *STOCK: Chinese export lacquer, papier-mâché, tortoiseshell, fans.* TEL: 01403 730554.

Victoriana Dolls

101 Portobello Rd. W11 2BQ. (Mrs H. Bond). Open Sat. 8-3 or by appointment. *STOCK: Dolls, toys and accessories.* TEL: Home - 01737 249525.

Virginia

98 Portland Rd., Holland Park. W11 4LQ. (V. Bates). Est. 1971. Open 11-6. SIZE: Medium. *STOCK: Clothes and lace, 1880-1940, from £100.* LOC: Holland Park Ave. PARK: Easy. TEL: 020 7727 9908; fax - 020 7229 2198. VAT: Stan.

Johnny Von Pflugh Antiques

286 Westbourne Grove. W11. Est. 1985. Open Sat. 8-5 at Portobello Market or by appointment. SIZE: Small. *STOCK: European works of art, Italian oil paintings, gouaches, 17th-19th C, £300-£1,500; fine ironware, 17th-18th C, £300-£800; medical and scientific instruments, 18th-19th C, £200-£1,000.* PARK: Easy. TEL: 020 8740 5306; mobile - 07949 086243. SER: Valuations; buys at auction (keys, caskets, medical instruments, Italian oil paintings and gouaches). FAIRS: Olympia (June); Scientific and Medical (April and Oct). VAT: Spec.

Trude Weaver `LAPADA`
71 Portobello Rd. W11 2QB. Est. 1968. Open Wed.-Sat. 9-5. SIZE: Medium. *STOCK: 18th-19th C furniture, associated accessories.* PARK: Easy. TEL: 020 7229 8738; fax - same. SER: Valuations.

Wolseley Fine Arts Ltd
12 Needham Rd. W11 2RP. (Rupert Otten and Hanneke van der Werf). SLAD. TEFAF. Open during exhibitions Wed., Thurs. and Fri. 11-6, Sat. 11-5 or by appointment. *STOCK: British and European 20th C works on paper and sculpture, works by David Jones, Eric Gill, John Buckland Wright, Pierre Bonnard, Edouard Vuillard, Ker Xavier Roussel and Eugeen van Mieghem; contemporary still life paintings, art, sculpture and carved lettering.* TEL: 020 7792 2788; fax - 020 7792 2988; e-mail - info@wolseleyfinearts.com; website - www.wolseleyfinearts.com. SER: Regular catalogues. FAIRS: Works on Paper; New York; TEFAF; Art London; 20th/21st C British Art.

World Famous Portobello Market
177 Portobello Rd. W11. (Angelo Soteriades). PADA. Est. 1951. Open Sat. 5.30-5.30. SIZE: 60 dealers. *STOCK: Stamps, coins, Art Deco, amber, jewellery, oils, watercolours, engravings, prints, maps, books, photographs, objects, teddy bears, toys, dolls, wood, soapstone, Africana, picture frames, ephemera, auction catalogues.* TEL: 020 7436 9416; mobile - 07956 277077; e-mail - info@portobello-antiques.com; website - www.portobello-collections.co.uk. SER: Valuations; framing.

W13

W.13 Antiques
10 The Avenue, Ealing. W13 8PH. Est. 1977. Open Tues., Thurs. and Sat. 10-5 or by appointment. SIZE: Medium. *STOCK: Furniture, china and general antiques, 18th-20th C.* LOC: Off Uxbridge Rd., West Ealing. PARK: Easy. TEL: 020 8998 0390; mobile - 07778 177102. SER: Valuations. VAT: Stan.

W14

Marshall Gallery
67 Masbro Rd. W14 0LS. (D. A. and J. Marshall). Resident. Est. 1978. Open 10-6, Sat. 10-5. CL: Mon. SIZE: Medium. *STOCK: French and decorative furniture, £500-£20,000; objects and lighting, £200-£12,000; pictures, from £100; all 18th-20th C.* LOC: Just behind Olympia, off Hammersmith Rd. PARK: Easy. TEL: 020 7602

3317. SER: Restorations (furniture, re-gilding, re-wiring). VAT: Spec.

D. Parikian
3 Caithness Rd. W14 0JB. ABA. Est. 1960. Open by appointment. *STOCK: Antiquarian books, mythology, iconography, emblemata, Continental books, pre-1800.* TEL: 020 7603 8375; fax - 020 7602 1178; e-mail - dparikian@aol.com.

J. Roger (Antiques) Ltd `BADA`
W14. (C. Bayley). Open by appointment. *STOCK: Late 18th to early 19th C small elegant pieces furniture, mirrors, prints, porcelain and boxes.* TEL: 020 7603 7627.

SW1

A.D.C. Heritage Ltd `BADA`
SW1V 4PB. (F. Raeymaekers and E. Bellord). Open by appointment. *STOCK: Silver, old Sheffield plate.* TEL: 020 7976 5271; fax - 020 7828 7432; mobile - 07747 692554. SER: Valuations; restorations; buys at auction.

Didier Aaron (London)Ltd `BADA`
21 Ryder St., St. James's. SW1Y 6PX. Open 10-1 and 2-5.30 and by appointment. SIZE: Large. *STOCK: Furniture, mainly French, 18th to early 19th C; paintings and drawings, 17th-19th C; all £5,000-£500,000; objets d'art, £1,000-£50,000.* LOC: 20 yds. from Christie's. TEL: 020 7839 4716; e-mail - contact@didieraaronltd.com. FAIRS: Paris Biennale, Maastricht (TEFAF); IFAAD, New York. VAT: Stan/Spec.

Ackermann & Johnson `BADA`
27 Lowndes St. SW1X 9HY. (Peter Johnson). Est. 1783. Open 9-5.30, Sat. by appointment. SIZE: Medium. *STOCK: British paintings and watercolours, especially sporting, marine and landscapes including the Norwich School, 18th-20th C.* PARK: Meters. TEL: 020 7235 6464; fax - 020 7823 1057; e-mail - ackermann johnson@btconnect.com; website - www. artnet.com/ackermann.johnson. SER: Valuations; restorations; framing. VAT: Spec.

Adam Gallery Ltd
35 Ponsonby Terrace. SW1P 4PZ. (Paul and Philip Dye). *STOCK: 20th C British and international paintings and prints especially St. Ives, Bacon, Nicholson, Francis, Piper, Debuffet, Kandinsky, Lanyon, Moore, Picasso, Delaunay, Hitchens, Hilton, Heron and Scott; British contemporary, £500-£50,000.* TEL: 020 7630 0599; fax - same; e-mail - enquiries@adam gallery.com; website - www.adamgallery.com.

ADEC
227 Ebury St. SW1W 8UT. (A. De Cacqueray).
Est. 1985. Open 10-6, Sat. 11-4. *STOCK: French
and Continental furniture, objets d'art.* TEL: 020
7730 5000; fax - 020 7730 0005. SER: Interior
design.

Verner Åmell Ltd
4 Ryder St., St. James's. SW1Y 6QB. SLAD. Est.
1988. Open 10-5.30. CL: Sat. *STOCK: Dutch and
Flemish Old Masters, 16th-17th C; 18th C
French and 19th C Scandinavian paintings.* TEL:
020 7925 2759. FAIRS: TEFAF; Grosvenor
House. VAT: Spec.

Albert Amor Ltd
37 Bury St., St. James's. SW1Y 6AU. Est. 1903.
Open 9.30-4.30. CL: Sat. SIZE: Small. *STOCK:
18th C English ceramics, especially first period
Worcester and blue and white porcelain.* PARK:
Meters. TEL: 020 7930 2444; fax - 020 7930
9067. SER: Valuations. VAT: Spec.

Anno Domini Antiques   `BADA`
**66 Pimlico Rd. SW1W 8LS. (F. Bartman). Est.
1960. Open 10-1 and 2.15-6, Sat. 10-3. SIZE:
Large. STOCK: Furniture, 17th to early 19th C,
£500-£20,000; mirrors, 17th-19th C, £300-
£3,000; glass, screens, decorative items and
tapestries, £15-£10,000. Not Stocked: Silver,
jewellery, arms, coins. LOC: From Sloane Sq.
go down Lower Sloane St., turn left at traffic
lights. PARK: Easy. TEL: 020 7730 5496;
home - 020 7352 3084. SER: Buys at auction.
VAT: Stan/Spec.**

Antiquus
90-92 Pimlico Rd. SW1W 8PL. (E. Amati). Open
9.30-5.30. SIZE: Large. *STOCK: Classical,
medieval and Renaissance works of art,
paintings, textiles and glass.* LOC: Near Sloane
Sq. underground station. PARK: Meters in
Holbein Place. TEL: 020 7730 8681; fax - 020
7823 6409; e-mail - enquiries@antiquus-
london.co.uk; website - www.antiquus-
london.co.uk.

Appley Hoare Antiques
30 Pimlico Rd. SW1W 8LJ. (Appley & Zoe
Hoare). Est. 1980. Open 10.30-6, Sat. 11-5. SIZE:
Medium. *STOCK: House and garden furniture,
French 18th-19th C, with original paint and
patination; decorative items.* LOC: Corner
Pimlico Green. PARK: Easy. TEL: 020 7730
7070; fax - 020 7730 8188; e-mail -
appley@appleyhoare.com; website - www.
appleyhoare.com. SER: Shipping. VAT: Spec.

**The Armoury of St. James's Military
Antiquarians**
17 Piccadilly Arcade, Piccadilly. SW1Y 6NH.
Open 9.30-6. SIZE: Small. *STOCK: British and
foreign Orders of Chivalry, 18th C to date, £50-
£50,000; militaria, including regimental
brooches and drums; toy and hand-painted model
soldiers, £4-£4,000.* LOC: Between Piccadilly
and Jermyn St. TEL: 020 7493 5082; e-mail -
welcome@armoury.co.uk; website - www.
armoury.co.uk/home. SER: Valuations. special
commissions. VAT: Stan/Spec.

Artemis Fine Arts Limited   `LAPADA`
15 Duke St., St. James's. SW1Y 6DB. (Timothy
Bathurst, Adrian Eeles, Armin Kunz and Francois
Borne). SLAD. Open 9.30-5.30. CL: Sat. *STOCK:
Old Master, 19th C and modern paintings,
drawings and prints; Scandinavian paintings.*
TEL: 020 7930 8733; fax - 020 7839 5009;
website - www.artemisfinearts.com. FAIRS:
Maastricht; London Original Print. VAT: Margin.

Nigel A. Bartlett
25 St Barnabas St. SW1W 8QB. Open 9.30-5.30.
CL: Sat. *STOCK: Marble, pine and stone
chimney pieces.* TEL: 020 7730 3223; fax - 020
7730 2332.

**Hilary Batstone Antiques inc. Rose
Uniacke Interiors**   `LAPADA`
8 Holbein Place. SW1W 8NL. Est. 1983. Open
10.30-5.30, Sat. by appointment. SIZE: Medium.
*STOCK: 19th-20th C decorative furniture,
mirrors and lighting.* TEL: 020 7730 5335; e-mail
- hilary@batstone.com. SER: Interior decorating.
FAIRS: Decorative Antiques and Textiles,
Chelsea. VAT: Spec.

Chris Beetles Ltd
10 Ryder St., St. James's. SW1Y 6QB. Est. 1976.
Open 10-5.30. SIZE: Large. *STOCK: English
watercolours, paintings and illustrations, 18th-
20th C, £500-£50,000.* LOC: 100yds. from Royal
Academy. PARK: Meters. TEL: 020 7839 7551;
e-mail - gallery@chrisbeetles.com; website -
www.chrisbeetles.com. SER: Valuations;
framing. VAT: Spec.

Belgrave Carpet Gallery Ltd
91 Knightsbridge. SW1. (A.H. Khawaja). Open
9.30-6.30. *STOCK: Hand knotted Oriental carpets
and rugs.* TEL: 020 7235 2541/7245 9749.

Blanchard Ltd   `LAPADA`
86/88 Pimlico Rd. SW1W 8PL. Est. 1990. Open
10-6, Sat. 10-3. SIZE: Medium. *STOCK: English
and Continental furniture, lighting and objets*

d'art, 1700-1950. LOC: Near Sloane Sq.
underground station. TEL: 020 7823 6310; fax -
020 7823 6303. SER: Valuations; restorations;
buys at auction. VAT: Stan/Spec.

N. Bloom & Son (1912) Ltd   `LAPADA`
12 Piccadilly Arcade, Piccadilly. SW1Y 6NH.
(Ian Harris). CINOA. Est. 1912. Open 10.30-
5.30. *STOCK: Jewellery, mainly 1870's-1970's;
small silver, objets d'art and vertu; paintings.*
TEL: 020 7629 5060; fax - 020 7493 2528;
mobile - 07973 149363; e-mail - nbloom@
nbloom.co.uk; website - www.nbloom.co.uk.
SER: Valuations; restorations and repairs; buys at
auction. VAT: Stan/Spec.

John Bly   `BADA`
**27 Bury St., St. James's. SW1Y 6AL. (J. and V.
Bly). CINOA. Est. 1891. Open by
appointment. STOCK: Fine English furniture,
silver, glass, porcelain and fine paintings, 18th-
19th C. TEL: 020 7930 1292; fax - 020 7839
4775; e-mail - john@johnbly.com; website -
www.johnbly.com. SER: Restorations;
valuations; consultancy. FAIRS: BADA;
Grosvenor House; W. Palm Beach.**

J.H. Bourdon-Smith Ltd   `BADA`
**24 Mason's Yard, Duke St., St. James's. SW1Y
6BU. CINOA. Est. 1954. Open 9.30-6. CL: Sat.
SIZE: Medium. STOCK: Silver, 1680-1830,
£50-£15,000; Victorian and modern silver, 1830
to date, £25-£10,000. PARK: Meters. TEL: 020
7839 4714/3951; e-mail - julia@bourdon
smith.co.uk. SER: Valuations; restorations
(silver); buys at auction. FAIRS: Olympia
(Nov); Harrogate; Grosvenor House; BADA;
New York; San Francisco. VAT: Stan/Spec.**

Robert Bowman
8 Duke St., St. James's. SW1Y 6BN. SLAD. Est.
1992. Open Mon.-Fri. 10-6. SIZE: Medium.
*STOCK: Sculpture in bronze, marble and
terracotta, 19th C to date, £3,000-£200,000.*
PARK: Meters. TEL: 020 7839 3100; fax - 020
7839 3223. SER: Valuations; restorations
(bronze, marble and terracotta). FAIRS: Olympia;
Maastricht; Palm Beach; New York. VAT: Spec.

Brisigotti Antiques Ltd
44 Duke St., St. James's. SW1Y 6DD. Open 9.30-
1 and 2-6. *STOCK: European works of art, Old
Master paintings.* TEL: 020 7839 4441; fax - 020
7976 1663.

Camerer Cuss and Co
17 Ryder St., St. James's. SW1Y 6PY. Est. 1788.
Open 9.30-5. CL: Sat. SIZE: Medium. *STOCK:*

Clocks, 1600-1910, £250-£30,000; watches, 1600-1930, £100-£35,000. TEL: 020 7930 1941; e-mail - camerercuss@17ryderstreet.freeserve.co. uk; website - www.camerercuss.com. SER: Valuations; restorations (clocks and watches); buys at auction. VAT: Stan/Spec.

John Carlton-Smith [BADA]
17 Ryder St., St. James's. SW1Y 6PY. Open 9.30-5.30. CL: Sat. STOCK: Clocks, barometers, chronometers, 17th-19th C. TEL: 020 7930 6622; fax - same; website - www. fineantiqueclocks.com. SER: Valuations. VAT: Spec.

Miles Wynn Cato
60 Lower Sloane St. SW1W 8BP. Est. 1995. Open Mon.-Fri. 9.30-5.30 and by appointment. SIZE: Medium. *STOCK: English and Welsh pictures and works of art, 1550-1950.* LOC: 100 yds. south of Sloane Sq. PARK: Meters. TEL: 020 7259 0306; fax - 020 7259 0305; e-mail - wynncato@welshart.co.uk; website - www. welshart.co.uk. SER: Valuations; restorations; framing; appraisals.

Chelsea Antique Mirrors
72 Pimlico Rd. SW1W 2LS. (A. Koll). Est. 1976. Open 10-6, Sat. 10-2. SIZE: Medium. *STOCK: Antique mirrors, £1,000-£25,000.* PARK: Easy. TEL: 020 7824 8024; fax - 020 7824 8233. SER: Valuations; restorations (gilding).

Ciancimino Ltd
99 Pimlico Rd. SW1W 8PH. Open 10-6, Sat. 11-5. *STOCK: Art Deco furniture, Oriental art and ethnography.* TEL: 020 7730 9950/9959; fax - 020 7730 5365.

Classic Bindings
61 Cambridge St. SW1V 4PS. (Sasha Poklewski-Koziell). Est. 1989. Open Mon. - Fri. 9.30-5.30 and by appointment. *STOCK: English and French literature, history and politics, first editions, travel, illustrated, fine bindings, architecture and furniture, biographies, natural history and sciences, art and sport.* LOC: Off Warwick Way, Pimlico. PARK: Easy. TEL: 020 7834 5554; fax - 020 7630 6632; e-mail - info@classicbindings.net; website - www.classicbindings.net. FAIRS: ABA Olympia and Chelsea; PBFA London.

Cobra and Bellamy
149 Sloane St. SW1X 9BZ. (V. Manussis and T. Hunter). Est. 1976. Open 10.30-5.30. SIZE: Medium. *STOCK: 20th C jewellery, £50-£5,000.* TEL: 020 7730 9993; e-mail - cobrabellamy@ hotmail.com. VAT: Stan/Margin.

Cornucopia
12 Upper Tachbrook St. SW1V 1SH. Est. 1967. Open 11-6. SIZE: Large. *STOCK: Jewellery, 20th C clothing and accessories.* PARK: Meters. TEL: 020 7828 5752.

Cox and Company
37 Duke St., St. James's. SW1Y 6DF. (Mr and Mrs R. Cox). Est. 1972. Open 10-5.30, Sat. by appointment. SIZE: Small. *STOCK: European paintings, 19th-20th C, £1,000-£20,000; sporting (racing) and wildlife paintings.* LOC: Off Piccadilly. TEL: 020 7930 1987/7839 4539; e-mail - coxco@bellatlantic.net; website - www. coxco.uk.com. SER: Valuations; restorations; buys at auction. VAT: Spec.

Peter Dale Ltd [LAPADA]
12 Royal Opera Arcade, Pall Mall. SW1Y 4UY. Est. 1955. Open 9.30-5. CL: Sat. SIZE: Medium. *STOCK: Firearms, 16th-19th C; edged weapons, armour, 14th-19th C; militaria.* LOC: Arcade behind Her Majesty's Theatre and New Zealand House. PARK: 350yds. Whitcomb St. public garage. TEL: 020 7930 3695; fax - 020 7930 2223. SER: Valuations; buys at auction. FAIRS: Arms (Spring and Autumn). VAT: Spec.

Kenneth Davis (Works of Art) Ltd
15 King St., St. James's. SW1Y 6QU. Open 9-5. CL: Sat. *STOCK: Antique silver and works of art.* TEL: 020 7930 0313; fax - 020 7976 1306.

Alastair Dickenson Ltd [BADA]
90 Jermyn St. SW1Y 6JD. (Alastair Dickenson and Melanie Cuchet). Est. 1996. Open 9.30-5.30. CL: Sat. SIZE: Small. STOCK: Fine English, Irish and Scottish silver, 16th to early 19th C; unusual silver - vinaigrettes, wine labels, card cases, caddy spoons, snuff boxes; Arts and Crafts silver including Omar Ramsden. LOC: Off Duke St. PARK: Meters. TEL: 020 7839 2808; fax - 020 7839 2809; mobile - 07976 283530. SER: Valuations; restorations (repairs, gilding, re-plating), replacement cruet and ink bottles; buys at auction. VAT: Spec.

Simon C. Dickinson Ltd
58 Jermyn St. SW1Y 6LX. (Simon Dickinson, David Ker and James Roundell). SLAD. Est. 1993. Open 10-5.30, Fri. 10-4.30. CL: Sat. SIZE: Large. *STOCK: Important Old Master and Modern Master paintings.* LOC: 2 mins. from Piccadilly. TEL: 020 7493 0340; fax - 020 7493 0796; website - www.simondickinson.com. SER: Valuations; restorations; buys at auction. VAT: Spec.

Douwes Fine Art Ltd
38 Duke St., St. James's. SW1Y 6DF. SLAD. Est.
1805. Open 9.30-5.30. CL: Sat. SIZE: Medium.
*STOCK: 16th-20th C paintings, drawings and
watercolours, Dutch, Flemish, French and
Russian schools.* PARK: Meters. TEL: 020 7839
5795. SER: Valuations; restorations. VAT: Spec.

Eaton Gallery `LAPADA`
34 Duke St., St. James's and 9 and 12a Princes
Arcade, Jermyn St. SW1Y 6DF. (Dr J.D. George).
Est. 1976. Open 10-5.30. *STOCK: English and
European paintings, 19th-20th C and
contemporary.* TEL: 020 7930 5950; fax - 020
7839 8076.

N. and I. Franklin `BADA`
**11 Bury St., St. James's. SW1Y 6AB. Open
9.30-5.30. CL: Sat. STOCK: Fine silver and
works of art. TEL: 020 7839 3131; fax - 020
7839 3132. FAIRS: Grosvenor House; New
York.**

Victor Franses Gallery `BADA`
**57 Jermyn St., St. James's. SW1Y 6LX. Est.
1972. Open 10-5, Sat. by appointment.
STOCK: 19th C animalier bronzes, paintings,
watercolours and drawings. TEL: 020 7493
6284/7629 1144; fax - 020 7495 3668. SER:
Valuations; restorations. FAIRS: Grosvenor
House.**

S. Franses Ltd
80 Jermyn St. at Duke St., St. James's. SW1Y
6JD. Est. 1909. Open 9-5. CL: Sat. SIZE: Large.
*STOCK: Historic and decorative tapestries,
carpets, fabrics and textiles.* TEL: 020 7976
1234; fax - 020 7930 8451; e-mail - gallery@
franses.com; website - www.franses.com. SER:
Valuations; restorations; cleaning. VAT: Spec.

Charles Frodsham & Co Ltd
32 Bury St., St. James's. SW1Y 6AU. Open by
appointment. SIZE: Medium. *STOCK: Clocks,
watches, marine chronometers and other
horological items.* LOC: Between Jermyn St. and
St. James's St. PARK: Meters. TEL: 020 7839
1234; fax - 020 7839 2000. VAT: Stan/Spec.

Frost and Reed Ltd (Est. 1808) `BADA`
**2-4 King St., St James's. SW1Y 6QP. SLAD.
Open 9-5.30. CL: Sat. STOCK: Fine 19th C
British and Continental paintings, marine and
sporting pictures, Post-Impressionist drawings
and watercolours; works by Sir Alfred
Munnings, Montague Dawson, Marcel Dyf,
Peter Smith, and Heather St Clair Davis.
PARK: Meters. TEL: 020 7839 4645; fax - 020-**
7839 1166; e-mail - frostandreed@btinternet.
com; website - www.frostandreed.co.uk. VAT:
Spec.

Gallery '25
26 Pimlico Rd. SW1W 8LJ. (D. Iglesis). Est.
1969. Open 10.30-5.30, Sat. 10.30-5. SIZE:
Medium. *STOCK: Art glass, £100-£5,000; signed
furniture, £1,000-£10,000; decorative fine art,
£500-£5,000; all 1900-1960's.* TEL: 020 7730
7516; fax - same. SER: Valuations; buys at
auction (as stock). FAIRS: Park Lane; Olympia.
VAT: Stan/Spec.

Christopher Gibbs Ltd `LAPADA`
3 Dove Walk, Pimlico Rd. SW1W 8PH. Est.
1960. Open Mon.-Fri. 9.30-5.30. SIZE: Large.
*STOCK: Unusual and decorative paintings,
furniture, works of art and sculpture.* TEL: 020
7730 8200; fax - 020 7730 8420. FAIRS:
Consultancy. VAT: Spec.

Nicholas Gifford-Mead `BADA` `LAPADA`
**68 Pimlico Rd. SW1W 8LS. Est. 1972. Open
9.30-5.30. CL: Sat. SIZE: Medium. STOCK:
Chimney pieces and sculpture, 18th-19th C,
from £1,000.** LOC: 3 mins. from Sloane Sq.
**TEL: 020 7730 6233; fax - 020 7730 6239. SER:
Valuations. VAT: Stan/Spec.**

Andi Gisel
69 Pimlico Rd. SW1W 8NE. Open 9-6, Fri. and
Sat. 9-5. *STOCK: 18th-19th C French furniture
and lighting.* TEL: 020 7730 4187; fax - same.
VAT: Stan/Spec/Export.

Joss Graham
10 Eccleston St. SW1W 9LT. Est. 1980. Open 10-
6. SIZE: 2 floors. *STOCK: Textiles including
rugs, kelims, embroideries, tribal costume and
shawls; jewellery, metalwork, furniture, masks
and primitive art - Indian, Middle Eastern,
Central Asian and African.* LOC: 5 mins. walk
from Victoria station. PARK: NCP, Semley Place.
TEL: 020 7730 4370; fax - same; e-mail -
joss.graham@btinternet.com. SER: Valuations;
restorations; conservation. FAIRS: Hali
International, London; Arts of Pacific Asia; Tribal
Art Show, San Francisco.

Martyn Gregory Gallery `BADA`
**34 Bury St., St. James's. SW1Y 6AU. SLAD.
Open 10-6. CL: Sat. SIZE: Medium. STOCK:
China Trade paintings relating to China and the
Far East; early English watercolours, 18th-20th
C; British paintings, both £500-£100,000.**
PARK: Meters. TEL: 020 7839 3731; fax - 020
7930 0812; e-mail - mgregory@dircon.co.uk;

website - www.martyngregory.com. SER: Valuations. FAIRS: Grosvenor House; Maastricht (TEFAF); New York (Winter); Boston (Ellis Memorial); London (Watercolours & Drawings). VAT: Spec.

Ross Hamilton Ltd   `LAPADA`
95 Pimlico Rd. SW1W 8PH. (Mark Boyce and John Underwood). Est. 1971. Open 9-6, Sat. 11-1 and 2.30-5. SIZE: Large. *STOCK: English and Continental furniture, 17th-19th C, £1,000-£100,000; porcelain and objects, 18th-19th C, £1,000-£3,000; paintings, 17th-19th C, £1,000-£10,000+.* LOC: 2 mins. walk from Sloane Square. PARK: Side streets. TEL: 020 7730 3015; website - www.lapada.co.uk/ross hamilton/. SER: Worldwide delivery. VAT: Stan/Spec.

Brian Harkins Oriental Art
3 Bury St., St. James's. SW1Y 6AB. Est. 1978. Open Mon.-Fri. 10-6. SIZE: Small. *STOCK: Japanese art, 19th-20th C, £2,000-£60,000; Japanese Art Deco, £500-£12,000; Chinese scholar's art and rocks from Ming (1368-1643) and Qing dynasties (1643-1912), £500-£20,000.* LOC: Near Green Park underground station. TEL: 020 7839 3338; fax - 0207 839 9339; e-mail - info@brianharkins.co.uk; website - www.brianharkins.co.uk. FAIRS: Asian Art, New York.

Harris Lindsay   `BADA`
67 Jermyn St. SW1Y 6NY. (Jonathan Harris and Bruce Lindsay). CINOA. Open 9.30-6. CL: Sat. *STOCK: English, Continental and Oriental furniture and works of art.* TEL: 020 7839 5767; fax - 020 7839 5768. FAIRS: Grosvenor House; IFAAD New York. VAT: Spec.

Harrods Ltd
Brompton Rd., Knightsbridge. SW1X 7XL. Open 10-7. SIZE: Large. *STOCK: Fine Victorian, Edwardian and period furniture and clocks.* PARK: Own. TEL: 020 7225 5940.

Julian Hartnoll
3rd. Floor, 14 Mason's Yard, Duke St., St. James's. SW1Y 6BU. Est. 1968. Open by appointment or by chance. *STOCK: 19th-20th C British paintings, drawings and prints especially pre-Raphaelite and works by the Kitchen Sink artists, including Bratby.* TEL: 020 7839 3842; e-mail - art@juliahartnoll.com. FAIRS: Olympia; Watercolours and Drawings. VAT: Spec.

Harvey and Gore   `BADA`
41 Duke St., St. James's. SW1Y 6DF. (B.E. Norman). CINOA. Est. 1723. Open 9.30-5. CL: Sat. SIZE: Small. *STOCK: Jewellery, £150-£50,000; silver, £50-£15,000; old Sheffield plate, £125-£15,000; antique paste.* TEL: 020 7839 4033; fax - 020 7839 3313; e-mail - norman@harveyandgore.co.uk; website - www.harveyandgore.co.uk. SER: Valuations; restorations (jewellery and silver); buys at auction. FAIRS: BADA. VAT: Stan/Spec.

Hazlitt, Gooden and Fox Ltd
38 Bury St., St. James's. SW1Y 6BB. SLAD. Open 9.30-5.30. CL: Sat. SIZE: Large. *STOCK: Paintings, drawings and sculpture.* PARK: Meters. TEL: 020 7930 6422; fax - 020 7839 5984. SER: Valuations; restorations. VAT: Spec.

Thomas Heneage Art Books   `LAPADA`
42 Duke St., St. James's. SW1Y 6DJ. Est. 1975. Open 9.30-6 or by appointment. CL: Sat. *STOCK: Art reference books.* TEL: 020 7930 9223; fax - 020 7839 9223; e-mail - artbooks@heneage.com.

Hermitage Antiques plc
97 Pimlico Rd. SW1W 8PH. (B. Vieux-Pernon). Est. 1967. Open 10-6, Sat. 10-5, Sun. by appointment. SIZE: Large. *STOCK: Biedermeier, Empire and Russian furniture; oil paintings; decorative arts; chandeliers; bronzes.* Not Stocked: Silver and jewellery. LOC: Off Sloane Square. PARK: Easy. TEL: 020 7730 1973; fax - 020 7730 6586; e-mail - info@hermitage-antiques.co.uk; website - www.hermitage-antiques.co.uk. SER: Consultancy. VAT: Stan/Spec.

Carlton Hobbs   `BADA`
Est. 1975. Open by appointment. *STOCK: English and Continental furniture, paintings, chandeliers, works of art, £4,000-£850,000.* LOC: Westminster. TEL: 020 7340 1000; fax - 020 7340 1001; e-mail - carlton@carlton hobbs.com; website - www. carltonhobbs.com.

Christopher Hodsoll Ltd inc. Bennison   `BADA`
89-91 Pimlico Rd. SW1W 8PH. Est. 1991. Open 9-6. *STOCK: Furniture, sculpture, pictures and objects.* PARK: Meters. TEL: 020 7730 3370; fax - 020 7730 1516; website - www.hodsoll.com. SER: Search; interior design. VAT: Stan/Spec.

Hotspur Ltd   `BADA`
14 Lowndes St. SW1X 9EX. (R.A.B. Kern). Est. 1924. Open 8.30-6. SIZE: Large. *STOCK: Fine English furniture, 1680-1800.* LOC: Between Belgrave Sq. and Lowndes Sq.

PARK: Underground within 100yds. TEL: 020 7235 1918; fax - 020 7235 4371; e-mail - hotspurltd@msn.com. FAIRS: Grosvenor House. VAT: Spec.

Christopher Howe

93 Pimlico Rd. SW1W 8PH. Est. 1982. Open 9-6, Sat. 10.30-4.30. SIZE: Large. *STOCK: English and European furniture, 16th-20th C, £100-£250,000; decorative objects and lighting.* LOC: Near Sloane Square. PARK: Meters nearby. TEL: 020 7730 7987; fax - 020 7730 0157; e-mail - antiques@howelondon.com. VAT: Stan/Spec.

Humphrey-Carrasco

43 Pimlico Rd. SW1W 8NE.. (David Humphrey and Marylise Carrasco). Est. 1987. Open 10-6, Sat. 10-5. *STOCK: English furniture and lighting, architectural objects, 18th-19th C.* LOC: 10 mins. walk from Sloane Sq. PARK: Easy. TEL: 020 7730 9911; fax - 020 7730 9944; e-mail - hc@humphreycarrasco.demon.co.uk. FAIRS: Olympia. VAT: Stan/Spec

Iconastas

5 Piccadilly Arcade. SW1Y 6NH. (John Gaze and Christopher Martin-Zakheim). Est. 1968. Open 10-6, Sat. 2-5. SIZE: Small. *STOCK: Russian art, 10th C to 1974.* PARK: Meters. TEL: 020 7629 1433; fax - 020 7408 2015; e-mail - info@iconastas.com; website - www.iconastas. com. SER: Valuations.

Jeremy Ltd `BADA`

29 Lowndes St. SW1X 9HX. (M. and J. Hill). Est. 1946. Open 8.30-6, Sat. by appointment. SIZE: Large. STOCK: English, French and Russian furniture, objets d'art, glass chandeliers, 18th to early 19th C. PARK: Nearby. TEL: 020 7823 2923; fax - 020 7245 6197; e-mail - jeremy@jeremique.co.uk; website - www.jeremy.ltd.uk. FAIRS: Grosvenor House; New York Armory Show. VAT: Spec.

Derek Johns Ltd

12 Duke St., St. James's. SW1Y 6BN. SLAD. Open 10-6. *STOCK: Old Master paintings.* TEL: 020 7839 7671; fax - 020 7930 0986. FAIRS: Maastricht (TEFAF); IFAAD, New York.

Keshishian `BADA`

73 Pimlico Rd. SW1W 8NE. Est. 1978. Open 9.30-6, Sat. 10-5. SIZE: Large. STOCK: European and Oriental carpets, to late 19th C; Aubussons, mid 19th C; European tapestries, 16th-18th C; Arts and Crafts and Art Deco carpet specialists. LOC: Off Lower Sloane St.

PARK: Easy. TEL: 020 7730 8810; fax - 020 7730 8803. SER: Valuations; restorations. VAT: Stan/Spec.

John King `BADA`

74 Pimlico Rd. SW1W 8LS. Est. 1970. Open 10-6, Sat. by appointment. SIZE: Medium. STOCK: Fine and unusual antiques, £500-£150,000. TEL: 020 7730 0427; fax - 020 7730 2515; e-mail - kingj896@aol.com. FAIRS: Olympia (June). VAT: Spec.

Knightsbridge Coins

43 Duke St., St. James's. SW1. Open 10-6. CL: Sat. *STOCK: Coins - British, American and South African; medals.* TEL: 020 7930 7597/7930 8215.

Lamberty Ltd

46 Pimlico Rd. SW1W 8LP. (Andrew Lamberty). Est. 1992. Open 10-6, Sat. 10-2. SIZE: Large. *STOCK: Furniture and decorative items, to £125,000.* PARK: Pay & Display nearby. TEL: 020 7823 5115; fax - 020 7823 4433; mobile - 07768 736687; e-mail - mail@lamberty.co.uk

Bob Lawrence Gallery

93 Lower Sloane St. SW1. Est. 1972. Open 10-6. SIZE: Medium. *STOCK: Decorative arts to Art Deco - furniture, paintings, objects and furnishings, £50-£10,000.* LOC: 2 mins. Sloane Sq., adjacent to Pimlico Rd. PARK: Easy. TEL: 020 7730 5900; fax - 020 7730 5902. SER: Valuations; restorations; buys at auction. VAT: Stan/Spec.

M. and D. Lewis

84 Pimlico Rd. SW1. Open 9.30-5.30, Sat. 9.30-12, Sun. by appointment. *STOCK: Continental and Victorian furniture, porcelain, bronzes.* TEL: 020 7730 1015; fax - 020 7727 3908 (after 6). VAT: Stan.

Longmire Ltd (Three Royal Warrants)

12 Bury St., St. James's. SW1Y 6AB. Open 9.30-5.30, Sat. in Nov. and Dec. only. *STOCK: Individual cufflink and dress sets: antique and contemporary, signed, platinum, gold, gem set, hardstone, pearl, carved crystal or enamel - four vices, fishing, polo, golfing, shooting, big game, ladybird and pigs.* LOC: Coming from Piccadilly, down Duke St., right into King St. past Christie's, first right into Bury St. PARK: Easy. TEL: 020 7930 8720; fax - 020 7930 1898. SER: Custom hand engraving or enamelling in colour - any corporate logo, initials, crest, coats of arms or tartan, any animal (cat, dog etc.), racing silks, sailing burgees, favourite hobbies or own automobiles.

MacConnal-Mason Gallery `BADA`
14 and 17 Duke St., St. James's. SW1Y 6DB.
TEFAF. Est. 1893. Open 9-6. SIZE: Large.
STOCK: Pictures, 19th-20th C. PARK: Meters.
TEL: 020 7839 7693; fax - 020 7839 6797; e-
mail - macconnal-mason@msn.com; website -
www.macconnal-mason-gallery.co.uk. SER:
Valuations; restorations. FAIRS: Maastricht;
New York; Palm Beach; Dallas; London. VAT:
Spec.

The Mall Galleries
The Mall. SW1. Est. 1971. Open 10-5 seven days.
*STOCK: Paintings, sculpture, prints and
drawings.* LOC: Near Trafalgar Sq. PARK:
Nearby. TEL: 020 7930 6844; fax - 020 7839
7830; website - www.mallgalleries.org.uk. SER:
Contemporary art exhibitions; commissioning;
gallery hire; workshops.

Paul Mason Gallery `BADA`
149 Sloane St. SW1X 9BZ. CINOA. Est. 1969.
Open 9-6, Wed. 9-7, Sat. 11-5. *STOCK: Marine,
yachting and naval paintings, prints, jewellery,
barometers, chronometers and furniture;
nautical artifacts; ship models; sporting and
decorative paintings and prints; portfolio stands
and old frames, 18th-20th C.* LOC: Sloane Sq.
end of Sloane St. PARK: Easy. TEL: 020 7730
3683; fax - 020 7730 7359; e-mail -
Paulmasonart@aol.com. SER: Valuations;
restorations (prints and paintings); buys at
auction. FAIRS: England and Europe. VAT:
Stan/Spec.

Jeremy Mason (Sainsbury & Mason)
145 Ebury St. SW1. Est. 1968. Open 10-12.30
and 4-5.30 by appointment. *STOCK: Period
Oriental and European works of art, especially
Chinese and Japanese, bronzes, lacquer,
porcelain, glass and pictures.* TEL: 020 7730
8331; fax - 020 7730 8334; mobile - 07939
240884. FAIRS: Olympia (June). VAT: Spec.

Mathaf Gallery Ltd `LAPADA`
24 Motcomb St. SW1X 8JU. (Brian and Gina
MacDermot). SLAD. Est. 1975. Open 9.30-5.30,
Sat. by appointment. *STOCK: Paintings, Middle
East subjects, 19th C.* LOC: Knightsbridge. TEL:
020 7235 0010; e-mail - art@mathafgallery.
demon.co.uk; website - www. mathafgallery.com.
SER: Valuations. VAT: Spec.

Matthiesen Fine Art Ltd.
7-8 Mason's Yard, Duke St., St. James's. SW1Y
6BU. Est. 1978. Open by appointment. *STOCK:
Fine Italian Old Master paintings, 1300-1800;
French and Spanish Old Master paintings.* TEL:

020 7930 2437; fax - 020 7930 1387. SER:
Valuations; buys at auction.

Thomas Mercer (Chronometers) Ltd
32 Bury St., St. James's. SW1Y 6AU. Open by
appointment. SIZE: Medium. *STOCK: Marine
chronometers.* LOC: Between Jermyn St. and St.
James's St. PARK: Meters. TEL: 020 7930 9300;
fax - 020 7321 0350. VAT: Stan/Spec.

Messums `BADA` `LAPADA`
40 Duke St., St James's. SW1Y 6DF. SLAD.
Open Mon.-Fri. 10-6, other times by
appointment. SIZE: Medium. *STOCK:
Traditional and British Impressionist paintings.*
TEL: 020 7839 5180; fax - 020 7839 5188. SER:
Valuations; restorations; framing. VAT:
Stan/Spec.

Duncan R. Miller Fine Arts `BADA` `LAPADA`
6 Bury St., St. James's. SW1Y 6AB. Open 10-
6. SIZE: Small. *STOCK: Modern British and
European paintings, drawings and sculpture,
especially Scottish Colourist paintings.* LOC:
Green Park underground station. TEL: 020
7839 8806. SER: Valuations; conservation and
restoration (oils, works on paper and Oriental
rugs); buys at auction. FAIRS: Grosvenor
House; BADA; Olympia. VAT: Spec.

Nigel Milne Ltd
38 Jermyn St. SW1Y 6DN. (Nigel and Cherry
Milne). Est. 1979. Open 9.30-5.30. SIZE: Small.
STOCK: Jewellery, silver frames and objects.
TEL: 020 7434 9343; e-mail - jewels@
nigelmilne.co.uk; website - www.nigelmilne.co.
uk. SER: Valuations. VAT: Stan/Spec.

Mrs Monro Ltd
Jubilee House, 70 Cadogan Place. SW1X 9AH.
(John Lusk). FBIDA. Est. 1926. Open 9.30-5.30,
Fri. 9.30-5. CL: Sat. SIZE: Medium. *STOCK:
Small decorative furniture, £500-£1,000+; china,
£50-£500+; rugs, prints, lamps, pictures and
general decorative items, from £50; all 18th-19th
C.* LOC: Between Sloane Sq. and Cadogan Place.
PARK: Garage nearby. TEL: 020 7235 0326; fax
- 020 7259 6305; e-mail - design@mrsmonro.
co.uk; website - www.mrsmunro.co.uk. SER:
Restorations (furniture and china). VAT:
Stan/Spec.

Moreton Street Gallery
40 Moreton St. SW1V 2PB. (W.M. Pearson -
Frasco International Ltd). Est. 1972. Open 9-1
and 2-6. CL: Sat. SIZE: Medium. *STOCK:
Contemporary oils, watercolours, limited*

editions, posters; early engravings - Bunbury, Rowlandson, Hogarth, Gilray and Heath. LOC: Off Belgrave Rd. PARK: Easy. TEL: 020 7834 7773/5; fax - 020 7834 7834. SER: Valuations; restorations; buys at auction (originals and engravings). VAT: Stan.

Peter Nahum at The Leicester Galleries
BADA

5 Ryder St. SW1Y 6PY. SLAD. CINOA. Est. 1983. Open 9.30-6, Sat. and Sun. by appointment. SIZE: Large. *STOCK: British and European paintings, works on paper and bronzes, including the Pre-Raphaelites, Symbolists and Modern British, 19th-20th C, £1,000-£100,000+.* LOC: 100yds. from Royal Academy. PARK: Meters. TEL: 020 7930 6059; fax - 020 7930 4678; e-mail - peternahum@leicestergalleries.com; websites - www.leicestergalleries.com and www.penseroso.com. SER: Valuations; restorations; framing. FAIRS: Grosvenor House; 20th/21st C British Art; IFAAD, New York. VAT: Spec.

The O'Shea Gallery
BADA
4 St. James's St. SW1A 1EF. ABA. Est. 1978. Open Mon.-Fri. 9.30-6. SIZE: Small. *STOCK: Maps, topographical, decorative, natural history, sporting and marine prints; rare atlases, illustrated books, 15th-19th C, £5-£5,000.* TEL: 020 7930 5880; fax - 020 7930 9500; e-mail - prints@osheagallery.com; website - www.osheagallery.com. SER: Valuations; framing; restorations. FAIRS: Olympia (June); International New York; San Francisco Fall. VAT: Stan/Spec.

Oakham Gallery
BADA LAPADA
27 Bury St., St. James's. SW1 6AL. (Dr A.J. Smith). Open 10-5, Sat. and other times by appointment. *STOCK: Continental oils and watercolours, Victorian and 19th C.* TEL: 020 7839 8800; fax - 020 7976 2266; mobile - 07885 281041; e-mail - asmith@oakhamgallery.fsnet.co.uk.

Odyssey Fine Arts Ltd
LAPADA
24 Holbein Place. SW1W 8NL. (Martin Cacrodain). Est. 1992. Open 10-6. SIZE: Small. *STOCK: 18th to early 19th C Italian and French provincial furniture; 18th C engravings.* TEL: 020 7730 9942; fax - 020 7259 9941; e-mail - odysseyfinearts@aol.com; website - www.odysseyart.co.uk. FAIRS: Olympia. *Trade Only.*

Old Maps and Prints
3rd Floor, Harrods, Knightsbridge. SW1X 7XL. Est. 1976. *STOCK: Maps, 16th C to 1890; engravings (all subjects); watercolours.* TEL: 020 7730 1234, ext. 2124.

Ossowski
BADA
83 Pimlico Rd. SW1W 8PH. Est. 1960. Open 10-6. CL: Sat. pm. SIZE: Medium. *STOCK: Carved gilt, 18th C; mirrors, consoles, wood carvings.* TEL: 020 7730 3256. SER: Restorations (gilt furniture). FAIRS: New York; Palm Beach. VAT: Stan/Spec.

Paisnel Gallery
22 Mason's Yard, Duke St., St James's. SW1Y 6BU. (Stephen and Sylvia Paisnel). SLAD. Est. 1977. Open 10-6. CL: Sat. SIZE: Small. *STOCK: Modern British paintings, especially Newlyn and St. Ives Schools, £5,000-£50,000.* LOC: Duke St. runs between Piccadilly and King St. 1 min. from Christies. PARK: St. James Sq. TEL: 020 7930 9293; fax - 020 7930 7280; e-mail - info@paisnelgallery.co.uk. VAT: Spec.

The Parker Gallery
BADA
28 Pimlico Rd. SW1W 8LJ. (Thomas H. Parker Ltd). SLAD. Est. 1750. Open 9.30-5.30, Sat. by appointment. SIZE: Medium. *STOCK: Historical prints, £45-£1,200; English paintings, £1,000-£30,000; ship models, £95-£30,000.* LOC: 5 mins. from Sloane Sq. TEL: 020 7730 6768; fax - 020 7259 9180; website - www.theparkergallery.com. SER: Restorations (as stock); mounting; framing. VAT: Stan/Spec.

Michael Parkin Fine Art Ltd
Studio 4, Sedding St., 1/6 Sloane Sq. SW1W 8EE. SLAD. Open by appointment. *STOCK: British paintings, watercolours, drawings and prints, 1860-1960, £50-£40,000.* PARK: Easy. TEL: 020 7730 9784; fax - 020 7730 9718. FAIRS: 20th-21st C British Art. VAT: Spec.

Trevor Philip and Sons Ltd
BADA
75a Jermyn St., St. James's. SW1Y 6NP. (T. and S. Waterman). Est. 1972. Open 9.30-6, Sat. by appointment. SIZE: Medium. *STOCK: Early scientific instruments, globes, barometers and ships models; silver and vertu.* PARK: At rear. TEL: 020 7930 2954; fax - 020 7321 0212; e-mail - globe@trevorphilip.com; website - www.trevorphilip.com. SER: Valuations; restorations (clocks and scientific instruments); buys at auction. FAIRS: Grosvenor House. VAT: Stan/Spec.

Portland Gallery
9 Bury St., St. James's. SW1Y 6AB. SLAD. Est. 1985. Open 10-6. CL: Sat. SIZE: Medium.

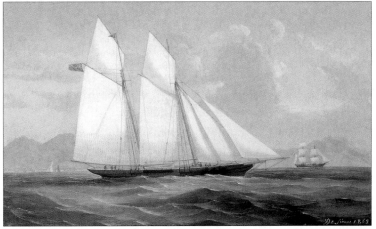

STOCK: Scottish pictures, 20th C, £500-£250,000. TEL: 020 7321 0422. SER: Valuations; buys at auction. VAT: Spec.

Pullman Gallery

14 King St., St. James's. SW1Y 6QU. (Simon Khachadourian). Est. 1980. Open 10-6, Sat. by appointment. SIZE: Medium. *STOCK: Objets de luxe, 19th-20th C, £200-£20,000; automobile art, pre-1950, £1,000-£20,000; cocktail shakers, bar accessories, cigar memorabilia, 1880-1950, £250-£25,000; René Lalique glass, 1900-1940, from £3,000.* LOC: Corner of Bury St., adjacent Christie's. PARK: Easy. TEL: 020 7930 9595; fax - 020 7930 9494; mobile - 07973 141606; e-mail - sk@pullmangallery.com; website - www. pullmangallery.com. VAT: Stan.

Mark Ransom Ltd

62 and 105 Pimlico Rd. SW1W 8LS. Est. 1989. Open 10-6. SIZE: Large. *STOCK: Furniture - French Empire and Russian, early 19th C; Continental, decorative, from late 18th C, all to £1,000+.* LOC: Close to Sloane Sq. underground station - turn left left, 5 mins. walk. PARK: Side streets. TEL: 020 7259 0220; fax - 020 7259 0323. VAT: Stan/Spec.

Steven Rich & Michael Rich

39 Duke St., St. James's. SW1Y 6DF. SLAD. Open daily, Sat. by appointment. SIZE: Medium. *STOCK: Master paintings, 16th-19th C; general items.* LOC: Just off Piccadilly. PARK: St. James's Sq. TEL: 020 7930 9308; fax - 020 7930 2088. SER: Valuations. VAT: Spec.

Rogier et Rogier

20A Pimlico Rd. SW1W 8LJ. (Miss Lauriance Rogier). Est. 1980. Open 10-6, Sat. 11-4. SIZE: Small. *STOCK: French and Continental painted and country furniture, 18th-19th C, £1,000-£5,000; lamps and wall sconces, 19th C, from £500; decorative antique and reproduction items, from £300.* LOC: 5 mins. walk from Sloane Sq. PARK: Meters. TEL: 020 7823 4780; e-mail - rogier@easynet.co.uk. SER: Restorations (decoration, painted effects, murals, trompe l'oeil). VAT: Spec.

Julian Simon Fine Art Ltd `BADA`

70 Pimlico Rd. SW1W 8LS. (M. and J. Brookstone). Open 10-6, Sat. 10-4 or by appointment. *STOCK: Fine English and Continental pictures, 18th-20th C.* LOC: Sloane Sq. TEL: 020 7730 8673; fax - 020 7823 6116; e-mail - juliansimon@compuserve.com; website - www.19thcenturypaintings.com. FAIRS: Olympia.

Sims, Reed Ltd

43a Duke St., St James's. SW1Y 6DD. ABA. Est. 1977. Open 10-6, Sat. 10-4. *STOCK: Illustrated, rare and in-print books on the fine and applied arts; leather-bound literary sets; contemporary books.* TEL: 020 7493 5660; fax - 020 7493 8468; e-mail - info@simsreed.com; website - www. simsreed.com. FAIRS: London ABA.

Peta Smyth - Antique Textiles `LAPADA`

42 Moreton St., Pimlico. SW1V 2PB. Est. 1977. Open 9.30-5.30. CL: Sat. *STOCK: European textiles, 16th-19th C - needlework, silks and velvets, hangings and curtains, tapestry panels and cushions, £50-£20,000.* PARK: Easy. TEL: 020 7630 9898; fax - 020 7630 5398; e-mail - petasmyth@uk.online.co.uk. FAIRS: Olympia. VAT: Spec.

Somlo Antiques `BADA`

7 Piccadilly Arcade. SW1Y 6NH. Est. 1972. Open 10-5.30, Sat. 10.30-5. SIZE: Medium. STOCK: Vintage wrist and antique pocket watches, from £1,000. LOC: Between Piccadilly and Jermyn St. PARK: Meters. TEL: 020 7499 6526. SER: Restorations.

Robin Symes Ltd

3 Ormond Yard, Duke of York St., St. James's. SW1. Open by appointment. SIZE: Large. *STOCK: Antiquities, ancient art.* PARK: Meters. TEL: 020 7930 9856/7; 020 7930 5300.

thesilverfund.com

1 Duke of York St. SW1Y 6JP. (Alastair Crawford and Michael James). Open daily, Sat. and Sun. by appointment. SIZE: Large. *STOCK: Old Georg Jensen silver, £500-£100,000.* LOC: Opposite Christies (King St/Bury St). PARK: NCP Mayfair. TEL: 020 7839 7664; fax - 020 7839 8935; e-mail - dealers@thesilverfund.com. SER: Valuations; restorations. VAT: Stan/Spec.

Bill Thomson - Albany Gallery

1 Bury St., St. James's. SW1Y 6AB. (W.B. Thomson). Open Mon.-Fri. 9-6 by appointment. *STOCK: British drawings, watercolours and paintings, 1700-1850 and some 20th C.* TEL: 020 7839 6119; fax - 020 7839 6614.

Trafalgar Galleries `BADA`

35 Bury St., St. James's. SW1Y 6AY. Open 9.30-6. CL: Sat. STOCK: Old Master paintings. LOC: Just south of Piccadilly. TEL: 020 7839 6466.

Tryon Gallery (incorporating Malcolm Innes)

7 Bury St., St James's. SW1Y 6AL. (Malcolm

Innes and Oliver Swann). SLAD. Open 10-6, CL: Sat. (except during some exhibitions). SIZE: Large. *STOCK: Sporting, wildlife and natural history subjects; Scottish landscape and military pictures; paintings, bronzes, books, £150-£50,000.* TEL: 020 7839 8083; fax - 020 7839 8085; e-mail - tryon@tryon.co.uk; website - www.tryongallery.co.uk. SER: Valuations; framing; advising; commission buying. FAIRS: Game. VAT: Spec.

Un Francais á Londres
202 Ebury St. SW1W 8UN. Est. 1990. Open 10-6, Sat. 10-4 or by appointment. SIZE: Large. *STOCK: 18th to early 19th C French and Continental furniture.* LOC: Near Pimlico Rd. PARK: Easy. TEL: 020 7730 1771/1881; fax - 020 7730 1881; e-mail - eburystreet@aol.com; website - www.unfrancaisalondres.com. SER: Valuations; restorations; buys at auction. VAT: Spec

Rafael Valls Ltd `BADA`
11 Duke St., St. James's. SW1Y 6BN. SLAD. Est. 1976. Open Mon.-Fri. 9.30-6. STOCK: Old Master paintings. TEL: 020 7930 1144; fax - 020 7976 1596. FAIRS: Maastricht: Grosvenor House: BADA. VAT: Spec.

Rafael Valls Ltd `BADA`
6 Ryder St., St. James's. SW1Y 6QB. SLAD. Open Mon.-Fri. 9.30-6. STOCK: Fine European paintings. TEL: 020 7930 0029; fax - 020 7976 1596. VAT: Spec.

Johnny Van Haeften Ltd `BADA`
13 Duke St., St. James's. SW1Y 6DB. (J. and S. Van Haeften). SLAD. TEFAF. Est. 1978. Open 10-6, Sat. and Sun. by appointment. SIZE: Medium. STOCK: Dutch and Flemish Old Master paintings, 16th-17th C, £5,000-£5m. LOC: Middle of Duke St. TEL: 020 7930 3062/3; fax - 020 7839 6303; e-mail - paintings@johnnyvanhaeften.com. SER: Valuations; restorations (Old Masters); buys at auction (paintings including Old Masters). FAIRS: Grosvenor House; Maastricht. VAT: Spec.

Waterman Fine Art Ltd
75A Jermyn St., St. James's. SW1Y 6NP. Open 9-6, Sat. 10-4. *STOCK: 20th C paintings and watercolours.* TEL: 020 7839 5203; fax - 020 7321 0212.

Westenholz Antiques Ltd
76-78 Pimlico Rd. SW1W 8PL. Open 10-6, Sat. by appointment. *STOCK: 18th-19th C furniture, pictures, objects, lamps, mirrors.* TEL: 020 7824 8090.

Whitford Fine Art
6 Duke St., St. James's. SW1Y 6BN. (Adrian Mibus). Est. 1973. Open 10-6. CL: Sat. *STOCK: Oil paintings and sculpture, late 19th to 20th C; Modernism, post war abstract and pop art.* TEL: 020 7930 9332; fax - 020 7930 5577; e-mail - whitfordfineart@btinternet.com; website - www.artnet.com/whitford.html. VAT: Spec.

Arnold Wiggins and Sons Ltd `BADA`
4 Bury St., St. James's. SW1Y 6AB. (M. Gregory). Open Mon.-Fri 9-5.30. STOCK: Picture frames, 16th-19th C. TEL: 020 7925 0195.

Wildenstein and Co Ltd
46 St. James's Place. SW1A 1NS. SLAD. Est. 1934. Open by appointment. *STOCK: Impressionist and Old Master paintings and drawings.* TEL: 020 7629 0602; fax - 020 7493 3924.

SW3

Norman Adams Ltd `BADA`
8/10 Hans Rd., Knightsbridge. SW3 1RX. Est. 1923. Open 9-5.30, Sat. and Sun. by appointment. SIZE: Large. STOCK: English furniture, 18th C, £650-£250,000; objets d'art (English and French) £500-£50,000; mirrors, glass pictures, 18th C; clocks and barometers. LOC: 30yds. off the Brompton Rd., opposite west side entrance to Harrods. TEL: 020 7589 5266; fax - 020 7589 1968; e-mail - antiques@ normanadams.com; website - www.norman adams.com. FAIRS: Grosvenor House; BADA. VAT: Spec.

After Noah
261 King's Rd. Chelsea. SW3 5EL. (M. Crawford and Z. Candlin). *STOCK: Arts and Craft oak and similar furniture, leather sofas and chairs, 1880's to 1950's, £1-£5,000; iron, iron and brass beds; decorative items, bric-a-brac including candlesticks, mirrors, lighting, kitchenalia and jewellery.* TEL: 020 7351 2610; fax - same; e-mail - enquiries@afternoah.com; website - www. afternoah.com. SER: Restorations. VAT: Stan.

The Andipa Gallery `LAPADA`
162 Walton St. SW3 2JL. Est. 1969. Open 11-6. *STOCK: Icons from Byzantium, Greece, Russia, Eastern Europe, Asia Minor and North Africa; Italian Masters and Old Masters, all from 14th-19th C; Asian art and antiquities, from 500 BC; modern and contemporary prints, drawings, paintings and sculpture.* LOC: Knightsbridge. TEL: 020 7589 2371; fax - 020 7225 0305; e-mail -

art@andipa.com; website - www.andipa.com. SER: Valuations; restorations; research; collections.

Antiquarius

131/141 King's Rd. SW3. (Atlantic Antiques Centres Ltd). Est. 1970. Open 10-6. LOC: On the corner of King's Rd. and Flood St., next to Chelsea Town Hall. TEL: Enquiries - 020 7351 5353; fax - 020 7969 1639; e-mail - antique@dial.pipex.com. Below are listed some of the many specialist dealers at this market.

225 Jewellery Exchange
Stand V21. (Mrs. Michelle Rowan). *Silver and jewellery.* TEL: 020 7352 8744.

Jaki Abbott
Stand M12. *Jewellery.* TEL: 020 7352 7989.

Aesthetics BADA LAPADA
Stand V2. (Peter and Philip Jeffs). *Silver, ceramics and decorative arts, 1860-1960.* TEL: 020 7352 0395.

AM-PM
Stand V11. (Jane Yeganeh). *Vintage watches.* TEL: 020 7351 5654.

Alexia Amato LAPADA
Stand V8. *Decorative antiques, Bohemian glass.* TEL: 020 7352 3666.

The Art Deco Pavillion
Stand V18. (Maxime Boulanger). *Art Deco furniture.* TEL: Mobile - 07960 321668.

Beauty & The Beast
Stands Q9/10. (J. Rothman). *Costume jewellery, BP Austrian bronzes, handbags.* TEL: 020 7351 5149.

Alexandra Bolla
Stand J1. *Jewellery.* TEL: 020 7352 7989.

Brown & Kingston
Stands V5/6. (Dennis Kingston). *Furniture, Imari, blue and white, Staffordshire porcelain.* TEL: 020 7376 8881.

T. Buchinger
Stand Q2. *Jewellery.* TEL: 020 7352 8734.

Jasmine Cameron
Stands M1/2/16. *Inkpots and pens, artists materials, glass.* TEL: 020 7351 4154.

Vivian Carroll
Stand N1. *General antiques.* TEL: 020 7352 8734.

Chelsea Antiques Rug Gallery
Stand V15. (N. Somnez). *Oriental carpets and Persian rugs.* TEL: 020 7351 6611.

Chelsea Military Antiques
Stands N13/14. (Dominic Abbott and Richard Black). *Militaria, swords, revolvers, uniforms, medals (WWII and British Empire).* TEL: 020 7352 0308.

Mrs. Cordell LAPADA
Stands J2/3*Fine jewellery.*

The Cufflink Shop
Stands G2/3. (John Szwarc). *Jewellery and cufflinks.* TEL: 020 7352 8201.

Glen Dewart
Stands P7/8. *Prints and paintings.* TEL: 020 7352 4777.

D. Donaghue
Stands P9/10/11. *Jewellery and objets de vertu.* TEL: 020 7352 8734.

S. Edmunds
Stand E6. *Militaria.* TEL: 020 7351 5357.

Makiko Featherstone
Stands J9/11. *Silver, jewellery, small objets d'art.* TEL: 020 7376 8845.

Ferguson Fine Art
Stand V13. (Serena Ferguson). *Sporting collectables.* TEL: 020 7352 5272.

Flight of Fancy LAPADA
Stands A9-A11. (Jesse Davis). *General antiques.* TEL: 020 7352 4314.

French Glass House
Stands P14/15/16, N4/5. (M. Aboudara). *Art Nouveau and Art Deco glass.* TEL: 020 7376 5394.

Galleria Italiana
Stands V3/4. *Arts and crafts.* TEL: 020 7352 0809.

Anthony J. Gibb
Stand D3. *Militaria.* TEL: Mobile - 07803 783857.

Angelo Gibson
Stand M10. *Silver plate, general antiques.* TEL: 020 7352 4690.

Brian Gordon LAPADA
Stand G1. *Silver and plate.* TEL: 020 7351 5808.

M. Gray
Stand V9. *Vintage movie posters.* TEL: 020 7351 5166.

Robin Haydock LAPADA
Stands L1/10. *Textiles and decorative furnishings.* TEL: 020 7349 9110.

ANTIQUARIUS

131-141 King's Road, London SW3

"A fine example of what the best
antiques centre can offer"

Antique Dealer and Collectors Guide

Enquiries: Mike Spooner/Neil Jackson

Tel: 020-7351 5353 Fax: 020-7969 1639

Hayman & Hayman
Stands K2-K5. *Photo frames, scent bottles.* TEL: 020 7351 6568.

Mr. Jones
Stand L2. *Silver.*

Michael Kelleher
Stand V7. *Decorative prints.* TEL: 020 7581 8739

Don Kelly
Stands L3, M13. *Antiquarian and reference books.* TEL: 020 7352 4690.

Claude & Martine Latreville
Stand V16. *Fine silver and jewellery.* TEL: 020 7352 5964.

Le Shop
Stand L9. (A. Canetti and J. Galisson). *Jewellery and decorative accessories.* TEL: 020 7352 4690.

Michael Lexton
Stands N8-11. *Silver.* TEL: 020 7351 5980.

Little River
Stands D1/2 and D5/6. (David Dykes). *Asian prints, Oriental china and porcelain.* TEL: 020 7349 9080. SER: Restorations (Oriental furniture).

A. Lopari (Sormeh)
Stand V20. *Jewellery.* TEL: 020 7352 5592.

Mariad Antique Jewellery
Stand V38. (Mrs M. McLean). *Vienna bronzes and jewellery.* TEL: 020 7351 9526.

Dolores Martin
Stands M14/15. *Silver and silver plate; Art Deco.* TEL: 020 7351 5829.

V. Martin
Stand V12. *Jewellery and objects.* TEL: 020 7352 1444.

Martinez-Negrillo
Stands P1/2/3. *Jewellery, porcelain, glass, paintings, objets de vertu.* TEL: 020 7349 0038; mobile - 07956 406954.

Gerald Mathias
Stands R3-6. *Victorian and Edwardian furniture, clocks, boxes.* TEL: 020 7351 0484.

Mrs N. McDonald-Hobley
Stand L7. *Jewellery.* TEL: 020 7351 0154.

William McLeod-Brown
Stands L5/6. *Prints.* TEL: 020 7352 4690; workshop - 020 7730 3547.

Phillipa & John Miller
Stands J4/5. *Jewellery and objets d'art.* TEL: 020 7352 4690/7351 0294.

Mrs. T. Molloy
Stands A12/13. *Oil paintings.*

Mrs. D. Mousavi
Stand D4. *Gold and silver, jade, netsuke.* TEL: 020 7352 8734.

Nicholson Jewellery
Stand V37. (James Nicholson). *Jewellery and silver.* TEL: Mobile - 07976 567992.

Sue Norman
Stand L4. (Mr and Mrs Alloway). *Blue and white china.* TEL: 020 7352 7217.

Maria Perez
Stands V23/24. *Jewellery.* TEL: 020 7351 1986.

Abdul Rabi
Stand P4. TEL: 020 7352 8734. SER: Jewellery and watch repairs.

Keiron Reilly
Stands K1/6. *Art Nouveau and Art Deco.* TEL: 020 7352 2099.

Ronco Antiques
Stand V1. (Alex Ronco). *Bronzes.* TEL: 020 7376 8116.

Simar Antiques
Stands A18/19 and H1/2. (A. Cohen). *Silver.* TEL: 020 7352 7155.

D. M. Simpson
Stand E1. *Ivory.* TEL: 020 7352 7989.

Miwa Thorpe
Stands M8/9. *Silver and jewellery.* TEL: 020 7351 2911.

Graham Tomlinson & Sotiris Papadimitriou
Stands T3/4. *Decorative antiques and garden ornaments.* TEL: Mobile - 07778 470983.

William Wain
Stand J6. *Vintage costume jewellery.* TEL: 020 7351 4905.

West Country Jewellery
Stands M5/6/7. (David Billing). *Jewellery, objects, silver.* TEL: 020 7376 8252.

XS Baggage
Stand A1-4, B1-5, C1/2. (Mr and Mrs Lehane). *Antique luggage and travel requisites; sporting memorabilia.* TEL: 020 7352 7989/7376 8781.

Ziggy
Stands E3/4. (Shigehura Aritake). *Watches and lighters.* TEL: 020 7376 5628.

Apter Fredericks Ltd `BADA`
265-267 Fulham Rd. SW3 6HY. Open 9.30-5.30, Sat. and evenings by appointment. SIZE: 6 showrooms. STOCK: English furniture, 17th to early 19th C. TEL: 020 7352 2188; fax - 020 7376 5619; e-mail - antiques@apter-fredericks.com; website - www.apter-fredericks.com. FAIRS: Grosvenor House; IFAAD, New York. VAT: Stan/Spec.

Joanna Booth `BADA`
247 King's Rd., Chelsea. SW3 5EL. Est. 1963. Open 10-6. SIZE: Medium. STOCK: Sculpture, 12th-17th C; tapestries, textiles, 16th-18th C; Old Master drawings, £50-£50,000; early furniture, works of art. PARK: Meters. TEL: 020 7352 8998; fax - 020 7376 7350; e-mail - joanna@joannabooth.co.uk; website - www.joannabooth.co.uk. SER: Buys at auction. FAIRS: Olympia; BADA (Chelsea); New York Javits Centre. VAT: Spec.

Bourbon-Hanby Antiques Centre
151 Sydney St. Chelsea. SW3 6NT. Open 10-6, Sun. 11-5. LOC: Just off Kings Road, opposite town hall. TEL: 020 7352 2106.

Butler and Wilson
189 Fulham Rd. SW3 6JN. Open 10-6, Wed. 10-7, Sun. 12-6. CL: Sat. *STOCK: Jewellery, Art Deco, vintage bags and clothes, 1950's jewellery, objects and accessories.* TEL: 020 7352 3045.

Campbell's of Walton Street
164 Walton St. SW3 2JL. Open 9.30-5.30. *STOCK: 20th C impressionist and modern British oils and watercolours.* TEL: 020 7584 9268; fax - 020 7581 3499; website - www.campbellsofwaltonstreet.co.uk. SER: Master framing, carving, gilding; restorations.

Richard Courtney Ltd `BADA`
112-114 Fulham Rd. SW3 6HU. Est. 1959. Open 9.30-1 and 2-6. CL: Sat. SIZE: Large. STOCK: English furniture, 18th C, £5,000-£50,000. PARK: Easy. TEL: 020 7370 4020. FAIRS: Grosvenor House; BADA. VAT: Spec.

Robert Dickson and Lesley Rendall Antiques `BADA`
263 Fulham Rd. SW3 6HY. Est. 1969. Open 10-6, Sat. 10-4.30 or by appointment. SIZE: Medium. STOCK: Late 18th to early 19th C furniture and works of art, £500-£100,000. PARK: Easy. TEL: 020 7351 0330; e-mail - antiques@dickson-rendall.demon.co.uk; website - www.dicksonrendall-antiques.co.uk. SER: Restorations; valuations. VAT: Spec.

Dragons of Walton St. Ltd
23 Walton St. SW3 2HX. (R. Fisher). Est. 1982. Open 9.30-5.30, Sat. 10-5. *STOCK: Mainly painted and decorated furniture; hand decorated children's furniture, decorative items.* LOC: Close to Harrods. PARK: Hasker St. or First St. TEL: 020 7589 3795; fax - 020 7584 4570.

Drummonds London Showroom
78 Royal Hospital Rd., Chelsea. SW3 4HN. SALVO. Est. 1988. Open 9-6, Sat. 10-3. SIZE: Large. *STOCK: Original architectural materials, restored period bathrooms, fire places, radiators and garden ornaments.* PARK: Easy. TEL: 020 7376 4499; fax - 020 7376 4488; e-mail - London@drummonds-arch.co.uk; website - www.drummonds-arch.co.uk. SER: Manufacturer of cast-iron baths, iron conservatories and brassware; restorations (stonework and gates); vitreous re-enamelling of baths.

Michael Foster BADA
118 Fulham Rd., Chelsea. SW3 6HU. (Margaret and Michael Susands). Est. 1963. Open 9.30-5.30, Sat. by appointment. STOCK: 18th C English furniture and works of art. PARK: Rear of premises. TEL: 020 7373 3636/3040. SER: Valuations. FAIRS: Grosvenor House.

Gallery Lingard
PO Box 33705, Chelsea Manor St. SW3 3FD. SLAD. Open by appointment. STOCK: Architectural drawings, watercolours, paintings, prints and books. TEL: 020 7352 6034; fax - same.

Gallery Yacou LAPADA
127 Fulham Rd. SW3 6RT. Open 10.30-6, Sat. 11.30-5. STOCK: Decorative and antique Oriental and European carpets (room-size and over-size). TEL: 020 7584 2929; fax - 020 7584 3535; e-mail - galleryyacou@aol.com. FAIRS: Olympia.

General Trading Co Ltd LAPADA
2 Symons St. SW3 2TJ. Est. 1920. Open 10-6.30. SIZE: Medium. STOCK: English furniture, £100-£10,000; objects, both 18th-20th C. LOC: Near Sloane Sq. TEL: 020 7730 0411, 020 7823 5426; e-mail - enquiries@general-trading.co.uk; website - www.general-trading.co.uk. VAT: Stan/Spec.

David Gill LAPADA
60 Fulham Rd. SW3 6HH. Est. 1986. Open 10-6. SIZE: Medium. STOCK: Decorative and fine arts, Picasso, Cocteau ceramics and drawings, 1900 to present day. PARK: Onslow Sq. TEL: 020 7589 5946; fax - 020 7584 9184. VAT: Stan.

Godson and Coles BADA
92 Fulham Rd. SW3 6HR. (Richard Godson and Richard Coles). Est. 1978. Open 9.30-5.30, Sat. by appointment. STOCK: Fine 17th to early 19th C English furniture and works of art. TEL: 020 7584 2200; fax - 020 7584 2223; e-mail - godsonandcoles@aol.com; website - www.godsonandcoles.co.uk. FAIRS: Grosvenor House.

Green and Stone
259 Kings Rd. SW3 5EL. (R.J.S. Baldwin). Est. 1927. Open 9-6, Sat. 9.30-6, Sun. 12-5. STOCK: 18th-19th C writing and artists' materials, glass and china. LOC: At junction with Old Church St. PARK: Meters. TEL: 020 7352 0837; fax - 020 7351 1098; e-mail - antiques@greenandstone. com. SER: Restorations (pictures and frames). VAT: Stan.

James Hardy and Co
235 Brompton Rd. SW3 2EP. Est. 1853. Open 10-5.30. STOCK: Silver including tableware, and jewellery. PARK: Meters. TEL: 020 7589 5050; fax - 020 7589 9009. SER: Valuations; repairs.

Peter Harrington Antiquarian Bookseller
100 Fulham Rd., Chelsea. SW3 6HS. Est. 1969. Open 10-6. SIZE: Large. STOCK: Antiquarian and collectable books, 1500-2000, £20-£50,000+. TEL: 020 7591 0220; fax - 020 7225 7054; e-mail - books@peter-harrington.demon. co.uk; website - www.peter-harrington.demon.co. uk. SER: Valuations; restorations (full bookbinding); buys at auction. FAIRS: Olympia Books & Antiques, Chelsea, New York, Boston, California. Trade Only.

Stephanie Hoppen Ltd
17 Walton St. SW3 2HX. Est. 1962. Open 10-6, Sat. 12-4. STOCK: Decorative picture specialist - watercolours, oils, drawings and prints, antique and modern. TEL: 020 7589 3678.

Michael Hughes BADA
88 Fulham Rd., Chelsea. SW3 6HR. Est. 1970. Open 9.30-5.30, Sat. by appointment. SIZE: Large. STOCK: Fine 18th-19th C English furniture and works of art. TEL: 020 7589 0660; fax - 020 7823 7618; mobile - 07880 505123; e-mail - antiques@michaelhughes. freeserve.co.uk. FAIRS: Olympia (June).

Hungry Ghost
122 Fulham Rd. SW3 6HU. (Virginia Kern). Est. 1998. Open 10-5.30. CL: Mon. STOCK: Chinese furniture and artefacts, 18th-19th C, to £15,000. TEL: 020 7370 6673; fax - same; e-mail - virginiakern@aol.com; website - www.hungry-ghost.co.uk. FAIRS: Decorative (Battersea). VAT: Stan.

Anthony James and Son Ltd BADA
88 Fulham Rd. SW3 6HR. CINOA. Est. 1949. Open 9.30-5.45, Sat. by appointment. SIZE: Large. STOCK: Furniture, 1700-1880, £200-£50,000; mirrors, bronzes, ormolu and decorative items, £200-£20,000. PARK: Easy. TEL: 020 7584 1120; fax - 020 7823 7618; e-mail - info@anthony-james.com; website - www.anthony-james.com. SER: Valuations; buys at auction. FAIRS: Olympia (June). VAT: Spec.

Peter Jones at PJ2 LAPADA
1st Floor, Draycott Ave. SW3 2NA. (John Lewis Partnership). CINOA. Est. 1915. Open 9.30-7.

Rogers de Rin Antiques

76

Specialists in WEMYSS WARE

76 Royal Hospital Road London SW3 4HN
Tel: 020 7352 9007 Fax: 020 7351 9407

OPEN 10AM TO 5.30PM, SAT. 10AM TO 1PM. NOW OPEN SUNDAY BY APPOINTMENT.
We would like to buy collections of Wemyss Ware or individual pieces
Email: rogersderin@rogersderin.co.uk

SIZE: Large. *STOCK: 18th-19th C furniture, mirrors and pictures.* LOC: Chelsea. TEL: 020 7730 3434, ext. 5734. VAT: Spec.

John Keil Ltd [BADA]
1st Floor, 154 Brompton Rd. SW3 1HX. Est. 1959. Open 9.30-5.30, Sat. by appointment. STOCK: Fine English furniture, 18th to early 19th C. LOC: Near Knightsbridge underground station. PARK: 200 yds. TEL: 020 7589 6454; fax - 020 7823 8235; e-mail - antiques@johnkeil.com; website - www. johnkeil.com. VAT: Spec.

Peter Lipitch Ltd [BADA]
120/124 Fulham Rd. SW3 6HU. Est. 1954. Open 9.30-5.30. SIZE: Large. STOCK: Fine English furniture and mirrors. TEL: 020 7373 3328; fax - 020 7373 8888; website - www. peterlipitch.com. FAIRS: BADA; Grosvenor House. VAT: Spec.

The Map House [BADA]
54 Beauchamp Place. SW3 1NY. (P. Curtis and P. Stuchlik). ABA. IMCOS. Est. 1907. Open 9.45-5.45, Sat. 10.30-5 or by appointment. STOCK: Antique and rare maps, atlases, engravings and globes. TEL: 020 7589 4325/7584 8559; fax - 020 7589 1041; e-mail - maps@themaphouse.com; website - www. themaphouse.com. VAT: Stan.

McKenna and Co [LAPADA]
28 Beauchamp Place. SW3 1NJ. (C. and M. McKenna). Est. 1982. Open 10-6. SIZE: Medium. *STOCK: Fine jewellery, Georgian to post war, £250-£25,000; some silver and objects.* LOC: Off Brompton Rd., near Harrods. PARK: Meters. TEL: 020 7584 1966; fax - 020 7225 2893; e-mail - info@mckennajewels.com; website - www.mckennajewels.com. SER: Valuations; restorations. VAT: Stan/Margin.

No. 12
12 Cale St., Chelsea Green. SW3 3QU. (Thomas Kerr Antiques Ltd). Open 10-6, Sat. 10-5. *STOCK: French country furniture and accessories.* PARK: Meters. TEL: 020 7581 5022; fax - 020 7581 3966. VAT: Spec.

Old Church Galleries
98 Fulham Rd., Chelsea. SW3 6HS. (Nicky Ranson and Mrs M. Harrington). FATG. ABA. Open 10-6. *STOCK: Maps and engravings, sporting and decorative prints.* TEL: 020 7591 8790; fax - 020 7591 8791; e-mail - sales@old-churchgalleries.com; website - www.old-church-galleries.com. SER: Framing. FAIRS: Olympia; Boston International.

Orientalist
LAPADA

152-154 Walton St. SW3 2JJ. (E., H. and M. Sakhai). Est. 1985. Open 10.30-5.15, appointment advisable. SIZE: Large. *STOCK: Oriental, European, antique and reproduction rugs - classic and tribal Persian, Caucasian, Indian and Turkish, especially over-sized; Aubusson, tapestries, cushions and contemporary rugs.* PARK: Easy. TEL: 020 7581 2332; e-mail - rugs@orientalist.demon.co.uk; website - www.orientalist.demon.co.uk/orientalist. SER: Valuations; restorations (cleaning and repairing rugs, carpets and tapestries).

Perez
199 Brompton Rd. SW3 1LA. (Mr Tyran). Est. 1983. Open 10-6. SIZE: Large. *STOCK: Antique carpets, rugs, tapestries and Aubussons.* LOC: 50 yards from Harrods. PARK: Easy. TEL: 020 7589 2199 (ansaphone). SER: Valuations; restorations; buys at auction. VAT: Stan/Spec.

Prides of London
15 Paultons House. Paultons Sq. SW3 5DU. Open by appointment. *STOCK: Fine 18th-19th C English and Continental furniture; objets d'art.* TEL: 020 7586 1227. SER: Interior design.

Rogers de Rin
BADA

76 Royal Hospital Rd., Chelsea. SW3 4HN. (V. de Rin). Est. 1950. Open 10-5.30, Sat. 10-1, Sun. by appointment, SIZE: Small. STOCK: Wemyss pottery, objets d'art, decorative furnishings (Regency taste), collectors' specialities, 18th-19th C, £50-£10,000. LOC: Just beyond Royal Hospital, corner of Paradise Walk. PARK: Easy. TEL: 020 7352 9007; fax - 020 7351 9407; e-mail - rogersderin@rogersderin.co.uk; website - www.rogersderin.co.uk. VAT: Spec.

Russell Rare Books
239A Fulham Rd., Chelsea. SW3 6HY. (C. Russell). ABA. PBFA. Est. 1978. Open Mon.-Fri. 11-6. SIZE: Small. *STOCK: Antiquarian books.* LOC: At junction Old Church St. TEL: 020 7351 5119; fax - 020 7376 7227; e-mail - c.russell@russellrarebooks.com; website - www.russellrarebooks.com. FAIRS: Russell Hotel (monthly); Olympia (June).

Charles Saunders Antiques
255 Fulham Rd. SW3 6HY. Open Mon.-Fri.9.30-5.30. *STOCK: Decorative furniture, objects and lamps, 18th to early 20th C.* TEL: 020 7351 5242; e-mail - info@charlessaundersantiques.com. VAT: Spec.

Christine Schell
15 Cale St. SW3 3QS. Est. 1973. Open 10-5.30. SIZE: Small. *STOCK: Unusual tortoiseshell, silver and enamel objects, late 19th-20th C, £150-£2,500.* LOC: North of King's Rd., between Sloane Ave. and Sydney St. PARK: Easy. TEL: 020 7352 5563; e-mail - c.schell@eidosnet.co.uk. SER: Valuations; restorations (tortoiseshell, ivory, shagreen, crocodile, leather, enamels, silver, hairbrush re-bristling). VAT: Stan/Spec.

Robert Stephenson
1 Elystan St. Chelsea Green. SW3 3NT. Open 9.30-5.30, Sat. 10.30-2. *STOCK: Antique and decorative room-sized carpets and kilims; antique Oriental rugs, European tapestries and Aubussons, textiles, needlepoints and cushions; modern Bessarabian kilims, traditional and own contemporary designs.* TEL: 020 7225 2343; fax - same. SER: Cleaning; restorations; valuations.

Gordon Watson Ltd
LAPADA

50 Fulham Rd. SW3 6HH. Est. 1977. Open 11-6. *STOCK: Art Deco and 1940's glass, jewellery and furniture, £1,000-£50,000; silver by Jensen and Jean E. Puiforcat, 1920's, £500-£30,000.* LOC: At junction with Sydney St. PARK: Sydney St. TEL: 020 7589 3108/7584 6328. VAT: Stan/Spec.

Rock crystal, sapphire and diamond sûreté *pin, c.1920. Sold at Sotheby's London, December 2002, for £5,451.*

From an article entitled "Art Deco Jewellery" by Daniela Mascetti which appeared in the May 2003 issue of *Antique Collecting*. For more details and to subscribe see page 21.

Clifford Wright Antiques Ltd.
Antiques and Works of Art

Telephone 020-7589 0986
Fax 020-7589 3565

104 & 106 Fulham Road,
London SW3 6HS

*A good late George III
Hepplewhite period
mahogany serpentine
fronted serving table.*

English Circa 1785.

*Height: 35¾" (91cm)
Width: 69½" (176.5cm)
Depth: 31" (79cm)*

O.F. Wilson Ltd [BADA] [LAPADA]
Queen's Elm Parade, Old Church St. (corner Fulham Rd.), Chelsea. SW3 6EJ. (P. and V.E. Jackson and K.E. Simmonds). Est. 1935. Open 9.30-5.30, Sat. 10.30-1. SIZE: 6 showrooms. *STOCK: English and French furniture, mirrors, mantelpieces, objets d'art.* TEL: 020 7352 9554; fax - 020 7351 0765. SER: Valuations. VAT: Spec.

Clifford Wright Antiques Ltd [BADA]
104-106 Fulham Rd. SW3 6HS. Est. 1964. Open Mon.-Fri. 9-5.30 or by appointment. SIZE: Large. *STOCK: Furniture, period giltwood, looking glasses and consoles, 18th to early 19th C.* LOC: Near Royal Marsden Hospital. PARK: Nearby. TEL: 020 7589 0986; fax - 020 7589 3565. VAT: Spec.

SW4

Antiques and Things
(Mrs V. Crowther). Est. 1986. Open by appointment. SIZE: Small. *STOCK: 18th-19th C French furniture, lighting and decorative items including curtain furniture and textiles, £5-£10,000.* LOC: Clapham. TEL: 020 7498 1303; fax - same; mobile - 07767 262096; website -

www.antiquesandthings.co.uk. FAIRS: Decorative Antiques and Textiles.

Places and Spaces
30 Old Town, Clapham. SW4 0LB. (Paul Carroll and Nick Hannam). Est. 1996. Open 10.30-6, Sun. 12-4. CL: Mon. SIZE: Small. *STOCK: Furniture, lighting, art and ceramics, 20th C, £45-£2,000.* LOC: Near Clapham Common underground station. PARK: Meters. TEL: 020 7498 0998; fax - 020 7627 2625. SER: Valuations.

SW5

Beaver Coin Room
Beaver Hotel, 57 Philbeach Gdns. SW5 9ED. (J. Lis). Est. 1971. Open by appointment. SIZE: Small. *STOCK: European coins, 10th-18th C; commemorative medals, 15th-20th C; all £5-£5,000.* LOC: 2 mins. walk from Earls Court Rd. PARK: Easy. TEL: 020 7373 4553; fax - 020 7373 4555; e-mail - hotelbeaver@hotmail.com. SER: Valuations; buys at auction (coins and medals). FAIRS: London Coin and Coinex. VAT: Stan.

SW6

20th Century Gallery
821 Fulham Rd. SW6 5HG. (E. Brandl and H. Chapman). Open 10-6, Sat. 10-1. SIZE: Small. *STOCK: Post impressionist and modern British oils and watercolours; original prints.* LOC: Near Munster Rd. junction. PARK: Easy. TEL: 020 7731 5888. SER: Restorations (paintings); framing. VAT: Spec.

275 Antiques
275 Lillie Rd., Fulham. SW6 7LL. (David Fisher). Open 10-5.30. SIZE: Medium. *STOCK: English and Continental decorative furniture, £200-£1,200; decorative objects and mirrors, £50-£500; unique American Lucite 1960's table lamps and furniture, £250-£800.* PARK: Easy. TEL: 020 7386 7382.

291 Antiques
291 Lillie Rd., Fulham. SW6 7LL. SIZE: Large. *STOCK: Highly decorative antiques, Gothic style and 18th C splendour; mirrors, garden statuary and textiles.* TEL: 020 7381 5008. SER: Lavish interior design.

313 Antiques
313 Lillie Rd., Fulham. SW6 7LL. (Marc Costantini Art & Antiques). Open 10.30-5.30. *STOCK: 17th-19th C furniture, £200-£3,000; decorative and interesting objects, £20-£500; pictures especially portrait oils; decorative wood frames, mirrors, carpets.* LOC: From Old Brompton Rd., west for half a mile after crossing Northend Rd. PARK: Easy and nearby. TEL: 020 7610 2380; fax - same;. SER: Shipping arranged.

(55) For Decorative Living
55 New King's Rd., Chelsea. SW6 4SE. (Mrs J. Rhodes). BFS. Est. 1987. Open 10.30-5.30. SIZE: Large. *STOCK: Furniture, lighting and decorative items, European, Colonial and garden.* PARK: Pay & Display. TEL: 020 7736 5623. SER: Design.

And So To Bed Limited
638/640 King's Rd. SW6. Est. 1973. Open 10-6. SIZE: Large. *STOCK: Brass, lacquered and wooded beds.* LOC: End of King's Rd., towards Fulham. PARK: Easy. TEL: 020 7731 3593/4/5; freephone - 0808 1444343; fax - 020 7371 5272; e-mail - enquiries@andsotobed.co.uk; website - www.andsotobed.co.uk. SER: Restorations; spares; interior design. VAT: Stan.

The Antique Lamp Shop

at Christopher Wray Lighting, 591-593 King's Rd. SW6 2YW. Est. 1964. Open 10-6. SIZE: Large. *STOCK: Victorian and Edwardian oil lamps, spare parts, wicks, chimneys, glass shades; 19th C French and English decorative light fittings, Art Deco wall brackets and pendants, piano candle sconces; also door furniture, old signage and some furniture.* LOC: From Sloane Sq. over Stanley Bridge. PARK: Own at rear. TEL: 020 7751 8701; fax - 020 7751 8699. SER: Repairs and renovations. VAT: Stan.

Christopher Bangs `BADA` `LAPADA`

P O Box 6077. SW6 7XS. CINOA. **Est. 1971. Open by appointment. STOCK: Domestic metalwork and metalware, works of art, decorative objects. TEL: 020 7381 3532 (24 hrs); fax - 020 7381 2192 (24 hrs); mobile - 07836 333532; e-mail - cbangs@beeb.net. SER: Research; commission buys at auction; finder. VAT: Stan/Spec.**

Sebastiano Barbagallo

661 Fulham Rd. SW6 5PZ. Est. 1975. Open 10-6 including Sun. *STOCK: Chinese furnitures; antiques and handicrafts from India, Tibet, SE Asia and China.* LOC: Near Fulham Broadway. TEL: 020 7751 0691.

Barclay Samson Ltd

65 Finlay St. SW6 6HF. (Richard Barclay). IVPDA. Open by appointment. *STOCK: Pre 1950 original lithographic posters: French, German, Swiss, American, British and Russian Constructivist schools.* TEL: 020 7731 8012; fax - 020 7731 8013; mobile - 07785 306401; e-mail - richard@barclaysamson.com. FAIRS: Olympia (June); USA. VAT: Spec.

Robert Barley Antiques

SW6. (R.A. Barley). Est. 1965. Open by appointment. SIZE: Medium. *STOCK: Rare and bizarre objects, sculpture and pictures, 2000BC-2003AD.* TEL: 020 7736 4429; fax - same. FAIRS: Olympia (Spring, Summer and Winter); Decorative Antiques and Textiles (Jan., April and Sept). VAT: Stan/Spec.

Big Ben Antique Clocks

5 Broxholme House, New King's Rd. SW6 4AA. (R. Lascelles). Est. 1978. *STOCK: Longcase painted dial clocks, from £1,500; decorative antiques and accessories.* LOC: At junction of Wandsworth Bridge Rd. and New King's Rd. TEL: 020 7736 1770; fax - 020 7384 1957; e-mail - info@lasc.demon.co.uk; website - www.roger lascelles.com. SER: Buys at auction.

Julia Boston `LAPADA`

588 King's Rd. SW6 2DX. CINOA. Est. 1976. Open 10-6 or by appointment. SIZE: Large. *STOCK: 18th-19th C furniture, tapestry cartoons, antiquarian prints and decoration.* TEL: 020 7610 6783; fax - 020 7610 6784; e-mail - julia@juliaboston.com; website - www.juliaboston.com. VAT: Spec.

Alasdair Brown

3/4 The Cranewell, The Gas Works, 2 Michael Rd. SW6 2AD. Est. 1986. Open Wed. and Thurs. 10-6, other days by appointment. SIZE: Medium. *STOCK: Furniture, to £15,000; decorative items, to £10,000; upholstery, lighting and the unusual.* LOC: Behind Christopher Wray (King's Road). PARK: Easy. TEL: 020 7736 6661; fax - 020 7384 3334; e-mail - ab@alasdairbrown.com; website - www.alasdairbrown.com. SER: Valuations; restorations; finder. FAIRS: Olympia (Feb., June and Nov). VAT: Stan/Spec.

I. and J.L. Brown Ltd

632-636 King's Rd. SW6 2DU. Open 9-6. SIZE: Large. *STOCK: English and French provincial furniture including tables, country chairs, dressers, armoires, side tables and servers; decorative items.* TEL: 020 7736 4141; fax - 020 7736 9164; e-mail - sales@brownantiqueslondon.com. SER: Restorations; chair re-rushing.

Rupert Cavendish Antiques

610 King's Rd. SW6 2DX. Est. 1980. Open 10-6. SIZE: Large. *STOCK: Louis XVI (Gustavian), Empire, Biedermeier and Art Deco furniture; 20th C oil paintings.* LOC: Just before New King's Rd. PARK: Easy. TEL: 020 7731 7041; fax - 020 7731 8302; e-mail - RCavendish @aol.com; website - www.rupertcavendish. co.uk. SER: Valuations; restorations (furniture). VAT: Spec.

Chelminski

616 King's Rd., Chelsea. SW6 2DU. (Hilary Chelminski). SALVO. Est. 1970. Open 10-6, Sat. 11-5. SIZE: Medium. *STOCK: Sculpture and garden ornaments in marble, bronze, stone and terracotta, 18th-19th C, £100-£250,000.* LOC: Near corner with Maxwell Rd. PARK: Easy. TEL: 020 7384 2227; fax - 020 7384 2229; mobile - 07989 033831. SER: Restorations (architectural and garden items and sculpture); buys at auction.

John Clay

263 New King's Rd., Fulham. SW6 4RB. Est. 1974. Open 10-6. SIZE: Medium. *STOCK: Furniture, £50-£10,000; objets d'art and animal objects, silver and clocks, £10-£5,000; all 18th-*

19th C. Not Stocked: Pine. LOC: Close to Parsons Green, A3. PARK: Easy. TEL: 020 7731 5677; e-mail - johnclayantiques@btconnect.com. SER: Restorations (furniture, objets d'art). VAT: Stan/Spec.

Fergus Cochrane and Leigh Warren Antiques
570 King's Rd. SW6 2DY. Est. 1981. Open 10-5. SIZE: Medium. *STOCK: Decorative lighting, furniture and objects, 1700-1930, £100-£3,000.* PARK: Easy. TEL: 020 7736 9166.

Decorative Antiques `LAPADA`
284 Lillie Rd., Fulham. SW6 7PX. (Anthony Harley). Est. 1991. Open 10-5.30. SIZE: Medium. *STOCK: French country furniture, 18th C; decorative items.* PARK: Easy. TEL: 020 7610 2694; fax - 020 7386 0103. SER: Valuations; restorations. VAT: Spec.

Charles Edwards `BADA`
19A Rumbold Rd. SW6 2HX. Est. 1972. Open 9.30-6, Sat. 10-5. SIZE: Medium. *STOCK: Antique and reproduction light fixtures; furniture, 18th-19th C; decorative items.* LOC: Just off King's Rd. PARK: Meters. TEL: 020 7736 7172; fax - 020 7731 7388; e-mail - charles@charlesedwards.com.VAT: Stan/Spec.

Nicole Fabre `LAPADA`
592 King's Rd. SW6 2DX. CINOA. Est. 1989. Open 10.30-6, Sat. 11-6, Sun. by appointment. SIZE: Medium. *STOCK: French furniture, provincial style, French textiles, decorative objects, to 1870.* PARK: Meters. TEL: 020 7384 3112; fax - 020 7610 6410. VAT: Spec.

Fairfax Antiques and Fireplaces
568 King's Rd. SW6 2DY. Open by appointment. *STOCK: Cast iron and pine fireplaces, architectural items, balustrades and railings, decorative furniture and collectables.* TEL: 020 7736 5023; fax - 01249 652030.

Hector Finch Lighting
88-90 Wandsworth Bridge Rd. SW6 2TF. (Mr and Mrs H. Finch). Est. 1988. Open 10-5.30. SIZE: Medium. *STOCK: Antiques and period lighting, early 20th C contemporary and reproduction.* LOC: Off New King's Rd. PARK: Side streets or Pay and Display. TEL: 020 7731 8886; fax - 020 7731 7408; e-mail - hector@hectorfinch.com; website - www.hectorfinch.com. SER: Restorations (period lighting). VAT: Global.

Floyd & James Antiques
592 Fulham Rd. SW6 5NT. (George Floyd and

Mark James). Est. 1972. Open 8.30-6, Sat. by appointment. SIZE: Large. *STOCK: 18th-19th C furniture, objects and mirrors, especially Georgian and Regency.* LOC: Junction of Parsons Green Lane. PARK: Meters. TEL: 020 7736 0183; mobile - 07973 279679; e-mail - info@plj-antiques.com; website - www.plj-antiques.com. FAIRS: Claridges; Olympia; Harrogate. VAT: Stan/Spec.

Birdie Fortescue Antiques `LAPADA`
Studio GJ, Cooper House, 2 Michael Rd. SW6 2AD. Open by appointment. SIZE: Large. *STOCK: French and Italian fruitwood furniture, 18th to early 19th C, £500-£10,000.* LOC: Off King's Rd. TEL: 01206 337557; fax - same; mobile - 07778 263467; e-mail - bfortescue antiques@btopenworld.com. FAIRS: Olympia (Feb. and June): Decorative (Sept). VAT: Spec.

Fulham Antiques
318-320 Munster Rd., Fulham. SW6 6BH. (Adrian Eves). Est. 1998. Open 10-5.30. SIZE: Large. *STOCK: English, Continental and decorative antique furniture, mirrors and lighting.* TEL: 020 7610 3644; e-mail - fulhamantique320@aol.com.

Fulham Marble
56 Tasso Rd., Fulham. SW6. (P.H. Davies). Est. 1946. Open 8.30-5, Sat. 9-1. SIZE: Medium. *STOCK: Marble and wood mantelpieces, grates, fenders, fire irons, chandeliers, including reproduction, £50-£20,000.* TEL: 020 7385 8519. SER: Valuations; restorations (marblework and wood mantelpieces). VAT: Stan.

Judy Greenwood
657-659 Fulham Rd. SW6 5PY. Est. 1978. Open 10-5.30, Sat. 10-5. *STOCK: French decorative furniture including armoires, tables and chairs, commodes, lighting, mirrors, beds, quilts, all 1900's.* LOC: Fulham Broadway, nearest underground station. TEL: 020 7736 6037; fax - 020 7736 1941; e-mail - judyg@dial.pipex.com.

Robin Greer
434 Fulham Palace Rd. SW6 6HX. ABA. PBFA. Est. 1965. Open by appointment. *STOCK: Children's and illustrated books, original illustrations.* TEL: 020 7381 9113; fax - 020 7381 6499; e-mail - rarities@rarerobin.com. SER: Catalogues issued.

Gregory, Bottley and Lloyd
13 Seagrave Rd. SW6 1RP. Est. 1858. Open 9.30-5. CL: Sat. SIZE: Medium. *STOCK: Mineral specimens, £1-£5,000; fossils, £5-£500.* LOC:

Nearest underground station - West Brompton. PARK: Easy. TEL: 020 7381 5522; fax - 020 7381 5512. VAT: Stan.

Guinevere Antiques
574/580 King's Rd. SW6 2DY. Open 9.30-6, Sat. 10-5.30 (warehouse by appointment only). SIZE: Large + trade warehouse. *STOCK: Period decorative antiques and accessories.* TEL: 020 7736 2917; fax - 020 7736 8267; e-mail - sales @guinevere.co.uk; website - www.guinevere. co.uk.

Gutlin Clocks and Antiques
606 King's Rd. SW6 2DX. Est. 1990. Open 10-6. SIZE: Large - two floors. *STOCK: Longcase clocks, £2,000-£8,000; mantel clocks, £300-£6,000; furniture and lighting, £500-£3,000; all 18th-19th C.* LOC: 200 yards from beginning of New King's Rd. PARK: Maxwell Rd. TEL: 020 7384 2439; fax - same; home - 020 8740 6830; e-mail - mark@gutlin.com; website - www.gutlin. com. SER: Valuations; restorations (clocks and clock cases); buys at auction (clocks).

House of Mirrors
597 King's Rd. SW6 2EL. (G. Witek). Est. 1960. Open 10-6. *STOCK: Mirrors.* TEL: 020 7736

5885; fax - 020 7610 9188; e-mail - grazyna @houseofmirrors.co.uk; website - www. houseofmirrors.co.uk.

HRW Antiques (London) Ltd LAPADA
26 Sulivan Rd. SW6 3DT. Open 9-5. CL: Sat. SIZE: Large. *STOCK: Furniture and objects of art, 18th-19th C.* LOC: Within easy reach of the King's Rd. and Chelsea Harbour. TEL: 020 7371 7995; fax - 020 7371 9522; e-mail - iain@hrw-antiques.com; website - www.hrw-antiques.com.

Indigo
275 New King's Rd., Parsons Green. SW6 4RD. (Richard Lightbown and Marion Bender). Est. 1983. Open 10-6. SIZE: Small. *STOCK: Chinese, Indian, Japanese and Tibetan furniture and accessories, Chinese porcelain, from early 19th C, to £3,600.* PARK: Nearby. TEL: 020 7384 3101; fax - 020 7384 3102; e-mail - antiques@indigo-uk.com; website - www.indigo-uk.com.

Christopher Jones Antiques
618-620 King's Rd. SW6 2DU. Open 10-5.30. *STOCK: Continental and British decorative objects and furniture, screens and mirrors, 18th-19th C, £500-£10,000.* TEL: 020 7731 4655; fax - 020 7371 8682; e-mail - florehouse@msn.com;

website - www.christopherjonesantiques.co.uk.
VAT: Spec.

King's Court Galleries

949/953 Fulham Rd. SW6 5HY. (Mrs J. Joel).
Est. 1983. Open 10-5.30. *STOCK: Antique maps,
engravings, decorative and sporting prints.*
PARK: Easy. TEL: 020 7610 6939; e-mail -
sales@kingscourtgalleries.co.uk; website - www.
kingscourtgalleries.co.uk. SER: Framing (on
site).

L. and E. Kreckovic

559 King's Rd. SW6 2EB. Open 10-6. *STOCK:
18th-19th C furniture.* TEL: 020 7736 0753; fax -
020 7731 5904. SER: Restorations.

Lewin

638 Fulham Rd. SW6 5RT. (David and Harriett
Lewin). Est. 1989. Open 10.30-6. SIZE: Medium.
*STOCK: Original Dutch colonial furniture and
teak and mahogany reproduction colonial-style
designs.* PARK: Pay & Display. TEL: 020 7731
1616; fax - 020 7371 7772; website -
www.lewincolonial.com. SER: Delivery (free
locally). FAIRS: House & Garden; Period Living;
various country house. VAT: Stan.

Lunn Antiques Ltd

86 New Kings Rd., Parsons Green. SW6 4LU.
Est. 1976. Open 10-6. *STOCK: Antique lace,
antique and modern bed linen, nightdresses,
christening robes.* TEL: 020 7736 4638; fax - 020
7371 7113; e-mail - lunnantiques@aol.com. SER:
Laundry and restoration (antique linen and lace).
VAT: Margin.

Michael Luther Antiques

590 King's Rd., Chelsea. SW6 2DX. (Michael
Luther and Peter Goodwin). Est. 1967. Open 10-
6. SIZE: Large. *STOCK: Furniture - 18th-19th C,
£500-£20,000; early 20th C, £300-£3,000;
lighting, 19th-20th C, £300-£5,000.* LOC:
Between Lots Rd. and Parsons Green. PARK:
Nearby. TEL: 020 7371 8492; fax - same. SER:
Valuations; buys at auction (furniture). VAT:
Spec.

Michael Marriott

Unit F7, 72 Farm Lane, Fulham. SW6 1QA. Est.
1979. Open 10-5.30, Sat. pm. and Sun. by
appointment. SIZE: Large. *STOCK: 18th & 19th
C furnishings.* PARK: Easy. TEL: 020 7610 3922;
fax - 020 7610 2908. SER: Valuations;
restorations. VAT: Stan/Spec.

David Martin-Taylor Antiques LAPADA

558 King's Rd. SW6 2DZ. Open 10-6, Sat. 11-5.

SIZE: Medium. *STOCK: Classic and decorative
furniture and unusual objects, 18th-19th C.*
PARK: Easy. TEL: 020 7731 4135; fax - 020
7371 0029; e-mail - dmt@davidmartintaylor.
com; website - www.davidmartintaylor.com.
SER: Hire. FAIRS: Olympia (June). VAT:
Stan/Spec.

Mark Maynard Antiques

651 Fulham Rd. SW6 5PU. Est. 1977. Open 10-
5, Sun. by appointment. SIZE: Medium. *STOCK:
Decorative items, £25-£300.* LOC: Near Fulham
Broadway underground station. PARK: Easy.
TEL: 020 7731 3533; home - 020 7373 4681.
VAT: Stan/Spec.

Mora & Upham Antiques

584 King's Rd. SW6 2DX. (Matthew Upham). Est.
1976. Open 10-6. SIZE: Medium. *STOCK:
Chandeliers, English and Continental furniture,
decorative items, garden statuary.* LOC: Corner
premises. PARK: Easy. TEL: 020 7731 4444; fax -
020 7736 0440; e-mail - mora.upham@talk21.com.
SER: Valuations; restorations (lighting). VAT: Spec.

Nimmo & Spooner

277 Lillie Rd., Fulham. SW6 7LL. (Catherine
Nimmo and Myra Spooner). Est. 1996. Open
10.30-5.30. SIZE: Medium. *STOCK: Objects and
furniture including painted dressers and chests of
drawers, tables, mirrors, 18th-20th C, to £3,500.*
LOC: Between Fulham Broadway and
Hammersmith. PARK: Nearby. TEL: 020 7385
2724; fax - same.

Old World Trading Co

565 King's Rd. SW6. (R.J. Campion). Est. 1970.
Open 9.30-6. *STOCK: Fireplaces, chimney pieces
and accessories, chandeliers, mirrors, furniture
including decorative, works of art.* TEL: 020
7731 4708; fax - 020 7731 1291; e-mail -
oldworld@btinternet.com.

Ossowski `BADA`

**595 King's Rd. SW6 2EL. Est. 1960. Open
9.30-5.30. SIZE: Large. STOCK: Furniture,
18th C. TEL: 020 7731 0334. SER: Valuations;
restorations. FAIRS: IFAAD, New York (Oct).
VAT: Spec.**

Anthony Outred `BADA`

**69 Finlay St. SW6 6HF. Open by appointment.
STOCK: Exceptional English and Continental
furniture especially unusual and amusing,
£1,000-£100,000. TEL: 020 7371 9863; fax -
020 7371 9869; mobile - 07767 848132; e-mail -
antiques@outred.co.uk; website - www.outred.
co.uk. FAIRS: Olympia. VAT: Stan/Spec.**

M. Pauw Antiques

Cooper House, 2 Michael Rd. SW6 2AD. Est. 1981. SIZE: Medium. *STOCK: English and Continental furniture, leather chairs, 18th-19th C; decorative items, lighting fixtures, zinc and lead planters.* PARK: Easy. TEL: 020 7731 4022; fax - 020 7731 7356; e-mail - info@mpauw; website - www.mpauw.com. VAT: Stan.

Perez Antique Carpets Gallery

150 Wandsworth Bridge Rd., Fulham. SW6 2UH. (K. Dinari). Est. 1984. Open 10-6.30, Wed. 10-7.30. SIZE: Large. *STOCK: Carpets, 19th C, £400-£40,000; rugs, 18th-20th C, £300-£3,000; textiles, 19th C, £70-£1,500.* PARK: Easy. TEL: 020 7371 9619. SER: Valuations; restorations; buys at auction (Oriental and European carpets, rugs and textiles, tapestries). VAT: Stan/Spec.

The Pine Mine (Crewe-Read Antiques)

100 Wandsworth Bridge Rd., Fulham. SW6 2TF. (D. Crewe-Read). Est. 1971. Open 9.45-5.45, Sat. till 4.30. SIZE: Large. *STOCK: Georgian and Victorian pine, Welsh dressers, farmhouse tables, chests of drawers, boxes and some architectural items.* LOC: From Sloane Sq., down King's Rd., into New King's Rd., left into Wandsworth Bridge Rd. PARK: Outside. TEL: 020 7736 1092. SER: Furniture made from old wood; stripping; export.

Daphne Rankin and Ian Conn `LAPADA`

608 King's Rd. SW6 2DX. Est. 1979. Open 10.30-6. SIZE: Medium. *STOCK: Oriental porcelain including Chinese, Japanese, Imari, Cantonese, Satsuma, Nanking, Famille Rose, £500-£25,000; Dutch Delft; tortoiseshell tea caddies.* PARK: Maxwell Rd. adjacent to shop. TEL: 020 7384 1847; fax - same; mobile - 07774 487713; e-mail - daphnerankin@aol.com; website - www.rankin-conn-chinatrade.com. SER: Valuations; buys at auction (as stock). FAIRS: Olympia (June and Nov). VAT: Stan/Spec.

Richardson and Kailas Icons `BADA`

65 Rivermead Court, Ranelagh Gardens. SW6 3RY. (C. Richardson). Open by appointment. *STOCK: Icons and frescoes.* TEL: 020 7371 0491; e-mail - chris.richardson1@virgin.net. SER: Consultancy; valuations; restorations.

Rogers & Co `LAPADA`

604 Fulham Rd. SW6 5RP. (M. and C. Rogers). Est. 1971. Open 10-6. SIZE: Large. *STOCK: Furniture, 18th-19th C, £100-£3,000; upholstery.* LOC: Near Fulham library, Parsons Green Lane. PARK: Side streets. TEL: 020 7731 8504; fax -

020 7610 6040. SER: Valuations. VAT: Stan/Spec.

Simon Horn Furniture Ltd

117-121 Wandsworth Bridge Rd. SW6 2TP. BIDDA. Est. 1982. Open 9.30-5.30, Sun. by appointment. SIZE: Large. *STOCK: Wooden classically styled bedframes £1,500-£6,500; bedside tables £250-£1,100; all 1790-1910 or recent larger copies.* LOC: South from New King's Rd., towards river down Wandsworth Bridge Rd., premises on left at first zebra crossing. PARK: Easy. TEL: 020 7731 1279; fax - 020 7736 3522; e-mail - info@simonhorn.com; website - www.simonhorn.com. SER: Restorations; gilding. FAIRS: House & Garden. VAT: Stan.

Soo San

598A King's Rd. SW6 2DX. Est. 1996. Open 10-6. SIZE: Small. *STOCK: Chinese furniture and accessories - cabinets, coffee tables, chairs, consol tables, desks, stools, beds, leather trunks, wedding baskets, wooden food containers, birdcages, porcelain, 18th-19th C; lacquer ware and Burmese buddhas; all £50-£18,000.* TEL: 020 7731 2063; fax - 020 7731 1566; e-mail - suze@soosan.co.uk; website - www.soosan.co.uk. SER: Valuations; restorations (re-lacquering, gilding and wood).

Trowbridge Gallery `LAPADA`

555 King's Rd. SW6 2EB. (M. Trowbridge). Est. 1980. Open 9.30-6, Sat. 10-5.30. SIZE: Large. *STOCK: Decorative prints, 17th-19th C, £35-£3,000.* LOC: Near Christopher Wray Lighting. PARK: Easy. TEL: 020 7371 8733. SER: Valuations; restorations; buys at auction (antiquarian books and prints); hand-made frames; decorative mounting. FAIRS: Decorative Antiques and Textiles; Olympia; LAPADA; City of London. VAT: Stan.

Whiteway and Waldron Ltd

305 Munster Rd., Fulham. SW6 6BJ. (M. Whiteway and G. Kirkland). Est. 1976. Open 10-6, Sat. 11-4. SIZE: Large. *STOCK: Religious antiques including candlesticks, statuary, gothic and carved church woodwork.* LOC: At junction with Lillie Rd. PARK: On forecourt for loading, or Strode Rd. TEL: 020 7381 3195; fax - same; e-mail - sales@whiteway-waldron.co.uk; website-www.whiteway-waldron.co.uk. SER: Buys at auction (religious items). VAT: Stan.

York Gallery Ltd `LAPADA`

569 King's Rd. SW6 2EB. (Jane and Gerd Beyer). Est. 1984. Open 10.30-5.30. SIZE:

Medium. *STOCK: Antique prints.* TEL: 020 7736 2260; fax - same; e-mail - prints@yorkgallery.co.uk; website - www.yorkgallery.co.uk. SER: Bespoke framing. VAT: Stan.

SW7

Anglo Persian Carpet Co
6 South Kensington Station Arcade. SW7 2NA. Est. 1910. Open 9.30-6. *STOCK: Carpets and rugs.* TEL: 020 7589 5457. SER: Valuations; restorations (carpets and rugs); cleaning.

Atlantic Bay Carpets Gallery `BADA`
14 Gloucester Rd. SW7 4RB. (W. Grodzinski). CINOA. Est. 1945. Open 9-4, Sat. by appointment. SIZE: Medium. *STOCK: Antique Oriental and European carpets and textiles; Islamic and Indian art.* TEL: 020 7689 8489; fax - 020 7581 8189; e-mail - atlantic baygallery@btinternet.com; website - www.btinternet.com/~atlanticbaygallery/. SER: Valuations; restorations; buys at auction (as stock). VAT: Stan/Spec.

The Gloucester Road Bookshop
123 Gloucester Rd., South Kensington. SW7 4TE. (Nicholas Dennys). Est. 1983. Open 9.30-10.30 pm, Sat. and Sun. 10.30-6.30. SIZE: Medium. *STOCK: Secondhand hardback and paperback books, all genres, mainly 19th-20th C, £1-£50; modern first editions, mainly 20th C, £5-£10,000; rare books, 17th-20th C, £70-£5,000.* LOC: 150 yards Gloucester Road underground station. Come out of station, cross road and turn right. PARK: Loading; easy weekends. Meters nearby. TEL: 020 7370 3503; fax - 020 7373 0610. SER: Valuations; book search.

M.P. Levene Ltd `BADA`
5 Thurloe Place. SW7 2RR. Est. 1889. Open 9.30-6. CL: Sat. pm. *STOCK: Silver, old Sheffield plate, scale silver models, various, all prices.* LOC: Few mins. past Harrods near South Kensington underground station. PARK: Easy. TEL: 020 7589 3755; fax - 020 7589 9908; e-mail - silver@mplevene.co.uk; website - www.mplevene.co.uk. SER: Valuations. VAT: Stan/Spec.

A. & H. Page (Est. 1840)
66 Gloucester Rd. SW7 4QT. NAG. Open 9-5.45, Sat. 10-2. *STOCK: Silver, jewellery, watches.* TEL: 020 7584 7349. SER: Valuations; repairs; silversmith; goldsmith.

The Taylor Gallery Ltd
1 Bolney Gate. SW7 1QW. (Jeremy Taylor). Est. 1986. Open by appointment. *STOCK: Irish, British, China Trade and marine paintings, 19th-20th C.* TEL: 020 7581 0253; fax - 020 7589 4495; e-mail - jeremy@taylor-gallery-london.com; website - www.taylor-gallery-london.com. FAIRS: Olympia (June); Palm Beach (Feb); Hong Kong (Oct).

The Wyllie Gallery
44 Elvaston Place. SW7 5NP. (J.G. Wyllie). Open by appointment. *STOCK: 19th-20th C marine paintings and etchings, especially works by the Wyllie family.* TEL: 020 7584 6024; e-mail - jgwyllie@hotmail.com.

SW8

Davies Antiques `LAPADA`
c/o The Packing Shop, 6-12 Ponton Rd. SW8 5BA. (H.Q.V. Davies). Est. 1976. Open 10-5.30, Sat. by appointment. *STOCK: Continental porcelain especially Meissen, 1710-1930.* PARK: Own. TEL: 020 8947 1902; fax - same; mobile - 07753 739689; e-mail - hugh.davies@btconnect.com; website - www.antique-meissen.com.

The French House (Antiques) Ltd
125 Queenstown Rd. SW8 3PH. (S.B. and M.J. Hazell). Est. 1995. Open 10-6. SIZE: Medium. *STOCK: Wooden beds, 18th-19th, £900-£2,500; gilt mirrors, 19th C, £300-£2,000; lighting, 19th-20th C, £200-£1,000; all French.* LOC: Short drive from Victoria station. PARK: Sidestreets. TEL: 020 7978 2228; fax - 020 7978 2340; website - www.thefrenchhouse.co.uk. SER: Restorations; cabinet making; upholstery; French polishing; painting. VAT: Stan/Spec.

Fay Lucas Artmetal `BADA`
Christies Fine Art Security, 42 Ponton Rd. SW8 5BA. Est. 1977. Open by appointment. *STOCK: Fine signed silver holloware, 20th C, £200-£50,000; signed furniture, 20th C, £5,000-£50,000; antique military and sporting jewellery, £100-£3,000.* TEL: 020 7371 4404; fax - same; mobile - 07767 660550; e-mail - info@faylucas.com. SER: Valuations; restorations; buys at auction. FAIRS: Olympia (Feb., June and Nov). VAT: Stan/Spec.

Paul Orssich
2 St. Stephen's Terrace, South Lambeth. SW8 1DH. Open by appointment. *STOCK: Old, rare and out of print books on Spain and Hispanic studies; old maps of all parts of the world, from £20.* TEL: 020 7787 0030; fax - 020 7735 9612; e-mail - paulo@orssich.com; website - www.orssich.com.

SW9

Rodney Franklin Antiques
Est. 1968. Open by appointment. *STOCK: French and English mirrors and beds, furniture, lighting, architectural and garden items.* TEL: 020 7274 0729. VAT: Stan/Spec.

SW10

Carlton Davidson Antiques
507 King's Rd.,Chelsea. SW10 0TX. Est. 1981. Open 10-6. *STOCK: Lamps, chandeliers, mirrors and decorative items, £500-£5,000.* TEL: 020 7795 0905.

Jonathan Clark & Co
18 Park Walk, Chelsea. SW10 0AQ. SLAD. Open 10-6.30, Sat. by appointment. *STOCK: Modern British paintings and sculpture.* TEL: 020 7351 3555; fax - 020 7823 3187.

Collins and Hastie Ltd
5 Park Walk, Chelsea. SW10 0AJ. (Caroline Hastie and Diana Collins). Open 10-6, Sat. 11-4. SIZE: Large. *STOCK: 20th C contemporary and modern paintings, European and British, £500-£30,000.* LOC: Park Walk runs between King's Rd. and Fulham Rd. PARK: Easy. TEL: 020 7351 4292. SER: Restorations (pictures). VAT: Spec.

The Furniture Cave
533 King's Rd. SW10 0TZ. Est. 1967. Open 10-6, Sun. 11-4. SIZE: Large. LOC: Corner of Lots Rd. PARK: Meters. TEL: 020 7352 4229/5478. SER: Shipping; forwarding. VAT: Stan/Spec. Below are listed the dealers trading from this address.

Paul Andrews Antiques
Basement. *English and Continental decorative furniture; sculpture, Old Master paintings, prints and drawings.* TEL: 020 7352 4584; fax - 020 7351 7815.

Brown's Antique Furniture
First Floor. *Library and dining, and decorative objects, from early 18th C.* TEL: 020 7352 2046; fax - 020 7352 3654.

Stuart Duggan
First Floor. *Georgian and Victorian furniture especially 19th-20th C pianos.* TEL: 020 7352 2046; fax - 020 7352 3654.

Robert Grothier
TEL: 020 7352 2045; fax - 020 7352 6803.

Harpur Dearden
TEL: 020 7352 3111; fax - 020 7351 5833.

Kenneth Harvey Antiques
LAPADA

Ground Floor. *Decorative furniture, mirrors, chandeliers, light fittings.* TEL: 020 7352 3775; fax - 020 7352 3759.

Simon Hatchwell Antiques
LAPADA

Ground Floor. Est. 1961. *English and Continental decorative furniture and objets d'art.* TEL: 020 7351 2344; fax - 020 7351 3520.

Hill Farm Antiques
General antiques including large tables. TEL: 020 7352 2046; fax - 020 7352 3654.

David Loveday
First Floor. *English and Georgian large furniture.* TEL: 020 7352 1100; fax - 020 7351 5833.

John Nicholas Antiques
TEL: 020 7352 2046; fax - 020 7352 3654.

Phoenix Trading Company
Furniture including Indian, porcelain, bronzes. TEL: 020 7351 6543; fax - 020 7352 9803.

Christopher Preston Antiques
Ground Floor. *Early 19th C and Regency furniture.* TEL: 020 7352 8587; fax - 020 7376 3627.

Anthony Redmile
Basement. *Marble resin neo-classical Grand Tour objects.* TEL: 020 7351 3813; fax - 020 7352 8131.

Hünersdorff Rare Books
P.O. Box 582. SW10 9RU. ABA. Est. 1969. Open by appointment. *STOCK: Continental books in rare editions, early printing, science and medicine, military, Latin America, natural history.* TEL: 020 7373 3899; fax - 020 7370 1244; e-mail - huner.rarebooks@dial.pipex.com; website - www.abebooks.com/home/hunersdorff. FAIRS: Olympia (June).

Thomas Kerr Antiques Ltd
at L'Encoignure, 517 King's Rd. SW10 0TX. Est. 1977. Open 10-6. SIZE: Large. *STOCK: French country furniture, paintings, mirrors and decorative items.* TEL: 020 7351 6465; fax - 020 7351 4744. VAT: Stan/Spec.

Lane Fine Art Ltd
8 Drayton Gardens. SW10 9SA. (C. Foley). Open by appointment. *STOCK: Oil paintings, 1500-1850, principally English, major works by the main artists of the period, £10,000-£1million+.* TEL: 020 7373 3130; fax - 020 7373 2277; e-mail - cf@lanefineart.co.uk. SER: Valuations. VAT: Stan/Spec.

Langford's Marine Antiques

BADA **LAPADA**

The Plaza, 535 King's Rd. SW10 0SZ. (L.L. Langford). Est. 1941. *STOCK: Ships models, marine instruments, globes, steam engine models.* **TEL: 020 7351 4881; fax - 020 7352 0763; e-mail - langford@dircon.co.uk; website - www.langfords.co.uk. VAT: Stan/Spec.**

Langton Street Gallery

13 Langton St. SW10 0JL. (P. and C. Kennaugh). Open 10.30-7.00, Sat. 10-4. *STOCK: Oils, watercolours, 20th C and contemporary £300-£3,000.* LOC: Worlds End, Chelsea. TEL: 020 7351 1973. SER: Framing; restorations. FAIRS: Affordable Art. VAT: Spec.

Stephen Long

348 Fulham Rd. SW10 9UH. Est. 1966. Open 9.30-1 and 2.15-5, Sat. pm. and Sun. by appointment. SIZE: Small. *STOCK: English pottery, 18th-19th C, to £400; English painted furniture, 18th to early 19th C; toys and games, household and kitchen items, chintz, materials and patchwork, to £1,000.* LOC: From South Kensington along road on right between Ifield Rd. and Billing Rd. PARK: Easy. TEL: 020 7352 8226. VAT: Spec.

McVeigh & Charpentier

LAPADA

498 King's Rd. SW10 0LE. (Maggie Charpentier). Est. 1979. Open 10.30-5, weekends by appointment only. SIZE: Medium. *STOCK: Continental furniture, mirrors, garden ironwork and stone, 17th-19th C.* LOC: Two blocks down from Earls Court. PARK: In cul de sac adjacent. TEL: 020 7351 1442/7352 6084; home - 020 7937 6459; mobile - 07801 480167. FAIRS: Olympia (June); Harvey (Sept., Jan. and March). VAT: Spec.

McWhirter

22 Park Walk, Chelsea. SW10 0AQ. (James McWhirter). Est. 1988. Open 9-6, Sat. by appointment. SIZE: Medium. *STOCK: Works of art, objects, unusual furniture.* LOC: Near Fulham Road Cinema. PARK: Meters. TEL: 020 7351 5399; fax - 020 7352 9821. SER: Consultancy (art). VAT: Spec.

Offer Waterman and Co. Fine Art

11 Langton St. SW10 0JL. Est. 1996. Open 10-6.30, Sat. 11-4, Sun. by appointment. SIZE: Small. *STOCK: Modern British paintings, 1900 to date, £500-£5,000.* LOC: Off Kings Rd. PARK: Easy. TEL: 020 7351 0068; fax - 020 7351 2269; e-mail - info@waterman.co.uk; website - www.waterman.co.uk. SER:

Valuations; restorations (as stock); framing; buys at auction (Modern British paintings). FAIRS: Art 2002; 20th/21st C Art, Olympia. VAT: Stan/Spec.

Orientation

2 Park Walk. SW10 0AD. (Evelyne Soler). Est. 1990. Open 10-5.30, Sat. by appointment. SIZE: Medium. *STOCK: Continental furniture, 18th-19th C; Chinese porcelain, ceramics, works of art, China trade items, to £20,000.* LOC: Off Fulham Rd. TEL: 020 7351 0234; fax - 020 7351 7535. FAIRS: Olympia. VAT: Spec.

Park Walk Gallery

BADA

20 Park Walk, Chelsea. SW10 0AQ. (J. Cooper). SLAD. Est. 1988. Open 10-6.30, Sat. 11-4. SIZE: Medium. *STOCK: Paintings, £250-£100,000; watercolours, £250-£20,000; drawings, £200-£15,000; all contemporary.* **LOC: Off Fulham Rd. PARK: Easy. TEL: 020 7351 0410; fax - same; website - www. jonathancooper.co.uk. SER: Valuations; restorations. FAIRS: Olympia; Watercolours and Drawings, Art London; Art 2003. VAT: Spec.**

H.W. Poulter and Son

279 Fulham Rd. SW10 9PZ. Est. 1946. Open 9.30-5. CL: Sat. pm. SIZE: Large. *STOCK: English and French marble chimney pieces, grates, fenders, fire-irons, brass, chandeliers.* PARK: Meters. TEL: 020 7352 7268. SER: Restorations (marble work). VAT: Stan/Spec.

John Thornton

455 Fulham Rd. SW10 9UZ. Open 10-5.30. *STOCK: Antiquarian books especially theology.* TEL: 020 7352 8810.

Vaughan Ltd

G1 Chelsea Harbour Design Centre, Chelsea Harbour. SW10 0XE. Est. 1980. Open 9-5.30. CL: Sat. SIZE: Large. *STOCK: Reproduction 18th-19th C lighting, furniture, decorative objects.* PARK: Easy. TEL: 020 7349 4600. VAT: Stan/Spec.

SW11

David Alexander Antiques & Kate Thurlow

BADA **LAPADA**

29a Battersea Bridge Rd. SW11 3BA. (Kate Thurlow and Rodney Robertson). CINOA. Est. 1970. Open by appointment or by chance. SIZE: Large. *STOCK: European furniture, 15th-17th C, £500-£20,000.* **LOC: At junction with Hammersmith Rd., opposite Olympia Exhibition Hall. PARK: Limited or meters.**

TEL: 020 7585 0315; fax - same; mobile - 07836 588776. SER: Valuations; restorations (furniture); buys at auction. FAIRS: Olympia. VAT: Spec.

Braemar Antiques
113 Northcote Rd., Battersea. SW11 6PW. (Maria Elisabeth Ramos-de-Deus and Elizabeth Henderson). Est. 1995. SIZE: Small. *STOCK: Painted furniture including armoires, chests of drawers, mirrors and lamps; quilts, eiderdowns, china and glass.* LOC: Near Clapham junction. PARK: Easy. TEL: 020 7924 5628; e-mail - ramos-de-deus@msn.com. FAIRS: Brocante, Chelsea.

Eccles Road Antiques
60 Eccles Rd., Battersea. SW11. (H. Rix). Open 10-5. *STOCK: General antiques, pine furniture and smalls.* LOC: Off Clapham Common. TEL: 020 7228 1638.

Christopher Edwards
36 Roseneath Rd. SW11 6AH.. Est. 1982. Open by appointment. SIZE: Medium. *STOCK: Architecturally inspired furniture, unusual works of art, 19th C, £100-£10,000.* TEL: 020 7223 9962; fax - same; mobile - 07831 707043. SER: Valuations; buys at auction. VAT: Stan/Spec.

Garland Antiques
74 Chatham Rd., Battersea. SW11 6HG. (Garland Beech). Open 10-6, Sun. 12-5. CL: Mon. SIZE: Small. *STOCK: Furniture, 19th C; decorative objects, 18th-19th C.* PARK: Easy. TEL: 020 7924 4284.

Gideon Hatch Rugs
1 Port House, Plantation Wharf, Battersea. SW11 3TY. Est. 1985. Open by appointment. SIZE: Small. *STOCK: Oriental and European rugs, 19th to early 20th C, £500-£25,000.* LOC: Off York Rd., behind Homebase. PARK: Easy. TEL: 020 7223 3996; fax - 020 7223 3997; e-mail - info@gideonhatch.co.uk; website - www.gideonhatch.co.uk. SER: Valuations; restorations; cleaning; buys at auction (rare rugs). FAIRS: Olympia; Battersea. VAT: Stan/Spec.

Lucy Johnson   `BADA` `LAPADA`
29A Battersea Bridge Rd. SW11 3BA. CINOA. Est. 1982. Open 10-5. SIZE: Medium. *STOCK: 17th to early 18th C furniture, Delftware and interiors.* TEL: 07974 149912; e-mail - lucy-johnson@lucy-johnson.com. FAIRS: BADA; Olympia.

Northcote Road Antiques Market
155A Northcote Rd., Battersea. SW11 6QB.

Open 10-6, Sun. 12-5. SIZE: 30 dealers. *STOCK: Victoriana and Art Deco collectables, silver, glass, furniture, lighting, jewellery, prints, mirrors, flatware.* TEL: 020 7228 6850.

Overmantels
66 Battersea Bridge Rd. SW11 3AG. (Seth Taylor). BCFA. Est. 1980. Open 9.30-5.30. SIZE: Medium. *STOCK: English giltwood mirrors, £400-£3,000; French giltwood mirrors, £700-£3,000; both 18th-19th C; 19th C furniture, £200-£2,000.* LOC: 200m south of Battersea Bridge. PARK: Outside shop. TEL: 020 7223 8151; fax - 020 7924 2283. SER: Valuations; restorations (gesso work and gilding). VAT: Stan/Spec.

Pairs Antiques Ltd
Unit 6 Parkfields Industrial Estate, Culvert Rd., Battersea. SW11 5BA. (Iain M. Brunt). Est. 1994. Open by appointment. SIZE: Large. *STOCK: Pairs only - 18th-19th C furniture, decorative objects and paintings, £500-£20,000.* PARK: Easy. TEL: 020 7622 6446; fax - 020 7622 3663; mobile - 07798 684694; e-mail - iain@pairs antiques.co.uk; website - www.pairsantiques. co.uk. SER: Valuations; restorations; buys at auction. VAT: Stan/Spec.

Regent House Gallery
223 St John's Hill. SW11 1TH. (Nick & Jayne Underwood Thompson). Est. 1988. Open 10-6, Thurs. 10-7.30. CL: Mon. SIZE: Small. *STOCK: Watercolours and paintings, 19th-20th C, £50-£1,000; prints, drawings, cartoons, 18th-20th C, £10-£400; small antiques, books, 19th to early 20th C, £10-£200.* LOC: Top of St John's Hill, mid-way between Clapham Junction and Wandsworth Town. PARK: Pay and display. TEL: 020 7228 9344; home and fax - 020 7228 9344; e-mail - nick@regenthousegallery.com; website - www.regenthousegallery.com. SER: Framing.

The Woodpigeon
71 Webbs Rd. SW11 6SD. (Lucy Kallin). Est. 1995. Open Tues.-Sat. 10.30-5.30. SIZE: Small. *STOCK: Country furniture, mainly French - painted armoires, chests, wardrobes and beds; small decorative items and country antiques, mainly mid to late 19th C, £5-£1,500.* LOC: Parallel with Northcote Rd. PARK: Side roads. TEL: 020 7223 8668; mobile - 07904 102442. SER: Furniture painting and re-upholstery. VAT: Spec.

Robert Young Antiques   `BADA`
68 Battersea Bridge Rd. SW11 3AG. (Robert and Josyane Young). Est. 1974. Open 10-6, Sat. 10-5. SIZE: Medium. *STOCK: Fine country furniture, 17th-18th C, £500-£50,000; English*

Kate Dyson

THE DINING ROOM SHOP

62-64 White Hart Lane • London SW13 0PZ

Tel: 020-8878 1020   Fax: 020-8876 2367   Website: www.thediningroomshop.co.uk

Antique tables and sets of chairs, glass, china, cutlery, prints,
table linen and lace – all for the dining room

---

and European treen and objects of folk art, £100-£25,000; English and European provincial pottery and metalwork, £100-£10,000. LOC: Turn off King's Rd. or Chelsea Embankment into Beaufort St., cross over Battersea Bridge Rd., 9th shop on right. PARK: Opposite in side street. TEL: 020 7228 7847; fax - 020 7585 0489; e-mail - office@robertyoungantiques.com. SER: Valuations; buys at auction (treen and country furniture). FAIRS: Olympia; Winter Antiques (New York); Fall (San Francisco). VAT: Stan/Spec.

SW12

Twentieth Century
(M. Taylor). Est. 1986. Open by appointment. STOCK: Art Deco, Art Nouveau, Arts and Crafts, decorative arts items, £50-£500. PARK: Easy. TEL: 020 8675 6351; fax - same; e-mail - martin@nbscoms.co.uk. FAIRS: Battersea Art Deco; Loughborough Art Deco; Manchester; Birmingham. VAT: Stan.

SW13

Christine Bridge   BADA LAPADA
78 Castelnau, Barnes. SW13 9EX. CINOA. Est. 1972. Open anytime by appointment.

SIZE: Medium. STOCK: Glass - 18th C collectors and 19th C coloured, engraved and decorative, £50-£15,000; small decorative items - papier mâché, bronzes, needlework, ceramics. LOC: Main road from Hammersmith Bridge. PARK: Easy. TEL: 020 8741 5501; fax - 020 8255 0172; mobile - 07831 126668; e-mail - christine@bridge-antiques.com; website - www.bridge-antiques.com. SER: Valuations; restorations (glass - cutting, polishing, de-clouding); buys at auction; shipping. FAIRS: Olympia (June and Nov); BADA; Brussels; Tokyo; Melbourne; Sydney; Singapore; Santa Monica; Cleveland; Chicago. VAT: Stan/Spec.

Simon Coleman Antiques
40 White Hart Lane, Barnes. SW13. Est. 1974. Open 9.30-6. SIZE: Large. STOCK: 18th-19th C farm tables. PARK: Easy. TEL: 020 8878 5037; e-mail - colemansimon@aol.com. VAT: Stan/Spec.

The Dining Room Shop
62/64 White Hart Lane, Barnes. SW13 0PZ. (K. Dyson). Est. 1985. Open 10-5.30, Sun. by appointment. SIZE: Medium. STOCK: Formal and country dining room furniture, 18th-19th C; glasses, china, pottery, cutlery, damask and lace table linen, 19th C; associated small and

The Clock Clinic

Antique Clocks

A Regency period striking bracket clock
signed Handley and Moore London

Open Tues – Fri 9-6, Sat 9-1, Closed Mondays

85, Lower Richmond Road, Putney, London, SW15 1EU
Tel: 020-8788 1407 Fax: 020-8780 2838

**Website: www.clockclinic.co.uk
Email: clockclinic@btconnect.com**

decorative items. LOC: Near Barnes rail bridge, turning opposite White Hart public house. PARK: Easy. TEL: 020 8878 1020; fax - 020 8876 2367; e-mail - enquiries@thediningroomshop.co.uk; website - www.thediningroomshop.co.uk. SER: Valuations; restorations; bespoke furniture; finder; interior decorating. FAIRS: Olympia (June). VAT: Stan/Spec.

Joy McDonald Antiques
50 Station Rd., Barnes. SW13 0LP. Resident. Est. 1966. Open 10.30-5.30, prior telephone call advisable. CL: Mon. SIZE: Small. *STOCK: 19th-20th C mirrors, chandeliers and lighting; decorative items and upholstered chairs.* TEL: 020 8876 6184.

New Grafton Gallery
49 Church Rd., Barnes. SW13 9HH. (Claudia Wolfers). Est. 1968. Open 10-5.30. CL: Mon. SIZE: Medium. *STOCK: Modern British and contemporary paintings, drawings and sculpture, from £150.* LOC: Off Castelnau which runs from Hammersmith Bridge. PARK: Easy. TEL: 020 8748 8850; fax - 020 8748 9818; e-mail - art@newgrafton.com; website - www.newgrafton.com. SER: Valuations; restorations. VAT: Stan/Spec.

John Spink
BADA

9 Richard Burbidge Mansions, 1 Brasenose Drive, Barnes. SW13 8RB. Est. 1972. Open by appointment. *STOCK: Fine English watercolours and selected oils, 1720-1920.* TEL: 020 8741 6152; e-mail - john@johnspink.com. FAIRS: World of Watercolours; Olympia (Summer and Winter).

Tobias and The Angel
68 White Hart Lane, Barnes. SW13 0PZ. (A. Hughes). Est. 1985. Open 10-6. SIZE: Large. *STOCK: Quilts, textiles, furniture, country and painted beds, decorative objects, from 1800.* LOC: Parallel to Barnes High St. PARK: Easy. TEL: 020 8878 8902; home - 01206 391003. SER: Interior design. VAT: Stan/Spec.

SW14

The Arts & Crafts Furniture Co Ltd
49 Sheen Lane, East Sheen. SW14 4AB. (Patrick Rogers). Est. 1985. Open 10-6, Sat. 10-5. SIZE: Medium. *STOCK: Arts and Crafts furniture and effects, Gothic and Aesthetic movement, 1850-1950, £500-£5,000.* LOC: Off Upper Richmond Road (South Circular A205). PARK: Nearby. TEL: 020 8876 6544; fax - same; website - www.acfc.co.uk. SER: Valuations; restorations including French polishing and upholstery; buys at auction. VAT: Spec.

Mary Cooke Antiques Ltd
BADA LAPADA

12 The Old Power Station, 121 Mortlake High St. SW14 8SN. Open by appointment. *STOCK: Silver.* TEL: 020 8876 5777; fax - 020 8876 1652. SER: Valuations; restorations. FAIRS: Chelsea (Autumn); BADA; LAPADA; Olympia. VAT: Stan/Spec.

Paul Foster's Bookshop
119 Sheen Lane, East Sheen. SW14 8AE. ABA. PBFA. Est. 1983. Open 10.30-6. SIZE: Medium. *STOCK: Books - antiquarian, 17th-19th C, £100-£1,000; out of print, 19th-20th C, £1-£500; general, 50p-£100.* LOC: 20 yards from South Circular. PARK: Easy. TEL: 020 8876 7424; fax - same. FAIRS: Hotel Russell, PBFA monthly.

SW15

The Clock Clinic Ltd
BADA LAPADA

85 Lower Richmond Rd., Putney. SW15 1EU. (R.S. Pedler). BHI. Est. 1971. Open 9-6, Sat. 9-1. CL: Mon. *STOCK: Clocks and barometers.* PARK: Meters. TEL: 020 8788 1407; fax - 020 8780 2838; e-mail - clockclinic@btconnect. com; website - www.clockclinic.co.uk. SER:

Valuations; restorations (as stock); buys at auction. FAIRS: Olympia (Feb., June and Nov). VAT: Stan/Spec.

Hanshan Tang Books

Unit 3 Ashburton Centre, 276 Cortis Rd. SW15 3AY. (John Constable, John Cayley and Myrna Chua). ABA. Open by appointment. *STOCK: Secondhand, antiquarian and new books and periodicals on Chinese, Japanese, Korean and Central Asian art and culture.* TEL: 020 8788 4464; fax - 020 8780 1565; e-mail - hst@hanshan.com; website - www.hanshan.com/. SER: Regular and special catalogues; wants lists welcome.

Thornhill Galleries Ltd. in association with A. & R. Dockerill Ltd

Rear of 78 Deodar Rd., Putney. SW15 2NJ. (Graham and Anthony Wakefield and Lindy Greig). Est. 1880. Open 9-5.15, Sat. 10-12. SIZE: Large. *STOCK: English and French period panelling, chimneypieces in wood, marble and stone; architectural items, wood carvings, 17th-19th C firegrates and fenders, fireplace accessories and iron interiors.* LOC: Off Putney Bridge Rd. PARK: Easy. TEL: 020 8874 2101/5669; fax - 020 8877 0313; e-mail - sales@thornhillgalleries.co.uk; website - www.thornhillgalleries.co.uk. SER: Valuations; restorations (architectural items); buys at auction (architectural items). VAT: Stan/Spec.

SW16

H.C. Baxter and Sons   BADA LAPADA

40 Drewstead Rd. SW16 1AB. (T.J., J. and G.J. Baxter and T.J. Hunter). Est. 1928. Open Wed. and Thurs. 8.30-5.15 or by appointment. SIZE: Medium. *STOCK: English furniture, 1730-1830, £1,000-£35,000.* LOC: Near Streatham Hill station. PARK: Easy. TEL: 020 8769 5869/5969; fax - 020 8769 0898; e-mail - partnershcbaxter@tiscali.co.uk; website - www.hcbaxter.co.uk. FAIRS: Grosvenor House; BADA; Olympia (Nov). VAT: Spec.

A. and J. Fowle

542 Streatham High Rd. SW16 3QF. Est. 1962. Open 9.30-7. SIZE: Large. *STOCK: General antiques, Victorian and Edwardian furniture.* LOC: A23 towards Brighton from London. PARK: Easy. TEL: 020 8764 2896; mobile - 07968 058790. FAIRS: Ardingly.

SW17

Ted Few

97 Drakefield Rd. SW17 8RS. Resident. Est.

1975. Open by appointment. SIZE: Medium. *STOCK: Paintings and sculpture, 1700-1940, £500-£5,000.* LOC: 5 mins. walk from Tooting Bec underground station. TEL: 020 8767 2314. SER: Valuations; buys at auction. VAT: Spec.

SW18

Earlsfield Bookshop

513 Garratt Lane, Wandsworth. SW18 4SW. (Charles Dixon). Est. 1985. Open 4-6, Fri. 11-6, Sat. 10-5. SIZE: Small. *STOCK: Books, £1-£50.* LOC: Next to Earlsfield station. PARK: Limited. TEL: 020 8946 3744.

Just a Second

284 Merton Rd., Wandsworth. SW18 5JN. (James Ferguson). Est. 1980. Open 9.30-5.30. CL: Mon. SIZE: Medium. *STOCK: Victorian, Edwardian, pre-1920's and reproduction furniture and bric-a-brac.* LOC: 5 mins. from Southfields underground station. PARK: Easy. TEL: 020 8874 2520. SER: Valuations; restorations.

Mr Wandle's Workshop Ltd

202 Garratt Lane, Wandsworth. SW18 4ED. (S. Zoil). Open 9-5.30. *STOCK: Victorian and Edwardian fireplaces and surrounds especially cast iron.* TEL: 020 8870 5873. SER: Shot-blasting.

SW19

Corfield Potashnick   LAPADA

39 Church Rd., Wimbledon Village. SW19 5DQ. (Jonathan Corfield Fry and Simon Potashnick). Open 10-6 or by appointment. SIZE: 1997. *STOCK: Fine antique furniture.* TEL: 020 8944 9022. SER: Restorations; valuations. FAIRS: LAPADA.

The David Curzon Gallery

35 Church Rd., Wimbledon Village. SW19 5DQ. Est. 1985. Open 10-6. CL: Mon. and Tues. SIZE: Medium. *STOCK: Paintings and watercolours, from 1900, £350-£10,000.* LOC: 7 mins. walk from Wimbledon underground/BR stations. PARK: Reasonable. TEL: 020 8944 6098; fax - same; e-mail - curzgal@aol.com. SER: Framing; restorations; valuations. VAT: Spec.

Shaikh and Son (Oriental Rugs) Ltd

139 Arthur Rd. SW19 8AB. (M. Shaikh). Open 10-6. CL: Sat. pm. *STOCK: Persian carpets, rugs, £100-£10,000.* TEL: 020 8947 9232. SER: Repairing and cleaning.

Mark J. West - Cobb Antiques Ltd BADA
39B High St., Wimbledon Village. SW19 5BY.
Open 10-5.30. SIZE: Large. *STOCK: Antique
glass, £5-£5,000.* PARK: Easy. TEL: 020 8946
2811. SER: Valuations; buys at auction.
FAIRS: Olympia; Grosvenor House.

SW20

W.G.T. Burne (Antique Glass) Ltd BADA
PO Box 9465. (Formerly of Chelsea) SW20
9ZD. (Mrs G. and A.T. Burne). Est. 1936.
Open by appointment. *STOCK: English and
Irish glassware, Georgian and Victorian
decanters, chandeliers, candelabra and lustres.*
TEL: 020 8543 6319; fax - same; mobile -
07774 725834. SER: Valuations; restorations.
VAT: Stan/Spec.

W. F. Turk Antique Clocks LAPADA
355 Kingston Rd., Wimbledon Chase. SW20 8JX.
CINOA. Est. 1970. Open Tues.-Fri. 9-5.30, Sat. 9-4.
SIZE: Medium. *STOCK: Clocks, including
longcase, 17th-19th C, £4,000-£150,000; bracket,
17th-19th C, £2,000-£40,000; mantel and carriage,
19th C, £450-£20,000.* LOC: Off A3. PARK: Easy.
TEL: 020 8543 3231; fax - same; website -
www.wfturk.com. SER: Valuations; restorations.
FAIRS: Olympia; LAPADA. VAT: Stan/Spec.

SE1

Antiques Exchange
170172 Tower Bridge Rd. SE1 3LS. (Mr and Mrs
R. Draysey). Est. 1966. Open 10-6, Sun. 11-5.
SIZE: Large. *STOCK: Furniture, smalls, lighting,
decorative items, from 1700.* PARK: Nearby.
TEL: 020 7403 5568; fax - 020 7378 8828; e-mail
- Ray@AntiquesExchange.com; website - www.
AntiquesExchange.com. SER: Restorations
(furniture).

Bermondsey Antiques Market
Corner of Long Lane and Bermondsey St. SE1.
(Bath Antiques Market Ltd). Est. 1959. Open Fri. 5
am-2 pm. *STOCK: Wide range of general antiques
and collectables including specialist dealers in most
fields especially jewellery and silver.* LOC:
Borough, Tower Hill or London Bridge underground
stations. TEL: Enquiries - 020 7969 1500; fax - 020
7969 1639. SER: Valuations; book binding.

**Victor Burness Antiques and Scientific
Instruments**
241 Long Lane, Bermondsey. SE1 4PR. (V.G.
Burness). Est. 1975. Open Fri. 6am-1pm or by
appointment. SIZE: Small. *STOCK: Scientific
instruments, marine items, 19th C, £20-£1,500.*
PARK: Easy. TEL: Home - 01732 454591; e-mail

- vcrosskeys@aol.com. SER: Valuations. FAIRS: Portman Hotel.

Robert Bush - Antique & Decorative Furniture

Open by appointment. *STOCK: Furniture.* TEL: Mobile - 07836 236911; e-mail - bush.antiques @virgin.net.

Europa House Antiques

160-164 Tower Bridge Rd. SE1 3LS. (G. Viventi). Est. 1976. Open 9.30-5.15, Sat. 10-5.15. SIZE: Large. *STOCK: Furniture and general antiques.* TEL: 020 7403 0022; e-mail - viventi @btinternet.com.

The Galleries

157 Tower Bridge Rd., Bermondsey. SE1 3LW. (Alan Bennett). Open 9.30-5.30, Fri. 8-4.30, Sat. and Sun. 12-6. SIZE: Very large. *STOCK: Georgian and Victorian English and Continental furniture, some collectables.* TEL: 020 7407 5371; fax - 020 7403 0359. VAT: Stan/Spec.

Tower Bridge Antiques

47 and 71 Tanner St. SE1 3PL. Open 9-5.30, Sat. 10.30-6, Sun. 11-5. SIZE: Large. *STOCK: Victorian, Georgian and Edwardian furniture, shipping goods.* TEL: 020 7403 3660; e-mail - towerbridgeant@aol.com. VAT: Stan.

SE3

Michael Silverman

PO Box 350. SE3 0LZ. ABA. ILAB. Est. 1989. Open by appointment. *STOCK: Manuscripts, autograph letters, historical documents.* PARK: Free. TEL: 020 8319 4452; fax - 020 8856 6006; e-mail - ms@michael-silverman.com; website - www.michael-silverman.com. SER: Catalogue available. FAIRS: ABA - Olympia (June) and Chelsea (Nov). *Postal Only.*

Vale Stamps and Antiques

21 Tranquil Vale, Blackheath. SE3 0BU. (H.J. and R.P. Varnham). BNTA. Est. 1952. Open 10-5.30. CL: Thurs. SIZE: Small. *STOCK: Georgian and Victorian jewellery, £25-£500; ancient and medieval coins, £20-£500.* LOC: Village centre, 100yds. from rail station. PARK: Nearby. TEL: 020 8852 9817. SER: Valuations. FAIRS: London Coin. VAT: Stan/Spec.

SE5

Camberwell Architectural Salvage & Antiques

47 Southampton Way, Camberwell. SE5 7SW.

(M. Tree). Est. 1993. Open Tues.-Sat. 10-5. SIZE: Medium. *STOCK: Architectural salvage including doors, floorboards, radiators, baths, sinks and taps, 19th-20th C, £15-£600; furniture, 19th-20th C; fireplaces.* LOC: From Camberwell Green towards Peckham - 6th turning on left, just past College of Art. PARK: Easy. TEL: 020 7277 0315; e-mail - info@camberwellsalvage.co.uk; website - www.camberwellsalvage.co.uk. SER: Fitting (fireplaces).

Coats Oriental Carpets

116 Grove Lane. SE5 8BJ. (A. Coats). Est. 1973. Open by appointment. *STOCK: Oriental carpets and rugs, kelims, £50-£2,000; Oriental textiles and embroideries, £10-£100; all 19th C.* TEL: 020 7274 6471. SER: Valuations; restorations (re-weaving); buys at auction. VAT: Stan.

Robert E. Hirschhorn   `BADA` `LAPADA`

CINOA. Est. 1979. Open by appointment. *STOCK: Distinctive English, Welsh and Continental country furniture, mainly oak, elm, walnut and fruitwood, and interesting objects, 18th C and earlier; European ceramics, especially delftware; textiles and metalwork.* PARK: Easy. TEL: 020 7703 7443; mobile - 07831 405937; e-mail - hirschhornantiques @macunlimited.net. FAIRS: BADA (March); Olympia (June and Nov.).

SE6

Wilkinson plc

5 Catford Hill. SE6 4NU. Est. 1947. Open 9-5. CL: Sat. SIZE: Medium. *STOCK: Glass especially chandeliers, 18th C and reproduction, art metal work.* LOC: Opposite Catford Bridge station. Entrance through Wickes D.I.Y. car park. PARK: Easy. TEL: 020 8314 1080; fax - 020 8690 1524; e-mail - enquiries@wilkinson-plc.com; website - www.wilkinson-plc.com. SER: Restorations and repairs (glass, metalwork).

SE7

Ward Antiques
267 Woolwich Rd., Charlton. SE7. (T. and M. Ward). Est. 1981. Open 10-5, Sun. 11-2. SIZE: Medium. *STOCK: Victorian fireplaces, Victorian and Edwardian furniture, £50-£1,000.* LOC: From A102 M take Woolwich/Woolwich ferry turn, 100yds. from roundabout, immediately under rail bridge across the road. PARK: Easy. TEL: 020 8305 0963; home - 020 8698 0771.

SE8

Antique Warehouse
9-14 Deptford Broadway. SE8 4PA. Est. 1986. Open 10-6, Sun. 11-4. SIZE: Large. *STOCK: Fine furniture, 1750 to 20th C; sofas, chairs, mirrors and lighting.* PARK: Opposite. TEL: 020 8691 3062; website - www.antiquewarehouse.co.uk. VAT: Stan.

SE9

Cobwebs
73 Avery Hill Rd., New Eltham. SE9 2BJ. (Martin Baker). Est. 1991. Open 10-5.30, Sun. 10-2. CL: Mon. am and Thurs. SIZE: Medium. *STOCK: Furniture, smalls, Oriental items.* LOC: Between A20 and A2 and 5 mins. from New Eltham BR station. PARK: Easy. TEL: 020 8850 5611; website - wwwantique-dealers.eu.com/cobwebs. SER: Valuations.

The Fireplace
257 High St., Eltham. SE9 1TY. (A. Clark). Est. 1978. Open daily. SIZE: Medium. *STOCK: Fireplaces, 19th-20th C, £100-£1,000.* PARK: Adjacent side streets. TEL: 020 8850 4887. SER: Restorations (fireplaces). VAT: Stan.

R.E. Rose FBHI
731 Sidcup Rd., Eltham. SE9 3SA. Est. 1976. Open 9-5. SIZE: Small. *STOCK: Clocks and barometers, 1750-1930, £50-£5,000.* LOC: A20 from London, shop on left just past fiveways traffic lights at Green Lane. PARK: Easy. TEL: 020 8859 4754. SER: Restorations (clocks and barometers); spare parts for antique clocks and barometers. VAT: Stan/Spec.

SE10

Creek Antiques
23 Greenwich South St. SE10 8NW. Est. 1986. Open 11-5, appointment advisable. SIZE: Small. *STOCK: Jewellery and silver, from Victorian, £5-*

£500; general antiques, amusement machines, enamel signs. LOC: 200 yards from British Rail station. PARK: Easy. TEL: 020 8293 5721; mobile - 07778 427521; e-mail - creekantiques @aol.com.

Greenwich Antiques Market
Greenwich High Rd. SE10. Est. 1972. Open Sun. 7.30-4.30, and Sat. (June-Sept.). SIZE: 80 stalls. *STOCK: General antiques and bric-a-brac.* LOC: Almost opposite rail station. PARK: Adjacent.

The Greenwich Gallery
9 Nevada St. SE10 9JL. (R.F. Moy). Est. 1965. Open 10-5.30 including Sun. *STOCK: Mainly English oil paintings and watercolours, 18th C to 1950.* PARK: Opposite. TEL: 020 8305 1666. SER: Restorations; framing; exhibitions. VAT: Spec.

The Junk Box
47 Old Woolwich Rd. SE10 9NW. (Robert Dodd and Marilyn Allen). Est. 1993. Open 10-5.30 including Sun. SIZE: Small. *STOCK: Furniture, pictures and prints, collectables, 19th-20th C, £5-£1,000.* PARK: Easy. TEL: 020 8293 5715.

The Junk Shop
9 Greenwich South St. SE10 8NW. (T. and R. Moy). Est. 1985. Open 10-6 including Sun. SIZE: Large. *STOCK: Larger antique and decorative items, 18th C to 1950's; furniture, architectural items and bric-a-brac.* TEL: 020 8305 1666. VAT: Stan/Spec.

Lamont Antiques Ltd
Tunnel Avenue Antique Warehouse, Tunnel Avenue Trading Estate, Greenwich. SE10 0QH. (N. Lamont and F. Llewellyn). Open 9-5.30. CL: Sat. SIZE: Large. *STOCK: Architectural fixtures and fittings, bars, stained glass, pub mirrors and signs, shipping furniture, £5-£25,000.* PARK: Own. TEL: 020 8305 2230; fax - 020 8305 1805. SER: Container packing.

Peter Laurie Antiques   `LAPADA`
28 Greenwich Church St. SE10 9BQ. Open 10-5 including Sun. CL: Fri. am. *STOCK: Nautical items, navigational instruments, maritime curiosities, weapons and photographic items.* TEL: 020 8853 5777; fax - same; e-mail - plaurie@maritimeantiques-uk.com; website - www.maritimeantiques-uk.com.

The Warwick Leadlay Gallery
5 Nelson Rd., Greenwich. SE10 9JB. (Warwick Leadlay and Anthony Cross). Est. 1974. Open 9.30-5.30, Sun. and public holidays 11-5.30.

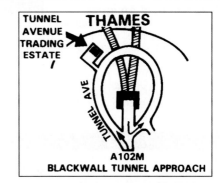
SIZE: Large. *STOCK: Antique maps, prints, fine arts, Nelson specialists, 17th-20th C.* LOC: Head of Greenwich Market. PARK: Nearby. TEL: 020 8858 0317; fax - 020 8853 1773; e-mail - info@warwickleadley.com; website - www.warwickleadley.com. SER: Framing; restorations; valuations. VAT: Stan.

Marcet Books
4A Nelson Rd., Greenwich. SE10 9JB. (Martin Kemp). PBFA. Est. 1980. Open 10-5.30 including Sun. SIZE: Small. *STOCK: General secondhand and antiquarian books.* LOC: In alley off Nelson Rd., leading to Greenwich market. PARK: 200 yards. TEL: 020 8853 5408; e-mail - marcet @dircon.co.uk; website - www.marcetbooks.co.uk. SER: Valuations. FAIRS: PBFA monthly Russell Hotel.

Rogers Turner Books
23a Nelson Rd., Greenwich. SE10 9JB. Est. 1975. Open Thurs.-Fri. 10-6 or by appointment. *STOCK: Antiquarian books especially on clocks and scientific instruments.* TEL: 020 8853 5271; fax - same; Paris - 0033 13912 1191; e-mail - rogersturner@compuserve.com; website - www.rogersturner@abebooks.com. SER: Buys at auction (British and European); catalogues available.

Spread Eagle Antiques
1 Stockwell St. SE10 9JL. (R.F. Moy). Est. 1954. Open 10-5.30 including Sun. SIZE: Large. *STOCK: Furniture, pictures and decorative items, 18th-19th C.* PARK: Opposite. TEL: 020 8305 1666; home - 020 8692 1618. SER: Valuations; restorations (pictures and furniture). VAT: Stan/Spec.

Spread Eagle Book & Curio Shop
8 Nevada St. SE10 9JL. (R.F. Moy). Est. 1954. Open 10-5.30 including Sun. SIZE: Large. *STOCK: Antiquarian and secondhand books, period costume, curios, china, bric-a-brac, prints, postcards.* LOC: A202. From London follow A2, then turn left at Deptford - or follow riverside road from Tower Bridge. TEL: 020 8305 1666. SER: Valuations; restorations (furniture, china and pictures). VAT: Stan/Spec/Global.

The Waterloo Trading Co.
Unit D Tunnel Ave. Trading Estate, Tunnel Ave., Greenwich. SE10 0QH. Est. 1989. Open 9-5. CL: Sat. SIZE: Large. *STOCK: Victorian, Edwardian and shipping furniture.* TEL: 020 8858 3355; fax - 020 8858 3344; e-mail - boysship@talk21.com. SER: Robert Boys Shipping; packing. VAT: Stan.

Robert Whitfield Antiques   LAPADA

Tunnel Avenue Antique Warehouse, Tunnel Avenue Trading Estate, Greenwich. SE10 0QH. Open 10-5. CL: Sat. *STOCK: Edwardian, Victorian and secondhand furniture, especially bentwood chairs.* PARK: Easy. TEL: 020 8305 2230; fax - 020 8305 1805; e-mail - robertwhitfield@btinternet.com. SER: Container packing.

SE13

Robert Morley and Co Ltd   BADA

34 Engate St. SE13 7HA. Est. 1881. Open 9.30-5. STOCK: Pianos, harpsichords, clavichords, spinets, virginals, harps; stools, music cabinets and stands. PARK: Own. TEL: 020 8318 5838; e-mail - jvm@morley-r.u-net.com; website - www.morleypianos.com. SER: Restorations (musical instruments). VAT: Stan.

The Old Station

72 Loampit Lane, Lewisham. SE13 7SX. (Robert Jacob). Open 10-5.30, Sun. 11-4. SIZE: Medium. *STOCK: Architectural items including doors, baths, panelling and sinks, cast iron radiators; antique furniture.* LOC: A20. PARK: Easy. TEL: 020 8694 6540; mobile - 07710 489895; e-mail - theoldstation@btinternet.com; website - www.the-old-station.co.uk. SER: Valuations; pine stripping. FAIRS: Ardingly, Newark, Swinderby.

SE18

The Walpole Galleries

Commonwealth Buildings, Woolwich Church St. SE18 5NS. (Graham Walpole). Est. 1975. By appointment. SIZE: Very large. *STOCK: Paintings, 1770-1940, £500-£50,000; works of art, 1700-1920, £250-£10,000; furniture, 1780-1920, £500-£25,000.* LOC: Immediately off A206; main road through London through Greenwich and east to Woolwich. .25 of mile before Woolwich Ferry. PARK: Own. TEL: 020 8316 7324; mobile - 07831 561042; e-mail - graham@walpoleantiques.com. FAIRS: Olympia (June). VAT: Stan/Spec.

SE20

Bearly Trading of London

202 High St., Penge. SE20 7QB. (Jake and Guy Aust). Open Sat. 10-6. *STOCK: Old bears, artist bears, rocking horses, antique furniture.* LOC: Opposite Kent House Rd., Beckenham, Kent. PARK: Opposite. TEL: 020 8659 0500; 020 8466 6696; fax - 020 8460 3166. SER: Repairs (bears).

SE21

Acorn Antiques

111 Rosendale Rd., West Dulwich. SE21 8EZ. (Mrs G. Kingham). Est. 1976. Open 10-6, Sat. 10-5.30. *STOCK: Furniture, sterling silver, jewellery, ceramics, glassware and fireplace accessories.* TEL: 020 8761 3349. VAT: Stan.

Francis Jevons

80 Dulwich Village. SE21 7AJ. Est. 1983. Usually open 9.30-1 and 2.30-5.30, Sat. until 5, other times by appointment. CL: Wed. *STOCK: China and small furniture, late 18th to 19th C; interior design, lamps and decorative items.* LOC: Off South Circular leading down from either Gallery or College roads. PARK: Easy. TEL: 020 8693 1991. SER: Valuations; restorations. VAT: Stan/Spec.

SE22

Melbourne Antiques & Interiors

8 Melbourne Grove, East Dulwich. SE22 0QR. (Ian Peters). Est. 1990. Open 10-6. SIZE: Large. *STOCK: French beds and armoires, £300-£1,000+; mirrors, £50-£1,000+; commodes, £500-£1,000+; painted furniture.* LOC: Off South Circular at Dulwich. PARK: Easy. TEL: 020 8299 6565; fax - 020 8299 4257. SER: Restorations (furniture).

SE25

Engine 'n' Tender

19 Spring Lane, Woodside Green. SE25 4SP. (Mrs Joyce M. Buttigieg). Est. 1957. Open Thurs. and Fri. 12-5.30, Sat. 10-5.30. SIZE: Small. *STOCK: Model railways, mainly pre 1939; Dinky toys, to 1968; old toys, mainly tinplate.* LOC: Near Croydon tramlink. PARK: Easy. TEL: 020 8654 0386. FAIRS: Local toy.

North London Clock Shop Ltd

Rear of 60 Saxon Rd. SE25 5EH. (D.S. Tomlin). Est. 1960. Open 9-6. CL: Sat. SIZE: Medium. *STOCK: Clocks, longcase, bracket, carriage, skeleton, 18th-19th C.* PARK: Easy. TEL: 020 8664 8089. SER: Restorations (clocks and barometers); wheel cutting; hand engraving; dial painting; clock reconversions. FAIRS: Olympia. VAT: Stan.

SE26

Abbott Antiques and Country Pine

109 Kirkdale, Sydenham. SE26 4QJ. Est. 1972. Open 10-5.30, Sat. 10-5. *STOCK: Victorian,*

Edwardian and stripped pine furniture; interesting items. LOC: 1/2 mile from South Circular Rd. at Forest Hill. TEL: 020 8699 1363; e-mail - abbottantiques@btinternet.com.

Behind the Boxes - Art Deco
98 Kirkdale, Sydenham. SE26 4BG. (Ray Owen). Est. 1987. Open 10.30-5, Sun. and Mon. by appointment. SIZE: Large. *STOCK: Furniture, lighting and costume jewellery, 1930's, from £5.* LOC: 1 mile from Crystal Palace. BR station Forest Hill. PARK: Loading, otherwise Fransfield Rd. TEL: 020 8291 6116. SER: Valuations; buys at auction. FAIRS: Decorama and Deco.

Oola Boola Antiques London
139-147 Kirkdale. SE26 4QJ. (R. Scales and S. Bramley). Est. 1968. Open 10-6, Sat.10-5, Sun. 11-5. SIZE: Large. *STOCK: Furniture, £5-£3,000; mahogany, oak, walnut, Victorian, Arts & Crafts, Art Nouveau, Edwardian, Art Deco, retro and shipping goods.* PARK: Forecourt. TEL: 020 8291 9999; fax - 020 8291 5759; e-mail - oola.boola@telco4u.net.

Sydenham Antiques Centre
48 Sydenham Rd., Sydenham. SE26 5QF. (Mrs L. Cockton). Est. 1996. Open 10-5. SIZE: Medium. *STOCK: China, glass, silver, collectables, furniture and jewellery, 19th-20th C, £5-£500.* LOC: 2 doors down from Post Office in High St. PARK: Easy and nearby. TEL: 020 8778 1706. SER: Valuations; restorations (china).

Vintage Cameras Ltd
256 Kirkdale, Sydenham. SE26 4NL. (J. and M. Jenkins). Est. 1959. Open 9-5. SIZE: Large. *STOCK: Vintage and classic cameras, £50-£5,000; general photographica, £5-£500; all 1840-2001.* LOC: Near South Circular Rd. PARK: Nearby. TEL: 020 8778 5416; fax - 020 8778 5841; e-mail - i@vintagecameras.co.uk; website - www.vintagecameras.co.uk. SER: Valuations. VAT: Stan.

E1

La Maison
107/108 Shoreditch High St. E1 6JN. (Guillaume and Louise Bacou). Open 10-6, Sat. 11.30-6. SIZE: Large. *STOCK: Beds.* TEL: 020 7729 9646; fax - 020 7729 6399. SER: Restorations. VAT: Margin.

E2

George Rankin Coin Co. Ltd
325 Bethnal Green Rd. E2. Est. 1965. *STOCK: Coins, medals, medallions and jewellery.* TEL: 020 7739 1840/7729 1280; fax - 020 7729 5023.

E4

Record Detector
3 & 4 Station Approach, Station Rd., North Chingford. E4 6AL. (N. Salter). Est. 1992. Open 10-6. CL: Thurs. SIZE: Small (2 shops). *STOCK: Secondhand and collectable records, L.P.'s, E.P.'s, singles and CD's.* LOC: In forecourt of North Chingford station. PARK: Easy. TEL: 020 8529 6361/2938; e-mail - sales@salter.co.uk; website - www.salter.co.uk.

Nicholas Salter Antiques
8 Station Approach, Station Rd., North Chingford. E4 6AL. (Sherley Salter). Est. 1971. Open Tues. and Wed. 10-5, Fri. and Sat. 10-6. SIZE: Large. *STOCK: Furniture, 1850-1930, £150-£1,500; china and linen, 1870-1950, £30-£150; antiquarian and secondhand books; vintage clothes and accessories, 1860's-1970's, £5-£500.* LOC: Next to North Chingford station. PARK: Easy. TEL: 020 8529 2938; e-mail - sales@salter.co.uk; website - www.salter.co.uk.

E8

Boxes and Musical Instruments
2 Middleton Rd., Hackney. E8 4BL. (A. and J. O'Kelly). Est. 1974. Open any time by appointment. SIZE: Medium. *STOCK: Boxes - caddies, sewing, writing, snuff, vanity, jewellery and desk, £300-£5,000; musical instruments, plucked string, £1,000-£3,000; all 18th-19th C.* LOC: Off Kingsland Rd., continuation of Bishopsgate. PARK: Easy. TEL: 020 7254 7074; home - same; fax - 0870 125 7669; e-mail - boxes@hygra.com; website - www.hygra.com. SER: Valuations; restorations (exceptional instruments only). Registered with the Conservation Unit of the Museums and Galleries Commission.

E11

Old Cottage Antiques LAPADA
8 High St., Wanstead. E11 2AJ. (P. Blake and B. Hawkins). Est. 1920. Open Fri. and Sat. 10-5. SIZE: Medium. *STOCK: Furniture, clocks, paintings, 19th-20th C.* LOC: Near Wanstead and Snaresbrook Central Line underground stations. PARK: Easy. TEL: 020 8989 2317/8504 9264; mobile - 07710 031079; e-mail - brianhawkinsantiques@hotmail.com. SER: Buys at auction. VAT: Stan/Spec.

A.R. ULLMANN LTD.
10 HATTON GARDEN
LONDON EC1N 8AH
TEL: 020 7405 1877
FAX: 020 7404 7071

e-mail: ar_ullmann27@hotmail.com
website:
http://freespace.virgin.net/ar.ullmann

ANTIQUE AND
SECONDHAND
JEWELLERY
SILVER
OBJETS D'ART
BOUGHT, SOLD &
REPAIRED

OPEN: Monday – Fri 9am-5pm
Sat 9.30am – 5pm

REPAIRS – VALUATIONS

E17

Collectors Centre - Antique City
98 Wood St. E17. Est. 1978. Open 9.30-5.30. CL: Thurs. SIZE: Large. *STOCK: Antiques, collectables, 40's, 50's, 60's, £1-£500.* PARK: Opposite. TEL: 020 8520 4032. *Trade Only.*

Georgian Village Antiques Market
100 Wood St., Walthamstow. E17 3HX. Est. 1972. Open 10-5. CL: Thurs. SIZE: 5 shops. *STOCK: Clocks, barometers, postcards, collectables, jewellery, brass, copper, stamps, silver, silver plate.* LOC: 50yds. from Dukes Head. PARK: Adjacent. TEL: 020 8520 6638.

E18

Victoria Antiques
166A George Lane, South Woodford. E18 2HL. (M. A. Holman). Est. 1998. Open 11-5. CL: Tues. and Thurs. SIZE: Small. *STOCK: Clocks and carved chairs, 18th-19th C, £100-£1,000; pictures, 19th C, £50-£500; silver, £20-£500; bronze figures, £100-£1,000.* LOC: 2 mins. walk from South Woodford station. PARK: George Lane. TEL: 020 8989 1002. SER: Valuations. VAT: Stan.

EC1

City Clocks
31 Amwell St. EC1R 1UN. (J. Rosson). FBHI. Est. 1960. Open Tues.-Fri. 8.30-5.30, Sat. 9.30-2.30 or by appointment. SIZE: Medium. *STOCK: Clocks, some furniture, 18th-20th C, £100-£12,000.* PARK: Easy. TEL: 020 7278 1154; website - www.cityclocks.co.uk. SER: Valuations; restorations (clocks and watches, house calls to longcase); buys at auction. VAT: Spec.

Eldridge London
99-101 Farringdon Rd. EC1R 3BT. (B. Eldridge). Est. 1953. Open 12-5. CL: Wed. SIZE: Large. *STOCK: Furniture, treen and items of social and historical importance.* PARK: Easy. TEL: 020 7837 0379. VAT: Spec.

Finecraft Workshop Ltd
10 Greville St. EC1N 8SB. (Martyn J. Pummell). NAG. Est. 1955. Open 10.15-5, Sat. 10.15-4.30, Sun. 10.15-2. SIZE: Medium. *STOCK: Jewellery, 19th-20th C, £100-£8,000+.* LOC: Between Farringdon Rd. and Hatton Garden. PARK: Nearby. TEL: 020 7242 3825; fax - 020 7404 0170. SER: Valuations; restorations; re-making and repairing; insurance claims undertaken; buys at auction. FAIRS: Europe and USA. VAT: Stan.

Frosts of Clerkenwell Ltd
60-62 Clerkenwell Rd. EC1M 5PX. BCWMG. BHI. Est. 1932. Open 10-5. CL: Sat. SIZE: Large. *STOCK: Quality vintage clocks, watches and barometers.* TEL: 020 7253 0315; website - www.frostsofclerkenwell.co.uk. SER: Restorations.

Jonathan Harris (Jewellery) Ltd
63-66 Hatton Garden (office). EC1N 8LE. (E.C., D. I. and J. Harris). Est. 1958. Open 9.30-4.30. CL: Sat. *STOCK: Antique and secondhand rings, brooches, pendants, bracelets and other jewellery, from £100.* PARK: Nearby. TEL: 020 7242 9115/7242 1558; fax - 020 7831 4417. SER: Valuations; export. VAT: Stan/Spec.

Hirsh Ltd
10 Hatton Garden. EC1N 8AH. (A. Hirsh). Open 10-5.30. *STOCK: Fine jewellery, silver and objets d'art.* TEL: 020 7405 6080; fax - 020 7430 0107; e-mail - enquiries@hirsh.co.uk. SER: Valuations; jewellery designed and re-modelled.

R. Holt and Co. Ltd
98 Hatton Garden. EC1N 8NX. (R. and J. Holt). GMC. BJA. London Diamond Bourse. Est. 1948. Open 9.30-5.30. CL: Sat. *STOCK: Gemstone*

specialists. TEL: 020 7405 5286/0197; fax - 020 7430 1279; e-mail - info@rholt.co.uk; website - www.rholt.co.uk. SER: Valuations; restorations (gem stone cutting and testing, bead stringing and inlaid work).

Joseph and Pearce Ltd   LAPADA
63-66 Hatton Garden. EC1N 8LE. Est. 1896. Open by appointment. *STOCK: Jewellery, 1800-1960, £100-£5,000.* TEL: 020 7405 4604/7; fax - 020 7242 1902. FAIRS: Earls Court, NEC, Inhorgenta, New York. VAT: Stan/Spec. *Trade Only.*

A.R. Ullmann Ltd
10 Hatton Garden. EC1N 8AH. (J.S. Ullmann). Est. 1939. Open 9-5, Sat. 9.30-5. SIZE: Small. *STOCK: Jewellery, gold, silver and diamond; silver and objets d'art.* LOC: Close to Farringdon and Chancery Lane underground stations. PARK: Multi-storey in St. Cross St. TEL: 020 7405 1877; fax - 020 7404 7071; home - 020 8346 2546. SER: Valuations; restorations. VAT: Stan/Spec.

EC2

D. Horton
69 Moorgate. EC2R 6BH. *STOCK: Modern*

British paintings. TEL: 020 7588 6004; fax - 020 7588 6005; website - www.hortonlondon.co.uk. SER: Valuations.

LASSCO   LAPADA
St. Michael's, Mark St. (off Paul St.). EC2A 4ER. (Anthony Reed). Est. 1977. Open 10-5. *STOCK: Architectural antiques including panelled rooms, chimney pieces, garden ornaments, lighting, door furniture, stained glass, columns and capitals, stonework, relics and curiosities.* TEL: 020 7749 9947; fax - 020 7749 9941; mobile - 07956 964193; e-mail - ant@lassco.co.uk; website - www.lassco.co.uk/antiques.

Westland London
St. Michael's Church, Leonard St. EC2A 4ER. (Geoffrey Westland). SALVO. Est. 1969. Open 9-6, Sat. 10-5, Sun. by appt. SIZE: Large. *STOCK: Period and prestigious chimneypieces, architectural elements, panelled rooms, light fittings, statuary, paintings and furniture, £100-£100,000.* LOC: Off Gt. Eastern St. PARK: Easy. TEL: 020 7739 8094; fax - 020 7729 3620; e-mail - westland@westland.co.uk; website - www. westland.co.uk. SER: Restorations; installations; shipping.

EC3

Ash Rare Books
153 Fenchurch St. EC3M 6BB. (L. Worms). ABA. ILAB. Est. 1946. Open by appointment. SIZE: Small. *STOCK: Books, 1550-1980, £20-£10,000; maps, 1550-1850, £25-£2,000; prints, 1650-1900, £20-£1,000.* LOC: First floor office opposite top of Rood Lane. TEL: 020 7626 2665; fax - 020 7623 9052; e-mail - books@ashrare.com; website - www.ashrare.com. SER: Buys at auction (books and maps). VAT: Stan.

Halcyon Days — BADA
4 Royal Exchange. EC3V 3LL. (Peter Norman). Est. 1950. Open 10-5.30. *STOCK: 18th to early 19th C enamels, Georgian and Victorian scent bottles, papier mâché, tôle, objects of vertu, treen, unusual small Georgian furniture.* TEL: 020 7626 1120; fax - 020 7283 1876; e-mail - info@halcyondays.co.uk; website - www.halcyondays.co.uk. VAT: Stan/Spec.

Nanwani and Co
2 Shopping Arcade, Bank Station, Cornhill. EC3V 3LA. Est. 1958. CL: Sat. *STOCK: Precious and semi-precious stones, Oriental items, objets d'art.* TEL: 020 7623 8232; fax - 020 7283 2548. VAT: Stan.

Searle and Co Ltd
1 Royal Exchange, Cornhill. EC3V 3LL. NAG. Est. 1893. Open 9-5.30. SIZE: Medium. *STOCK: Georgian, Victorian, Art Nouveau, Art Deco and secondhand silver and jewellery; novelty pieces and collectibles.* LOC: Near Bank underground station - exits 3 & 4. PARK: Meters. TEL: 020 7626 2456; fax - 020 7283 6384; e-mail - mail@searleandco.ltd.uk; website - www.searleandco.ltd.uk. SER: Commissions; valuations; restorations; repairs; engraving. VAT: Stan/Spec.

EC4

Gladwell and Company — LAPADA
68 Queen Victoria St. EC4N 4SJ. (Anthony Fuller). SLAD. Open 8-8, Sat. and Sun. by appointment. SIZE: Small. *STOCK: Oil paintings, watercolours, drawings, etchings and bronzes, £50-£50,000.* LOC: Near St Paul's cathedral and Bank of England. PARK: Easy. TEL: 020 7248 3824; fax - 020 7236 6875; e-mail - gladwells@btopenworld.com; website - www.gladwells.com. SER: Valuations; restorations; buys at auction. FAIRS: LAPADA; NEC; Manchester, Glasgow and Tatton Watercolours and Drawings; New York; Chicago.

N1

After Noah
121 Upper St., Islington. N1 1QP. (M. Crawford and Z. Candlin). Est. 1990. Open 10-6, Sun. 12-5. SIZE: Medium. *STOCK: Arts and Craft oak and similar furniture, leather sofas and chairs, 1880's to 1950's, £1-£5,000; iron, iron and brass beds; decorative items, bric-a-brac including candlesticks, mirrors, lighting, kitchenalia and jewellery.* PARK: Side streets. TEL: 020 7359 4281; fax - same; e-mail - enquiries@afternoah.com; website - www.afternoah.com. SER: Restorations. VAT: Stan.

The Angel Arcade
116 Islington High St., Camden Passage. N1 8EG. Open Wed. and Sat. 7.30-4.30. *STOCK: Decorative items and general antiques.* PARK: Business Design Centre. Below are listed some of the dealers in this arcade.

Argosy Antiques
Shop 4. (Pat Buttigieg). *Silver and plate, bronzes, early lighting and early door knockers.* TEL: 020 7359 2517; home - 020 7402 4422.

Matthew Austin-Cooper
Shop C. *French and English decorative furniture, leather and antler items, Black Forest carvings, mirrors and lighting.* TEL: 020 7226 4901; mobile - 07958 631690.

Kate Bannister
Shop C. *Decorative antiques - tramp art, twig and bamboo furniture, lighting, inkwells, papier mâché and tôle trays, tôle scuttles, antler and horn accessories.* TEL: 020 7704 6644.

Marilyn Bookal Antiques
Shop 10. *French and painted decorative furniture, majolica, tôle, papier mâché and miniature bamboo furniture.* TEL: Mobile - 07768 997687.

Burlington Designs
Shop 9. (Martin Lynn). *Boule d'escaliers, lighting and fireside furniture.* TEL: Mobile - 07730 037671. SER: Polishing and gilding.

Peter Collingridge Antiques Ltd
Shop 2. *18th-20th C metalware and lighting.* TEL: 020 7354 9189; mobile - 07860 581858.

Val Cooper Antiques
Shop E. *Bamboo furniture, majolica, papier mâché, brass frames, Black Forest carvings, decorative accessories.* TEL: 020 7226 4901; 020 8505 2922; mobile - 07930 634015; e-mail - valcooperantique@aol.com. SER: Restorations.

Feljoy Antiques
Shop 3. (J. Humphreys and F. Finburgh). Est. 1985. *Chintzware, decorative items, beadwork cushions and textiles.* TEL: 020 7354 5336; e-mail - joy@feljoy-antiques.demon.co.uk.

Rosemary Hart
Shop 8. Est. 1980. *Victorian silver plated tableware, decorative serving ware and small silver.* TEL: 020 7359 6839; e-mail - contact@rosemaryhart.co.uk; website - www.rosemaryhart.co.uk. SER: Restorations; replating.

Lou, John & Chris
Shop 1. *Decorative items.*

Maureen Lyons
Shop 5. *Chandeliers, decorative furniture and accessories.* TEL: 020 7354 4245; fax - 020 7354 0508.

Lans Pickup
Shop G. *Textiles and 18th C country furniture.* TEL: 020 7359 8272.

Annie's Vintage Costume & Textiles
12 Camden Passage, Islington. N1 8ED. (A. Moss). Open 11-6 including Sun. PARK: Nearby and meters. TEL: 020 7359 0796.

The Antique Trader
The Millinery Works, 85/87 Southgate Rd. N1 3JS. (B. Thompson and D. Rothera). Est. 1968. Open 11-6 or by appointment. SIZE: Large. *STOCK: Arts & Crafts, Art furniture and effects; £100-£15,000.* LOC: Close to Camden Passage Antiques Centre. PARK: Free. TEL: 020 7359 2019; fax - 020 7359 5792; e-mail - antiquetrader @millineryworks.co.uk; website - www.millinery works.co.uk. VAT: Stan/Spec.

Banbury Fayre
6 Pierrepont Row Arcade, Camden Passage, Islington. N1. (N. Steel). Est. 1984. Open Wed. and Sat. SIZE: Small. *STOCK: Collectables including commemoratives, shipping, Boy Scout movement, Boer War, air line travel.* PARK: 200yds. TEL: Home - 020 8852 5675.

Camden Passage Antiques Market and Pierrepont Arcade Antiques Centre
Pierrepont Arcade, Islington. N1 8EF. Est. 1960. Open Wed. and Sat. 7.30-3.30 or by appointment. Thurs. - book market. SIZE: Over 400 dealers. *STOCK: Wide range of general antiques and many specialists.* PARK: Multi-storey and meters. TEL: 020 7359 0190; mobile - 07960 877035; e-mail - murdochdkr@aol.com; website - www.antiquesnews.co.uk/camdenpassage. SER: Shipping.

Peter Chapman Antiques and Restoration
LAPADA
10 Theberton St., Islington. N1 0QX. (P.J. and Z.A. Chapman). CPTA. CINOA. Est. 1971. Open 9.30-6, Sun. and public holidays by appointment. SIZE: Medium. *STOCK: Furniture and decorative objects, 1700-1900; paintings, drawings and prints, 17th to early 20th C; stained glass, hall lanterns; Grand Tour items.* LOC: 5 mins. walk from Camden Passage down Upper St. PARK: Easy. TEL: 020 7226 5565; fax - 020 8348 4846; mobile - 07831 093662; e-mail - pchapmanantiques@easynet.co.uk; website - www.antiques-peterchapman.co.uk. SER: Valuations; restorations (furniture and period objects); buys at auction. VAT: Stan/Spec.

Chapter One
2 Pierrepont Row Arcade, Camden Passage. N1 9EG. (Yvonne Gill). Est. 1993. Open Wed. 9-3, Sat. 9-5 or by appointment. SIZE: Small. *STOCK: Handbags, costume jewellery, vintage accessories, fabrics, unusual collectors items, 1880-1960, £1-£300.* TEL: 020 7359 1185; e-mail - yg@platinum.demon.co.uk. SER: Jewellery repairs; search.

Charlton House Antiques
18/20 Camden Passage, Islington. N1 8ED. Open Wed. and Sat. 8-5, Tues. and Fri. 10-4. SIZE: Large. *STOCK: European and Art Deco furniture, 1840-1930, £100-£5,000; general antiques.* LOC: Near Angel underground station. PARK: Easy. TEL: 020 7226 3141; fax - 020 7226 1123; e-mail - charlhse@aol.com. VAT: Stan/Spec.

Chest of Drawers
281 Upper St., Islington. N1 2TZ. (J. Delf). Open 10-6 including Sun. *STOCK: Pine and oak.* TEL: 020 7359 5909; fax - 020 7704 6236; website - www.chestofdrawers.co.uk.

Rosemary Conquest
4 Charlton Place, Camden Passage. N1 8AJ. Open 11-5.30, Wed. and Sat. 9-5.30. CL: Mon. SIZE: Small. *STOCK: Chandeliers and European decorative items.* PARK: Easy. TEL: 020 7359 0616; mobile - 07710 486384. SER: Shipping. FAIRS: Battersea Decorative; Chelsea Village Brocante.

Carlton Davidson Antiques
33 Camden Passage, Islington. N1 8EA. Est. 1981. Open Wed.-Sat. 10-4. SIZE: Medium. *STOCK: Lamps, chandeliers, mirrors and decorative items, £100-£3,000.* LOC: Near Charlton Place. PARK: Meters. TEL: 020 7226 7491. VAT: Stan.

Donay Games & Pastimes

3 Pierrepont Row, Camden Passage, Islington. N1 8EF. (Carol E. Goddard). Est. 1980. Open Wed. and Sat. 9.30-3.30, office Mon.-Fri. SIZE: Medium. *STOCK: Board and mechanical games - horse racing, cricket, golf and football; treen, paper and metal puzzles including Journet and mechanical Hoffman; chess, backgammon, cribbage, dominoes; card games and scorers; tinplate including Schuco; dice, shakers, mah-jong, marbles, artists' colourboxes; animal bronzes, Punch & Judy puppets including ephemera, 1780-1950, £5-£5,000.* LOC: Near Angel underground station. PARK: Charlton Place, Colebrook Row. TEL: 020 7359 1880; office - 01444 250230; fax - 01444 250231; e-mail - donaygames@aol.com; website - www. donaygames.com.

Eccentricities   LAPADA

The Merchants Hall, 46 Essex Rd. N1 8LN. (K. Skeel). SIZE: Very large. *STOCK: General small items especially curiosities and eccentricities.* TEL: 020 7359 5633.

Eclectica

2 Charlton Place. N1 8AJ. (Liz Wilson). Est. 1988. Open Tues. Thurs. and Fri. 11-6, Wed. and Sat. 9-6. *STOCK: Vintage costume jewellery.* TEL: 020 7226 5625; fax - same.

The Fleamarket

7 Pierrepont Row Arcade, Camden Passage, Islington. N1 8EE. Open 9.30-6. CL: Mon. SIZE: Large. 26 stand-holders. *STOCK: Jewellery, furniture, objets d'art, militaria, guns, swords, pistols, porcelain, coins, medals, stamps, 18th-19th C, £1-£500; antiquarian books, prints, fine art, china, silver, glass and general antiques.* PARK: Easy. TEL: 020 7226 8211. SER: Valuations; buys at auction.

Vincent Freeman

1 Camden Passage, Islington. N1 8EA. Est. 1966. Open Wed. and Sat. 10-5. SIZE: Large. *STOCK: Music boxes, furniture and decorative items, from £100.* TEL: 020 7226 6178; fax - 020 7226 7231; e-mail - freemanvj@hotmail.com. FAIRS: Olympia (June). VAT: Stan/Spec.

Furniture Vault

50 Camden Passage, Islington. N1 8AE. (David Loveday). Est. 1969. Open Tues.-Sat. 9.30-4.30. SIZE: Large. *STOCK: Furniture, 18th-20th C.* TEL: 020 7354 1047; e-mail - davidloveday1 @aol.com.

Georgian Village

30-31 Islington Green. N1. Open 10-4, Wed. and Sat. 7-5. PARK: Nearby. TEL: 020 7226 1571.

Get Stuffed

105 Essex Rd., Islington. N1 2SL. Est. 1975. Open 1-5, Sat. 1-3. *STOCK: Stuffed birds, fish, animals, trophy heads; rugs; butterflies, insects.* TEL: 020 7226 1364; fax - 020 7359 8253; mobile - 07831 260062; e-mail - taxidermy@ thegetstuffed.co.uk; website - www.thegetstuffed. co.uk. SER: Restorations; taxidermy; glass domes and cases supplied.

David Griffiths Antiques

17 Camden Passage, Islington. N1 8EA. Open Tues., Wed., Fri. and Sat. 10-4 or by appointment. *STOCK: Decorative antiques including military and campaign furniture, leather chairs, pub accessories, club fenders and other fittings from hotels and gentlemen's clubs; quality vintage luggage.* TEL: 020 7226 1126; fax - 020 7226 1991.

House of Steel Antiques

400 Caledonian Rd. N1 1DN. (J. Cole). Est. 1974. Open 11-6, Sat. by appointment. SIZE: Warehouse. *STOCK: Metal items - fireplaces, 18th-19th C, £50-£1,000; spiral staircases, £300-£1,000; balconies, railings, garden furniture, £50-£500; all 19th C.* LOC: Near King's Cross. PARK: Own. TEL: 020 7607 5889. SER: Valuations; restorations (welding, polishing and sandblasting); steel furniture manufactured, items made to order. VAT: Stan.

Diana Huntley   LAPADA

8 Camden Passage, Islington. N1 8ED. Est. 1970. Open Tues. and Fri. 10-4, Wed. 7.30-5, Thurs. by appointment, Sat. 9-5. *STOCK: European porcelain, £50-£10,000; objets d'art; all 19th C.* TEL: 020 7226 4605; fax - 020 7359 0240; e-mail - diana@dianahuntleyantiques.co.uk; website -

www.dianahuntleyantiques.co.uk. SER: Valuations. VAT: Stan/Spec.

Intercol London

Gallery, 114 Islington High St. (within Camden Passage). Correspondence - 43 Templars Crescent, N3 3QR. N1. (Yasha Beresiner). Est. 1977. Open Wed.-Sat. 9-5, other times by appointment. SIZE: Large. *STOCK: Playing cards, maps and banknotes and related literature, £5-£1,000+.* PARK: Easy. TEL: 020 8349 2207; fax - 020 8346 9539; e-mail - yasha@ compuserve.com; website - www.intercol.co.uk. SER: Valuations; restorations (maps including colouring); buys at auction (playing cards, maps, banknotes and books). FAIRS: Major specialist European, U.S.A. and Far Eastern. VAT: Stan/Spec.

Jonathan James   `LAPADA`

52/53 Camden Passage, Islington. N1 8EA. (Norman Petre). Est. 1970. Open 10-4.30, Wed. 9.30-4.30. CL: Mon. SIZE: Medium. *STOCK: Furniture, 18th-19th C, £1,000-£20,000.* PARK: 100 yds. TEL: 020 7704 8266; fax - same. SER: Valuations. VAT: Stan/Spec.

Japanese Gallery

23 Camden Passage, Islington. N1 8EA. Open 10-6. *STOCK: Japanese woodcut prints; books, porcelain, screens, kimonos, scrolls, furniture, netsuke, inro and Tsuba.* TEL: 020 7226 3347; fax - 020 7229 2934. SER: Framing; free authentification; interior design, ie. Tatami.

Jubilee Photographica

10 Pierrepont Row Arcade, Camden Passage, Islington. N1 8EE. (Richard Meara). Est. 1966. Open Wed. and Sat. 10-4 or by apppointment. SIZE: Small. *STOCK: Photographica - images, daguerreotypes, ambrotypes, tintypes, vintage paper prints, stereoscopic cards and viewers, magic lanterns and slides, topographical and family albums, cabinet cards and cartes de visite, £1-£1,000.* LOC: From Piccadilly Circus, take 19 bus to Angel, Islington. PARK: Meters. TEL: Home - 01932 863924; e-mail - meara@btconnect.com. SER: Buys at auction. FAIRS: London Photograph; Photographica; Bievres, France; American Photo Historical Society, New York.

Carol Ketley Antiques   `LAPADA`

PO Box 16199. N1 7WD. Est. 1979. Open by appointment. SIZE: Medium. *STOCK: Mirrors, decanters, drinking glasses, decorative furniture and objects, 1780-1900, £10-£10,000.* LOC: Showroom close to Camden Passage. PARK: Easy. TEL: 020 7359 5529; fax - 020 7226 4589;

Jubilee Photographica
Richard Meara
Fine Books and Photographs Ltd
Phone: 01932 863924 Fax: 01932 860318
Mobile:07860 793707 meara@btconnect.com
10 Pierrepont Row, Camden Passage Antiques Market, ISLINGTON,
London N1 8EE (Nearest underground station - ANGEL)

mobile - 07831 827284. SER: Gilding. FAIRS: Olympia; LAPADA; Decorative Antiques and Textiles. VAT: Global.

Judith Lassalle

7 Pierrepont Row Arcade, Camden Passage, Islington. N1 8EF. Est. 1765 Cornhill. Open Wed. 7.30-4, Sat. 9.30-4, other times by appointment. *STOCK: Books, children's games, optical toys and rocking horses, 17th C to 1914, £25-£5,000.* PARK: Nearby. TEL: 020 7607 7121; shop - 020 7354 9344. SER: Valuations; restorations; buys at auction. FAIRS: Ephemera; PBFA; American Ephemera.

John Laurie (Antiques) Ltd   `LAPADA`

351/352 Upper St., Islington. N1 0PD. (R. Gewirtz). Est. 1962. Open 9.30-5. SIZE: Large. *STOCK: Silver, Sheffield plate.* TEL: 020 7226 0913/6969; fax - 020 7226 4599. SER: Restorations; packing and shipping. VAT: Stan.

London Militaria Market

Angel Arcade, Camden Passage, Islington. N1. (S. Bosley and M. Warren). Est. 1987. Open Sat. 8-2. SIZE: Large. 35 dealers. *STOCK: Militaria, 1800 to date.* LOC: Near Angel underground station. PARK: Meters and nearby. TEL: 01628 822503 or 01455 556971.

THE MALL
ANTIQUES ARCADE
Camden Passage, London N1

Over 35 Dealers in
London's premier centre for dealers,
decorators and collectors.

Enquiries: Mike Spooner/Neil Jackson
Tel: 020-7351 5353 Fax: 020-7969 1639

The Mall Antiques Arcade
359 Upper St., Islington. N1. (Atlantic Antiques
Centres Ltd). Est. 1979. Open 10-5, Wed. 7.30-5,
Sat. 9-6. CL: Mon. LOC: 5 mins. from Angel
underground station. PARK: Meters. TEL: 020
7351 5353; enquiries - 020 7969 1634; e-mail -
antique@dial.pipex.com. Below are listed the
dealers at this Arcade.

Alexandra Alfandary
LAPADA
Stand G9. *Meissen porcelain.* TEL: 020 7354 9762.

R. Arantes
Stand G27. *Lalique glass.* TEL: 020 7253 5303.

Banana Dance Ltd
Stand G16. (Jonathan Daltrey). *Clarice Cliff, 20th
C decorative arts.* TEL: Mobile - 07976 296987.

Chancery Antiques
Stand G2. (R. Rote). *Oriental and Continental
works of art.* TEL: 020 77359 9035.

Leolinda Costa
Stand G3. *Ethnic silver and gemstone jewellery.*
TEL: 020 7226 3450.

Chris Dunn St. James
Stand G7. *Vintage jewellery.* TEL: 020 7704 0127.

John Harvey
Stand G21. *Art Deco and Art Nouveau.* TEL: 020
7354 3349.

Leon's Militaria
Stand G25. *Militaria.* TEL: Mobile - 07989
649972.

Andrew Lineham
BADA
**Stand G19. *Glass and porcelain.* TEL: 020 7704
0195.**

F. MacDonnel
Stand G11. *Prints.* TEL: 020 7354 1706.

Paul Mayhew
Stand G28. *Clocks.* TEL: 020 7704 6510.

Laurence Mitchell Antiques
Stand G20. *European and English porcelain;
Oriental works of art, Chinese export and Japanese
porcelain; Meissen, 18th and especially 19th C.*
TEL: 020 7359 7579; mobile - 07968 065110; fax -
020 7359 7579; e-mail - info@buymeissen.com;
website - www.buymeissen.com.

Linda Morgan
Stand G26. *Jewellery.* TEL: 020 7359 0654.

Nadine Okker
LAPADA
Stand G8. *Porcelain, glass and bronzes.* TEL: 020
7354 9496.

John Pearman
Stand G24. *Glass and porcelain.* TEL: 020 7359
0591.

Tom Pelc
Stand G1. *Watches and clocks.* TEL: 020 7704
6510.

Rumours
LAPADA
Stands G4/5. (J. Donovan). *Art Nouveau, Art Deco
china and objets d'art.* TEL: 020 7704 8416.

Count Alexander von Beregshasy
Stand G13. *Jewellery, French paste and tiaras
(reproduction crown jewels).* TEL: 020 7354 0059.

Michael Young
Stand G22. *Decorative items, model boats.* TEL:
020 7226 2225.

Lower Mall, London N1

The Antique Barometer Co.
Stand B5. (Jill Liddell). *Barometers, scientific
instruments and related accessories, SM furniture,
medical.* TEL: 020 7226 4992.

Patricia Baxter
Stand B3. *Furniture.* TEL: 020 7354 0886.

James Petre
Stand B8. *Furniture.* TEL: Mobile - 07950 561588.

Malcolm D. Stevens   LAPADA
Stand B2. *Furniture.* TEL: 020 7359 1020; home - 01992 574607.

Turner Brown Antiques
Stands B9/10. (V. Brown). *Furniture and general antiques.* TEL: 020 7359 9402.

Charles Woodage   LAPADA
Stands B4/6/7. *Furniture.* TEL: Mobile - 07767 304317.

Graham Woodage
Stand B1. *Furniture and accessories.*

Michel André Morin   LAPADA
7 Charlton Place, Camden Passage, Islington. N1 8AQ. Open Wed. 8.30-4.30, Sat. 9-4.30, other days by appointment. SIZE: Medium. *STOCK: French decorative furniture, 18th-19th C; French chandeliers.* PARK: Easy. TEL: 020 7226 3803; fax - 020 7704 0708; mobile - 07802 832496. FAIRS: Olympia; Decorative, Battersea. VAT: Spec.

Chris Newland Antiques
Lower Ground Floor, Georgian Village, 30/31 Islington Green. N1. Est. 1964. Open 9-5.30. SIZE: Large. *STOCK: Mahogany furniture, 19th C, £300-£1,000; office furniture, 19th-20th C; shipping furniture, marble, works of art.* PARK: NCP 100 yards. TEL: 020 7359 9805. SER: Valuations; restorations (furniture, French polishing). VAT: Stan/Spec.

Kevin Page Oriental Art   LAPADA
2, 4 and 6 Camden Passage, Islington. N1 8ED. Est. 1968. Open 10.30-4. CL: Mon. and Thurs. SIZE: Large. *STOCK: Oriental porcelain and furniture, fine Japanese works of art from the Meiji period.* LOC: 1 min. from Angel underground station. PARK: Easy. TEL: 020 7226 8558. SER: Valuations. VAT: Stan.

The Passage Antiques
26 Camden Passage, Islington. N1 8ED. (Ian Savage and Ian Wilson). Est. 1992. Open 9.30-5.30. SIZE: Medium. *STOCK: Mainly 19th C furniture including dining, library and consul tables, chairs, sideboards, buffets, linen presses, coffers, chaise longue, settees, trunks, mainly English, some French and German, £150-£7,500.* TEL: 020 7226 3403; fax - 020 7288 1305; mobile - 07968 390845; e-mail - ian.savage @virgin.net. SER: Valuations; restorations (French polishing, repairs, upholstery).

Piers Rankin
14 Camden Passage, Islington. N1 8ED. Est. 1983. Open Tues.-Sat. 9.30-5.30, Mon. by appointment only. SIZE: Medium. *STOCK: Silver and plate, old Sheffield plate, 1700-1930.* PARK: NCP. TEL: 020 7354 3349; fax - 020 7359 8138; e-mail - rankinfamily@rankinpfsbusiness.co.uk.

Regent Antiques
Barpart House, North London Freight Depot, York Way. N1 0UZ. (T. Quaradeghini). Est. 1983. Open 9-5.30, other times by appointment. SIZE: Large. *STOCK: Furniture, 18th C to Edwardian.* LOC: 1/4 mile from Kings Cross station. PARK: Own. TEL: 020 7833 5545; fax - 020 7278 2236; e-mail - regentantiques@aol.com. SER: Restorations (furniture). VAT: Stan/Spec. *Trade Only.*

Relic Antiques at Camden Passage
21 Camden Passage, Islington. N1 8EA. (Malcolm Gliksten). Est. 1975. Open Wed,. Fri. and Sat. 10-4.30. *STOCK: Decorative antiques and painted furniture, childhood memorabilia and paintings, Black Forest carving, fairground art, marine items, period shopfittings, architectural ornaments, trade signs and naive art.* PARK: Meters. TEL: 020 7359 2597; fax - 020 7388 2691; mobile - 07831 785059. FAIRS: Battersea; Montpellier. VAT: Stan.

Restall Brown and Clennell Ltd
Adelaide Wharf, 120 Queensbridge Rd., E2 8PD. (S. Brown). Open Mon.-Fri. 9-5.30 appointment advisable. *STOCK: English furniture, 17th-19th C.* TEL: 020 7739 6626; fax - 020 7739 6123; e-mail - sales@rbc-furniture.co.uk. VAT: Stan/ Spec.

Marcus Ross Antiques
16 Pierrepont Row Arcade, Camden Passage, Islington. N1 8EF. Est. 1972. Open 10.30-4.30. CL: Mon. *STOCK: Oriental porcelain especially Imari, general antiques.* TEL: 020 7359 8494; fax - 020 7359 0240.

Style Gallery
10 Camden Passage, Islington. N1 8ED. (M. Webb and P. Coakley-Webb). Open Wed. and Sat. 9.30-4 or by appointment. *STOCK: Art Nouveau, WMF and Liberty pewter, Art Deco bronzes including Preiss and Chiparus, ceramics and glass.* TEL: 020 7359 7867; home - 020 8361 2357; fax - same; mobile - 07831 229640; website - www.styleantiques.co.uk; e-mail - coakleywebb@btinternet.com.

Sugar Antiques

8-9 Pierrepont Arcade, Camden Passage, Islington. N1 8EF. (Elayne and Tony Sugarman). Est. 1990. Open Wed. and Sat. 7.30-3.30. SIZE: Medium. *STOCK: Wrist and pocket watches, 19th-20th C, £25-£2,000; fountain pens and lighters, early 20th C to 1960's, £15-£1,000; costume jewellery and collectables, 19th-20th C, £5-£500.* LOC: 5 mins. walk from the Angel underground station (Northern Line). PARK: Meters. TEL: 020 7354 9896; fax - 020 8931 5642; mobile - 0793 179 980; e-mail - tony@ sugarantiques.com; website - www.sugar antiques.com. SER: Repairs (as stock); buys at auction (as stock). VAT: Stan.

Swan Fine Art

12b Camden Passage, Islington. N1 8ED. (P. Child). Open 10-5, Wed. and Sat. 9-5 or by appointment. SIZE: Medium. *STOCK: Paintings, fine and decorative sporting and animal, portraits, 17th-19th C, £500-£25,000+.* PARK: Easy, except Wed. and Sat. TEL: 020 7226 5335; fax - 020 7359 2225; mobile - 07860 795336. VAT: Spec.

Tadema Gallery `BADA` `LAPADA`

10 Charlton Place, Camden Passage, Islington. N1 8AJ. (S. and D. Newell-Smith). CINOA. Est. 1978. Open Wed. and Sat. 10-5 or by appointment. SIZE: Medium. *STOCK: Jewellery - Art Nouveau, Art & Crafts, Art Deco to 1960's; artist designed pieces and 20th C abstract art.* PARK: Reasonable. TEL: 020 7359 1055; fax - same; e-mail - info@tademagallery.com; website - www. tademagallery.com. FAIRS: Grosvenor House; International Art & Design, New York. VAT: Spec.

C. Tapsell

Christopher House, 5 Camden Passage, Islington. N1 8EA. Est. 1970. Open Tues. and Fri. 10-5, Wed. 9-4.30, Sat. 9-5, other times by appointment. SIZE: Medium. *STOCK: English mahogany and walnut furniture, 18th-19th C, £300-£15,000; Oriental china, 17th-19th C, £20-£5,000; French furniture, 18th-19th C, £500-£5,000.* LOC: Near Angel underground station. PARK: Opposite. TEL: 020 7354 3603. VAT: Stan/Spec.

The Textile Company

P.O Box 2800. N1 4DQ. (Judy Wentworth). Est. 1982. Open by appointment. *STOCK: 18th C silks, British and French printed cottons, lace, 1600-1850; Paisley and Kashmir shawls, period costume and accessories.* Not Stocked:

Tapestries, upholstery and cushions. TEL: 020 7381 4500; e-mail - jwentworth@beeb.net. SER: Buys at auction; hire; photographic archive. VAT: Stan/Spec.

Turn On Lighting

116/118 Islington High St., Camden Passage. N1 8EG. (J. Holdstock). Est. 1976. Open Tues.-Fri. 10.30-6, Sat. 9.30-4.30. *STOCK: Lighting, 1840-1940.* LOC: Angel underground station. PARK: Business Design Centre. TEL: 020 7359 7616; fax - same. SER: Interior design; museum commissions.

Vane House Antiques

15 Camden Passage, Islington. N1 8EA. (Michael J. Till). Est. 1950. Open 10-5. CL: Mon. and Thurs. *STOCK: 18th to early 19th C furniture.* TEL: 020 7359 1343; fax - same. VAT: Spec.

Mike Weedon `LAPADA`

7 Camden Passage, Islington. N1 8EA. (Mike and Hisako Weedon). Est. 1977. Open Wed. 9-5, Sat. 10-5. *STOCK: Large selection Art Nouveau glass - Gallé, Daum, Lötz; antique glass by artists and designers, from 1880 to 1939; Art Deco sculpture - bronze, bronze and ivory including Chiparus, Preiss, Lorenzl.* TEL: Wed and Sat. only - 020 7226 5319; fax - 020 7700 6387; home - 020 7609 6826; e-mail - info@mikeweedonantiques. com; website - www.mikeweedonantiques.com.

Agnes Wilton

3 Camden Passage, Islington. N1 8EA. Est. 1974. Open 9.30-3. *STOCK: Furniture, decorative items including perfume bottles, collectables, silver and boxes.* TEL: 020 7226 5679; fax - 020 7226 0779.

Yesterday Child `LAPADA`

Angel Arcade, Camden Passage, 118 Islington High St. N1 8EG. (D. and G. Barrington). Est. 1970. Open Wed. and Sat. 8.30-3. SIZE: Small. *STOCK: Dolls, miniatures and toys, 1800-1925, £25-£5,000.* PARK: Business Design Centre opposite. TEL: 020 7354 1601; home and fax - 01908 583403; e-mail - djbarrington@ btopenworld.com. SER: Valuations; restorations. FAIRS: Kensington Town Hall Doll. VAT: Spec.

York Gallery Ltd

51 Camden Passage. N1 8EA. (Jane and Gerd Beyer). Est. 1984. Open Wed. and Sat. 10-5. *STOCK: Antique prints.* TEL: 020 7354 8012; e-mail - prints@yorkgallery.co.uk; website - www. yorkgallery.co.uk. SER: Bespoke framing.

N2

Amazing Grates - Fireplaces Ltd
61-63 High Rd., East Finchley. N2. (T. Tew). Resident. Est. 1971. Open 10-6. SIZE: Large. *STOCK: Mantelpieces, grates and fireside items, £200-£5,000; Victorian tiling, £2-£20; early ironwork, all 19th C.* LOC: 100yds. north of East Finchley underground station. PARK: Own. TEL: 020 8883 9590/6017. SER: Valuations; reproduction mantelpieces in stone and marble; restorations (ironwork, welding of cast iron and brazing, polishing); installations. VAT: Stan.

Martin Henham (Antiques)
218 High Rd., East Finchley. N2 9AY. Est. 1967. Open 10-6. SIZE: Medium. *STOCK: Furniture and porcelain, 1710-1920, £5-£3,500; paintings, 1650-1940, £10-£4,000.* PARK: Easy. TEL: 020 8444 5274. SER: Valuations; restorations (furniture); buys at auction.

Barrie Marks Ltd
24 Church Vale, Fortis Green. N2 9PA. ABA. PBFA. Open by appointment. *STOCK: Antiquarian books - illustrated, private press, colourplate, colour printing; modern first editions.* TEL: 020 8883 1919.

Lauri Stewart - Fine Art
36 Church Lane. N2 8DT. Open Mon. and Tues. 10.30-4.30. *STOCK: Modern British oils and watercolours.* TEL: 020 8883 7719; e-mail - lste181072@aol.com.

N4

Chaucer Fine Arts Ltd
5 Victoria Terrace. N4 4DA. Est. 1978. Open by appointment. *STOCK: Old Master paintings, sculpture and works of art; 19th C European paintings, 20th C Russian paintings and drawings.* TEL: 020 7281 4689; fax - 020 7281 4721; e-mail - chaucer@atlas.co.uk. FAIRS: Milan. VAT: Margin.

Alexander Juran and Co   `BADA`
at Nathan Azizollahoff, OCC, Top Floor & Lift, Building A, 105 Eade Rd. N4 1TJ. Est. 1951. Open 9.15-5.30. CL: Sat. STOCK: Caucasian rugs, nomadic and tribal; carpets, rugs, tapestries. TEL: 020 7435 0280; fax - same; 020 8809 5505. SER: Valuations; repairs. VAT: Stan/Spec.

Kennedy Carpets
OCC Building 'G', 105 Eade Rd. N4 1TJ. (M. Kennedy and V. Eder). Est. 1974. Open 9.30-6. SIZE: Large. *STOCK: Decorative carpets, collectable rugs and kelims, mid-19th C to new, £500-£50,000.* LOC: Off Seven Sisters Road. PARK: Free. TEL: 020 8800 4455; fax - 020 8800 4466; e-mail - kennedycarpets@ukonline.co.uk; website - www.cloudband.com/occ/kennedy carpets. SER: Valuations; making to order. FAIRS: Domotex. VAT: Stan.

Joseph Lavian
OCC, Building E, Ground Floor, 105 Eade Rd. N4 1TJ. Est. 1950. Open 9.30-5.30. SIZE: Large. *STOCK: Oriental carpets, rugs, kelims, tapestries and needlework, Aubusson, Savonnerie and textiles, 17th-19th C.* TEL: 020 8800 0707; fax - 020 8800 0404; mobile - 07767 797707; e-mail - Lavian@Lavian.com; website - www.Lavian.com. SER: Valuations; restorations.

Michael Slade Antiques
42 Quernmore Rd. N4 4QP. Est. 1987. Open 10-6. SIZE: Small. *STOCK: Period oak, Georgian, Victorian, Edwardian and Art Deco furniture, £300-£1,000.* PARK: Easy. TEL: 020 8341 3194; mobile - 07813 377029; website - www.antiques northlondon.co.uk. SER: Valuations; restorations (furniture including upholstery, French polishing and cabinet repairs). FAIRS: Alexandra Palace.

Teger Trading
318 Green Lanes. N4 1BX. Open 9-6. CL: Sat. SIZE: Large. *STOCK: Reproduction bronzes, furniture, marble figures, paintings, mirrors, porcelain and unusual items.* TEL: 020 8802 0156; fax - 020 8802 4110; e-mail - les@teger-trading.demon.co.uk. SER: Restorations; film hire. *Trade Only.*

N5

Nicholas Goodyer
15 Calabria Rd., Highbury Fields. N5 1JB. ABA. ILAB. PBFA. Est. 1951. Open 9.30-5, but prior telephone call advisable. CL: Sat. *STOCK: Antiquarian books especially illustrated.* PARK: Nearby. TEL: 020 7226 5682; fax - 020 7354 4716; e-mail - email@nicholasgoodyer.com; website - www.nicholasgoodyer.com. FAIRS: International ILAB (London, Boston, San Francisco); monthly PBFA, London.

Strike One   `BADA`
48a Highbury Hill. N5 1AP. (J. Mighell). Est. 1968. Open by appointment. SIZE: Medium. STOCK: Clocks, pre-1870, especially early English wall and tavern, £2,000-£25,000; English longcase, 1675-1820, £3,000-£40,000; English bracket, lantern, skeleton and French

carriage; Vienna regulators; barometers, music boxes. **PARK: Easy. TEL: 020 7354 2790; fax - same; e-mail - milo@strikeone.co.uk; website - www.strikeone.co.uk. SER: Valuations; restorations (clocks and barometers); catalogue available. VAT: Stan/Spec.**

N6

At the Sign of the Chest of Drawers
164 Archway Rd. N6 5BB. (A. Harms). Open Sat. 10-6. *STOCK: Pine and country furniture.* TEL: 020 8340 7652

Fisher and Sperr
46 Highgate High St. N6 5JB. (J.R. Sperr). Est. 1945. Open daily 10.30-5. SIZE: Large. *STOCK: Books, 15th C to date.* LOC: From centre of Highgate Village, nearest underground stations Archway (Highgate), Highgate. PARK: Easy. TEL: 020 8340 7244; fax - 020 8348 4293. SER: Valuations; restorations (books). VAT: Stan.

Betty Gould and Julian Gonnermann Antiques
408-410 Archway Rd., Highgate. N6 5AT. Est. 1964. Open 10-5.30, Sat. 9.30-5.30. CL: Mon. and Thurs. SIZE: Medium. *STOCK: Furniture, 18th-20th C, £50-£5,000.* LOC: On A1, just below Highgate underground station (corner of Shepherds Hill). TEL: 020 8340 4987. SER: Restorations; French polishing; upholstery.

N7

Dome Antiques (Exports) Ltd `LAPADA`
40 Queensland Rd., Islington. N7 7AJ. (Adam and Louise Woolf). Est. 1961. Open Mon.-Fri. SIZE: Large. *STOCK: 19th C furniture, £250-£10,000.* LOC: Near junction of Holloway and Hornsey roads. PARK: Easy. TEL: 020 7700 6266; fax - 020 7609 1692; mobile - 07831 805888; e-mail - info@domeantiques.co.uk. SER: Valuations; restorations (furniture). FAIRS: LAPADA (NEC, April; Olympia, Feb. and June; Commonwealth Institute, Oct). VAT: Stan/Spec.

N8

Solomon
49 Park Rd., Crouch End. N8 8SY. (Solomon Salim). Est. 1982. Open 9.30-6. SIZE: Medium. *STOCK: Furniture including upholstered and Arts and Crafts, £200-£4,000; decorative items, £100-£500; all 1800-1920.* LOC: 20 mins. off North Circular at Muswell Hill turn-off. PARK: Easy. TEL: 020 8341 1817; e-mail - solomon@solomonantiques.fsnet.co.uk. SER:

Valuations; restorations (furniture including upholstery). VAT: Spec.

N9

Anything Goes
83 Bounces Rd. N9 8LD. (C.J. Bednarz). Est. 1977. Open 10-5. CL: Mon. SIZE: Medium. *STOCK: General antiques including 18th-19th C furniture and bric-a-brac.* PARK: Easy. TEL: 020 8807 9399. SER: Valuations. FAIRS: Newark.

N10

Crafts Nouveau
112 Alexandra Park Rd., Muswell Hill. N10 2AE. (Laurie Strange). Open Wed.-Sat. 10.30-6.30, Tues. and Sun. by appointment. CL: Mon. SIZE: Large. *STOCK: Arts and Crafts, Art Nouveau furniture and decorative art - desks and writing accessories, ceramics including Doulton, Moorcroft; glassware including Loetz; copper and pewter (Hugh Wallis, Archibald Knox, Liberty, Newlyn and Keswick schools); postcards, stamps, ephemera, Gallé and Daum reproduction lamps and glass.* LOC: Parade of shops, off Colney Hatch Lane. PARK: Easy and nearby. TEL: 020 8444 3300; fax - 020 8883 4587; mobile - 07958 448380; e-mail - craftsnouveau@btconnect.com; website - www.craftsnouveau.co.uk. SER: Restorations (furniture including upholstery).

N11

The Collector Limited
4 Queens Parade Close, Friern Barnet. N11 3FY. (Tom Power). Est. 1973. Open 9-5.30. SIZE: Large. *STOCK: Decorative ceramics especially Royal Doulton, from 1900, £50-£3,000; Beswick, from 1920, £40-£1,000; Moorcroft, £150-£750; Lladro, Worcester and Spode.* LOC: Near Arnos Grove/Bounds Green, B550/A406. PARK: Easy. TEL: 020 8361 7787; fax - 020 8361 4143; e-mail - collector@globalnet.co.uk. SER: Valuations. FAIRS: Specialist Decorative Art. VAT: Stan.

N12

Finchley Fine Art Galleries
983 High Rd., North Finchley. N12 8QR. (Sam Greenman). Est. 1972. Open 1-7; Wed. by appointment. SIZE: Large. *STOCK: 18th-20th C watercolours, paintings, etchings, prints, mostly English, £25-£10,000; Georgian, Victorian, Edwardian furniture, £50-£10,000; china and porcelain - Moorcroft, Doulton, Worcester, Clarice Cliff, £5-£2,000; musical and scientific instruments, bronzes, early photographic apparatus, fire-arms, shotguns.* LOC: Off M25,

Finchley Fine Art Galleries

983 High Road, North Finchley, London N12 8QR Telephone:
020-8446-4848 Fax: 020-8445-2381
Mobile: 077 1262 9282
E-mail: finchleyfineart@onetel.net.uk

*200 plus fine 18th-20th Century English watercolours and
paintings in a constantly changing stock. Four galleries of good
quality Georgian, Victorian and Edwardian furniture, pottery,
porcelain, smalls, etc.*

Sir William Russell Flint 1880-1969
*A watercolour of Sibylle wearing a Coster Hat.
My first recorded impression of the smiling handsome seated girl who
later became my adored wife for fifty five years. 7¾ x 3¾ inches*

OPENING TIMES:
MON, TUES, THURS, FRI, SAT, SUN, 1.00-7.00.
WEDNESDAY BY APPOINTMENT

THE COSTER HAT

junction 23, take Barnet road. Gallery on right 3
miles south of Barnet church, opposite Britannia
Road. PARK: Easy. TEL: 020 8446 4848; fax -
020 8445 2381; mobile - 07712 629282; e-mail -
finchleyfineart@onetel.net.uk. SER: Valuations;
restorations; picture re-lining, cleaning; framing.

Frames Direct
218 Woodhouse Rd., Friern Barnet. N12 0RS. (D.
Georgiou and S. Kerr). Est. 1976. Open 10-5.30.
SIZE: Small. *STOCK: General antiques, mirrors
and frames.* LOC: Near Muswell Hill. PARK:
Nearby. TEL: 020 8446 8409. SER: Restorations.

Zeno Booksellers
57a Nether St. North Finchley. N12 7NP. (Maria
and Loui Loizou). Est. 1944. Open 9.30-5.30, Sat.
10-4.30. *STOCK: Antiquarian books on Greece,
Cyprus, Byzantium, Turkey, Middle East and the
Balkans.* TEL: 020 8446 1985/6; fax - 020 8446
1985; e-mail - info@thegreekbookshop.com;
website - www.thegreekbookshop.com.

N13

Palmers Green Antiques Centre
472 Green Lanes, Palmers Green. N13 5PA.
(Michael Webb). Est. 1976. Open 10-5.30, Sun.
11-5. CL: Tues. SIZE: Large. *STOCK: Furniture,
general antiques and collectables.* PARK:
Nearby. TEL: 020 8350 0878. SER: Valuations.
FAIRS: Alexandra Palace.

N14

C.J. Martin (Coins) Ltd **LAPADA**
85 The Vale, Southgate. N14 6AT. Open by

appointment. *STOCK: Ancient and medieval
coins and ancient artefacts.* TEL: 020 8882
1509/4359.

N16

The Cobbled Yard
1 Bouverie Rd., Stoke Newington. N16 0AB. (C.
Lucas). Open Wed.-Sun. 11-5.30. SIZE: Small.
*STOCK: Victorian pine furniture, £50-£750; iron
and brass beds, 19th C, £200-£500; Edwardian
and some period furniture, from £100; general
antiques, collectors and decorating items, bric-a-
brac, £5-£500.* LOC: Off Church St. PARK: Easy.
TEL: 020 8809 5286; e-mail - info@cobbled-
yard.co.uk; website - www.cobbled-yard.co.uk.
SER: Valuations; restorations (small furniture
repairs, upholstery).

N19

Chesney's Antique Fireplace Warehouse
734-736 Holloway Rd. N19 3JF. Est. 1983. Open
9-5.30, Sat. 10-5. SIZE: Large. *STOCK: 18th-
19th C marble, stone and timber chimney pieces,
£1,000-£150,000; reproduction chimney pieces,
£250-£7,500.* LOC: South of Archway
roundabout on A1. PARK: Side streets adjacent.
TEL: 020 7561 8280; fax - 020 7561 8288. SER:
Valuations. VAT: Stan/Spec.

Old School (Gardens & Interiors)
130c Junction Rd., Tufnel Park. N19 5LB. Open
11-7 including Sun. *STOCK: Decorative objects,
original pine and reclaimed furniture, period
garden furniture and some reproduction, tools
and general antiques.* TEL: 020 7272 5603.

N20

Julian Alexander Antiques
40 Totteridge Lane. N20 9QJ. (Julian A. Gonnermann). Est. 1991. Open 9.30-5. CL: Mon. and Thurs. SIZE: Medium. *STOCK: 18th-20th C furniture, £50-£5,000.* LOC: Close to Totteridge and Whetstone underground stations. TEL: 020 8446 6663; e-mail - julian@jag.uk.com; website - www.jag.uk.com. SER: French polishing; re-upholstery.

The Totteridge Gallery
61 Totteridge Lane. N20 0HD. Est. 1985. Open daily, Sun. by appointment. SIZE: Small. *STOCK: Oil paintings, £1,000-£25,000; watercolours, £300-£10,000; both 18th-20th C. Limited edition Russell Flint prints, 20th C, £500-£3,000.* LOC: Opposite Totteridge and Whetstone underground station. PARK: Easy. TEL: 020 8446 7896; website - www.totteridgegallery.com. SER: Valuations; restorations; frame repairs. FAIRS: NEC. VAT: Stan/Spec.

N21

Dolly Land
864 Green Lanes, Winchmore Hill. N21 2RS. Est. 1987. Open 9.30-4.30. CL: Mon. and Wed. *STOCK: Dolls, teddies, trains, die-cast limited editions.* PARK: Easy. TEL: 020 8360 1053; fax - 020 8364 1370; website - www.dollyland.com. SER: Restorations; part exchange; dolls' hospital. FAIRS: Doll and Bear.

NW1

Art Furniture
158 Camden St. NW1 9PA. Open 12-5 including Sun. SIZE: Warehouse. *STOCK: Decorative arts 1851-1951, Arts & Crafts furniture by Heal's, Liberty and others.* LOC: Under rail bridge on Camden St. going south. PARK: Easy. TEL: 020 7267 4324; fax - 020 7267 5199; e-mail - arts-and-crafts@artfurniture.co.uk; website - www.artfurniture.co.uk. SER: Export; hire. VAT: Stan/Spec.

Madeline Crispin Antiques
95 Lisson Grove. NW1 6UP. Est. 1971. Open 10-5.30. *STOCK: General antiques.* TEL: 020 7402 6845. VAT: Stan. *Trade Only.*

Angela Hone Watercolours `LAPADA`
CINOA. Open by appointment. *STOCK: English and French watercolours and pastels, 1850-1930.* TEL: 01628 48470; fax - same; e-mail - honewatercolours@aol.com. FAIRS: Chelsea; Olympia; LAPADA.

Laurence Corner
62-64 Hampstead Rd. NW1 2NU. Est. 1955. Open 9.30-6. SIZE: Large. *STOCK: Uniforms, helmets, militaria, theatrical costumes, props, fancy dress, flags.* LOC: From Tottenham Court Rd. - Warren St. end - continue into Hampstead Rd., then Drummond St. is first turning on right by traffic lights. PARK: Easy. TEL: 020 7813 1010; fax - 020 7813 1413; website - www.laurencecorner.com. SER: Hire; catalogue on request.

Relic Antiques Trade Warehouse
127 Pancras Rd. NW1 1UN. (Malcolm and Matthew Gliksten). Est. 1968. Open 10-5.30, Sat. and Sun. by appointment. *STOCK: English and French decorative and country; architectural and garden; mirrors and French posters; fairground art, trade signs and marine antiques; shopfittings and showcases.* PARK: Meters. TEL: 020 7387 6039; fax - 020 7388 2691; mobile - 07831 785059. VAT: Stan.

David J. Wilkins
27 Princess Rd., Regents Park. NW1 8JR. Est. 1974. Open by appointment. SIZE: Large, warehouses. *STOCK: Oriental rugs.* LOC: Off Regent's Park Rd., near St Mark's church. PARK: Free. TEL: 020 7722 7608; home - 01799 542246; website - www.orientalrugexperts.com. SER: Valuations; restorations; Oriental rug broker. VAT: Stan.

NW2

G. and F. Gillingham Ltd
62 Menelik Rd. NW2 3RH. (George and Fryda Gillingham). Est. 1960. Open by appointment. *STOCK: Furniture, 1750-1950.* TEL: 020 7435 5644; fax - same; mobile - 017958 484140. SER: Valuations; export.

Sabera Trading Co
2 Oxgate Parade, Crest Rd. NW2 7EU. (Sabera Nawrozzadeh). Open 10-6. SIZE: Large. *STOCK: Oriental carpets, 19th-20th C, £100-£12,000; porcelain, early 20th C, £100-£1,000; antiques and fine art, jewellery.* PARK: Easy. TEL: 020 8450 0012; fax - same; home - 020 8450 4058. SER: Valuations.

Soviet Carpet & Art Galleries
303-305 Cricklewood Broadway. NW2 6PG. (R. Rabilizirov). Est. 1983. Open 10.30-5, Sun. 10.30-5.30. CL: Sat. SIZE: Large. *STOCK:*

Hand-made rugs, £100-£1,500; Russian art, £50-£5,000; all 19th-20th C. LOC: A5. PARK: Side road. TEL: 020 8452 2445. SER: Valuations; restorations (hand-made rugs). VAT: Stan.

NW3

Patricia Beckman Antiques `LAPADA`
(Patricia and Peter Beckman). Est. 1968. Open by appointment. *STOCK: Furniture, 18th-19th C.* LOC: Hampstead. TEL: 020 7435 5050/0500. VAT: Spec.

Tony Bingham `LAPADA`
11 Pond St. NW3 2PN. Est. 1964. Open Mon.-Fri. 10-6.30. *STOCK: Musical instruments, books, music, oil paintings, engravings of musical interest.* TEL: 020 7794 1596; fax - 020 7433 3662; e-mail - tbingham@easynet.co.uk. VAT: Stan/Spec.

P.G. de Lotz
20 Downside Cres., Hampstead. NW3 2AP. Est. 1967. *STOCK: Antiquarian books on history warfare - naval, military and aviation.* TEL: 020 7794 5709; fax - 020 7284 3058. SER: Catalogue available; search. *Mail Order only.*

Keith Fawkes
1-3 Flask Walk, Hampstead. NW3 1HJ. Est. 1970. Open 10-5.30. SIZE: 2 shops. *STOCK: Antiquarian and general books.* LOC: Near Hampstead underground station. TEL: 020 7435 0614.

Otto Haas (A. and M. Rosenthal)
49 Belsize Park Gardens. NW3 4JL. Est. 1866. Open by appointment. CL: Sat. *STOCK: Manuscripts, printed music, autographs, rare books on music.* TEL: 020 7722 1488; fax - 020 7722 2364; e-mail - AlbiRosenthal@aol.com.

Hampstead Antique and Craft Emporium
12 Heath St., Hampstead. NW3 6TE. Est. 1967. Open 10.30-5, Sat. 10-6, Sun. 11.30-5.30. CL: Mon. SIZE: 24 units. *STOCK: General antiques, craft work and gifts.* LOC: 2 mins. walk from Hampstead underground station. TEL: 020 7794 3297.

Klaber and Klaber `BADA`
PO Box 9445. NW3 1WD. (Mrs B. Klaber and Miss P. Klaber). Est. 1968. Open by appointment. *STOCK: English and Continental porcelain and enamels, 18th-19th C.* TEL: 020 7435 6537; fax - 020 7435 9459; e-mail - info@klaber.com; website - wwwklaber.com. FAIRS: Grosvenor House. VAT: Spec.

Leask Ward `LAPADA`
Open by appointment. *STOCK: Oriental and European antiques and paintings.* TEL: 020 7435 9781; fax - same; e-mail - wardl5@aol.com. SER: Consultancy. VAT: Spec.

Duncan R. Miller Fine Arts `BADA`
17 Flask Walk, Hampstead. NW3 1HJ. CINOA. Open by appointment. SIZE: Small. *STOCK: Modern British and European paintings, drawings and sculpture, especially Scottish Colourist paintings.* LOC: Off Hampstead High St., near underground station. PARK: Nearby. TEL: 020 7435 5462. SER: Valuations; conservation; restorations (oils, works on paper and Oriental rugs); buys at auction. FAIRS: Grosvenor House; BADA; Olympia. VAT: Spec.

Newhart (Pictures) Ltd
PO Box 1608. NW3 3LB. (Ann and Bernard Hart). Open by appointment. *STOCK: Oil paintings and watercolours, 1850-1930, from £500.* TEL: 020 7722 2537; fax - 020 7722 4335; e-mail - hart@newhartpictures.co.uk; website - www.newhartpictures.co.uk. SER: Valuations; restorations; framing. VAT: Spec.

Recollections Antiques Ltd
The Courtyard, Hampstead Antiques Emporium, 12 Heath St., Hampstead. NW3 6TE. (June Gilbert). Est. 1987. Open Tues.-Sat. 10.30-5. SIZE: Small. *STOCK: English blue and white transfer print pottery, 1820-1850; pine and oak furniture, 19th C; children's furniture and toys; unusual decoartive items - glass and kitchenalia.* PARK: Nearby. TEL: 020 7431 9907; fax - 020 7794 9743; mobile - 07930 394014; e-mail - junalantiques@aol.com.

Malcolm Rushton - Early Oriental Art
13 Belsize Grove. NW3 4UX. (Dr Malcolm Rushton). Est. 1997. Open by appointment, mainly evenings and weekends. SIZE: Small. *STOCK: Fine early Oriental art, neolithic to Tang dynasty, to £15,000.* LOC: Near Belsize Park underground station, off Haverstock Hill. PARK: Easy. TEL: 020 7722 1989. SER: Valuations; restorations (ceramics, sculpture mounting). VAT: Stan.

M. and D. Seligmann `BADA`
26 Belsize Park Gardens. NW3 4LH. (Maja and David Seligman). CINOA. Est. 1948. Open by appointment. *STOCK: Fine vernacular furniture, mainly English, 17th to early 19th C; antiquities and objets d'art.* PARK: Meters. TEL: 020 7722 4315; fax - same; mobile - 07946 634429. FAIRS: Olympia (June). VAT: Stan/Spec.

NW4

Talking Machine
30 Watford Way, Hendon. NW4 3AL. Open 10-5, Sat. 9.30-1.30, prior telephone call advisable. *STOCK: Mechanical music, old gramophones, phonographs, vintage records and 78's, needles and spare parts, early radios and televisions, typewriters, sewing machines, juke boxes, early telephones.* LOC: 1 min. from Hendon Central underground station. TEL: 020 8202 3473; mobile - 07774 103139; e-mail - davepaul50@ hotmail.com and talkingmachine@gramophones. ndirect.co.uk; website - www.gramophones. ndirect.co.uk. SER: Buys at auction. VAT: Spec.

NW5

Acquisitions (Fireplaces) Ltd
24-26 Holmes Rd., Kentish Town. NW5. (K. Kennedy). NFA. GMC. Est. 1974. Open 9-5. SIZE: Large. *STOCK: Fireplaces in marble, wood, cast-iron and stone, Georgian, Victorian, Edwardian reproduction, fire-side accessories, £195-£5,000.* LOC: 3 mins. walk from Kentish Town underground station. PARK: Forecourt. TEL: 020 7485 4955. SER: Bespoke manufacture of chimney pieces. VAT: Stan.

Lida Lavender   `LAPADA`
39-51 Highgate Rd. NW5 1RS. (Lida and Paul Lavender). Est. 1992. Open 10-6. SIZE: Large. *STOCK: Carpets including Aubusson, tapestries and textiles.* TEL: 020 7424 0600; fax - 020 7424 0404; e-mail - info@lavenders.co.uk; website - www.lavenders.co.uk. SER: Restorations. FAIRS: Olympia (Feb. and June).

Orientalist
74-78 Highgate Rd. NW5 1PB. (E. and H. Sakhai). Est. 1885. SIZE: Large. *STOCK: Rugs, carpets, needlepoints, tapestries and Aubussons, including reproduction.* PARK: Easy and nearby. TEL: 020 7482 0555; fax - 020 7267 9603. SER: Valuations; restorations (cleaning and repairing rugs, carpets and tapestries); buys at auction (Oriental carpets, rugs and textiles). VAT: Stan/Spec.

NW6

Gallery Kaleidoscope incorporating Scope Antiques
64-66 Willesden Lane. NW6 7SX. (K. Barrie). Est. 1965. Open 10-6. SIZE: Large. *STOCK: Oils, watercolours, prints, ceramics and sculpture, 19th-21st. C.* LOC: 10 mins. from Marble Arch. PARK: Easy. TEL: 020 7328 5833; fax - 020

7624 2913. SER: Restorations; framing. FAIRS: Affordable Art (Spring). VAT: Stan/Spec.

Hosains Books and Antiques
12 Honeybourne Rd., West Hampstead. NW6 1JJ. (K.S. and Mrs. Y. Hosain). Est. 1979. Open by appointment. *STOCK: Secondhand and antiquarian books on India, Middle East, Central Asia; miniatures; prints of India and Middle East; Islamic manuscripts.* TEL: 020 7794 7127; fax - 020 7433 3126.

NW8

Alfies Antique Market
13-25 Church St. NW8. Open Tues.-Sat. 10-6. SIZE: 300 stands with 180+ dealers on 4 floors. TEL: 020 7723 6066; fax - 020 7724 0999; e-mail - post@Alfies.com. Below are listed the dealers at this market.

20th Century Runway
Stand S1. (Nicole Borevec). *Fashion and collectables, late '60s and '70s.* TEL: 020 7723 6105.

Beth Adams
Stands G43/44. *Decorative arts, 1860-1950's, £8-£750.* TEL: Mobile - 07776 136003.

Kami Allahyari
Stand F100. TEL: 020 7723 1370. SER: Rug restoration.

David and Diana Bennett Antiques
Stands G104/5. *Boxes, scent bottles, small furniture, silver inkwells, fish servers, clocks, brass scales, glasses, decanters, wooden watch stands, 1800-1900, £20-£300.* TEL: 020 7724 2229.

Bibliopola
Stand F17. (Joe Del-Grosso). *Antiquarian illustrated, childrens books; modern first editions, 1600-1940.* TEL: 020 7724 7231.

M. J. Black
Stands F59/61. *Furniture, decorative and unusual objects.* TEL: 020 7724 0678.

Shelley Blake
Stands G108/9. *Paintings, frames and mirrors.* TEL: 020 7723 1513.

Paolo Bonino
Stands G116/121/122/129. *Collectables, frames, mirrors and glass.* TEL: 020 7723 1513.

Darren Brindell
Stands F57/58. *Furniture and decorative items.* TEL: 020 7724 0678.

Naneen and Peter Brooks
Stands G139/40. *Jewellery, figures, mugs and objets d'art, Georgian to 1960, £25-£1,500.* TEL: 020 7723 0564; mobile - 07785 786395.

Ian Broughton
Stands S59/60. *1930s to 1950s items.* TEL: 020 7723 6105.

Bernie Bruno
Stand G115. *Clocks and watches.* TEL: 020 7723 0564

Vincenzo Cafferella
Stands G33/34. *Furniture, oil paintings, frames and mirrors.* TEL: 020 7724 3701.

Sheila Cameron
Stand G135. *Jewellery.* TEL: 020 7723 0564.

William Campbell
Stands G5-8. *Period picture frames and mirrors, 18th-20th C, £20-£1,000.* TEL: 020 7723 7730. SER: Framing.

Mia Cartwright
Stand G52. *Luggage.* TEL: 020 7723 0449.

Castaside
Stands B40-42. (David Smith). *Theatre memorabilia, ephemera.* TEL: 020 7723 7686.

Linda Chan
Stand G120. *Jewellery.* TEL: 020 7724 0362.

Cushion Corner
Stand F113/126. *Cushions.* TEL: 020 7723 1370.

Vera Da Silva
Stands G87/88. *Decorative items.* TEL: 020 7723 0449.

Dodo
Stands F71/73. (Liz Farrow). *Posters, tins and advertising signs, 1890-1940.* TEL: 020 7723 1515.

Gerald Dougall
Stand F16. *Decorative antiques, 18th-20th C, £20-£1,000.* TEL: 020 7723 0678.

Gill Drey
Stand F21. *Paintings.* TEL: 020 7723 0678.

Hillary Duffield
Stand S54. *Lighting.* TEL: 020 7723 2548.

Antonio Durante
Stands S57/58. *Decorative items, collectables and costume jewellery.* TEL: 020 7723 6105.

East-West Antiques
Stands G113/114/117. (Colin Thomson). *Books and Oriental objects, from 1800, £5-£500.* TEL: 020 7723 0564.

Eastgate Antiques
Stands S7/9. (Joan Latford) *China teasets, wall plates, cups and saucers; Victorian coloured and Art Deco pressed glass; oil lamps and silver, 19th-20th C, £15-£1,500.* TEL: 020 7723 6105.

Renato Ferrari
Stands G64/65. *Art Nouveau.* TEL: 020 7723 0449.

Julia Foster-Fogle
Stand F56. *19th C decorative antiques.* TEL: 020 7723 0678; mobile - 07973 146610.

The Girl Can't Help It
Stand G100. (Sparkle Moore). *Clothing and costume, costume jewellery.* TEL: 020 7724 8984.

Goldsmith and Perris   `LAPADA`
Stands G59/61. (Gloria Goldsmith). *Silver and plate. lighting.* TEL: 020 7724 7051.

Theresa Gore
Stand S10. *Buttons.* TEL: 020 7723 6105.

Linette Greco
Stand G26. *Jewellery.* TEL: 020 7723 1513.

Guillou-Emary
Stand F80. (Jean Gillou). *General decorative items, 18th-20th C, £25-£800.* TEL: 020 7723 0429.

Stephen Hall
Stand F77. *Decorative items.* TEL: 020 7723 0678.

George Hepburn
Paintings, watercolours and drawings, 18th-20th C, £50-£2,000. TEL: 020 7723 3437; mobile - 07721 598487.

Kate Keats
Stand F51. TEL: 020 7774 0678.

Barry Landsman
Stand G911. *Watercolours, 18th-19th C, £50-£1,000.* TEL: 020 7723 1513.

Legacy
Stands G50/51. (J. Rosser and W. Garraway). *Postcards, old tins, ephemera, commemoratives, decorative and miniature objects.* TEL: Mobile - 07855 164954.

Sarah Lewis
Stand S40. *Textiles - cushions, curtains, tapestries and embroideries; trims, tassels, prints, linen and lace, silk, shawls and clothes, 19th-20th C, £10-£10,000.* TEL: 020 7723 6105.

Libra Design
Stands F40/44/45. (Marie Gottlieb). *Furniture, lighting and decorative furniture.* TEL: 020 7723 2688.

Mark Locke
Stands F54/55. TEL: 020 7724 0678.

Marie Antiques
Stands G136/138. (Marie Warner). *Jewellery.* TEL: 020 7706 3727.

Francesca Martire
Stands F103-105. *Arts and Crafts, 20th C paintings, costume jewellery, decorative arts.* TEL: 020 7724 4802.

Mason Blanc
Stand S121. (Abigail Smith). *Linen and lace.* TEL: 020 7723 5731.

Robert McCoy
Stand F20. *Paintings, 19th-20th C, £50-£500.* TEL: 020 7723 0678.

Moji Mohamadi
Stand G31. *Jewellery, clocks and watches.* TEL: 020 7723 1513. SER: Restorations (jewellery).

Bruna Naufal
Stand G1. *Furniture, from 1920.* TEL: 020 7724 3439.

Noe & Chiesa
Stands S50/51. *Art Deco and bakelite, 20th C, from £4.* TEL: Mobile - 07751 084135.

Kenneth Norton-Grant
Stands F109/111. *Brass, pewter, pottery and china, 16th-20th C, £1-£250.* TEL: 020 7723 1370.

NS Watches
Stands G12/13. (Mo Heidarieh). *Watches, clocks, prints, pens, cameras and silver, from 1850, from £10.* TEL: 020 7723 1513.

Pari & Maryam
Stands G26/30. *Jewellery, clocks and watches.* TEL: 020 7723 1513.

Stevie Pearce
Stands G114-115,G144. *Costume jewellery, fashion accessories, linen and lace, 1900-1970, from £10.* TEL: 020 7723 2526.

Persiflage
Stands S6/8. (G. Trefor Jones). *Costume, clothing, linen and lace.* TEL: 020 7724 7366.

Francesco Petillo
Stands G47/48. *Decorative items including furniture.* TEL: 020 7723 0449.

Katherine Pole
Stands F52/53. *Textiles, furniture and decorative antiques, 18th-19th C, £5-£500.* TEL: 020 7724 0678.

Geoffrey Robinson
Stands G77/78. *Glass, lighting, chrome, Art Deco, 1925-1960's.* TEL: 020 7724 8984.

Hoshang Samii
Stand S105. *French decorative antiques, 18th-19th C, £10-£600.* TEL: 020 7723 5731.

Andreas Schmid
Stands G69/70/72. *Furniture.* TEL: 020 7723 0449.

Ophelia Scremini
Stand S109. *Textiles.* TEL: 020 7723 5731.

Kyra Segal
Stand S11. *Textiles, clothing and costume.* TEL: 020 7723 6105.

Gloria Sinclair
Stand F23. *Porcelain and jewellery, 18th-19th C.* TEL: 020 7724 7118.

Connie Speight
Stands G125/127. *Dolls and bears, handbags and jewellery.* TEL: 020 7723 1513.

Kelvin Spooner
Stand S107. *Prints.* TEL: 020 7723 5731.

Cad Van Swankster
Stands G89/90/115. *Clothing and costume, collectables.* TEL: 020 7724 8984.

Eugene Tiernan
Stand F14. *Decorative antiques, furniture, frames and mirrors, 19th-20th C, £50-£1,500.* TEL: 020 7723 8964; fax - same.

Tin Tin Collectables
Stands G38/39/42. (Peter Pinnington). *Antique luggage, costume and clothing, ceramics.* TEL: 020 7258 1305.

Travers Antiques
Stands F74/76. (Paula Kluth). TEL: 020 7258 0662.

June Victor
Stands S41/43. *Decorative textiles and linen, clothing and costume, 17th-20th C, £5-£500.* TEL: 020 7723 6105.

D. F. Wallis
Stand F15. *Medical and scientific items, corkscrews, 19th C, £1-£500.* TEL: 020 7402 1038; fax - same.

Jessie Western
Stands S2/4. *Western clothing and Native American jewellery.* TEL: Mobile - 07775 750486.

G. Wetzel
Stand S110. TEL: 020 7723 5731. SER: Restorations.

Fiona Wicks
Stands G14/15. *Furniture and decorative items.* TEL: 020 7723 0449.

Wolfbridge
Stand S16. (Nigel Brooke). TEL: 020 7723 9755.

Beverley
30 Church St., Marylebone. NW8 8EP. Open 10-6 or by appointment. *STOCK: Art Nouveau, Art Deco, decorative objects.* TEL: 020 7262 1576.

D. and A. Binder
34 Church St. NW8 8EP. Open 10-6. *STOCK: Traditional shop-fittings, counters, cabinets, vitrines and display stands.* LOC: Near Lisson Grove. TEL: 020 7723 0542; fax - 020 7724 0837.

Bizarre
24 Church St., Marylebone. NW8 8EP. (A. Taramasco and V. Conti). Open 10-5. *STOCK: Art Deco and Art Nouveau.* TEL: 020 7724 1305; fax - 020 7724 1316.

Church Street Antiques
8 Church St. NW8 8ED. (Stuart Shuster). Est. 1975. Open 10-5.30. CL: Mon. SIZE: Medium. *STOCK: English brown furniture, 18th to early 20th C, £500-£2,000.* LOC: Between Edgeware Rd. and Lisson Grove. PARK: Meters. TEL: 020 7723 7415; fax - 020 7723 7415; home - 020 8952 2249. SER: Valuations; restorations (polishing). FAIRS: NEC. VAT: Stan.

Davidson and Morgan
5 Church St. NW8 8EE. (Edward Davidson). Est. 1982. Open 10-6. SIZE: Medium. *STOCK: Fine and decorative antiques; French, Continental and English furniture, 1780-1930; architectural antiques, objets d'art, paintings and eclectic items.* PARK: Easy. TEL: 020 7724 9236; fax - 020 7723 9387; e-mail - sales@davidsonand morgan.com; website - www.davidsonand morgan.com. SER: Free sourcing; valuations. FAIRS: Decorative Antiques.

Nicholas Drummond/Wrawby Moor Art Gallery Ltd
6 St. John's Wood Rd. NW8 8RE. (J.N. Drummond). Est. 1972. Open by appointment. *STOCK: English and European oils, £250-£30,000; works on paper.* LOC: Pass Lords entrance and next lights, house last bow front on left, facing down Hamilton Terrace. TEL: 020 7286 6452; home - same; fax - 020 7266 9070; e-mail - drummonds@nixpix.fsnet.co.uk. SER: Valuations; restorations (oils); buys at auction. VAT: Spec.

Gallery of Antique Costume and Textiles
2 Church St., Marylebone. NW8 8ED. Est. 1975. Open 10-5.30. *STOCK: Curtains, needleworks, paisley shawls, original clothing up to 1940's and English quilts, 19th-20th C; tassles, decorative borders, silk panels, velvets and brocades, £5-£20,000.* LOC: 500yds. from Marylebone underground station and 1/2 mile from Marble Arch. PARK: Easy. TEL: 020 7723 9981 (ansaphone); e-mail - info@gact.co.uk; website - www.gact.co.uk. FAIRS: Hali; Vintage Fashion and Textiles; New York.

Robert Gordon Antiques
22 Church St. NW8 8EP. Open 10-5. SIZE:

Diagonal barometer, signed in a cartouche on the scale 'Made by P Sullivan LONDON 1710'. Unusually, the vertical tube is exposed. A paper scale underlies the brass one shown here, on its cartouche is 'Made by P Sullivan in Essex Street LONDON'. (Private collection. Photo Patrick Marney Barometers)

From an article entitled "Diagonal and Reticulated Barometers" by Patrick Marney and Anita McConnell which appeared in the April 2002 issue of *Antique Collecting*. For more details and to subscribe see page 21.

Medium. *STOCK: 18th-19th C furniture.* LOC: Off Edgware Rd. PARK: Easy. TEL: 020 7262 3613. VAT: Spec.

Patricia Harvey Antiques and Decoration LAPADA
42 Church St., Marylebone. NW8 8EP. Est. 1961. Open 10-5.30. SIZE: Medium. *STOCK: Decorative furniture, objets, accessories and paintings, £100-£20,000.* LOC: Between Lisson Grove and Edgware Rd., near Alfies Antique Market. TEL: 020 7262 8989; fax - same; home - 020 7624 1787; e-mail - info@patriciaharvey antiques.co.uk; website - www.patricia harveyantiques.co.uk. SER: Valuations; buys at auction; interior decoration. FAIRS: Decorative Antiques and Textiles. VAT: Stan.

Just Desks LAPADA
20 Church St. NW8 8EP. (G. Gordon and N. Finch). Est. 1967. Open 9.30-6, Sat. 9.30-5 or by appointment. *STOCK: Victorian, Edwardian and reproduction desks, writing tables, bureaux, chairs, filing cabinets and roll tops.* PARK: Meters/Pay & Display. TEL: 020 7723 7976; fax - 020 7402 6416. VAT: Stan.

Andrew Nebbett Antiques
35-37 Church St., Marylebone. NW8 8ES. Est. 1986. Open 10-5.30. CL: Mon. SIZE: Large. *STOCK: Shop fittings, leather chesterfields, decorative, military and ships furniture; creamware and glass.* LOC: 50m from Alfie's Antique Market. TEL: 020 7723 2303; e-mail - anebbett@aol.com. FAIRS: Olympia (Feb). VAT: Stan/Spec.

No. 28 Antiques
28 Church St. NW8 8EP. (David Tulissio, Dominic de Beaumont and Alan Isenberg). Est. 1998. Open 10-6. SIZE: Medium. *STOCK: Chandeliers, wall lights and lamps, 18th-20th C, £200-£3,000; bronzes and sculpture, 18th-19th C,* £200-£4,000; general decorative antiques, 18th-20th C, £100-£5,000; furniture, 19th-20th C, £300-£5,000.* LOC: Opposite Alfie's Antique Market, between Lisson Grove and Edgware Rd. (nearest underground station - Edgware Road). TEL: 020 7724 4631; mobiles - 07973 186305/07770 920405/07802 425835. VAT: Stan/Spec.

The Studio
(John Beer). Open by appointment. *STOCK: British Arts and Crafts, Gothic and Art Deco, especially furniture, 1830-1960's.* TEL: 01242 576080; mobile - 07976 704306. SER: Valuations; buys at auction.

Tara Antiques
6 Church St. NW8 8ED. (G. Robinson). Est. 1971. Open 10-6. CL: Mon. SIZE: Medium. *STOCK: Unusual marble and bronze statuary; Vienna bronzes, silver, furniture, paintings, ivory and tortoiseshell.* PARK: Easy. TEL: 020 7724 2405. SER: Buys at auction. VAT: Stan.

Townsends
81 Abbey Rd., St. John's Wood and 106 Boundary Rd. NW8 0AE. (M. Townsend). Est. 1972. Open 10-6. SIZE: Large + warehouse 96A Clifton Hill. *STOCK: Fireplaces, £250-£6,000; stained glass, £80-£1,000; architectural and garden antiques, £50-£2,000; all mainly 18th-19th C.* LOC: Corner of Abbey Rd. and Boundary Rd. PARK: Easy. TEL: 020 7624 4756; warehouse - 020 7372 4327; fax - 020 7372 3005. SER: Valuations; site surveys; free delivery. VAT: Stan.

Wellington Gallery
1 St John's Wood High St. NW8 7NG. (Mrs K. Barclay). Open 10.30-6. *STOCK: Furniture, 18th-19th C; paintings, Georgian glass, fine porcelain, silver and Sheffield plate, general antiques.* TEL: 020 7586 2620; fax - 020 7483

0716. SER: Valuations; restorations (silver and plate, furniture, paintings, glass and porcelain); curtain making; upholstery; gilding; engraving.

Young & Son `LAPADA`
12 Church St. NW8 8EP. (L. and S. Young). CINOA. Est. 1990. Open Tues.-Sat. 10-6. SIZE: Medium. *STOCK: Furniture, paintings, £1,000-£5,000; lighting and mirrors, £200-£500; decorative items, £100-£5,000; all 18th-20th C.* LOC: Off Lisson Grove and Edgeware Rd. PARK: Easy. TEL: 020 7723 5910; fax - same; mobile - 07958 437043; e-mail - leon@dircon.co.uk; website - www.youngandson.com. SER: Valuations; restorations (gilding, framing, French polishing, paintings lined, cleaned and restored). VAT: Stan/Spec.

NW9

B.C. Metalcrafts
69 Tewkesbury Gardens. NW9 0QU. (F. Burnell). Est. 1946. Open by appointment. *STOCK: Lighting, ormolu and marble lamps; Oriental and European vases; clocks, pre-1900, £5-£500.* TEL: 020 8204 2446; fax - 020 8206 2871. SER: Restorations; conversions; buys at auction. *Trade Only.*

NW10

David Malik and Son Ltd
5 Metro Centre, Britannia Way, Park Royal. NW10 7PA. Open 9-5. CL: Sat. *STOCK: Chandeliers, wall lights.* PARK: Easy. TEL: 020 8965 4232; fax - 020 8965 2401. VAT: Stan.

Willesden Green Architectural Salvage
189 High Rd., Willesden. NW10 2SD. (D. Harkin). Est. 1996. *STOCK: Architectural items.* TEL: 020 8459 2947; fax - 020 8415 1515; mobile - 07971 176547.

NW11

Christopher Eimer
P.O. Box 352. NW11 7RF. BNTA. IAPN. Est. 1970. Open 9-5 by appointment. *STOCK: Commemorative and historical medals and related art.* TEL: 020 8458 9933; fax - 020 8455 3535; e-mail - art@christophereimer.co.uk; website - www.christophereimer.co.uk. VAT: Global/Margin.

WC1

Abbott and Holder
30 Museum St. WC1A 1LH. (Philip Athill). Est.

1936. Open 9.30-6, Thurs. till 7. SIZE: 3 floors. *STOCK: English watercolours, drawings, oils and prints, 1760-2000.* LOC: Opposite British Museum. TEL: 020 7637 3981; fax - 020 7631 0575; e-mail - abbott.holder@virgin.net; website - www.abbottandholder.co.uk. VAT: Spec

Atlantis Bookshop
49a Museum St. WC1A 1LY. (Geraldine and Bali Beskin). Est. 1922. Open 10.30-6. *STOCK: Antiquarian books on the occult and paranormal; occasional related artefacts and paintings.* LOC: Tottenham Court or Holborn underground stations. TEL: 020 7405 2120; e-mail - atlantis@theatlantisbookshop.com; website - www.theatlantisbookshop.com.

Austin/Desmond Fine Art
Pied Bull Yard, 68/69 Great Russell St. WC1B 3BN. (J. Austin). SLAD. Open 10.30-5.30. *STOCK: Modern and contemporary British paintings and prints.* TEL: 020 7242 4443; fax - 020 7404 4480; website - www.austindesmond.com.

Book Art & Architecture Bookshop & Volume Gallery
12 Woburn Walk, Bloomsbury. WC1. (Prof. Dennis Sharp and Y. Shariff). Est. 1964. Open Mon.-Fri. 11-6 or by appointment. SIZE: Small. *STOCK: Rare, out-of-print and secondhand architectural books and prints, 20th C, £3.50-£2,500; art, design, planning of modern movement; books published by Book Art Ltd.* LOC: Pedestrian street off Tavistock Sq., opposite Euston. PARK: Nearby. TEL: 020 7387 5006; fax - 01707 875286; e-mail - sharpd@globalnet.co.uk; website - sharparchitects.co.uk. SER: Valuations; restorations; buys at auction (books and prints). FAIRS: Various book; Historic Buildings Show. VAT: Stan.

Cinema Bookshop
13-14 Great Russell St. WC1B 3NH. (F. Zentner). Est. 1969. Open 10.30-5.30. SIZE: Small. *STOCK: Books, magazines, posters and stills.* LOC: First right off Tottenham Court Rd. PARK: Easy. TEL: 020 7637 0206; fax - 020 7436 9979. SER: Mail order. VAT: Stan.

George and Peter Cohn
Unit 21, 21 Wren St. WC1X 0HF. Est. 1947. Open 9-5, Sat. and Fri. pm. by appointment. *STOCK: Decorative lights.* PARK: Forecourt. TEL: 020 7278 3749. SER: Restorations (chandeliers and wall-lights). *Trade Only.*

Fine Books Oriental

38 Museum St. WC1A 1LP. (Jeffrey Somers). PBFA. Est. 1970. Open 9.15-5.30, Sat. 11-5.30. SIZE: Medium. *STOCK: Books.* LOC: Near British Museum. PARK: Meters. TEL: 020 7242 5288; fax - 020 7242 5344.

Michael Finney Antique Prints and Books

31 Museum St. WC1A 1LG. (Michael and Mirka Finney). ABA. PBFA. Est. 1979. Open 10-6. SIZE: Large. *STOCK: Prints, 17th-19th C; decorative plate books and watercolours especially David Roberts, Piranesi and Spain; caricatures.* PARK: Meters. TEL: 020 7631 3533; fax - 020 7637 1813; e-mail - prints@michael finney.co.uk; website - www.michaelfinney. co.uk. FAIRS: ABA Olympia (June).

Robert Frew Ltd

106 Gt. Russell St. WC1B 3NB. ABA. PBFA. Open 10-6, Sat. 10-2. *STOCK: Books, 15th-20th C, £5-£25,000; maps and prints, 15th-19th C, £5-£5,000.* LOC: Turn right off Tottenham Court Rd. to British Museum, shop on left past YMCA. PARK: Easy. TEL: 020 7580 2311; fax - 020 7580 2313; e-mail - shop@robertfrew.com; website - www.robertfrew.com. FAIRS: ABA Olympia; Chelsea; PBFA; Hotel Russell; various USA. VAT: Stan.

Jessop Classic Photographica

67 Great Russell St. WC1B 3BN. Open 9-5.30. *STOCK: Classic photographic equipment, cameras and optical toys.* TEL: 020 7831 3640; fax - 020 7831 3956.

The Museum Bookshop

36 Gt. Russell St. WC1B 3QB. (Ashley Jones). Est. 1982. Open 10-5.30. *STOCK: Books on antiquities - Egyptian, Middle Eastern, classical; glass, ceramics, conservation.* LOC: 3 mins. from Tottenham Court Rd. underground station. TEL: 020 7580 4086; fax - 020 7436 4364; e-mail - mbooks@btconnect.com; website - www. museumbookshop.com. SER: Catalogues, mail order.

Nortonbury Antiques   LAPADA

BCM Box 5345. WC1N 3XX. Open by appointment. *STOCK: Silver, 17th-19th C.* TEL: 01984 631668; fax - same; mobile - 07774 174092; e-mail - nortonbury.antiques@virgin.net.

Rennies

13 Rugby St. WC1. (Paul and Karen Rennie). Open Tues.-Sat. 12-6.30. *STOCK: Decorative arts, 1880-1960; vintage posters, mainly British; ceramics by Ravilious; vintage scarves.* TEL: 020 7405 0220; e-mail - info@rennart.co.uk; website - www.rennart.co.uk.

Simmons Gallery

53 Lambs Conduit St. WC1N 3NB. (Howard and Frances Simmons). BNTA. Est. 1982. Open 10.30-5.30, Wed. 10.30-7. CL: Sat. SIZE: Small. *STOCK: Coins and medals, from 2000BC to contemporary; scales and weights, ancient to 1900; contemporary jewellery and sculpture.* LOC: Off Theobalds Rd, Holborn. Close to Gt Ormond St. Hospital. PARK: Meters. TEL: 020 7831 2080; fax - 020 7831 2090; e-mail - info@simmonsgallery.co.uk; website - www. simmonsgallery.co.uk. SER: Valuations; buys at auction (coins and medals). FAIRS: London Coin (Feb., June, Nov); ANA Midsummer Convention (Aug). VAT: Stan/Spec/Global.

Skoob Russell Square

10 Brunswick Centre, Off Bernard St. WC1N 1AE. (C.Y. Loh). Est. 2001. Open 11-7, Sun. 12-5. SIZE: Large. *STOCK: Secondhand books specialising in philosophy, cultural studies, literature, psychology, science. Art house videos.* LOC: Near Russell Sq. underground station. PARK: Easy. TEL: 020 7278 8760; fax - 020 7278 3137; e-mail - books@skoob.com; website - www.skoob.com. SER: Publishers of Skoob Seriph, Esoterica and Pacifica series.

Spink and Son Ltd   BADA

69 Southampton Row. WC1B 4ET. BNTA. IAPN. Est. 1666. Open 9.30-5.30. CL: Sat. STOCK: Coins, medals, stamps, bank notes and related books. TEL: 020 7563 4000; fax - 020 7563 4066; e-mail - info@spinkandson.com; website - www.spink-online.com. SER: Valuations. VAT: Stan/Spec.

WC2

Anchor Antiques Ltd

Suite 31, 26 Charing Cross Rd. WC2H 0DG. (K.B. Embden and H. Samne). Est. 1964. Open by appointment. *STOCK: Continental and Oriental ceramics, European works of art and objets de vertu.* TEL: 020 7836 5686. VAT: Spec. *Trade Only.*

Apple Market Stalls

Covent Garden Market. WC2E 8RF. Est. 1980. Open every Monday 10-6.30. SIZE: 48 stalls. *STOCK: General antiques and quality collectables.* LOC: North Hall. TEL: 020 7836 9136; e-mail - info@coventgardenmarket.co.uk; website - www.coventgardenmarket.co.uk.

A.H. Baldwin and Sons Ltd `BADA`
11 Adelphi Terrace. WC2N 6BJ. IAPN. BNTA. Est. 1872. Open 9-5. CL: Sat. SIZE: Medium. *STOCK: Coins, 600 BC to present; commemorative medals, 16th C to present, numismatic literature.* LOC: Off Robert St., near Charing Cross. TEL: 020 7930 6879; fax - 020 7930 9450; e-mail - coins@baldwin.sh. SER: Valuations; auctioneers and auction agents for selling and purchasing. VAT: Stan/Spec.

Blackwell's
100 Charing Cross Rd. WC2H 0JG. SIZE: Small. *STOCK: Antiquarian and rare modern books.* TEL: 020 7292 5100.

M. Bord (Gold Coin Exchange)
16 Charing Cross Rd. WC2H 0HR. Est. 1969. Open 10.30-6. SIZE: Small. *STOCK: Gold, silver and copper coins, Roman to Elizabeth II, all prices.* LOC: Near Leicester Sq. underground station. TEL: 020 7836 0631/7240 0479. SER: Valuations; buys at auction. FAIRS: All major coin. VAT: Stan/Spec.

Philip Cohen Numismatics
20 Cecil Court. WC2N 4HE. BNTA. Est. 1977. SIZE: Medium. *STOCK: English coins, 16th-20th C, £1-£1,000.* LOC: Off Charing Cross Road, near Leicester Sq. underground station. TEL: 020 7379 0615; fax - 020 7240 4300. SER: Valuations.

Covent Garden Flea Market
Jubilee Market, Covent Garden. WC2E 8RB. (Sherman and Waterman Associates Ltd). Est. 1975. Open every Mon. from 6 am. SIZE: 150 stalls. *STOCK: General antiques.* LOC: South side of piazza, just off The Strand, via Southampton St. PARK: Easy and NCP Drury Lane. TEL: 020 7836 2139/7240 7405.

David Drummond at Pleasures of Past Times
11 Cecil Court, Charing Cross Rd. WC2N 4EZ. Est. 1962. Open 11-2.30 and 3.30-5.45 and usually 1st Sat. monthly, other times by appointment. SIZE: Medium. *STOCK: Scarce and out-of-print books of the performing arts; early juvenile and illustrated books; vintage postcards, valentines, entertainment ephemera.* Not Stocked: Coins, stamps, medals, jewellery, maps, cigarette cards. LOC: In pedestrian court between Charing Cross Rd. and St. Martin's Lane. TEL: 020 7836 1142; fax - same; e-mail - drummond@poptfsnet.co.uk. VAT: Stan.

Elms-Lesters Tribal Art `LAPADA`
1-5 Flitcroft St. WC2H 8DH. (Paul Jones and Fiona McKinnon). Est. 1972. Open 11-6 during exhibitions, other times by appointment. SIZE: Medium. *STOCK: Tribal art from Africa, Oceania and south-east Asia - sculptures, masks, ethnographic objects, furniture and textiles, 19th to mid-20th C.* LOC: Between Soho, Covent Garden and Bloomsbury. PARK: Meters and NCP nearby. TEL: 020 7836 6747; fax - 020 7379 0789; e-mail - gallery@elms-lesters.demon.co.uk; website - www.elms-lesters.demon.co.uk. SER: Valuations. FAIRS: LAPADA.

Stanley Gibbons
399 Strand. WC2R 0LX. Est. 1856. Open 9-5.30, Sat. 9.30-5.30. SIZE: Large. *STOCK: Popular and specialised stamps, postal history, catalogues, albums, accessories; autographs and memorabilia.* LOC: Opposite Savoy Hotel. TEL: 020 7836 8444; fax - 020 7836 7342. SER: Valuations; auctions. VAT: Stan/Spec.

Gillian Gould at Ocean Leisure
Embankment Place, 11-14 Northumberland Avenue. WC2N 5AQ. Est. 1988. Open 9.30-6, Thurs. 9.30-7, Sat. 9.30-5.30 or by appointment. SIZE: Small. *STOCK: Marine antiques and collectables, scientific instruments, £30-£1,000.* LOC: Embankment underground station. TEL: Home - 020 7419 0500; fax - 020 7419 0400; mobile - 07831 150060; e-mail - gillgould@dealwith.com. SER: Valuations; restorations; hire; sources gifts for personal and corporate presentation; buys at auction. VAT: Stan.

Grosvenor Prints
28 Shelton St., Covent Garden. WC2H 9JE. Est. 1975. Open 10-6, Sat. 11-4. SIZE: Large. *STOCK: 18th-19th C topographical and decorative prints, specialising in portraits, dogs and British field sports.* LOC: One street north of Covent Garden underground station. PARK: Easy. TEL: 020 7836 1979; fax - 020 7379 6695; website - www.grosvenorprints.com; e-mail - grosvenorprints@btinternet.com. SER: Valuations; restorations; buys at auction. VAT: Stan/Spec.

P. J. Hilton (Books)
12 Cecil Court. WC2N 4HE. (Paul Hilton). Est. 1980. Open 11-6, Sat. 11-5. SIZE: Medium. *STOCK: Antiquarian books, 16th-20th C, £75-£500; secondhand books; leather cloth bindings by the yard.* LOC: Off Charing Cross Rd. TEL: 020 7379 9825. SER: Valuations.

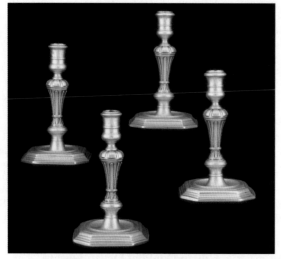
Lee Jackson
2 Southampton St., Covent Garden. WC2E 7HA. PBFA. Est. 1996. Open 10-5.30. SIZE: Large. *STOCK: Maps and views of the world, 16th-19th C, £10-£3,000.* LOC: Off the Strand, opposite the Savoy Hotel. PARK: Meters. TEL: 020 7240 1970; e-mail - leejackson@btinternet.com; website - www.leejackson.btinternet.co.uk. FAIRS: London Map; Miami International Map. VAT: Stan.

S. and H. Jewell Ltd
26 Parker St. WC2B 5PH. Est. 1830. Open 9-5.30, Sat. by appointment. SIZE: Large. *STOCK: Furniture.* TEL: 020 7405 8520; fax - 020 7405 8521. SER: Valuations; restorations. VAT: Stan/Spec.

Koopman Ltd & Rare Art (London) Ltd

BADA

Entrance to London Silver Vaults, Ground Floor, 53/64 Chancery Lane. WC2A 1QS. (Timo Koopman and Lewis Smith). Open 9-5.30, Sat. 10-1. *STOCK: Fine quality English Georgian and Continental silverware.* TEL: 020 7242 7624; fax - 020 7831 0221; e-mail - enquiries@ rareartlondon.com; website - www. rareartlondon.com. FAIRS: Milan; Olympia; New York; Maastricht (TEFAF); Gotha, Parma.

The London Silver Vaults
Chancery House, 53-64 Chancery Lane. WC2A 1QS. Est. 1892. Open 9-5.30, Sat. 9-1. SIZE: 34 shops. *STOCK: Antique and modern silver, plate, jewellery, objets d'art, clocks, watches, general items.* TEL: 020 7242 3844. The following are some of the dealers at these vaults.

A. M. W. Silverware
Vault 52-53. TEL: 020 7242 3620; fax - 020 7831 3923.

Argenteus Ltd   LAPADA
Vault 2. TEL: 020 7831 3637; fax - 020 7430 0126. VAT: Stan/Spec.

Belmonts

A. Bloom
Vault 27. *Victorian and Edwardian silver miniatures to monumental table centres.* TEL: 020 7242 6189; fax - same; e-mail - bloomvault @aol.com; website - www.bloomvault.com.

Luigi Brian Antiques
Vault 17. *Fine English and European silver, objets d'art and icons.* TEL: 020 7405 2484; fax - same.

B.L. Collins
Vault 20. (Barry Collins). TEL: 020 7404 0628; fax

- 020 7404 1451; e-mail - b.collins@silvervaults. idps.co.uk; website - www.blcollins.co.uk.

Crown Silver
Vault 30. TEL: 020 7242 4704. *Trade Only.*

P. Daniels
Vault 51. TEL: 020 7430 1327.

Bryan Douglas LAPADA
Vault 12/14. (Ian Bryan). *Antique, old and modern silverware.* TEL: 020 7242 7073; fax - same; e-mail - sales@bryandouglas.co.uk; website - www.bryandouglas.co.uk.

R. Feldman Ltd LAPADA
Vault 6. *Unusual and rare items, old Sheffield and Victorian plate, silver centrepieces, candelabra, epergnes combined with argenteus specialising in all patterns of flatware.* TEL: 020 7405 6111; fax - 020 7430 0126; e-mail - rfeldman@rfeldman. co.uk; website - www.rfeldman.co.uk.

I. Franks LAPADA
Vault 9/11. Est. 1926. *Old and antique English silver and plate especially tableware, teasets, cutlery, epergnes, candlesticks and candelabra.* TEL: 020 7242 4035; fax - same; e-mail - info@ifranks.com; website - www.ifranks.com.

Anthony Green Antiques
Vault 54. *Vintage wrist watches.* TEL: 020 7430 0038

M. & J. Hamilton
Vault 25. *17th -20th C silver including cutlery.* TEL: 020 7831 7030; fax - 020 7831 5483; e-mail - hamiltonsilver@hotmail.com.

Gary Hyams
Vault 48-50. *Silver and Sheffield Plate.* TEL: 020 7831 4330.

Stephen Kalms LAPADA
Vault 15, 31, 32. TEL: 020 7430 1265; fax - 020 7405 6206; e-mail - stephen@skalms.freeserve. co.uk; website - www.kalmsantiques.com.

B. Lampert
Vault 19. TEL: 020 7242 4121.

Langfords LAPADA
Vault 8/10. (Adam and Joel Langford). Est. 1940. *Silver and plate especially cutlery.* TEL: 020 7242 5506; fax - 020 7405 0431; e-mail - vault@langfords.com; website - www.langfords. com. SER: Valuations. VAT: Stan/Spec.

Leon Antiques
Vault 57.

Nat Leslie Ltd
Vault 21-23. (Mark Hyams). Est. 1940. *Victorian and 20th C silverware especially flatware and contemporary designers, especially Stuart Devlin.* TEL: 020 7242 4787; fax - 020 7242 4504; e-mail - nat.leslie@which.net; website - www.natleslie.co. uk. VAT: Stan/Spec.

Linden and Co. (Antiques) Ltd
Vault 7. (H. F., H.M. and S. C. Linden). *Silver and plate, specialising in gift items for weddings, christenings, silver weddings and retirements, £100-£750.* TEL: 020 7242 4863; fax - 020 7405 9946; e-mail - lindenandco@aol.com; website - www.lindenantiquesilver.com. VAT: Stan/Spec.

C. and T. Mammon
Vault 55-64. (Claude Mammon). *Victorian and old Sheffield plate, Continental and English silver and cutlery, mirror plateaux and centrepieces.* TEL: 020 7405 2397; fax - 020 7405 4900; e-mail - claudemammon@btinternet.com; website - www.candtmammon.com.

I. Nagioff (Jewellery)
Vault 63 and 69. (I. and R. Nagioff). Est. 1955. *Jewellery, 18th-20th C, £5-£2,000+; objets d'art, 19th C, to £200.* TEL: 020 7405 3766. SER: Valuations; restorations (jewellery). VAT: Stan.

Percy's (Silver) Ltd LAPADA
Vault 16. (David and Paul Simons). *Fine decorative silver especially claret jugs, candelabra, candlesticks, flatware and collectables.* TEL: 020 7242 3618; fax - 020 7831 6541; e-mail - sales@percys-silver.com; website - www.percys-silver.com.

A coffee jug in old Naples style probably made by the Ginori family late in the 19th century, well past the glory days of Doccia.

From an article entitled "Italian Porcelain" by John Sandon which appeared in the June 2003 issue of *Antique Collecting*. For more details and to subscribe see page 21.

Terry Shaverin
Vault 143. TEL: 020 8368 5869; fax - 020 8361 7659; e-mail - terryshaverin@silverflatware.co.uk; website - www.silverflatware.co.uk.

David S. Shure and Co
Vault 1. (Lynn Bulka). Est. 1900. Author. *Antique and modern silverware, old Sheffield plate, cutlery and jewellery.* TEL: 020 7405 0011; fax - same. SER: Valuations. VAT: Stan.

Silstar (Antiques Ltd)
Vault 29. (B. Stern). Est. 1955. TEL: 020 7242 6740; fax - 020 7430 1745; e-mail - antique@silstar.fsnet.co.uk. VAT: Stan/Spec.

B. Silverman `BADA`
Vault 26. Est. 1927. *Fine antique silver including flatware.* TEL: 020 7242 3269; fax - 020 7430 1949; e-mail - robin@silverman-london.com; website - www.silverman-london.com. SER: Valuations; buys at auction. VAT: Stan/Spec.

S. and J. Stodel. `BADA`
Vault 24. (Jeremy Stodel). *Chinese export to English Art Deco silver including flatware.* TEL: 020 7405 7009; fax - 020 7242 6366; e-mail - stodel@msn.com; website - www.chinesesilver.com.

J. Surtees
Vault 65. *Silver.* TEL: 020 7242 0749.

William Walter Antiques Ltd
`BADA` `LAPADA`
Vault 3/5. (Elizabeth Simpson). Est. 1927. *Georgian silver, old Sheffield plate; also modern silver.* TEL: 020 7242 3284; fax - 020 7404 1280; e-mail - enq@wwantiques.prestel.co.uk; website - www.williamwalter.co.uk. SER: Valuations; restorations (silver, plate).

Peter K. Weiss
Vault 18. Est. 1955. *Watches, clocks.* TEL: 020 7242 8100; fax - 020 7242 7310. VAT: Stan.

Wolfe (Jewellery)
Vault 41. (John Petrook). TEL: 020 7405 2101; fax - same. VAT: Stan/Spec.

Marchpane
16 Cecil Court, Charing Cross Rd. WC2N 4HE. (Kenneth Fuller). ABA. PBFA. ILAB. Est. 1989. Open 10.30-6. SIZE: Medium. *STOCK: Antiquarian children's and illustrated books, from 18th C to date.* TEL: 020 7836 8661; fax - 020 7497 0567; e-mail - k_fuller@btclick.com.

Arthur Middleton
12 New Row, Covent Garden. WC2N 4LF. Est. 1968. Open 10-6, Sat. by appointment. SIZE: Medium. *STOCK: Globes, 1720-1950, from miniatures to large library pairs; scientific instruments - navigation, astronomy, surveying, microscopes, 18th-19th C, £100-£50,000.* LOC: New Row runs between Leicester Sq. and Covent Garden. Shop 300yds. east from Leicester Sq. TEL: 020 7836 7042/7062; fax - 020 7497 2486; e-mail - arthur@antique-globes.com; website - www.antique-globes.com. SER: Valuations; buys at auction; prop hire. VAT: Stan.

Henry Pordes Books Ltd
58-60 Charing Cross Rd. WC2H 0BB. Open 10-7. *STOCK: Secondhand, antiquarian and remainder books on most subjects including antiques.* TEL: 020 7836 9031; fax - 020 7240 4232; e-mail - henrypordes@clara.net; website - www.home.clara.net/henrypordes.

The Rae-Smith Gallery
8 Cecil Court. WC2N 4HE. (John and Felicity Rae-Smith). Est. 1992. Open 11.30-6, Mon. by appointment. SIZE: Medium. *STOCK: 20th C original cartoon artwork and book illustrations, £30-£3,000.* LOC: Between Charing Cross Road and St. Martin's Lane - Leicester Square underground station. PARK: Meters or NCP. TEL: 020 7836 7424; fax - same; e-mail - raesmithg@aol.com. SER: Valuations. FAIRS: Watercolours and Drawings. VAT: Margin.

Reg and Philip Remington
18 Cecil Court, Charing Cross Rd. WC2N 4HE. ABA. Est. 1979. Open 10-5, Sat. by appointment. SIZE: Medium. *STOCK: Voyages and travels, 17th-20th C, £5-£1,000.* LOC: Near Trafalgar Sq. TEL: 020 7836 9771. SER: Buys at auction. FAIRS: London Book, Olympia. VAT: Stan.

Bertram Rota Ltd
1st Floor, 31 Long Acre. WC2E 9LT. Est. 1923. Open 9.30-5.30. CL: Sat. *STOCK: Antiquarian and secondhand books, especially first editions, private presses, English literature, and literary autographs.* TEL: 020 7836 0723/7497 9058; e-mail - bertramrota@compuserve.com.

The Silver Mouse Trap
56 Carey St. WC2A 2JB. (A. Woodhouse). Est. 1690. Open 10-5. CL: Sat. SIZE: Medium. *STOCK: Jewellery, silver.* LOC: South of Lincoln's Inn Fields. TEL: 020 7405 2578. SER: Valuations; restorations. VAT: Spec.

Stage Door Prints
9 Cecil Court, Charing Cross Rd. WC2N 4EZ. (A. Reynold). Open 11-6. *STOCK: Prints of performing arts, sports and topographical;*

signed photographs, maps, Victorian cards, valentines; film shop - posters, stills, books, memorabilia; performing arts book room and bargain basement. TEL: 020 7240 1683.

Storey's Ltd
3 Cecil Court, Charing Cross Rd. WC2N 4EZ. (T. Kingswood). Est. 1929. Open 10-6. *STOCK: Antiquarian prints and engravings, especially naval and military; natural history and topography, including David Roberts; antiquarian maps and books.* LOC: Between Charing Cross Rd. and St. Martin's Lane. PARK: Trafalgar Square garage. TEL: 020 7836 3777; fax - 020 7836 3788; e-mail - storeysltd@ btinternet.com; website - www.storeysltd.co.uk.

Tindley and Chapman
4 Cecil Court. WC2N 4HE. Est. 1974. Open 10-5.30, Sat. 11-4. *STOCK: 20th C first editions English and American literature including detective fiction.* TEL: 020 7240 2161; fax - 020 7379 1062; e-mail - bellbr@dial.pipex.com.

Tomtom
42 New Compton St. WC2H 8DA. (T. S. Roberts). Est. 1990. Open 12-7, Sat. 11-6. CL: Mon. SIZE: Medium. *STOCK: Post war design furniture, art, glass and ceramics, 1940-1980, to £1,000+.* LOC: Adjacent Charing Cross Rd. PARK: Meters. TEL: 020 7240 7909; fax - same; e-mail - sales@tomtomshop.co.uk; website - www.tomtomshop.co.uk. SER: Valuations; buys at auction (designer furniture and post war art). FAIRS: Pier Show, New York. VAT: Spec.

Trafalgar Square Collectors Centre
7 Whitcomb St. WC2H 7HA. (D.C. Pratchett and R.D. Holdich). Est. 1979. Open 10-5. CL: Sat. *STOCK: Coins and military medals, bonds, banknotes, badges and militaria, 18th-20th C, £5-£10,000.* LOC: Next to National Gallery. PARK: NCP. TEL: 020 7930 1979; fax - 020 7930 1152; e-mail - rdhmedals@aol.com. SER: Valuations; buys at auction (coins and military medals). VAT: Stan/Spec.

Travis and Emery
17 Cecil Court, Charing Cross Rd. WC2N 4EZ. ABA. PBFA. Est. 1960. Open 11-6 including Sun. SIZE: Medium. *STOCK: Musical literature, sheet music and prints.* LOC: Between Charing Cross Rd. and St. Martin's Lane. PARK: Meters. TEL: 020 7240 2129; fax - 020 7497 0790; e-mail - enqasb@travis-and-emery.com. SER: Valuations.

Watkins Books Ltd
19 Cecil Court, Charing Cross Rd. WC2N 4EZ.

A lesser-known bone china vase, height 7½in., moulded with aerographed decoration in salmon pink with sgraffito decoration of stylised buds. About 1956-57.

From an article entitled "Susie Cooper Bone China 1950-1966" by Ann Eatwell which appeared in the March 2002 issue of *Antique Collecting*. For more details and to subscribe see page 21.

Est. 1880. Open 10-6, Thurs. 10-8, Sat. 10.30-6. *STOCK: Mysticism, occultism, Oriental religions, astrology, psychology, complementary medicine and a wide selection of books in the field of mind, body and spirit - both new and secondhand.* LOC: Near Leicester Sq. underground station. TEL: 020 7836 2182; fax - 020 7836 6700; e-mail - service@ watkinsbooks.com; website - www.watkins books.com.

Nigel Williams Rare Books
25 Cecil Court, Charing Cross Rd. WC2N 4HE. ABA. Est. 1988. Open 10-6. SIZE: Medium. *STOCK: Books - literature first editions, 18th-20th C; children's and illustrated, original artwork and prints, detective fiction.* LOC: Near Leicester Sq. underground station. TEL: 020 7836 7757; fax - 020 7379 5918; e-mail - sales@nigelwilliams.com; website - www. nigelwilliams.com. FAIRS: ABA, Olympia.

The Witch Ball
2 Cecil Court, Charing Cross Rd. WC2N 4HE. (R. Glassman). Resident. Est. 1969. Open 10.30-6.30. SIZE: Small. *STOCK: Prints relating to the performing arts, from 17th C, 20th C posters.* LOC: 2 mins. from Leicester Square underground station. PARK: NCP nearby. TEL: 020 7836 2922; e-mail - thewitchball@btinternet.com; website - www.thewitchball.co.uk. VAT: Stan.

BEDFORDSHIRE

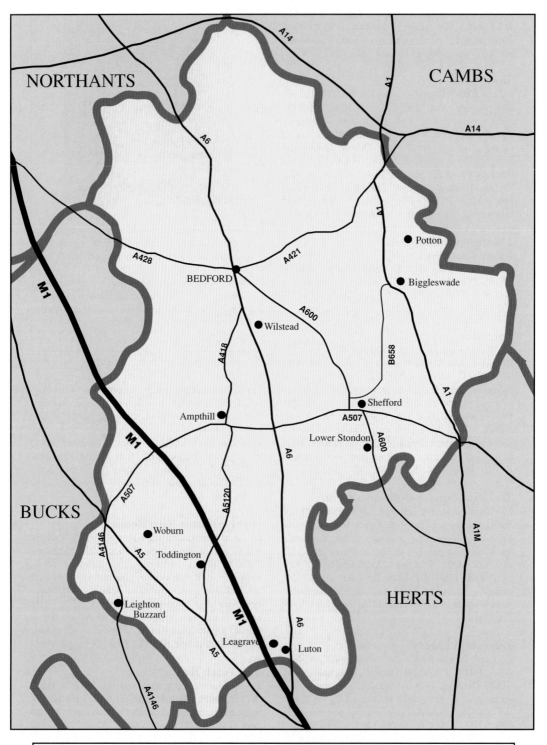

AMPTHILL

Ampthill Antiques

Market Sq. MK45 2EH. (Lord J.E. Shayler). Est. 1980. Open 11-6 including Sun. SIZE: Large. *STOCK: Furniture, collectables, jewellery, clocks, china, glass, pictures.* LOC: Town centre. PARK: Easy and at rear. TEL: 01525 403344.

Ampthill Antiques Emporium

6 Bedford St. MK45 2NB. (Marc Legg). Est. 1979. Open 10-5 including Sun. CL: Tues. SIZE: Large – 40 dealers. *STOCK: Antique furniture, fireplaces, architectural items, smalls, ceramics, glass and jewellery.* LOC: 5 mins. from Junction 13, M1. PARK: Easy. TEL: 01525 402131; fax – 01582 737527; e-mail – info@ampthillantiquesemporium. co.uk; website – www.ampthillantiquesemporium. co.uk. SER: Restorations (upholstery); stripping (pine).

Antiquarius of Ampthill

107 Dunstable St. MK45 2NG. (Peter Caldwell). Est. 1997. Open 10.30-5, Sun. 1-5. SIZE: Small. *STOCK: Sitting and dining room furniture, 1800-1900, to £3,000.* LOC: Town centre. PARK: Nearby. TEL: 01525 841799; e-mail – peter. caldwell@tesco.net SER: Restorations; re-upholstery.

House of Clocks

102-104 Dunstable St. MK45 2JP. (John and Helga Ginty, Ian and Hazel Proud). Resident. Est. 1957. Open 9-5, Sun. 11-4. SIZE: Medium. *STOCK: Clocks including longcase, bracket, carriage and wall, £150-£12,000.* PARK: Through narrow archway by shop, behind Market Sq. TEL: 01525 403136; fax – 01525 718577; e-mail – helgaginty@aol.com. SER: Valuations; restorations (clocks). FAIRS: Manchester; Birmingham: Uxbridge: Kettering: Luton. VAT: Stan/Spec.

David Litt Antiques

The Old Telephone Exchange, Claridges Lane. MK45 2NG. (David and Helen Litt). Est. 1967. Open 7.30-5, Sat. and Sun. by appointment. SIZE: Large. *STOCK: French country items especially armoires, farmhouse tables, sets of chairs, chandeliers and mirrors.* LOC: Off Woburn St. PARK: Easy. TEL: 01525 404825; fax – 01525 404563; mobile – 07802 449027; home – 01525 750359; e-mail – litt@ntlworld. com. SER: Restorations (cabinet work). FAIRS: Decorative Antiques & Textile, Battersea; House & Garden; Olympia.

Paris Antiques

97B Dunstable St. MK45 2NG. (Paul and Elizabeth Northwood). Est. 1985. Open 9.30-5. CL: Mon. SIZE: Medium. *STOCK: Furniture,*

AMPTHILL ANTIQUES EMPORIUM

Experience shopping as it was nearly a century ago at this unique antique centre, housed in a purpose built Victorian department store, virtually unchanged since 1898. Three floors offering a variety of town, country & decorative Antiques to suit all tastes. Visit our rear yard for Architectural & Garden Antiques. Marvel at our magnificent mahogany pharmacy interior, which now incorporates our payment counter & reception area.

IN-HOUSE SERVICES

Traditional Upholsterer • Furniture Restorer • Picture Framer

and the most comprehensive range of restoration materials in the area

Open every day **10.00am-5.00pm**
(except Tuesday closed all day)
6 Bedford Street, Ampthill
Telephone: 01525 402131
www.ampthillantiquesemporium.co.uk
email: info@ampthillantiquesemporium.co.uk

18th to early 20th C, £250-£4,000; brass and copper, silver and plate, pictures and smalls. LOC: Off junction 12, M1. PARK: Opposite. TEL: 01525 840488; home – 01525 861420; mobile – 07802 535059. SER: Valuations; restorations (mainly furniture, some metal); buys at auction.

Pilgrim Antiques

111 Dunstable St. MK45 1BY. (Gary Lester). Est. 1982. Open 10-5.30 including Sun. SIZE: Large. *STOCK: Furniture including dining tables, bookcases, chairs, wardrobes, 18th-20th C, £500-£5,000.* LOC: Town centre. PARK: Rear of premises. TEL: 01525 633023; home – 01525 403266. SER: Restorations.

The Pine Parlour

82a Dunstable St. MK45 2LF. (Lynn Barker). Est. 1989. Open 10-5 including Sun. CL: Mon. SIZE: Small. *STOCK: Pine furniture, 19th C, £200-£800; kitchenalia, £5-£60.* PARK: Easy. TEL: 01525 403030; home – same. SER: Valuations.

Transatlantic Antiques & Fine Art Ltd

101 Dunstable St. MK45 2NG. (I.J. and D. M. Higgins). Est. 1995. Open 10.30-5, Sun. 12-5. SIZE: Large. *STOCK: 19th C furniture, £150-*

£4,000; glass, ceramics, silver and metalware, 19th C, £5-£3,000; pictures and interesting objects, 18th-19th C, £50-£1,000. LOC: Main street. PARK: Easy, nearby. TEL: 01525 403346; fax – same; e-mail – transatlantic@talk21.com; website – www.antiquesweb.co.uk/transatlantic. SER: Restorations; buys at auction. VAT: Spec.

BEDFORD

Architectural Antiques
70 Pembroke St. MK40 3RQ. (Paul and Linda Hoare). Est. 1989. Open 12-5, Sat. 10-5. SIZE: Medium. *STOCK: Early Georgian to early 20th C fireplaces, £500-£1,000; sanitary ware, from late Victorian, £100-£500; doors, panelling, pews, chimney pots and other architectural items, Georgian and Victorian, £50-£100.* LOC: Follow signs to town centre, turn on The Embankment or Castle Rd., shop is off Castle Rd., near Post Office. PARK: Easy. TEL: 01234 213131/ 343421; fax – 01234 309858. SER: Valuations; restorations; installations (period fireplaces).

BIGGLESWADE

Old Mother Hubbard's
38 Shortmead St. SG18 0AP. (Derry Anne Dynes). Est. 1994. Open 10-5, Sat. 9.30-5. CL: Thurs. SIZE: Medium. *STOCK: China, 1920's-30's, £15-£100; Victoriana, 19th C, £10-£500; Victorian pine, £100-£1,000.* PARK: Easy. TEL: 01767 600959. FAIRS: Janba, St Ives; Regal Promotions, Dunstable.

Shortmead Antiques
46 Shortmead St. SG18 0AP. (S.E. Sinfield). Open 10.30-4. CL: Mon. and Thurs. SIZE: Small. *STOCK: Furniture, £50-£1,000; boxes, porcelain, silver, bronzes, copper and brass, all pre-1930.* LOC: 1/2 mile from A1. TEL: 01767 601780 (ansaphone); website – www.shortmeadantiques. co.uk.

Simply Oak
Oaktree Farm, Potton Rd. SG18 0EP. (R. Sturman and A. Kilgarriff). Est. 1996. Open 10-5, Sun. 11-4. SIZE: Large. *STOCK: Restored oak furniture, late Victorian to 1930's, £100-£2,000.* LOC: Off A1 towards Biggleswade, right turn onto B1040 – 3 miles towards Potton. PARK: Own. TEL: 01767 601559; fax – 01767 312855; e-mail – antiques@simplyoak.freeserve.co.uk. SER: Valuations; restorations (furniture especially oak).

LEAGRAVE

Tomkinson Stained Glass
2 Neville Rd. LU3 2JQ. (S. Tomkinson). Open by appointment. *STOCK: Stained glass windows.* TEL: 01582 527866; mobile – 07831 861641. LOC: 5 minutes from station. PARK: Easy. SER: Valuations; restorations. VAT: Stan.

LEIGHTON BUZZARD

David Ball Antiques
59 North St. LU7 7EQ. Est. 1967. Open 10-5. CL: Mon except by appointment. SIZE: Medium.

Some examples of scoops bearing initials.

From an article entitled "Bone Apple Scoops" by Geoffrey Smaldon which appeared in the September 2002 issue of **Antique Collecting**. For more details and to subscribe see page 21.

STOCK: Paintings and watercolours, 18th-20th C, £100-£1,000; furniture, £100-£4,500; clocks, £60-£3,000. PARK: Easy. TEL: 01525 377737; home – 01525 210753; mobile – 07831 11161. SER: Valuations. FAIRS: Luton.

Nick & Janet's Antiques
Buffalo House, Mill Rd., Slapton. LU7 9BT. (Janet and Nick Griffin). Est. 1992. Open by appointment. SIZE: Small. STOCK: Pottery – South Devon including Torquay, £1-£2,000; North Devon including Brannam and Baron, £1-£1,000; Wesuma, £20-£400; Martin Brothers, £200-£5,000; modern Moorcroft, £30-£4,000; Cobridgeware, £20-£1,000. PARK: Easy. TEL: 01525 220256; home – same; fax – 01525 220757; e-mail – janet@nickandjanets.co.uk; website – www.nickandjanets.co.uk. SER: Valuations.

LOWER STONDON

Memory Lane Antiques
14 Bedford Rd. SG16 6EA. (Elizabeth Henry). Est. 1985. Open 10.30-5, Sun. 11-4. CL: Wed. and Thurs. SIZE: Medium. STOCK: General antiques including 19th oak, silver and plate, glass including coloured. LOC: On A600 near RAF Henlow. PARK: Easy. TEL: 01462 811029/812716; fax – same. SER: Valuations.

LUTON

Bargain Box
4 & 6a Adelaide St. LU1 5BB. Open 9-6, Wed. 9-1. STOCK: General antiques and collectables. TEL: 01582 423809.

Bernadette's Antiques & Collectables & Auctioneers
19a Adelaide St. LU1 5BB. Open 9-6, Wed. 9-1. STOCK: General antiques. TEL: 01582 423809.

Foye Gallery
15 Stanley St. LU1 5AL. Est. 1960. Open 9.30-5 or by appointment. STOCK: Engravings, etchings, drawings, watercolours, paintings, maps, books. TEL: 01582 738487. VAT: Stan.

POTTON

W. J. West Antiques
58 High St. SG19 2QZ. (Alan, Richard and Wesley West). Est. 1930. Open 9-5.30, Sat. 9-12. SIZE: Small. STOCK: Furniture, mainly Victorian, including upholstered, to £4,000. LOC: Town centre. PARK: Easy. TEL: 01767 260589;

fax – 01767 261513; mobile – 07989 257260; home – 01767 260289; e-mail – emma_west32 @yahoo.com. SER: Valuations; restorations (furniture including upholstery).

SHEFFORD

S. and S. Timms Antiques Ltd [LAPADA]
2/4 High St. SG17 5DG. Est. 1976. Open 9.30-5, Sat. and Sun. 11-5 or by appointment. SIZE: Large. STOCK: 18th-19th C town and country furniture. LOC: A507, centre of village. PARK: Easy. TEL: 01462 851051; mobile – 07885 458541; e-mail – info@timmsantiques.com; website – www.timms antiques.com. FAIRS: LAPADA (London and NEC); Chelsea; Battersea. VAT: Stan/Spec.

TODDINGTON

Books for Collectors Ltd.
Unit 1, Rear 24/26 High St, LU5 6BY. (Frank and Shirley Horn). Open 10-4, prior telephone call advisable. STOCK: New and secondhand collectors books. PARK: Easy. TEL: 01525 875100/01582 738624; fax – 01525 877600. FAIRS: Most large UK.

Town Hall Antiques

We stock Georgian, Victorian &
Edwardian furniture.
Local county maps, 19th/20thC
prints, oils & watercolours.
A large selection of porcelain,
glass, silver & plate, from
Georgian through to early 20thC
Clocks, sporting goods, jewellery &
antiquities, the list is endless!
Come along & see for yourself
how much we have to offer.

Opening Hours
Mon - Sat 10.00 - 5.30
Sunday 11.00 - 5.30
Market Place, Woburn, Beds
Tel. 01525 290950

WILSTEAD (WILHAMSTEAD)
Nr. Bedford

Manor Antiques
The Manor House, Cottonend Rd. MK45 3BT.
(Mrs S. Bowen). Est. 1976. Open Tues.-Sat. 10-5,
Sun. by appointment. SIZE: Large. *STOCK:
Furniture, 19th C to Edwardian, £100-£5,000;
lighting, mirrors, decorative objects.* LOC: Just
off A6, 4 miles south of Bedford. PARK: Own.
TEL: 01234 740262; home – same. SER:
Restorations (furniture); buys at auction. FAIRS:
Olympia. VAT: Stan/Spec.

WOBURN

Christopher Sykes Antiques
The Old Parsonage. MK17 9QL. (C. and M.
Sykes). Est. 1949. Open 9-5. SIZE: Large.
*STOCK: Collectors' items – attractive, early
brass, copper and pewter; scientific and medical
instruments; specialist in rare corkscrews, £10-
£800; silver decanter labels, tastvins and funnels,
pottery barrels and bin labels, glass decanters
and tantalus.* LOC: In main street opposite Post
Office on A50. PARK: Easy. TEL: 01525

290259/290467; fax – 01525 290061; e-mail –
sykes.corkscrews@sykes-corkscrews.co.uk;
website – www.sykes-corkscrews.co.uk. SER:
130 page illustrated mail order catalogue on
corkscrews and wine related antiques available
£7 each. VAT: Stan/Spec.

Town Hall Antiques
Market Place. MK17 9PZ. (Elfyn and Elaine
Groves). Est. 1993. Open 10-5.30, Sun. 11-5.30.
SIZE: Medium. *STOCK: Furniture, £50-£5,000;
lighting, clocks, ceramics, glass, silver and plate,
£10-£2,000; prints and pictures, £5-£2,000; all
18th to early 20th C; mirrors, domestic metalware; some antiquities; cigarette cards, tools,
sporting memorabilia.* LOC: Off A5 and off
junction 12 or 13, M1. PARK: Easy. TEL: 01525
290950; e-mail – elfyngroves@tinyworld.co.uk.
SER: Valuations; framing.

The Woburn Abbey Antiques Centre
BADA **LAPADA**

**MK17 9WA. (The Bedford Estates). Est. 1967.
Open every day (including Bank Holidays) 10-
5.30. CL: Christmas holidays. SIZE: Over 75
shops and showcases on two floors. *STOCK:
English and Continental furniture, porcelain,
glass, paintings, silver and decorative items.* Not
stocked: Reproduction. LOC: From M1
junction 13, A5 to Woburn Abbey, Centre is in
South Courtyard. PARK: Easy. TEL: 01525
290350; fax – 01525 292102; e-mail – antiques
@woburnabbey.co.uk. SER: Carriage for
large items; worldwide shipping.**

Woburn Fine Arts
12 Market Place. MK17 9PZ. (Z. Bieganski). Est.
1983. Open Tues.-Sun. 2.30-5.30. SIZE: Medium.
*STOCK: Post-impressionist paintings, 1880-
1940; European paintings, 17th-18th C; British
paintings, 20th C.* PARK: Easy. TEL: 01525
290624; fax – 01525 290733. SER: Restorations
(oils and watercolours); framing.

Art Deco
and Other Figures

Bryan Catley

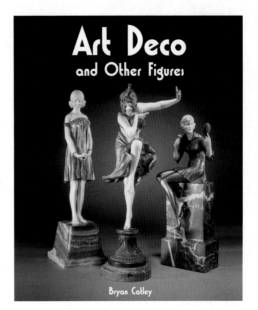

- *Contains the most comprehensive range of art deco figures ever published*

- *Sumptuously illustrated throughout*

- *Compiled by the leading specialist dealer in these figures*

- *A popular collecting subject which is reflected in the enduring success of this important work of reference*

This important book contains the most complete range of art deco figures ever published. It is based partly on the original importers' catalogues and partly on the wide range of pieces handled by the author – the leading specialist dealer in the subject.

Between the wars an entirely 'modern' style of decorative sculpture emerged which was a complete break with the heavy romantic late nineteenth century schools, and was totally in sympathy with the vibrant young society of the 1920s.

The unconventional use of bronze and ivory for a great number of these sensual figures in no way obscures the fact that many of them are of exceptionally high quality; add to this their sense of movement and rhythm and one realises that the large sums they command is a reflection of a discriminative international collectors' market. This new edition provides an almost complete listing of the great variety and range of figures, of which there are still more to be found.

Bryan Catley's original interest in the subject was fired when he inherited an art deco figure from his late grandmother's collection. During his student days at engineering college and after he was inspired to go on and buy every figure he could afford; his searches resulted in a large collection. Later he and John Sparrow set up the business known as 'Catspa' which has for many years become synonymous with Art Deco sculpture.

11 x 8½in. / 279 x 216mm.
348pp., 100 col., 1,100 b.&w. illus.
1 85149 382 4
£45.00

Available from all good booksellers and direct from the publisher:
ANTIQUE COLLECTORS' CLUB
Sandy Lane, Old Martlesham, Woodbridge, Suffolk, IP12 4SD.
Tel: 01394 389950   Fax: 01394 389999
Email: sales@antique-acc.com
Website: www.antique-acc.com

BERKSHIRE

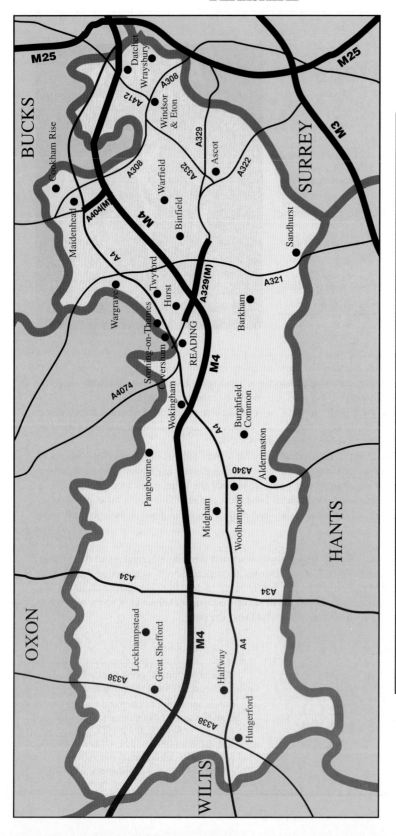

Dealers and Shops in Berkshire

Place	Count
Aldermaston	1
Ascot	1
Barkham	1
Binfield	1
Burghfield Common	1
Caversham	1
Cookham Rise	1
Datchet	1
Great Shefford	1
Halfway	1
Horton	1
Hungerford	17
Hurst	1
Leckhampstead	1
Maidenhead	1
Midgham	1
Pangbourne	1
Reading	3
Sandhurst	1
Sonning-on-Thames	1
Twyford	1
Warfield	1
Wargrave	2
Windsor and Eton	16
Wokingham	1
Woolhampton	1
Wraysbury	1

ALDERMASTON, Nr. Reading

Aldermaston Antiques
The Old Dispensary. RG7 4LW. (Vivian and Roger Green). Est. 1994. Open 10-5.30. SIZE: Medium + yard. *STOCK: Longcase clocks, furniture, lamps, silver, desks, mainly 19th C; architectural and garden stone and iron items.* LOC: A340, village centre. PARK: Easy and at rear. TEL: 01189 712370; home – same.

ASCOT

Omell Galleries
The Corner House, Course Rd. SL5 7HL. (Omell Galleries (Windsor) Ltd.). Est. 1947. Open 9.30-1 and 2-5 or by appointment. SIZE: Medium. *STOCK: Fine paintings, £400-£6,000.* LOC: Off High St. opposite garage. PARK: Easy. TEL: 01344 873443; fax – 01344 873467; e-mail – aomell@aol.com; website – www. omellgalleries. co.uk. SER: Valuations; restorations; cleaning; repairs (oils, watercolours and frames). VAT: Spec.

BARKHAM, Nr. Wokingham

Barkham Antique Centre
Barkham St. RG40 4PJ. (Len and Mary Collins). Open 10.30-5 including Sun. SIZE: Large – 50+ dealers. *STOCK: General antiques including furniture, china, kitchenalia, coins, Dinky toys, paintings, glassware, scientific instruments and brass; collectables including Beswick, Moorcroft, Royal Doulton, Wade.* LOC: Off M4, junction 10, A329M to Wokingham, over station crossing to Barkham (B3349), left at Bull public house, centre 300 yards on left. PARK: Easy. TEL: 0118 976 1355. SER: Valuations; restorations (china, French polishing, upholstery, cabinet making).

BINFIELD

Ulla Stafford Antiques   BADA
Binfield Lodge. RG42 5QB. Open by appointment. *STOCK: Georgian and Continental furniture; European ceramics, 17th-18th C.* TEL: 0118 934 3208; fax – same. FAIRS: Olympia (June). VAT: Spec.

BURGHFIELD COMMON, Nr. Reading

Graham Gallery
Highwoods. RG7 3BG. (J. Steeds). Est. 1976. Open by appointment at any time. SIZE: Medium.

STOCK: English watercolours, £50-£1,500; English oil paintings, £200-£8,000; English prints, £25-£200; mainly 19th to early 20th C. LOC: 4 miles from Reading on Burghfield road. PARK: Easy. TEL: 0118 9832320; fax – 0118 9831070; e-mail – grahamgallery@freeuk.com; website – www.grahamgallery.org.uk. SER: Valuations; restorations; cleaning; framing.

CAVERSHAM, Nr. Reading

The Clock Workshop   LAPADA
17 Prospect St. RG4 8JB. (J. M. Yealland) FBHI. TVADA. CINOA. Est. 1980. Open 9.30-5.30, Sat. 10-1. SIZE: Small. *STOCK: Clocks, late 17th to late 19th C, £350-£60,000; barometers, 18th-19th C, £500-£12,000.* LOC: Prospect St. is the beginning of main Reading to Henley road. PARK: Behind shop in North St. TEL: 0118 9470741; e-mail – theclockworkshop@supanet. com. SER: Valuations; restorations (clocks, barometers, chronometers, barographs); buys at auction. FAIRS: TVADA; LAPADA; Olympia. VAT: Stan/Spec.

COOKHAM RISE

Cookham Antiques
35 Station Parade. SL6 9BR. (Gary Lloyd Wallis). TVADA. Est. 1990. Open daily including Sun. SIZE: Large. *STOCK: Furniture including bookcases, desks, chests of drawers, 18th-20th C, £50-£1,000.* PARK: Easy and at rear. TEL: 01628 523224; mobile – 07778 020536. SER: Valuations; restorations.

DATCHET

The Studio Gallery
The Old Bank, The Green, SL3 9JH. (Julian Bettney). Est. 1990. Open 11-7, until 6 Sun. CL: Tues. am. and Fri. *STOCK: Fine paintings and prints, 1740-1940.* LOC: Off junction 5, M4, opposite Manor Hotel. PARK: Horton Rd. or railway station. TEL: 01753 544100; fax – same; mobile – 07770 762468; e-mail – Julianbettney @talk21.com. SER: Landscape paintings in oils painted to commission; bespoke framing (hand built, coloured, gilded, marbled, veneered).

GREAT SHEFFORD, Nr. Hungerford

Alan Hodgson
No 2 Ivy House, Wantage Rd. RG16 7DA. *STOCK: Boxes, country and general antiques,*

collectors' items. LOC: A338, 10 mins. from Hungerford towards Wantage. TEL: 01488 648172; e-mail – alanh.ivy@pop3.hiway.co.uk. SER: Restorations (furniture).

HALFWAY, Nr. Newbury

Alan Walker   BADA

Halfway Manor. RG20 8NR. TVADA. Est. 1987. Open by appointment. SIZE: Large. *STOCK: Fine barometers and weather instruments.* LOC: 4 miles west of Newbury on A4. PARK: Easy. TEL: 01488 657670; mobile – 07770 728397; website – www.alanwalkerbarometers. com. SER: Restorations.

HORTON, Nr. Slough

John A. Pearson Antiques   BADA

Horton Lodge, Horton Rd. SL3 9NU. (Mrs J.C. Sinclair Hill). Est. 1902. Open by appointment. SIZE: Large. *STOCK: English and Continental furniture, 1700-1850, £50-£30,000; oil paintings, 17th-19th C, £50-£50,000; decorative objects.* Not Stocked: Items after 19th C. LOC: From London turn off M4, exit 5, past London Airport; from M25 take exit 14. 10 mins from Heathrow. PARK: Easy. TEL: 01753 682136; fax – 01753 687151.

HUNGERFORD

Beedham Antiques Ltd   BADA

Charnham Close. RG17 0EJ . Open 10-5 or by appointment. *STOCK: English oak furniture, 16th-18th C; objects and works of art.* TEL: 01488 684141; fax – 01488 684050. VAT: Spec.

Below Stairs of Hungerford

103 High St. RG17 0NB. (Stewart. L. Hofgartner). Est. 1974. Open 10-6, including Sun. and Bank Holidays. SIZE: Large. *STOCK: Kitchen and decorative garden items, bedroom furniture, lighting, collectables, sporting items and memorabilia, interior fittings and taxidermy, mainly 19th C English, £20-£2,500.* Not Stocked: Reproductions. LOC: Main street. PARK: Easy. TEL: 01488 682317; fax – 01488 684294; e-mail – hofgartner@belowstairs.co.uk; website – www. belowstairs.co.uk. SER: Valuations; on-line catalogue. VAT: Stan.

Sir William Bentley Billiards (Antique Billiard Table Specialist Company)

Standen Manor Farm. RG17 0RB. GMC. Est. 1989. Open by appointment seven days a week. SIZE: Large. *STOCK: Billiard tables, billiard/dining tables; antique and modern accessories including panelling, brass lights, marker boards and seating.* PARK: Own; helicopter facilities. TEL: 01488 681711; 020 8940 1152; fax – 01488 685197; website – www.billiards.co.uk. SER: Restorations; removals and storage. FAIRS: House & Garden; Ideal Home; Period Living; Decorex; Antiques & Fine Art; Palm Beach.

Bow House

3-4 Faulkner Sq., Charnham St. RG17 0HH. (Jo Preston). Open 9.30-5.30, Sun. 10-4. SIZE: 2 floors. *STOCK: 18th-19th C furniture and decoratives, contemporary accessories and gifts.* LOC: First shop in Hungerford from Newbury A4. PARK: Own. TEL: 01488 680826. VAT: Spec.

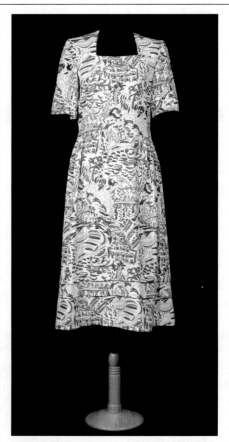

Alec Walker, blockprinted dress in linen, c.1930.

From an article entitled "Artists' Textiles in Britain 1945-1970" by Geoffrey Rayner and Richard Chamberlain which appeared in the April 2003 issue of **Antique Collecting**. For more details and to subscribe see page 21.

Bridge House Antiques & Interiors

7 Bridge St. RG17 0EH. (Kate Pols). Est. 1991. Open Tues.-Sat. 10-5.30. SIZE: Large. *STOCK: 19th C French, Georgian, Regency and Edwardian antiques and decorative items.* PARK: Easy. TEL: 01488 681999; fax – same; mobile – 07810 753048. SER: Restorations.

The Fire Place (Hungerford) Ltd

Hungerford Old Fire Station, Charnham St. RG17 0EP. (E.B. and E.M. Smith). Est. 1976. Open 10-1.30 and 2.15-5. SIZE: Large. *STOCK: Fireplace furnishings and metalware especially fenders; paintings.* LOC: A4. TEL: 01488 683420. VAT: Stan/Spec.

Franklin Antiques

25 Charnham St. RG17 0EJ. (Lynda Franklin). Est. 1973. Open 10-5.30. SIZE: Large. *STOCK: 18th-19th C French and English furniture and decorative items.* LOC: A4. PARK: Easy. TEL: 01488 682404; fax – 01488 686089; mobile – 07831 200834; home – 01488 684072; e-mail – antiques@lyndafranklin.com; website – www.lyndafranklin.com. SER: Valuations; restorations.

Garden Art

Barrs Yard, 1 Bath Rd. RG17 0HE. (Susan and Arnie Knowles). Est. 1980. Open 10-6, Sun. 11-4. SIZE: Large. *STOCK: Period garden items.* PARK: Easy. TEL: 01488 681881; home – 01488 681882; website – www.bigbronze.co.uk. VAT: Stan/Spec.

Great Grooms of Hungerford

Riverside House, Charnham St. RG17 0EP. Open 9.30-5.30, Sun.and Bank Holidays 10-4. SIZE: 3 floors. *STOCK: Wide variety of specialist dealers in 18th-19th C English and Continental town and country furniture, pottery and porcelain, silver and plate, works of art, metalware, glass, clocks, Oriental, oils and watercolours, prints, clocks and watches.* LOC: From M4 junction 14 on to A338. PARK: Own. TEL: 01488 682314; fax – 01488 686677; e-mail – antiques@great-grooms. co.uk; website – www.great.grooms.co.uk. SER: Valuations; restorations (furniture including upholstery, pictures, silver, jewellery, ceramics). VAT: Spec.

Hungerford Arcade

High St. RG17 0NF. (Wynsave Investments Ltd). Est. 1972. Open 9.30-5.30, Sun. 11-5. SIZE: Over 80 stallholders. *STOCK: General antiques and period furniture.* PARK: Easy. TEL: 01488 683701.

Roger King Antiques

111 High St. RG17 0NB. (Mr and Mrs R.F. King). Est. 1974. Open 9.30-5 and most Sun. 11-5. SIZE: Large. *STOCK: Furniture, 1750-1910, £100-£2,000; china, 19th C; oil paintings.* Not Stocked:

Silver, jewellery. LOC: Opposite Hungerford Arcade. PARK: Easy. TEL: 01488 682256; website – www.kingantiques.co.uk. VAT: Spec.

MJM Antiques

13 Bridge St. RG17 0EH. (Michael Mancey). Est. 1997. Open 10-4. SIZE: Small. *STOCK: Fine guns and swords, 1700-1900, £300-£15,000.* LOC: Town centre. PARK: Easy. TEL: 01488 684905; fax – 01488 684090; home – 01488 684999; e-mail – mike@oldguns.co.uk; website – www.oldguns.co.uk. SER: Valuations. FAIRS: London Arms; International Arms; Park Lane Arms; Bisley Arms.

The Old Malthouse `BADA`

15 Bridge St. RG17 0EG. (P.F.Hunwick). CINOA. Est. 1963. Open 10-5.30. SIZE: Large. *STOCK: 18th to early 19th C walnut and mahogany furniture – dining tables, sets of chairs, mirrors, chests of drawers; clocks, barometers, decorative items and glass.* Not Stocked: Orientalia. LOC: A338, left at Bear Hotel, shop is approx. 120 yards on left, just before bridge. PARK: Front of premises. TEL: 01488 682209; fax – same; e-mail – hunwick@oldmalthouse30.freeserve.co.uk. SER: Valuations. FAIRS: Chelsea (March, Sept). VAT: Spec.

Principia Fine Art

35A High St. RG17 0NF. (Michael Forrer). Est. 1970. Open 9.30-5.30. SIZE: Large. *STOCK: Collectors items, scientific instruments, maritime, country furniture, treen, pictures, Oriental china, porcelain, books and clocks.* PARK: Easy. TEL: 01488 682873; fax – 01189 341989; e-mail – majingforrer@yahoo.com.cn. SER: Valuations. FAIRS: Scientific Instrument. VAT: Spec.

Styles Silver `LAPADA`

12 Bridge St. RG17 0EH. (P. and D. Styles). Est. 1974. Open 9.30-5.30, other times by appointment. SIZE: Medium. *STOCK: Antique, Victorian and secondhand silver including cutlery.* PARK: Easy. TEL: 01488 683922; home – same; fax – 01488 683488; mobile – 07778 769559; e-mail – dpgstyles@btinternet.com; website – www.styles-silver.co.uk. SER: Repairs; finder.

Turpins Antiques `BADA` `LAPADA`

17 Bridge St. RG17 0EG. (Jane Sumner). CINOA. Open Wed., Fri. and Sat. or by appointment. SIZE: Small. *STOCK: 17th-18th C walnut, oak and mahogany furniture and metalware.* TEL: 01488 681886; home – 01672 870727. FAIRS: Olympia. VAT: Spec.

Youll's Antiques

28 Charnham St. RG17 0EJ. (B.Youll). Est. 1935. Open 10.30-5.30, Sun. 11-5. *STOCK: French and*

English furniture and decorative items. TEL: 01488 682046; fax – 01488 684335; e-mail – bruce.youll@virgin.net; website – www.youll.com. FAIRS: Newark.

HURST, Nr. Reading

Peter Shepherd Antiques

Penfold, Lodge Rd. RG10 0EG. Est. 1962. Open by appointment. *STOCK: Glass, rarities and books.* TEL: 0118 934 0755.

LECKHAMPSTEAD, Nr. Newbury

Hill Farm Antiques

Hill Farm, Shop Lane. RG20 8QG. (Mike Beesley). Open 9-5, Sun. by appointment. *STOCK: 19th C dining tables, chairs and library furniture.* LOC: Off B4494 between Stag public house and church. PARK: Own at rear. TEL: 01488 638541/638361; website: www.hillfarmantiques.co.uk. SER: Restorations; shipping arranged; buys at auction.

MAIDENHEAD

Widmerpool House Antiques

7 Lower Cookham Rd., Boulters Lock. SL6.

(M.L. Coleman). Open by appointment. *STOCK: English furniture, oil paintings, watercolours, prints; porcelain and Swansea pottery, glass, silver, 18th-19th C.* PARK: Nearby. TEL: 01628 623752.

MIDGHAM, Nr. Reading

Berkshire Antiques Centre
Unit 1 Kennetholme Farm Buildings, Bath Rd. RG7 5UX. (J. Bradley). Est. 2000. Open 10.30-4.30 including Sun. CL: Wed. SIZE: Medium. *STOCK: Antique and reproduction furniture, smalls including china, glass and collectables; garden art and artifacts.* LOC: A4 London to Newbury road. PARK: Easy. TEL: 01189 710477; fax – same; e-mail – enquiries@berkshire-antiques.fsnet. co.uk. FAIRS: Ardingly, Kempton.

PANGBOURNE

Rita Butler
4 Station Rd. RG8 7AN. TVADA. Est. 1999. Open Tues.-Sat. 10-5. SIZE: 2 floors. *STOCK: General antiques including small furniture especially oak; early 19th C to early 20th C ceramics especially Art Deco; glass, early 1800s; silver.* PARK: Opposite. TEL: 01189 845522; mobile – 07752 936327; e-mail – rbutler@amserve.com. FAIRS: TVADA; Thames; Silhouette: Jay.

READING

Fanny's Antiques
1 Lynmouth Rd. RG1 8DE. (Julia Lyons). Est. 1988. Open 10.30-4, Sun. 12-4. SIZE: Large. *STOCK: Decorative, period and new furniture, smalls.* PARK: Easy. TEL: 01189 508261; home – 01491 671471. SER: Valuations; restorations. FAIRS: House & Gardens; Battersea Decorative.

Rupert Landen Antiques
Church Farm, Reading Rd., Woodcote. RG8 0QX. TVADA. Open 9-5, Sat. 10-3. CL: Mon. *STOCK: Late 18th to early 19th C furniture.* TEL: 01491 682396; mobile – 07974 732472.

P.D. Leatherland Antiques
68 London St. RG1 4SQ. (Susan, Paul and Peter Leatherland). Est. 1970. Open 9-6, Sun. 10-5.30. SIZE: Large. *STOCK: Furniture, 18th C to 1920's; decorative china, clocks, metalware, mirrors and pictures, £5-£4,000.* LOC: 1/2 mile from rail station. PARK: Easy. TEL: 0118 958 1960. VAT: Stan/Spec.

SANDHURST

Berkshire Metal Finishers Ltd
3 Factory, Vulcan Close. GU47 9DD. (J.A. and Mrs. J. Sturgeon). Est. 1957. Open 8-1 and 2-6, Sat. 8-1 and 2-4, Sun. 9-1. SIZE: Large. *STOCK: Brass, copper and steel metalware; silver plate.* LOC: Off A30 towards Wokingham on A321, after 1.25 miles turn left into Swan Lane, estate 1st turning right, last factory near car park. PARK: Easy. TEL: 01252 873475; fax – 01252 875434. SER: Restorations (metalware polishing and lacquering).

SONNING-ON-THAMES

Cavendish Fine Arts   BADA
The Dower House. RG4 6UL. (Janet Middlemiss and Guy Hazel). TVADA. Est. 1972. Open by appointment. *STOCK: Fine Queen Anne and English Georgian furniture, glass and porcelain.* LOC: 5 mins. from M4. TEL: 01189 691904; mobile – 07831 295575; e-mail – janet@cavendishfinearts.com; website – www. cavendishfinearts.com. SER: Valuations; shipping; interior decoration. FAIRS: Olympia; Chelsea; BADA; TVADA. VAT: Stan/Spec.

TWYFORD, Nr. Reading

Bell Antiques
2B High St. RG10 9AE. (Nigel, Chris and Russell Timms). Est. 1989. Open 9.30-5.30, Sun. 10-5.30. SIZE: Small. *STOCK: General antiques including china and glass, silver and plate, small furniture, 18th-20th C, £10-£300.* LOC: Village centre on crossroads. PARK: Nearby. TEL: 0118 934 2501. VAT: Spec.

WARFIELD

Moss End Antique Centre
Moss End Garden Centre. RG12 6EJ. TVADA. Est. 1988. Open 10.30-5. CL: Mon. SIZE: Large – 25 dealers. *STOCK: General antiques and collectables.* LOC: A3095. PARK: Own. TEL: 01344 861942; website – www.mossendantiques. co.uk. FAIRS: TVADA (Spring and Autumn).

WARGRAVE

John Connell – Wargrave Antiques
66 High St. RG10 8BY. Est. 1979. Open Wed.-Sun. other times by appointment. SIZE: Large – several

dealers. *STOCK: Furniture, Georgian-Edwardian; small items, china, glass, metal.* PARK: Nearby. TEL: 01189 402914. SER: Restorations (furniture); silver plating; metal polishing.

Ferry Antiques
70 High St. RG10 8BY. (Kate and Peter Turner). Est. 1982. Open 10-5.30, Sun. 10.30-4.30. CL: Mon. and Tues. SIZE: Medium. *STOCK: Furniture, 18th-19th C, £250-£5,000; glass and porcelain, 18th-19th C, £25-£500; silver and plate, 19th C, £50-£1,000.* LOC: At crossroads. PARK: 100 yards. TEL: 01189 404415; e-mail – kasiapj@aol.com. SER: Valuations; restorations (furniture and clocks). FAIRS: East Berkshire, Burchetts Green.

WINDSOR AND ETON

Art & Antiques and Bridge Miniatures
69 High St., Eton. SL4 6AA. (Vivien and Eddie Rand). Est. 1982. Open 10.30-5.30, Sat. 10.30-6, Sun. 2.30-6. SIZE: Medium. *STOCK: Collectors' items, jewellery, furniture, dolls house miniatures, from Victorian, £1-£600.* LOC: 1st shop over Thames from Windsor at Eton. PARK: Nearby. TEL: 01753 855727; home – 01628 527127. SER: Restorations (furniture, dolls houses, jewellery).

Roger Barnett Antiques
91 High St., Eton. SL4 6AF. Est. 1975. Open by appointment. *STOCK: Mahogany furniture and clocks.* TEL: 01753 867785/541861.

Berkshire Antiques Co Ltd
42 Thames St., Windsor. SL4 1YY. Est. 1980. Open 10.30-5.30 including Sun. (Jan. to April – Sun. by appointment). SIZE: Large. *STOCK: Antique and modern designer jewellery; general antiques, china, porcelain and glass, silver and plate, Royal commemoratives, toys and dolls, £10-£25,000.* LOC: Opposite George V memorial fountain. PARK: Nearby. TEL: 01753 830100; fax – 01753 832278; e-mail – sales@jewels2go. co.uk; website – www.jewels2go.co.uk. SER: Valuations; repairs.

Dee's Antique Pine
89 Grove Rd. SL4 1HT. (Dee Waghorn). Est. 1975. Open Wed.-Sat. 10-6, Sun. 11-3, other times by appointment. SIZE: Medium. *STOCK: 19th to early 20th C pine wardrobes and chests of drawers.* LOC: 5 mins. from town centre. PARK: Easy. TEL: 01753 865627; mobile – 07711 902887; e-mail – dee@deesantiquepine.fsnet.co.uk. SER: Free storage, local delivery and wardrobe assembly.

Eton Antique Bookshop
88 High St., Eton. SL4 6AF. (Maurice Bastians). Est. 1975. Usually 10-5.30 and Sun.pm. SIZE: Medium. *STOCK: Secondhand and antiquarian books; antiquarian prints.* PARK: Easy and at rear. TEL: 01753 855534. SER: Book search and repairs.

Eton Antiques Partnership
80 High St., Eton. SL4 6AF. (Mark Procter). Est. 1967. Open 10-5, Sun. 11-5.30. SIZE: Large. *STOCK: Mahogany and rosewood furniture, 18th-19th C.* LOC: Slough East exit from M4 westbound. PARK: Nearby. TEL: 01753 860752; home – same. SER: Exporting; interior design consultants. VAT: Stan/Spec.

Marcelline Herald Antiques   LAPADA
41 High St., Eton. SL4 6BD. TVADA. Est. 1993. Open Tues.,Thurs., Fri. and Sat. 10-5, other days by appointment. SIZE: Medium. *STOCK:*

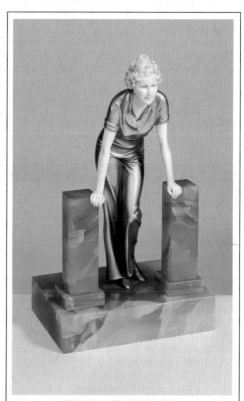

F. Preiss, The Stile, 9¼in.

From an article entitled "Art Deco Figures" by Bryan Catley which appeared in the May 2003 issue of *Antique Collecting*. For more details and to subscribe see page 21.

Furniture, £500-£15,000; mirrors, pelmets and screens, £200-£2,500; ceramics, lamps and prints, £50-£1,000; all 18th to early 19th C. PARK: Loading and nearby. TEL: 01753 833924; fax – 0118 971 4683; home – same. FAIRS: TVADA; Decorative Antiques & Textile. VAT: Spec.

J. Manley
27 High St., Eton. SL4 6AX. Est. 1891. Open 10-5. STOCK: Watercolours, old prints. TEL: 01753 865647. SER: Restorations; framing; mounting.

Peter J. Martin
LAPADA
40 High St., Eton. SL4 6BD. (Peter J. Martin & Son). TVADA. Est. 1963. Open 9-1 and 2-5. CL: Sun. SIZE: Large and warehouse. STOCK: Period, Victorian and decorative furniture and furnishings, £50-£20,000; metalware, £10-£500, all from 1800. PARK: 50yds. opposite. TEL: 01753 864901; home – 01753 863987; e-mail – pjmartin.antiques@btopenworld.com; website – www.pjmartin-antiques.co.uk. SER: Restorations; shipping arranged; buys at auction. VAT: Stan/Spec.

Mostly Boxes
93 High St., Eton. SL4 6AF. (G.S. Munday). Est. 1977. Open 10-6.30. STOCK: Wooden, mother of pearl and tortoiseshell boxes. PARK: 100 yds. TEL: 01753 858470. SER: Restorations (boxes). VAT: Spec.

O'Connor Brothers
Trinity Yard, 59 St. Leonards Rd., Windsor. SL4 3BX. (Bernard O'Connor). Est. 1970. Open 10-5.30. STOCK: Furniture and general antiques. LOC: 5 mins. from the castle. PARK: Easy. TEL: 01753 866732/869852. SER: Restorations; upholstery. VAT: Stan.

Oriental Rug Gallery Ltd
115-116 High St., Eton. SL4 6AN. (Richard Mathias and Julian Blair). BORDA. Est. 1989. Open 10-5.30. SIZE: Large. STOCK: Old and new Russian, Afghan, Turkish and Persian carpets, rugs and kelims; Oriental objets d'art. PARK: Behind showroom. TEL: 01753 623000; fax – same; e-mail – rugs@orientalruggallery.com; website – www.orientalruggallery.com. SER: Cleaning; repairs.

Rules Antiques
62 St Leonard's Rd. SL4 3BY. (Sue Rule and Kathryn Cale). Open 10.30-6. STOCK: Lighting, door furniture, period fixtures & fittings; unusual small furniture. LOC: Next to Arts Centre. PARK: Meters. TEL: 01753 833210.

Studio 101
101 High St., Eton. SL4 6AF. (Anthony Cove). Est. 1959. SIZE: Medium. STOCK: Mahogany furniture, some 18th C, mainly 19th C, £50-£1,000; brass, silver plate, 19th C, £10-£200. LOC: Walk over Windsor Bridge from Windsor and Eton Riverside rail station. PARK: Public, at rear of premises. TEL: 01753 863333.

Times Past Antiques
59 High St., Eton. SL4 6BL. (P. Jackson). MBHI. Est. 1970. Open 10-6, Sun. 12-5. SIZE: Medium. STOCK: Clocks and music boxes, £100-£3,000. PARK: Reasonable. TEL: 01753 857018; home – same; e-mail – philliptimespast@aol.com. SER: Valuations; restorations (clocks and watches); buys at auction (clocks). VAT: Stan/Spec.

Turks Head Antiques
98 High St., Eton. SL4 6AF. Open 10-5. CL: Mon. STOCK: Silver and plate, porcelain, glass and interesting collectables. TEL: 01753 863939.

WOKINGHAM

Wokingham Antiques Centre
152 London Rd. RG40 1SU. (Elisabeth Ballard). Est. 1998. Open 10.30-5.30, 1st Sun. monthly 9-4.30, other times by appointment. CL: Wed. SIZE: Small. STOCK: Furniture, 18th C to 1950's, £50-£2,500; curios, £1-£1,000; porcelain, pottery and silver, to modern collectables, £1-£500. LOC: Off A329, follow signs for town centre, first shop on right opposite St. Crispin's school. PARK: Easy. TEL: 0118 9790202. SER: Restorations (caning, small upholstery, wood); buys at auction.

WOOLHAMPTON, Nr. Reading

The Old Bakery Antiques
Bath Rd. RG7 5RE. (S. Everard). Resident. Est. 1969. Open 10.30-5.30 including Sun. SIZE: Medium. STOCK: Furniture, objets d'art, collectors' items, general antiques. PARK: Easy. TEL: 0118 9712116. FAIRS: Newark; Ardingly.

WRAYSBURY

Wyrardisbury Antiques
23 High St. TW19 5DA. (C. Tuffs). Est. 1978. Open 10-5. CL: Mon. except by appointment. SIZE: Small. STOCK: Clocks, £100-£6,000; barometers, small furniture, £100-£1,500. LOC: A376 from Staines by-pass (A30) or from junction 5 M4/A4 via B470, then B376. PARK: Easy. TEL: 01784 483225. SER: Restorations (clocks).

BUCKINGHAMSHIRE

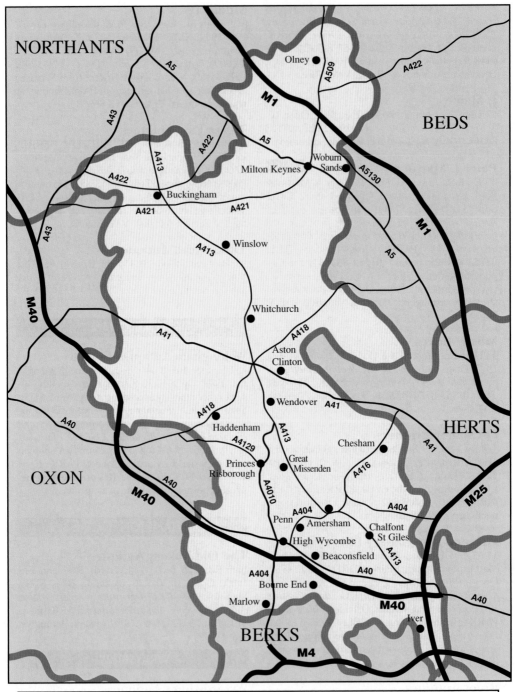

Dealers and Shops in Buckinghamshire

				Milton Keynes	1
Amersham	4	Chesham	6	Olney	4
Aston Clinton	1	Great Missenden	2	Penn	2
Beaconsfield	5	Haddenham	1	Princes Risborough	1
Bourne End	2	High Wycombe	3	Wendover	2
Buckingham	1	Iver	1	Whitchurch	1
Chalfont St. Giles	2	Marlow	2	Winslow	1

AMERSHAM

Carlton Clocks
Station Rd., Little Chalfont. HP7 9PP. (Ian Cherkas). BWCG. Est. 1981. Open 9-5.30, Sat. 9-4. *STOCK: Longcase, mantel, wall and carriage clocks, barometers and pocket watches, from 1700's to reproduction, £200-£10,000.* PARK: Easy. TEL: 01494 763793; fax – 01494 764989; e-mail – info@ukclocks.com; website – www. ukclocks.com. SER: Valuations; restorations (clocks, watches and barometers).

The Cupboard Antiques   LAPADA
80 High St., Old Amersham. HP7 0DS. (N. and C. Lucas). Est. 1965. Open 10-5. CL: Fri. SIZE: 4 showrooms. *STOCK: Georgian, Regency and early Victorian furniture and decorative items.* PARK: Easy. TEL: 01494 722882. FAIRS: Olympia (June).

Michael and Jackie Quilter
38 High St. HP7 0DJ. Est. 1970. Open 10-5. SIZE: 3 floors. *STOCK: General antiques, stripped pine, copper, brass, unusual objects.* PARK: Easy. TEL: 01494 433723; e-mail – jackie@quilters-antiques.fsnet.co.uk. SER: Free local delivery. VAT: Stan.

Sundial Antiques
19 Whielden St. HP7 0HU. (A. and Mrs M. Macdonald). Est. 1970. Open 9.30-5.30. CL: Thurs. SIZE: Small. *STOCK: English and European brass, copper, metalware, fireplace equipment, 18th-19th C, £5-£500; small period furniture, 1670-1910, £25-£1,500; horse brasses, £10-£300; decorative items, 1750-1910, £5-£500; pottery, porcelain, curios, pre-1930, £10-£750.* Not Stocked: Jewellery, clocks, coins, oil paintings, stamps, books, silver, firegrates. LOC: On A404, in Old Town 200yds. from High St. on right; from High Wycombe, 500yds. from hospital on left. PARK: Easy. TEL: 01494 727955.

ASTON CLINTON

Dismantle and Deal Direct – Architectural Salvage Brokers
108 London Rd. HP22 5HS. (Tony Pattison). Est. 1992. Open 9-5, Sat. 9-1. SIZE: Large *STOCK: Doors, glass, 18th C to 1930, £5-£1,000; fireplaces, marble and stone, 18th C to 1920, £500-£3,000; garden ornaments, 19th C to 1950, £1,000-£2,000.* LOC: Off M25 junction 20, take A41. PARK: Easy. TEL: 01296 632300; fax – 01923 282214; e-mail – info@dismandealdirect.com; website – www. dismandealdirect.com. SER: Restorations (glass, marble, stone). VAT: Stan/ Spec.

Buck House Antique Centre

47 Wycombe End, Old Town. HP9 1LZ. (C. and
B. Whitby). Est. 1979. Open 10-5, Sun. 12-4. CL:
Wed. SIZE: Medium – 10 dealers. *STOCK: Wide
variety of general antiques including English and
Oriental porcelain, clocks, barometers, oak and
mahogany furniture, boxes and beds, to 1930's,
£5-£5,000.* LOC: A40. PARK: Easy. TEL: 01494
670714; e-mail – bachantiques@supanet.com.
SER: Valuations.

Ellison Fine Art   `BADA`

(Claudia Hill). Est. 2000. Open by appointment. *STOCK: 16th-19th C portrait miniatures,
enamels and silhouettes, English and Continental, £250-£20,000+.* PARK: Easy. TEL:
01494 678880; home – 01494 670053; mobile –
07720 317899; e-mail – claudia.hill@ellison
fineart.co.uk; website – www.ellisonfineart.
com. SER: Valuations; restorations (framing,
glazing and conservation). FAIRS: BADA,
Chelsea; Olympia; Harrogate.

June Elsworth – Beaconsfield Ltd

Clover House, 16 London End. HP9 2JH. (Mrs J.
Elsworth). Est. 1983. CL: Mon. SIZE: Large.
*STOCK: Fine English furniture, 18th-19th C;
decorative accessories and silver, 19th C; oil
paintings, 19th-20th C.* LOC: In old town, on
A40. PARK: Easy. TEL: 01494 675611; fax –
01494 671273. VAT: Spec.

Grosvenor House Interiors

51 Wycombe End, Beaconsfield Old Town. HP9
1LX. (T.I. Marriott). Est. 1970. Open 10-1 and 2-
5. CL: Wed. SIZE: Large. *STOCK: 18th-19th C
furniture especially upholstered and mid-19th C
walnut; fireplaces and accessories; 19th C
watercolours and oils.* PARK: Easy. TEL: 01494
677498. SER: Interior architectural design,
fireplace specialists. VAT: Stan/Spec.

Period Furniture Showrooms

49 London End. HP9 2HW. (R.E.W. Hearne and
N.J. Hearne). TVADA. Est. 1965. Open Mon.-
Sat. 9-5.30. SIZE: Large. *STOCK: Furniture,
1700-1900, £50-£5,000.* LOC: A40 Beaconsfield
Old Town. PARK: Own. TEL: 01494 674112; fax
– 01494 681046; e-mail – sales@periodfurniture.
net; website – www.periodfurniture.net. SER:
Restorations (furniture). VAT: Stan/Spec.

Bourne End Antiques Centre

67 The Parade. SL8 5SB. (S. Shepheard). Est.

1995. Open 10-5.30, Sun. 12-4. SIZE: Large.
*STOCK: Furniture – pine, £100-£900, darkwood,
£100-£800; both from 19th C; china and glass,
£1-£250.* LOC: A4155, 2 miles from Marlow.
PARK: Easy. TEL: 01628 533298; home – 01300
320125. VAT: Stan.

La Maison

The Crossings, Cores End Rd. SL8 5AL. (Jeremy
D. Pratt). Est. 1995. Open 9.30-5.30, Mon. 1-5,
Sat. 10-5.30, Sun. 11-5. SIZE: Medium. *STOCK:
French antiques including beds and chandeliers,
19th C, to £1,000.* LOC: Take Marlow by-pass
from junction 3, M40. PARK: Easy. TEL: 01628
525858; fax – 01494 670363. SER: Valuations;
restorations (re-upholstery). FAIRS: Burchetts
Green. VAT: Stan/Spec.

Buckingham Antiques Centre

5 West St. MK18 1HL. (Peter Walton). Est. 1975.
Open 9.15-5.30, Sat. 9-5.30, Wed. and Sun. by
appointment. SIZE: Medium. *STOCK: Furniture,
19th C, £50-£1,000; clocks, 18th-20th C, £50-
£2,000; general antiques, £2-£500.* LOC: On
A422 towards Brackley, near town centre. PARK:
Nearby. TEL: 01280 824464; home – same; e-
mail – peterwalton@whsmith.net.co.uk. SER:
Valuations; restorations (clocks).

Gallery 23 Antiques

High St. HP9 4QH. (Mrs A. Vollaro). Est. 1991.
Open 10-5. *STOCK: Furniture, clocks, silver,
Continental and English porcelain, glass, paintings,
prints and watercolours, tapestry cushions.* TEL:
01494 871512.

T. Smith

The Furniture Village, London Rd. HP8 4NN.
Est. 1982. Open 10-5 including Sun. SIZE:
Medium. *STOCK: Antique pine and architectural
items.* LOC: Opposite Pheasant public house.
PARK: Easy. TEL: 01494 873031. SER: Valuations; restorations (including upholstery); buys
at auction (furniture).

Chess Antiques   `LAPADA`

85 Broad St. HP5 3EF. (M.P. Wilder). Est. 1966.
Open 9-5, Sat. 10-5. SIZE: Small. *STOCK: Fur-
niture and clocks.* PARK: Easy. TEL: 01494 783043.
SER: Valuations; restorations. VAT: Stan/Spec.

Omniphil Prints
Germains Lodge, Fullers Hill. HP5 1LR. (Ross Muddiman). Est. 1953. Open 9-5 by appointment. SIZE: Warehouse. *STOCK: Rare prints on all subjects and Illustrated London News from 1842.* PARK: Easy. TEL: 01494 771851; e-mail – omniphil@talk21.com.

Queen Anne House
57 Church St. HP5 1HY. (Miss A.E. Jackson). Est. 1918. Open Wed., Fri. and Sat. 9.30-5, other times by appointment. SIZE: Large. *STOCK: Furniture, decorative and furnishing pieces, porcelain figures, other china, glass, silver plate, copper, brass, Victoriana, Persian rugs.* Not Stocked: Silver, weapons, jewellery. PARK: Easy. TEL: 01494 783811. SER: Buys at auction.

The Sovereign Furniture Gallery
115 High St. HP5 1DE. (Mr and Mrs Leadbeater). Est. 1999. Open 10-5.30, Sun. 12-4. CL: Wed. SIZE: Large. *STOCK: Furniture, 18th to early 20th C, £25-£1,500.* LOC: A41 – Chesham turning on to A416 to High St. PARK: Nearby. TEL: 01494 783103. SER: Valuations; restorations (furniture including upholstery). FAIRS: NEC; Milton Keynes Centre.

Stuff and Nonsense
68-70 Broad St. HP5. (Elaine and Helen Robb). Open 9.30-5.30, Sun. 11-5.30. SIZE: Medium. *STOCK: General antiques and collectables – furniture including reproduction mahogany, books, commemoratives, records and clocks.* LOC: Just out of High St., on main road. PARK: Easy and at rear. TEL: 01494 775988; fax – same.

M.V. Tooley, CMBHI
at Chess Antiques, 85 Broad St. HP5 3EF. Est. 1960. Open 9-6, Sat. 10-5. SIZE: Small. *STOCK: Clocks and barometers.* TEL: 01494 783043. SER: Valuations; restorations; spare parts.

GREAT MISSENDEN

The Hampden Trading Company
The Old Barn, Solinger Farm, Little Hampden. HP16 9PT. (Callie Hope-Morley). Open by appointment. *STOCK: 18th-19th C country and painted furniture, textiles, pictures and decorative items.* TEL: 01494 488853; fax – 01494 488818.

Peter Wright Antiques
(Incorporating Missenden Restorations and Abbey Clocks & Repairs), 32b High St. HP16 0AU. Est. 1992. Open by appointment. SIZE: Small. *STOCK: Clocks, curios and furniture.* LOC: A413. PARK: Opposite. TEL: 01494 891330. SER: Restorations; repairs (clocks).

HADDENHAM

H.S. Wellby Ltd
The Malt House, Church End. HP17 8AH. (C.S.Wellby). BAPCR. Est. 1820. Open by appointment 9-6. *STOCK: 18th-19th C paintings.* TEL: 01844 290036. SER: Restorations. VAT: Spec.

HIGH WYCOMBE

Browns' of West Wycombe
Church Lane, West Wycombe. HP14 3AH. BFM. Est. Pre 1900. Open 8-5.30. CL: Sat. *STOCK: Furniture.* LOC: On A40 approximately 3 miles west of High Wycombe on Oxford Road. PARK: Easy. TEL: 01494 524537; fax – 01494 439548. SER: Restorations; hand-made copies of period chairs.

Glade Antiques
BADA LAPADA
PO Box 873. HP14 3PF. (Sonia Vaughan). CINOA. Open by appointment. *STOCK: Fine Oriental ceramics, bronzes and jades: Chinese items from Han, Tang, Song, Ming and Quing periods; Japanese items – mainly Kakiemon, Nabeshima, Kutani, Satsuma and Imari; also Korean Koryo, Yi and Choson periods.* TEL: 01494 882818; fax – 01628 487255; mobile – 07771 552328; e-mail – sonia@gladeantiques.com; website – www.gladeantiques.com. FAIRS: BADA; Olympia; LAPADA.

Windmill Fine Art
2 Windmill Drive, Widmer End. HP15 6BD. (Ray White). Open by appointment. *STOCK: Fine Victorian and early 20th C watercolours.* TEL: 01494 713757; fax – same; mobile – 07885 370408. SER: Valuations; commission search. FAIRS: Most major.

IVER

Yester-year
12 High St. SL0 9NG. (P.J. Frost). Resident. Est. 1969. Open 10-6. SIZE: Small. *STOCK: Furniture, porcelain, pottery, glass, metalwork, 18th to early 20th C.* PARK: Easy. TEL: 01753 652072. SER: Valuations; restorations (furniture and pictures); framing; buys at auction.

Jack Harness Antiques

Westfield Farm, Henley Rd., Medmenham. SL7. Est. 1981. Open 9-5 or by appointment. SIZE: Large warehouse. *STOCK: Pine and country furniture, especially period pine and original painted French provincial furniture.* PARK: Easy. TEL: 01491 410691; fax – 01491 410699; mobile – 07768 666833; home – 01628 471775; e-mail – jackharness@aol.com. SER: Restorations; courier. VAT: Stan/Spec. *Mainly Trade.*

Marlow Antique Centre

35 Station Rd. SL7 1NW. Est. 1995. Open 10.30-5, Sun. 11-4. SIZE: 30+ dealers. *STOCK: 18th-20th C furniture, collectors' china from Worcester to Clarice Cliff, Staffordshire figures and dogs, chandeliers, silver, decorative glass, writing slopes, tea caddies, postcards, pens, cuff-links, equestrian items, jewellery.* LOC: Town centre. PARK: Nearby. TEL: 01628 473223; fax – 01628 478989. SER: International packing and shipping.

Temple Lighting (Jeanne Temple Antiques)

Stockwell House, Wavendon. MK17 8LS. Est. 1968. Open 10-5, Sun. by appointment. CL: Mon. SIZE: Medium. *STOCK: Victorian, Edwardian and 1930's light fittings; 19th C furniture; decorative items.* LOC: Just off A5130 Woburn Sands to Newport Pagnell road. PARK: Easy. TEL: 01908 583597; fax – 01908 281149. FAIRS: Luton; Silsoe.

The Antiques Centre at Olney

13 Osborns Court, Off High St. South. MK46 4LA. (Robert Sklar). Open 10-5, Sun. 12-5. CL: Mon. SIZE: Large, 80 dealers. *STOCK: General antiques, furniture, porcelain.* LOC: Town centre. PARK: Easy. TEL: 01234 710942; fax – 01234 710947; website – www.antiques-of-britain.co.uk.

Archer's Antique and Country Furniture

Wood View Cottage, Yardley Rd. MK46 5EL. (Katherine Haslam and Neil Carter). Est. 1999. Open by appointment. *STOCK: 19th C English and Continental pine, mahogany, French and upholstered furniture, to £2,000.* PARK: TEL: 01234 713050; fax – same. VAT: Stan/Spec.

Pine Antiques

10 Market Place. MK46 4EA. (Linda Wilkinson). Est. 1976. Open 10-5, Sat. 9.30-5.30, Sun. 12-5. SIZE: 3 floors. *STOCK: Pine furniture, antique and reclaimed.* PARK: Easy. TEL: 01234 711065; 01908 510226; e-mail – pine-antiques@hotmail.com. SER: Restorations; bespoke furniture.

Robin Unsworth Antiques

1 Weston Rd. MK46 5BD. (R. and Z. M.

A teapot, cover and stand from the 'Horatia' service. £32,700. (Sotheby's)

From an article entitled "19th Century British Porcelain" by Fergus Gambon which appeared in the July/August 2002 issue of **Antique Collecting**. For more details and to subscribe see page 21.

ANTIQUES AT...WENDOVER
Datelined Antiques Centre
Established 1987

30 dealers in a period building offering
quality town and country antiques – car park

Monday – Saturday 10-5.30 Sundays & B. Hols 11-5.00

The Old Post Office, 25 High Street, Wendover, Bucks HP22 6DU
Tel: 01296 625335   www.antiquesatwendover.co.uk
Email: antiques@antiquesatwendover.co.uk

Unsworth). Est. 1971. Open 9-5, Sun. 9-4.30. SIZE: Small. *STOCK: Longcase and wall clocks, £500-£15,000; period and Victorian furniture, £1,000-£10,000; objects of art, £200-£5,000.* LOC: 6 miles from junction 14, M1. PARK: Easy. TEL: 01234 711210; home – 01908 617193. VAT: Spec.

PENN, Nr. High Wycombe

Penn Barn
By the Pond, Elm Rd. HP10 8LB. (P. J. M. Hunnings). Est. 1968. Open Tues.-Sat.10.30-4, (sometimes closed 1-2). SIZE: Medium. *STOCK: Antiquarian books, maps and prints, 19th C, £5-£500; watercolours and oils, 19th-20th C, £50-£1,500.* LOC: B474. PARK: Easy. TEL: 01494 815691.

Penn Village Antique Centre
3 Hazlemere Rd., Potters Cross. HP10 8AA. (M. and V. Thomas). Est. 1955. Open 10-5, Sun. 12-5. SIZE: Large. *STOCK: Many dealers selling a variety of specialist items.* LOC: B474. PARK: Easy. TEL: 01494 812244; home – same.

PRINCES RISBOROUGH

Well Cottage Antiques Centre
20-22 Bell St. HP27 0AD. Est. 1985. Open 10-5, Sun. and Bank Holidays 1-5. SIZE: 9 showrooms. *STOCK: Furniture including pine; silver, jewellery, china, glass, brass, copper, silhouettes, miniatures, treen, pictures and collectables.* LOC: A4010. TEL: 01844 342002.

WENDOVER

Antiques at . . .Wendover Antiques Centre
The Old Post Office, 25 High St. HP22 6DU. (N.

Gregory). Est. 1987. Open 10-5.30, Sun. and Bank Holidays 11-5. SIZE: Large – 30 dealers. *STOCK: General antiques dateline 1940/50 – town and country furniture, flatware, kitchenalia, gardenalia, pottery and porcelain, jewellery, Art Deco, Belleek, silver, lamps and lighting, clocks, barometers, telescopes, scientific and medical instruments, beds and bathroom fittings, decorative items, glass, metalware, lace and linen, garden statuary, architectural salvage and antiquities.* LOC: A431. PARK: Own. TEL: 01296 625335; fax – 01296 620401; e-mail – antiques@antiquesatwendover.co.uk; website – www.antiquesatwendover.co.uk. SER: Restorations (china and furniture); metal polishing.

Sally Turner Antiques **LAPADA**
Hogarth House, High St. HP22 6DU. TVADA. Open 10-5. CL: Wed. and Sun. except Dec. SIZE: 7 showrooms + barn. *STOCK: Decorative and period furniture, general antiques and jewellery.* PARK: Own. TEL: 01296 624402; fax – same; mobile – 07860 201718.

WHITCHURCH

Deerstalker Antiques
28 High St. HP22 4JT. (R.J. and L.L. Eichler). Est. 1980. Open 10-5.30. CL: Mon. SIZE: Small. *STOCK: General antiques.* PARK: Easy. TEL: 01296 641505. SER: Restorations (furniture pre 1880). FAIRS: Milton Keynes.

WINSLOW

Winslow Antiques Centre
15 Market Sq. MK18 3AB. Est. 1992. Open 10-5, Sun. 1-5. CL: Wed. SIZE: 20 dealers. *STOCK: Furniture, English pottery, silver and jewellery, general antiques.* LOC: A413. TEL: 01296 714540; fax – 01296 714556.

CAMBRIDGESHIRE

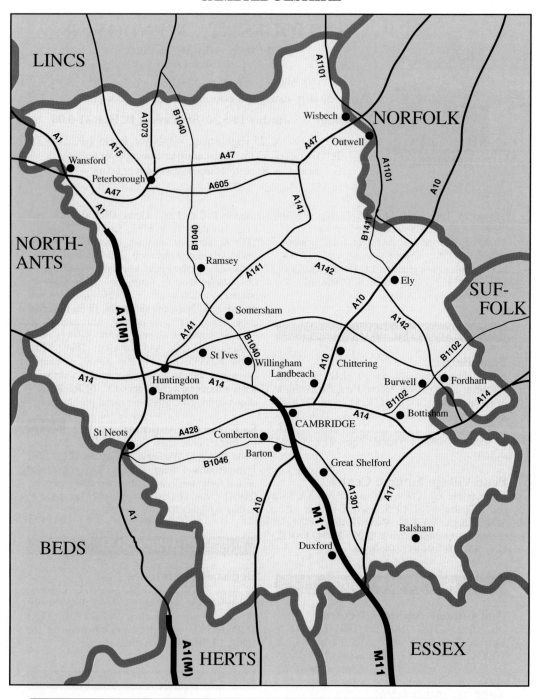

Dealers and Shops in Cambridgeshire

Balsham	1	Chittering	1	Huntingdon	1	St. Ives	1
Barton	1	Comberton	1	Landbeach	1	St. Neots	1
Bottisham	1	Duxford	1	Outwell	1	Wansford	1
Brampton	1	Ely	7	Peterborough	4	Willingham	1
Burwell	1	Fordham	1	Ramsey	2	Wisbech	4
Cambridge	15	Great Shelford	1	Somersham	1		

BALSHAM, Nr. Cambridge

Ward Thomas Antiques
7 High St. CB1 6DJ. (Christian Ward Thomas). Est. 1997. Open 9-5, Sat. 10-5, Sun. 10-4. *STOCK: Pine furniture, £210-£950.* LOC: Village centre, opposite primary school. TEL: 01223 892431; fax – 01223 892367; mobile – 07887 986566; e-mail – christian@ward-thomas.fsnet. co.uk. SER: Valuations; restorations (pine).

BARTON, Nr. Cambridge

Bagatelle Antiques
Burwash Manor Barns, New Rd. CB3 7AY. (A. M. and M. H. Jeffery). Est. 1998. Open 10-5, Sat. 2-5, Sun. by appointment. SIZE: Medium. *STOCK: Furniture, 19th C, £100-£2,000; decorative items, 19th C to 1930's, £10-£250.* LOC: Signed from New Rd. PARK: Easy. TEL: 01223 264400; fax – 01223 264445. SER: Restorations (furniture including re-caning).

BOTTISHAM, Nr. Cambridge

Cambridge Pine
Hall Farm, Lode Rd. CB5 9DN. (Mr and Mrs D. Weir). Est. 1980. Open seven days. SIZE: Large. *STOCK: Pine, 18th-19th C and reproduction, £25-£2,000.* LOC: Midway between Bottisham and Lode, near Anglesey Abbey. PARK: Easy. TEL: 01223 811208; home – same; e-mail – cambridgepine@btconnect.com; website – www. cambridgepine.co.uk. SER: Copies made in old timber with or without painted finish.

BRAMPTON, Nr. Huntingdon

David's
The Old Forge, 41 High St. PE28 4TG. (David Clark and David Collet). Est. 1957. Open Fri. and Sat. 10-4.30, Sun. 11-4. SIZE: Medium. *STOCK: English furniture, 18th-19th C.* PARK: Easy. TEL: 01480 434389; fax – same. SER: Valuations; buys at auction. VAT: Spec.

BURWELL

Peter Norman Antiques and Restorations
Sefton House, 55 North St. CB5 0BA. (P. Norman and A. Marpole). Est. 1975. Open 9-12.30 and 2-5.30. SIZE: Medium. *STOCK: Furniture, clocks, arms and Oriental rugs, 17th-19th C, £250-*

£10,000. PARK: Easy. TEL: 01638 616914. SER: Valuations; restorations (furniture, oil paintings, clocks and arms). VAT: Spec.

CAMBRIDGE

Jess Applin Antiques   BADA
8 Lensfield Rd. CB2 1EG. Est. 1968. Open 10-5. *STOCK: Furniture, 17th-19th C; works of art.* **LOC: At junction with Hills Rd. opposite church. PARK: Pay and display nearby. TEL: 01223 315168. VAT: Spec.**

John Beazor and Sons Ltd   BADA
78-80 Regent St. CB2 1DP. Est. 1875. Open 9.15-5, Sat. 10-5 and by appointment. *STOCK: English furniture, late 17th to early 19th C; clocks, barometers and period accessories.* PARK: Pay & Display and multi-storey. TEL: 01223 355178; fax – 01223 355183; e-mail – martin@johnbeazorantiques.co.uk; website – www.johnbeazorantiques.co.uk. SER: Valuations; sourcing.

The Bookshop
24 Magdalen St. CB3 0AF. (Hugh Hardinge and Peter Bright). Open 10.30-5.30. SIZE: Medium. *STOCK: Secondhand and antiquarian books.* LOC: North of river. PARK: Meters. TEL: 01223 362457; e-mail – peter.bright@care4free.net.

Buckies   LAPADA
31 Trinity St. CB2 1TB. (G. McClure-Buckie). NAG. GMC. Est. 1972. Open 9.45-5. CL: Mon. SIZE: Medium. *STOCK: Jewellery, silver, objets d'art.* PARK: Multi-storey nearby. TEL: 01223 357910. SER: Valuations; restorations; repairs. VAT: Stan/Spec.

Cambridge Fine Art Ltd   LAPADA
Priesthouse, 33 Church St., Little Shelford. CB2 5HG. (R. and J. Lury). Resident. Est. 1972. Open daily 10-6, Sun. by appointment. SIZE: Large. *STOCK: British and European paintings, 1780-1900; modern British paintings, 1880-1940; British prints by J.M. Kronheim to the Baxter Process.* LOC: Next to church. PARK: Easy. TEL: 01223 842866/843537. SER: Valuations; restorations; buys at auction. VAT: Stan/Spec.

Gabor Cossa Antiques
34 Trumpington St. CB2 1QY. (D. Theobald). Est. 1948. Open 10-6. *STOCK: English ceramics, glass, bijouterie.* LOC: Opposite Fitzwilliam Museum. PARK: 400yds. TEL: 01223 356049. VAT: Global.

Peter Crabbe Antiques
3 Pembroke St. CB2 3QY. Open 10-4.30. *STOCK: Furniture and Oriental porcelain and works of art.* TEL: 01223 357117. VAT: Spec.

G. David
16 St. Edward's Passage. CB2 3PJ. (D.C. Asplin, N.T. Adams and B.L. Collings). ABA. PBFA. Est. 1896. Open 9-5. *STOCK: Antiquarian books, fine bindings, secondhand and out of print books, selected publishers remainders.* LOC: 100 yards from Market Sq. PARK: Lion Yard. TEL: 01223 354619.

Galloway and Porter Ltd
30 Sidney St. CB2 3HS. ABA. Est. 1900. *STOCK: Antiquarian and secondhand books.* TEL: 01223 367876.

Gwydir Street Antiques Centre
Units 1 & 2 Dales Brewery, Gwydir St. CB1 2LJ. (Pamela Gibb). Est. 1994. Open 10-5, Sat. 10-5.30, Sun. 11-5. SIZE: Medium. *STOCK: Victorian and Edwardian furniture in mahogany, walnut, pine, satinwood and oak; upholstered arm chairs and sofas; lamps, mirrors and other decorative items.* LOC: Off Mill Rd. PARK: Opposite. TEL: 01223 356391.

The Hive
Unit 3, Dales Brewery, Gwydir St. CB1 2LG. (B. Blakemore and A. Morgan). Open 10-5, Sun. 11-5. SIZE: 11 dealers. *STOCK: Victorian and Edwardian furniture, antique pine, kitchenalia, period lighting, pictures, ceramics, tiles, costume jewellery and Oriental rugs.* LOC: Off Mill Rd. PARK: Opposite. TEL: 01223 300269.

Sarah Key
The Haunted Bookshop, 9 St. Edward's Passage. CB2 3PJ. PBFA. Est. 1987. Open 10-5. *STOCK: Children's and illustrated books, literature and antiquarian.* LOC: City centre. PARK: Lion Yard multi-storey. TEL: 01223 312913; e-mail – sarahkey@hauntedbooks.demon.co.uk.SER: Shipping. FAIRS: Major UK.

The Lawson Gallery
7-8 King's Parade. CB2 1SJ. (Leslie J. and Lucinda J. Lawson). FATG. Est. 1967. Open 9.30-5.30. SIZE: Medium. *STOCK: Posters, prints, limited editions, original artwork, specialists in antiquarian and modern prints of Cambridge.* LOC: Opposite King's College. PARK: Lion Yard. TEL: 01223 313970. VAT: Stan.

Solopark Plc
Station Rd., Pampisford. CB2 4HB. (R.J. Bird). SALVO. Est. 1976. Open 8-5, Fri. and Sat. 8-4, Sun. 9-1. *STOCK: Traditional and new building materials, timber and period architectural items.* PARK: Easy. TEL: 01223 834663; fax – 01223 834780; e-mail – info@solopark.co.uk; website – www.solopark.co.uk.

Those were the Days
91-93 Mill Rd. CB1 2AW. Est. 1984. Open 10-5, Sat. 9.30-5.30, Sun. 11-5. SIZE: Medium. *STOCK: General antiques including furniture, period lighting and fireplaces, 19th C, £5-£1,500.* LOC: Opposite St. Barnabas Church. PARK: Pay & Display. TEL: 01223 300440.

CHITTERING, Nr. Cambridge

Simon and Penny Rumble Antiques
LAPADA

Causeway End Farmhouse. CB5 9PW. Open by appointment. *STOCK: Early oak, country furniture, woodcarving and works of art.* LOC: 6 miles north of Cambridge, off A10. TEL: 01223 861831.

COMBERTON

Comberton Antiques
5a West St. CB3 7DS. (Mrs M. McEvoy). Est. 1980. Open Mon., Fri. and Sat. 10-5, Sun. 2-5. SIZE: Large. *STOCK: Furniture, 1780-1920, £50-£2,000; bric-a-brac, 1830-1920, £5-£100; hand-made Turkish kelims; shipping goods.* LOC: 6 miles west of Cambridge, 2 miles junction 12, M11. PARK: Easy. TEL: 01223 262674; home – 01223 263457. VAT: Margin.

DUXFORD

Riro D. Mooney
4 Moorfield Rd. CB2 4PS. Est. 1946. Open 9-6.30. SIZE: Medium. *STOCK: General antiques, 1780-1920, £5-£2,600.* LOC: 1 mile from M11. PARK: Easy. TEL: 01223 832252; website – www.riromooney-antiques.com. SER: Restorations (furniture). VAT: Stan/Spec.

ELY

Cloisters Antiques
1A Lynn Rd. CB7 4EG. (Barry Lonsdale). PBFA. Est. 1999. Open 10-4.30, Sun. 12.30-4.30. CL: Wed. SIZE: Small. *STOCK: Small antiques and collectables, paintings and clocks; antiquarian and secondhand books.* LOC: Opposite Lamb Inn, close to cathedral. PARK: St Mary's St. TEL:

01353 668558; mobile – 07767 881677; e-mail – cloisters.antiques@virgin.net; website – www.cloistersantiques.co.uk

Sara Lemkow Antiques

Waterside Antiques Centre, The Wharf. CB7 4AU. Est. 1962. Open 9.30-5.30 including Bank Holidays, Sun. 11-4.30. SIZE: Small. *STOCK: French enamel and English kitchenalia, copper and brass, scales and weights, oil lamps.* LOC: River edge. PARK: Easy. TEL: 01353 667066; fax – 01284 735161; mobile – 07789 405635; e-mail – rachel.lemkov@btinternet.com; website – www.antique-kitchenalia.co.uk. FAIRS: Newark.

Mrs Mills Antiques

1a St. Mary's St. CB7 4ER. Est. 1968. Open 10-5. CL: Tues. SIZE: Small. *STOCK: China, jewellery, silver.* Not Stocked: Furniture. LOC: Near cathedral. PARK: Nearby. TEL: 01353 664268.

Rookery Farm Antiques

Waterside Antiques Centre, The Wharf. CB7 4AU. (Rachel Lemkov). Est. 1972. Open 9.30-5.30 including Bank Holidays, Sun. 11-4.30. SIZE: Small. *STOCK: Stripped and painted pine and decorative items.* LOC: River edge. PARK: Easy. TEL: 01353 667066; fax – 01294 735161; mobile – 07789 405635; e-mail – rachel.lemkov@btinternet.com; website – www.antique.kitchenalia.co.uk. FAIRS: Newark.

Valued History

9 Market Place. CB7 4NP. (Paul Murawski). Est. 1995. Open 10-5. CL: Mon. SIZE: Small. *STOCK: Antiquities, ancient to Tudor, £25-£1,000+; coins and other artifacts, £5-1,000.* TEL: 01353 654080. SER: Valuations. FAIRS: Cumberland Coin. VAT: Spec.

Waterside Antiques Centre

The Wharf. CB7 4AU. Est. 1986. Open 9.30-5.30 including Bank Holidays, Sun. 11.30-5.30. SIZE: Large. *STOCK: General antiques.* LOC: Waterside area. PARK: Easy. TEL: 01353 667066.

Marie West Antiques

Waterside Antiques Centre, The Wharf. CB7 4AU. Open 9.30-5.30 including Bank Holidays, Sun. 11-4.30. SIZE: Small. *STOCK: Decorative furniture and smalls; painted and stripped pine.* LOC: River edge. PARK: Easy. TEL: 01353 667066; home – 01799 586305; e-mail – mariewest@sellarwest.fsnet.co.uk. FAIRS: Newark.

FORDHAM, Nr. Ely

Phoenix Antiques

1 Carter St. CB7 5NG. Est. 1966. Open by appointment. SIZE: Medium. *STOCK: Early European furniture, domestic metalwork, pottery and delft, carpets, scientific instruments, treen and bygones.* LOC: Centre of village. PARK: Own. TEL: 01638 720363. SER: Valuations.

GREAT SHELFORD, Nr. Cambridge

Storm Fine Arts Ltd

Church Street Barns. CB2 5EL. (Bill and Sue Mason). Resident. Est. 1998. Open by appointment. SIZE: Medium. *STOCK: Paintings and pictures, 1500 to date, £500-£100,000; porcelain, pottery and glass, 1800-1900, £150-£1,500; decorative arts, 1700 to date, £100-£15,000; textiles, 1700-1900, £1,000-£30,000.* PARK: Easy. TEL: 01223 844786; fax – 01223 847871; website – www.stormfinearts.com SER: Valuations; restorations; buys at auction. VAT: Stan.

HUNTINGDON

Huntingdon Trading Post

1 St Mary's St. PE29 3PE. (Mrs D. J. A. De'Ath). Est. 1980. Open daily. SIZE: 30+ dealers. *STOCK: Wide range of general antiques, to £10,000.* PARK: Easy. TEL: 01480 450998; fax – 01480 431142; website – www.huntingdontradingpost.co.uk.

LANDBEACH

J.V. Pianos and Cambridge Pianola Company

The Limes, 85 High St. CB4 8DR. (F.T. Poole). Est. 1972. Open Mon.-Fri., evenings and weekends by appointment. SIZE: Medium. *STOCK: Pianos, pianolas and pianola rolls.* LOC: First building on right in Landbeach from A10. PARK: Easy. TEL: 01223 861348/861507; home – same; fax – 01223 441276; website – www.cambridgepianolacompany.co.uk. SER: Valuations; restorations. VAT: Stan.

OUTWELL, Nr. Wisbech

A.P. and M.A. Haylett

Glen-Royd, 393 Wisbech Rd. PE14 8PG. Open 9-6 including Sun. *STOCK: Country furniture, pottery, treen and metalware, 1750-1900, £5-*

£500. Not Stocked: Firearms. LOC: A1101. PARK: Easy. TEL: 01945 772427; home – same. SER: Buys at auction.

PETERBOROUGH

Antiques & Curios
249 Lincoln Rd., Millfield. PE2 5NZ. (M. and Mrs R. Mason). Est. 1990. Open 10-5. SIZE: Medium. *STOCK: Pine furniture, 19th C, £50-£500; mahogany and oak furniture, 19th to early 20th C, £50-£500; fireplaces, 19th C, £50-£1,000; collectables, 19th-20th C, £10-£100.* LOC: North from city centre. PARK: Easy. TEL: 01733 314948; home – same. SER: Valuations; restorations (furniture stripping and polishing, fireplaces). FAIRS: Peterborough Festival of Antiques.

Francis Bowers Chess Suppliers
1 Marriott Court, Oxney Rd. PE1 5NQ. Resident. Est. 1991. Open by appointment. SIZE: Small. *STOCK: Chess books, boards, sets and timers; clocks.* PARK: Easy. TEL: 01733 897119; e-mail – chessbower@aol.com.

Fitzwilliam Antiques Centre
Fitzwilliam St. PE1 2RX. Open 10-5. SIZE: 25 dealers. *STOCK: General antiques.* LOC: Near city centre. PARK: Easy. TEL: 01733 565415/566346.

Ivor and Patricia Lewis Antique and Fine Art Dealers   `LAPADA`
30 Westwood Park Rd. PE3 6JL. Open by appointment. *STOCK: Decorative English and French furniture, 19th to early 20th C.* TEL: 01733 344567; mobile – 07860 553388.

RAMSEY, Nr. Huntingdon

Abbey Antiques
63 Great Whyte. PE26 1HL. (R. and J. Smith). Est. 1977. Open 10-5 including Sun. CL: Mon. SIZE: Medium. *STOCK: Furniture including pine, 1850-1930, £50-£500; porcelain, glass, Goss and crested china, 1830-1950, £3-£500; Beswick, Fen pottery, Mabel Lucie Attwell, small collectables.* PARK: Easy. TEL: 01487 814753. SER: Mabel Lucie Attwell Museum and Collectors' Club: Memories UK (Enesco Memories of Yesterday figurines sold). FAIRS: Alexandra Palace.

Antique Barometers
Wingfield, 26 Biggin Lane. PE26 1NB. (William and Helen Rae). Open by appointment. *STOCK:*

A Lambert Negro smoker automaton, French, c.1890, with a Jumeau bisque head, the figure exhales smoke whilst looking around and lifting his cane, 24in. high. £4,935. (Christie's London)

From an article entitled "Music and Movement" by Jon Baddeley which appeared in the December/January 2003 issue of *Antique Collecting*. For more details and to subscribe see page 21.

Fine barometers, 18th-19th C, barographs, £400-£10,000. PARK: Easy. TEL: 01487 814060; home/fax – same; e-mail – antiquebarometers @talk21.com. SER: Valuations; restorations.

SOMERSHAM, Nr. Huntingdon

T. W. Pawson – Clocks

31A High St. PE28 3JA. BWCG. Est. 1981. Open by appointment. SIZE: Small. *STOCK: Antique clocks, £150-£5,000; mercury barometers, to mid-19th C.* LOC: Main road through village. PARK: Easy. TEL: 01487 841537; home – same; e-mail – thomas.pawson@btinternet.com. SER: Restorations, overhauls, repairs (clocks and barometers).

ST. IVES

B.R. Knight and Sons

Quay Court, Bull Lane, Bridge St. PE17 4AU. (M. Knight). Est. 1972. Open Mon., Wed., Fri. 11-2, Sat. 10.30-4.30 or by appointment. SIZE: Medium. *STOCK: Porcelain, pottery, jewellery, paintings, watercolours, prints, decorative arts.* LOC: Off Bridge St. PARK: Nearby. TEL: 01480 468295/300042; e-mail – michaelknight9@ hotmail. com.

ST. NEOTS

Tavistock Antiques

Cross Hall Manor, Eaton Ford. PE19 7GB. Open by appointment. *STOCK: Period English furniture.* TEL: 01480 472082. *Trade Only.*

WANSFORD, Nr. Peterborough

Starlight Period Lighting

16 London Rd. PE8 6JB. (Richard P. Rimes and Lynne Ayres). Resident. Est. 1989. Open Tues.-Fri. 9.30-1 and 2.15-5 and most Sats. 10-1 and 2.30-5. SIZE: Medium. *STOCK: Period and new lighting.* LOC: On A1 near A47 junction. PARK: Easy. TEL: 01780 783999; fax – same; e-mail – starlight@lampsandcandles.co.uk; website – www.lampsandcandles.co.uk. SER: Restorations (period lighting). FAIRS: Historic Buildings; Parks & Gardens Exhibition. VAT: Stan/Spec.

WILLINGHAM

Q Antiques

27 Green St. CB4 5JA. (Helen H. Dunne). Est. 2000. Open 10.30-5, Sun. 10.30-4. CL: Tues. SIZE: Medium. *STOCK: Paintings, furniture, porcelain, silver and jewellery, brass and copper, fishing items, racing memorabilia, rugs, early oak to Edwardian, £5-£2,000; Art Deco.* LOC: A14. PARK: Easy. TEL: 01954 260280; home – 01954 231220. SER: Valuations; restorations (furniture, silver and porcelain); buys at auction.

WISBECH

Antiques & Curios (Steve Carpenter)

95-96 Norfolk St. PE13 2LF. Est. 1985. Open 9-5, Sun., Mon. and Wed. by appointment. SIZE: Medium. *STOCK: Georgian and Victorian longcase clocks, £1,000-£3,000; Georgian, Victorian and Edwardian furniture, 19th C, £100-£5,000; bygones and collectables, 18th-20th C, £5-£3000.* LOC: Town centre, just off A47. PARK: Easy. TEL: 01945 588441; e-mail – scarpenterantiques@amserve.net. SER: Valuations; restorations (structural, veneering and polishing); shipping.

Peter A. Crofts

BADA

117 High Rd., Elm. PE14 0DN. (Mrs Pat L. Crofts). Est. 1949. Open by appointment. *STOCK: General antiques, furniture, porcelain, silver, jewellery.* LOC: A1101. TEL: 01945 584614. VAT: Stan/Spec.

Granny's Cupboard

34 Old Market. PE13 1NF. (R.J. Robbs). Est. 1982. Open Tues. and Thurs. 10.30-4, Sat. 10.30-3. SIZE: Medium. *STOCK: China, glass, small furniture, Victorian to 1950's, £5-£500.* PARK: Easy. TEL: 01945 589606; home – 01945 870730. FAIRS: The Maltings, Ely.

R. Wilding

Lanes End, Gadds Lane, Leverington. PE13 5BJ. Resident. *STOCK: Bamboo furniture and mirrors; period furniture including walnut chests; gilt/polished mirrors.* TEL: 01945 588204; fax – 01945 475712. SER: Veneering; polishing; compo carving; gilding; conversions; replicas. *Trade Only.*

CHESHIRE

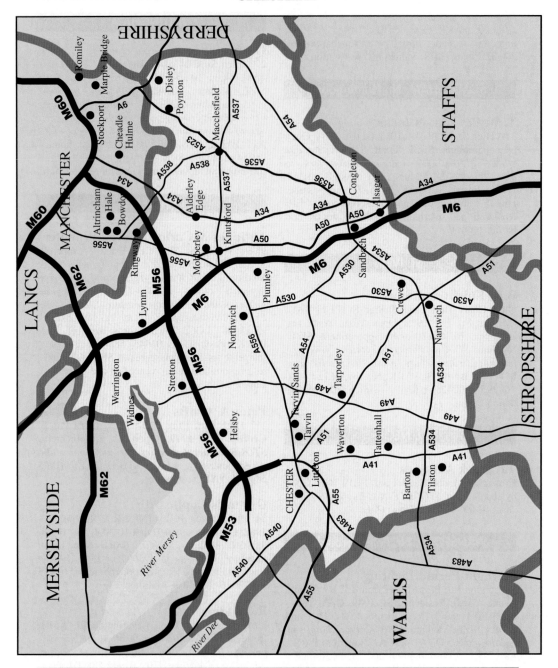

Dealers and Shops in Cheshire

Alderley Edge	2	Hale	1	Plumley	1	Tattenhall	1
Alsager	1	Helsby	1	Poynton	2	Tilston	1
Altrincham	4	Knutsford	5	Ringway	1	Warrington	1
Barton	1	Littleton	1	Romiley	1	Waverton	1
Bowdon	2	Lymm	1	Sandbach	1	Widnes	1
Cheadle Hulme	2	Macclesfield	4	Stockport	9		
Chester	23	Marple Bridge	1	Stretton	1		
Congleton	2	Mobberley	2	Tarporley	1		
Crewe	2	Nantwich	7	Tarvin	1		
Disley	2	Northwich	1	Tarvin Sands	1		

ALDERLEY EDGE

Sara Frances Antiques `LAPADA`
32 South St. SK9 7ES. (Mrs F.S. Waterworth). Est. 1990. Open Sat. 10-4. SIZE: Small. *STOCK: Furniture, 17th-19th C, £100-£6,000; silver, 19th-20th C, £50-£500; decorative items, 17th-20th C, £100-£2,500.* LOC: Off London Rd. PARK: Easy. TEL: 01625 585549; mobile – 07801 458852. SER: Valuations; restorations (furniture and silver).

D.J. Massey and Son
51a London Rd. SK9 7DY. Est. 1900. Open 9.15-5.15, Wed. 9.15-4.45. SIZE: Large. *STOCK: Victorian jewellery, silverware, gold and diamond jewellery.* LOC: On A34. PARK: Easy. TEL: 01625 583565. VAT: Stan/Spec.

ALSAGER, Nr. Crewe

Trash 'n' Treasure
48 Sandbach Rd. South. ST7 2LP. (G. and D. Ogden). Est. 1979. Open Tues., Thurs., Fri. and Sat. 10-4. SIZE: Medium. *STOCK: Late Georgian to 1930's furniture, pictures, ceramics, £5-£10,000.* LOC: 10 mins. junction 16, M6. PARK: Nearby. TEL: 01270 872972/873246. SER: Valuations; lectures.

ALTRINCHAM

Bizarre Decorative Arts North West
118 Manchester Rd. WA14 4PY. (Malcolm C. and Rebecca Lamb). Resident. Est. 1986. Open 10-6, Sun. by appointment. SIZE: Large. *STOCK: Furniture and lighting, £100-£15,000; figurines, bronzes, ceramics including Clarice Cliff, and jewellery, £5-£2,000; all Art Nouveau and Art Deco.* LOC: A56. PARK: Own. TEL: 0161 926 8895; home – same; fax – 0161 929 8310. SER: Valuations; restorations (furniture and lighting; silver and chrome plating, pewter polishing). FAIRS: NEC Aug; Loughborough Art Deco; Kensington Decorative Arts. VAT: Stan/Spec.

Church Street Antiques `LAPADA`
4/4a Old Market Place. WA14 4NP. (Alex Smalley and Nick Stanley). Est. 1991. Open 10-5.30, Sun. 12-4. CL: Tues. SIZE: Large. *STOCK: Furniture, 18th-19th C, £100-£10,000; silver and plate, 19th C, £50-£1,000; paintings, 19th C to contemporary, £100-£5,000.* PARK: Easy. TEL: 0161 929 5196; fax – same; mobile – 07768 318661; website – www.churchstreetantiques.com. SER: Valuations; restorations. FAIRS: Tatton; Chester; GMex; Arley; Harrogate. VAT: Spec.

Robert Redford Antiques & Interiors
48 New St. WA14 2QS. (S. and R. Redford). Est. 1989. By appointment. *STOCK: General antiques, furniture, small silver, porcelain, glass.* LOC: Town centre. PARK: Easy. TEL: Home – 0161 926 8232; fax – 0161 928 4827.

Squires Antiques
25 Regent Rd. WA14 1RX. (V. Phillips). Est. 1977. Open 10-5. CL: Mon. and Wed. SIZE: Medium. *STOCK: Small furniture, 1800-1930, £60-£1,500; small silver, 1850-1970, £20-£400; brass, copper and bric-a-brac, 1850-1940, £10-£400; jewellery, porcelain, fire accessories, light fittings and interior design items.* Not Stocked: Large furniture, coins and badges. LOC: Adjacent hospital and large car park. PARK: Easy. TEL: 0161 928 0749. SER: Valuations.

BARTON, Nr. Farndon

Derek and Tina Rayment Antiques
`BADA` `LAPADA`
Orchard House, Barton Rd. SY14 7HT. (D.J. and K.M. Rayment). Est. 1960. Open by appointment every day. **STOCK: Barometers, 18th-20th C, from £100.** LOC: A534. PARK: Easy. TEL: 01829 270429; home – same; e-mail – raymentantiques@aol.com; website – www. antique-barometers.com. SER: Valuations; restorations (barometers only); buys at auction (barometers). FAIRS: Olympia; Chelsea; LAPADA, (NEC and London); BADA. VAT: Stan/Spec.

BOWDON

Eureka Antiques
7A Church Brow. WA14 2SF. (Noel Gibson and Alex O'Donnell). Est. 1965. Open by appointment. SIZE: Medium. *STOCK: Mahogany furniture, 1800-1850; objets d'art, papier maché, glass.* PARK: Nearby. TEL: 0161 941 5453; fax – same; mobile – 07798 573332. SER: Valuations. FAIRS: Olympia; NEC.

Richmond Antiques
Richmond Rd. WA14 2TT. (Joe and Leslie Freeman). Est. 1992. Open 12-6, Sun. by appointment. CL: Mon. *STOCK: Mirrors, 19th C, £300-£2,000; French decorative furniture, 19th C, £150-£1,500; chandeliers, early 20th C, £200-£2,000.* LOC: Near Manchester airport, junction 7, M56, junction 19, M6. PARK: Easy. TEL: 01619 281229; home – same. SER: Restorations. VAT: Spec.

Allan's Antiques and Reproductions

10 Ravenoak Rd. SK8 7DL. (S. Allan). Est. 1979. Open Thurs., Fri. and Sat. *STOCK: Furniture, general antiques, metalware.* LOC: Opposite war memorial. TEL: 0161 485 3132.

Andrew Foott Antiques

4 Claremont Rd. SK8 6EG. Est. 1985. Open by appointment. SIZE: Small. *STOCK: Barometers, 18th-20th C, £200-£2,500; small furniture, 18th-20th C, £500-£3,000.* LOC: 5 mins. from new A34 by-pass. PARK: Easy. TEL: 0161 485 3559; e-mail – andrew.foott@tesco.net. SER: Restorations (barometers and furniture). FAIRS: NEC Antiques for Everyone.

Adams Antiques `LAPADA`

65 Watergate Row. CH1 2LE. (B. and T. Adams). Est. 1973. Open 10-5. CL: Sun. except by appointment. SIZE: Medium. *STOCK: English and Continental furniture, £200-£4,000; English and French clocks, £150-£4,000; objets d'art, £10-£3,000; all 18th to early 20th C.* PARK: Nearby. TEL: 01244 319421. SER: Valuations; restorations (furniture and clocks). VAT: Stan/Spec.

Aldersey Hall Ltd

Town Hall Sq., 47 Northgate St. CH1 2HQ. (Kim Wilding-Welton). Est. 1990. Open 8.30-5.30. SIZE: Medium. *STOCK: Art Deco and general British ceramics, £5-£500; small furniture, £50-£200; all 1880-1940.* LOC: Between library and Odeon cinema. PARK: Own 100 yards. TEL: 01244 324885. SER: Valuations; buys at auction (Art Deco ceramics). FAIRS: Alexandra Palace, Loughborough, Ardingly, Newark; Birmingham. VAT: Stan/Spec.

Antique Exporters of Chester

CH3 7RZ. (Michael Kilgannon). Est. 1970. Open 8-8 including Sun. SIZE: Warehouse. *STOCK: Furniture.* LOC: Waverton. TEL: 01829 741001; home – 01244 570069. SER: Packing; oak farmhouse tables made to order.

The Antique Garden

Grosvenor Garden Centre, Wrexham Rd. CH4 9EB. (Maria Hopwood). Est. 1991. Open 10-4.30 including Sun. *STOCK: Garden-related bygones.* LOC: A483. PARK: Easy. TEL: 01244 629191; mobile – 07976 539990. SER: Valuations.

The Antique Shop

40 Watergate St. CH1 2LA. (Peter Thornber). Est. 1985. Open 10-5.30, Sat. 10-6, Sun. (May-Dec.) 1-5, other times by appointment. SIZE: Small. *STOCK: Metalware – brass, pewter, copper, iron, 1700-1900, £35-£350; Doulton – character jugs, figures and series ware, 1890-1960, £35-£350; blue and white transfer printed ware; Prattware pot lids, British Army cap badges; fountain pens; boxes and treen; cranberry glass.* LOC: Off Bridge St. PARK: Nearby. TEL: 01244 316286; home – 0151 327 1725; e-mail – antiques chester@tinyworld.co.uk. SER: Restorations (metalwork). FAIRS: Cheshire.

Avalon Post Card and Stamp Shop

1 City Walls, Rufus Court, Northgate St. CH1 2JG. (G.E. Ellis). Est. 1980. Open Tues.-Sat. 10-4. *STOCK: Postcards, stamps and collectables.* LOC: City centre. TEL: 01244 318406; e-mail – avalon@fsbdial.co.uk; website – www.postcard. co.uk/npf.

Baron Fine Art `LAPADA`

68 Watergate St. CH1 2LA. (S. and R. Baron). Est. 1984. Open 9.30-5.30. *STOCK: Watercolours and oils, some etchings, late 19th to early 20th C, some contemporary, £50-£60,000.* PARK: Easy. TEL: 01244 342520. SER: Restorations; framing. FAIRS: Tatton Park; LAPADA; NEC (April, Aug. and Nov); Watercolours & Drawings (Jan/Feb). VAT: Stan/Spec.

Boustead-Bland Antiques `LAPADA`

59 Watergate Row South. CH1 2LE. Est. 1985. Open 10-5.30. *STOCK: 17th-19th C town and country furniture; portraits, clocks, metalware, pottery, porcelain and lighting.* LOC: City centre. PARK: Nearby. TEL: 01244 342300; home – 01244 350366; e-mail – bousteadbland@attglobal. net.uk. SER: Restorations (furniture, French polishing). FAIRS: NEC. VAT: Spec.

Cameo Antiques

19 Watergate St. CH1 2LB. Est. 1994. Open 9-5, Sat. 9-5.30. SIZE: Small. *STOCK: Jewellery and English silver, 1800-1990, £20-£2,000; English (including Moorcroft and Sally Tuffin pottery) and Continental porcelain, 1750-1960.* LOC: Off Bridge St. PARK: Easy. TEL: 01244 311467; fax – same. SER: Valuations. VAT: Stan/Spec.

Farmhouse Antiques

21-23 Christleton Rd., Boughton. CH3 5UF. (K. Appleby). Est. 1973. Open 9-5. SIZE: Large. *STOCK: Farmhouse furniture, longcase clocks, Staffordshire pottery, country bygones, mechan-*

ical music, Manchester United football pro-grammes. LOC: 1 mile from City centre on A41. PARK: Easy. TEL: 01244 322478; evenings – 01244 318391. SER: Export. VAT: Stan/Spec.

Grosvenor Antiques and Interiors
61 Watergate Row. CH1 2LE. (John R. Martin). Est. 2002. Open 10-5.30. SIZE: Medium. *STOCK: Dining and bedroom furniture, paintings, silver plate, lighting and interior design.* LOC: City centre, 200 metres west of Cross. PARK: Multi-storey nearby. TEL: 01244 401185; fax – 01244 401695. SER: Interior design; restorations (furniture including polishing). FAIRS: NEC.

Harris & Holt
Grange Farm, Parkgate Rd., Mollington. CH1 6NP. (Sandra Harris). Est. 1978. Open Thurs., Fri. and Sat. or by appointment. SIZE: Medium. *STOCK: English and Continental furniture, £500-£10,000; oil paintings including portraits, £1,000-£10,000; works of art, £100-£5,000; all 17th-19th C.* LOC: A540 Chester to Parkgate road, opposite Mollington Banastre Hotel. PARK: Easy. TEL: 01244 851180; fax – 0151 353 8107; mobile – 07860 560875. SER: Valuations; buys at auction. FAIRS: Battersea; Olympia (June). VAT: Spec.

J. Alan Hulme
Antique Maps & Old Prints, 52 Mount Way, Waverton. CH3 7QF. Est. 1965. Open Mon.-Sat. by appointment. *STOCK: Maps, 16th-19th C; prints, 18th-19th C.* TEL: 01244 336472.

Jamandic Ltd
22 Bridge St. Row. CH1 1NN. Est. 1975. Open 9.30-5.30, Sat. 9.30-1. SIZE: Medium. *STOCK: Decorative furniture, mirrors, lighting, pictures and prints.* TEL: 01244 312822. SER: Interior design and decoration; export. VAT: Stan/Spec.

K D Antiques
11 City Walls. CH1 1LD. (Dorothea Gillett). Est. 1990. Open 10-5. SIZE: Small. *STOCK: Stafford-shire figures, 18th-19th C, £50-£500; wooden boxes, 18th-19th C, £20-£300; collectables, £5-£50; pottery, porcelain and glass, 19th C, £50-£150; pictures and prints, small furniture.* LOC: City centre, next to Eastgate Clock, wall level. PARK: Nearby. TEL: 01244 314208.

Kayes of Chester
LAPADA
9 St. Michaels Row. CH1 1EF. (A.M. Austin-Kaye and N.J. Kaye). NAG. Est. 1948. Open 9-5.30. SIZE: Medium. *STOCK: Diamond rings and jewellery, 1850-1950, £20-£20,000; silver and plate, 1700-1930, £20-£8,000; small objects and ceramics, 19th to early 20th C, £50-£1,000.*

PARK: Nearby. TEL: 01244 327149; fax – 01244 318404; website – www.Kayeschester.com. SER: Valuations; restorations (silver, jewellery and plate); buys at auction. VAT: Stan/Spec.

Lowe and Sons
11 Bridge St. Row. CH1 1PD. Est. 1770. *STOCK: Jewellery and silver, Georgian, Victorian and Edwardian; unusual collectors' items.* TEL: 01244 325850. VAT: Stan/Spec.

Melody's Antiques
LAPADA
The Old School House, Kinnerton Rd., Lower Kinnerton. CH4 9AE. (M. and M. Melody). Est. 1977. Open 10-5.30 by appointment. SIZE: Large. *STOCK: 18th-20th C oak, mahogany, walnut and pine furniture; porcelain, lighting, decorative items.* LOC: 3 miles from Chester. TEL: 01244 660204. SER: Courier; container packing. FAIRS: Newark; NEC. VAT: Stan/Spec.

Moor Hall Antiques
27 Watergate Row. CH1 2LE. (John Murphy). Resident. Est. 1992. Open 10-5.30, Mon., Fri. and Sat. 10.30-5.30. SIZE: Large. *STOCK: Furniture, 18th-19th C, £1,000-£2,000; prints, 19th C, £50-£200; modern decorative items, £20-£100.* LOC: City centre. PARK: Easy. TEL: 01244 340095. SER: Restorations (oils, watercolours and furn-iture). VAT: Stan/Spec.

The Old Warehouse Antiques
7 Delamere St. CH1 4DS. (Mr and Mrs M. O'Donnell). Est. 1990. Open 10-5. SIZE: Large. *STOCK: Victorian and Edwardian furniture, £50-£1,000.* LOC: Opposite Delamere bus station. PARK: Nearby. TEL: 01244 383942; mobile – 07876 633111. SER: French polishing. VAT: Spec

Stothert Old Books
4 Nicholas St. CH1 2NX. (Alan and Marjory Checkley). PBFA. Est. 1977. Open 10-5. SIZE: Medium. *STOCK: Books, 17th-20th C, £2-£1,000.* LOC: At junction with Watergate St. TEL: 01244 340756; e-mail – alancheckley@ yahoo.com.

Watergate Antiques
56 Watergate St. CH1 2LD. (A. Shindler). Est. 1968. Open 9.30-5.30. SIZE: Medium. *STOCK: Porcelain and pottery, jewellery; specialist in silver and silver plate to the Trade.* LOC: From Liverpool first set of traffic lights past Waterfall Roundabout, turn left. PARK: At rear. TEL: 01244 344516; fax – 01244 320350; e-mail – watergate.antiques@themail.co.uk. SER: Silver plating; restorations; repairs (ceramic and jewel-lery). VAT: Stan.

Wheatsheaf Antiques
57 Christleton Rd., Boughton. CH3. Est. 1988. Open 11-4, Sun. 12-4. SIZE: Medium. *STOCK: Furniture, 18th C to 1930's, £500-£2,000; vintage clothing, Victorian to 1970's; prints, 18th C to 1930's.* PARK: Adjacent. TEL: 01244 403743; fax – 01244 351713; e-mail – info@ antiquesonlineuk.com; website – www.antiques onlineuk.com. SER: Restorations. VAT: Spec.

CONGLETON

W. Buckley Antiques Exports
35 Chelford Rd. CW12 4QA. Open 7 days by appointment. *STOCK: Mainly shipping and Victorian furniture.* TEL: 01260 275299. SER: Shipping.

Littles Collectables
8/10 Little St. CW12 1AR. (Mrs J. Storey). Est. 1989. CL: Wed. SIZE: Medium. *STOCK: Pottery and glass, Doulton, pine furniture, French period furniture, lighting, mirrors and objets d'art, £5-£1,000.* LOC: Town centre. PARK: Nearby. TEL: 01260 299098.

CREWE

Antique and Country Pine Ltd
102 Edleston Rd. CW2 7HD. Est. 1988. Open 9.30-5, Sat. 10-5, Sun. by appointment. CL: Wed. SIZE: Small. *STOCK: Stripped pine, 19th to early 20th C, £25-£600; satinwood furniture, 1900, £100-£500.* LOC: Turn off Nantwich Rd. (A534), shop 250 yards on left. TEL: 01270 258617; home – 01270 665991.

Copnal Books
18 Meredith St. CW1 2PW. (P. Ollerhead). Est. 1980. Open Mon. and Fri. 9.30-4.30, Sat. 9.30-5. SIZE: Small. *STOCK: Books, £1-£50.* LOC: 200 yards north of market. PARK: Easy. TEL: 01270 580470; home – 01270 585622. SER: Valuations; buys at auction.

DISLEY, Nr. Stockport

Michael Allcroft Antiques
203 Buxton Rd., Newtown. SK12 2RA. Est. 1984. Open Tues.-Fri. 12-6, Sat. 10-5, other times by appointment. SIZE: Large. *STOCK: Edwardian and 1930's furniture.* LOC: A6 south of Stockport. TEL: Mobile – 07798 781642; fax – 01663 744014. SER: Container packing.

Mill Farm Antiques
50 Market St. SK12 2DT. (F.E. Berry). Est. 1968. Open every day. SIZE: Medium. *STOCK: Pianos, clocks, mechanical music, shipping goods, general antiques, £50-£10,000.* LOC: A6, 7 miles south of Stockport. PARK: Easy. TEL: 01663 764045; fax – 01663 762690; e-mail – mfa@ millfarmantiques.fsbusiness.co.uk. SER: Valuations; restorations (clocks, watches, barometers and music boxes). VAT: Stan/Spec.

HALE, Nr. Altrincham

French Countrystyle
61 Stamford Park Rd. WA15 9EZ. (Bernard and Margaret Ernstone). Open Tues.-Sat.10-5. SIZE: Small. *STOCK: French decorative furniture, beds, lighting, mirrors and unusual items, 1800-1910, £150-£2,000.* PARK: Easy. TEL: 0161 927 9041; fax – 0161 904 8949; e-mail – bernard@ frenchcountrystyle.co.uk; website – www.french countrystyle.co.uk. FAIRS: Newark.

HELSBY

Sweetbriar Gallery
Robin Hood Lane. WA6 9NH. (Mrs A. Metcalfe). Est. 1986. Open 9-5.30 or by appointment to see full stock. *STOCK: Antique and modern paperweights, £5-£8,000.* LOC: Off M56, junction 14. First left at traffic lights, first right after Elf Garage, past three right turns. Premises on hillside with long, low sandstone wall in front . PARK: Easy. TEL: 01928 723851; home – same; fax – 01928 724153; mobile – 07860 907532; e-mail – sweetbr@globalnet.co.uk; website – www.sweetbriar.co.uk. SER: Valuations; buys at auction (paperweights). FAIRS: Glass (May and Nov.); National Motorcycle Museum (Birmingham); Great Antiques; Shepton Mallet; Newark; Ardingly. VAT: Stan/Spec.

KNUTSFORD

B.R.M. Coins
3 Minshull St. WA16 6HG. (Brian Butterworth). Est. 1968. Open 11-3, Sat. 11-1 or by appointment. SIZE: Small. *STOCK: Coins, medals and banknotes, worldwide, BC to date, from 5p; money boxes, coin scales and weights.* LOC: A50. PARK: Nearby. TEL: 01565 651480; home – 01606 74522. SER: Valuations; buys at auction (as stock).

Cranford Galleries
10 King St. WA16 6DL. (M.R. Bentley). Est. 1964. Open 11-5. CL: Wed. SIZE: Small.

STOCK: Pictures, prints and Victoriana. Not Stocked: Glass. LOC: Main St. PARK: Easy. TEL: 01565 633646. SER: Framing and mounting. VAT: Stan.

Glynn Interiors
92 King St. WA16 6ED. Est. 1963. Open 10-4. CL: Mon. and Wed. SIZE: Large. *STOCK: Furniture, 1750-1900, £50-£2,000; Victorian chairs, £50-£650.* Not Stocked: Porcelain. LOC: 10 mins. drive after leaving M6 at Exit 19. PARK: Own. TEL: 01565 634418. SER: Restorations (re-upholstery); cabinet repairs. VAT: Stan/Spec.

Knutsford Antiques Centre
113 King St. WA16 6EH. (David and Patricia McLeod). Est. 1995. Open 10-5, Sun. 12-5. CL: Mon. SIZE: 20+ dealers. *STOCK: Furniture, 18th C, £100-£2,000; pine, £200-£600; early British porcelain, ceramics and collectables, £10-£2,000; British silver, £10-£1,000; books, £1-£50; glass, £10-£500; jewellery, £25-£500.* LOC: Main street, 5 mins. from junction 19, M6. PARK: Easy. TEL: 01565 654092; website – www.knutsfordantiques.com. SER: Valuations.

Lion Gallery and Bookshop
15a Minshull St. WA16 6HG. (R.P. Hepner). Est. 1964. Open Fri. 10.30-4.30, Sat. 10-4.30. *STOCK: Antiquarian maps, prints and books, watercolours and oils, 16th-20th C; O.S. maps and early directories.* LOC: King St. 3 mins. M6. PARK: Nearby. TEL: 01565 652915; fax – 01565 75014; mobile – 07850 270796. SER: Restorations; binding; cleaning; framing; mounting. VAT: Stan.

John Titchner and Sons
Littleton Old Hall, Little Heath Rd. CH3 7DW. Open 9-5. CL: Sat. *STOCK: Furniture, 18th-19th C.* TEL: 01244 336986.

Willow Pool Garden Centre
Burford Lane. WA13 0SH. (S. Brunsveld). Open 9-6, including Sun. *STOCK: Architectural and general antiques.* TEL: 01925 757827; fax – 01925 758101.

Gatehouse Antiques
5/7 Chester Rd. SK11 8DG. (W.H. Livesley). Est. 1973. Open 9-5. CL: Sun. except by appointment and Wed. pm. *STOCK: Small furniture, silver and plate, glass, brass, copper, pewter, jewellery, 1650-1880.* PARK: Opposite. TEL: 01625 426476; home – 01625 612841.

Hills Antiques
Indoor Market, Grosvenor Centre. SK11 6SY . (D. Hill). Est. 1968. Open 9.30-5.30. *STOCK: Small furniture, jewellery, collectors' items, stamps, coins, postcards.* LOC: Town Centre. PARK: Easy. TEL: 01625 420777/420467; e-mail – hillsantiques@tinyworld.co.uk; website – www.hillsantiques.co.uk.

D.J. Massey and Son
47 Chestergate. SK11 6DG. Est. 1900. Open 9.30-5.15. *STOCK: Jewellery, gold and diamonds, all periods.* TEL: 01625 616133.

Mereside Books
75 Chestergate. SK11 6DG. (Miss S. Laithwaite and K. S. Kowalski). Est. 1996. Open 10-5, Mon. and Tues. by appointment. SIZE: Small. *STOCK: Books – secondhand, 20th C, £2-£100; antiquarian, 19th C, £10-£300; illustrated, 20th C, £10-£1,000.* TEL: 01625 425352; home – 01625 431160. SER: Valuations; restorations (books including re-binding). FAIRS: Buxton Book.

Town House Antiques
21 Town St. SK6 5AA. (Paul and Jeri Buxcey). Open 10-6 most days. *STOCK: Antique pine, French beds and decorative items.* PARK: Forecourt. TEL: 0161 427 2228; home – 0161 427 1343.

David Bedale
WA16 7HR . Est. 1977. By appointment. SIZE: Medium. *STOCK: 18th-19th C furniture, unusual and decorative items.* TEL: 01565 872270; mobile – 07836 623021. VAT: Stan/Spec.

Limited Editions
The Barn, Oak Tree Farm, Knutsford Rd. WA16 7PU. (C.W. Fogg). Est. 1978. Open Thurs., Fri. and Sat. 10-5.30, Sun. 12-4. SIZE: Large. *STOCK: Furniture, 19th C, especially dining tables and*

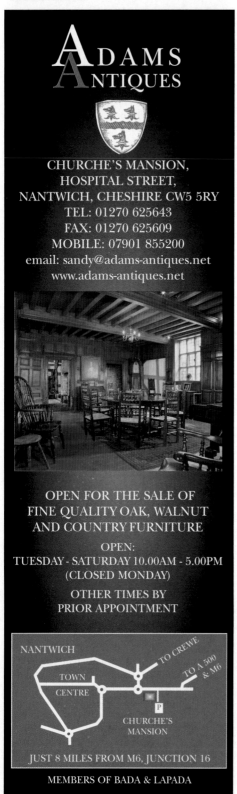

chairs, £100-£5,000; arm chairs and couches for re-upholstery. LOC: Main road between Knutsford and Wilmslow. PARK: Own. TEL: 01565 874075; e-mail – info@ltd-editions.co.uk; website – www.antique-co.com. SER: Valuations; restorations (furniture). VAT: Stan/Spec.

NANTWICH

Adams Antiques   BADA LAPADA
Churche's Mansion, Hospital St. CW5 5RY. (Sandy Summers). Resident. Est. 1975. Open 10-5. CL: Mon., other times by prior appointment. SIZE: Large, 8 showrooms. *STOCK: Mainly oak, walnut and fruitwood country furniture, Welsh dressers, corner cupboards, tables and chairs; longcase clocks, Mason's Ironstone.* LOC: A500 towards town centre, shop on left on main roundabout. PARK: Own. TEL: 01270 625643; fax – 01270 625609; e-mail – sandy@adams-antiques.net; website – www. adams-antiques.net. SER: Valuations; restorations (furniture). FAIRS: BADA; LAPADA; NEC; Olympia (Nov). VAT: Stan/Spec.

Barn Antiques
8 The Cocoa Yard, Pillory St. CW5 5BL. (J.B. Lee). Est. 1993. CL: Wed. SIZE: Small. *STOCK: Carltonware, Beswick, Royal Doulton and Shelley china and collectables.* LOC: Town centre. TEL: 01270 627770.

Chapel Antiques
47 Hospital St. CW5 5RL. (Miss D.J. Atkin). Est. 1983. Open 9.30-5.30, Wed. 9.30-1 or by appointment. CL: Mon. SIZE: Medium. *STOCK: Oak, mahogany and pine furniture, Georgian and Victorian, £100-£3,000; longcase clocks, pre-1830, £1,000-£3,000; copper, brass, silver, glass, porcelain, pottery and small items, 19th C, £10-£500.* LOC: Enter town via Pillory St., turn right into Hospital St. PARK: Easy. TEL: 01270 629508; home – same. SER: Valuations; restorations (furniture and clocks).

Roderick Gibson
70 Hospital St. CW5 5RP. (R. and L. Gibson). Est. 1975. Open Tues.-Sat. 10-5. *STOCK: Furniture and decorative collectors' pieces.* PARK: Nearby. TEL: 01270 625301; website – www.sfc. co.uk/antiques. SER: Valuations. VAT: Stan/ Global.

Love Lane Antiques
Love Lane. CW5 5BH. (M. Simon). Est. 1982. Open 10-5. CL: Wed. SIZE: Small. *STOCK: General antiques, 19th-20th C, £5-£500.* LOC: 2 mins. walk from town square. PARK: Nearby. TEL: 01270 626239.

Coppelia Antiques

Valerie and Roy Clements

Holford Lodge, Plumley Moor
Road, Plumley, Nr. Knutsford,
Cheshire WA16 9RS
Telephone: 01565 722197
Fax: 01565 722744
4 miles from J.19, M6

Fine quality mahogany longcase clock, c.1770, London maker, ht. 7ft. 8in. Dial with chapter ring and spandrels with strike-silent in the arch

We currently have one of the finest selections of quality longcase clocks in the U.K. We also stock mantel, bracket, English and Vienna wall clocks. Established 1970, all our clocks are fully restored and guaranteed 1 year. Free delivery U.K. mainland. Why not pay us a visit, you will receive a warm welcome, free coffee and constructive, expert advice.

OPEN 7 DAYS BY APPOINTMENT

Nantwich Antiques and The Passage to India

The Manor House, 7 Beam St. CW5 5LR. (A. S. Coupe). Est. 1982. Open 10-5. SIZE: Medium. *STOCK: 18th-19th C English furniture, to £1,000; field sports accessories; period and reproduction Indian and Chinese furniture.* LOC: Town centre. PARK: Own. TEL: 01270 610615; website – www.indianfurniture.co.uk. SER: Valuations; restorations. FAIRS: CLA Game; Lowther House.

Richardson Antiques Ltd

90 Hospital St. CW5 5RP. (Terry Richardson). Est. 1981. Open by appointment. SIZE: Medium. *STOCK: Furniture, collectables and china.* TEL: 01270 625963; home – 01270 628348. SER: Valuations; restorations (French polishing, upholstery, clocks). VAT: Spec/Global.

NORTHWICH

Northwich Antiques Centre

132 Witton St. (F.J. Cockburn). Est. 1990. Open 10-5 including Sun. SIZE: Large. *STOCK: Georgian, Victorian and Edwardian furniture, £50-£1,000+; china, clocks and barometers; Royal Doulton, Beswick, Moorcroft; prints,* paintings, books, jewellery. LOC: Town centre. PARK: Easy. TEL: 01606 47540; fax – 01606 889262.

PLUMLEY

Coppelia Antiques

Holford Lodge, Plumley Moor Rd. WA16 9RS. (V. and R. Clements). Resident. Est. 1970. Open 10-6 including Sun. by appointment. SIZE: Medium. *STOCK: Over 500 clocks (mainly longcase and wall), £1,000-£50,000; tables – Georgian mahogany, wine, oak gateleg and side; bureaux, desks, chests of drawers, lowboys, coffers – all stock guaranteed.* LOC: 4 miles junction 19, M6. PARK: Own. TEL: 01565 722197; fax – 01565 722744; website – www.pendulumofmayfair. co.uk. SER: Restorations. FAIRS: Buxton (May). VAT: Spec.

POYNTON, Nr. Stockport

Harper Fine Paintings

"Overdale", Woodford Rd. SK12 1ED. (P.R. Harper). Est. 1967. Open by appointment. SIZE: Large. *STOCK: Watercolours, £100-£35,000; oils including European, £250-£60,000.* LOC: From A523 centre of Poynton lights, turn into Chester Rd., over railway. After 1/4 mile turn right, 1st drive on left after railway bridge. PARK: Easy. TEL: 01625 879105; home – same; fax – 01625 850128; e-mail – Peteevette@aol.com. SER: Valuations; restorations; buys at auction (as stock). VAT: Stan/Spec.

Recollections

69 Park Lane. SK12 1RD. (Angela Smith). Open 10-5. SIZE: Medium. *STOCK: Antique, pre-war and secondhand furniture; costume jewellery and decorative collectables.* PARK: Own at rear and Civic Centre. TEL: 01625 859373.

RINGWAY, Nr. Altrincham

Cottage Antiques

Hasty Lane. WA15 8UT. (J. and J. M. Gholam). Est. 1967. SIZE: Medium. *STOCK: Furniture, metalware, ceramics, glass, early 18th to mid 19th C.* Not Stocked: Jewellery, jade and ivory. LOC: Off junction 6, M56, off A538, very close to airport. PARK: Easy. TEL: 0161 980 7961. SER: Valuations.

ROMILEY, Nr. Stockport

Romiley Antiques & Jewellery
42 Stockport Rd. SK6 3AA. (P. Green). Est. 1983.
Open Thurs., Fri. and Sat. 9-5. SIZE: Medium.
*STOCK: Furniture, 18th-19th C, £100-£2,000;
ceramics, 18th-19th C, £5-£1,000; jewellery, 19th
C, £5-£1,000.* LOC: 5 miles from Stockport.
PARK: Nearby. TEL: 0161 494 6920; home –
same. SER: Valuations. VAT: Stan/Spec.

SANDBACH

Saxon Cross Antiques Emporium
Town Mill, High St. CW11 1AH. (John and
Christine Jones). Est. 1972. Open 10-5, Tues. 10-
4.30, Sun. 11-4, Mon. by appointment. SIZE:
Large. *STOCK: Furniture, 16th to early 20th C,
£50-£1,000; glass, silver, china and porcelain,
19th-20th C, £50-£1,000;* LOC: .75 miles off
junction 17, M6. PARK: Easy and nearby. TEL:
01270 753005; fax – same. SER: Valuations;
restorations; buys at auction. FAIRS: Cheshire
Show. VAT: Stan/Spec.

STOCKPORT

Antique Furniture Warehouse
Units 3/4 Royal Oak Buildings, Cooper St. SK1
3QJ. Est. 1982. Open 9-5. SIZE: Large. *STOCK:
English and Continental mahogany, walnut and
inlaid furniture, paintings, clocks, shipping
goods, pottery, porcelain and curios, decorative
items, architectural.* LOC: 5 mins. off M56
towards town centre, 2 mins. off M60. PARK:
Easy. TEL: 0161 429 8590; fax – 0161 480 5375.
SER: Courier; packing. VAT: Stan.

Antiques Import Export
20 Buxton Rd., Hevley. SK2 6NU. Open 9.30-
5.30. SIZE: Large. *STOCK: American and pre-
1930 English furniture, to £5,000.* PARK: Easy.
TEL: 0161 476 4013; fax – 0161 285 2860; e-
mail – paul@antiquesimportexport.freeserve.
co.uk. SER: Valuations; restorations. FAIRS:
Newark.

Flintlock Antiques
28 and 30 Bramhall Lane. SK2 6HD. (F.
Tomlinson and Son). Est. 1968. Open 9-5. SIZE:
Large. *STOCK: Furniture, clocks, pictures,
scientific instruments.* PARK: Easy. TEL: 0161
480 9973. VAT: Stan/Spec.

Halcyon Antiques
435/437 Buxton Rd., Great Moor. SK2 7HE.

(Mrs Jill A. Coppock). Est. 1980. Open 10-5.
SIZE: Large. *STOCK: Porcelain and glass, £1-
£2,000; furniture, £50-£2,000; both 1750-1940:
jewellery, silver and plate, linen and lace.* LOC:
A6, 3 miles south of town. PARK: Easy. TEL:
0161 483 5038; home – 0161 439 3524.

Imperial Antiques   LAPADA
295 Buxton Rd., Great Moor. SK2 7NR. (A.
Todd). Est. 1972. Open 10-5, Sun. by appointment. SIZE: Large. *STOCK: Decorative French
and English antiques; silver and plate, 19th-20th
C; porcelain especially Japanese and Chinese,
18th-19th C; all £100-£10,000.* LOC: A6 Buxton
Rd., 1.5 miles south of town centre. PARK: Easy.
TEL: 0161 483 3322; fax – 0161 483 3376; e-
mail – Alfred@imperialantiques.com; website –
www.imperialantiques.com. SER: Buys at auction
(as stock). VAT: Stan/Spec.

Manchester Antique Company
MAC House, St Thomas's Place. SK1 3TZ. Open
9.30-4.30. SIZE: Large. *STOCK: Antique furniture, English, Continental and shipping goods,
mainly walnut and mahogany.* TEL: 0161 355
5566/5577; e-mail – sales@manchesterantique.
co.uk; website – www.manchester-antique.co.uk.

Nostalgia Architectural Antiques
LAPADA
Holland's Mill, Shaw Heath. SK3 8BH. (D. and
E. Durrant). Est. 1975. Open Tues.-Fri. 10-6, Sat.
10-5. SIZE: Large. *STOCK: Fireplaces, £200-
£50,000; bathroom fittings and architectural
items, £50-£2,000; all 18th-19th C.* LOC: 5 mins.
from junction 1, M60. PARK: At rear. TEL: 0161
477 7706; fax – 0161 477 2267; website – www.
nostalgia-uk.com. SER: Valuations. VAT: Stan/
Spec.

The Old Curiosity Shop
123 Stockport Rd. West, Bredbury. SK6 2AN.
(Sandra Crook). Est. 1984. Open 10-6, Sun. 12-5.
CL: Wed. SIZE: Medium. *STOCK: 1920's, 1930's
oak furniture, especially barley twist; brass coal
buckets, fire tools.* LOC: 2 miles from M60.
PARK: Forecourt or opposite. TEL: 0161 494
9469; home – same. SER: Restorations (furniture
– hand stripping).

Victoria Imports
MAC House, St. Thomas's Place. SK1 3TZ. (S.
Harris and T. Finn). Est. 1973. Open 8-5. CL: Sat.
*STOCK: General antiques especially four-poster
beds.* PARK: Nearby. TEL: 0161 285 1167;
mobile – 07946 417074. SER: Valuations; restorations; export. FAIRS: Newark. VAT: Stan/Spec.

STRETTON, Nr. Warrington

Antiques Etc.
Shepcroft House, London Rd. WA4 5PJ. (M. Clare). Est. 1978. Resident, usually available. SIZE: Medium. *STOCK: Furniture, pine, barometers, clocks, instruments and items of interest, £5-£2,000.* LOC: A49, towards Warrington, through Stretton traffic lights, next turning on left. PARK: Easy. TEL: 01925 730431; mobile – 07836 570663.

TARPORLEY

Tarporley Antique Centre
76 High St. CW6 0DP. Est. 1992. Open 10-5, Sun. 11-4. SIZE: 9 dealers on two floors. *STOCK: Furniture, ceramics, commemoratives, treen, Studio pottery, glass, oils, watercolours, prints.* LOC: Main road, near Crown public house. PARK: In front of premises and opposite. TEL: 01829 733919. SER: Buys at auction.

TARVIN, Nr. Chester

Antique Fireplaces
The Manor House, Church St. CH3. (Mrs G. O'Toole). Est. 1979. Open Fri., Sat. and Sun. 10-5 or by appointment. SIZE: Medium. *STOCK: Fireplaces and ranges, 18th-19th C, £150-£3,000.* LOC: At junction of A556 and A51. PARK: Easy. TEL: 01829 740936; home – 01606 46717. SER: Valuations; restorations; installations (fireplaces and ranges); new tiles and fenders ordered from suppliers on request. FAIRS: Tatton Park, Knutsford.

TARVIN SANDS, Nr. Chester

Cheshire Brick and Slate Co
Brook House Farm, Salters Bridge. CH3 8HL. (Malcolm and Jason Youde). Est. 1978. Open 7.30-5.30, Sat. 8-4.30. SIZE: Large. *STOCK: Reclaimed conservation building materials, 16th-20th C; architectural antiques – garden statuary, stonework, lamp posts, gates, fireplaces, bathroom suites, chimney pots and ironwork, 18th-20th C, £50-£1,000; furniture, pews, leaded lights, pottery, 18th-20th C, £5-£1,000.* LOC: Directly off A54 just outside Tarvin. PARK: Own. TEL: 01829 740883; fax – 01829 740481; e-mail – enquiries@cheshirebrickandslate.co.uk; website – www.cheshirebrickandslate.co.uk. SER: Valuations; restorations (fireplaces, timber treatment); building/construction and demolition; renovations. VAT: Stan/Global.

TATTENHALL, Nr. Chester

The Great Northern Architectural Antique Company Ltd
New Russia Hall, Chester Rd. CH3 9AH. Open 9.30-5 including Sun. SIZE: Large. *STOCK: Period doors, fire surrounds, stained glass, sanitary ware, garden statuary, furniture and curios.* LOC: Off A41. PARK: Easy. TEL: 01829 770796; fax – 01829 770971. SER: Stripping; restorations (stained glass); repairs (metalwork). VAT: Stan.

TILSTON, Nr. Malpas

Well House Antiques
The Well House. SY14 7DP. (S. French-Greenslade). Est. 1968. Open by appointment. SIZE: Small. *STOCK: Collectors' items, china, glass, silver.* PARK: Easy. TEL: 01829 250332.

WARRINGTON

The Rocking Chair Antiques
Unit 3, St. Peter's Way. WA2 7BL. (Mike and Jane Barratt). Est. 1976. Open 8.30-5, Sat. 10-4. SIZE: Large. *STOCK: Furniture and bric-a-brac.* LOC: Off Orford Lane. PARK: Easy. TEL: 01925 652409; fax – same; mobile – 07774 492891. SER: Valuations; packing and shipping. VAT: Stan.

WAVERTON, Nr. Chester

The White House
Whitchurch Rd. CH3 7PB. (Mrs Elizabeth Rideal). Est. 1979. Open 10-5. SIZE: Medium. *STOCK: Stripped pine furniture, 19th-20th C, £50-£2,000; Victorian china, 19th C, £5-£100; bric-a-brac.* LOC: A41, 2.5 miles south of Sainsbury's roundabout on Whitchurch Rd. PARK: Easy. TEL: 01244 335063; home – same; fax – 01244 335098. VAT: Margin.

WIDNES

Iain Campbell
Unit A5, Moor Lane Business Centre. WA8 7AQ. PBFA. Est. 1970. Open by appointment. SIZE: Small. *STOCK: Prints, 18th-19th C, £1-£100; drawings and watercolours, printed ephemera, books, 19th C, £1-£500.* LOC: On B5419. PARK: Easy. TEL: 0151 420 5545. FAIRS: Newark DGM; PBFA – London, Oxford, Cambridge, York, Haydock Park, Chester; Ephemera, London (June and Dec.). VAT: Stan.

CORNWALL

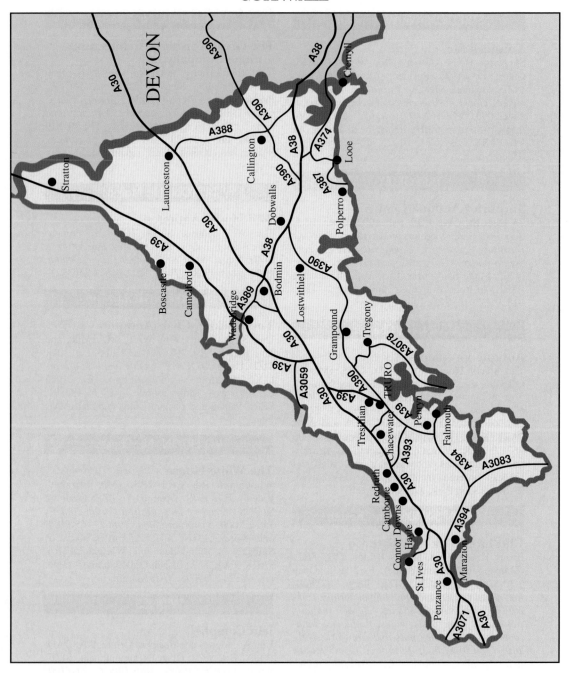

Dealers and Shops in Cornwall

Bodmin	1	Cremyll	1	Lostwithiel	2	Stratton	1
Boscastle	2	Dobwalls	1	Marazion	1	Tregony	1
Callington	1	Falmouth	4	Penryn	3	Tresillion	1
Camborne	1	Grampound	2	Penzance	9	Truro	6
Camelford	1	Hayle	1	Polperro	2	Wadebridge	2
Connor Downs	1	Launceston	2	Redruth	2		
Chacewater	1	Looe	2	St. Ives	3		

BODMIN

Bodmin Antiques Centre
Town End. PL31 1LN. (Ralph and Nola Solomons). Est. 1996. Open 10-4. SIZE: Medium - several dealers. *STOCK: Ceramics and glass, £5-£350, small furniture, £10-£350, both 19th-20th C; commemoratives, kitchenalia, toys, brass, 20th C, £5-£75.* LOC: Main road. PARK: Nearby. TEL: 01208 78661; home - 01208 74609; e-mail - bodminantiques@hotmail.com; website - www. bodminantiquescentre.co.uk. SER: Valuations.

BOSCASTLE

Newlyfe Antiques
The Old Mill. PL35 0AQ. (Harry Ruddy). Open seven days a week May-Sept., prior telephone call advisable at other times. *STOCK: Collectables, 18th-19th C furniture, French beds.* LOC: Village centre. PARK: Nearby. TEL: 01840 250230.

Pickwick Antiques
Dunn St. PL35 0AA. (David Lamond). Est. 1970. Open Mon.-Thurs. 10-4, Sat. 10-12. SIZE: Small. *STOCK: General small antiques including silver and plate, glass, pre-1950, £5-£500+.* PARK: Easy. TEL: 01840 250770; home/fax - 01566 880085; mobile - 07971 648107; e-mail - david-peter@craigmoor.freeserve.co.uk. SER: Valuations.

CALLINGTON

Country Living Antiques
Weston House, Haye Rd. PL17 7JJ. (Ian Baxter CBE). Resident. Est. 1990. Open 10-6. SIZE: Large - including barn. *STOCK: 19th C oak and pine country furniture, general antiques, £1-£2,000.* LOC: Town centre. PARK: Own. TEL: 01579 382245; fax - same. SER: Valuations; buys at auction.

CAMBORNE

Victoria Gallery & Bookshop
28 Cross St. TR14 8EX. (B.J. and J.P. Maker). Open Mon.-Fri. 10.30-5.15, other times by appointment. *STOCK: Books, pictures, general antiques, small furniture, silver and jewellery.* TEL: 01209 719268. SER: Valuations.

CAMELFORD

Corner Shop Antiques and Gallery
68 Fore St. PL32 9PG. (P.J. Tillett). Est. 1982. Open 9.30-5.30. SIZE: Small. *STOCK: General antiques including Torquay ware, Victorian watercolours, collector's items and bric-a-brac, £2-£1,000.* LOC: Main road. PARK: Nearby. TEL:

01840 212573; home - same; mobile - 07884 456247; e-mail - tillett18@aol.com. *Trade Only.*

CHACEWATER, Nr. Truro

Chacewater Antiques
5 Fore St. TR4 8PS. (Sandra McCall). Est. 1991. Open 10.30-4, Sat. 10-1. CL: Wed. *STOCK: Furniture, 17th-19th C, £100-£1,000; brass and copper, paintings, 19th to early 20th C, £80-£450.* LOC: 5 mins. from Truro. From A30 Chiverton roundabout towards Truro. PARK: Nearby. TEL: 01872 561411; home - 01209 711545.

CONNOR DOWNS, Nr. Hayle

Julie Strachey
Trevaskis Barn, Gwinear Rd. TR27 5JQ. Est. 1975. Open by appointment. SIZE: Medium. *STOCK: Decorative 18th-19th C farm and country furniture, especially tables, dressers, chests, wrought iron and unusual garden items.* TEL: 01207 613750; mobile - 07711 249939. SER: Packing and shipping. FAIRS: NEC. VAT: Stan.

CREMYLL

Cremyll Antiques
The Cottage, Cremyll Beach, Torpoint. PL10 1HX. (E. Kaszewski). BHI. Est. 1949. SIZE: Small. *STOCK: Clocks and watches, small items, jewellery, Victorian trinkets.* PARK: Own. TEL: 01752 823490. SER: Repairs (barometers, barographs, watches, clocks and jewellery).

DOBWALLS, Nr. Liskeard

Olden Days
Five Lanes. PL14 6JD. (F.J.C. Nancarrow and K.E.C. Trevellian). Est. 1980. Open 9.30-5.30, Sun. 11-4. SIZE: Medium. *STOCK: Period furniture, £50-£1,500; reclaimed and new pine furniture; bric-a-brac and collectables.* LOC: A38 between Liskeard and Bodmin. PARK: Easy and private behind shop. TEL: 01579 321577; home - same; e-mail - dobwallsantiques@ btinternet.com; website - www.oldendays.org. SER: Restorations; furniture made to order. VAT: Stan/Spec.

FALMOUTH

John Maggs
54 Church St. TR11 3DS. (C.C. Nunn). Est. 1900. Open 10-5. SIZE: Medium. *STOCK: Antiquarian prints and maps, exclusive limited editions.* LOC: Main street. PARK: At rear of shop. TEL: 01326 313153; fax - same; website - www.johnmaggs. co.uk. SER: Restorations; framing.

Old Town Hall Antiques
3 High St. TR11 2AB. (Mary P. Sheppard and Terence J. Brandreth). Est. 1986. Open 10-5.30, Sun. 11-4. SIZE: Large + trade store. *STOCK: Furniture including French, beds and mirrors, 19th-20th C, £100-£2,000; country smalls, china and collectables, 19th-20th C, £10-£60.* LOC: From edge of Falmouth follow signs towards marina, shop situated on right under road arch (one-way street). PARK: Easy. TEL: 01326 319437; home - 01326 377489; website - www.oldtownhallantiques.co.uk. SER: Storage and delivery. VAT: Global.

Rosina's
4 High St. TR11 2AB. (Mrs R. Gealer). Est. 1977. Open 11-4.30. *STOCK: Old dolls, bears, including limited edition, Steiff and artist bears, toys, linen and lace, clothes; modern miniatures. Fairies especially designed for Rosina's.* TEL: 01326 311406; home - 01326 219491. SER: Restorations.

Waterfront Antiques Market
1st Floor, 4 Quay St. TR11 3HH. Open 10-5. SIZE: 20 dealers. *STOCK: Furniture, pottery, porcelain, glass, silver, metalware, kitchenalia, pictures, books, clocks, jewellery, decorative and collectors' items.* TEL: 01326 311491.

GRAMPOUND, Nr. Truro

Pine and Period Furniture
Fore St. TR2 4QT. (S. Payne). Est. 1971. Open 10.30-5. *STOCK: Pine and period furniture.* TEL: 01726 883117. SER: Restorations.

Radnor House
Fore St. TR2 4QT. (P. and G. Hodgson). Est. 1972. Open 10-5. SIZE: Medium. *STOCK: Furniture and accessories, pre-1900.* Not Stocked: Jewellery, coins and weapons. LOC: A390. PARK: Easy. TEL: 01726 882921; home - same; e-mail - radnorantiques@aol.com. SER: Valuations; buys at auction.

HAYLE

Copperhouse Gallery - W. Dyer & Sons
14 Fore St. TR27 4DX. (A.P. Dyer). Est. 1900. Open 9-5.30. SIZE: Medium. *STOCK: Watercolours and oils, including Newlyn and St. Ives schools; small antiques, Art Deco and studio pottery.* LOC: Main road. PARK: Easy. TEL: 01736 752787; home - 01736 752960. SER: Framing.

LAUNCESTON

Antique Chairs and Museum
Colhay Farm, Polson. PL15 9QS. (Tom and Alice Brown). Est. 1988. Open seven days. SIZE: Large. *STOCK: Chairs, 18th to early 20th C.* LOC: Signed from A30. PARK: Easy. TEL: 01566 777485; fax - same; home - same; e-mail - chairs@brown7368.fslife.co.uk; website - www.antiquechairscolhay.co.uk. SER: Restorations; buys at auction.

Todd's
2 High St. and 8 Tower St. PL15 8ER. (B. Gallant and T. Mead). Est. 1997. Open 9-5, Sat. 9-4. SIZE: Medium and small. *STOCK: Furniture, from 18th C, £100-£2000; ceramics, from 18th C, £10-£400; reproduction period lighting, £40-£500.* PARK: Nearby. TEL: 01566 775007/ 772749; fax - 01566 775007. SER: Restorations. VAT: Stan/Spec.

LOOE

Dowling and Bray
Fore St., East Looe. PL13 1AE. Est. 1920. *STOCK: General antiques, furniture and brassware.* TEL: 01503 262797.

Tony Martin
Fore St. PL13 1AE. Est. 1965. Open 9.30-1 and 2-5 appointment advisable. SIZE: Medium. *STOCK: Porcelain, 18th C; silver, 18th-19th C, both £20-£200; glass, furniture, oils and watercolours.* LOC: Main street. TEL: 01503 262734; home - 01503 262228.

LOSTWITHIEL

John Bragg Antiques
35 Fore St. PL22 0BN. Open 10-5. CL: Wed. pm. *STOCK: Furniture, mainly period mahogany and Victorian.* LOC: 100yds. off A390. TEL: 01208 872827.

The Higgins Press
South St. PL22 0BZ. (Mrs Doris Roberts). Est. 1982. Open 10-4, Wed. and Sat. 10-1. SIZE: Small. *STOCK: Porcelain, Victorian and collectable, £5-£1,000; clocks and glass, Victorian to Art Deco, £5-£750; furniture, Georgian to 1930's, £10-£3,000.* LOC: Just off A390. PARK: Easy and nearby. TEL: 01208 872755; home - same; mobile - 07748 993370.

Old Palace Antiques
Old Palace, Quay St. PL22 0BS. (D. Bryant). Open 10-1 and 2-5. CL: Wed. pm. *STOCK: Pine, general antiques, books, postcards and collectors' items.* TEL: 01208 872909.

MARAZION

Antiques
The Shambles, Market Place. TR17 0AR.
(Andrew S. Wood). Est. 1988. Open Mon.-Fri.
10.15-5.30, also Sats. 1 Nov.-31 March. SIZE:
Medium. *STOCK: General antiques and
collectors' items including 19th-20th C pottery
and porcelain; Victorian to 20th C glass
including pressed; blue and white china, Art
Deco ceramics, Devon pottery, commemorative
ware, Goss and crested china, 1950's-60's pottery
and glass, bottles.* LOC: Main street. PARK:
Easy. TEL: 01736 711381; home - same.

PENRYN

Old School Antiques
Church Rd. TR10 8DA. (J.M. Gavin). Open 8.30-
6. *STOCK: General antiques.* TEL: 01326 375092.

Ruby Antiques Ltd
Grays Wharf, Commercial Rd. TR10 8AE. (Tracey
E. and Martin T. Platt). Est. 2001. Open Tues.-Sat.
10-5, Sun. and Bank Holidays 11-4. SIZE: Medium.
*STOCK: Victorian and Edwardian furniture
including chaises longues, chairs, pine boxes,
pictures, fire furniture including brass fenders,
candlesticks, brass and copper, paintings and prints;
blue and white, Gaudy Welsh and other ceramics,
£1-£2,500.* LOC: Old main road from Truro, by
river. PARK: Free nearby. TEL: 01326 379322;
mobile - 07989 537891/537892; home - 01872
863879; e-mail - mandtplatt@ntlworld.com.

Neil Willcox & Mark Nightingale
Jobswater, Mabe. TR10 9BT. Open by
appointment. *STOCK: Sealed wine and other
bottles, British and Continental 1650-1850, and
related items.* TEL: 01326 340533; fax - same; e-
mail - nightdes@aol.com; website - www.
earlyglass.com. SER: Valuations; mail order -
catalogue and photos supplied.

PENZANCE

Antiques & Fine Art
1 Queens Buildings, The Promenade. TR18 4DL.
(Elinor Davies and Geoffrey Mills). Est. 1985.
Open 10-4. SIZE: Medium. *STOCK: Furniture,
17th C to Edwardian, to £10,000; some
decorative pieces, to £250.* LOC: Next to
Queen's Hotel. PARK: Nearby. TEL: 01736
350509; home - 01736 350677; e-mail - enquiries
@antiquesfineart.co.uk; website - www.antiques
fineart.co.uk. SER: Valuations; restorations
(furniture including upholstery).

Chapel Street Antiques Arcade
61/62 Chapel St. TR18 4AE. Est. 1985. Open
9.30-5. SIZE: 20 dealers. *STOCK: Furniture,
pottery, porcelain, glass, silver, metalware,
kitchenalia, pictures, books, clocks, jewellery,
decorative and collectors' items.* TEL: Mobile -
07890 542708.

Daphne's Antiques
17 Chapel St. TR18 4AW. Est. 1976. Open 10-5.
SIZE: Medium. *STOCK: Early country furniture,
Georgian glass, Delft, pottery and decorative
objects.* TEL: 01736 361719.

Peter Johnson
62 Chapel St. TR18 4AE. (Peter Chatfield-
Johnson). Est. 1961. Open 9.30-5, Mon. by
appointment. SIZE: Small. *STOCK: Lighting,
19th-20th C, £25-£500; Oriental ceramics and
furniture, 18th-19th C, £25-£2,000; handmade
silk lampshades, 20th C, £25-£250.* LOC: Left at
top of Market Jew St. PARK: Easy. TEL: 01736
363267; home - 01736 368088. SER: Valuations;
restorations (soft furnishings).

Little Jem's
69 Causewayhead. TR18 2SR. (J. Lagden). Open
9.30-5. *STOCK: Antique and modern jewellery
(specialising in opal and amber), gem stones,
objets d'art, paintings, clocks and watches.* TEL:
01736 351400. SER: Repairs; commissions.

New Street Bookshop
4 New St. TR18 2LZ. (K.E. Hearn and C.J.
Bradley). Open 10-5. *STOCK: Books and
ephemera.* LOC: Close to town centre, just off
Chapel St. TEL: 01736 362758; e-mail -
eankelvin@yahoo.com.

The Old Custom House
53 Chapel St. TR18 4AF. (Manfred Baker and
Ulrich Grote). Est. 1997. Open 9-5.30. SIZE:
Medium. *STOCK: Porcelain and glass, silver and
small furniture, contemporary paintings.* TEL:
01736 331030.

Penzance Rare Books
43 Causewayhead. TR18 2SS. (Patricia
Johnstone). Est. 1990. Open 10-5. SIZE: Small.
STOCK: Anitquarian and secondhand books.
LOC: Top of Causewayhead. PARK: Nearby.
TEL: 01736 362140; home - 01736 367506; e-
mail - patricia.johnstone@btinternet.com. SER:
Valuations.

**Tony Sanders Penzance Gallery and
Antiques**
14 Chapel St. TR18 4AW. Est. 1972. Open 9-

5.30. SIZE: 3 floors. *STOCK: Oils and watercolours, 19th-20th C, £50-£5,000; glass, silver, china and small furniture; specialist in Newlyn and J F Pool of Hayle copper; contemporary art, paintings and bronzes.* TEL: 01736 366620/368461. VAT: Stan.

POLPERRO

Gentry Antiques
c/o Rod & Line, Little Green. PL13 2RF. (Marilyn Gentry). Est. 2000. Open 10-5. SIZE: Small. *STOCK: Ceramics, mainly blue and white; country furniture especially stickback chairs, Cornishware, kitchenalia, brass and copper, £10-£1,000.* PARK: At entrance to village. TEL: 01503 272361; website - www.cornishware collector.co.uk. SER: Valuations.

Past & Presents
1 Lansallos St. PL13 2QU. (Joe Askew and Melanie Jane Wray). Est. 1998. Open Nov.-Mar. 10-4, summer months 9-7. SIZE: Small. *STOCK: Oak and pine country furniture, oil lamps, Victorian kitchen enamelware and utensils, Staffordshire pottery, Beswick, Beatrix Potter, Royal Doulton character jugs, crested china.* LOC: Village centre. PARK: Nearby. TEL: 01503 272737; home - 01503 272984; e-mail - info@polperro-antiques.com; website - www.polperro-antiques.com.

REDRUTH

Evergreen Antiques
38 Fore St. TR15 2AE. (Miss A. Champion and Miss M. Jelf). Est. 1993. Open 10-4.30. SIZE: Medium. *STOCK: Victorian and Edwardian furniture including pine, table lamps, copper and brass.* LOC: Main street, opposite Post)ffice. PARK: Nearby. TEL: 01209 215634; mobile - 07870 195717.

The Old Steam Bakery
60A Fore St. TR14 7NU. (Stephen J. Phillips). Est. 1986. Open 10.30-5. SIZE: Large. *STOCK: Furniture including oak, 19th to early 20th C, £50-£100+; china and glass, early 20th C.* LOC: Next to main Post Office. PARK: Easy. TEL: 01209 315099; home - 01209 710650. SER: Valuations; restorations (furniture). VAT: Stan.

ST. IVES

Courtyard Collectables
Cyril Noall Sq., Fore St. TR26 1HE. (Janice Mosedale). Est. 1994. Open June to end Sept. 7 days 10-10; Oct., April and May 7 days 10-6; Nov. to March, Sat. and Sun. 10.30-4.30. SIZE:

Medium. *STOCK: 20th C collectables.* TEL: 01736 798809. SER: Valuations; buys at auction.

Mike Read Antique Sciences
1 Abbey Meadow, Lelant. TR26 3LL . Est. 1974. Open by appointment. SIZE: Small. *STOCK: Scientific instruments - navigational, surveying, mining, barometers, telescopes and microscopes, medical, 18th-19th C, £10-£5,000; maritime works of art and nautical artifacts.* LOC: Turn left on hill in village, heading towards St. Ives. PARK: Easy. TEL: 01736 757237. SER: Valuations; restorations. FAIRS: Scientific & Medical Instrument.

Tremayne Applied Arts
Street-an-Pol. TR26 2DS. (Roger and Anne Tonkinson). Est. 1998. Summer - Open 10.30-4.30, Sat. 10-1.30. CL: Wed. Winter - Open Mon., Fri. and Sat. mornings. *STOCK: Furniture, china, glass, paintings and prints, late 19th to late 20th C, £50-£3,000.* LOC: Central, close to tourist information office. PARK: Station. TEL: 01736 797779; fax - 01736 793222; home - 01736 753537.

STRATTON, Nr. Bude

Marhamchurch Antiques
Coach House, Cann Orchard. EX23 9TD. (Paul Fitzsimmons). Est. 1991. Open 9-5 by appointment only. SIZE: Small. *STOCK: Early oak, 16th-17th C; country oak, 17th-18th C including tables, chairs, coffers.* LOC: 1 mile from Marhamchurch village. PARK: Easy. TEL: 01288 359352; mobile - 07779 038891; e-mail - paul@marham churchantiques.co.uk; website - www. marhamchurchantiques.co.uk. FAIRS: Coopers.

TREGONY, Nr. Truro

Tregony Antiques
The Old Rectory, Fore St. TR2 5RW. (The Oliver Family). Open 10.30-5, (extended in summer), evenings and Sun. by appointment. SIZE: Medium. *STOCK: Ceramics, including Doulton stoneware, £10-£500; paintings and prints, 19th to early 20th C, £50-£1,000; furniture, 18th to early 20th C, £75-£3,000; brass, copper and treen, £10-£300.* Not Stocked: Silver and jewellery. LOC: Village centre, B3287. PARK: Easy. TEL: 01872 530225; home - same.

TRESILLIAN, Nr. Truro

Tresillian Antiques
The Elms. TR2 4BA. (Philip and Linda Buddell). Est. 1972. Open 9.30-5.30, Sun. by appointment. SIZE: Small. *STOCK: Oak and mahogany furniture,*

ALAN BENNETT

18th and 19th century Furniture, Porcelain Silver, Jewellery and Paintings

NEW BRIDGE HOUSE NEW BRIDGE STREET TRURO CORNWALL 01872 273296

Georgian, Victorian and Edwardian; collectables including china, ivory, silver and teddy bears; oils and watercolours, mainly landscape and marine. LOC: A390. PARK: Easy. TEL: 01872 520173; home - same; mobile - 07951 425937; e-mail - lulubudd@aol.com. SER: Valuations; restorations (furniture, canework and paintings).

TRURO

Alan Bennett
24 New Bridge St. TR1 2AA. Est. 1954. Open 9-5.30. SIZE: Large. STOCK: Furniture, £50-£5,000; jewellery and porcelain, to 1900, £5-£1,000; paintings and prints, £20-£2,000. LOC: Eastern side of cathedral. PARK: 100yds. from shop. TEL: 01872 273296. VAT: Stan/Spec.

Blackwater Pine Antiques
Blackwater. TR4 8ET. (J.S. Terrett). Open 9-6. STOCK: Pine and country furniture. TEL: 01872 560919. SER: Restorations; stripping; furniture made to order.

Bonython Bookshop
16 Kenwyn St. TR1 3BU. (Rosemary Carpenter). Est. 1996. Open 10.30-4.30. SIZE: Small. STOCK: Cornish books, £5-£200; topography, £5-£50; art, £5-£100. TEL: 01872 262886; e-mail - bonythonbooks@mobooks.freeserve.co.uk; website - www.abebooks.com. SER: Valuations; book search.

Bric-a-Brac
16A Walsingham Place. TR1 2RP. (Lynne and Richard Bonehill). Est. 1991. Open 9.30-5. SIZE: Small. STOCK: Militaria, £5-£2,000; small furniture, £20-£1,000; commemorative and crested china, £5-£150; collectors' items and bric-a-brac, 50p-£2,000; all 19th-20th C. LOC: Town centre, just off Victoria Sq. PARK: Multi-storey nearby. TEL: 01872 225200; e-mail - richard@bonehill3.freeserve.co.uk; website - www.bonehill3.freeserve.co.uk. FAIRS: Lostwithiel.

The Coinage Hall Antiques Centre
1 Boscawen St. TR1 2QU. (Graham and Pippa Kennedy). Est. 1994. Open 10-4.30. SIZE: Medium. STOCK: Fine art, furniture, paintings, sculpture, lighting, architectural items, collectables including postcards. LOC: City centre. PARK: Easy. TEL: 01872 262520; fax - same. SER: Valuations; restorations (fine art, furniture). FAIRS: Newark, Shepton Mallet, Westpoint.

Collector's Corner
45-46 Pannier Market, Back Quay. TR1 2LL. (Alan McLoughlin and John Lethbridge). Est. 1980. Open 9.30-4.30, Sat. 9-4. SIZE: Small. STOCK: Stamps, coins, postcards, medals, postal history, militaria, £5-£500. LOC: City centre. PARK: Nearby. TEL: 01872 272729; home - 01326 573509; mobile - 07815 668551; website - www.militarycollectables.co.uk. SER: Valuations.

WADEBRIDGE

St. Breock Gallery
St. Breock Churchtown. PL27 7JS. (R.G.G. Haslam-Hopwood). Est. 1970. Open 10-5. STOCK: Oils and watercolours, 20th-21st C; furniture, general antiques and objets d'art, £20-£2,000. LOC: Near Royal Cornwall Showground. PARK: Own. TEL: 01208 812543; fax - 01208 814671; e-mail - hopscotch@stbroeck.freeserve.co.uk; website - www.tomorrows-antiques.com. SER: Restorations; buys at auction; furniture copies made to order. VAT: Spec.

Victoria Antiques
21 Molesworth St. PL27 7DQ. (M. and S. Daly). Open Mon.-Sat. SIZE: Large. STOCK: Furniture, 17th-19th C, £25-£10,000. LOC: On A39 between Bude and Newquay. PARK: Nearby. TEL: 01208 814160. SER: Valuations; restorations. VAT: Stan/Spec/Global.

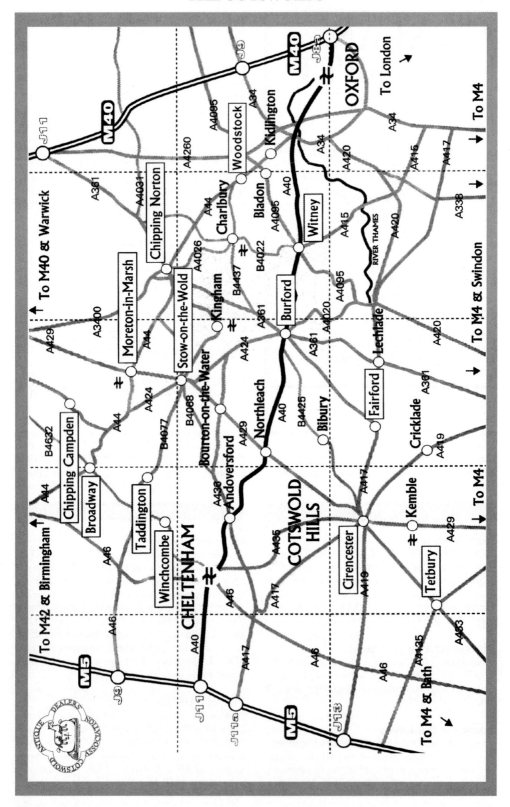

THE COTSWOLD ANTIQUE DEALERS' ASSOCIATION

*Buy Fine Antiques and Works of Art
at provincial prices in England's lovely
and historic countryside*

The Cotswolds, one of the finest areas of unspoilt countryside in the land, have been called "the essence and the heart of England." The region has a distinctive character created by the use of honey-coloured stone in its buildings and dry stone walls. Within the locality the towns and villages are admirably compact and close to each other and the area is well supplied with good hotels and reasonably priced inns. The Cotswolds are within easy reach of London (1½ hour by road or rail) and several major airports.

Cotswold sheep – which inspired the logo for the Cotswold Antique Dealers' Association – a quatrefoil device with a sheep in its centre – have played an important part in the region's history with much of its wealth created by the woollen industry. As for antiques, shops and warehouses of the CADA offer a selection of period furniture, pictures, porcelain, metalwork, and collectables unrivalled outside London.

With the use of the CADA directory on the following pages, which lists the names of its members, their specialities and opening times, visitors from all over the world can plan their buying visit to the Cotswolds. CADA members will assist all visiting collectors and dealers in locating antiques and works of art. They will give you advice on where to stay in the area, assistance with packing, shipping and insurance and the exchange of foreign currencies. They can advise private customers on what can realistically be bought on their available budgets, and if the first dealer does not have the piece which you are selecting he will know of several other members who will. The CADA welcomes home and overseas buyers in the certain knowledge that there are at least fifty dealers with a good and varied stock, a reputation for fair trading and an annual turnover in excess of £15,000,000.

BROADWAY

Fenwick and Fenwick Antiques
88-90 High St. WR12 7AJ. (George and Jane Fenwick). CADA. Est. 1980. Open 10-6 and by appointment. SIZE: Large. *STOCK: Furniture, oak, mahogany and walnut, 17th to early 19th C; samplers, boxes, treen, Tunbridgeware, Delft, decorative items and corkscrews.* PARK: Outside and own by arrangement. TEL: 01386 853227; after hours - 01386 841724; fax - 01386 858504. VAT: Spec.

Haynes Fine Art of Broadway   BADA LAPADA
Picton House Galleries, 42 High St. WR12 7DT. (A.C. Haynes). CADA. Open 9-6. SIZE: Large - 12 showrooms. *STOCK: Over 2000 British and European 16th-21st C oil paintings and watercolours.* LOC: From Lygon Arms, 100 yards up High St. on left. PARK: Easy. TEL: 01386 852649; fax - 01386 858187; e-mail - enquiries@haynes-fine-art.co.uk; website - www.haynesfineart.com. SER: Valuations; restorations; framing; catalogue available (£10). VAT: Spec.

H.W. Keil Ltd   BADA
Tudor House. WR12 7DP. CADA. Est. 1925. Open 9.15-12.45 and 2.15-5.30. SIZE: Large. *STOCK: Walnut, oak, mahogany and rosewood furniture; early pewter, brass and copper, tapestry, glass and works of art, 17th-18th C.* LOC: By village clock. TEL: 01386 852408; fax - 01386 852069. VAT: Spec.

John Noott Galleries   BADA LAPADA
28 High St., 14 Cotswold Court, and at The Lygon Arms, High St. WR12 7AA. (John, Pamela and Amanda Noott). CADA. Est. 1972. Open 9.30-1 and 2-5. SIZE: Large. *STOCK: Paintings, watercolours and bronzes, 19th C to Contemporary.* PARK: Easy. TEL: 01386 854868/858969; fax - 01386 854919. SER: Valuations; restorations; framing. VAT: Stan/Spec.

BURFORD

Jonathan Fyson Antiques
50 High St. OX18 4QF. (J.R. Fyson). CADA. Est. 1970. Open 9.30-1 and 2-5.30, Sat. from 10. SIZE: Medium. *STOCK: English and Continental furniture, decorative brass and steel including lighting and fireplace accessories; club fenders, mirrors, porcelain, table glass, jewellery.* LOC: At junction of A40/A361 between Oxford and Cheltenham. PARK: Easy. TEL: 01993 823204; fax - same; home - 01367 860223; e-mail - j@fyson.co.uk. SER: Valuations. VAT: Spec.

Gateway Antiques
Cheltenham Rd., Burford Roundabout. OX18 4JA. (M.C. Ford and P. Brown). CADA. Est. 1986. Open 10-5.30 and Sun. 2-5. SIZE: Large. *STOCK: English and Continental furniture, 18th to early 20th C; decorative accessories.* LOC: On roundabout (A40) Oxford/Cheltenham road, adjacent to the Cotswold Gateway Hotel. PARK: Easy. TEL: 01993 823678/822624; fax - 01993 823857; e-mail - enquiries@gatewayantiques. co.uk; website - www.gatewayantiques.co.uk. SER: Courier (multi-lingual). VAT: Stan/Spec.

David Pickup   BADA
115 High St. OX18 4RG. CADA. Est. 1977. Open 9.30-1 and 2-5.30, Sat. 10-1 and 2-4. SIZE: Medium. *STOCK: Fine furniture, works of art, from £500+; decorative objects, from £100+; all late 17th to mid 20th C, specialising in Arts and Crafts.* PARK: Easy. TEL: 01993 822555. FAIRS: Olympia. VAT: Spec.

Richard Purdon Antique Carpets   BADA
158 The Hill. OX18 4QY. CADA. Est. 1959. Open 10-5. SIZE: Medium. *STOCK: Antique Eastern and European carpets, village and tribal rugs, needlework, textiles and related items.* TEL: 01993 823777; fax - 01993 823719; e-mail - rp@richardpurdon.demon.co.uk; website - www.purdon.com. SER: Valuations; restorations. FAIRS: Hali (Olympia). VAT: Stan/Spec.

Manfred Schotten Antiques
109 High St. OX18 4RG. CADA. Est. 1974. Open 9.30-5.30 or by appointment. *STOCK: Sporting antiques and library furniture.* PARK: Easy. TEL: 01993 822302; fax - 01993 822055; e-mail - antiques@schotten.com; website - www.schotten.com. SER: Restorations; trophies. FAIRS: Olympia (Spring, Summer and Winter). VAT: Stan/Margin.

Brian Sinfield Gallery
150 High St. OX18 4QU. CADA. Est. 1972. Open 10-5.30, Mon. by appointment. SIZE: Medium. *STOCK: Mainly contemporary and late 20th C paintings, watercolours and sculpture.* PARK: Easy. TEL: 01993 824464; fax - 01993 824525; e-mail - gallery@briansinfield.com; website - www.briansinfield.com. SER: 8 exhibitions annually. VAT: Spec.

Swan Gallery

High St. OX18 4RE. (D. Pratt). CADA. Est. 1966. Open 10-5.30. SIZE: Large. *STOCK: Country furniture in oak, yew, walnut and fruitwood, 17th-19th C, £300-£12,000; Staffordshire figures and small decorative items, 18th-20th C, £50-£800.* PARK: Easy. TEL: 01993 822244. VAT: Mainly Spec.

CHIPPING NORTON

Antique English Windsor Chairs   BADA

9 Horse Fair. OX7 5AL. CINOA. CADA. Est. 1971. Open 10-5, prior telephone call advisable. CL: Mon. and Tues. except by appointment. *STOCK: 18th-19th C Windsor chairs, including sets.* TEL: 01608 643322; fax - 01608 644322; e-mail - michael@antique-english-windsor-chairs.com; website - www.antique-english-windsor-chairs.com. FAIRS: BADA; Olympia (June, Nov). VAT: Stan/Spec.

Key Antiques

11 Horse Fair. OX7 5AL. (J. Riley). CADA. Open 10-5.30 or by appointment. CL: Mon. and Tues. SIZE: Medium. *STOCK: English period oak and country furniture, 17th-19th C; domestic metalware, pottery and associated items.* LOC: Main road. PARK: Easy. TEL: 01608 644992/643777; e-mail - key.antiques@ btopenworld.com; website - www.keyantiques. com. VAT: Spec.

CIRENCESTER

William H. Stokes   BADA

The Cloisters, 6/8 Dollar St. GL7 2AJ. (W.H. Stokes and P.W. Bontoft). CADA. Est. 1968. Open 9.30-5.30, Sat. 9.30-4.30. *STOCK: Early oak furniture, £1,000-£50,000; brassware, £150-£5,000; all 16th-17th C.* LOC: West of parish church. TEL: 01285 653907; fax - 01285 640533; e-mail - post@williamstokes.co.uk; website - www.williamstokes.co.uk. VAT: Spec.

Rankine Taylor Antiques   LAPADA

34 Dollar St. GL7 2AN. CADA. Est. 1969. Open 9-5.30, Sun. by appointment. SIZE: Large. *STOCK: Furniture, 17th to early 19th C, £300-£35,000; silver, glass, rare and interesting objects.* Not Stocked: Victoriana. LOC: From church, turn right into West Market Place, via Gosditch St. into Dollar St. PARK: Own - private opposite. TEL: 01285 652529; website - www.antiquesnews.co.uk /rankin-taylor. VAT: Spec.

Patrick Waldron Antiques

18 Dollar St. GL7 2AN. Resident. CADA. Est.

1965. Open 9.30-1 and 2-6, Sun. by appointment. SIZE: Medium. *STOCK: Town and country furniture, 17th to early 19th C.* LOC: In street behind church. PARK: Easy and public behind shop. TEL: 01285 652880; home - same; workshop - 01285 643479; e-mail - patrick. waldron@virgin.net. SER: Restorations (furniture); buys at auction. VAT: Stan/Spec.

FAIRFORD

Blenheim Antiques

Market Place. GL7 4AB. (N. Hurdle). CADA. Resident. Est. 1972. Open 9.30-6.30. SIZE: Medium. *STOCK: 18th-19th C furniture and accessories.* PARK: Easy. TEL: 01285 712094. VAT: Stan/Spec.

Mark Carter Antiques

Gloucester House, Market Place. GL7 4AB. (Mark and Karen Carter). CADA. Est. 1979. Open 10-5.30, other times by appointment. SIZE: Large. *STOCK: English oak, fruitwood and country furniture, 17th-19th C, £500-£10,000.* PARK: Easy. TEL: 01285 712790; mobile - 07836 260567; e-mail - markcarterantiques@ hotmail.com. SER: Valuations. VAT: Stan/Spec.

MORETON-IN-MARSH

Astley House - Fine Art   LAPADA

Astley House, High St. GL56 0LL. (David, Nanette and Caradoc Glaisyer). CADA. CINOA. Est. 1973. Open 9-5.30 and by appointment. SIZE: Medium. *STOCK: Oil paintings, 19th-21st C, £800-£20,000.* LOC: Main street. PARK: Easy. TEL: 01608 650601; fax - 01608 651777; e-mail - astart333@aol.com; website - www.art-uk.com. SER: Restorations (oils and watercolours); framing. VAT: Spec.

Astley House - Fine Art   LAPADA

Astley House, London Rd. GL56 0LE. (David, Nanette and Caradoc Glaisyer). CADA. CINOA. Est. 1973. Open 10-1 and 2-5 and by appointment. CL: Wed. SIZE: Large. *STOCK: Oil paintings, 19th-21st C; large decorative oils and portraits.* LOC: Town centre. PARK: Easy. TEL: 01608 650608; fax - 01608 651777; e-mail - astart333@aol.com; website - www.art-uk.com. SER: Restorations (oils and watercolours); framing (porcelain). VAT: Spec.

Jon Fox Antiques

High St. GL56 0AD. CADA. Est. 1982. Open 9.30-5.30, Sun. 11-4, Tues. by appointment. SIZE: Large - 2 adjacent shops. *STOCK: 19th C garden items including urns, seats, troughs and* tools, £50-£5,000+; 18th -19th C country furniture £300-£3,000; treen, bygones, metalware, fireplace items. PARK: Easy. TEL: 01608 650325/650714. VAT: Spec.

Seaford House Antiques — LAPADA
Seaford House, High St. GL56 0AD. (Derek and Kathy Young). CINOA. CADA. Est. 1988. Open 10-5.30, Mon. and Tues. by appointment. SIZE: Medium. STOCK: Furniture, 18th C to Edwardian especially upholstered, £500-£5,000; English and Continental porcelain including Worcester, Coalport, Meissen, Sitzendorf, Sampson and Copeland, mirrors and paintings, 19th C, £100-£3,000. PARK: Easy. TEL: 01608 652423; fax - same. VAT: Spec.

STOW-ON-THE-WOLD

Duncan J. Baggott — LAPADA
Woolcomber House, Sheep St. GL54 1AA. CADA. Est. 1967. Open 9-5.30 or by appointment. CL: Bank Holidays. SIZE: Large. STOCK: 17th-20th C English oak, mahogany and walnut furniture, paintings, domestic metalwork and decorative items; garden statuary and ornaments. PARK: Sheep St. or Market Sq. TEL: 01451 830662; fax - 01451 832174. SER: Worldwide shipping; UK delivery. FAIRS: Exhibition Oct. annually (CADA).

Baggott Church Street Ltd — BADA
Church St. GL54 1BB. (D.J. and C.M. Baggott). CADA. Est. 1978. Open 9.30-5.30 or by appointment. SIZE: Large. STOCK: English furniture, 17th-19th C; portrait paintings, metalwork, pottery, treen and decorative items. LOC: South-west corner of market square. PARK: Market square. TEL: 01451 830370; fax - 01451 832174. SER: Annual exhibition - Oct.

Christopher Clarke Antiques Ltd — LAPADA
The Fosseway. GL54 1JS. (I.D., D.S. and S.F. Clarke). CADA. Est. 1961. Open 9.30-5.30 or by appointment. SIZE: Large. STOCK: Furniture including campaign, 17th-20th C; works of art, metalware, treen, pictures, decorative items, animal antiques. LOC: Corner of The Fosseway and Sheep St. PARK: Easy. TEL: 01451 830476; fax - 01451 830300; e-mail - cclarkeantiques@ aol.com; website - www.antiques-in-england. com. FAIRS: Olympia (June, Nov. and Feb).

Cotswold Galleries
The Square, GL54 1AB. (Richard and Cherry Glaisyer). CADA. FATG. Est. 1961. Open 9-5.30 or by appointment. SIZE: Large. STOCK: Oil paintings especially 19th-20th C landscape. PARK: Easy. TEL: 01451 870567; fax - 01451 870678; website - www.cotswoldgalleries.com. SER: Restorations; framing.

The John Davies Gallery
Church St. GL54 1BB. CADA. Est. 1977. Open 9.30-1.30 and 2.30-5.30. SIZE: Large. STOCK: Contemporary and late period paintings; limited edition bronzes. PARK: In square. TEL: 01451 831698; fax - 01451 832477; e-mail - daviesart @aol.com; website - www.the-john-davies-gallery.co.uk. SER: Restorations and conservation to museum standard.

Keith Hockin Antiques — BADA
The Square. GL54 1AF. CADA. Est. 1968. Open Thurs., Fri. and Sat., 10-5, other times by appointment or ring the bell. SIZE: Medium. STOCK: Oak furniture, 1600-1750; country furniture in oak, fruitwoods, yew, 1700-1850; pewter, copper, brass, ironwork, all periods. Not Stocked: Mahogany. PARK: Easy. TEL: 01451 831058; fax - same; e-mail - keithhockin@aol.com. SER: Buys at auction (oak, pewter, metalwork). VAT: Stan/Spec.

Huntington Antiques Ltd — LAPADA
Church St. GL54 1BE. (M.F. and S.P. Golding). CADA. CINOA. Resident. Est. 1974. Open 9.30-5.30 or by appointment. SIZE: Large. STOCK: Early period and fine country furniture, metalware, treen and textiles, tapestries and works of art. LOC: Opposite main gates to church. TEL: 01451 830842; fax - 01451 832211; e-mail - info@huntington-antiques.com; website - www.huntington-antiques.com. SER: Valuations; buys at auction. FAIRS: LAPADA. VAT: Spec.

Roger Lamb Antiques & Works of Art
LAPADA
The Square. GL54 1AB. CADA. Open 10-5. STOCK: 18th to early 19th C furniture especially small items, lighting, decorative accessories, oils and watercolours. TEL: 01451 831371. SER: Search.

Antony Preston Antiques Ltd — BADA
The Square. GL54 1AB. CADA. Est. 1965. Open 9.30-5.30 or by appointment. STOCK: 18th-19th C English and Continental furniture and objects; barometers and period lighting. TEL: 01451 831586; fax - 01451 831596. VAT: Stan/Spec.

Queens Parade Antiques Ltd — BADA
The Square. GL54 1AB. (Sally and Antony Preston). CADA. Est. 1965. Open 9.30-5.30.

SIZE: Large. *STOCK: 18th-19th C furniture, papier mâché, tôle peinte, needlework and period lighting.* LOC: Off Fosse Way. PARK: Easy. **TEL: 01451 831586; e-mail - antony@ antonypreston.com.** FAIRS: Grosvenor House; BADA. VAT: Stan/Spec.

Ruskin Decorative Arts

5 Talbot Court. GL54 1DP. (Anne and William Morris). CADA. Est. 1990. Open 10-1 and 2-5.30. SIZE: Small. *STOCK: Interesting and unusual decorative objects, Arts and Crafts furniture, Art Nouveau, Art Deco, glass and pottery, metalwork, 1860-1940.* LOC: Between the square and Sheep St. PARK: Nearby. TEL: 01451 832254; fax - 01451 832167; home - 01993 831880; e-mail - william.anne@ruskin decarts.co.uk. SER: Valuations. FAIRS: NEC.

Samarkand Galleries   `LAPADA`

7 & 8 Brewery Yard, Sheep St. GL54 1AA. (Brian MacDonald). CADA. CINOA. FRGS. Est. 1979. Open 10-5.30, Sun. by appointment. SIZE: Medium. *STOCK: Tribal and village rugs and artefacts, 19th C, £100-£10,000; fine decorative carpets, 19th-20th C, £1,000-£10,000+; kelims, 19th-20th C, £200-£2,000; also unique contemporary rugs and carpets.* LOC: Street adjacent to Market Sq. PARK: Easy. TEL: 01451 832322; fax - same; e-mail - mac@samarkand.co. uk; website - www.samarkand.co.uk. SER: Exhibitions; valuations; restorations; cleaning. FAIRS: Hali, Olympia (June). VAT: Stan/Spec.

Stow Antiques   `LAPADA`

The Square. GL54 1AF. (Mr and Mrs J. and Bruce Hutton-Clarke). CADA. Resident. Est. 1969. Open Mon.-Sat. 10-5.30, other times by appointment. SIZE: Large. *STOCK: Furniture, mainly Georgian, £500-£30,000; decorative items, gilded mirrors, £50-£10,000.* PARK: Easy. TEL: 01451 830377; fax - 01451 870018; e-mail - hazel@stowantiques.demon.co.uk. SER: Shipping worldwide.

Talbot Court Galleries

Talbot Court. GL54 1BQ. (J.P. Trevers). CADA. IMCOS. Est. 1988. Open 9.30-1 and 1.30-5.30. SIZE: Medium. *STOCK: Prints and maps, 1580-1880, £10-£5,000.* LOC: Behind Talbot Hotel in precinct between the square and Sheep St. PARK: Nearby. TEL: 01451 832169; fax - 01451 832167. SER: Valuations; restorations; cleaning; colouring; framing; buys at auction (engravings). VAT: Stan.

The Titian Gallery   `LAPADA`

Sheep St. GL54 1JS. (Ilona Johnson Gibbs). CADA. CINOA. Est. 1978. Open 10-5.30 and by appointment. SIZE: Medium. *STOCK: Fine 18th-19th C British and European oil paintings and watercolours, £1,000-£40,000.* LOC: Near The Fosseway. PARK: Adjacent and nearby. TEL: 01451 830004; fax - 01451 830126; e-mail - ilona@titiangallery.co.uk; website - www.titian gallery.co.uk. SER: Valuations; buys at auction (oils and watercolours). FAIRS: CADA exhibition. VAT: Spec.

STRETTON-ON-FOSSE

Astley House - Fine Art   `LAPADA`

The Old School. GL56 9SA. (David, Nanette and Caradoc Glaisyer). CADA. CINOA. Est. 1973. Open by appointment. SIZE: Large. *STOCK: Large decorative oil paintings, 19th-21st C.* LOC: Village centre. PARK: Easy. TEL: 01608 650601; fax - 01608 651777; e-mail - astart333@aol.com; website - www.art-uk.com. SER: Exhibitions; mailing list. VAT: Spe

TADDINGTON, Nr. Cheltenham

Architectural Heritage

Taddington Manor. GL54 5RY. (Adrian, Suzy, Alex and Adam Puddy). CADA. Est. 1978. Open 9.30-5.30, Sat. 10.30-4.30. SIZE: Large. *STOCK: Oak and pine period panelled rooms; stone and marble chimney pieces; stone, marble, bronze and terracotta statuary; garden ornaments, fountains, temples, well-heads, seats, urns, cisterns, sundials and summer houses.* PARK: Easy. TEL: 01386 584414; fax - 01386 584236; e-mail - puddy@architectural-heritage.co.uk; website - www.architectural-heritage.co.uk. SER: Worldwide delivery; shipping; bespoke ornaments, chimneypieces and panelled rooms. FAIRS: Chelsea Flower Show. VAT: Stan.

TETBURY

Breakspeare Antiques   `LAPADA`

36 and 57 Long St. GL8 8AQ. (M. and S.

Witney Antiques

LSA & CJ JARRETT AND RR SCOTT
96-100 CORN STREET, WITNEY,
OXON OX28 6BU, ENGLAND.
TEL: 01993 703902. FAX: 01993 779852.
E-mail: witneyantiques@community.co.uk
Website: www.witneyantiques.com

A fine bracket clock by Haley & Son, London. English. Circa 1830.

Antique Furniture, Clocks, Samplers & Early Needlework.

Breakspeare). CADA. Resident. Est. 1962. Open 10-5 or by appointment. CL: Thurs. SIZE: Medium. *STOCK: English period furniture - early walnut, 1690-1740, mahogany, 1750-1835.* PARK: Own. TEL: 01666 503122; fax - same. VAT: Spec.

Day Antiques BADA
5 New Church St. GL8 8DS. CADA. TADA. Est. 1975. Open 10-5. SIZE: Medium. *STOCK: Early oak furniture and related items.* PARK: Easy. TEL: 01666 502413; fax - 01666 505894; e-mail - dayantiques@lineone.net; website - www.dayantiques.com VAT: Spec.

Bobbie Middleton
58 Long St. GL8 8AQ. CADA, TADA. Open 10-1 and 2.30-5, Sun. by appointment. *STOCK: Country house furniture, mirrors and upholstered furniture, 18th-19th C.* LOC: On corner with New Church St. TEL: 01666 502761; e-mail - bobbiemiddleton@lineone.net. VAT: Spec.

WINCHCOMBE

Prichard Antiques
16 High St. GL54 5LJ. (K.H. and D.Y. Prichard). CADA. Est. 1979. Open 9-5.30, Sun. by appointment. SIZE: Large. *STOCK: Period and decorative furniture, £10-£20,000; treen and metalwork, £5-£5,000; interesting and decorative*

accessories. LOC: On B4632 Broadway to Cheltenham road. PARK: Easy. TEL: 01242 603566. VAT: Spec.

WITNEY

Colin Greenway Antiques
90 Corn St. OX28 6BU. CADA. Resident. Est. 1975. Open 9.30-5, Sat. 10-4, Sun. by appointment. SIZE: Large. *STOCK: Furniture, 17th-20th C; metalware, decorative and unusual items; garden furniture.* LOC: Along High St. to town centre, turn right, shop 400yds. on right. PARK: Easy. TEL: 01993 705026; fax - same; mobile - 07831 585014. VAT: Stan/Spec.

W.R. Harvey & Co (Antiques) Ltd LAPADA
86 Corn St. OX28 6BU. CADA. GMC. Open 9.30-5.30 and by appointment. SIZE: Large. *STOCK: Fine English furniture, £500-£150,000; clocks, mirrors, objets d'art, £250-£50,000; all 1680-1830.* LOC: 300 yards from Market Place. PARK: Easy. TEL: 01993 706501; fax - 01993 706601; e-mail - antiques@wrharvey.co.uk; website - www.wrharvey.co.uk. SER: Valuations; restorations; consultancy. FAIRS: BADA; Chelsea (March & Sept.); Olympia (June). VAT: Stan/Spec.

Witney Antiques BADA LAPADA
96/100 Corn St. OX28 6BU. (L.S.A. and C.J. Jarrett and R.R. Jarrett-Scott). CADA. Est. 1962. Open 10-5, Mon. and Tues. by appointment. SIZE: Large. *STOCK: English furniture, 17th-18th C; bracket and longcase clocks, mahogany, oak and walnut, early needlework and samplers.* LOC: From Oxford on old A40 through Witney via High St., turn right at T-junction, 400yds. on right. PARK: Easy. TEL: 01993 703902/703887; fax - 01993 779852; e-mail - witneyantiques@ community.co.uk; website - www.witney antiques.com. SER: Restorations. FAIRS: BADA; Grosvenor House. VAT: Spec.

WOODSTOCK

John Howard BADA
Heritage, 6 Market Place. OX20 1TE. TVADA. CADA. Open 10-5.30. SIZE: Small. *STOCK: 18th-19th C British pottery especially rare Staffordshire animal figures, bocage figures, lustre, 18th C creamware and unusual items.* PARK: Easy. TEL: 0870 4440678; fax - same; mobile - 07831 850544; e-mail - john@ johnhoward.co.uk; website - www.antique pottery.co.uk and www.Staffordshires.com. SER: Packing; insurance service to USA. FAIRS: Olympia; BADA. VAT: Spec.

CUMBRIA

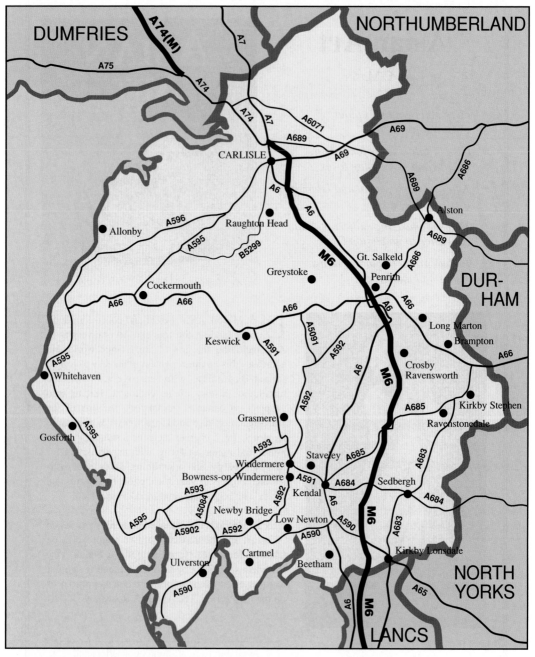

Dealers and Shops in Cumbria

Allonby	1	Grasmere	2	Penrith	5
Alston	2	Great Salkeld	1	Raughton Head	1
Beetham	1	Greystoke	1	Ravenstonedale	2
Bowness-on-Windermere	2	Kendal	7	Sedbergh	2
Brampton	3	Keswick	4	Staveley	1
Carlisle	3	Kirkby Lonsdale	1	Ulverston	2
Cartmel	4	Kirkby Stephen	2	Whitehaven	1
Cockermouth	3	Long Marton	2	Windermere	1
Crosby Ravensworth	1	Low Newton	2		
Gosforth	1	Newby Bridge	1		

ALLONBY

Cottage Curios
Main St. CA15 6PX. (B.Pickering). Est. 1965.
Open Sat. and Sun. 2-5.

ALSTON

Alston Antiques
Front St. CA9 3HU. (Mrs J. Bell). Est. 1976.
Open 10-5. CL: Tues. SIZE: Medium. *STOCK:
General antiques.* PARK: Easy. TEL: 01434
382129; mobile - 07876 501929.

Just Glass
Cross House, Market Place. CA9 3HS. (M.J.
Graham). Est. 1987. Open Wed., Thurs., Sat. 11-
4, Sun. 12-4. *STOCK: Glass, 1780-1920's, to
£800.* LOC: Town centre. PARK: Easy. TEL:
Home - 01434 381263; mobile - 07833 994948.
FAIRS: Narworth Castle.

BEETHAM, Nr. Milnthorpe

Peter Haworth
Temple Bank. LA7 7AL. Open by appointment.
*STOCK: Scottish and Staithes Group paintings
and watercolours, 1850-1950, £100-£30,000.*
LOC: 2 miles south of Milnthorpe on A6 to
Lancaster. PARK: Easy. TEL: 015395 62352; fax
- 015395 63438; e-mail - prhaworth@yahoo.com.
SER: Valuations; restorations; commissions.
VAT: Spec.

BOWNESS ON WINDERMERE

Something Old Something New
(Behind Royal Hotel), St Martin's Parade. Est.
1994. Open 11-5.30 including Sun. SIZE: 3
rooms. *STOCK: Rare vinyl, books, collectables,
antiques, cameras and bric-a-brac.* TEL: 01524
781718.

J.W. Thornton Antiques Supermarket
North Terrace. LA23 3AU. Est. 1972. Open by
appointment. SIZE: Large. *STOCK: Fine art,
general antiques, furniture, shipping and
architectural items, pine, bric-a-brac, paintings,
decorators items.* PARK: Nearby. TEL: 01229
580284; mobile - 07759 282142. SER:
Valuations; buys at auction; fairs vetting.

BRAMPTON

The Cumbrian Antiques Centre
St Martin's Hall, Front St. CA8 1NT. (S.T.
Summerson-Wright). Est. 1976. Open 10-5, Sun.
12-5. SIZE: Large. *STOCK: Wide range of
general antiques from silver and china to
longcase clocks and furniture.* LOC: A69 Carlisle
to Newcastle road into village, premises on right
as road forks. PARK: Easy. TEL: 016977 42515;
fax - same; home - 07889 924843; e-mail -
cumbrianantiques@hotmail.com. SER: Valuations;
restorations.

Something Old, Something New
46 Main St. CA8 1SB. (Joan Potts). Est. 1980.
Open 10-4.30. SIZE: Medium. *STOCK: Victorian
pine, country oak, mahogany, painted furniture
and decorative items.* LOC: A69. PARK: Easy.
TEL: 01697 741740; home - 01228 675587. SER:
Valuations; buys at auction.

CARLISLE

Carlisle Antiques Centre
Cecil Hall, Cecil St. CA1 1NT. (Wendy Mitton).
Open 9-4. *STOCK: Furniture, porcelain, clocks,
silver, jewellery, quilts and textiles.* LOC: M6
junction 43. PARK: Easy. TEL: 01228 536910; fax -
same; e-mails - wendymitton@aol.com; websites -
www.carlisleantiquescentre.co.uk and www.carlisle-
antiques.co.uk. SER: Repairs (clocks). FAIRS:
Naworth Castle, Brampton (March and Aug). Below
are listed the dealers at this centre.

Fine Pine
*Old and original stripped pine furniture;
mahogany and oak bedroom suites, large
furniture, china, quilts.*

It's About Time
(B. and W. Mitton). Est. 1985. *Period furniture,
porcelain, jewellery, textiles, glass, bric-a-brac.*
TEL: 01228 536910.

Warwick Antiques
(J. T. Wardrope). CMBHI. *Period furniture, wall,
bracket and longcase clocks.* SER: Valuations;
restorations (clocks).

**Saint Nicholas Galleries Ltd. (Antiques
and Jewellery)**
39 Bank St. CA3 8HJ. (C.J. Carruthers). Open
10-5. CL: Mon. SIZE: Medium. *STOCK:
Jewellery, silver, plate, Rolex and pocket watches,
clocks; collectables; Royal Doulton; Dux,
Oriental vases; pottery, porcelain; watercolours,
oil paintings; brass and copper.* LOC: City
centre. PARK: Nearby. TEL: 01228 544459.

Souvenir Antiques
Treasury Court, Fisher St. CA3 8RF. (J. Higham).
Est. 1985. Open 10-5. SIZE: Small. *STOCK:
Porcelain and pottery, Victorian to Art Deco, £5-
£500; coronation ware, crested china, local
prints, maps, postcards, Roman and medieval

The Antique Shop

*English antique furniture,
also decorative items*

Open 10.00am – 5.00pm
every day including Sunday

CARTMEL
GRANGE-OVER-SANDS
CUMBRIA

TELEPHONE 015395-36295
MOBILE TELEPHONE 07768 443757
www.anthemionantiques.co.uk

coins, antiquities, costume jewellery. Not Stocked: Textiles. LOC: City centre between Fisher St. and Scotch St. PARK: Nearby. TEL: 01228 401281; websites - www.souvenir antiques.co.uk and www. cumbriamaps.co.uk.

CARTMEL

Anthemion - The Antique Shop
BADA LAPADA
LA11 6QD. (J. Wood). Est. 1982. Open 10-5 including Sun. SIZE: Large. STOCK: English period furniture, 17th to early 19th C, £100-£30,000; decorative items, 17th-19th C, £20-£2,000. Not Stocked: Victoriana, bric-a-brac. LOC: Village centre. PARK: Easy. TEL: 01539 536295; mobile - 07768 443757. FAIRS: Olympia; LAPADA; NEC; Harrogate. VAT: Stan/Spec.

Norman Kerr - Gatehouse Bookshop
The Square. LA11 6PX. (H. and J.M. Kerr). PBFA. Est. 1933. Open weekend afternoons or by appointment. *STOCK: Antiquarian and secondhand books.* TEL: 01539 536247.

Peter Bain Smith (Bookseller)
Bank Court, Market Sq. LA11 6QB. Open 1.30-5 including Sun. From mid Nov. to Easter open

Wed.-Sat. 1.30-4.30. *STOCK: Books including antiquarian, especially children's and local topography.* LOC: A590 from Levens Bridge, off roundabout at Lindale by-pass through Grange-over-Sands. PARK: Nearby. TEL: 01539 536369. SER: Valuations.

Simon Starkie Antiques
Gatehouse Cottage, Cavendish St. LA11 6QA. Est. 1980. Open Wed., Fri. and Sat. 10.30-4.30, Sun. 11.30-4.30 and by appointment. SIZE: Small. *STOCK: Oak furniture, 17th-19th C, £100-£8,000; painted country furniture and clocks, 18th-19th C, £50-£2,500; Delftware and pewter, 18th-19th C, £30-£1,000.* LOC: 10 miles from M6, follow signs for Cartmel priory. PARK: Nearby. TEL: 015395 36453; home - 01229 861222. SER: Valuations; buys at auction (furniture and earthenware). VAT: Stan/Spec.

COCKERMOUTH

CG's Curiosity Shop
43 Market Place. CA13 9LT. (Colin Graham). Est. 1985. Open 10-12.30 and 1.30-5. SIZE: Medium. *STOCK: China, glass, collectables, militaria, books, linen, furniture, advertising, radios and unusual items, from 1800, £5-£1,000+.* LOC: End of main street, over the bridge. PARK: Nearby. TEL: 01900 824418; home - 01697 321108; mobile - 07712 206786; e-mail - cgcuriosity@hotmail.com; website - www.cgcuriosityshop.fws1.com. SER: Valuations; restorations; buys at auction; internet search. FAIRS: Newark.

Cockermouth Antiques
5 Station St. CA13 9QW. (E. Bell and G. Davies). Est. 1983. Open 10-5. SIZE: Large. *STOCK: General antiques especially jewellery, silver, ceramics, furniture, pictures, glass, books, metalware, quilts.* LOC: Just off A66, in town centre. PARK: Easy. TEL: 01900 826746; e-mail - elainebell54@aol.com.

Cockermouth Antiques Market
Courthouse, Main St. CA13 9LU. Est. 1979. Open 10-5. SIZE: Large - 4 stallholders. *STOCK: Victorian, Edwardian and Art Deco items, furniture, printed collectables, postcards, books, linen, china, glass, textiles, jewellery and pictures.* LOC: Town centre, just off A66. PARK: 50 yds. TEL: 01900 824346. SER: Restorations (furniture); stripping (pine). VAT: Stan/Spec.

CROSBY RAVENSWORTH, Nr. Penrith

Jennywell Hall Antiques
CA10 3JP. (Mrs M. Macadie). Resident. Est.

1975. Open most days, but phone call advisable. SIZE: Medium. *STOCK: Oak and mahogany furniture, paintings, interesting objects.* LOC: 5 miles from junction 39, M6. PARK: Easy. TEL: 01931 715288; home - same.

GOSFORTH

Archie Miles Bookshop
Beck Place. CA20 1AT. (Mrs C.M. Linsley). Open 10-5, Sun. 1-5.30, out of season opening times may vary. CL: Mon. *STOCK: Secondhand, antiquarian and out-of-print books, maps and prints.* TEL: 01946 725792.

GRASMERE

Lakes Crafts & Antiques Gallery
3 Oak Bank, Broadgate. LA22 9TA. (Joe and Sandra Arthy). Est. 1990. Open 15th Mar. - 31st Oct. 9.30-6 including Sun., other times 10-4.30. CL: 5th Jan. - 1st Feb. SIZE: Medium. *STOCK: Books, 18th-20th C, £1-£500; collectables and postcards, £1-£100; general antiques, 17th-20th C, £5-£250.* LOC: North side of village, off A591 on Ambleside to Keswick road. PARK: Easy. TEL: 01539 435037; fax - 01539 444271; home - 01539 444234. VAT: Stan.

The Stables
College St. LA22 9SW. (J.A. and K.M. Saalmans). Est. 1971. Open daily 10-6 Easter-November, other times, and in May, telephone call advisable. SIZE: Small. *STOCK: Brass and copper items, oil lamps, domestic bygones; pottery, silver, prints, Royal commemoratives, books.* Not Stocked: Weapons, furniture. LOC: By the side of Moss Grove Hotel. PARK: Easy. TEL: 01539 435453; home - same; e-mail - a.saalmans@btopenworld.com.

GREAT SALKELD, Nr. Penrith

G.K. Hadfield
Beck Bank. CA11 9LN. (G.K. and J.V. Hadfield (Hon. FBHI) and D.W. and N.R. Hadfield-Tilly). Est. 1972. Open 9-5. *STOCK: Clocks - longcase, dial, Act of Parliament, skeleton and carriage; secondhand, new and out of print horological books.* LOC: From M6, junction 40 take A686 towards Alston for 3 miles, left on B6412 signed Great Salkeld, about 1.5 miles, turn left at sign for Salkeld Dykes, 1st house on right. TEL: 01768 870111; fax - same; e-mail - gkhadfield@dial. pipex.com; website - www.gkhadfield.tilly.co.uk. SER: Restoration materials (antique clocks including hand cut hands and gilding); valuations (clocks and horological books). VAT: Stan/Spec.

GREYSTOKE, Nr. Penrith

Roadside Antiques
Watsons Farm, Greystoke Gill. CA11 0UQ. (K. and R. Sealby). Resident. Est. 1988. Open 10-6 including Sun. SIZE: Medium. *STOCK: Ceramics, longcase clocks, glass, Staffordshire figures, pot-lids, paintings, furniture, small collectables, jewellery, mainly 19th C, £5-£2,000.* LOC: B5288 Penrith/Keswick road to Greystoke, through village, first left then left again, premises second on right. PARK: Easy. TEL: 01768 483279.

KENDAL

Architectural Antiques
146 Highgate. LA9 4HW. (G. Fairclough). Est. 1984. Open 9.30-5. SIZE: Medium. *STOCK: Fireplaces, hobs, grates, marble and wooden chimney pieces, cast-iron inserts; Victorian tiles and kitchen ranges, unusual architectural items, Flemish brass chandeliers.* PARK: Easy. TEL: 01539 737147; fax - same; mobile - 07801 440031; e-mail - gordonfairclough@cs.com; website - www.architecturalantiques.co.uk. SER: Valuations; restorations (cast-iron).

Dower House Antiques
38/40 Kirkland. LA9 5AD. Open 10-6. *STOCK: Pottery, porcelain, paintings, furniture.* TEL: 01539 722778.

Granary Collectables
29 All Hallows Lane. LA9 4JH. (B. J. Cross). Est. 1998. Open 10-4.30. CL: Mon. SIZE: Small. *STOCK: Small collectables, pictures, kitchenalia, pottery, advertising and unusual items, £5-£100.* LOC: 100 yards from town centre, off main road. PARK: Easy. TEL: 01539 740770. SER: Valuations.

Kendal Studios Antiques
2/3 Wildman St. LA9 6EN. (R. Aindow). Est. 1950. Open 10.30-4, prior telephone call advisable. SIZE: Medium. *STOCK: Ceramics, maps and prints, paintings, oak furniture, art pottery.* LOC: Leave M6 at junction 37, follow one-way system, shop on left. PARK: Nearby. TEL: 01539 723291 (24 hrs. answering service). SER: Finder; shipping. VAT: Stan/Spec.

Shambles Antiques
17-19 New Shambles. LA9 4TS. (John G. and Janet A. Smyth). Est. 1992. Open Tues.-Sat. 10-5. SIZE: Medium. *STOCK: Arts and Crafts, art pottery, paintings, furniture; English pottery and porcelain, 18th-19th C; 20th C Scandinavian*

A South German giltmetal and patinated brass automaton 'blackamoor' clock, Augsburg, c.1610. 12¾in. high.

From an article entitled "Renaissance Clocks" by Richard Garnier which appeared in the April 2002 issue of *Antique Collecting*. For more details and to subscribe see page 21.

ceramics and glass; collectors' items, silver, all £5-£5,000. LOC: Off Market Place. PARK: Multi-storey nearby. TEL: 01539 729947; home - 01539 821590; mobile - 07710 245059; e-mail - jansmyth@btinternet.com; website - www. kendalantiques.co.uk. SER: Valuations.

The Silver Thimble
39 All Hallows Lane. LA9. (V. Ritchie). Est. 1980. Open 10-4. SIZE: Large. *STOCK: Jewellery, silver, glass, linen and lace, porcelain, copper and brass.* LOC: Turn left at second set of traffic lights on main road into Kendal from south, shop 200yds. on right. PARK: Easy. TEL: 01539 731456; e-mail - gmvritchie@aol.com. VAT: Spec.

Westmorland Clocks
Gillinggate. LA9 4HW. (G. and I. Fairclough). Est. 2002. Open 9.30-5. SIZE: Small. *STOCK: Clocks, especially Lancashire and Lake District longcase.* PARK: Easy. TEL: 01539 737147; website - www.westmorlandclocks.com. SER: Valuations; restorations.

KESWICK

Cat in the Window
29 Station St., (Beneath Ravensworth Hotel). CA12 5HH. (E. Fell). Est. 1980. Open 10.30-4.30. CL: Mon-Wed. SIZE: Small. *STOCK: Porcelain and pottery, copper, brass and pewter, small furniture.* LOC: Near Fitz Park. PARK: Easy and nearby. TEL: Mobile - 07989 717088. SER: Valuations; buys at auction. FAIRS: Colin Caygill in Cumbria.

The Country Bedroom
Lake Rd. CA12 5BZ. (W.I. Raw). Est. 1981. Open 9.30-5. *STOCK: Brass beds, iron and brass beds, mattress and base sets for antique beds, mirrors, linen, quilts, £150-£2,000.* LOC: Top of Main St. TEL: 017687 74881; fax - 017687 71424. VAT: Stan.

Keswick Bookshop
4 Station St. CA12 5HT. (Jane and John Kinnaird). PBFA. Est. 1994. Open April to end Oct. 10.30-5, and by appointment in winter. SIZE: Medium. *STOCK: Books, 18th-20th C; prints and maps, 18th-20th C.* LOC: Town centre. PARK: Nearby. TEL: 01768 775535; fax - 01228 528567; home - same. VAT: Stan/Spec.

John Young and Son (Antiques) LAPADA
12-14 Main St. CA12 5JD. Est. 1890. Open 9-5. SIZE: Large. *STOCK: 17th-20th C. furniture, clocks and decorative items for the home and garden.* LOC:

Town centre. PARK: At rear. TEL: 017687 73434; fax - 017687 73306. VAT: Stan/Spec.

KIRKBY LONSDALE

Architus Antiques
14 Main St. (J. Pearson). Est. 1990. Open 10-4.30, Sat. 10-5.30. SIZE: Medium. *STOCK: Victorian oil lamps, £100-£250; china and glass, jewellery and silver, Victorian to early 20th C.* LOC: First antique shop on left in village from A65 towards Kendal. TEL: 015242 72409; home - 015242 71517. SER: Valuations.

KIRKBY STEPHEN

Haughey Antiques   LAPADA
28/30 Market St. CA17 4QW. (D.M. Haughey). Est. 1969. Open 10-5 or by appointment. SIZE: Large. *STOCK: 17th-19th C oak, walnut and mahogany furniture.* LOC: M6, junction 38, 10 mins. to east. PARK: Own. TEL: 017683 71302; fax - 017683 72423; e-mail - info@haugheyantiques.co.uk; website - www.haugheyantiques.co.uk. SER: Valuations. FAIRS: Olympia; LAPADA, NEC. VAT: Stan/Spec.

David Hill
36 Market Sq. CA17 4QT. Est. 1965. Open

Thurs., Fri. and Sat. 9.30-4. SIZE: Medium. *STOCK: Country clocks and furniture, £10-£1,000; both 18th-19th C; glassware, £5-£75; curios, £5-£50; shipping goods, kitchenalia, iron and brassware.* LOC: On A685; M6 junction 38. PARK: Easy. TEL: 017683 71598.

LONG MARTON, Nr. Appleby

Ben Eggleston Antiques Ltd
The Dovecote. CA16 6BJ. (Ben and Kay Eggleston). Est. 1976. Open by appointment. SIZE: Large. *STOCK: Pine furniture, £5-£2,500.* LOC: 2 miles east of A66 between Appleby and Penrith. PARK: Easy. TEL: 017683 61849; home and fax - same; e-mail - ben@beneggleston antiques.co.uk. FAIRS: Newark. VAT: Stan/Spec.

LOW NEWTON, Nr. Grange-over-Sands

Utopia Antiques Ltd
Yew Tree Barn. LA11 6JP. (P.J. and Mrs J. Wilkinson). Est. 1970. Open 10-5 including Sun. SIZE: Large + warehouse. *STOCK: Indian Colonial furniture including reproduction, handicrafts and fabrics.* LOC: A590, 2 miles south of Newby Bridge. PARK: Easy. TEL: 015395 30065; e-mail - utopiaantique@utopiaantique.com; website - www.utopiaantique.com. VAT: Stan.

W.R.S. Architectural Antiques

Yew Tree Barn. LA11 6JP. (Clive Wilson). Open 10-5, Sun. 12-6 (winter 11-5). *STOCK: General architectural antiques including fireplaces; period furniture.* TEL: 01539 531498.

NEWBY BRIDGE

Townhead Antiques — LAPADA

LA12 8NP. (E.M. and C.P. Townley). Est. 1960. Open 10-5. SIZE: Large. *STOCK: 18th-19th C furniture, silver, porcelain, glass, decorative pieces; clocks, pictures.* LOC: A592. 1 mile from Newby Bridge on the Windermere road. PARK: Easy. TEL: 01539 531321; fax - 01539 530019; e-mail - Townhead@aol.com; website - www. Townhead-Antiques.co.uk. SER: Valuations. VAT: Stan/Spec.

PENRITH

Antiques of Penrith

4 Corney Sq. CA11 7PX. (Sylvia Tiffin and Lilian Cripps). Est. 1964. Open 10-12 and 1.30-5, Sat. 10-12.30. CL: Wed. SIZE: Large. *STOCK: Early oak and mahogany furniture, clocks, brass, copper, glass, china, silver plate, metal, Staffordshire figures, curios, paintings and collectables.* Not Stocked: Jewellery, books, rugs. LOC: Near Town Hall. PARK: Easy. TEL: 01768 862801. VAT: Stan/Spec/Global.

Brunswick Antiques

8 Brunswick Rd. CA11 7LU. (M. and L. Hodgson). Est. 1985. Open 10-5. SIZE: Small. *STOCK: Furniture, clocks, pottery, glass, metalware, 19th-20th C.* LOC: Town centre. PARK: Easy. TEL: 01768 899338; home - 01768 867164; e-mail - brunswickantiques@msn.com. VAT: Spec.

Joseph James Antiques

Corney Sq. CA11 7PX. (G.R. Walker). Est. 1970. Open 9-5. CL: Wed. SIZE: Medium. *STOCK: Furniture and upholstery, 18th C and Victorian, £10-£3,000; porcelain and pottery, £5-£1,000; silver and plate, pictures, £2-£800; all 18th-19th C.* LOC: On the one-way system in the town, 100yds. from the main shopping area (Middlegate), 50yds. from the town hall. PARK: Easy and 100yds. TEL: 01768 862065. SER: Re-upholstery; soft furnishings. VAT: Stan.

Penrith Coin and Stamp Centre

37 King St. CA11 7AY. (Mr and Mrs A. Gray). Resident. Est. 1974. Open 9-5.30. CL: Wed. Sept.-May. SIZE: Medium. *STOCK: Coins, B.C. to date, 1p-£500; jewellery, secondhand, £5-£500; Great Britain and Commonwealth stamps.* LOC: Just off town centre. PARK: Behind shop. TEL: 01768 864185; fax - same. SER: Valuations; repairs (jewellery). FAIRS: Many coin and stamp. VAT: Stan.

Sandgate Antiques

21 Sandgate. CA11 7TJ. (Steve Bates). Est. 1983. Open Mon., Tues., Fri. and Sat. 10-5 or by appointment. SIZE: Medium. *STOCK: Oak and country furniture, 17th to early 19th C; longcase clocks, Delft, decorative items.* LOC: Near town centre, past bus station up hill on right. PARK: Easy. TEL: 01768 899599; fax - same. VAT: Stan/Spec.

RAUGHTON HEAD, Nr. Carlisle

Cumbria Architectural Salvage

Birkshill. CA5 7DH. (K. Temple). SALVO. Est. 1988. Open 9-5, Sat. 9-12. SIZE: Medium. *STOCK: Fireplaces, 1700-1930, £150-£1,500; kitchen ranges, cast-iron radiators, bathroom fittings, doors, bricks and granite setts, building materials, sandstone, flags, balusters and staircase parts.* LOC: 9 miles from Carlisle. PARK: Easy. TEL: 01697 476420; home - same; fax - 01697 476754. SER: Valuations; restorations (fireplaces and ranges).

RAVENSTONEDALE, Nr Kirkby Lonsdale

The Book House

Fallowfield. CA17 4NG. (C. and M. Irwin). PBFA. Est. 1963. Open 9-5. CL: Tues. *STOCK: Books, mainly 19th-20th C, £1-£1,000; some postcards, 20th C, 25p-£20.* LOC: Off A685. Near top of village street set back on left. PARK: Easy. TEL: 015396 23634; fax - same; e-mail - enquiries@thebookhouse.co.uk SER: Valuations. FAIRS: Northern PBFA. VAT: Stan.

Winton Hall Antiques

Rowfoot Farm. CA17 4NN. (S. Baldwick). Resident. Est. 1975. Open 9-5 including Sun. SIZE: Large. *STOCK: Oak and country furniture, 1600-1800, £100-£12,000; mahogany, 1750-1830, £100-£10,000.* LOC: Midway between village and The Fat Lamb Inn, 1.5 miles from A685. PARK: Easy. TEL: 015396 23669. SER: Valuations; buys at auction. VAT: Stan/Spec. *Trade Only.*

SEDBERGH

R. F. G. Hollett and Son

6 Finkle St. LA10 5BZ. (R. F. G. and C. G. Hollett). Est. 1951. Open Wed.-Sat.10-12 and

1.30-5. SIZE: Large. *STOCK: Antiquarian books, 15th-20th C, £20-£20,000+; maps, prints and paintings, 17th-19th C, £20-£5,000+.* LOC: Town centre. PARK: Free nearby. TEL: 015396 20298; fax - 015396 21396; e-mail - hollett@sedbergh.demon.co.uk; website - www. holletts-rarebooks.co.uk. SER: Valuations. VAT: Stan.

Stable Antiques

Wheelwright Cottage, 15-16 Back Lane. LA10 5AQ. Est. 1970. Open 10-6 or by appointment. *STOCK: Small furniture, early metal, brass, copper, silver, china, prints, small collectors' items, treen, tools.* LOC: 5 miles from exit 37, M6. PARK: Outside shop. TEL: 015396 20251; e-mail - antique.thurlby@amserve.net. SER: Search.

Staveley Antiques

27/29 Main St. LA8 9LU. (P. John Corry). Est. 1991. Open 10-5, Sun. by appointment. SIZE: Large. *STOCK: Brass and iron bedsteads, 1830-1930, £200-£1,200; French walnut bedsteads, from 1880, £500-£2,000; lighting, 1880-1935, from £50; fire-irons, kerbs and metalware, from 1850, from £50.* LOC: Between Kendal and Windermere on A591 (now bypassed). PARK: Easy. TEL: 01539 821393; home - 01539 821123; e-mail - john@staveley-antiques.co.uk; website - www.staveley-antiques.co.uk. SER: Valuations; restorations (brass and iron bedsteads, metalware).

A1A Antiques

59B Market St. LA12 7LT. (J.W. Thornton). Est. 1960. Telephone for appointment, preferably before 8am or between 8-11pm. SIZE: Large. *STOCK: Bric-a-brac, clocks, furniture, shipping items, pictures, decorators items.* PARK: Easy. TEL: 01229 580284; mobiles - 07974 788525 and 07759 282142. SER: Valuations; restorations; buys at auction; fairs vetting.

Elizabeth and Son

Market Hall. (J.R. Bevins). Est. 1960. Open 9-5. CL: Wed. SIZE: Medium. *STOCK: Victorian and Edwardian glass, silver, brass and copper, gold and silver jewellery, books.* LOC: Town centre. PARK: Easy. TEL: 01229 582763.

Michael Moon - Antiquarian Booksellers

19 Lowther St. CA28 7AL. (M. and S. Moon).

SBA. PBFA. Est. 1970. Open 9.30-5. SIZE: Large. *STOCK: Antiquarian books including Cumbrian topography.* LOC: Opposite Clydesdale Bank. PARK: Nearby. TEL: 01946 599010. FAIRS: PBFA Northern. VAT: Stan.

Joseph Thornton Antiques

4 Victoria St. LA23 1AB. (J.W. Thornton). Est. 1971. Open by appointment. SIZE: Large. *STOCK: General antiques, art, architectural and decorators' items, clocks, bric-a-brac.* LOC: 50yds. from rail station. PARK: Easy. TEL: 01229 580284; mobiles - 07759 282142 and 07974 788525. SER: Valuations; buys at auction; fairs vetting.

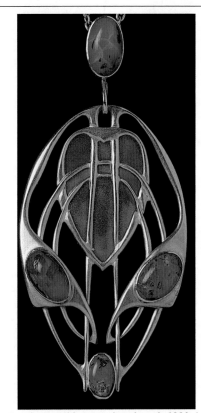

Pendant; gold, enamel and opal, 1900-4. Around £10,000. (John Jesse Collection. Photograph Michael Bruce)

From an article entitled "A Passionate Endevour Collecting Archibald Knox" by Stephen A. Martin which appeared in the December/January 2002 issue of ***Antique Collecting***. For more details and to subscribe see page 21.

DERBYSHIRE

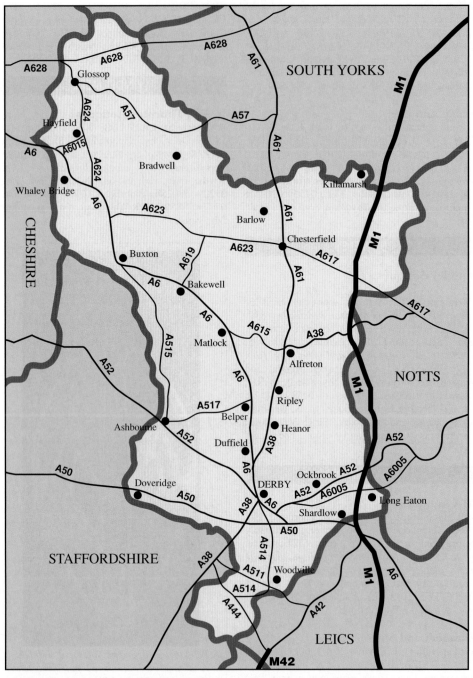

Dealers and Shops in Derbyshire

Alfreton	2	Derby	5	Matlock	1
Ashbourne	10	Doveridge	1	Ockbrook	1
Bakewell	4	Duffield	1	Ripley	2
Barlow	2	Glossop	1	Shardlow	1
Belper	3	Hayfield	2	Whaley Bridge	2
Bradwell	1	Heanor	1	Woodville	1
Buxton	5	Killamarsh	1		
Chesterfield	3	Long Eaton	1		

ALFRETON

Alfreton Antiques Centre
11 King St. DE55 7AF. (Helen Dixon). Est. 1996. Open 10-4.30, Sun. 11-4.30. SIZE: Large - 40 dealers. *STOCK: Wide range of furniture, ceramics, books, postcards, lighting, metalware, glass, collectables, Deco, costume jewellery, pictures, Langley Artware pottery, militaria, silver.* LOC: Off junction 28, M1, A38 to Alfreton, King St. is main street up to traffic lights, shop on right before the lights. PARK: Easy. TEL: 01773 520781; home - 01773 852695; mobile - 07970 786968; e-mail - alfreton antiques@supanet.com; website - www. alfretonantiques.supanet.com. SER: Valuations; Denby replacement service; restorations (ceramics). FAIRS: Antiques in the Park, Kedleston.

Steam-models.uk.com
31-32 South St., Riddings. DE55 4EJ. (Richard Evison). Est. 1990. Open 9-5, Sat. by appointment. SIZE: Small. *STOCK: Steam models and advertising figures, 20th C.* LOC: A610 from junction 26, M1 to Codnor. Right at traffic lights, right again to Riddings. PARK: Easy. TEL: 01773 541527; fax - 01773 541527; e-mail - raevison@aol.com; website - www. steam-models.uk.com. SER: Valuations; restorations (steam models); buys at auction (steam models). VAT: Stan.

ASHBOURNE

Ashbourne Antiques Ltd
Warehouse, Blake House, Shirley. DE6 3AS. (Robert Allsebrook). Est. 1977. Open by appointment. SIZE: Small. *STOCK: English furniture, 17th-20th C and hand-made copies.* LOC: A52 Ashbourne/Derby. PARK: Easy. TEL: 01335 361236; mobile - 07970 094883. SER: Restorations; cabinet making; removals; packing and shipping. VAT: Stan.

Daniel Charles Antiques
33 Church St. DE6 1AE. (Keith and Hayley Phillips-Moul). Est. 2000. Open 10-5.30. SIZE: Medium. *STOCK: Furniture and fine art, 17th-18th C, to £1,000+.* PARK: Easy. TEL: 01335 300002; fax - 01335 348200; mobile - 07050 129250. SER: Restorations (furniture and porcelain); buys at auction. VAT: Stan/Spec.

Pamela Elsom - Antiques
5 Church St. DE6 1AE. Est. 1963. Open Thurs., Fri. and Sat. 10-5, other days and times by appointment. SIZE: Medium. *STOCK: Furniture,* £20-£10,000, metalware, both 17th-19th C; period smalls, general antiques, treen, pottery, glass, secondhand books. Not Stocked: Coins, militaria. LOC: On A52. PARK: Easy. TEL: 01335 343468/344311. SER: Valuations. VAT: Spec.

Folk & Country Antiques
21 Church St. DE6 1AE. (R. and K. Beech). Est. 1977. Open 10-5. CL: Mon. SIZE: Small. *STOCK: Painted and country furniture and associated smalls.* PARK: Easy. TEL: 01335 342598; home - 01335 360229.

J H S Antiques Ltd `LAPADA`
45 Church St. (Julian Howard Snodin). CINOA. Est. 1972. Open 10-5. CL: Mon. and Wed. SIZE: Medium. *STOCK: 17th C oak, £1,000-£15,000; metalware, 17th to early 19th C, £50-£1,000; carvings, 17th to early 18th C, £300-£1,000.* LOC: A52 from junction 25, M1. PARK: Easy. TEL: 01335 347733. VAT: Spec.

Manion Antiques
23 Church St. DE6 1AE. (Mrs V.J. Manion). Est. 1984. Open Thurs., Fri. and Sat. 10-5.30, other times by appointment. SIZE: Small. *STOCK: Porcelain, paintings, silver, jewellery, small furniture, £50-£100+.* PARK: Outside. TEL: 01335 343207; home - same; mobile - 07968 067316. SER: Valuations.

Pine and Decorative Items
38 Church St. DE6 1AJ. (M. and G. Bassett). Est. 1980. Open 10-5. CL: Wed. and Sun. except by appointment. SIZE: Small + warehouse. *STOCK: English and French pine and country furniture; garden furniture, ironwork, kitchenalia, 18th C to 1950's, from £10.* TEL: 01335 300061; fax - same; e-mail - mgbassett@aol.com; website - www.antiques-atlas.com. VAT: Stan.

Rose Antiques
37 Church St. DE6 1AJ. Est. 1982. Open 10-5. SIZE: Medium. *STOCK: Furniture, silver, porcelain, jewellery, copper, brass and pine.* LOC: A52. PARK: Easy. TEL: 01335 343822; home - 01335 324333.

Spurrier-Smith Antiques `LAPADA`
28, 30 and 39 Church St. DE6 1AJ. (I. Spurrier-Smith). Est. 1973. Open 10-5, Wed. and Sun. by appointment. SIZE: Large (8 showrooms) + warehouse. *STOCK: Furniture, oils, watercolours, porcelain, pottery, metalware, instruments, Oriental bronzes, collectables, pine, decorative items. Warehouse - pine and American export goods.* PARK: Easy. TEL:

01335 343669/342198; home - 01629 822502; e-mail - ivan@spurrier-smith.fsnet.co.uk; website - www.spurrier-smith.co.uk. SER: Valuations; restorations (furniture). VAT: Stan/Spec.

Kenneth Upchurch
30B Church St. DE6 1AE. Est. 1972. *STOCK: Oil paintings and watercolours, mainly 19th C; pottery and porcelain.* TEL: 01332 754499.

BAKEWELL

Peter Bunting Antiques `BADA` `LAPADA`
Harthill Hall, Alport. DE45 1LH. Est. 1980. Open by appointment. SIZE: Medium. STOCK: Early oak, country furniture, portraits and period decoration. LOC: On B5056. PARK: Own. TEL: 01629 636203; fax - 01629 636101; mobile - 07860 540870. VAT: Stan/Spec.

Chappells Antiques Centre `BADA`
King St. DE45 1DZ. Est. 1992. Open 10-5, Sun. 12-5. STOCK: Period furniture, decorative and collectors' items, 17th-20th C. LOC: King St is signposted B5055, Monyash, off the A6. PARK: Agricultural Centre (entrance off A6) and Smith's Island (off Baslow Rd.) 5 mins walk from Centre. TEL: 01629 812496; fax - 01629 814531; website - www.chappells antiquescentre.com. Below are listed the dealers at this market.

Allens
20th C ceramics and secondhand books.

Barbara Austin
Linen, lace and small textile items.

Rex Boyer Antiques
18th-19th C furniture and decorative objects.

Cambridge Fine Art
(Nicholas Lury). *Period British and Continental paintings.*

Chappell's Antiques & Fine Art `BADA`
Est. 1940. 17th-19th C English furniture, oil paintings, porcelain, pottery, metalwork, clocks and decorative items. VAT: Stan/Spec.

Clocks in the Peak
Longcase clocks, specialising in Derbyshire makers.

Cottage Antiques `LAPADA`
18th-19th C furniture, glass, treen, textiles, furnishing and decorative items.

Stephanie Davison Antiques
Early English oak and country furniture.

Roger de Ville
19th C pottery and porcelain, specialising in commemoratives.

J. Dickinson
Maps, prints and books.

Elizabeth Ann Antiques
Furniture and decorative items.

Elizabeth Antiques
General antiques and collectables.

G.W. Ford & Son Ltd `LAPADA`
(I.G.F. Thomson). Est. 1890. *Mahogany and country furniture, 18th-19th C, £50-£5,000; sculpture, 19th to early 20th C, £50-£3,000; collectable and decorative items, 18th-19th C, £10-£1,200.* TEL: Home - 01246 410512; fax - same. SER: Valuations; restorations (furniture, silver and EP). VAT: Stan/Spec.

Ganymede Antiques
18th-19th C clocks, furniture, silver and plate, pewter, brass, pharmaceutical and scientific instruments.

Brian L. Hills
Period furniture, decorative items, paintings, sculpture and works of art.

J.H.S. Antiques Ltd `LAPADA`
17th to early 19th C country furniture, Staffordshire, treen and metalware.

Shirley May Antiques & Collectables
Kitchenalia, Cornish, Denby and textiles.

Millennium Antiques
Fine English silver, silver plate, glass and bijouterie.

Walter Moores & Son LAPADA
18th-19th C furniture and decorative items.

M.F. Morris Antiques
Fine Derby, Royal Crown Derby and Lynton porcelain.

Old Country Antiques
Sporting antiques, luggage and Beswick animals.

Paraphernalia Lighting
Antique lighting and decorative arts.

Judy Portway
(Benjamin Henry & Co)Vintage and designer costume jewelley and accessories.

Pye Antiques
Early blue and white, ironstone, Dux, wall clocks and barometers.

Renaissance Antiques
Pottery, papier-mâché, metals, glass and objects d'art.

Scarlett Antiques
Victorian to 1930's jewellery, clocks and watches.

Sandra Wallhead Antiques
19th to early 20th C furniture, cranberry glass, dolls, jewellery and objets d'art.

N.I. Wilkinson
19th-20th C collectables.

Michael Wisehall Antiques BADA
Furniture, plate, glass, pictures, metalware and pottery.

Martin and Dorothy Harper Antiques
LAPADA
King St. DE45 1DZ. Est. 1973. Open 10-5, Sun. and other times by appointment. CL: Mon. and Thurs. SIZE: Medium. *STOCK: Furniture, £75-£7,500; metalware, £30-£500; glass, £15-£150; all 17th to late 19th C.* PARK: Easy. TEL: 01629 814757; mobile - 07885 347134. SER: Valuations; restorations; buys at auction. VAT: Stan/Spec.

Michael Pembery Antiques
Peppercorn House, King St. DE45 1FD. (M. and L. Pembery). Est. 1967. Open 10-5. SIZE: Medium. *STOCK: Furniture, £500-£4,000; metalware, £100-£1,000; objets d'art, £100-£1,500; all 18th-19th C.* PARK: Nearby. TEL:

01629 814161. SER: Valuations; restorations. VAT: Stan/Spec.

BARLOW, Nr. Dronfield

Byethorpe Furniture
Shippen Rural Business Centre, Church Farm. S18 7TR. (Brian Yates). Est. 1977. Open 9.30-5.30. SIZE: Medium. *STOCK: Oak, mahogany and pine country and classical furniture.* PARK: Easy. TEL: 01142 899111; fax - same; website - www.byethorpe.com. SER: Restorations (furniture); specialist woodwork; upholstery; French polishing; hand-made reproductions. VAT: Stan/Spec.

Hackney House Antiques
Hackney Lane, S18 7TD. (Mrs J.M. Gorman). Resident. Est. 1984. Open Tues.-Sun. 9-6. SIZE: Small. *STOCK: Furniture, 18th-19th C; prints, linen, silver, longcase and wall clocks.* LOC: B6051 NW of Chesterfield. PARK: Easy. TEL: 01142 890248.

BELPER

Derwentside Antiques
Derwent St. DE56 1WN. Est. 1995. Open 8.30-5.30, Sun. 8.30-5. SIZE: Large. *STOCK: General antiques mainly furniture.* LOC: Just off A6. PARK: Own. TEL: 01773 828008; fax - 01773 828983; e-mail - enquires@derwentsidehome centre.co.uk; website - www.derwentsidehome centre.co.uk. SER: Restorations; sourcing of period furniture.

Sweetings (Antiques 'n' Things)
1 & 1a The Butts. DE56 1HX. (K.J. and J.L. Sweeting). Est. 1971. Open daily. SIZE: Large. *STOCK: Pre 1940's furniture including stripped pine, oak, mahogany, satinwood, £20-£1,000.* LOC: Off A6, near Market Place. PARK: Easy. TEL: 01773 825930/822780. SER: Valuations; restorations (pine and satinwood); shipping. VAT: Stan.

Neil Wayne "The Razor Man"
The Cedars (rear of 55 Field Lane), DE56 1DD. Resident. Est. 1969. Open every day 9.30-6 by appointment. SIZE: Medium. *STOCK: Razors and shaving items, 18th to early 19th C, £20-£300.* PARK: Easy. TEL: 01773 824157; fax - 01773 825573; e-mail - neil.wayne@derbyshire-holidays.com.

BRADWELL

Bradwell Antiques Centre
Newburgh Hall, Netherside. Est. 2000. Open 10-5, Sun. 11-5. SIZE: 30 dealers. *STOCK: Wide range of general antiques, 18th-20th C, £5-£5,000.* LOC: A625 Hope Valley road, turn opposite Travellers Rest public house on to B6049. PARK: Own. TEL: 01433 621000; fax - same; e-mail - info@bradwellantiques.com; websites - www.bradwellantiques.com and www.antiquestrail.com. SER: Restorations (furniture); buys at auction.

BUXTON

The Antiques Warehouse
25 Lightwood Rd. SK17 7BJ. (N.F. Thompson). Est. 1983. Open 10.30-4 or by appointment. SIZE: Large. *STOCK: British furniture, mainly mahogany, rosewood and walnut, 17th-20th C; paintings, silver, metalware, smalls, clocks including longcase, Victorian brass and iron bedsteads.* LOC: Off A6. PARK: Own at rear. TEL: 01298 72967; home/fax - 01298 22603; mobile - 07947 050552. SER: Valuations; restorations; buys at auction.

Maggie Mays
Unit 10, Cavendish Arcade. SK17. (Mrs J. Wild). Est. 1993. Open 10.30-5. CL: Mon. *STOCK: Victorian furniture and effects, £35-£800; Art Deco glassware, mirrors, pottery, £20-£500; Edwardian furniture, £100-£800.* LOC: Opposite Turners Memorial on Terrace Road. PARK: Easy. TEL: Mobile - 07831 606003; home - 01663 733935. SER: Valuations; buys at auction.

The Penny Post Antiques
9 Cavendish Circus. SK17 6AT. (D. and R. Hammond). Est. 1978. Open 10-5. SIZE: Small. *STOCK: Pictures, commemoratives, crested china, shaving mugs and other collectables; furniture; general antiques.* LOC: Town centre, opposite Palace Hotel. PARK: Easy. TEL: Home - 01298 25965.

West End Galleries
8 Cavendish Circus. SK17 6AT. (A. and A. Needham). Est. 1955. Open 9-5, Sat. 9-4. SIZE: Medium. *STOCK: French and English furniture; clocks, paintings, works of art, bronzes.* LOC: A6. PARK: Easy. TEL: 01298 24546. VAT: Spec.

What Now Antiques
Cavendish Arcade, The Crescent. SK17 6BQ. (L. Carruthers). Est. 1987. Open 10-5, Sun. 2-5. CL: Mon. SIZE: Small. *STOCK: General antiques and collectables including Art Deco pottery, small silver items, jewellery, textiles, lighting, clocks, Victorian and Edwardian furniture, £1-£1,000.* LOC: Central. PARK: Nearby. TEL: 01298 27178; mobile - 07977 369878; e-mail - ally4antiques@ic24.net. SER:Valuations; export; foreign trade.

CHESTERFIELD

Anthony D. Goodlad
26 Fairfield Rd., Brockwell. S40 4TP. Est. 1974. Open by appointment. SIZE: Small. *STOCK: General militaria, WWI and WWII.* LOC: Close to town centre. PARK: Easy. TEL: 01246 204004. FAIRS: Major UK Arms.

Ian Morris
479 Chatsworth Rd. S40 3AD. Est. 1970. Open 1-5 or by chance or appointment. SIZE: Medium. *STOCK: Furniture, 18th-20th C, £50-£2,000; pictures, small items.* LOC: A619 to Baslow and Chatsworth House. PARK: Easy. TEL: 01246 235120. VAT: Stan/Spec.

Marlene Rutherford Antiques
401 Sheffield Rd., Whittington Moor. S41 8LS. Est. 1985. Open Mon. and Tues. 12-4, Thurs. 10-4, Fri. and Sat. 1-4. *STOCK: Furniture, pottery, clocks and lamps, £5-£1,000.* PARK: Easy. TEL: 01426 450209; mobile - 07885 665440. SER: Valuations. FAIRS: Bowman, Newark; Pandora; Buxton.

DERBY

Abbey House
115 Woods Lane. DE22 3UE. (Shirley White). Resident. Est. 1959. Open by appointment. *STOCK: Dolls, teddy bears and all things juvenile.* TEL: 01332 331426; e-mail - shirley.white1@btinternet.com. SER: Repairs (dolls and teddies); restorations (furniture).

Derventio Books
43a Sadler Gate. DE1 1NR. (D. A. Harper). Est. 1996. Open 10.15-5. SIZE: Medium. *STOCK: Out-of-print, secondhand and antiquarian books especially modern first editions, Derbyshire,*

science fiction, mainly 19th-20th C, 50p to £500; some antiquarian maps and prints. LOC: 1st floor via short passageway off Sadler Gate. PARK: Nearby. TEL: 01332 343538; website - www.derventio-books.co.uk SER: Valuations.

Finishing Touches
224 Uttoxeter Old Rd., The Rowditch. DE1 1NF. (Lynne Robinson). Est. 1994. Open 10-5.30, Sun. by appointment. CL: Mon. SIZE: Small. *STOCK: Fire surrounds, £200-£800; pine furniture, £50-£500; kitchenalia and pottery, £1-£25; all late 19th to early 20th C.* LOC: Off A38 at junction with A52. PARK: Rear of church. TEL: 01332 721717; website - www.derbyantiques.co.uk. SER: Restorations.

Friargate Pine Company Ltd
The Pump House, Friargate Goods Wharf, Stafford St. Entrance. DE1 1JL. (N. J. Marianski). Open 9-5. *STOCK: Antique and reproduction pine furniture.* TEL: 01332 341215.

Brian Matsell
1 Friar Gate Court, Friar Gate. DE1 1HE. Resident. Est. 1965. Open by appointment. SIZE: Small. *STOCK: Georgian and Regency furniture, decorative antiques, Oriental porcelain and objects; oil paintings and watercolours.* LOC: Town centre. PARK: Easy. TEL: 01332 365211; mobile - 07747 702741. SER: Valuations; buys at auction; consultancy. VAT: Stan/Spec.

DOVERIDGE

Pine Antiques Workshop
Bell Farm, Yelt Lane. DE6 5JU. (M.A. and A. Groves). Est. 1975. Open Tues.-Sat. 9-5.30, other times by appointment. SIZE: Large. *STOCK: English and Welsh pine, pottery, linen and kitchenalia.* PARK: Own. TEL: 01889 564898; fax - same.

DUFFIELD, Nr. Derby

Wayside Antiques
62 Town St. DE56 4GG. (B. and Mrs J. Harding). Est. 1975. Open 10-6 or by appointment. *STOCK: Furniture, 18th-19th C, £50-£5,000; porcelain, pictures, boxes and silver.* PARK: Forecourt. TEL: 01332 840346. SER: Restorations (furniture). VAT: Stan/Spec.

GLOSSOP

Derbyshire Clocks
104 High St. West. SK13 8BB. (J.A. and T.P. Lees). Est. 1975. CL: Tues. *STOCK: Clocks.*

PARK: Easy. TEL: 01457 862677. SER: Restorations (clocks and barometers). VAT: Spec.

HAYFIELD, Nr. New Mills

Michael Allcroft Antiques
1 Church St. Est. 1984. Open Sat. 2-5, Sun. 1-5, other times by appointment. *STOCK: Pine furniture and decorative items.* TEL: 01663 742684; mobile - 07798 781642; fax - 01663 744014.

Paul Pickford Antiques
Top of the Town, Church St. SK22 2JE. Est. 1975. Open Tues., Thurs. and Sat. 11-4, Sun. 1-5, other times by appointment. SIZE: Medium. *STOCK: 19th C furniture, stripped pine, lighting and general antiques, £50-£1,000.* LOC: Off A6 at Newtown, near Disley, take A6015. PARK: Easy. TEL: 01663 747276; home - 01663 743356; e-mail - paul@pickfordantiques.co.uk; website - www.pickfordantiques.co.uk.

HEANOR

Heanor Antiques Centre
1-3 Ilkeston Rd. (Jane Richards). Est. 1998. Open 10.30-4.30. SIZE: Large. *STOCK: Wide range of general antiques and collectables.* LOC: Off M1, junction 26 or A38. PARK: Easy. TEL: 01773 531181. SER: Valuations; restorations.

KILLAMARSH

Havenplan's Architectural Emporium
The Old Station, Station Rd. S21 1EN. Est. 1972. Open Tues., Wed., Thurs. and Sat. 10-2.30. SIZE: Large. *STOCK: Architectural fittings and decorative items, church interiors and furnishings, fireplaces, doors, decorative cast ironwork, masonry, bygones, garden ornaments, 18th to early 20th C.* LOC: M1, exit 30. Take A616 towards Sheffield, turn right on to B6053, turn right on to B6058 towards Killamarsh, turn right between two railway bridges. PARK: Easy. TEL: 01142 489972; home - 01246 433315. SER: Hire.

LONG EATON

Miss Elany
2 Salisbury St. NG10 1BA. (D. and Mrs Mottershead). Est. 1977. Open 9-5. SIZE: Medium. *STOCK: Pianos, 1900 to date, £150-£1,000; general antiques, Victorian and Edwardian, £180-£500.* PARK: Easy. TEL: 0115 9734835. VAT: Stan.

MATLOCK

Matlock Antiques and Collectables Centre
7 Dale Rd. DE4 3LT. (W. Shirley). Open 10-5 including Sun. SIZE: Large - 70 dealers. *STOCK: Furniture, clocks, art and general antiques.* LOC: Town centre. PARK: Easy. TEL: 01629 760808; e-mail - bmatlockantiques@aol.com; website - www.matlockantiques.f9.co.uk.

OCKBROOK

The Good Olde Days
6 Flood St. DE72 3RP. (Mr and Mrs S. Potter). Est. 1992. Open 10-5, Wed. 12-5. CL: Mon. SIZE: Medium. *STOCK: Beswick, Doulton, Wedgwood, Moorcroft, small furniture.* LOC: Village centre. PARK: Rear of shop. TEL: 01332 544244; home - 01332 663586. SER: Valuations. FAIRS: Coventry, Kettering, Wickstead Park, RAF Swinderby, Ipswich, Norwich.

RIPLEY

A.A. Ambergate Antiques
c/o Upstairs & Downstairs, 8 Derby Rd. DE5 3HR. (C.V. Lawrence). Est. 1972. Open 10-4. SIZE: Medium. *STOCK: Victorian and Edwardian furniture including bedroom, sideboards, tables and chairs, display cabinets, pottery and pictures, to £1,500.* LOC: Town centre. PARK: Easy. TEL: 01773 745201; mobile - 07885 327753. SER: Valuations; restorations.

Memory Lane Antiques Centre
Nottingham Rd. DE5 3AS. (James Cullen). Est. 1994. Open 10.30-4 including Sun. SIZE: Large. *STOCK: Victoriana and 20th C collectables, pine furniture, specialist in old Denby, Bourne and Langley, lighting.* LOC: 200 yards from town centre - 500 yds from A610 (Sainsburys) roundabout. PARK: Easy. TEL: 01773 570184; mobile - 07703 115626. SER: Valuations; stripping (pine); old Denby replacement service and plate pattern library, 1940 to date. FAIRS: Derby University; Newark; Abacus; Kedleston Hall; Swinderby.

SHARDLOW, Nr. Derby

Shardlow Antiques Warehouse
24 The Wharf. DE72 2GH. (Nigel Critchlow). Est. 1986. Open 10.30-5, Sun. 12-5. CL: Fri. SIZE: Large. *STOCK: Furniture, Georgian to shipping.* LOC: Off M1, junction 24. PARK: Own. TEL: 01332 792899/662899. VAT: Spec.

WHALEY BRIDGE

Richard Glass
Hockerley Old Hall, Hockerley Lane. Resident. Est. 1985. Open by appointment. SIZE: Small. *STOCK: Oak furniture, 17th-18th C, £1,000-£5,000; paintings, drawings, metal and stoneware, 17th-19th C, £200-£2,000.* LOC: From town centre towards Stockport, turn left at station car park, up hill and 2nd right into Hockerley Lane, up farm track at the end of the lane, house on left. PARK: Easy. TEL: 0161 236 1520; fax - 0161 237 5174. SER: Valuations. VAT: Spec.

Nimbus Antiques
14 Chapel Rd. SK23 7JZ. (L.M. and H.C. Brobbin). Est. 1978. Open 9-5.30, Sun. 2-5.30. SIZE: Large. *STOCK: Furniture, mainly mahogany, walnut and some oak, including desks, dining tables, clocks, chests, 18th-19th C.* LOC: A6, 20 mins. from Stockport. PARK: Easy. TEL: 01663 734248; fax - 01663 734248; e-mail - nimbusantiques@hotmail.com; website - www.antiques-atlas.com/nimbus.htm. VAT: Stan/Spec.

WOODVILLE

Wooden Box Antiques
32 High St. DE11 7EH. (Mrs R. Bowler). Est. 1982. Open 10-5 including some Sun. SIZE: Medium. *STOCK: Furniture, Georgian-Edwardian, £75-£400; original cast-iron fireplaces, surrounds, £50-£600; Victorian tiles, country pine furniture, pine doors.* LOC: A511 (was A50), between Ashby-de-la-Zouch and Burton-on-Trent. PARK: Easy. TEL: 01283 212014; 01297 444451; mobile - 07733 160349.

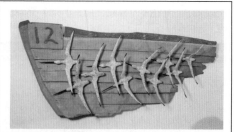

Guy Taplin (b.1939), 'Ten Flying Sanderlings', carved and painted driftwood, 72in. long. (David Messum Fine Art)

From an article entitled "Painters and Sculptors of East Anglia" by Geoffrey Munn which appeared in the February 2003 issue of **Antique Collecting**. For more details and to subscribe see page 21.

All new format and size!

Starting to Collect Series

The *Starting to Collect* series is intended to respond to the demand for inexpensive practical books which will satisfy the needs of the beginner who is interested in exploring possible new collecting areas. They give the historical and geographical background to their subjects, together with a wealth of factual information on the individual representative pieces. They offer guidance on where and how to buy, as well as advice on how not to be taken in by fakes and copies. Each book has been written by an expert in that particular area. A key feature of each book is the suggestions for further reading. This best-selling series is now available in a new, larger format.

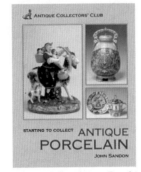

Starting to Collect Antique Silver
Ian Pickford

Provides in compact form, the essential background knowledge to silver and the techniques of silver-smithing. Over 50 types of silver objects are discussed and there is useful information on marks.

Starting to Collect Antique Porcelain
John Sandon

Compact and fact-filled, this book includes porcelain from both the West and the Far East. All price ranges are comprehensively covered; the book goes on to discuss sources of purchase, with advice on fakes and caring for a collection.

Starting to Collect Antique Furniture
John Andrews

A concise yet wide-ranging survey of collectable antique furniture, illustrated throughout in full colour, guides the new collector through almost three centuries of furniture with clarity and authority.

Starting to Collect Antique Glass
John Sandon

John Sandon tells the whole story of glass from its discovery in Ancient Egypt to the advanced designs and forward-looking techniques of the 20th century. Carefully chosen illustrations focus on available and affordable specimens, offering practical advice to keen novice collectors.

Starting to Collect Antique Jewellery
John Benjamin

A comprehensive introduction to the subject, tracking the progress of jewellery designs from early times to the 20th century. It will assist the professional jeweller, the collector and the student in making informed and balanced judgements upon scores of crucial topics – from the setting of old gems, to fakes and forgeries.

Starting to Collect Antique Oriental Rugs
Murray Eiland III

Novice collectors are in good hands here; Murray Eiland III guides them through the initial problematic areas – where to buy, what to look for, care and restoration, before turning his attention to the materials and techniques, dyes and designs, involved in the manufacture of rugs.

Series specifications: 7¾ x 9½ inches, 192 pages, colour throughout, Hardbound
Retail price £12.50 each

Available from all good booksellers and direct from the publisher:
ANTIQUE COLLECTORS' CLUB
Sandy Lane, Old Martlesham, Woodbridge, Suffolk, IP12 4SD.
Tel: 01394 389950   Fax: 01394 389999
Email: sales@antique-acc.com   Website: www.antique-acc.com

DEVON

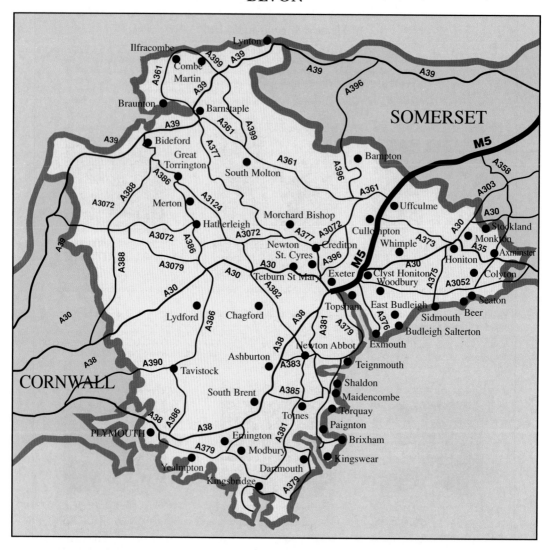

Dealers and Shops in Devonshire

Ashburton	8	Exeter	12	Plymouth	5
Axminster	1	Exmouth	2	Seaton	1
Bampton	2	Great Torrington	1	Shaldon	1
Barnstaple	6	Hatherleigh	2	Sidmouth	3
Beer	1	Honiton	25	South Brent	1
Bideford	2	Ilfracombe	1	South Molton	6
Braunton	1	Kingsbridge	1	Stockland	1
Brixham	2	Kingswear	1	Tavistock	1
Budleigh Salterton	2	Lydford	1	Tedburn St Mary	1
Chagford	3	Lynton	2	Teignmouth	3
Clyst Honiton	1	Maidencombe	1	Topsham	4
Combe Martin	1	Merton	1	Torquay	4
Colyton	1	Modbury	2	Totnes	8
Crediton	1	Monkton	1	Uffculme	1
Cullompton	5	Morchard Bishop	1	Whimple	1
Dartmouth	1	Newton Abbot	2	Woodbury	1
East Budleigh	1	Newton St. Cyres	1	Yealmpton	1
Ermington	1	Paignton	2		

ASHBURTON

Antiques Ad Hoc
17 North St. TQ13 7QH. (Helen Harvey and Lisa Goddard-Smith). Est. 1994. Open 10-5, Sat. 11-5. CL: Wed. SIZE: Small. *STOCK: Period furniture and decorative items, mirrors and lamps, pottery and porcelain, woolwork pictures, line and stipple engravings, copper and brass, English and French, 1770-1910.* LOC: North end of North St. PARK: Loading and nearby. TEL: 01364 654667; mobile - 07778 764424; home - 01752 402130.

Ashburton Marbles
Great Hall, North St. TQ13 7DU. (Adrian Ager). Est. 1976. Open 8-5, Sat. 10-4. SIZE: Warehouse and showrooms. *STOCK: Marble and wooden fire-surrounds, decorative cast iron inserts; scuttles, fenders, overmantels, 1790-1910; architectural decorative antiques, garden statuary and related items, chandeliers, soft furnishings and furniture; mid-Victorian dining tables and bedroom furniture.* PARK: Easy. TEL: 01364 653189; fax - same; e-mail - afager@tinyworld. co.uk; website - www.adrianager.co. uk.

Dartmoor Bookshop
2 Kingsbridge Lane. TQ13 7DX. (Paul and Barbara Heatley). PBFA. Est. 1982. Open 9.30-5.30. SIZE: Large. *STOCK: Books - secondhand and antiquarian.* LOC: On lane facing car park. PARK: Easy. TEL: 01364 653356; e-mail - Dartmoorbks@aol.com; website - www. dartmoorbks.dabsol.co.uk. SER: Valuations.

Kessler Ford
9 North St. TQ13 7QJ. (Elisabeth Kessler and Matthew Ford). Est. 1999. Open Tues., Thurs., Fri. 10-5, Sat. 10.30-5. SIZE: Medium. *STOCK: Period oak and Georgian mahogany furniture; pictures, carvings, bronzes.* LOC: Main street. PARK: Easy. TEL: 01364 654310; fax - 01364 652141. SER: Valuations. VAT: Spec.

Mo Logan Antiques
11 North St. TQ13 7AG. (Martin & Mo Logan). Est. 1972. Open Tues., Thurs., Fri. and Sat. 10-4.30. SIZE: Small. *STOCK: Textiles, early 20th C; rugs, gilt furniture and mirrors, lamps, small period furniture, decorative items.* LOC: Town centre. TEL: 01364 654179; mobile - 07967 234129.

Moor Antiques
19a North St. TQ13 7QH. (T. and Mrs D. Gatland). Est. 1984. CL: Wed. pm. SIZE: Small. *STOCK: Small furniture, 1780-1900, £250-*£2,500; clocks, 1830-1910, £150-£2,000; silver and china, 1750-1900, £25-£500; jewellery, £30-£250.* LOC: A38 town centre, 100 yards past town hall. PARK: Nearby. TEL: 01364 653767. SER: Valuations.

Pennsylvania Pine Co
18 East St. TQ13 7AZ. (S. F. Robinson and C. A. Tolchard). Est. 1967. Open 10.30-4.30. CL: Wed. SIZE: Medium. *STOCK: Unusual English pine furniture, 18th-20th C, £50-£5,000.* PARK: Easy. TEL: 01364 652244; fax - same; mobile - 07941 891640; home - 01364 652594. SER: Valuations; restorations (pine); furniture made to order.

The Shambles
24 North St. TQ13 7QD. Est. 1982. Open 10-5. SIZE: 5 dealers. *STOCK: Country and general antiques and decorative items, £5-£2,000.* LOC: Town centre. PARK: Opposite. TEL: 01364 653848. SER: Valuations. FAIRS: Sandown Park; Westpoint Exeter; Shepton Mallet. VAT: Stan/Spec.

AXMINSTER

W.G. Potter and Son
1 West St. EX13 5HS. Est. 1863. Open 9-5. CL: Sat. pm. SIZE: Medium. *STOCK: Pine, 19th-20th C; some mahogany and oak.* LOC: Main street (A35) opposite church. PARK: Easy. TEL: 01297 32063. SER: Restorations (furniture); buys at auction. VAT: Stan/Spec.

BAMPTON, Nr. Tiverton

Bampton Gallery
2-4 Brook St. EX16 9LY. (Gerald Chidwick). FRICS. Est. 1997. Open 9.30-5.30, Sat. 9.30-1, Sun. and other times by appointment. SIZE: Medium. *STOCK: Furniture including upholstered, porcelain, pottery and glass, 1750-1900, £10-£10,000; pictures and prints, £10-£1,000.* LOC: Main street. PARK: Outside. TEL: 01398 331119; fax - same; home - 01398 331354. SER: Restorations (furniture including traditional upholstery, ceramics); buys at auction (porcelain and furniture).

Robert Byles and Optimum Brasses
7 Castle St. EX16 9NS. (Robert and Rachel Byles). Est. 1966. Open Mon.-Fri. 9-1 and 2-5 or by appointment. SIZE: Medium. *STOCK: Furniture, 16th-18th C; local farmhouse tables and settles, metalwork, pottery, unstripped period pine, architectural items.* PARK: Nearby. TEL: 01398 331515; fax - 01398 331164; website - www.obida.com. SER: Restoration materials;

replica brass handles for antique furniture. VAT: Stan/Spec.

BARNSTAPLE

Barn Antiques
73 Newport Rd. EX32 9BG. (T. Cusack). Open 9.30-5, Wed. 9.30-1. SIZE: Large. *STOCK: General antiques.* TEL: 01271 323131.

Medina Gallery
80 Boutport St. EX31 1SR. (R. Jennings). Est. 1972. Open 9.30-5. SIZE: Medium. *STOCK: Maps, prints, photographs, oils and watercolours, £1-£500.* PARK: Easy. TEL: 01237 371025. SER: Picture framing, mounting. VAT: Stan.

North Devon Antiques Centre
The Old Church, 18 Cross St. EX31 1BD. (P. Broome). Est. 1985. Open 10-4.30. SIZE: Large. *STOCK: Furniture, china, clocks, 18th C to 1960's, £5-£2,500; Victorian and Art Deco fireplaces, £100-£900.* LOC: 40 yards off High St. PARK: Nearby. TEL: 01271 375788. SER: Valuations; restorations (woodwork and clocks). FAIRS: Newark, Shepton Mallet, Exeter Westpoint.

Mark Parkhouse Antiques and Jewellery
106 High St. EX31 1HP. Est. 1976. CL: Wed. *STOCK: Jewellery, furniture, silver, paintings, clocks, glass, porcelain, small collectors' items, 18th-19th C, £100-£10,000.* PARK: Nearby. TEL: 01271 374504; fax - 01271 323499. SER: Valuations; buys at auction. VAT: Stan/Spec.

Selected Antiques & Collectables
19 Newport Rd. EX32 9BG. (Helen Chugg). Est. 1994. Open Tues.-Sat. 10-4. SIZE: Large. *STOCK: North Devon pottery, 19th C; porcelain and ceramics, glass, collectables, 19th-20th C; linen, books, memorabilia, toys, dolls.* PARK: Easy. TEL: 01271 321338 (24hr. answerphone); mobile - 07866 024831. SER: Valuations. FAIRS: Specialist pottery.

Tudor House
115 Boutport St. EX31 1TD. (C. and D. Pilon). Est. 1980. Open 9.30-3.30, Wed. 9.30-1. SIZE: Large. *STOCK: Furniture and bric-a-brac, late 18th C and reproduction.* LOC: Off M5, Tiverton link road to town centre. PARK: Easy. TEL: 01271 375370; home - 01271 371750. SER: Valuations; restorations (furniture).

BEER

Beer Collectables
Dolphin Courtyard. EX12 3EQ. (L. R. Forkes).

Est. 1985. Open 10-5 including Sun. SIZE: Medium. *STOCK: Antique fishing tackle, from £25; jewellery, £50-£2,000; china and smalls, £2-£50.* PARK: Easy. TEL: 01297 24362; home - 01460 65294. SER: Valuations; buys at auction. FAIRS: Taunton, Torquay, Beaminster; some local.

BIDEFORD

J. Collins and Son   BADA   LAPADA
The Studio, 28 High St. EX39 2AN. (J. and P. Biggs). CINOA. Est. 1953. Open by appointment. SIZE: Large. *STOCK: Georgian and Regency furniture; general antiques including framed and restored 19th-20th C oils and watercolours, £100-£100,000.* LOC: On quayside. PARK: Easy. TEL: 01237 473103; fax - 01237 475658; home - 01237 476485; e-mail - biggs@collinsantiques.co.uk; website - www.collinsantiques.co.uk. SER: Valuations; restorations (period furniture, paintings and watercolours); cleaning; framing. FAIRS: BADA (March); Olympia (Nov). VAT: Spec.

Cooper Gallery
Cooper St. EX39 2DA. (Mrs J. Bruce). Est. 1975. Open 10-4.30, Wed. 10-1.30, Sat. 10-2.30. SIZE: Small. *STOCK: Watercolours, mainly West Country views, late 19th to early 20th C, £200-£2,500.* LOC: Just off the quay, opposite HSBC bank. PARK: Nearby. TEL: 01237 477370; fax - same; home - 01237 423415; e-mail - cooper gallery@freecall-uk.co.uk; website - www. coopergalleryuk.com. SER: Valuations; restorations (watercolours); cleaning; framing. VAT: Spec.

BRAUNTON

Timothy Coward Fine Silver   LAPADA
Marisco, Saunton. EX33 1LG. Open by appointment. *STOCK: Antique and early 20th C silver.* TEL: 01271 890466.

BRIXHAM

Around the Clock
Ye Olde Coffin House, King St. TQ5 9TF. (Dr. Paul Strickland). NAWCC. Est. 1996. Open by appointment. SIZE: Small. *STOCK: Antique and early electric clocks.* PARK: Loading only and nearby. TEL: 01803 856307; e-mail - clocks@forall.fsnet.co.uk. website - www. forall.fsnet.co.uk. SER: Valuations; restorations.

JOHN PRESTIGE ANTIQUES

Greenswood Court,
Greenswood Road,
Brixham Devon, TQ5 9HN
Tel: 01803 856141
Fax: 01803 851649
E-mail: sales@john-prestige.co.uk

2 WAREHOUSES OF ANTIQUE ENGLISH & CONTINENTAL FURNITURE AND DECORATIVE SMALLS. FULL RESTORATION FACILITIES ON SITE. WE SPECIALISE IN SUPPLYING THE AMERICAN AND OVERSEAS TRADE

John Prestige Antiques
1 and 2 Greenswood Court. TQ5 9HN. (John and Patricia Prestige). Est. 1971. Open 8.45-6, appointment advisable. CL: Sat. and Sun. except by appointment. SIZE: Large + warehouse. *STOCK: Period and Victorian furniture; shipping goods; decorative smalls.* PARK: Own. TEL: 01803 856141; home - 01803 853739; fax - 01803 851649; e-mail - sales@john-prestige. co.uk; website - www.john-prestige.co.uk. SER: Restorations (furniture); desk re-lining; courier (West Country). VAT: Stan/Spec.

BUDLEIGH SALTERTON

Days of Grace
15 Fore St. EX9 6NH. (L. Duriez). *STOCK: Antique lace, vintage textiles and costume, china, jewellery, furniture, interesting decorating items.* TEL: 01395 443730.

David J. Thorn
2 High St. EX9 6LQ. Est. 1950. Open Tues., Fri. and Sat. 10-1. SIZE: Small. *STOCK: English, Continental and Oriental pottery and porcelain, 1620-1850, £5-£5,000; English furniture, 1680-1870, £20-£5,000; paintings, silver, jewellery, £1-£1,000.* PARK: Easy. TEL: 01395 442448. SER: Valuations. VAT: Stan/Spec.

CHAGFORD

Godolphin Antiques
11 The Square. TQ13 8AA. (S. Freeman). Est. 2000. Open 10-5, Sun. by appointment. SIZE: Medium. *STOCK: Watercolours and oils, 18th to early 20th C, £200-£35,000; oak and country furniture, 17th-18th C; clocks.* LOC: Off the square. Turn opposite Easton Court Hotel on A382 Moretonhampstead-Okehampton road. PARK: Easy. TEL: 01647 433999; website - www.godolphinfineart.com. SER: Buys at auction (watercolours and oils).

Rex Antiques
The Old Rex Cinema. TQ13 8AB. (John Meredith). Est. 1979. Open by appointment. SIZE: Large. *STOCK: Country oak, 16th-19th C, £5-£2,000; Oriental brass and copper, weapons, large unusual items, granite, architectural items, old iron work.* PARK: Easy. TEL: 01647 433405. SER: Buys at auction. VAT: Stan/Spec. *Trade only.*

Whiddons Antiques and Tearooms
6 High St. TQ13 8AJ. (D. Meldrum). Est. 1979. Open 10-5.30, Sun. 12-5.30. SIZE: Medium. *STOCK: General and country items - furniture*

including pine, clocks, prints, paintings, copper, brass, books and collectables. LOC: Opposite church. PARK: Easy. TEL: 01647 433406; home - 01647 433303.

CLYST HONITON, Nr. Exeter

Home Farm Antiques
STOCK: Antiques and collectables. LOC: Off A30 Exeter Airport exit. PARK: Easy. TEL: 01392 444491. SER: Restorations; delivery.

COLYTON

Colyton Antiques Centre
Dolphin St. EX24. (R.C. Hunt and M.J. Conway). Est. 2000. Open 10-5, Sun. 11-4. SIZE: Large. *STOCK: General antiques.* PARK: Easy. TEL: 01297 552339; fax - same.

COMBE MARTIN

Sherbrook Antiques and Collectables
1 Borough Rd. EX34 0AN. (Trevor and Mrs Lesley Pickard). Est. 1997. Open 10-5.30. CL: Mon and Wed. SIZE: Small. *STOCK: General antiques and collectables.* LOC: Sea front. PARK: Nearby. TEL: 01271 889060; mobile - 07887 806493; e-mail - Trevor@sherbrook antiques.fsbusiness.co.uk. SER: Valuations; some restorations (furniture).

CREDITON

Musgrave Bickford Antiques
15 East St. EX17 3AT. (Mr and Mrs D.M. Bickford). Est. 1983. Open by appointment. SIZE: Small. *STOCK: Clocks and barometers, mainly 19th C, from £400.* LOC: From Exeter on A377 on right entering one-way system, towards Tiverton. PARK: Easy and at rear by arrangement. TEL: 01363 775042. SER: Restorations (longcase, mantel, wall clock and barometer movements, dials, cases). VAT: Stan/Spec.

CULLOMPTON

Cobweb Antiques
The Old Tannery, Exeter Rd. EX15 1DT. (R. Holmes). Est. 1980. Open 10-5. SIZE: Large. *STOCK: Pine and country furniture, painted, decorative and mahogany items, £5-£5,000.* LOC: Half a mile from junction 28, M5. PARK: Easy. TEL: 01884 855748. SER: Stripping; restorations; packing; courier.

Cullompton Old Tannery Antiques
Exeter Rd. EX15 1DT. (Cullompton Antiques). Est. 1989. Open 10-5, Sun. by appointment. SIZE: Large. *STOCK: Pine, oak, mahogany and fruitwood country furniture; beds, china, decorative items and mirrors.* LOC: Off M5, junction 28, through town centre, premises on right, approximately 1 mile. PARK: Easy. TEL: 01884 38476; fax - same; e-mail - tannery@ cullompton-antiques.co.uk; website - www. cullompton-antiques.co.uk.

Miller Antiques
The Old Tannery, Exeter Rd. EX15 1DT. (Nick Miller). Open 10-5.30, Sat. 10-5, Sun. by appointment. SIZE: Large. *STOCK: Furniture, 18th-19th C, £25-£2,000, country, 17th-19th C, £25-£3,000; decorative accessories, £5-£2,000.* LOC: M5 junction 28, bottom of the High St. opposite Somerfield. PARK: Easy. TEL: 01884 38476; fax - same. SER: Valuations; buys at auction.

Mills Antiques
The Old Tannery, Exeter Rd. EX15 1DT. Est. 1979. Open 10-5.30, Sat. 10-5. *STOCK: 17th C to Edwardian furniture; French bedroom suites, country furniture and decorative items.* PARK: Easy. TEL: 01392 860945.

R.C. Associates
The Old Tannery, Exeter Rd. EX15 1DT. Open 10-5.30, Sat. 10-5. *STOCK: French provincial furniture - beds, armoires, tables, buffets.* PARK: Easy.

DARTMOUTH

Chantry Bookshop and Gallery
11 Higher St. TQ6 9RB. (M.P. Merkel). Est. 1969. Open 10.30-5. CL: 15th Jan.-20th Mar. SIZE: Small. *STOCK: Antiquarian books and watercolours; decorative maps, town plans, prints, sea charts and battle plans.* LOC: Next to 'The Cherub' public house. PARK: Nearby. TEL: 01803 832796; home - 01803 834208.

EAST BUDLEIGH

Antiques at Budleigh House
Budleigh House. EX9 7ED. (W. Cook). Est. 1981. Open 10-5, Sat. 10-1. CL: Mon. and Wed. SIZE: Small. *STOCK: 18th-19th C small furniture and decorative objects, porcelain, glass, silver and metalware, £5-£1,000.* LOC: Opposite Sir Walter Raleigh public house. PARK: Easy. TEL: 01395 445368; home - same. SER: Valuations; buys at auction.

ERMINGTON, Nr. Ivybridge

Mill Gallery
PL21 9NT. (Christopher Trant). Resident. Est. 1984. CL: Sat. SIZE: Small. *STOCK: Oils and watercolours, 18th-20th C, £300-£1,000.* LOC: From A38 take Ivybridge exit, follows signs, 1st premises in village. PARK: Easy. TEL: 01548 830172; website - www.millgallery.com. SER: Valuations; restorations (oils). VAT: Spec.

EXETER

The Antique Centre on the Quay
The Quay. EX2 4AP. Est. 1983. Open winter 10-5, Sat. and Sun. 10-5.30; summer 10-6 including Sun. SIZE: 20+ dealers. *STOCK: Antiques - small furniture, ceramics, glass, collectables, books, pictures, postcards, records, tools and jewellery.* PARK: Nearby. TEL: 01392 493501; website - www.exeterquayantiques.co.uk.

Eclectique
Cellars 18 & 23, The Quay. EX2 4AP. (E.J. Henson and C. Frank). Est. 1992. Open 7 days 11-5. SIZE: Medium. *STOCK: Mainly Victorian and Edwardian furniture including pine and oak; dining tables, chests of drawers, chairs and pictures.* LOC: Town centre. PARK: Nearby.

TEL: 01392 250799; e-mail - sales@eclectique.co.uk; website - www.eclectique.co.uk.

Exeter Rare Books
Guildhall Shopping Centre. EX4 3HG. (R.C. Parry). ABA. PBFA. Est. 1975. Open 10-1 and 2-5. SIZE: Small. *STOCK: Books, antiquarian, secondhand, out-of-print, 17th-20th C; Devon and West Country topography. £5-£500.* LOC: City centre. PARK: Easy. TEL: 01392 436021. SER: Valuations; buys at auction. FAIRS: ABA Chelsea, Bath; Edinburgh.

Fagins Antiques
The Old Whiteways Cider Factory, Hele. EX5 4PW. (C.J. Strong). Open 9.15-5, Sat. 11-5. SIZE: Large. *STOCK: Furniture, decorative items, pictures, porcelain, garden furniture, architectural and shipping items.* LOC: 10 mins. from junction 28, M5 on the B3181 Cullompton - Exeter road. PARK: Easy. TEL: 01392 882062; fax - 01392 882194; e-mail - info@faginsantiques.com; website - www.faginsantiques.com. SER: Stripping (pine); pine furniture made to order.

Gold and Silver Exchange
Eastgate House, Princesshay. EX4 3JT. *STOCK: Jewellery, watches including Rolex.* TEL: 01392 217478.

The House that Moved
24 West St. EX1 1BA. (L. Duriez). Est. 1980. Open 10-5. SIZE: 3 floors and courtyard. *STOCK: Lace, shawls, babywear, linen, 1920's costume, Victorian and Edwardian bridal wedding dresses.* LOC: West Quarter. PARK: Easy. TEL: 01392 432643.

McBains Antiques
LAPADA

Exeter Airport Industrial Estate, Westcott Lane. EX5 2BA. Est. 1975. Open 9-6, Sat. 10-1. CL: Bank Holidays. SIZE: Large warehouse complex. *STOCK: Georgian, Victorian and Edwardian furniture; Arts and Crafts; Continental, decorated and painted furniture.* LOC: 3 miles from junction 29, M5. After airport, turn left and follow sign to Westcott for 1 mile. PARK: Easy. TEL: 01392 366261; fax - 01392 365572; e-mail -mcbains@netcomuk.co.uk SER: Container packing and shipping; courier. FAIRS: Newark. VAT: Spec/Global/Export. Below are listed the dealers trading from this address.

Ash Brothers Antiques
Shipping furniture, decorative items, Chinese imports. TEL: 01392 364483; fax - same.

J. Buchanan Antiques
Furniture.

M. Burbidge Antiques
Furniture.

J. Huggett Antiques
Georgian furniture.

McBain Antique Exports
Est. 1963. *English, French and Belgium furniture suitable for export worldwide; architectural garden items.* TEL: 01392 466304; fax - 01392 447304; e-mail - mcbain.exports@zetnet.co.uk SER: Container packing; European courier service.

Miscellany Antiques
Furniture, Georgian to Edwardian. TEL: 01684 566671.

P & A
Arts & Crafts and decorative furniture.

Portobello Antiques
Furniture.

P. Reynolds Antiques
Mirrors, armchairs and tables.

Leon Robertson Antiques
Chests, desks and pine furniture. TEL: Mobile - 07971 171909.

Tredantiques
Fine quality period furniture and decorative items. TEL: Mobile - 07967 447082; website - www.tredantiques.com.

Wilford Antiques
Small furniture.

Youll's Antiques
French beds, tables, chairs and large furniture.

Mortimers
87 Queen St. EX4 3RP. (B. Mortimer). Est. 1970. Open 9-5. SIZE: Small. *STOCK: Jewellery, silver, clocks, watches and objet d'art.* LOC: City centre. PARK: Easy. TEL: 01392 279994. SER: Valuations; repairs. VAT: Stan/Spec.

John Nathan Antiques
1st floor, Ivor Doble Ltd. 24 Sidwell St. EX4 1AS. (I. Doble). Est. 1950. Open 9-5.30. SIZE: Small. *STOCK: Silver and jewellery, £5-£5,000; clocks, including Georgian and Victorian, £25-£3,000.* PARK: Easy. TEL: 01392 210864. SER: Valuations; restorations (silver and jewellery); buys at auction. VAT: Stan.

Phantique
47 The Quay. EX2 4AN. (Patsy Bliss). Est. 1996. Open daily - summer 10.30-5.30, winter 10.30-5. SIZE: Several dealers. *STOCK: Antiques,*

collectables, prints, books, toys, jewellery, small furniture, kitchenalia. PARK: Nearby. TEL: 01392 498995; website - www.phantique.co.uk.

The Quay Gallery Antiques Emporium
43 The Quay. EX2 4AP. (Mark Davis and Danielle Rawstron). Est. 1984. Open 10-5 including Sun. SIZE: Large - 15 dealers. *STOCK: 18th-20th C oak and mahogany furniture, marine items, porcelain, silver, plate, glass, paintings, prints, antiquities, carpets and decorative items.* LOC: Next to Old Customs House. PARK: Easy. TEL: 01392 213283.

Peter Wadham Antiques
3 Crane Cellars, Exeter Quay. EX2 4AN. Est. 1967. Open 10-5, Sun. and Mon. by appointment. SIZE: Small. *STOCK: Small furniture and mirrors, 1780-1880, £100-£1,000; glass, metalwork, topographical prints and local views, 1750-1870, £10-£500.* LOC: Close to Customs House. PARK: Easy. TEL: Home - 01392 255801. SER: Valuations; restorations (small furniture and picture frames). VAT: Spec.

Boase Antiques
5 High St. EX8 1NN. Open 10-5. *STOCK: Jewellery, silver, Victorian collectables.* LOC: Town centre. PARK: Easy. TEL: 01395 271528.

Treasures
34 Exeter Rd. EX8 1PS. (L. Treasure). Open 9-5. *STOCK: General antiques.* TEL: 01395 279512.

C. Short Antiques
12 Potacre St. EX38 8BH. (C. J. Short). Est. 1985. Open 10-4, Sat. 10-1. SIZE: Small. *STOCK: Victorian pine furniture, £100-£500.* TEL: Mobile - 07720 962729; home - 01805 624105. SER: Valuations; restorations; stripping; polishing. VAT: Stan.

Shaw Edwards
43 Market Place. EX20 3JP. Est. 1988. Open by appointment only. SIZE: Medium. *STOCK: Primitive furniture, early oak, metalware.* PARK: Easy. TEL: 01837 811101; mobile - 07968 288281; e-mail - shaw-edwards@yahoo.co.uk

Hatherleigh Antiques
BADA
15 Bridge St. EX20 3HU. (M. Dann). Open by appointment. SIZE: Medium. *STOCK:*

Collectors' furniture and works of art, pre-1700.
**PARK: Easy. TEL: 01837 810159/810500.
VAT: Spec.**

HONITON

Jane Barnes Antiques & Interiors
59 High St. EX14 1PW. (J.A.C. and S.J. Barnes).
Open 10-4. CL: Wed. SIZE: Medium. *STOCK:
General antiques and country pine, glass, clocks.*
LOC: Main St. PARK: Easy. TEL: 01404 41712;
e-mails - jane@janebarnesantiques.co.uk and
john@devonshirehilldesign.co.uk. SER: Furniture
copies made to order.

Roderick Butler
BADA
**Marwood House. EX14 1PY. (Roderick and
Valentine Butler). Est. 1948. Open 9.30-5
(during August by appointment only). SIZE:
Large. *STOCK: 17th-18th C and Regency
furniture, curiosities, unusual items, early
metalwork.* LOC: Adjacent to roundabout at
eastern end of High St. PARK: In courtyard.
TEL: 01404 42169. SER: Restorations
(furniture). VAT: Spec.**

C & S Antiques
159 High St. EX14 1LJ. (I. Crackston and H.
Sledge). Est. 1986. Open 10-5. SIZE: Medium.
*STOCK: Oak and period country antiques,
copper, brass, samplers, ceramics, 17th-19th C.*
PARK: Nearby. TEL: 01404 43436.

Collectables
134B High St. EX14 1JP. (Chris Guthrie). Est.
1993. Open 10-1 and 1.30-5. CL: Thurs. Jan.,
Feb., Mar. SIZE: Small. *STOCK: Railwayana,
Wade, cigarette and 'phone cards, toys and
games, breweriana, commemoratives.* PARK:
Nearby. TEL: 01404 47024; e-mail -
chris@collectableshoniton.co.uk.

Evans Emporium
140 High St. EX14 1JP. (Bob Evans). Est. 1992.
Open 10-5. SIZE: Small. *STOCK: General
antiques and collectables, sheet music and
musical instruments, silver and jewellery,
furniture and furnishings, 19th-20th C, £1-£500.*
PARK: Nearby. TEL: 01404 47869; mobile -
07790 546495.

Fountain Antiques
132 High St. EX14 1JP. (J. Palmer and G. York).
Est. 1980. Open 9.30-5.30. *STOCK: General
antiques including pictures, books and linen.*
PARK: Nearby. TEL: 01404 42074; fax - 01404
44993; e-mail - antiques@gyork.co.uk.

Alison Gosling Antiques Studio
31 High St. EX9 6LJ. Est. 1983. Open 12-5. CL:
Mon. and Thurs. SIZE: Medium. *STOCK:
Furniture, early 18th to early 19th C , £400-
£8,500; porcelain and decorative items, early
18th to early 20th C, £20-£1,000.* LOC: Next to
Barclay's Bank. PARK: Easy. TEL: 01404
549952; evenings - 01395 271451. SER:
Valuations.

The Grove Antiques Centre
55 High St. EX14 1PW. (Lesley V. Phillips). Est.
1998. Open 10-5. SIZE: Large. *STOCK: Regency,
Victorian and country furniture; iron and
mahogany beds; glass, porcelain, Staffordshire,
silver and jewellery, pictures, bears, carpets.*
PARK: Easy. TEL: 01404 43377; fax - 01404
43390; e-mail - info@groveantiquescentre.com;
website - www.groveantiquescentre.com. SER:
Shipping; delivery.

Hermitage Antiques
37 High St. EX14 1PJ. (C. Giltsoff and N.R.
Kirk). Est. 1993. Open 10-5, Sun. by
appointment. SIZE: Large. *STOCK: English
furniture, 18th-20th C, £50-£10,000+; Arts and
Crafts furniture, metalware, tiles, art pottery, £5-
£7,500+; clocks, barometers, glass, lighting,
china and collectables, 18th-20th C, £1-£5,000+.*
LOC: M5 junction 28 or A30. TEL: 01404 44406;
home - 01884 820944; mobile - 07768 960144.

High Street Books
150 High St. EX14 8JB. (G. Tyson). PBFA. Est.
1978. Open 10-5. SIZE: Medium. *STOCK:
Books, prints and maps, 18th-20th C, £1-£1,000.*
LOC: Opposite police station. PARK: Easy. TEL:
01404 45570; fax - same; home - 01404 41771.
SER: Valuations. FAIRS: Major London Book.

Honiton Antique Centre
Abingdon House, 136 High St. EX14 8JP.
(N.D.A. and E.K. Thompson). Est. 1985. Open
9.30-5.30. SIZE: Large - 20 dealers. *STOCK:
17th-20th C furniture, metalwork, copper, brass,
tools, sporting items, pottery, porcelain, pictures
and collectables.* LOC: Exeter end of High St.
PARK: Nearby. TEL: 01404 42108; e-mail -
tbumble84@aol.com.

Honiton Antique Toys
38 High St. EX14 1PJ. (L. and S. Saunders). Est.
1986. Open 10.30-5. CL: Mon. and Thurs.
STOCK: Toys, dolls, teddies and children's books.
PARK: Easy. TEL: 01404 41194; e-mail -
honitonantiquetoys38@hotmail.com.

Honiton Clock Clinic

16 New St. EX14 1EY. (David P. Newton). BHI; BWCG. Est. 1992. Open 10-12.30 and 1.30-4, Sat. 10-1. CL: Thurs. SIZE: Small. *STOCK: Clocks - mantel, bracket, carriage and longcase, fully restored, 30 hour and 8 day, painted and brass dial, 1 year guarantee; aneriod and mercurial barometers; clock and watches keys, clock and barometer spares.* LOC: Near town centre. PARK: Nearby. TEL: 01404 47466; fax - same. SER: Valuations; restorations (clocks and barometers); collection and delivery; home calls.

Honiton Fine Art

189 High St. EX14 8LQ. (C.B. and P.R. Greenberg). Est. 1974. Open 11.30-5. SIZE: Medium. *STOCK: English watercolours and oil paintings, 18th-20th C, £300-£5,000; Old Master drawings, Dutch, Italian and French, 16th-18th C, £300-£1,500.* LOC: Town centre. PARK: Easy. TEL: 01404 45942. SER: Valuations; restorations (oil paintings and watercolours).

The Honiton Lace Shop

44 High St. EX14 8PJ. (Jonathan Page). Est. 1983. Open 9.30-1 and 2-5. SIZE: Medium. *STOCK: Lace including wedding veils, specialist and collectors; quilts, shawls and other textiles, bobbins and lace making equipment.* PARK: Easy. TEL: 01404 42416; fax - 01404 47797; e-mail - shop@honitonlace.com; website - www.honitonlace.com. SER: Valuations; repairs. VAT: Stan.

Honiton Old Bookshop

Felix House, 51 High St. EX14 1PW. (R. Collicott). ABA. PBFA. Est. 1991. Open 10-5.30. *STOCK: Books - travel, childrens' illustrated, topography, natural history, antiquarian, sciences; West Country maps; bindings; all £5-£2,000.* LOC: Main street. PARK: Easy. TEL: 01404 47180. SER: Catalogues available (2 per annum). FAIRS: London PBFA; ABA, Chelsea and Olympia. VAT: Stan.

Honiton Pottery

30 High St. EX14 1PU. (E. H. Stephenson). Open 9-5, Sat. 10-4. SIZE: Large. *STOCK: Honiton pottery, from 1908.* PARK: Easy. TEL: 01404 42106; fax - same; home - 01404 831865; website - www.hpcs.info. SER: Valuations; restorations.

Lombard Antiques

14 High St. EX14 8PU. (B. and T. Sabine). Est. 1984. Open 10-5.30. SIZE: Small. *STOCK: 18th-19th C English furniture, porcelain and decorative items.* PARK: Easy. TEL: 01404 42140.

Merchant House Antiques

19 High St. EX14 1PR. (C. Giltsoff and R. Kirk). Open 10-5, Sun. by appointment. SIZE: Large. *STOCK: English and French fine and provincial furniture, 17th-19th C; works of art, ironstone and later china, collectables and decorative items, upholstery and furnishings, £10-£20,000+.* PARK: Easy. TEL: 01404 42694; fax - 01404 42471; home - 01884 820944; mobile - 07768 960144. SER: Valuations. VAT: Stan/Spec.

Otter Antiques

69 High St. EX14 1PW. (Kate Skailes). Open 9.30-5. CL: Thurs. pm. *STOCK: Fine antique silver, jewellery and plate including flatware; modern silver.* TEL: 01404 42627; e-mail - otterantiques@jspencer.co.uk.

Pilgrim Antiques   `LAPADA`

145 High St. EX14 8LJ. (G. and J.E. Mills). Est. 1970. Open 9-5.30. SIZE: Large - trade warehouse. *STOCK: Period English and Continental furniture.* PARK: Easy. TEL: 01404 41219/45316; fax - 01404 45317; e-mail - pilgrimantiques@globalnet.co.uk. SER: Packing and shipping. VAT: Stan/Spec.

Jane Strickland & Daughters   `LAPADA`

71 High St. EX14 1PW. Est. 1977. Open 10-5. SIZE: Medium. *STOCK: 18th-19th C furniture; 19th C English and French mirrors; 19th C armchairs, sofas and chaise longues; lighting, needlepoint and Aubusson rugs and cushions; decorative items.* LOC: 10 miles from M5. PARK: Easy. TEL: 01404 44221; e-mail - JSandDaughtersUK@aol.com; website - www.janestricklandanddaughters.co.uk. SER: Restorations (upholstery). FAIRS: Decorative Antique Textile, Battersea; Penmans Chester. VAT: Stan/Spec.

Upstairs, Downstairs

12 High St. EX14 8PU. (T. and B. Sabine). Est. 1975. Open 10-5.30. SIZE: Large. *STOCK: 18th-19th C furniture, porcelain, metalware, pictures and clocks.* PARK: Easy. TEL: 01404 42140.

Graham York Rare Books

225 High St. EX14 1LB. ABA. ILAB. PBFA. Est. 1982. Open 9.30-5. SIZE: Medium. *STOCK: Travel especially Spain and South Africa; art - fine and applied, especially lace, costume and textiles; literature, natural history, history, biography, children's, British topography especially West Country, gypsies, George Borrow; maps and prints.* LOC: Last shop at west end of High St. PARK: Nearby. TEL: 01404 41727; fax - 01404 44993; mobile - 07831 138011; e-mail -

books@gyork. co.uk; website - www.gyork.co.uk.
FAIRS: Monthly (Hotel Russell, Bloomsbury);
ABA Chelsea; International Book, Olympia
(June); PBFA Bath (April).

ILFRACOMBE

Relics
113 High St. EX34 9ET. (Nicola D. Bradshaw).
Resident. Est. 1977. Open 10-5. SIZE: Small.
*STOCK: General antiques and small collectables,
Victorian and Edwardian.* PARK: Nearby. TEL:
01271 865486; home/fax - same; e-mail -
nikkibradshaw@ukonline.co.uk. SER: Valuations.

KINGSBRIDGE

**Avon House Antiques/Hayward's
Antiques**
13 Church St. TQ7 1BT. (D.H. and M.S.
Hayward). Est. 1969. Open 10-1 and 2-5. SIZE:
Small. *STOCK: General antiques.* PARK:
Limited. TEL: 01548 853718; e-mail - enquiries
@haywardsantiques.com.uk. SER: Valuations;
stripping (pine). FAIRS: Devon County.

KINGSWEAR, Nr. Dartmouth

David L.H. Southwick Rare Art `BADA`
Beacon Lodge, Beacon Lane. TQ6 0BU. **Open
by appointment.** *STOCK: Chinese and
Japanese works of art.* **TEL: 01803 752533; fax
- 01803 752535; website - www.rareart.co.uk.**

LYDFORD, Nr. Okehampton

Skeaping Gallery
Townend House. EX20 4AR. Est. 1972. Open by
appointment. *STOCK: Oils and watercolours.*
TEL: 01822 820383; fax - same. VAT: Spec

LYNTON

Farthings
Churchill House. EX35 6NF. (Mrs L. R. Farthing
and Miss I. J. Farthing). Est. 1996. Open 10-4.30
(4pm in winter) including Sun. SIZE: Small.
*STOCK: Pictures, 19th-20th C, £50-£5,000;
small furniture, Victorian and Edwardian, £50-
£1,000; collectibles, 19th-20th C, £5-£2,000.*
LOC: Opposite church. PARK: Easy. TEL: 01598
753744; home - 01598 753465; e-mail - jane@
farthingsI.freeserve.co.uk. SER: Valuations;
restorations; buys at auction.

Wood's Antiques
29A Lee Rd. EX35 6BS. (Pat and Brian Wood).
Est. 1994. Open 9-5.30; in winter Sun. 9.30-2.

CL: Thurs. *STOCK: General antiques including
small furniture, mainly Victorian, £10-£8,000.*
PARK: Easy. TEL: 01598 752722.

MAIDENCOMBE, Nr. Torquay

G.A. Whiteway-Wilkinson
Sunsea, Teignmouth Rd. TQ1 4TP. Est. 1943.
Open by appointment. *STOCK: General
antiques, fine art and jewellery.* LOC:
Approximately half-way on main
Torquay/Teignmouth road. TEL: 01803 329692.
VAT: Spec.

MERTON, Nr. Okehampton

Barometer World Ltd
Quicksilver Barn. EX20 3DS. Est. 1979. Open
Tues.-Sat. 9-5. SIZE: Medium. *STOCK:
Mercurial wheel and stick barometers, 1780-
1900, £650-£12,500; aneroid barometers, 1850-
1930, £100-£1,500.* LOC: Between Hatherleigh
and Torrington on A386. PARK: Easy. TEL:
01805 603443; fax - 01805 603344; e-mail -
enquiries@barometerworld.co.uk; website -
www.barometerworld.co.uk. SER: Valuations;
restorations (barometers). VAT: Stan/Spec.

MODBURY, Nr. Ivybridge

Collectors Choice
27 Church St. PL21 0QR. (Allan Jenkins).
Resident. Est. 1994. Open 10-5.30. CL: Some
Wed. SIZE: Small. *STOCK: Clocks, £20-£1,000;
valve radios, ceramics, fountain pens and small
furniture, £5-£500; all 19th-20th C; garden urns
and statues.* LOC: A379 between Plymouth and
Kingsbridge. PARK: Easy. TEL: 01548 831111.
SER: Valuations; restorations (clocks and fountain
pens); repairs (clocks); cleaning; re-silvering.

Wild Goose Antiques
34 Church St. PL21 0QR. (Mr and Mrs T.C.
Freeman). Open 10-5.30. *STOCK: Old pine,
country furniture, decorative items.* LOC: A379
between Plymouth and Kingsbridge. PARK:
Nearby. TEL: 01548 830715. SER: Delivery.
VAT: Stan.

MONKTON, Nr. Honiton

Pugh's Farm Antiques
Pugh's Farm. EX14 9QH. (G. Garner and C.
Cherry). Est. 1974. Open 9-5.30. SIZE: Large.
*STOCK: French furniture, armoires, farm tables,
country furniture, neo-rustique, especially
wooden beds; Victorian and Edwardian furniture.*
LOC: A30 2 miles from Honiton. PARK: Easy.

TEL: 01404 42860; home - same; fax - 01404 47792; e-mails - sales@pughsantiques.com, and sales@antiquebeds.com; websites - www.pughs-antiques-export.com; www.pughsantiques.com and www.antiquebeds.com. SER: Importers and exporters. VAT: Stan.

MORCHARD BISHOP, Nr Crediton

Morchard Bishop Antiques
Meadowbank. EX17 6PD. (J.C. and E.A. Child). Resident. Est. 1970. Open by appointment. SIZE: Small. *STOCK: General antiques.* LOC: 8 miles west of Crediton, off A377 at Morchard Rd. PARK: Easy. TEL: 01363 877456.

NEWTON ABBOT

The Attic
9 Union St. TQ12 2JX. (G.W. Gillman). Est. 1976. CL: Mon. and Thurs., prior telephone call advisable. SIZE: Medium. *STOCK: General antiques, to £1,000.* LOC: Town centre. PARK: Easy. TEL: 01626 355124. SER: Valuations.

St Leonards Antiques & Craft Centre
Wolborough St. TQ12 1JQ. (Derick Wilson). Est. 1970. Open 10-4.30 including Sun., Tues. 9.30-4.30. SIZE: Large. *STOCK: General antiques,*
19th C, £5-£1,000. LOC: At start of main road to Totnes. PARK: Adjacent and opposite. TEL: 01626 335666; fax - same. SER: Valuations; restorations; buys at auction (furniture, decorative items). FAIRS: All major.

NEWTON ST. CYRES, Nr. Exeter

Gordon Hepworth Fine Art
Hayne Farm, Sand Down Lane. EX5 5DE. (C.G. and I.M. Hepworth). Est. 1990. Open Wed.-Sat. during exhibitions or by appointment. SIZE: Large barn - 2 floors. *STOCK: Modern British paintings, post-war and contemporary especially West Country - West Cornwall and St. Ives School, £300-£5,000.* LOC: A377, 3 miles nw. of Exeter turn left by village sign, into Sand Down Lane, farm entrance on left, after last white house. PARK: Easy. TEL: 01392 851351; home - same.

Hyde Road Antiques
23 Hyde Rd. TQ4 5BW. (David Pentecost). Est. 1975. Open 10-5, Thurs. 10-12.30 and 1.30-5. SIZE: Medium. *STOCK: Collectables and general antiques, 16th-20th C, £1-£5,000.* LOC: Off Torquay Rd. PARK: Opposite. TEL: 01803 554000. SER: Valuations; restorations (clocks, furniture, china); buys at auction. FAIRS: Westpoint; Matford, Exeter.

The Pocket Bookshop
159 Winner St. TQ3 3BP. (L. and A.R. Corrall). Est. 1985. Open Tues.-Sat. 10.30-5.30. SIZE: Small. *STOCK: Books, secondhand and out of print.* LOC: Outskirts. PARK: Nearby. TEL: 01803 529804.

PLYMOUTH

Annterior Antiques
22 Molesworth Rd., Millbridge. PL1 5LZ. (A. Tregenza and R. Mascaro). Est. 1987. Open 9.30-5.30, Sat. 10-5 or by appointment. CL: Tues. SIZE: Small. *STOCK: Stripped pine, 18th-19th C, £50-£3,000; some painted, mahogany and decorative furniture; brass and iron beds, 19th C, £250-£1,500; decorative small items.* LOC: Follow signs to Torpoint Ferry from North Cross roundabout, turn left at junction of Wilton St. and Molesworth Rd. PARK: Easy. TEL: 01752 558277; fax - 01752 564471; e-mail - info@ annterior.co.uk. SER: Buys at auction; finder. VAT: Stan/Spec.

Barbican Antiques Centre
82-84 Vauxhall St., Barbican. PL4 0EX. (T. Cremer-Price). Est. 1971. Open 9.30-5 including Sun. SIZE: 60+ dealers. *STOCK: Silver and plate, art pottery, porcelain, glass, jewellery, furniture, pictures, clocks, collectables.* PARK: Own. TEL: 01752 201752; fax - 020 8546 1618.

New Street Antique Centre
27 New St., The Barbican. PL1 2LS. (Turner Properties). Est. 1980. Open 10-5. SIZE: Medium. *STOCK: Clocks, silver, jewellery, weapons, general antiques.* PARK: Nearby. TEL: 01752 661165. VAT: Stan/Spec.

Parade Antiques Market
17 The Parade, The Barbican. PL1 2JW. (John Cabello). Est. 1982. Open 10-5 including Sun. SIZE: Medium. *STOCK: Collectables, 19th-20th C, £1-£1,000; militaria, 18th-20th C, £1-£7,000.* PARK: Easy. TEL: 01752 221443; fax - 01752 291208.

Michael Wood Fine Art
The Gallery, 1 Southside Ope, The Barbican. PL1 2LL. Est. 1967. Open Tues.-Sat.10-5, other times by appointment. SIZE: Medium. *STOCK: Oils, watercolours, original prints, sculptures, ceramics, art glass and books, contemporary, RA exhibitors, modern British, Newlyn, St Ives and Victorian, £50-£250,000.* LOC: Harbour front. PARK: Nearby. TEL: 01752 225533; mobiles - 07971 847722 and 07764 377899; e-mail - michael@michaelwoodfineart.com. SER:

Valuations; conservation/preservation/security advice. VAT: Stan/Spec.

SEATON

Etcetera Antiques
12 Beer Rd. EX12 2PA. (Michael and Deborah Rymer). Est. 1969. Open 10-1 and 2-5, Thurs. and other times by appointment. SIZE: Medium. *STOCK: General antique furniture and shipping goods.* PARK: Own. TEL: 01297 21965; mobile - 07780 840507.

SHALDON

Leigh Extence Antique Clocks
49 Fore St. TQ14 0EA. Open 10-5. CL: Sat. pm. *STOCK: Clocks, 1730-1880; barometers.* LOC: Opposite Royal Standard public house. PARK: Outside shop. TEL: 01626 872636; mobile - 07967 802160; e-mails - clocks@extence.co.uk and info@tompion.co.uk; website - www. extence.co.uk. SER: Buys at auction; finder (clocks); horological research.

SIDMOUTH

The Old Curiosity Shop
Old Fore St. EX10 8LP. (Thomas and Sally

Koch). Est. 1994. Open 9.30-5, Sun. 11-5. SIZE: Medium. *STOCK: Glass and china, including Moorcroft, Clarice Cliff, Lalique, Royal Doulton, Beswick; Oriental rugs, furniture; mantel and grandfather clocks; paintings.* LOC: Down High St. towards sea, in pedestrianised Old Fore St. PARK: Nearby. TEL: 01395 515299. FAIRS: Matford, West Point; Shepton Mallet.

Sidmouth Antiques & Collectors Centre
All Saints Rd. EX10 8ES. Open 10-5 (Easter-end Oct. 10-5.30). SIZE: 10 dealers. *STOCK: Wide range of antiques and collectables, militaria, antiquarian and out of print books, postcards, stamps, limited edition plates, pictures and prints, linen, lace and crochet items.* PARK: Nearby. TEL: 01395 512588; website - www. sidmouth.ws. FAIRS: DCAF Westpoint, Exeter.

The Vintage Toy and Train Shop
Sidmouth Antiques and Collectors Centre, All Saints Rd. EX10 8ES. (R.D.N., M.E. and J.W. Salisbury). Est. 1995. Open 10-5. *STOCK: Hornby Gauge 0 and Dublo trains, Dinky toys, Meccano and other die-cast and tinplate toys, wooden jig-saw puzzles.* LOC: Near main Post Office. PARK: Limited and opposite. TEL: 01395 512588; home - 01395 513399.

SOUTH BRENT

P.M. Pollak
Moorview, Plymouth Rd. TQ10 9HT. (Dr Patrick Pollak and Mrs Jeanne Pollak). ABA. Est. 1973. Open by appointment. SIZE: Small. *STOCK: Antiquarian books especially medicine and science; prints, some instruments, £50-£5,000.* LOC: On edge of village, near London Inn. PARK: Own. TEL: 01364 73457; fax - 01364 649126; e-mail - patrick@rarevols.co.uk; website - www.rarevols.co.uk. SER: Valuations; buys at auction; catalogues issued, computer searches.

SOUTH MOLTON

The Dragon
77 South St. EX36 3AG. (Mrs J. E. Aker). Est. 1994. Open 9-5. SIZE: Small. *STOCK: Pine and country furniture, from 19th C; bric-a-brac, books and pictures.* LOC: Near town centre. PARK: Limited or nearby. TEL: 01769 572374; mobile - 07712 079818; e-mail - snapdragon antiques@hotmail.com; website - www.visit southmolton.co.uk/dragon.htm. SER: Restorations (furniture).

The Dragon and the Phoenix
24 East St. EX36 3DB. (Paul Williams and Caroline Bennett). Open 10-4. SIZE: Small. *STOCK: Antique Chinese and Tibetan furniture.* PARK: Easy. TEL: 01769 574104; e-mail - antiques@dragonphoenix.co.uk; website - www. antiquechinesefurniture.co.uk.

The Furniture Antique Market
14a Barnstaple St. EX36 3BQ. (P. Soton). Est. 1992. CL:Wed. SIZE: Large. *STOCK: Wide range of general antiques.* LOC: On old A361, 100 yards from town centre. PARK: Nearby. TEL: 01769 573401; e-mail - lohardy@ madasafish.com. SER: Valuations.

Snap Dragon
80 South St. EX36 3AG. (Mrs J. E. Aker). Est. 1994. Open 9-5. SIZE: Small. *STOCK: Pine and country furniture, kitchenalia and tools, architectural and garden artefacts.* LOC: Near town centre. PARK: Limited and opposite. TEL: 01769 572374; mobile - 07712 079818; e-mail - snapdragonantiques@hotmail.com; website - www.snapdragondevon.co.uk. SER: Restorations (furniture).

J.R. Tredant
50/50a South St. EX36 4AG. Usually open. *STOCK: General antiques.* TEL: 01769 573006; home - 01769 572416. SER: Valuations.

R. M. Young Bookseller
17 Broad St. EX36 3AQ. (Mark Young). Est. 1970. Open 10-5, Thurs., Fri. and Sat. 9-5. SIZE: Medium. *STOCK: Books especially Exmoor, the countryside, Henry Williamson, £5-200.* LOC: Main street. PARK: Free nearby. TEL: 01769 573350. SER: Restorations; out-of-print book search.

STOCKLAND, Nr. Honiton

Colystock Antiques
Rising Sun Farm. EX14 9NH. (D.C. McCollum). Est. 1975. Open seven days. SIZE: Large. *STOCK: Pine and oak including English, Irish and Continental, 18th-19th C.* TEL: 01404 861271. SER: Container packing and documentation; courier.

TAVISTOCK

King Street Curios
5 King St. PL19 0DS. (T. and P. Bates). Est. 1979. Open 9-4. SIZE: Medium. *STOCK: Pine furniture, postcards, cigarette cards, china, glass, general collectables, jewellery, to £100.* LOC: Town centre. TEL: 01822 615193.

TEDBURN ST MARY, Nr. Exeter

A. E. Wakeman & Sons Ltd
Newhouse Farm. EX6 6AL. (A.P., G.M. and A. A. Wakeman). Est. 1967. Open Mon.-Fri. 9-5.30 or by appointment. SIZE: Large. *STOCK: Mahogany, walnut and rosewood furniture, mainly 19th C, £200-£5,000; some 18th C mahogany and oak, £300-£5,000.* LOC: 6 miles from Exeter. PARK: Easy. TEL: 01647 61254; home/fax - same; mobile - 07836 284765; e-mail - a.e.wakeman@btopenworld.com FAIRS: Newark. VAT: Stan/Spec. *Trade Only.*

TEIGNMOUTH

Extence Antiques
2 Wellington St. TQ14 8HH. (T.E. and L.E. Extence). Est. 1928. Open 9.30-5. SIZE: Medium. *STOCK: Jewellery, silver, objets d'art.* PARK: Limited. TEL: 01626 773353. VAT: Stan/Spec.

Queen's House Emporium
27 Fore St. TQ14 8DZ. (Teresa Nicholls). Est. 1982. Open Tues.-Sat. 10-1 and 1.30-5. SIZE: Small. *STOCK: Furniture, china, brass, general antiques and collectables.* LOC: Main street. PARK: Nearby. TEL: 01626 776675; mobile - 07768 076360. FAIRS: Westpoint; Marsh Barton.

Timepiece
125 Bitton Park Rd. TQ14 9BZ. (Clive and Willow Pople). Est. 1988. Open Tues.-Sat. 9.30-5.30, Sat. 9.30-6. SIZE: Medium. *STOCK: Country furniture, clocks, 19th C, £25-£2,000; collectables, 19th-20th C, £1-£100.* LOC: On A379 next to Bitton Park. TEL: 01626 770275.

TOPSHAM, Nr. Exeter

Bounty Antiques
76 Fore St. EX3 0HQ. (John Harding and John Purves). MADA. Est. 2000. Open 9.30-5. SIZE: Small. *STOCK: Marine, aviation, transport items, to £500; clocks, cameras, ceramics, tools, glass, ephemera, collectables, steam engines, to £500.* LOC: Next to Lloyds TSB. PARK: Nearby. TEL: 01392 875007; home - 01395 266077/232397. SER: Valuations. FAIRS: Westpoint; Matford, Exeter.

Mere Antiques   LAPADA
13 Fore St. EX3 0HF. (Marilyn Reed). Resident. Est. 1986. Open 9.30-5.30, Sat. 10-5.30, Sun. by appointment. SIZE: 3 rooms. *STOCK: English porcelain, 18th-19th C, £50-£10,000; furniture, 17th-20th C, £200-£5,000; decorative items.*

PARK: Easy and nearby. TEL: 01392 874224; e-mail - bob@ntlbusiness.com. SER: Valuations. FAIRS: NEC; LAPADA. VAT: Spec.

Pennies
40 Fore St. EX3 0HU. (Michael Clark). Open 10-5. *STOCK: Antiques and collectables.* TEL: 01392 877020. VAT: Stan/Spec.

Topsham Quay Antiques Centre
The Quay. EX3 0JA. (Stonewall Ltd). Est. 1993. Open seven days 10-5. SIZE: Large. *STOCK: Furniture, 18th-19th C, £100-£3,000+; ceramics and tools, 18th-20th C, £5-£1,000+; collectables, 20th C, £5-£200; silver and plate, 18th-20th C, £10-£1,500+; textiles, 18th-20th C, £5-£500.* LOC: 4 miles from Exeter, M5 junction 30. PARK: Easy. TEL: 01392 874006; fax - same; e-mail - office@antiquesontopshamquay.co.uk; website - www.antiquesontopshamquay.co.uk. SER: Valuations; buys at auction. FAIRS: Local.

TORQUAY

The Old Cop Shop
Castle Lane. TQ1 3AN. (L. Rolfe). Est. 1971. Open 9-5. SIZE: Medium. *STOCK: General antiques and shipping items.* PARK: Easy. TEL: 01803 294484; fax - 01803 316620. SER: Valuations. FAIRS: Local.

The Schuster Gallery
P O Box 139. TQ1 2XX. ABA. Est. 1973. Open by appointment. *STOCK: Antique prints, maps, medieval manuscripts, fine and rare colour plate books, atlases; children's illustrated books including Beatrix Potter, Kate Greenaway and Alice in Wonderland and related items.* TEL: 01803 211422; fax - 01803 211290; e-mail - tschuster@easynet.co.uk; website - www.acid.co.uk/acid/schus. htm.

Sheraton House Antiques
Sheraton House, 1 Laburnum Row, Torre. TQ2 5QX. (I.S. Hutton). Open 9.30-4.45. *STOCK: General antiques.* TEL: 01803 293334.

Toby's Architectural Antiques
Torre Station, Newton Rd. TQ2 2DD. (Paul and John Norrish). SALVO. Est. 1985. Open 10.30-5 seven days. SIZE: Large. *STOCK: Furniture, £15-£3,000; pianos, fireplaces, lighting, collectables, 19th-20th C, £5-£2,000.* LOC: Main Newton Abbott road, 1 mile from sea front. PARK: Easy. TEL: 01803 212222; fax - 01803 200523; e-mail - paul4tobys@yahoo.co.uk; website - www.tobysreclamation.co.uk. SER: Valuations; delivery (UK). VAT: Spec.

TOTNES

The Antique Dining Room
93 High St. TQ9 5PB. (P. Gillo). Est. 1983. Open Tues.-Sat. 10.30-5.30. SIZE: Small. *STOCK: Victorian and Edwardian furniture especially Victorian wind-out tables.* PARK: Nearby. TEL: 01803 847800; fax - same. SER: Restorations.

Bogan House Antiques
43-45 High St. TQ9 5NP. (Chris Mitchell). Est. 1977. Open Fri. 10-1 and 2-4, Sat. 10.30-1 and 2-4.30, some Tues., otherwise by appointment. SIZE: Small. *STOCK: Silver flatware, £5-£200; metalware, Victorian and Delft tiles, £5-£40; Japanese woodblock prints, £20-£400.* PARK: Nearby. TEL: 01803 862075; home - 01803 865386; mobile - 07989 416518.

Collards Books
4 Castle St. TQ9 5NU. (B. Collard). Est. 1970. Open 10.30-5, restricted opening in winter. *STOCK: Antiquarian and secondhand books.* LOC: Opposite castle. PARK: Nearby. TEL: Home - 01548 550246.

The Exchange
76 High St. TQ9 5SN. (J. and M. Caley). Est. 1997. Open 10-5. SIZE: Small. *STOCK: Antiquarian and secondhand books, papers and ephemera; general antiques and curios.* LOC: Town centre. PARK: Nearby. TEL: 01803 866836; home - 01803 868598; e-mail - bookworm1700@yahoo.co.uk. SER: Valuations.

Fine Pine Antiques
Woodland Rd., Harbertonford. TQ9 7SX. (Nick and Linda Gildersleve). Est. 1973. Open 9.30-5, Sun. 11-4. SIZE: Large. *STOCK: Stripped pine and country furniture.* LOC: A381. PARK: Easy. TEL: 01803 732465; home - 01548 821360; e-mail - info@fine-pine-antiques.co.uk; website - www.fine-pine-antiques.co.uk. SER: Restorations; stripping.

Pandora's Box
51/2 High St. TQ9 5NN. (Sarah Mimpriss and Mark and June Anderson). Est. 1989. Open Thurs., Fri. and Sat. 10.30-4.30. SIZE: Small. *STOCK: Etchings, small boxes, small Victorian furniture and trunks.* PARK: Nearby. TEL: 01803 867799; home - 01803 762112.

Pedlars Pack Books
4 The Plains. TQ9 5DR. (P. D. and A. Elliott). PBFA. Est. 1991. Open 9-5. SIZE: Medium. *STOCK: Books, £5-500.* LOC: Near river. PARK: Nearby. TEL: 01803 866423; e-mail - pedlar @aol.com. SER: Valuations; buys at auction.

Rotherfold Antiques
The Rotherfold. TQ9 5ST. (Mrs S. M. van Heck). Est. 1999. Open 10-1 and 2-5. CL: Thurs. SIZE: Medium. *STOCK: Furniture and fine art, 19th C; objets d'art, ceramics, mirrors.* LOC: At the end of The Narrows. PARK: Easy. TEL: 01803 840303. SER: Delivery; restorations.

UFFCULME, Nr. Cullompton

English Country Antiques
The Old Brewery, High St. EX15 3AB. (M.C. Mead). Est. 1996. Open 9-5, prior telephone call preferred. SIZE: Large. *STOCK: Country and decorating antiques - furniture - pine including painted, fruitwoods, oak and mahogany, bamboo, bentwood, leather and upholstered; metalware including lighting, brass, copper and iron, gardenalia, architectural; china and glass, mainly 19th-20th C; textiles, leatherwork, bric-a-brac, basketware, wooden items, model yachts, pictures and paintings, mirrors.* LOC: Village centre. PARK: Own. TEL: 01884 841110; home/fax - 01803 845480; mobile - 07768 328433; e-mail - mike@englishcountry antiques.co.uk; website - www.englishcountry antiques.co.uk. FAIRS: NEC.

WHIMPLE, Nr. Exeter

Anthony James Antiques
Brook Cottage, The Square. EX5 2SL. Open by appointment. *STOCK: 17th-19th C furniture and works of art.* LOC: A30 between Exeter and Honiton. PARK: Easy. TEL: 01404 822146. SER: Valuations. VAT: Spec.

WOODBURY, Nr Exeter

Woodbury Antiques
Church St. EX5 1HN. (H. Ballingall). Est. 1966. Open Mon., Tues., Fri. 10-3, Sat. 10-1. SIZE: Large. *STOCK: Victorian and Edwardian furniture and items.* PARK: Easy. TEL: 01395 232727. VAT: Stan/Spec.

YEALMPTON, Nr. Plymouth

Carnegie Paintings & Clocks
15 Fore St. PL9 2JN. (Chris Carnegie). Open Thurs.-Sat. 10-5.30 or by appointment. *STOCK: Clocks, barometers, paintings and small furniture.* TEL: 01752 881170; mobile - 07970 968337; website - www.paintingsandclocks.com. SER: Restorations (paintings, clocks and barometers).

DORSET

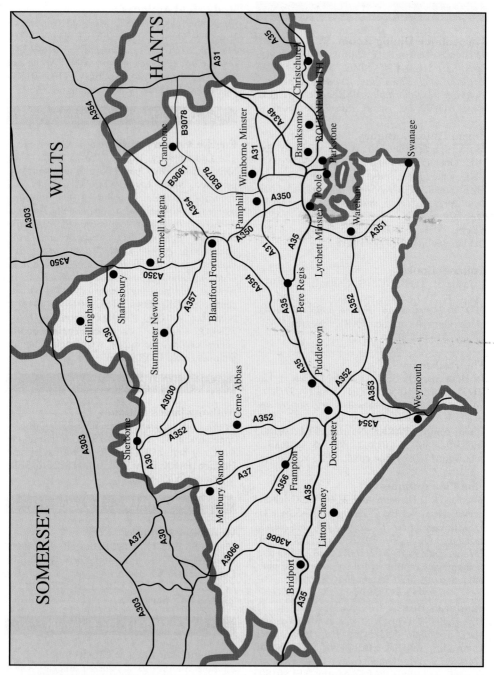

Dealers and Shops in Dorset

Bere Regis	2	Fontmell Magna	1	Puddletown	1
Blandford Forum	2	Frampton	1	Shaftesbury	2
Bournemouth	23	Gillingham	1	Sherborne	15
Branksome	3	Litton Cheney	1	Sturminster Newton	1
Bridport	4	Lytchett Minster	1	Swanage	2
Cerne Abbas	1	Melbury Osmond	1	Wareham	2
Christchurch	4	Pamphill	1	Weymouth	4
Cranborne	1	Parkstone	3	Wimborne Minster	3
Dorchester	8	Poole	4		

BERE REGIS, Nr. Wareham

Dorset Reclamation
Cow Drove. BH20 7JZ. (Tessa Pearce). SALVO. Open 8-5, Sat. 9-4. SIZE: Large. *STOCK: Decorative architectural and garden antiques, hard landscaping materials, fireplaces and bathrooms.* TEL: 01929 472200; fax - 01929 472292; e-mail - info@dorsetrec.uk.net.com; website - www.dorsetreclamation.co.uk. SER: Delivery; restorations.

Legg of Dorchester
The Old Mill Antiques, West St. BH20 7HS. (W. and H. Legg & Sons). Est. 1930. *STOCK: General antiques, Regency and decorative furniture, stripped pine.* PARK: Easy. TEL: 01929 472051; e-mail - jerry@legg ofdorchester.co.uk; website - www.leggof dorchester.co.uk. SER: Restorations (furniture). VAT: Spec.

BLANDFORD FORUM

Ancient and Modern Bookshop (including Garret's Antiques)
84 Salisbury St. DT11 7QE. (Mrs P. Davey). Est. 1988. Open 9.30-12.30 and 1.30-4.30. CL: Wed. *STOCK: Books and small antiques.* TEL: 01258 455276; e-mail - pegdavey@tinyworld.co.uk; websites - www.ancientandmodernbooks.co.uk; www.calcraft.co.uk; www.ukbookworld.com/ members/ancient.

Milton Antiques
Market Place. DT11 7HU. Open 9-5. CL: Wed pm. SIZE: Medium. *STOCK: Furniture, 18th-19th C, £50-£2,000; decorative items, 18th-20th C, £5-£200.* LOC: Opposite church, adjacent to town museum. PARK: Easy. TEL: 01258 450100. SER: Valuations; restorations including polishing.

BOURNEMOUTH

Altamiradeco
14 Seamoor Rd. BH4 9AR. (A. Benarroch). Est. 1994. Open Tues.-Sat. 9.30-5. SIZE: Medium. *STOCK: Art Deco - bronzes including Chiparus, Preiss, Colinet and Lorenz; furniture, glass, ceramics.* PARK: Loading only and nearby. TEL: 01202 766444; mobile - 07885 778342; e-mail - gallery@altamiradeco.com; website - www. altamiradeco.com. SER: Valuations.

Antiques and Furnishings
339 Charminster Rd. BH8 9QR. (P. Neath). Open 10-5.30. *STOCK: Furniture, brass, copper, china, textiles and decorative objects.* TEL: 01202 527976.

Antiques Exchange
873-877 Christchurch Rd., Boscombe. BH7 6AT. (Mr and Mrs R. Draysey). Est. 1972. Open 10.30-6. SIZE: Medium. *STOCK: Furniture, smalls, lighting, decorative, from 1700.* PARK: Easy. TEL: 01202 433456; e-mail - jo.draysey@virgin. net; website - www.antiquesexchange.com. SER: Restorations (furniture).

Boscombe Militaria
86 Palmerston Rd., Boscombe. BH1 4HU. (E.A. Browne). Est. 1981. Open 10-1 and 2-5. CL: Wed. *STOCK: German militaria, £10-£500; British and American militaria, £5-£300, all 1914-1918 and 1939-1945.* LOC: Just off Christchurch Rd. PARK: Easy. TEL: 01202 304250; fax - 01202 733696. FAIRS: Farnham; Cheshunt; major South of England Arms.

Boscombe Models and Collectors Shop
802c Christchurch Rd., Boscombe. BH7 6DD. (Sylvia Hart). Open Thurs., Fri. and Sat. 10-1 and 2-4.30. *STOCK: Collectors' toys, 19th-20th C, £1-£1,000.* TEL: 01202 398884.

Chorley-Burdett Antiques
828-830 Christchurch Rd., Pokesdown. BH7 6DF. (Raymond Burdett). Open 9-5.30. SIZE: Large. *STOCK: Furniture, pine furniture including reclaimed, late 19th to early 20th C, £50-£1,000.* LOC: Corner of Warwick Rd. PARK: Easy. TEL: 01202 423363; fax - same. VAT: Stan/Spec.

Lionel Geneen Ltd `LAPADA`
811 Christchurch Rd., Boscombe. BH7 6AP. Est. 1902. Open 9-5, Sat. 9-12, (closed lunchtimes), other times by appointment. SIZE: Large. *STOCK: English, Continental and Oriental furniture, china and works of art including some bronzes, enamels, ivories, jades, all mainly 19th C, Art Nouveau and Art Deco; specialising in tea, dinner and dessert services.* LOC: Main road through Boscombe. PARK: Own. TEL: 01202 422961; home - 01202 520417; mobile - 07770 596781. SER: Valuations. VAT: Stan/Spec.

H.L.B. Antiques
139 Barrack Rd. BH23 2AW. (H.L. Blechman). Est. 1969. SIZE: Large. *STOCK: Collectable items.* PARK: Easy. TEL: 01202 429252/482388.

Hampshire Gallery `LAPADA`
18 Lansdowne Rd. BH1 1SD. Est. 1971. *STOCK: Paintings and watercolours, 17th to early 20th C.*

TEL: 01202 551211. SER: Valuations. VAT: Spec.

Libra Antiques
916 Christchurch Rd. BH7 6DL. Est. 1997. Open 10-5. SIZE: Medium. *STOCK: Silver and plate, objects, furniture, metalware, china and glass.* PARK: Opposite. TEL: 01202 427615; mobile - 07836 680928. VAT: Stan.

G.B. Mussenden and Son Antiques, Jewellery and Silver
24 Seamoor Rd., Westbourne. BH4 9AR. Est. 1948. Open 9-5. CL: Wed. SIZE: Medium. *STOCK: Antiques, jewellery, silver.* LOC: Central Westbourne, corner of R.L. Stevenson Ave. PARK: Easy. TEL: 01202 764462. SER: Valuations. VAT: Stan/Global/Spec.

Geo. A. Payne and Son Ltd
742 Christchurch Rd., Boscombe. BH7 6BZ. (H.G. and N.G. Payne). FGA. Est. 1946. Open 9-5.30. SIZE: Small. *STOCK: Jewellery, 19th-20th C, £10-£3,000; silver, 18th-20th C, £30-£1,000; plate, £10-£200.* LOC: Opposite Browning Ave. and Chessel Ave. PARK: Browning Ave. TEL: 01202 394954. SER: Valuations; gemstone testing; restorations (silver, jewellery, clocks and watches). VAT: Stan/Spec.

R.E. Porter
2-6 Post Office Rd. BH1 1BA. Est. 1934. Open 9.30-5. SIZE: Medium. *STOCK: Silver including early antique spoons, Georgian, £20-£5,000; jewellery, pot lids, Baxter and Le Blond prints, clocks including second-hand. Not Stocked: Furniture, arms, armour, carpets.* LOC: Walking from the square, take the Old Christchurch Rd., then the first turning on the left. PARK: 300yds. at top of Richmond Hill. TEL: 01202 554289. SER: Valuations. VAT: Stan/Spec.

Portique
15/16/17 Criterion Arcade. BH1 1BU. (N. and E. Harkness). NAG. Est. 1968. Open Tues.- Fri. 9.30-5, Sat. 9.30-4.30. *STOCK: Silver, jewellery, Derby china, glass paperweights, cloisonné, clocks.* LOC: Coming from the square take the Old Christchurch Rd. from roundabout, arcade entrance is between first and second turnings on left. TEL: 01202 552979. SER: Repairs; restorations (silver and jewellery); valuations. VAT: Stan/Spec.

Recollections
5 Royal Arcade, Boscombe. BH1 4BT. (David and Brenda Francis). Est. 1994. Open 9.30-4.30. CL: Tues. and Wed. SIZE: Medium. *STOCK:*

Mainly collectables, 1920's to modern, including Poole, royal commemoratives, crested china, Art Deco, Beatrix Potter, Doulton, to £1,000. LOC: Off pedestrian precinct, opposite Sea Rd. PARK: Sovereign centre. TEL: 01202 304441.

Sainsburys of Bournemouth Ltd `LAPADA`
23-25 Abbott Rd. BH9 1EU. Est. 1918. Open 8-1 and 2-6, appointment advisable. CL: Sat. *STOCK: Furniture especially bookcases and dining tables, 18th C, to £40,000.* PARK: Own. TEL: 01202 529271; home - 01202 763616; fax - 01202 510028; ; e-mail - sales@sainsburys-antiques.com. SER: Custom-made furniture from re-cycled Georgian wood including exceptionally large pieces. VAT: Stan/Spec.

Sandy's Antiques
790-792 Christchurch Rd., Boscombe. BH7 6DD. BDADA. Open 10-5.30. SIZE: 2 large shops + warehouse. *STOCK: Victorian, Edwardian and shipping goods.* TEL: 01202 301190; evenings - 01202 304955. VAT: Stan/Spec.

Sterling Coins and Medals
2 Somerset Rd., Boscombe. BH7 6JH. (W.V. Henstridge). Est. 1969. Open 9.30-4. CL: Wed. pm. SIZE: Small. *STOCK: Coins, medals, militaria, World War II German items.* LOC: Next to 806 Christchurch Rd. TEL: 01202 423881. SER: Valuations. VAT: Stan.

M.C. Taylor
995 Christchurch Rd., Boscombe East. BH7 6BB. (Mark Taylor). MAPH, CMBHI. Est. 1982. Open Tues.-Sat. 9-5. SIZE: Small. *STOCK: Clocks, barometers, music boxes and turret clocks, £500-£20,000.* LOC: Opposite St. James' School and Kings Park entrance. PARK: Easy. TEL: 01202 429718; website - www.taylorclocks.com. SER: Valuations; restorations. VAT: Stan/Spec.

Tregoning Antiques
57 Westover Rd. BH1 2BZ. (Barry Papworth). NAG. Est. 1969. Open Mon., Tues., Fri. and Sat. SIZE: Small. *STOCK: Fine jewellery, 18th-19th C, £50-£24,000; silver, 18th-19th C, £10-£5,000; collectables, 19th C, £10-£200.* LOC: At junction with Bath Rd., opposite Royal Bath Hotel. PARK: Easy. TEL: 01202 312100; fax - same; mobile - 07813 820624; e-mail - sales@tregoning jewellers.uk.com; website - www.tregoning jewellersuk.com. SER: Valuations; restorations (jewellery and silver). VAT: Stan.

Victorian Chairman
883 Christchurch Rd., Boscombe. BH7 6AU. (M. Leo). Open 10-5. *STOCK: Furniture especially*

chairs, sofas and tables. TEL: 01202 420996. SER: Restorations (upholstery).

Vintage Clobber
874 Christchurch Rd., Boscombe. BH7 6DQ. (R.A. Mason). Open 10-5. *STOCK: Clothing and fabrics, from Victorian.* TEL: 01202 429794; website - www.vintageclobber.com.

Yesterday Tackle and Books
42 Clingan Rd., Boscombe East. BH6 5PZ. (David and Alba Dobbyn). Est. 1983. Open by appointment. *STOCK: Fishing tackle and associated items including taxidermy; books especially by 'BB' (D.J. Watkins-Pitchford); ephemera and prints.* PARK: Easy. TEL: 01202 476586. SER: Catalogues issued.

BRANKSOME

Allen's (Branksome) Ltd
447/449 Poole Rd. BH12 1DH. (P.J. D'Ardenne). Est. 1948. Open 9-5.30. SIZE: Large. *STOCK: Furniture.* TEL: 01202 763724; fax - 01202 763724; e-mail - allens@branksome447.fsnet.co.uk. VAT: Stan/Spec.

Branksome Antiques
370 Poole Rd. BH12 1AW. (B.A. Neal). Est. 1973. Open 10-5. CL: Wed. and Sat. SIZE: Medium. *STOCK: Scientific and marine items, furniture and general small items.* PARK: Easy. TEL: 01202 763324; home - 01202 679932. SER: Buys at auction (as stock). VAT: Stan/Spec.

David Mack Antiques
434-436 Poole Rd. and 21 Crommer Rd. BH12 1DF. Est. 1963. Open 9-5.30. SIZE: Large. *STOCK: 18th-19th C tables, chairs, display cabinets, desks, bureaux, bookcases; later furniture.* LOC: 2 doors from Branksome rail station. PARK: Own. TEL: 01202 760005; fax - 01202 765100; website - www.davidmack antiques.co.uk. SER: Restorations. VAT: Stan/Spec.

BRIDPORT

Batten's Jewellers
26 South St. DT6 3NQ. (R. and G. Batten). Est. 1974. Open 9.30-5. *STOCK: Jewellery and silver.* LOC: Town centre. PARK: Easy and nearby. TEL: 01308 456910. SER: Valuations; repairs.

Bedford Antiques
81 East St. DT6 3LB. (P.E.L. Bedford). Est. 1955. Usually open but prior telephone call advisable. SIZE: Medium. *STOCK: Oriental and European*

porcelain and bronzes, hardstone and ivory carvings, paintings and drawings, jewellery and portrait miniatures, snuff boxes, scent bottles, enamels and other objets de vertu, antiquities. LOC: Eastern end of town. PARK: Opposite. TEL: 01308 421370; home - same.

Benchmark Antiques
West Allington. DT6 5BJ. (Megan Standage). BAFRA. Est. 1992. Open by appointment. SIZE: Small. *STOCK: English furniture and related items, 1700-1880, £100-£15,000.* LOC: B3167 (West St.) 450yds from town centre. PARK: Easy. TEL: 01308 420941; home - same. SER: Valuations; restorations; buys at auction. FAIRS: NEC; Olympia.

Bridport Old Books
11 South St. DT6 3NR. PBFA. Est. 1998. Open 10-5. SIZE: Small. *STOCK: Antiquarian and secondhand books and prints.* LOC: Town centre. PARK: Nearby. TEL: 01308 425689. FAIRS: PBFA, Hotel Russell, London; Oxford; Bath; Glasgow; Edinburgh; H&D Hotel Royal National, London.

CERNE ABBAS

Cerne Antiques
DT2 7LA. (I. Pulliblank). Est. 1972. Open 10-1 and 2-5, Sun. 2-5. CL: Mon. and Fri. SIZE: Medium. *STOCK: Silver, porcelain, furniture including unusual items, mainly 19th C, £1-£400.* LOC: A352. PARK: Easy. TEL: 01300 341490; home - same.

CHRISTCHURCH

J.L. Arditti
20 Twynham Ave. BH23 1QU. Est. 1964. Open by appointment. SIZE: Medium. *STOCK: Oriental carpets and rugs, 18th to early 20th C, £500-£20,000.* LOC: From town centre take road towards Hurn airport, left turn. PARK: Twynham Avenue. TEL: 01202 485414/481500; e-mail - mike@arditti.freeserve.co.uk; website - www.arditti.freeserve.co.uk. SER: Valuations; restorations; cleaning (Persian rugs). VAT: Stan/Spec.

Christchurch Carpets
55/57 Bargates. BH23 1QE. (J. Sheppard). Est. 1963. Open 9-5.30. SIZE: Large. *STOCK: Persian carpets and rugs, 19th-20th C, £100-£5,000.* LOC: Main road. PARK: Adjacent. TEL: 01202 482712. SER: Valuations; repairs; cleaning. VAT: Stan/Spec.

Hamptons

12 Purewell. BH23 1EP. (G. Hampton). Open 10-6. CL: Sat. am. SIZE: Large. *STOCK: Furniture, 18th-19th C; general antiques, clocks, china, instruments, metalware, oil paintings, Chinese and Persian carpets and rugs.* PARK: Easy. TEL: 01202 484000.

Tudor House Antiques   LAPADA

420 Lymington Rd., Highcliffe, BH23 5HE. (P. Knight and D. Burton). Est. 1940. Open 10-5. CL: Mon. and Wed. SIZE: Medium. *STOCK: General antiques.* LOC: Main road, A337. PARK: Easy. TEL: 01425 280440. VAT: Stan/Spec.

CRANBORNE, Nr. Wimborne

Tower Antiques

The Square. BH21 5PR. (P.W. Kear and P. White). Est. 1975. Open 8.30-5.30. CL: Sat. *STOCK: Georgian and Victorian furniture.* TEL: 01725 517552.

DORCHESTER

Box of Porcelain Ltd

51d Icen Way. DT1 1EW. (R.J. and Mrs. S.Y. Lunn). Est. 1984. Open 10-5. CL: Thurs. *STOCK: Porcelain including Worcester, Doulton, Spode, Coalport, Beswick.* LOC: Close town centre, near Dinosaur Museum. TEL: 01305 267110; fax - 01305 263201; e-mail - rlunn@boxofporcelain. com; website - www.boxofporcelain.com. SER: Finder (Beswick and Doulton).

Colliton Antique Centre

Colliton St. DT1 1XH. Open daily, Sun. by appointment. SIZE: 14 dealers. *STOCK: 18th-20th C furniture, £25-£5,000; brass, bric-a-brac, pictures, china, pine, clocks, jewellery and silver, toys.* LOC: By town clock. PARK: Easy. TEL: 01305 269398/260115. SER: Restorations (cabinet work and metalware). VAT: Stan/Spec.

De Danann Antique Centre

25/27 London Rd. DT1 1NF. (J. Burton). Est. 1993. Open 9-5. SIZE: Large - 20 dealers. *STOCK: 17th-20th C furniture, bedsteads, ceramics, rugs, clocks, pine, kitchenalia, brass and copper, collectables.* PARK: Easy. TEL: 01305 250066; fax - 01305 250113; e-mail - dedanann@supanet.com; website - www. dedanann.co.uk. SER: Restorations (furniture including French polishing, cabinet making).

Finesse Fine Art

Empool Cottage, West Knighton. DT2 8PE.

(Tony Wraight). Open strictly by appointment. *STOCK: Pre-war motoring accessories - metal mascots and Lalique glassware, including mascots, fine bronzes, automobilia, picnic hampers, £1,000-£50,000.* TEL: 01305 854286; fax - 01305 852888; mobile - 07973 886937.

Michael Legg Antiques

8 Church St. DT1 1JN. (E.M.J. Legg). Open 9-5.30 or any time by appointment. SIZE: Medium. *STOCK: 17th-19th C furniture, clocks, porcelain, pictures, silver, glass.* TEL: 01305 264596. SER: Lectures on the Arts. VAT: Stan/Spec.

Legg of Dorchester

Regency House, 51 High East St. DT1 1HU. (W. and H. Legg & Sons). Est. 1930. Open 9.15-5.15. *STOCK: General antiques, Regency and decorative furniture, stripped pine.* TEL: 01305 264964; e-mail - jerry@leggofdorchester.co.uk; website - www.leggofdorchester.co.uk. SER: Restorations (furniture). VAT: Stan/Spec.

The Poet's Eye   BADA

52 High West St. DT1 1UT. (John Walker). Open 9.30-5 or by appointment. SIZE: Small. *STOCK: Early furniture, textiles, metalwork, ceramics, wood carvings, 16th-18th C; British folk art, 16th-19th C; 20th C and contemporary British arts and crafts.* LOC: Main street. PARK: Easy. TEL: 01305 260324. SER: Valuations; buys at auction. VAT: Spec.

Words Etcetera

2 Cornhill. DT1 1BA. (Julian Nangle). PBFA. ABA. Est. 1970. Open 9.30-5.30. SIZE: Medium. *STOCK: Antiquarian and quality second-hand books and prints; remainders on all subjects.* LOC: Close to museum. TEL: 01305 251919; fax - 01305 266898; home - 01258 820415. SER: Buys at auction (books). FAIRS: ABA London (June).

FONTMELL MAGNA

Quarterjack Antiques

The Old Coach House, Lurmer St. SP7 0PA. (Jon Neilson). Est. 1969. Open 9-5.15, Sun. 9.30-5. SIZE: Small. *STOCK: 18th-19th C glassware, furniture, pictures, corkscrews, walking sticks and horse brasses.* LOC: A350 between Blandford Forum and Shaftesbury. PARK: Easy. TEL: 01747 812222; website - www.quarterjack.com.

FRAMPTON, Nr. Dorchester

Georgina Ryder   LAPADA

Frampton House, DT2 9NH. Est. 1977. Open by

appointment. SIZE: Medium. *STOCK: 18th-19th C French furniture and decorative objects.* PARK: Easy. TEL: 01300 320308; fax - 01300 321600; mobile - 07785 391710; e-mail - maynardryder@aol.com. SER: Valuations; restorations (upholstery). FAIRS: Olympia; LAPADA; Decorative & Textile, Battersea. VAT: Spec.

GILLINGHAM

Talisman
`LAPADA`
The Old Brewery, Wyke. SP8 4NW. Est. 1980. Open 9-5, Sat. 10-4. SIZE: Large. *STOCK: Unusual and decorative items, garden furniture, architectural fittings, 18th-19th C; English and Continental furniture.* PARK: Easy. TEL: 01747 824423/824222; fax - 01747 823544. FAIRS: Olympia (June). VAT: Stan/Spec.

LITTON CHENEY, Nr. Dorchester

F. Whillock
Court Farm. DT2 9AU. Est. 1979. Open by appointment. *STOCK: Maps and prints.* LOC: Village centre. PARK: Easy. TEL: 01308 482457. SER: Framing.

LYTCHETT MINSTER

Old Button Shop Antiques
BH16 6JF. (T. Johns). Est. 1970. Open Tues.-Fri. 2-5, Sat 11-1. *STOCK: Small antiques, brass, copper, curios, unusual items and antique Dorset buttons.* TEL: 01202 622169.

MELBURY OSMOND, Nr. Dorchester

Hardy Country
Meadow View. DT2 0NA. (Steven and Caroline Groves). Est. 1980. Open by appointment. SIZE: Large. *STOCK: Georgian, Victorian, Edwardian pine and country furniture, £40-£2,500.* LOC: Off A37. PARK: Easy. TEL: 01935 83440; website - www.hardycountry.com.

PAMPHILL, Nr. Wimborne

Rectory Rocking Horses
The Barn, Pamphill Dairy. BH21 4ED. (Geoff Boyd and Ali Nicol). Est. 1996. Open 9-4. SIZE: Small. *STOCK: Rocking horses, various sizes, from early 20th C.* PARK: Easy. TEL: 01202 881100; fax - same; website - www.antique rockinghorses.co.uk. SER: Valuations; restorations.

PARKSTONE, Nr. Poole

Derek J. Burgess - Horologist
470 Ashley Rd. BH14 0AD. Est. 1980. Open Tues.-Fri. 9-1.30. *STOCK: Clocks, watches.* TEL: 01202 730542. SER: Restorations (clocks and watches of all periods); parts made.

Dorset Coin Company
193 Ashley Rd. BH14 9DL. (E.J. and C.P. Parsons). BNTA, IBNS. Est. 1977. Open 9.30-4, Sat. 9.30-1. *STOCK: Coins, 19th-20th C, £1-£50; banknotes, 20th C, £3-£50.* LOC: Main road through Upper Parkstone. PARK: Easy. TEL: 01202 739606; fax - 01202 739230. SER: Valuations. FAIRS: BNTA London. VAT: Stan/Global/Exempt

Christopher Williams Antiquarian Bookseller
19 Morrison Ave. BH12 4AD. PBFA. *STOCK: Books especially on antiques, art, needlework, lacemaking and leatherbound volumes and sets.* TEL: 01202 743157; fax - same; e-mail - cw4finebooks@lineone.net. FAIRS: Various. *Postal only.*

POOLE

G.D. and S.T. Antiques
(G.D. and S.T. Brown). Open by appointment. *STOCK: General antiques.* TEL: 01202 676340.

Great Expectations
115 Penn Hill Ave., Lower Parkstone. BH14 9LY. (A. Carter). Est. 1999. Open Wed.-Sat. 10.30-4.30. SIZE: Small. *STOCK: Furniture, mahogany, pine, burr walnut, oak and French, from 1800, to £1,250; English pottery, to £375.* PARK: Nearby. TEL: 01202 740645. SER: Restorations (furniture including upholstery).

Laburnum Antiques
Lonbourne House, 250 Bournemouth Rd. BH14 9HZ. (Doreen Mills). Est. 1998. Open Tues.-Sat. 10-5.30. *STOCK: Fine Georgian and Victorian furniture and artifacts.* LOC: A35. PARK: Forecourt. TEL: 01202 746222; fax - 01202 736777. SER: Restorations (furniture); upholstery. FAIRS: Wilton House.

Stocks and Chairs
11 Bank Chambers, Penn Hill Ave. BH14 9NB. (Mrs C.E. Holding-Parsons). Est. 1992. Open Tues., Thurs. and Fri. 11-5, Sat. 9.30-5 and by appointment. SIZE: Medium. *STOCK: Furniture, 18th to early 20th C, mainly £500-£5,000; specialist in hand-dyed leather chairs and settees.*

PARK: Easy. TEL: 01202 718618; mobile - 07970 010512; e-mail - stocksand.chairs@ virgin.net; website - www.stocksandchairs antiques.com. SER: Restorations (cabinet work, polishing).

PUDDLETOWN, Nr. Dorchester

Antique Map and Bookshop
32 High St. DT2 8RU. (C.D. and H.M. Proctor). ABA. PBFA. Est. 1976. Open 9-5. *STOCK: Antiquarian and secondhand books, maps, prints and engravings.* PARK: Easy. TEL: 01305 848633; e-mail - proctor@puddletown.demon. co.uk; website - www.abebooks.com/home/ proctorbooks. SER: Postal; catalogues.

SHAFTESBURY

Mr. Punch's Antique Market
33 Bell St. SP7 8AE. Est. 1994. Open 10-5.30. CL: Mon. SIZE: Large. *STOCK: Wide variety of general antiques, fine art and collectables. Also Punch and Judy collection.* LOC: On corner with Muston's Lane. PARK: Easy 100 yards. TEL: 01747 855775; fax - same. SER: Valuations; restorations; repairs (ceramics); delivery.

Shaston Antiques
16A Bell St. SP7 8AE. (J. D. Hine). Resident. Est. 1996. Open 9.30-1 and 2-5, Wed. 9.30-1. SIZE: Medium. *STOCK: Furniture, 18th-19th C, £300-£5,000.* LOC: From town centre, turn right opposite Grosvenor Hotel into Bell St. TEL: 01747 850405; home - same. SER: Restorations (furniture).

SHERBORNE

Abbas Antiques
at Sherborne World of Antiques, Long St. DT9 3BS. (T.F.J. Jeans). Est. 1991. Open 9.30-5. *STOCK: Small collectables and furniture, 18th-19th C.* PARK: Opposite. TEL: 01935 816451. SER: Restorations.

Antiques of Sherborne   LAPADA
1 The Green. DT9 3HZ. (C. and L. Greenslade). CINOA. SAADA. Est. 1988. Open 10-5. *STOCK: 18th-19th C furniture, sofas and armchairs, chess sets and linen.* LOC: Top of Cheap St., just off A30. PARK: Nearby. TEL: 01935 816549; mobile - 07971 019173; e-mail - clive@antiquesofsherborne.fsnet.co.uk. SER: Delivery (overseas). FAIRS: Shepton Mallet. VAT: Spec.

Chapter House Books
Trendle St. DT9 3NT. (Carol and Robert Hutchison). PBFA. Est. 1988. Open 10-5. SIZE: Large. *STOCK: Out-of-print, secondhand and antiquarian books, to £400.* LOC: Next to Almshouse and Abbey. TEL: 01935 816262; e-mail - chapterhousebooks@tiscali.com. SER: Valuations; restorations (bookbinding and repair); search.

Dodge and Son   LAPADA
28-33 Cheap St. DT9 3PU. (S. Dodge). Est. 1918. Open 9-5.30, Sun. by appointment. SIZE: Large. *STOCK: Furniture, including dining, all periods.* PARK: At rear. TEL: 01935 815151; e-mail - sales@dodgesherborne.co.uk. SER: Restorations; furniture makers; worldwide delivery. VAT: Stan/Spec.

Greystoke Antiques
Swan Yard, Off Cheap St. DT9 3AX. (F.L. and N.E. Butcher). Est. 1970. Open 10-4.30. *STOCK: Silver, Georgian, Victorian and later; early 19th C English blue transfer printed pottery.* LOC: Off main street. PARK: Adjacent to Swan Yard or outside shop. TEL: 01935 812833. VAT: Stan/Margin/Global.

Keeble Antiques
2 Tilton Court, Digby Rd. DT9 3NL. (C.P. Keeble). Est. 1965. Open 9-6, Sat. 8.30-6, Sun. 9.30-5.30. SIZE: Medium. *STOCK: Clocks, 19th C, £250-£850; Venetian mirrors, 19th C, £500-£900; books, 16th-20th C, £1-£800; maps, 17th-19th C, £100-£750.* LOC: Adjacent tourist information centre, near abbey. PARK: Easy. TEL: 01935 816199; fax - same; e-mail - info@keebleantiques.co.uk; website - www. keebleantiques.co.uk. SER: Valuations (books and maps).

Macintosh Antiques
The Courtyard, Newland. DT9 3JG. (Patrick and Elona Macintosh). Est. 1985. Open 10-5. SIZE: Large. *STOCK: 17th-20th C country house furniture and accessories including Arts & Craft movement, £100-£10,000.* PARK: Own. TEL: 01935 815209; home - 01935 815584; mobile - 07768 606811; e-mail - patrick@macintosh antiques.fsnet.co.uk. SER: Valuations. FAIRS: Olympia (Feb., June, Nov); Little Chelsea.

Phoenix Antiques
21 Cheap St. DT9 3PU. (Sally and Neil Brent Jones). Est. 1998. Open 9.30-5.30. SIZE: Medium. *STOCK: Furniture, 17th-20th; lighting, mirrors, furnishings, decorative and unusual items.* LOC: Town centre. PARK: Easy. TEL: 01935 812788; e-mail - phoenixantique@aol.com. SER: Valuations; restorations. VAT: Spec.

Piers Pisani Antiques
The Courtyard, Newland. Est. 1987. Open 10-5. SIZE: Medium. *STOCK: Furniture including sofas and armchairs, dining tables and sets of chairs, English and French country house and reproduction; decorative items.* LOC: Next to Sherborne House. PARK: Own. TEL: 01935 815209; fax - same; mobile - 07973 373753; e-mail - pp@pierspisani.com; website - www. pierspisani.com. SER: Valuations; restorations (upholstery, chairs copied, cabinet-making). VAT: Spec.

Renaissance
South St. DT9 3NG. (Malcolm Heygate Browne). Open 10-5. SIZE: Large. *STOCK: 18th-19th C furniture, pottery and porcelain.* LOC: Off Cheap St. towards station. PARK: Easy. TEL: 01935 815487; e-mail - antiquemalcolm@aol.com. SER: Valuations; restorations. VAT: Stan/Spec.

Sherborne World of Antiques
Long St. DT9 3BS. (S. Mattar). Open 9.30-5. SIZE: 40+ dealers. *STOCK: Fine arts, painting, furniture, rugs, objets d'art, jewellery, ceramics, glass.* LOC: From A30 via Greenhill. PARK: Easy - opposite. TEL: 01935 816451; fax - 01935 816240; e-mail - info@sherborneworldantiques. co.uk. SER: Restorations; upholstery; delivery.

The Swan Gallery
51 Cheap St. DT9 3AX. (S. and Mrs K. Lamb). Est. 1977. Open 9.30-5, Wed. 9.30-1. SIZE: Large. *STOCK: Watercolours, 18th to early 20th C; oil paintings, antiquarian maps and prints.* PARK: Easy, at rear. TEL: 01935 814465; fax - 01308 868195. SER: Valuations; restorations (paintings, watercolours and prints); framing. FAIRS: Watercolours and Drawings, Park Lane, London. VAT: Stan/Spec.

Timecraft Clocks
Unit 2, 24 Cheap St. DT9 3PX. (Gordon M. Smith). MBHI. Est. 1993. Open 10-5.30, , Mon. and other times by appointment. SIZE: Small. *STOCK: Clocks, 18th-20th C, £200-£4,000; barometers, 18th-20th C, £80-£1,200; telephones, 20th C, £80-£250.* PARK: Easy. TEL: 01935 817771. SER: Restorations (clock and barometer movements, cases and dials).

Wessex Antiques
6 Cheap St. DT9 3PX. (Mrs Frances Bryant). Est. 1986. Open Tues.-Sat. 10-5. SIZE: Small. *STOCK: Staffordshire figures, 1800-1900, £100-£3,000; English drinking glasses, 1680-1820, £50-£2,000; small English furniture, 1500-1850, £300-£6,000; Oriental rugs, 1800-1950, £400-*

£6,000. PARK: Loading and nearby. TEL: 01935 816816; fax - same. SER: Valuations; restorations (ceramics).

Henry Willis (Antique Silver)
38 Cheap St. DT9 3PX. Est. 1974. Open 10-5. SIZE: Small. *STOCK: Silver, 16th-20th C, £15-£15,000.* LOC: Town centre, just off A30. PARK: Nearby. TEL: 01935 816828. SER: Valuations; restorations (silver); buys at auction (silver). FAIRS: Olympia (June). VAT: Stan/Spec.

STURMINSTER NEWTON

Tom Tribe and Son
Bridge St. DT10 1BZ. CMBHI. Resident. Open 9-5, Sat. 9-1 and by appointment. *STOCK: Longcase and mantel clocks, barometers.* PARK: At side of shop. TEL: 01258 472311. VAT: Stan/Spec.

SWANAGE

Georgian Gems Antique Jewellers
28 High St. BH19 2NU. (Brian Barker). NAG. Est. 1971. Open 9.30-1 and 2.30-5 or by appointment. SIZE: Small. *STOCK: Jewellery, £5-£2,000; silver, £5-£500; both from 1700.* LOC: Town centre. PARK: Nearby. TEL: 01929 424697; freephone - 0800 471 0242; mobile - 07932 794742. SER: Valuations; repairs; gem testing; special search.

Reference Works Ltd.
at The Last Resort, 9 Commercial Rd. BH19 1DF. (B. and J.E. Lamb). Est. 1984. Open 10-4, Sat. 10-1. *STOCK: Reference books and catalogues on ceramics, all subjects, new and out-of-print; small range of ceramics, 18th-20th C.* TEL: 01929 424423; fax - 01929 422597; e-mail - sales@referenceworks.co.uk; website - www. referenceworks.co.uk. SER: Mail order, catalogue available; six newsletters each year; ceramic research and consultancy.

WAREHAM

Heirlooms Antique Jewellers and Silversmiths
21 South St. BH20 4LR. (M. and Mrs G. Young). FGA, DGA, RJDip. Est. 1986. Open 9.15-5. CL: Wed. SIZE: Medium. *STOCK: Jewellery, £30-£1,000; silver, £20-£500; both Georgian to Edwardian.* LOC: On main thoroughfare. PARK: At rear. TEL: 01929 554207. SER: Valuations; restorations; repairs; gem testing.

Yesterdays
13A North St. BH20 4AB. Est. 1995. Open 9.30-

4.30, Wed. 9.30-1.30. *STOCK: Pottery and porcelain - Dennis, Poole, blue and white, Beswick, Isle of Wight, Wade, Carlton and Spode, Jonathan Harris; okra glass.* LOC: Town centre opposite Post Office. PARK: Nearby. TEL: 01929 550505; home - 01929 556381. SER: Valuations; buys at auction. FAIRS: Shepton Mallet, Exeter; Winchester. VAT: Stan.

WEYMOUTH

Books Afloat
66 Park St. DT4 7DE. (J. Ritchie). Est. 1983. Open 9.30-5.30. SIZE: 2 floors. *STOCK: Rare and secondhand books especially nautical; maritime ephemera, liner memorabilia, ship models, paintings, prints.* LOC: Near rail station. PARK: Easy. TEL: 01305 779774.

Books & Bygones
Great George St. DT4 7AR. (Mrs Denise Nash). Est. 1981. Open 11-5.30, Sun. 12-5. SIZE: Medium. *STOCK: Books including antiquarian, 50p to £1,000; antiques and collectables, from 18th C, £1-£750; ephemera, from 50p.* LOC: Near King's statue, on esplanade. PARK: Easy. TEL: 01305 777231; home - 01305 771529. SER: Valuations; buys at auction.

Nautical Antique Centre
3a Cove Passage, off Hope Sq. DT4 8TR. (D.C. Warwick). Est. 1989. Open 10-1 and 2-5 prior telephone call advisable, Sat., Sun. and Mon. by appointment. SIZE: Medium. *STOCK: Exclusively original nautical, including sextants, logs, clocks, flags, blocks, old sails, old rope, bells, ship models, telescopes, ship badges, portholes and memorabilia, also restaurant/pub decorative items, 19th-20th C, £5-£2,000.* LOC: Near Hope square opposite Brewers Quay, adjacent harbour. PARK: Nearby. TEL: 01305 777838; home - 01305 783180; mobile - 07833 707247; e-mail - nauticalantiques@tinyworld. co.uk; website - www.nauticalantiques weymouth.co.uk. SER: Buys at auction (nautical items).

The Treasure Chest
29 East St. DT4 8BN. (P. Barrett). Open 10-1 and 2.30-5. CL: Wed. pm. *STOCK: Maps, prints, coins, medals; army, RN and RAF badges.* PARK: Next door. TEL: 01305 772757. SER: Lost medals replaced; medal mounting - full size or miniature, brooches and new ribbons.

WIMBORNE MINSTER

Four Seasons Gallery
24 West Borough. BH21 1NF. (Nigel Cox). Est. 1996. Open Wed.- Sat. 11-5.30. SIZE: Small. *STOCK: Small 18th-19th furniture, paintings, collectables; contemporary art gallery with regular exhibitions.* LOC: Near Minster. PARK: Easy and nearby. TEL: 01202 882204; website - www.fourseasonsgallery.co.uk.

J.B. Antiques
10A West Row. BH21 1LA. (J. Beckett). Est. 1978. Open 10-4, Fri. and Sat. 9.30-4. CL: Wed. SIZE: Small. *STOCK: Copper, £5-£360; brass, £1-£350; furniture, £30-£1,200; all 18th-20th C.* LOC: 2 mins. from Sq. PARK: Nearby. TEL: Home - 01202 882522. SER: Valuations; restorations (metalware); buys at auction (copper). FAIRS: Hinchingbrooke House, Huntingdon.

Minster Books
12 Corn Market. BH21 1HW. (John and Angela Child). Est. 1970. Open 10-5. SIZE: Medium. *STOCK: Books, £5-£100.* LOC: In road at side of Minster. PARK: King St. TEL: 01202 883355. SER: Valuations; restorations (book binding).

A carved Portland stone seat, early 19th century. £15,000-£25,000.

From an article entitled "Ancestral Seats" by James Rylands which appeared in the May 2002 issue of ***Antique Collecting***. For more details and to subscribe see page 21.

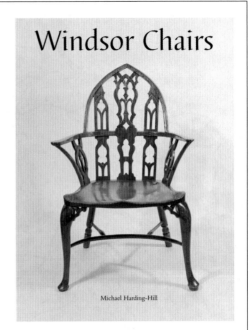

Windsor Chairs

Michael Harding-Hill

- *A visual record of the crème de la crème of Windsor chairs*

- *Beautiful colour illustrations*

- *Written by a hands-on specialist*

The Windsor chair, whether simple or complicated in construction, plain or ornate in appearance, has always served its purpose – to be utilitarian, durable, comfortable and even handsome.

Many excellent academic works have been written on the subject, but this book does not attempt to improve on their expertise. The intention rather is to complement them by showing the finest designs in greater detail. The form and construction of the chairs speak for themselves. All the chairs illustrated, although made in different centuries, are in use today. Is there another example of utilitarian furniture made in such numbers that still survives and is in everyday use?

More than 150 colour plates illustrate the very best Windsor chairs from the earliest stick-backs – literally stools with a few sticks added to the back – of the eighteenth century to those mass-produced for offices, schools, public institutions and the armed forces in the nineteenth century. There is a special section on American Windsors and an Epilogue outlines the story of the Windsor chair through the twentieth century and concludes by illustrating a 2002 Golden Jubilee chair.

This book is a celebration of the beautiful Windsor chair.

Michael Harding-Hill is a Cotswold antiques dealer who has specialised in Windsor chairs since 1971. Nearly all the chairs illustrated in this book have been in his possession and he has been able to look at them closely, to inspect the workmanship and to appreciate their beauty. There is no doubt in his mind that the Windsor chair could not be improved in any way.

9½ x 7½in./240 x 195mm.
160pp.,
180 col. and b.&w.
1 85149 429 4
£25.00

Available from all good booksellers and direct from the publisher:
ANTIQUE COLLECTORS' CLUB
Sandy Lane, Old Martlesham, Woodbridge, Suffolk, IP12 4SD.
Tel: 01394 389950   Fax: 01394 389999
Email: sales@antique-acc.com
Website: www.antique-acc.com

DURHAM

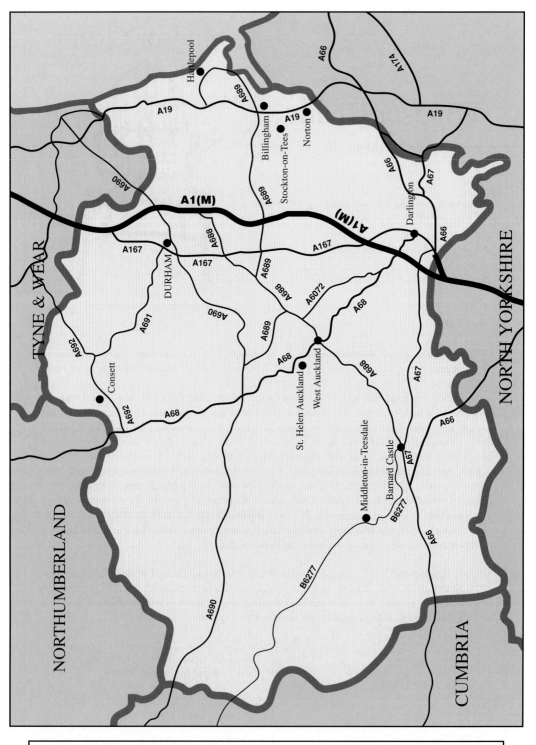

BARNARD CASTLE

Edward Barrington-Doulby
23 The Bank. (M. A. Venus). Est. 1990. Open Wed.-Sat. 11-5.30, Sun.12-5.30. SIZE: Warehouse + shop. *STOCK: 18th-20th C unusual tools, implements, kitchenalia, eccentricities, cast-iron, pottery, pictures, £1-£1,000; 17th-20th C pine, oak, mahogany, rustic and provincial furniture.* PARK: Easy. TEL: 01833 630500; home - 01325 264339; website - www.barnard-castle.co.uk/antiques/edwardbarrington-doulby. SER: Delivery.

The Collector
Douglas House, The Bank. DL12 8PH. (Robert A. Jordan). Est. 1970. Open Sat. 10-5 or by appointment. SIZE: Medium. *STOCK: Early furniture and complementary objects, decorative interior fittings and Eastern rugs.* PARK: Own. TEL: 01833 637783; fax - same; e-mail - JordanTheCollector@btinternet.com; website - www.barnard-castle.co.uk/antiques. SER: Restorations (especially metal work, early furniture and interiors).

Grant's Antiques
26 Newgate. DL12 8NG. (Carl and Stephanie Grant). Resident. Est. 1976. Open Wed. and Sat. 10.30-5. SIZE: Small. *STOCK: Oak and mahogany furniture, £100-£4,000; pottery, £15-£500; rugs, £50-£500; all 17th-19th C; paintings, 17th C to contemporary.* PARK: Easy. TEL: 01833 695700; e-mail - amh@rapidial.co.uk.

James Hardy Antiques Ltd
12 The Bank. DL12 8PQ. (Alan Hardy). Est. 1993. Open 10-5. CL: Thurs. SIZE: Medium. *STOCK: Furniture, 18th C to Edwardian, £500-£25,000; silver and porcelain, 18th-20th C, £25-£5,000.* PARK: Nearby. TEL: 01833 695135; fax - same; mobile - 07710 162003; e-mail - alan@jameshardyantiques.co.uk; website - www.jameshardyantiques.co.uk. SER: Restorations (silver and furniture); buys at auction (furniture). FAIRS: Harrogate; NEC. VAT: Spec.

Kingsley & Co. `LAPADA`
7 Newgate. DL12 8NQ. (David Harper). Est. 1992. Open 10.30-5. SIZE: Medium. *STOCK: Fine 17th to early 20th C antiques.* PARK: Nearby. TEL: 01833 650551; fax - same; home - 01833 650551; e-mail - kingsleyandco@btopenworld.com; website - www.kingsleyantiques.co.uk. SER: Valuations; restorations; re-upholstery.

Robson's Antiques
36 The Bank. DL12 8PN. (Anne, David and Dale Robson). Est. 1977. Open 10-5.30, Sun. 1.30-5.30. SIZE: Medium. *STOCK: Smalls including cutlery and canteens; silver perfume bottles, cruets, photograph frames; Victorian and north east glass; pottery including Maling, Carltonware and Losol; Durham and patchwork quilts; Georgian, Victorian and Edwardian fireplaces, ranges, marble and wooden surrounds, inserts.* LOC: Below Market Cross. PARK: Easy. TEL: 01833 690157/638700; mobile - 07977 146584; e-mail - dale.hunter.robson@virgin.net; website - www.robsonantiques.co.uk. SER: Valuations; restorations (fireplace fitting and stripping). FAIRS: NEC; Newark; Birmingham Glass; Manchester Armatage Centre Textile. VAT: Global.

Joan and David White Antiques
Neville House, 10 The Bank. DL12 8PQ. Est. 1975. Open Tues., Wed., Fri. and Sat. 11-5. *STOCK: Georgian, Victorian and export furniture and decorative items.* LOC: 100yds. from Market Cross. PARK: Front of shop. TEL: 01833 638329; home - 01325 374303. VAT: Stan/Spec.

BILLINGHAM

Margaret Bedi Antiques & Fine Art `LAPADA`
5 Station Rd. TS23 1AG. Est. 1976. Open by appointment. *STOCK: Mainly English period furniture, 1720-1920; oils and watercolours, 19th-20th C.* LOC: 300yds. off A19, by village green. PARK: Easy. TEL: 01642 782346; mobile - 07860 577637. FAIRS: Harrogate; North of England. VAT: Stan/Spec.

CONSETT

Harry Raine Antiques
Kelvinside House, Villa Real Rd. DH8 6BL. Appointment advisable. *STOCK: General antiques.* TEL: 01207 503935.

DARLINGTON

Robin Finnegan (Jeweller)
39 Cornmill Centre. DL1 1LS. NAG. Est. 1974. Open 9-5.30. SIZE: Medium. *STOCK: Jewellery, general antiques, coins, medals, military blazor badges and ties, £1-£10,000.* LOC: Town centre. PARK: Easy. TEL: 01325 489820; fax - 01325 357674; website - www.militarybadges.co.uk. SER: Valuations; repairs (jewellery); mounting (medals). VAT: Stan.

Alan Ramsey Antiques LAPADA

Unit 10-11 Dudley Rd, Yarm Road Industrial Estate. DL1 4GG. Est. 1973. Open Mon.-Fri. 9.30-4 or by appointment. SIZE: Warehouse. *STOCK: Victorian, Edwardian and Georgian furniture; interesting pine.* PARK: Easy. TEL: 01325 361679; home - 01642 711311; mobile - 07702 523246. VAT: Stan/Spec. *Trade Only.*

DURHAM

Old & Gold

87B Elvet Bridge. DH1 3AG. (Pam Tracey). Est. 1989. SIZE: Small. *STOCK: Jewellery and china, 19th C, £50-£100.* LOC: Next to Marriott Royal County Hotel. PARK: Multi-storey nearby. TEL: 0191 386 0728; mobile - 07831 362252. SER: Valuations; restorations (jewellery); buys at auction. FAIRS: Newark.

J. Shotton Antiquarian Books, Prints and Coins

89 Elvet Bridge. DH1 3AG. Est. 1967. Open 9.30-5. CL: Mon. *STOCK: Antiquarian books, prints, maps and coins.* TEL: 0191 386 4597.

HARTLEPOOL

Antique Fireplace Centre

134 Lyne St. South, TS24 7LX. (D.J. Crowther). Est. 1983. Open 9-5. SIZE: Large. *STOCK: Victorian and Edwardian fireplaces, Victorian 4-panel pine doors, architectural antiques.* TEL: 01429 279007/222433; mobile - 07774 639754. FAIRS: Swinderby.

MIDDLETON-IN-TEESDALE Nr. Barnard Castle

Brown's Antiques & Collectables

13 Chapel Row. DL12 0SN. (John and Val Brown). Resident. Est. 1990. Open 10-5, Sun. by appointment. SIZE: Medium. *STOCK: Furniture, metalware and collectables, 18th-20th, £20-£2,000.* LOC: North of A66. PARK: Easy. TEL: 01833 640276; e-mail - antiques@13chapelrow. freeserve.co.uk; website - www.browns-antiques.co.uk. SER: Buys at auction.

NORTON, Nr. Stockton-on-Tees

Paraphernalia

12 Harland Place, High St. TS20 1AA. (Rena Thomas). Est. 1982. Open 9.30-5. SIZE: Large. *STOCK: Mainly 19th C mahogany furniture, to £1,000.* LOC: Next to Red Lion public house. PARK: Easy. TEL: 01642 535940. SER: Restorations (furniture and French polishing). VAT: Stan/Spec.

ST HELEN AUCKLAND

Something Different

34a Maude Terrace. DL14 9BD. (P. Reeves and M. Holmes). Est. 1968. Open 9.30-5.30, Sun. 10-4.30. SIZE: Large. *STOCK: Furniture, clocks, decorative items, 19th-20th C.* PARK: Easy. TEL: 01388 664366. SER: Repairs (clocks); delivery (UK and Europe).

STOCKTON-ON-TEES

T.B. and R. Jordan (Fine Paintings) LAPADA

Aslak, Eaglescliffe. TS16 0QN. Est. 1974. Open by appointment. *STOCK: Oil paintings and watercolours especially Staithes group, 19th-20th C, £200-£15,000.* LOC: Village centre. PARK: Easy. TEL: 01642 782599; fax - 01642 780473; e-mail - info@tbrjordan.co.uk; website - www. tbrjordan.co.uk. SER: Commissions. FAIRS: Harrogate. VAT: Spec.

WEST AUCKLAND

Eden House Antiques

10 Staindrop Rd. DL14 9JX. (C.W. and M. Metcalfe). Est. 1978. Open daily including Sun. SIZE: Small. *STOCK: Clocks, furniture, 18th-20th C; collectables, bric-a-brac, oak and mahogany reproductions, Continental furniture.* LOC: A68, approx. 7 miles west of A1M. PARK: Easy. TEL: 01388 833013; e-mail - chris@antiques-e.co.uk; website - www.antiques-e.co.uk. SER: Valuations; restorations.

A pair of vases painted by William Mussill, made for the Australian market, unmarked, c.1870. Estimate £1,500-£2,000.

From an article entitled "The Minton Museum Sale" by Andrew Leston which appeared in the June 2002 issue of ***Antique Collecting***. For more details and to subscribe see page 21.

ARTISTS' TEXTILES
in BRITAIN
1945-1970

Geoffrey Rayner,
Richard Chamberlain and
Annamarie Stapleton

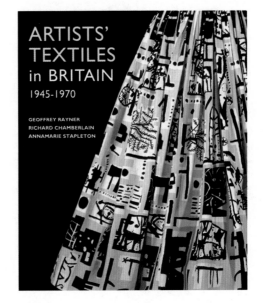

Artists' Textiles has over 100 stunning new illustrations of textiles for fashion (including headscarves) and furnishings designed by artists living or working in Britain for British companies during the period 1945-1970. This was a time of belief in 'Art for the People' in the new democratic spirit of Post-war Britain and has parallels in other media.

A comprehensive introduction by Geoff Rayner puts the period in its context, giving an historical perspective and covering contemporary events such as the Painting into Textiles exhibition at the ICA in 1953.

The final section of the book features an alphabetical biography; included are the artists and the manufacturers. The text concentrates on the artists' involvement with applied or decorative arts rather than a list of their fine art achievements.

Artists Include:

Edward Bawden	Zandra Rhodes
Jon Catleugh	William Scott
Jean Cocteau	Graham Sutherland
André Derain	
Barbara Hepworth	**Companies Include:**
Patrick Heron	Ascher
Henry Moore	Cresta Silks
Henri Matisse	Edinburgh Weavers
Ben Nicholson	Heal & Son
Eduardo Paolozzi	Liberty & Co.
Pablo Picasso	Porthia Textiles Prints
John Piper	Sanderson
	Warner & Sons

11¾ x 9¾in./300 x 250mm.
128pp.,120 col., 10 b.&w.
1 85149 432 4
£19.95 (paperback with flaps)

Available from all good booksellers and
direct from the publisher:
ANTIQUE COLLECTORS' CLUB
Sandy Lane, Old Martlesham, Woodbridge,
Suffolk, IP12 4SD.
Tel: 01394 389950   Fax: 01394 389999
Email: sales@antique-acc.com
Website: www.antique-acc.com

ESSEX

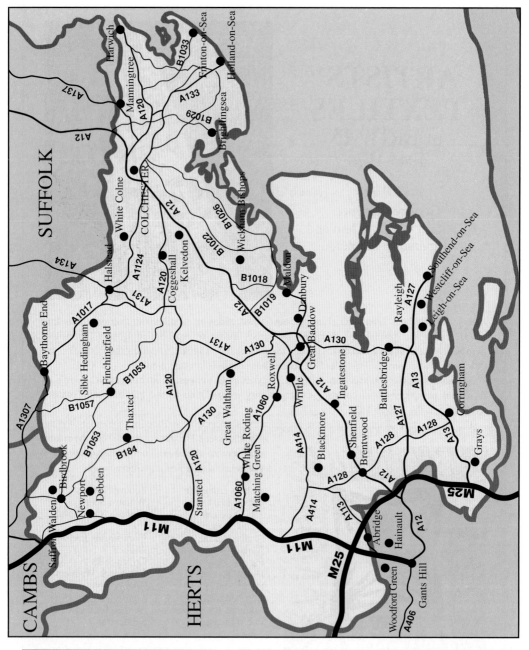

Dealers and Shops in Essex

Abridge	1	Debden	1	Ingatestone	1	Sible Hedingham	3
Battlesbridge	1	Finchingfield	1	Kelvedon	3	Southend-on-Sea	1
Baythorne End	1	Frinton-on-Sea	3	Leigh-on-Sea	7	Stansted	2
Birdbrook	1	Gants Hill	1	Maldon	3	Thaxted	1
Blackmore	1	Grays	1	Manningtree	1	Westcliff-on-Sea	2
Brentwood	3	Great Baddow	1	Matching Green	1	White Colne	1
Brightlingsea	1	Great Waltham	1	Newport	2	White Roding	1
Coggeshall	4	Hainault	1	Rayleigh	1	Wickham Bishops	1
Colchester	7	Halstead	2	Roxwell	1	Woodford Green	1
Corringham	1	Harwich	1	Saffron Walden	6	Writtle	1
Danbury	1	Holland-on-Sea	1	Shenfield	1		

ABRIDGE

Revival
Coach House, Market Place. RM4 1UA. (R. Y. Jefferson). Est. 1988. Open 11-5.30 and some Sun. CL: Fri. SIZE: Large. *STOCK: Furniture, Georgian to Deco, £20-£3,000; china and glass, silver, 1800-1960, £5-£500.* LOC: From London - off M11, junction 5, turn right then left on to A113. From M25, junction 26 follow A121, then B172. PARK: Opposite. TEL: 01992 814000; fax - 01992 814300. SER: Valuations; restorations (ceramics); repairs (watches and clocks).

BATTLESBRIDGE

Battlesbridge Antique Centre
SS11 7RF. (Jim and Fraser Gallie and Joseph Pettitt). Est. 1967. Open 7 days 10-5. SIZE: Over 80 units within adjacent premises (see below). *STOCK: Wide range from large furniture to jewellery, all periods with specialist dealers for most items.* LOC: A130, mid-way between Chelmsford and Southend. Junction 29, M25, east on A127 to A130, then north for 3 miles. By rail: Liverpool St.-Southend-on-Sea, change at Wickford for Battlesbridge. PARK: Own. TEL: Fax - 01268 575001; e-mail - info@battlesbridge. com; website - www.battlesbridge.com. SER: Restorations (furniture); container facilities; delivery (UK and overseas).

Cromwell House Antique Centre
TEL: Management : Jim Hamilton - 01268 762612; ground floor dealers - 01268 762612; first floor dealers - 01268 734030.

Haybarn and Bridgebarn Antique Centres
(J. P. Pettitt). TEL: 01268 763500/735884.

Muggeridge Farm Buildings
(Jim Gallie). TEL: 01268 732927.

The Old Granary Antique and Craft Centre
(Jim Gallie). TEL: Management - Justine Gallie - 01268 575000; showrooms - 01268 764197.

BAYTHORNE END

Swan Antiques
The Swan. CO9 4AF. (Mr and Mrs K. Mercado). Est. 1983. Open 9.30-6 including Sun. SIZE: Medium. *STOCK: Furniture, 18th-19th C and some Edwardian, £50-£2,000; porcelain, 19th C, £5-£1,000; small silver and collectables, 19th-20th C, £5-£500.* LOC: A1017 (formerly A604) junction with A1092 to Clare and Long Melford. PARK: Easy. TEL: 01440 785306; home - same. SER: Valuations. FAIRS: Newark; Ardingly.

BIRDBROOK, Nr. Halstead

I. Westrope
The Elms. CO9 4AB. Est. 1958. Open 9-5, Sat. 10-1 or by appointment. *STOCK: Furniture, china, dolls house furniture, garden ornaments including birdbaths, fountains, statues, animals.* LOC: A604. TEL: 01440 780034; evenings - 01440 730594.

BLACKMORE, Nr. Ingatestone

Megarry's and Forever Summer
Jericho Cottage, The Duckpond Green. CM4 0RR. (Peter and Judi Wood). EADA. Est. 1986. Open Wed.-Sun. 11-5 or by appointment. SIZE: Medium. *STOCK: Furniture, mainly 18th-19th C, some 20th C, £60-£3,500; ceramics, glass, treen and metalware, 19th-20th C, £5-£200; small silver and plate, jewellery and collectables, 19th-20th C, £5-£100; pine, 19th to early 20th C, £75-£1,000.* LOC: From A12, in Blackmore turn left at war memorial, premises behind Bull garden. PARK: Own. TEL: 01277 821031. SER: Valuations; restorations (furniture including French polishing, clocks and jewellery).

BRENTWOOD

Brandler Galleries
1 Coptfold Rd. CM14 4BM. (J. Brandler). FATG. Est. 1973. Open 10-5.30, Sun. by appointment. CL: Mon. SIZE: Medium. *STOCK: British pictures, 20th C, £100-£30,000; original artwork for books and comics.* LOC: Near Post Office. PARK: Own at rear. TEL: 01277 222269 (24 hrs); e-mail - john@brandler-galleries.com; website - www-brandler-galleries.com. SER: Valuations (photographs); restorations (watercolour and oil cleaning, relining); framing; buys at auction (pictures); 2-3 free catalogues annually. VAT: Spec.

Neil Graham Gallery
11 Ingrave Rd. CM15 8AP. (Mr. and Mrs. Neil Graham Firkins). EADA. FATG. Est. 1977. CL: Mon. SIZE: Large. *STOCK: 19th to early 20th C watercolours, oils and prints, £50-£1,000; Victorian and Edwardian occasional furniture, £100-£1,500; silver, pottery and porcelain, 19th-20th C, £25-£500.* LOC: Near junction of Wilson's Corner, town centre. PARK: Easy and High St. TEL: 01277 215383; fax - same; e-mail -info@neilgrahamgallery.com; website - www.neilgrahamgallery.com. SER: Valuations;

restorations (paintings); buys at auction. VAT: Stan/Spec.

Simpsons - Mirrors & Carvings
449 Ongar Rd. CM15 9JG. (S. Yardy). Open by appointment. *STOCK: Mirrors - antique including pine and new hand-carved; decorative pieces.* TEL: 01277 374541.

BRIGHTLINGSEA

The Shipwreck
22e Marshes Yard, Victoria Place. CO7 0BX. (Michael Kettle). Est. 1994. Open 10.15-5, Sun. 11.15-5 (Nov.-Feb. 2-5). SIZE: Medium. *STOCK: General antiques and collectables, £1-£100.* LOC: Between High St. and Promenade. PARK: Easy. TEL: 01206 307307; mobile - 07980 357456.

COGGESHALL

Argentum Antiques
1 Church St. CO6 1TU. (Mrs Dianne M. Carr). Open 10-5. CL: Wed. SIZE: Medium. *STOCK: Silver and Old Sheffield plate, 18th-20th C, £100-£2,000; furniture, mainly oak, 17th-19th C, £200-£3,000; decorative items, object d'art, garden ornaments, 19th C.* LOC: Between A120 and A12, village centre. PARK: Nearby. TEL: 01376 561365. VAT: Spec.

English Rose Antiques
7 Church St. CO6 1TU. (Mark and Iryna Barrett). Est. 1983. Open 10-5.30, Sun. 10.30-5.30. CL: Wed. *STOCK: English and Continental pine including dressers, chests, tables and wardrobes, 18th-19th C, £50-£2,000; fruitwood, ash and elm country furniture and kitchenalia.* LOC: Town centre. PARK: Loading or 50 yds. TEL: 01376 562683; home - same; fax - 01376 563450; mobile - 07770 880790; e-mail - englishrose antiques@hotmail.com. SER: Valuations; restorations; stripping; repairs; finishing. FAIRS: Newark, Swinderby, Ardingly.

Mark Marchant (Antiques)
3 Market Sq. CO6 1TS. Resident. Est. 1960. Open 11-5, Sun. 2.30-5.30. SIZE: Small. *STOCK: Clocks, barometers and music boxes only.* LOC: A120. PARK: Market square. TEL: 01376 561188. SER: Valuations; restorations; buys at auction.

Partners in Pine
63/65 West St. CO6 1NS. (W.T. and P.A. Newton). Resident. Est. 1982. Open 10-5. CL: Wed. SIZE: Small. *STOCK: Victorian stripped pine.* PARK: Easy. TEL: 01376 561972; e-mail -

newton65@supanet.com. SER: Restorations; bespoke furniture from reclaimed timber.

COLCHESTER

Barntiques
Lampitts Farm, Turkeycock Lane, Stanway. CO3 5ND. (S. Garrard). Resident. Est. 1978. Open weekends. SIZE: Medium. *STOCK: General antiques and pine.* LOC: Turn left at Eight Ash Green from A604. PARK: Easy. TEL: 01206 210486; home - 01206 212421.

S. Bond and Son
Olivers Orchard, Olivers Lane. CO2 0HH. (R. Bond). Open by appointment. SIZE: Large. *STOCK: Furniture and pictures.* TEL: 01206 331175; mobile - 07710 823800. SER: Valuations; restorations. VAT: Stan/Spec. *Trade only.*

Elizabeth Cannon Antiques
85 Crouch St. CO3 3EZ. (Elizabeth and Brian Cooksey). Est. 1978. Open 10-5. *STOCK: General antiques including jewellery, silver, glass, porcelain and furniture.* PARK: Easy. TEL: 01206 575817. VAT: Spec.

Castle Bookshop
40 Osborne St. CO2 7DB. (R.J. Green). PBFA. Est. 1947. Open 9-5. SIZE: 2 floors. *STOCK: Antiquarian and secondhand books, maps & prints.* TEL: 01206 577520; fax - same. SER: Book search. FAIRS: PBFA.

Grahams of Colchester
19 Short Wyre St. CO1 1LN. Open 9-5.30. *STOCK: Jewellery and silver.* TEL: 01206 576808. SER: Valuations; restorations.

E. J. Markham & Son Ltd
122/3 Priory St. CO1 2PX. (Mrs S. Campbell). NAG, NPA. Est. 1836. Open 8.30-5.30. SIZE: Medium. *STOCK: Jewellery, 19th-20th C, £25-£8,000; porcelain, 18th-20th C, £25-£2,000; furniture, 19th-20th C, £100-£1,500.* LOC: Opposite St Botolph's priory ruins. PARK: NCP Priory St. TEL: 01206 572646. SER: Valuations; restorations (porcelain). VAT: Stan.

Trinity Antiques Centre
7 Trinity St. CO1 1JN. Est. 1976. Open 9.30-5. SIZE: 7 dealers + cabinets. *STOCK: General antiques - small furniture, copper, clocks, brass, porcelain, silver, jewellery, collectors' items, Victoriana, maps and prints, linen, pine furniture.* LOC: Town centre, near library. PARK: Nearby. TEL: 01206 577775.

CORRINGHAM, Nr. Stanford-le-Hope

Bush House

Church Rd. SS17 9AP. (F. Stephens). Est. 1976. Open by appointment. *STOCK: Staffordshire animals, portrait figures, 1770-1901, £50-£5,000.* LOC: Opposite church. PARK: Own. TEL: 01375 673463; home - same; fax - same; e-mail - francis_j_stephens@hotmail.com; website - www.mysite.freeserve.com/StaffordshireFigures; www.mysite.freeserve.com/francisstephens. FAIRS: NEC, Birmingham; Westminster Ceramics; Glass. VAT: Spec.

DANBURY

Danbury Antiques

Eves Corner (by the Village Green). CM3 4QF. (Mrs Pam Southgate). EADA. Est. 1983. Open 10-5, Wed. 10-1, Sun. 10.30-1. CL: Mon. SIZE: Medium. *STOCK: Jewellery and silver, ceramics, metalware, furniture, 18th to early 20th C, £5-£3,000.* LOC: Off M25, take A12, then A414. PARK: Easy. TEL: 01245 223035. SER: Valuations; restorations (jewellery, upholstery, furniture). FAIRS: Furzehill, Margaretting. VAT: Stan/Spec.

DEBDEN, Nr. Saffron Walden

Debden Antiques

Elder St. CB11 3JY. (Robert Tetlow and Edward Norman). EADA. Est. 1995. Open 10-5.30, Sun. and Bank Holidays 11-4. SIZE: Large. *STOCK: Furniture, 17th-19th C, £100-£10,000; pictures, £50-£5,000, jewellery, silver, glass, porcelain, £5-£500, garden furniture, architectural, £50-£1,000; all 19th C.* LOC: Follow signs to Carver Barracks. PARK: Own. TEL: 01799 543007; fax - 01799 542482; e-mail - info@debden-antiques.co.uk; website - www.debden-antiques.co.uk. SER: Valuations; restorations. VAT: Stan/Spec.

FINCHINGFIELD

Finchingfield Antiques Centre

The Green. CM7 4JX. (Peter Curry). Est. 1992. Open 10-5.30 including Sun. SIZE: Large - 40 dealers. *STOCK: Wide range of general antiques and collectables.* LOC: From M11, A120 to Gt. Dunmow, then B1057. PARK: Easy. TEL: 01371 810258; fax - 01371 810625.

FRINTON-ON-SEA

Dickens Curios

151 Connaught Ave. CO13 9AH. (Miss M.Wilsher). Est. 1970. Open 9.45-1 and 2-5.30, Sat. 9.45-1 and 2-5. CL: Wed. pm. SIZE: Small. *STOCK: Postcards and ephemera, Victorian and later items, £5-£200.* LOC: From Frinton Station quarter of mile down Connaught Ave. PARK: Easy. TEL: 01255 674134.

Number 24 of Frinton

24 Connaught Ave. CO13 9PR. (Chris Pereira). Est. 1993. Open 10-5, Sun. 2-4. CL: Wed. SIZE: Medium. *STOCK: Art Deco and Victorian prints, general antiques, furniture and collectables.* PARK: Easy. TEL: 01255 670505.

Phoenix Trading

130 Connaught Ave. CO13 9AD. (Tom Sheldon). Est. 1996. Open 10-4, Mon. by appointment. SIZE: Large. *STOCK: Pine and painted furniture, 19th C, £500-£1,000.* LOC: Main shopping street. PARK: Easy. TEL: 01255 851094; fax - same. SER: Restorations. FAIRS: Ardingly; Kempton. VAT: Stan/Spec.

GANTS HILL

Antique Clock Repair Shoppe

26 Woodford Ave. IG2 6XG. (K. Ashton). Est. 1971. Open 10-5. *STOCK: Clocks, pictures, bric-a-brac.* TEL: 020 8550 9540.

GRAYS

Atticus Books

8 London Rd. RM17 5XY. (Robert Drake). Est. 1981. Open Thurs.-Sat. 9-4. SIZE: Small. *STOCK: Books.* LOC: Town centre, 5 mins from station, 10 mins from M25. PARK: Nearby. TEL: 01375 371200. SER: Search; binding.

GREAT BADDOW

Baddow Antique Centre

The Bringey, Church St. CM2 7JW. EADA. Est. 1969. Open 10-5, Sun. 11-5. SIZE: 22 dealers. *STOCK: 18th-20th C furniture, porcelain, silver, paintings, Victorian brass bedsteads, shipping goods.* PARK: Easy. TEL: 01245 476159. SER: Restorations; upholstery; framing; stripping (pine).

GREAT WALTHAM, Nr. Chelmsford

The Stores

CM3 1DE. (E. Saunders). Est. 1974. Open Wed.-Sat. 10-5, Sun. 11-4. SIZE: Large. *STOCK: Period pine and country furniture.* LOC: Village centre. PARK: At rear. TEL: 01245 360277; home - 01245 360260.

HAINAULT, Nr. Ilford

Gallerie Antiques
62-70 Fowler Rd. IG6 3XE. (M. Johnson). EADA. Est. 1998. Open 10-5.30, Sun. 10-4. SIZE: 80 dealers. *STOCK: Wide range of general antiques including 18th-20th C furniture, £500-£1,000; china, porcelain, glass, linen and lace, books, collectables.* LOC: A1112 Eastern Ave. At Moby Dick public house, turn towards Hainault Forest Country Park. PARK: Easy. TEL: 020 8501 2229; fax - 020 8501 2209. SER: Valuations; restorations (furniture, paintings, ceramics, clocks, re-caning); buys at auction. VAT: Stan/Spec.

HALSTEAD

Antique Bed Shop
Napier House, Head St. CO9 2BT. (Veronica McGregor). Est. 1977. Open Thurs.-Sat., other times by appointment. SIZE: Large. *STOCK: Antique wooden bedsteads - 19th C mahogany, rosewood, chestnut, oak, bergere and painted, £1,295-£3,500.* Not Stocked: Brass, iron or pine beds. LOC: On A131 to Sudbury. PARK: Own. TEL: 01787 477346; fax - 01787 478757. SER: Free UK delivery.

Townsford Mill Antiques Centre
The Causeway. CO9 1ET. (M.T. Stuckey). Open 10-5, Sun. and Bank Holidays 11-5. SIZE: 70 dealers. *STOCK: General antiques and collectables.* LOC: On A131 Braintree/Sudbury road. TEL: 01787 474451.

HARWICH

Harwich Antiques Centre
19 Kings Quay St. CO12 3ER. (Patrick and Hans Scholz). Open 10-5, Sun. and Bank Holidays 1-5. CL: Mon. SIZE: Medium. *STOCK: Furniture, porcelain, china, glass, silverware, jewellery, 19th C, £10-£2,000; collectables, 19th-20th C; decorative items.* LOC: Between the pier and Electric Palace cinema. PARK: Nearby. TEL: 01255 554719; e-mail - hac@antiques-access-agency.com; website - www.antiques-access-agency.com.

HOLLAND-ON-SEA

Bookworm
100 King's Ave. CO15 5EP. (Andrew M'Garry-Durrant). Est. 1995. Open 9-5 and most Bank Holidays. SIZE: Small. *STOCK: Modern fiction, first editions, 1930-2001, £10-£500; rare and out-of-print, military history, motor and general sport, transport, nautical, £5-£100.* LOC: On junction with Holland Rd. PARK: Easy. TEL: 01255 815984; fax - same; e-mail - question@ bookwormshop.com; website - www. bookwormshop.com. SER: Valuations.

INGATESTONE

Kendons
122a High St. CM4 0BA. (Mrs Hilary A. O'Connor). Est. 1978. Open 10-5. CL: Wed. and Tues. *STOCK: Jewellery, silver, china, small furniture, clocks, medals, coins, stamps.* LOC: 10 mins. from A12. PARK: Easy. TEL: 01277 353625. SER: Valuations. FAIRS: Ardingly; Sandown Park; Alexandra Palace.

KELVEDON, Nr. Colchester

Colton Antiques
Station Rd. CO5 9NP. (Gary Colton). Est. 1993. Open 8-5, Sun. by appointment. SIZE: Medium. *STOCK: Furniture, 17th to early 20th C, £300-£15,000; decorative items.* PARK: Own. TEL: 01376 571504; mobile - 07973 797098. SER: Restorations (furniture). VAT: Stan/Spec.

Chris L. Papworth Antique Clocks and Watches
2 High St. CO5 9AG. MBHI. BWCG. Est. 1970. Open 9-5, Sat 10-5. CL: Fri. SIZE: Medium. *STOCK: Clocks, watches (including pocket) and barometers.* LOC: Near mainline rail station. PARK: Own. TEL: 01376 573434; home - same; mobile - 07802 615461. SER: Repairs. FAIRS: Brunel, Uxbridge.

G.T. Ratcliff Ltd
Brick House Farm, Braxted Rd. C05 9BS. (F.D. Campbell). Est. 1935. Open by appointment. SIZE: Medium. *STOCK: Furniture, mainly 18th-19th C.* LOC: A12. PARK: Easy. TEL: 01376 570234; fax - 01376 571764. VAT: Stan. *Trade Only, mainly export.*

LEIGH-ON-SEA

K.S. Buchan
135 The Broadway. SS9 1PJ. Open 10-5. *STOCK: Furniture and general antiques.* TEL: 01702 479440.

Collectors' Paradise
993 London Rd. SS9 3LB. (H.W. and P.E.Smith). Est. 1967. Open 10-5.30. CL: Fri. SIZE: Small. *STOCK: Clocks, 1830-1930, from £85; bric-a-brac; postcards, 1900-1930s; cigarette cards, 1889-1939.* LOC: On A13. PARK: Easy. TEL: 01702 473077.

WEST ESSEX ANTIQUES
Stonehall

Dealer in English and Continental Furniture 18ᵗʰ – 20ᵗʰ C.

e-mail: chris@essexantiques.demon.co.uk

Tel/Fax: 01279 730609

Down Hall Road
Matching Green
Nr. Harlow ESSEX. CM17 0RA

Mobile: 07702 492111

15 mins. from M11
15 mins. Stansted Airport
45 mins. London

Deja Vu Antiques
876 London Rd. SS9 3NQ. (Stuart D. Lewis). Est. 1990. Open 9.30-5.30, Sun. 10.30-2.30. SIZE: Large. *STOCK: French and English furniture, late 18th to 19th C; antique bedsteads and lighting.* PARK: Easy. TEL: 01702 470829; e-mail - info@deja-vu-antiques.co.uk; website - www.deja-vu-antiques.co.uk. SER: Valuations; restorations. FAIRS: Newark; Ardingly.

Pall Mall Antiques
104c/d Elm Rd. SS9 1SQ. (R. and J. Webb). EADA. Open 10-5. CL: Wed. SIZE: Large. *STOCK: Porcelain, glass, metalware, furniture, and collectables.* PARK: Own. TEL: 01702 477235; website - www.pallmallantiques.co.uk. FAIRS: Newark.

John Stacey and Sons
86-90 Pall Mall. SS9 1RG. Est. 1946. Open 9-5.30. CL: Sat. pm. *STOCK: General antiques.* TEL: 01702 477051. SER: Valuations; exporters; auctioneers. VAT: Stan.

J. Streamer Antiques
86 Broadway and 212 Leigh Rd. SS9 1AE. Est. 1965. Open 9.30-5.30. CL: Wed. *STOCK: Jewellery, silver, bric-a-brac, small furniture.* TEL: 01702 472895.

Tilly's Antiques
1801 London Rd. SS9 2ST. (S.T. and R.J. Austen). Est. 1972. Open 10-5. CL: Wed. SIZE: Medium. *STOCK: Furniture, 19th C, £100-£500+; Victorian and Edwardian dolls, £100-£500; general antiques, 19th-20th C, £5-£200.* LOC: A13. PARK: Easy. TEL: 01702 557170. SER: Valuations; restorations (furniture and dolls).

MALDON

The Antique Rooms
63D High St. CM9 7EB. (Mrs E. Hedley). Est. 1966. Open 10-4. CL: Wed. SIZE: Medium. *STOCK: Furniture, pottery, porcelain, glass and silver, costume, linen and lace, jewellery, lace-making equipment, collectors' items.* LOC: Just off High St. PARK: Nearby. TEL: 01621 856985.

Clive Beardall Antiques
104B High St. CM9 5ET. BAFRA. EADA. Est. 1982. Open 8-5.30, Sat 8-2. SIZE: Medium. *STOCK: Furniture, 18th-19th C, £100-£5,000.* LOC: Off High St. up alleyway between Just Fabrics and Peter Foulkes. PARK: Easy. TEL: 01621 857890; fax - 01621 850753; website - www.clivebeardall.co.uk. SER: Restorations (furniture). VAT: Stan/Spec.

Maldon Antiques and Collectors Market
All Saints Church Hall, London Rd. CM9. (Rita Willson). Est. 1975. Open first Sat. every month 9-4. *STOCK: Jewellery, gold and silver, medals and badges, Victoriana, unusual items.* LOC: Top of High St., opposite police station. PARK: Own. TEL: 01702 230746.

MANNINGTREE

Antiques
49 High St. CO11 1AH. (A. Patterson). Open 10-1 and 2-5. *STOCK: General and country antiques.* PARK: Easy. TEL: 01206 396170.

MATCHING GREEN, Nr. Harlow

West Essex Antiques (Stone Hall)
Downhall Rd. CM17 0RA. Est. 1982. Open 9-5, Sat and Sun. by appointment. SIZE: Warehouse. *STOCK: English and Continental furniture, 18th-20th C, £100-£3,000.* LOC: Turning off A1060 at Hatfield Heath. PARK: Own. TEL: 01279 730609; mobile: 07702 492111; e-mail - chris@essexantiques.demon.co.uk; website - www.essexantiques.co.uk. VAT: Stan.

LITTLEBURY ANTIQUES — LITTLEBURY RESTORATIONS
58/60 FAIRYCROFT ROAD SAFFRON WALDEN ESSEX CB10 1LZ
TELEPHONE & FAX: SAFFRON WALDEN (01799) 527961
Evenings and Weekends: (01279) 771530

Barometers, marine antiques, fine ship models, walking sticks, chess sets and other high quality interesting pieces

Expert restoration by craftsmen; barometers, clocks, all forms of furniture repair, replacement of marquetry, all inlay work carefully matched

Business hours 9am-5pm Monday to Friday, Weekend by appointment only
Railway station: Audley End (1½ miles away) London to Cambridge line

---

NEWPORT, Nr. Saffron Walden

Newport Gallery
High St. CB11 3QZ. (W. Kemp and E.C. Hitchcock). Open 10-4.30, Wed. and Sat. 10-1. CL: Mon. *STOCK: Watercolours, prints and oils.* LOC: On B1383, two miles from Saffron Walden. PARK: At rear. TEL: 01799 540623. SER: Framing.

Omega
High St. CB11 3PF. (Tony Phillips and Sybil Hooper). Est. 1982. Open 10-6, Sat. 10-5.30. CL: Thurs. SIZE: Small. *STOCK: Furniture and lighting, 1880-1960, £20-£1,000; jewellery, objects, 1900-1960, £20-£300.* LOC: B1383. PARK: Easy. TEL: 01799 540720; home - same. SER: Valuations; restorations (furniture including French polishing, repairs and re-veneering). FAIRS: Art Deco - Battersea, Brighton, Tunbridge Wells.

RAYLEIGH

F.G. Bruschweiler (Antiques) Ltd
LAPADA
41-67 Lower Lambricks. SS6 8DA. Est. 1963. Open 9-5, Sat. by appointment. SIZE: Warehouses. *STOCK: Furniture, 18th-19th C.* LOC: A127 to Weir roundabout through Rayleigh High St. and Hockley Rd., first left past cemetery, then second left, warehouse round corner on left. PARK: Easy. TEL: 01268 773761/773932; home - 01621 828152; fax - 01268 773318; e-mail - info@fgbantiques.com; website - www.fgb antiques.com. VAT: Stan.

ROXWELL, Nr. Chelmsford

Freemans Antiques
CM1 4NJ. Open by appointment. *STOCK: 17th-18th C oak especially coffers.* TEL: 01245 231286.

SAFFRON WALDEN

Bush Antiques
26-28 Church St. CB10 1JQ. (Mrs J.M. Hosford). EADA. Est. 1962. Open 10.30-4.30. CL: Thurs. SIZE: Medium. *STOCK: English ceramics including blue and white transfer printed pottery, copper and pink lustre, £25-£250; mahogany and country furniture, to £1,000; copper and brass, to £250; all 1800-1860.* LOC: 300 yards north of Market Sq., on crossroads with Museum St. PARK: Nearby. TEL: 01799 523277.

Ickleton Antiques
4A Gold St. CB10 1EJ. (B. Arbery). Est. 1983. Open 10-4, Mon. 10-3, Sat. 10-5. SIZE: Small. *STOCK: Militaria including badges, medals and weapons; advertising and packaging, postcards.* LOC: Just off centre of town. PARK: Nearby. TEL: 01799 513114; home - 01799 527474. SER: Valuations.

Lankester Antiques and Books
Old Sun Inn, Church St., and Market Hill. CB10 1JW. (P. Lankester). Est. 1965. Open 10-5. SIZE: Large. *STOCK: Furniture, porcelain, pottery, metalwork, general antiques, books, prints and maps.* TEL: 01799 522685. VAT: Stan

Littlebury Antiques - Littlebury Restorations Ltd
58/60 Fairycroft Rd. CB10 1LZ. (N.H. D'Oyly). Est. 1962. Open 9-5. CL: Sat. and Sun. except by appointment. SIZE: Medium. *STOCK: Barometers, marine antiques, chess sets, walking sticks and curios.* PARK: Easy. TEL: 01799 527961; fax - same; home - 01279 771530; e-mail - heather@doyly.fsnet.co.uk. SER: Valuations; restorations; buys at auction. VAT: Stan/Spec.

Maureen Morris
BADA LAPADA
CB11 4TA. CINOA. Open by appointment. *STOCK: Samplers, needleworks, textiles.* TEL: 01799 521338; fax - 01799 522802; e-mail - mm@antiqueembroidery.com. VAT: Spec.

Saffron Walden Antiques Centre
1 Market Row. CB10 1HA. Est. 1996. Open 10-5, Sun. 11-4. SIZE: Large - 50+ dealers. *STOCK: Wide range of general antiques and collectibles.* LOC: Town centre. PARK: Nearby. TEL: 01799 524534.

SHENFIELD

The Chart House
33 Spurgate, Hutton Mount. CM13 2JS. (C.C. Crouchman). Est. 1974. Open by appointment. SIZE: Small. *STOCK: Nautical items.* PARK: Easy. TEL: 01277 225012; home - same. SER: Buys at auction.

SIBLE HEDINGHAM, Nr Halstead

Hedingham Antiques
100 Swan St. CO9 3HP. (Patricia Patterson). Est. 1978. Open by appointment. SIZE: Small. *STOCK: Mainly silver, some plate, china and glass, small furniture.* LOC: On A1017, village centre. PARK: Forecourt. TEL: 01787 460360; home - same; fax - 01787 469109; e-mail - patriciapatterson @totalise.co.uk; website - www. silberausengland.co.uk. SER: Repairs (silver, including re-plating); restorations (furniture). VAT: Spec/Global/Stan/Export.

Lennard Antiques   LAPADA
c/o W.A. Pinn & Sons, 124 Swan St. CO9 3HP. (Gill Meddings). Est. 1978. Open 9.30-6. *STOCK: Oak and country furniture, 17th to early 19th C; English Delftware.* LOC: On A1017 opposite Shell garage in village centre. PARK: Easy. TEL: 01787 461127. FAIRS: Chelsea; West London; Olympia (June); Harrogate.

W.A. Pinn and Sons   BADA LAPADA
124 Swan St. CO9 3HP. (K.H. and W.J. Pinn). Est. 1943. Open 9.30-6. CL: Sun. except by appointment. SIZE: Medium. *STOCK: Furniture, 17th to early 19th C, £100-£5,000; Chinese export porcelain, £25-£1,000; interesting items, prior to 1830, £10-£1,500.* LOC: On A1017 opposite Shell Garage. PARK: Easy. TEL: 01787 461127. FAIRS: Chelsea (Spring and Autumn); Olympia (June); Harrogate. VAT: Stan/Spec.

SOUTHEND- ON- SEA

Curio City.
Chartwell North, Upper Level, Victoria Plaza Shopping Centre. SS2 5SP. (T.W. Cornforth). Est. 1996. Open 10-5, Sat. 9-5. SIZE: Large - 80 dealers. *STOCK: 18th-20th C furniture, Oriental*

Exceptional Edwardian inlaid mahogany Sheraton Revival longcase clock with choice of quarter chime on tubular chimes or gongs, anon, c.1905, 108in. high. £16,000 at Christie's South Kensington, December 2002.

From an article entitled "The Post '9/11' Market for Clocks" by Richard Garnier which appeared in the April 2003 issue of **Antique Collecting**. For more details and to subscribe see page 21.

items, ceramics and collectables. LOC: Town centre. PARK: Nearby multi-storey. TEL: 01702 611350; fax - 01702 710383; website - www. ridgeweb.co.uk.

STANSTED

Linden House Antiques
3 Silver St. CM24 8HA. (A.W. and K.M. Sargeant). Est. 1961. Open 9-4.30, Sun. 1-4. SIZE: Large. STOCK: English furniture, 18th-19th C, £100-£2,000; small decorative items, including library and dining room furniture. LOC: A11. TEL: 01279 812372. VAT: Spec.

Valmar Antiques   BADA LAPADA
Croft House Cottage, High Lane. CM24 8LQ. (John and Marina Orpin). Resident. Est. 1960. Open by appointment. SIZE: Large. STOCK: Furniture and decorative items including Arts and Crafts, £50-£10,000. TEL: 01279 813201; fax - 01279 816962; mobile - 07831 093701; e-mail - valmar-antiques@cwcom.net. FAIRS: Major British.

THAXTED

Harris Antiques
24 Town Street. CM6 2LA. (F.A.D. and B.D.A. Harris and E.V. Bradshaw). Resident. BAFRA. EADA. UKIC. Est. 1956. Open 9-5, Sun. by appointment. SIZE: Medium. STOCK: Quality period furniture, ceramics, barometers and clocks, 16th-19th C, £50-£20,000+. LOC: Near M11 and Stansted Airport. PARK: Easy. TEL: 01371 832832; home - same. SER: Valuations; restorations (furniture and ceramics). VAT: Spec.

WESTCLIFF-ON-SEA

It's About Time
863 London Rd. SS0 9SZ. (R. and V. Alps and P. Williams). EADA. Est. 1980. Open 9-5.30. SIZE: Large. STOCK: Clocks, 18th-19th C, £200-£5,000; barometers, Victorian and Edwardian furniture. LOC: A13. PARK: Easy. TEL: 01702 472574; fax - same; home - 01702 205204; e-mail - shop@antiqueclock.co.uk; website - www.antiqueclock.co.uk.

Ridgeway Antiques
66 The Ridgeway. SS0 8NU. (Trevor Cornforth). EADA. Est. 1987. Open 10.30-5. SIZE: Small. STOCK: General antiques and Oriental, £5-£1,000. LOC: A13 London road, right at Chalkwell Ave., right to The Ridgway. PARK: Easy. TEL: 01702 710383. SER: Valuations. FAIRS: Ridgeway; Hallmark.

WHITE COLNE, Nr. Colchester

Fox and Pheasant Antique Pine
CO6 2PS. (J. and J. Kearin). Est. 1978. Open 8-6. SIZE: Small. STOCK: Stripped pine. LOC: A604. PARK: Easy. TEL: 01787 223297. SER: Stripping; restorations; kitchens; joinery.

WHITE RODING, Nr. Dunmow

White Roding Antiques
'Ivydene', Chelmsford Rd. CM6 1RG. (F. and J. Neill). Est. 1971. Open by appointment. SIZE: Medium. STOCK: Furniture and shipping goods, 18th-19th C, £10-£1,500. LOC: A1060 between Bishops Stortford and Chelmsford. PARK: Easy. TEL: 01279 876376; home - same. VAT: Stan/Spec.

WICKHAM BISHOPS

Barling Fine Porcelain Ltd   LAPADA
(S. Parish). Open by appointment. STOCK: English porcelain including Royal Worcester and Royal Crown Derby, £100-£12,000; watercolours, £300-£2,500. TEL: 01621 890058; e-mail - stuart@barling.uk.com; website - www.barling.uk.com. FAIRS: Wakefield Ceramic; NEC.

WOODFORD GREEN

Mill Lane Antiques
29 Mill Lane. IG8 0NG. (Niki Wood and Bonnita Read). Open Tues.-Sun. SIZE: Medium. STOCK: French lighting, furniture and Venetian mirrors. TEL: 020 8502 9930; fax - same; mobile - 07980 419956. SER: Valuations; restorations. FAIRS: Kempton Park.

WRITTLE, Nr. Chelmsford

Whichcraft Jewellery
54-56 The Green. CM1 3DU. (A. Turner). EADA. Est. 1978. Open 9.30-5.30. CL: Mon. SIZE: Small. STOCK: Jewellery, silver and watches, 19th C, £30-£5,000. PARK: Easy. TEL: 01245 420183; fax - 01245 420030. SER: Valuations; restorations (jewellery). VAT: Stan/Spec.

GLOUCESTERSHIRE

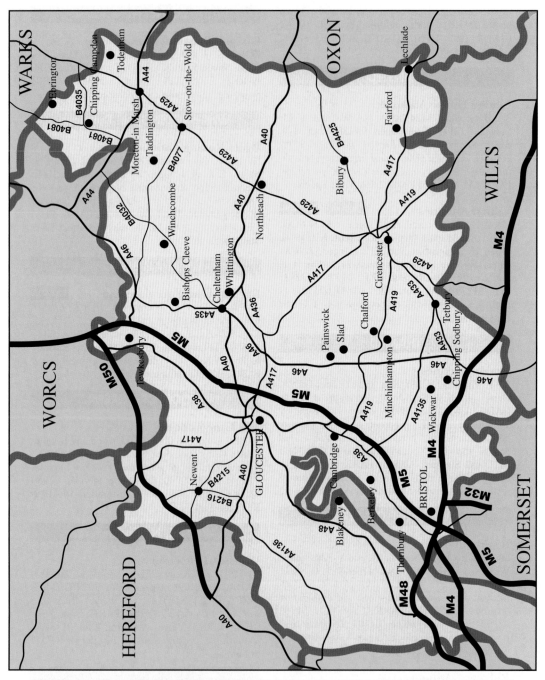

Dealers and Shops in Gloucestershire

Berkeley	2	Chipping Campden	5	Moreton-in-Marsh	16	Tewkesbury	3
Bibury	1	Chipping Sodbury	1	Newent	1	Thornbury	1
Bishops Cleeve	2	Cirencester	11	Northleach	3	Todenham	1
Blakeney	1	Ebrington	1	Painswick	1	Whittington	1
Bristol	28	Fairford	3	Slad	1	Wickwar	1
Cambridge	1	Gloucester	3	Stow-on-the-Wold	34	Winchcombe	6
Chalford	1	Lechlade	3	Taddington	1		
Cheltenham	23	Minchinhampton	1	Tetbury	25		

Berkeley Antiques Market
GL13 9BP. Est. 1985. Open 9.30-1 and 2-5. CL: Mon. SIZE: Large - 10 dealers. *STOCK: General antiques, oak, mahogany, pine, linen and smalls, £1-£5,000.* LOC: Village centre, 1 mile from A38. PARK: Easy. TEL: 01453 511032; mobile - 07802 304534.

Peter and Penny Proudfoot
16-18 High St. GL13 9BJ. FATG. Est. 1956. Open 9-6, Sun. by appointment. SIZE: Small. *STOCK: Furniture, 1600-1900, £100-£3,000; silver, 1700 to date, £5-£1,000; pictures, 1800 to date, £20-£3,000.* LOC: Village centre. PARK: Easy. TEL: 01453 811513; home - same; fax - 01453 511616; e-mail - pclaireproudfoot@ aol.com. SER: Valuations; restorations (furniture and oil paintings). VAT: Stan/Spec.

Mill Antiques of Bibury
Arlington Mill. GL7 5NL. Est. 1999. Open 7 days from 9 am. SIZE: 3 floors. *STOCK: Antiques, collectables, oils and prints.* PARK: Easy. TEL: 01285 740199; mobile - 07788 681998. FAIRS: TBA.

Cleeve Picture Framing
Church Rd. GL52 8RL. (J. Gardner). FATG. Est. 1974. Open 9-1 and 2-5.30, Sat. 9-1. *STOCK: Prints and pictures.* TEL: 01242 672785. SER: Framing; cleaning; restorations (oils, watercolours and prints).

The Priory Gallery LAPADA
The Priory, Station Rd. GL52 4HH. (R.M. and E. James). Est. 1977. SIZE: Large. *STOCK: British and European watercolours and oils, late 19th-20th C, £500-£50,000.* LOC: A435. PARK: Easy. TEL: 01242 673226. SER: Buys at auction (as stock). VAT: Stan/Spec.

Lion, Witch and Lampshade
Birmingham House, High St. GL15 4EB. (Mr. and Mrs N. Dixon). Open by appointment. *STOCK: Unusual decorative objects, 18th to early 20th C, £5-£150; lamps, wall brackets, chandeliers and candlesticks, £50-£1,000.* TEL: 01594 516422/020 7730 1774; fax - 01594 516422. SER: Restorations (porcelain and glass); lamp rewiring.

Alexander Gallery
122 Whiteladies Rd. BS8 2RP. (P.J. Slade and H.S. Evans). Open 9-5.30. *STOCK: 19th-20th C paintings, watercolours and prints.* TEL: 0117 9734692; fax - 0117 9466991; website - www.alexander-gallery.co.uk.

Antique Corner with A & C Antique Clocks
86 Bryants Hill, Hanham. BS5 8QT. (D.A. and J.P. Andrews). BWCMG. Est. 1985. Open 10-4. CL: Mon. and Wed. SIZE: Large - 2 floors. *STOCK: Clocks including longcase, wall and mantel; furniture and ceramics, £5-£5,000; aneroid and mercurial barometers; dolls and dolls houses.* LOC: Next to The Trooper public house, A431 Bristol to Bath road. PARK: Easy. TEL: 0117 9476141; website - www. antiquecorner.org.uk. SER: Repairs (clocks and barometers).

The Antiques Warehouse Ltd
430 Gloucester Rd., Horfield. BS7 8TX. (Chris Winsor). Resident. Est. 1994. Open 10-6, Sun. 12-4. SIZE: Large. *STOCK: Furniture, 18th to early 20th C, £200-£2,500; mirrors, from 19th C, £60-£1,000; rugs, from 19th C, £150-£600; lighting £100-£1,000.* LOC: A38 4 miles from M4/M5 interchange, 2 miles from city centre. PARK: Easy. TEL: 0117 942 4500; fax - 0117 942 4140; mobile - 07785 532173; e-mail - theantiqueswarehouseltd. co.uk. SER: Valuations; restorations (furniture and upholstery). VAT: Stan/Spec.

Arcadia Antiques & Interiors
4 Boyces Ave., Clifton. BS8 4AA. Est. 1993. Open 10-5.30. CL: Mon. SIZE: Small. *STOCK: General antiques including sofas and chairs, paintings, jewellery and decorative items, £5-£2,500.* LOC: Near The Mall. TEL: 01179 144479; fax - 01179 239308

Aristocratz
115 Coldharbour Rd., Redland. BS6 7SD. (Z. Bouyamourn). Est. 1980. Open 9.30-5.30. SIZE: Medium + warehouse. *STOCK: General antiques, French, Islamic and decorative items.* LOC: Junction 17, M4/M5. TEL: 0117 904 0091; mobile - 07770 393020; e-mail - aristocratz@ yahoo.com. SER: Delivery (UK and overseas). FAIRS: DMG; Exeter.

Bizarre Antiques
210 Gloucester Rd., Bishopston. BS7 8NZ. (E.J. Parkin). Open 8.15-5. *STOCK: General antiques.* TEL: 0117 9427888; home - 0117 9503498.

Bristol Brocante
123 St. Georges Rd., College Green, Hotwells. BS1 5UW. (David and Elizabeth Durant). Est. 1966. Open 12-6, Sun. by appointment. SIZE: Small. *STOCK: 19th-20th C French decorative antiques - small furniture, crystal and brass, hanging and wall lights and unusual items, £80-£1,000.* LOC: Junction of Anchor Rd. and Hotwells Rd., 3 mins. walk from library and city centre. PARK: Meters. TEL: 0117 909 6688; mobile - 07986 612056. FAIRS: Kensington Brocante, Newark, Sandown Park, Ardingly.

Bristol Guild of Applied Art Ltd
68/70 Park St. BS1 5JY. Est. 1908. Open 9-5.30, Mon. and Sat. 9.30-5.30. *STOCK: Furniture, late 19th-20th C.* TEL: 0117 9265548; fax - 0117 9255659.

Bristol Trade Antiques
192 Cheltenham Rd. BS6 5RB. (L. Dike). Est. 1970. SIZE: Large and warehouse. *STOCK: General antiques.* TEL: 0117 9422790.

Caledonian Antiques
6 The Mall, Clifton. BS8 4DR. Open 9-5.30. SIZE: Small. *STOCK: Antique and secondhand jewellery, silver and plate; modern classic jewellery.* LOC: Central. PARK: Nearby. TEL: 01179 743582; fax - 01179 667997. SER: Valuations; restorations (jewellery).

Cleeve Antiques
282 Lodge Causeway, Fishponds. BS16 3RD. (T. and S.E. Scull). Est. 1978. Open 9-5.30. *STOCK: Furniture and bric-a-brac.* TEL: 0117 9658366; home - 0117 9567008.

Cotham Antiques
1c Pitville Place, 39 Cotham Hill. BS6 6JZ. (Susan Miller and Cornelius Cummins). Est. 1983. Open Tues.-Sat.10.30-5.30. SIZE: Small. *STOCK: Jewellery, 1800 to designer modern, £50-£500; ceramics, 19th C to Art Deco, £100-£300; small furniture, 19th to early 20th C, £100-£700.* LOC: Off Whiteladies Rd from Clifton - turn left at Whiteladies shopping centre. PARK: Limited. TEL: 0117 973 3326. SER: Valuations; buys at auction.

Cotham Galleries
22 Cotham Hill, Cotham. BS6 6LF. (D. Jury). Est. 1960. Open 9-5.30. SIZE: Small. *STOCK: Furniture, glass and metal.* LOC: From city centre up Park St. into Whiteladies Rd. Turn right at Clifton Down rail station. PARK: Easy. TEL: 0117 9736026. SER: Valuations.

Flame and Grate
159 Hotwells Rd., Hotwells. BS8 4RU. Open 9-5. *STOCK: Original cast-iron fireplaces, marble surrounds and fireplace accessories.* PARK: Easy. TEL: 0117 9252560/9292930.

Focus on the Past
25 Waterloo St., Clifton. BS8 4BT. (K. Walker and A. Roylance). Est. 1976. Open 9.30-5.30, Sat. 9.30-6, Sun. 11-5. SIZE: Large. *STOCK: 19th-20th C furniture including mahogany, country, pine, French, English; ceramics, kitchenalia, glass, silver, plate, jewellery, to £1,000+.* LOC: Off Princess Victoria St. PARK: Nearby. TEL: 0117 973 8080. FAIRS: Shepton Mallet, Newark.

Grey-Harris and Co
12 Princess Victoria St., Clifton. BS8 4BP. Est. 1963. Open 10-5. *STOCK: Jewellery, Victorian; silver, old Sheffield plate.* TEL: 0117 9737365. SER: Valuations. VAT: Stan/Spec.

Chris Grimes Militaria
13 Lower Park Row. BS1 5BN. Open 11-5.30. *STOCK: Militaria, scientific instruments, nautical items.* TEL: 0117 9298205.

Copeland, c.1930s. Collection of jade figures. (Private collection)

From an article entitled "Spode-Copeland-Spode Art & Design" by Vega Wilkinson which appeared in the March 2002 issue of ***Antique Collecting***. For more details and to subscribe see page 21.

Margaret R. Jubb Antiques
6 Clifton Arcade, Boyces Ave., Clifton. BS8 4AA. Est. 1973. Open 11-5.30. SIZE: Small. *STOCK: Furniture, 1700-1900, £100-£3,000; metalware, lighting, Oriental rugs, old prints, clocks.* LOC: 1 mile from city centre. PARK: Limited and nearby. TEL: 01179 733105; home - 01179 624031; mobile - 07974 095554; e-mail - margaret.jubbs.antiques@virgin.net.co.uk; website - www.business.virgin.net.co.uk/margaret.jubbs.antiques. SER: Valuations.

Kemps
9 Carlton Court, Westbury-on-Trym. BS9 3DF. Open 9-5.30. *STOCK: Jewellery.* TEL: 0117 9505090.

Robert Mills Architectural Antiques Ltd
Narroways Rd., Eastville. BS2 9XB. SALVO. Est. 1969. Open 9.30-5. CL: Sat. SIZE: Large. *STOCK: Architectural items, panelled rooms, shop interiors, Gothic Revival, stained glass, church woodwork, bar and restaurant fittings, 1750-1920, £50-£30,000.* LOC: Half mile from junction 2, M32. PARK: Easy. TEL: 0117 9556542; fax - 0117 9558146; e-mail - sales@rmills.co.uk; website - www.rmills.co.uk. VAT: Stan.

Jan Morrison
3 Victorian Arcade, Boyce's Avenue, Clifton. BS8 4AA. Est. 1982. Open Tues.-Sat. 10-5.30. SIZE: Small. *STOCK: Silver, 1750 to date; glass, 18th C to Victorian.* PARK: Victoria Square. TEL: 0117 970 6822; fax - same; home - 0117 924 7995; mobile - 07789 094428; e-mail - jan@artibition.com.

Oldwoods
4 Colston Yard. BS1 5BD. (S. Duck). Open 11-5.30, Sat. 11-4. *STOCK: Victorian and Edwardian furniture, pine and other woods.* TEL: 0117 9299023. SER: Restorations.

Pastimes
23 Lower Park Row. BS1 5BN. (A.H. Stevens). Est. 1970. Open 10.30-1.45 and 2.45-5. SIZE: Medium. *STOCK: Militaria and military books, £1-£1,000.* LOC: Opposite Christmas Steps, off Colston St. PARK: Meters. TEL: 0117 929 9330.

Period Fireplaces
The Old Station, Station Rd., Montpelier. BS6 5EE. (John and Rhian Ashton and Martyn Roberts). Est. 1987. Open daily. SIZE: Medium. *STOCK: Fireplaces, original and reproduction, £100-£1,000.* LOC: Just off Gloucester Rd. PARK: Easy. TEL: 0117 944 4449; website - www.periodfireplaces.co.uk. SER: Valuations; restorations; fitting. VAT: Stan.

Porchester Antiques
58 The Mall, Clifton. BS8 4JG. (Devonia Andrews). Est. 1978. Open Tues.-Sat. 10-6. SIZE: Small. *STOCK: Moorcroft pottery and enamels, Sally Tuffin, Dennis chinaworks, diamond jewellery, £250-£10,000.* PARK: Easy. TEL: 0117 3730256; fax - 01275 810629; mobile - 07970 970449; e-mail - devonia.porchester.antiques@deepacres.freeserve.co.uk. SER: Valuations.

Potter's Antiques and Coins
60 Colston St. BS1 5AZ. (B.C. Potter). Est. 1965. Open 10.30-5.30. SIZE: Small. *STOCK: Antiquities, 500 B.C. to 1600 A.D., £5-£500; commemoratives, 1770-1953, £4-£300; coins, 500 B.C. to 1967, £1-£100; drinking glasses, 1770-1953, £3-£200; small furniture, from 1837, £10-£200.* LOC: Near top of Christmas Steps, close to city centre. PARK: NCP Park Row. TEL: 0117 9262551. SER: Valuations; buys at auction. VAT: Stan/Spec.

Raw Deluxe
148-150 Gloucester Rd. BS7 5NT. (James Stewart). Est. 1998. Open Thurs., Fri. and Sat. 10-5. SIZE: Small. *STOCK: Georgian and Victorian furniture, general smalls, Art Deco, 1950's-1970's furniture and lights.* LOC: Bishopston, 2 miles from city centre. TEL: 0117 942 6998; fax - 0117 942 6998. FAIRS: Kempton Park; Newark; Swinderby.

Relics - Pine Furniture
109 St. George's Rd., College Green. BS1 5UW. (R. Seville and S. Basey). Est. 1972. Open 10-5.30. SIZE: Large. *STOCK: Victorian style and reclaimed pine and hardwood furniture; nauticalia, mirrors, model yachts and Harmony Kingdom figurines.* LOC: Near cathedral, 1/2 mile from city centre. PARK: Easy. TEL: 0117 9268453; fax - same. VAT: Stan.

St. Nicholas Markets
The Exchange Hall, Corn St. BS1 1JQ. (Steve Morris). Est. 1975. Open 9.30-5. *STOCK: Wide range of general antiques and collectors' items.* TEL: 0117 9224014.

CAMBRIDGE, Nr. Gloucester

Bell House Antiques
Bell House. GL2 7BD. (G. and J. Hawkins). Resident. Open 10-1 and 2-5. SIZE: Medium. *STOCK: Furniture, shipping goods, stripped pine, small items, bygones, £5-£500.* LOC: Near Slimbridge, on main A38. PARK: Easy. TEL: 01453 890463. SER: Valuations.

CHALFORD

J. and R. Bateman Antiques [LAPADA]

Green Court, High St. GL6 8DS. Est. 1975. Open 9-6 or by appointment. *STOCK: Furniture, oak and country, 17th-19th C; decorative items.* PARK: Easy. TEL: 01453 883234. SER: Restorations; cabinet making; rushing and caning. VAT: Stan/Spec.

CHELTENHAM

David Bannister FRGS

26 Kings Rd. GL52 6BG. PBFA. Est. 1963. Open by appointment. SIZE: Medium. *STOCK: Early maps and prints, 1480-1850, from £25; decorative and topographical prints; atlases and colour plate books.* TEL: 01242 514287; fax - 01242 513890; e-mail - db@antiquemaps.co.uk. SER: Valuations; restorations; lectures; buys at auction. FAIRS: Antique Map & Print, Bonnington Hotel. VAT: Stan.

Edward Bradbury and Son

32 High St. GL50 1DZ. (O. Bradbury). Resident. Est. 1986. Open by appointment. SIZE: Small. *STOCK: Works of art, tribal art, furniture, 18th-19th C; books on art reference, monographs on artists and photographers, manuscripts.* PARK: Nearby. TEL: 01242 254952; e-mail - hardenhuish53@hotmail.com. SER: Valuations.

Cheltenham Antique Market

54 Suffolk Rd. GL50 2AQ. (K.J. Shave). Est. 1970. Open 9.30-5.30. SIZE: 6 dealers. *STOCK: General antiques.* TEL: 01242 529812.

Cocoa

9 Clarence Parade. GL50 3NY. (Cara Wagstaff). Est. 1973. Open 10-5. CL: Wed. SIZE: Small. *STOCK: Lace, antique wedding dresses and accessories, 19th-20th C, £1-£2,000.* LOC: Town centre. TEL: 01242 233588. SER: Re-creations; restorations (period textiles). VAT: Stan.

Giltwood Gallery

30/31 Suffolk Parade. GL50 2AE. (Mrs G. Butt). Resident. Est. 1992. Open 9-5.30, Sat. 10-5.30. SIZE: Large. *STOCK: Furniture, £500-£3,000; mirrors, £500, all 18th to early 20th C.* PARK: Easy. TEL: 01242 512482; fax - same. SER: Valuations; restorations (upholstery); buys at auction. VAT: Stan/Spec.

Greens of Cheltenham Ltd

15 Montpellier Walk. GL50 1SD. Est. 1946. Open 9-5. CL: Wed. SIZE: Large. *STOCK: Jewels, objets, porcelain and silver, some furniture.* LOC: Conjunction of Promenade and main shopping centre. PARK: Easy. TEL: 01242 512088; e-mail - steve@greensofcheltenham. co.uk. SER: Buys at auction. VAT: Stan/Spec.

Latchford Antiques

203 London Rd., Charlton Kings. GL52 6HX. (K. and R. Latchford). Est. 1985. Open 10-5.30. SIZE: Medium. *STOCK: Furniture, china, glass and objets d'art, 18th-19th C, £5-£2,000.* LOC: 2 miles from Cheltenham, on A40 towards London at Sixways Shopping Centre, on right. PARK: Easy. TEL: 01242 226263.

The Loquens Gallery

3 Montpellier Avenue. GL50 1SA. Est. 1992. Open 10.15-5. SIZE: Small. *STOCK: 18th-20th C watercolours and some oils.* LOC: Adjacent to The Queens Hotel. PARK: Nearby. TEL: 01242 254313; e-mail - info@loquensgallery.co.uk; website - www.loquensgallery.co.uk. SER: Valuations: framing; restorations.

Manor House Gallery

16 Royal Parade, Bayshill Rd. GL50 3AY. (Geoff Hassell). Resident. Open any time by appointment. *STOCK: British oils and watercolours, £200-£2,000; prints, under £100; all 20th C.* LOC: Central. PARK: Easy. TEL: 01242 228330; home - same; e-mail - geoff@manorhousegallery.net; website - www. manorhousegallery.net. SER: Valuations; restorations (oils). VAT: Stan/spec.

Martin and Co. Ltd

19 The Promenade. GL50 1LP. (I.M. and N.C.S. Dimmer). Est. 1890. *STOCK: Silver, Sheffield plate, jewellery, objets d'art.* TEL: 01242 522821; fax - 01242 570430. VAT: Stan/Spec.

Montpellier Clocks [BADA]

13 Rotunda Terrace, Montpellier. GL50 1SW. (B. Bass and T. Birch). Est. 1959. Open 9-5. SIZE: Medium. STOCK: Clocks, 17th-19th C; barometers. LOC: Close to Queens Hotel. PARK: Easy. TEL: 01242 242178; fax - same; website - www.montpellierclocks.com. SER: Repairs and restorations by West Dean/BADA Dip. conservator. VAT: Spec.

Patrick Oliver [LAPADA]

4 Tivoli St. GL50 2UW. Est. 1896. SIZE: Large. *STOCK: Furniture and shipping goods.* PARK: Easy. TEL: 01242 519538. VAT: Stan/Spec.

Eric Pride Oriental Rugs

44 Suffolk Rd. GL50 2AQ. Est. 1980. Open by appointment. SIZE: Medium. *STOCK: Rugs and carpets, £100-£4,000; kilims, £300-£2,000; saddle-bags and horse covers, £150-£800; all*

19th to early 20th C. LOC: A40 near Cheltenham College. PARK: Nearby. TEL: 01242 580822 (answerphone); fax - 01242 700549; e-mail - ericpride@hotmail.com; website - www.antiqueorientalrugs.co.uk. SER: Valuations; restorations; cleaning; repairs.

Q & C Militaria
22 Suffolk Rd. GL50 2AQ. (J.F. and B.M. Wright). OMRS, MCCOFI, BACSEA. Est. 1970. Open 10-5. CL: Mon. SIZE: Medium. *STOCK: Military memorabilia - British orders, decorations and medals; military drums, edged weapons, cap badges.* LOC: A40 ring road. PARK: At rear, off Old Bath Rd. TEL: 01242 519815; fax - same; mobile - 07778 613977; e-mail - john@qc-militaria.freeserve.co.uk; website - www.qcmilitaria.com. SER: Valuations; restorations (drums and military equipment); framing and mounting (medals); buys at auction. FAIRS: OMRS Convention, Aldershot, Yate, Stratford-upon-Avon; Aldershot Collectors (Farnham).

Michael Rayner
11 St. Luke's Rd. GL53 7JQ. Est. 1988. Open 10-6, other times by appointment. CL: Mon. and Tues. *STOCK: Books, antiquarian and secondhand.* PARK: Nearby. TEL: 01242 512806.

Scott-Cooper Ltd   `BADA`
52 The Promenade. GL50 1LY. Est. 1912. *STOCK: Silver, plate, jewellery, clocks, ivory, enamel, objets de vertu.* **TEL: 01242 522580. SER: Restorations and repairs (silver and jewellery). VAT: Stan/Spec.**

Catherine Shinn Decorative Textiles
5/6 Well Walk. GL50 3JX. Open 10-5. SIZE: 2 floors. *STOCK: Antique tapestry cushions, hangings, bell pulls; passe menterie and upholstery pieces, old curtains and table covers, toile.* PARK: Rear of library. TEL: 01242 574546; fax - 01242 578495. SER: Valuations; restorations; buys at auction (European textiles). VAT: Stan.

Sixways Antique Centre
199 London Rd., Charlton Kings. GL52 6HU. Est. 1984. Open 9.30-5.30, Sun. 11-5. SIZE: Large - 15 dealers. *STOCK: General antiques, pine and painted furniture, china, glass, prints, silver and plate, linen, books, toys, flatware and collectibles, £5-£5,000.* LOC: A40. PARK: Opposite. TEL: 01242 510672. SER: Restorations (furniture).

Tapestry
33 Suffolk Parade. GL50 2AE. Open 10.30-5.30. SIZE: Medium. *STOCK: Antique and decorative furniture and objects including soft furnishings, garden items, mirrors and lighting.* LOC: 10 mins. walk from The Promenade. PARK: Easy. TEL: 01242 512191.

Julian Tatham-Losh Ltd
Crescent House, 19 Eldorado Crescent. GL50 2PY. (Julian and Patience Tatham-Losh). Resident. TADA. Est. 1980. Open any time by appointment. SIZE: Medium. *STOCK: 19th C decorative smalls, bamboo and interesting furniture, majolica, flow blue, Staffordshire figures and animals, boxes and caddies, candlesticks, decorative glass, primitive and folk art items, kitchenalia, mirrors, desk-related items, brass and copper, luggage, £2-£10,000.* LOC: Town centre near station. PARK: Own. TEL: 0871 2881100; fax - 0871 2881101; mobile - 07850 574924; e-mail - jtlantiques@onetel.net.uk. SER: Antique and decorative items supplied to order, especially repeat bulk shipping items; courier (air-conditioned transport); free storage. FAIRS: NEC; Newark. VAT: Stan/Spec. *Trade & Export Only.*

John P. Townsend
Ullenwood Park Farm, Ullenwood. GL53 9QX. Est. 1969. Open 9-5. CL: Sat. SIZE: Medium. *STOCK: Furniture - stripped pine, country and shipping, to 1940's; books and bric-a-brac.* LOC: 4 miles from Cheltenham. PARK: Easy. TEL: 01242 870169; home - 01242 870223.

Triton Gallery
27 Suffolk Parade. GL50 2AE. (L. Bianco). Resident. Est. 1984. Open 9-5.30, other times by appointment. *STOCK: Period furniture, 18th C paintings, mirrors and lighting.* PARK: Easy. TEL: 01242 510477. VAT: Spec.

Peter Ward Fine Paintings
Nothill Cowley. GL53 9NJ. Est. 1972. Open 9-5. *STOCK: 17th-19th C paintings.* TEL: 01242 870178; mobile - 07979 857347; website - www.coriniumfinepaintings.co.uk. SER: Valuations; restorations; framing. VAT: Spec.

CHIPPING CAMPDEN

Antique Heritage
High St. GL55 6AT. (D.B. Smith). Est. 1981. Open 10-5, Sun. 11-4. SIZE: Small. *STOCK: Small items, china, porcelain, tables, boxes, Georgian and Victorian, £15-£400.* LOC: Village centre. PARK: Easy. TEL: 01386 840727.

Cottage Farm Antiques
Cottage Farm, Aston sub Edge. GL55 6PZ. (A.E. and E.A. Willmore). Est. 1986. Open 9-5 including Sun. SIZE: Large. *STOCK: Furniture including 19th C wardrobes, 18th-19th C dressers and tables, to £1,500.* LOC: Follow brown tourist signs. PARK: Easy. TEL: 01386 438263; fax and home - same; e-mail - info@cottagefarm antiques.co.uk; website - www.cottagefarm antiques.co.uk. SER: Delivery. VAT: Spec.

Ross Hardie
Lower High St. GL55 6AL. Est. 2001. Open Tues.-Sat. 10-5. SIZE: Small. *STOCK: Antique and secondhand jewellery and silver.* PARK: Easy. TEL: 01386 840539; fax - 01386 841902. SER: Valuations. FAIRS: NEC. VAT: Stan/Spec.

School House Antiques
School House, High St. GL55 6HB. (G. and M. Hammond). Est. 1895. Open 9.30-5 including Sun. (June-Sept.). CL: Thurs. (Oct.-May). SIZE: Large. *STOCK: Clocks, 18th-19th C; Georgian and Victorian furniture; works of art, oils and watercolours.* PARK: At rear. TEL: 01386 841474; e-mail - hamatschoolhouse@aol.com; website - www.schoolhouseantiques.co.uk. SER: Restorations; valuations.

Stuart House Antiques
High St. GL55 6HB. (J. Collett). Est. 1985. Open 10-1 and 2-5.30 including Sun. SIZE: Large. *STOCK: China, 19th C; general antiques, from 18th C; all £1-£1,000.* LOC: Opposite market hall. PARK: Easy. TEL: 01386 840995. SER: Valuations; china search; restorations (ceramics).

CHIPPING SODBURY, Nr. Bristol

Sodbury Antiques
70 Broad St. BS37 6AG. (Millicent Brown). Est. 1986. CL: Wed. SIZE: Small. *STOCK: Porcelain and china, mainly 18th-19th C; antique and secondhand jewellery, £5-£1,000.* PARK: Easy. TEL: 01454 273369.

CIRENCESTER

Walter Bull and Son (Cirencester) Ltd
10 Dyer St. GL7 2PF. NAG. Est. 1815. Open 9-5. SIZE: Small. *STOCK: Silver, from 1700, £50-£3,000; objets d'art.* LOC: Lower end of Market Place. PARK: At rear. TEL: 01285 653875; fax - 01285 641751. VAT: Stan/Spec.

Cirencester Arcade
25 Market Place. GL7 2NX. (M.J. and P.J. Bird).

Open Mon.-Sun. SIZE: 70 dealers. *STOCK: General antiques.* PARK: Opposite. TEL: 01285 644214. SER: Shipping.

Corner Cupboard Curios
2 Church St. GL7 1LE. (P. Larner). Est. 1972. Usually open but prior telephone call advisable. SIZE: Small. *STOCK: Collectables including gramophones, radios, records.* LOC: Swindon side of town. PARK: Easy. TEL: 01285 655476; home - same.

Forum Antiques
Springfield Farm, Perrotts Brook. GL7 7DT. (W. Mitchell). Est. 1986. Open Mon.-Fri. 8.30-5.30 by appointment only. SIZE: Small. *STOCK: Period furniture, pre-1850.* TEL: 01285 831821. SER: Valuations; restorations. VAT: Spec.

Hares
4 Black Jack St. GL7 2AA. (Allan G. Hare). Est. 1972. Open 10-5.30, Sun. by appointment. SIZE: Large. *STOCK: Furniture, especially dining tables and long sets of chairs, 18th to early 19th C, £100-£50,000; upholstery and decorative objects.* LOC: Near market square. PARK: Own. TEL: 01285 640077; mobile - 07860 350097; e-mail - hares@hares-antiques.com; website - www.hares-antiques.com. SER: Restorations; traditional upholstery. FAIRS: Olympia. VAT: Spec.

Parlour Farm Antiques
Unit 12 Wilkinson Rd., Love Lane Industrial Estate. GL7 1YT. (N. Grunfeld). Est. 1995. Open 10-5. SIZE: Large. *STOCK: Eastern European antique pine.* PARK: Easy. TEL: 01285 885336; fax - 01285 885338; e-mail - info@parlour farm.com; website - www.parlourfarm.com.

Silver Street Antiques and Things
9 Silver St. GL7 2BJ. (S.A. Tarrant). Resident. Est. 1992. Open 10-5. SIZE: Medium. *STOCK: General antiques including small furniture, £1-£1,500.* LOC: Between Corn Hall and museum. PARK: Nearby. TEL: 01285 641600.

William H. Stokes   `BADA`
The Cloisters, 6/8 Dollar St. GL7 2AJ. (W.H. Stokes and P.W. Bontoft). CADA. Est. 1968. Open 9.30-5.30, Sat. 9.30-4.30. STOCK: Early oak furniture, £1,000-£50,000; brassware, £150-£5,000; all 16th-17th C. LOC: West of parish church. TEL: 01285 653907; fax - 01285 640533; e-mail - post@williamstokes.co.uk; website - www.williamstokes.co.uk. VAT: Spec.

Rankine Taylor Antiques

34 Dollar St. GL7 2AN. CADA. Est. 1969. Open 9-5.30, Sun. by appointment. SIZE: Large. *STOCK: Furniture, 17th to early 19th C, £300-£35,000; silver, glass, rare and interesting objects.* Not Stocked: Victoriana. LOC: From church, turn right into West Market Place, via Gosditch St. into Dollar St. PARK: Own - private opposite. TEL: 01285 652529; website - www.antiquesnews.co.uk/rankin-taylor. VAT: Spec.

Patrick Waldron Antiques

18 Dollar St. GL7 2AN. Resident. CADA. Est. 1965. Open 9.30-1 and 2-6, Sun. by appointment. SIZE: Medium. *STOCK: Town and country furniture, 17th to early 19th C.* LOC: In street behind church. PARK: Easy and public behind shop. TEL: 01285 652880; home - same; workshop - 01285 643479; e-mail - patrick.waldron@virgin.net. SER: Restorations (furniture); buys at auction. VAT: Stan/Spec.

Bernard Weaver Antiques

28 Gloucester St. GL7 2DH. Open by appointment. SIZE: Medium. *STOCK: Furniture, mahogany and oak, 18th-19th C.* LOC: Continuation of Dollar St. PARK: Easy. TEL: 01285 652055. SER: Valuations; restorations.

EBRINGTON, Nr. Chipping Campden

John Burton Natural Craft Taxidermy

21 Main St. GL55 6NL. Est. 1973. Open by appointment. SIZE: Medium. *STOCK: Taxidermy - Victorian and Edwardian cased fish, birds and mammals, from £40-£2,500; glass domes, sporting trophies.* LOC: Village centre. PARK: Easy. TEL: 01386 593231; home - same; mobile - 07850 356354. SER: Valuations; restorations (taxidermy); buys at auction (taxidermy).

FAIRFORD

Blenheim Antiques

Market Place. GL7 4AB. (N. Hurdle). CADA. Resident. Est. 1972. Open 9.30-6.30. SIZE: Medium. *STOCK: 18th-19th C furniture and accessories.* PARK: Easy. TEL: 01285 712094. VAT: Stan/Spec.

Mark Carter Antiques

Gloucester House, Market Place. GL7 4AB. (Mark and Karen Carter). CADA. Est. 1979. Open 10-5.30, other times by appointment. SIZE: Large. *STOCK: English oak, fruitwood and country furniture, 17th-19th C, £500-£10,000.* PARK: Easy. TEL: 01285 712790; mobile - 07836 260567; e-mail - markcarterantiques@hotmail.com. SER: Valuations. VAT: Stan/Spec.

Anthony Hazledine

Antique Oriental Carpets, High St. GL7 4AD. Est. 1976. Open Mon., Fri. and Sat. 9-5, other days by appointment. SIZE: Small. *STOCK: Oriental carpets and textiles, 18th-19th C, £150-£4,000.* PARK: Easy. TEL: 01285 713400; home and fax - same. SER: Restorations; cleaning. VAT: Stan/Spec.

GLOUCESTER

Gloucester Antique Centre

1 Severn Rd. GL1 2LE. Est. 1949. Open 10-5, Sun. 1-5. SIZE: 140 dealers. 50p admission charge weekends and Bank Hols. - Trade free. *STOCK: General antiques - furniture, jewellery, silver, clocks, ceramics, collectables.* LOC: Within the Dock area. PARK: Easy. TEL: 01452 529716; fax - 01452 307161.

Arthur S. Lewis

Est. 1969. By appointment. *STOCK: Mechanical music, automata, clocks.* TEL: 01452 780258; website - www.arthurlewisantiques.com.

Military Curios, HQ84

(The Curiosity Shop), Southgate. GL1 2DX. (B. Williams). Est. 1964. Open 10-5 including Sun. *STOCK: Medals, badges, (3rd Reich specialities),*

militaria, blazer badges, Govt. surplus, edged weapons, replicas, air weapons; Jaguar - spares, mascots. LOC: A38, city centre. PARK: 100 yds (Docks). TEL: 01452 556038; fax - 01452 554056. SER: Valuations; finder (medals); mounting; framing; costume hire; badge-making; mail order;

LECHLADE

Jubilee Hall Antiques Centre
Oak St. GL7 3AY. Open 10-5, Sun. 11-5. SIZE: Large. *STOCK: 18th-19th C furniture, metalwork, prints, pictures, mirrors, pottery and porcelain, rugs, lighting, 19th C and earlier collectables, glass and silver.* LOC: On left 350 yards from town centre going north towards Burford. PARK: Own. TEL: 01367 253777; website - www.jubileehall.co.uk. SER: Shipping. Listed below are the dealers at this centre.

Mandy Barnes
Georgian and Victorian furniture, decorative objects, some textiles.

Keith and Lin Bawden
18th-19th C English furniture, boxes, mirrors, barometers and objects.

John Calgie
Period furniture, mirrors, copper, brass and interesting objects.

Andrew Crawforth
Antique metalwork, treen, glass and unusual items.

Francoise Daniel
Small silver, ivory, shibayama, tortoiseshell, art objects, Tunbridge ware, jewellery and glass.

Marc Drogin
Antiquities, from 2000 years.

Paul Eisler
18th-19th C ceramics, metalware, treen, small furniture, prints and maps.

Peter Gibbons
Period pewter, treen, brass, arms and armour, country furniture.

Anita Harris
Porcelain, decorative objects, soft furnishings, small furniture.

Colin and Mary Lee
Glass, porcelain, silver, silhouettes, pottery and objects.

Colin Morris
Country furniture, Staffordshire, brass, copper and period objects.

NAAS Antiques
18th-19th C decorative furnishings, mirrors, pictures, re-upholstered items, Worcester porcelain.

Oak Antiques
(David and Vicky Wilson). Period country oak furniture and metalware.

Clive Payne
Georgian furniture, works of art, blue and white, Masons ironstone.

Mary Pennel
Porcelain, small silver and jewellery.

Judi Pollitt (Times Past)
Ceramics including old blue and white and interesting objects, sewing items.

Red Lane Antiques
(Terry Sparks). 17th-19th C ironwork, treen, copper, brass and country furniture.

Lindsey Richardson
Glass, Staffordshire, pottery, porcelain, inkwells.

Keith Robinson
18th-19th C engravings, ceramics, lighting and Japanese and English objects of art.

Jackie & Richard Stent

18th-19th C furniture, prints, pottery, porcelain, chrystoleums, Belleek and small items.

Winson Antiques

Georgian and Victorian furniture, lead garden statuary and Masons ironstone.

Lechlade Arcade

5, 6 and 7 High St. GL7 3AD. (J. Dickson). Est. 1990. Open 9-5 including Sun. SIZE: 20+ dealers. *STOCK: Bric-a-brac, books, furniture (reclaimed pine), collectables, militaria, medals, pistols.* PARK: Riverside boat yard. TEL: 01367 252832; mobile - 07949 130875.

The Old Ironmongers Antiques Centre

Burford St. GL7. (Mark A. Serle and Geoff Allen). Open 10-5 including Sun. *STOCK: Old ironmongery, £5-£200; furniture including country, £40-£2,000; textiles, £10-£200; Georgian glass, £20-£250; decorative china, £10-£500; treen, £50-£200; militaria including medals, £5-£300; tools and rural implements, £5-£300.* LOC: A361. PARK: Easy. TEL: 01367 252397.

MINCHINHAMPTON, Nr. Stroud

Mick and Fanny Wright

The Trumpet. GL6 9JA. Est. 1979. Open Wed.-Sat. 10.30-5.30. SIZE: Medium. *STOCK: General antiques, decorative items, clocks, furniture, china, silver, plate and books, 50p-£2,000.* LOC: 200 yards west of crossroads at bottom of High St. PARK: Nearby. TEL: 01453 883027; e-mail - antiques@thetrumpet.free-online.co.uk. SER: Valuations. FAIRS: Kempton Park. VAT: Margin.

MORETON-IN-MARSH

Astley House - Fine Art   LAPADA

Astley House, High St. GL56 0LL. (David, Nanette and Caradoc Glaisyer). CADA. CINOA. Est. 1973. Open 9-5.30 and by appointment. SIZE: Medium. *STOCK: Oil paintings, 19th-21st C, £800-£20,000.* LOC: Main street. PARK: Easy. TEL: 01608 650601; fax - 01608 651777; e-mail - astart333@aol.com; website - www.art-uk.com. SER: Restorations (oils and watercolours); framing. VAT: Spec.

Astley House - Fine Art   LAPADA

Astley House, London Rd. GL56 0LE. (David, Nanette and Caradoc Glaisyer). CADA. CINOA. Est. 1973. Open 10-1 and 2-5 and by appointment. CL: Wed. SIZE: Large. *STOCK: Oil paintings, 19th-21st C; large decorative oils and portraits.* LOC: Town centre. PARK: Easy. TEL: 01608 650608; fax - 01608 651777; e-mail - astart333@aol.com; website - www.art-uk.com. SER: Restorations (oils and watercolours); framing (porcelain). VAT: Spec.

August Antiques and Interiors

Unit 3 Fosseway Business Park. GL56 9NQ. (Mike Robinson). Open 9.30-6. SIZE: Large. *STOCK: English and European oak, mahogany and pine furniture, 18th to early 20th C, £100-£5,000; associated items, general antiques and shipping goods.* PARK: Easy. TEL: 01608 651515; fax - same; mobile - 07970 429255; e-mail - mike.augustantiques@virgin.net. SER: Valuations; restorations.

Benton Fine Art   LAPADA

Regent House, High St. GL56 0AX. (J.G. Benton). Est. 1972. Open 10-5.30, Sun. 11-5.30, Tues. by appointment. SIZE: Large. *STOCK: Paintings, furniture, 18th to early 20th C, £500-£30,000.* PARK: Easy. TEL: 01608 652153; fax - same; mobile - 07885 575139; e-mail - bentonfineart@excite.com. FAIRS: LAPADA; Antiques for Everyone.

Berry Antiques Ltd   LAPADA

3 High St. GL56 0AH. (Chris Berry). Est. 1985. Open 10-5.30, Sun. 11-5.30. CL: Tues. SIZE: Medium. *STOCK: Furniture, late 18th to 19th C, £1,000-£15,000; porcelain, £50-£500; paintings, £200-£10,000; both 19th C.* LOC: Near junction with Broadway road. PARK: Easy. TEL: 01608 652929; home - same; e-mail - chris@berryantiques.co.uk; website - www.berryantiques.com. SER: Valuations. FAIRS: NEC, LAPADA. VAT: Spec.

Cox's Architectural Reclamation Yard

Unit 10, Fosseway Industrial Estate. GL56 9NQ. (P. Watson). SALVO. Est. 1991. Open 9-5, Sun. by appointment. SIZE: Large. *STOCK: Architectural antiques, fire surrounds and fireplaces, £250-£4,000; doors, £50-£500; all 19th C.* LOC: Just off Fosseway, northern end of Moreton-in-Marsh. PARK: Easy. TEL: 01608 652505; fax - 01608 652881; e-mail - coxs@fsbdial.co.uk; website - www.coxsarchitectural.co.uk. SER: Valuations. VAT: Stan.

Dale House Antiques

High St. GL56 0AD. (N. and A. Allen). Open 10-5.30, Sun. 11-5. SIZE: Large. *STOCK: 17th-19th C town and country furniture, clocks, barometers, pictures, porcelain and pottery, metalwork, objets.* LOC: Main street. PARK: Easy. TEL: 01608 652950; fax - 01608 652424. VAT: Spec.

August Antiques & Interiors (Warehouse)
Moreton-in-Marsh, Glos.

18th, 19th & 20th c. English & European Furniture & Associated Items, General Antiques & Shipping Goods.

3 Fosseway Business Park, Moreton-in-Marsh, Glos. GL56 9NQ

Telephone/Fax: 01608 651515
Mobile: 07970 429255

E-mail: mike.augustantiques@virgin.net

James Duffield Harding, Shooting in the Highlands, signed and inscribed, watercolour heightened with bodycolour, 16½in. x 22in., sold for £2,400 in 2001. (Sotheby's)

From an article entitled "James Duffield Harding 1797-1863 A Prince of Art Instructors" by Charles Hind which appeared in the October 2002 issue of *Antique Collecting*. For more details and to subscribe see page 21.

Jeffrey Formby Antiques `BADA`
Orchard Cottage, East St. GL56 0LQ. Resident. Est. 1994. Open by appointment. SIZE: Small. *STOCK: Fine English clocks, pre 1850, £2,000-£15,000; horological books, old and new, £5-£500.* **LOC: 100 yards from High St. PARK: Easy. TEL: 01608 650558; e-mail - jeff@formby-clocks.co.uk; website - www.formby-clocks.co.uk. FAIRS: BADA; Olympia. VAT: Spec.**

Jon Fox Antiques
High St. GL56 0AD. CADA. Est. 1982. Open 9.30-5.30, Sun. 11-4, Tues. by appointment. SIZE: Large - 2 adjacent shops. *STOCK: 19th C garden items including urns, seats, troughs and tools, £50-£5,000+; 18th -19th C country furniture £300-£3,000; treen, bygones, metalware, fireplace items.* PARK: Easy. TEL: 01608 650325/650714. VAT: Spec.

Grimes House Antiques & Fine Art
High St. GL56 0AT. (S. and V. Farnsworth). FATG. Est. 1978. Open 9.30-1 and 2-5, other times by appointment. *STOCK: Old cranberry and antique coloured glass, fine paintings.* LOC: Town centre. PARK: Free nearby. TEL: 01608 651029; fax - same; e-mail - grimes_house@cix.co.uk; websites - www.grimeshouse.co.uk and www.cranberry glass.co.uk. VAT: Spec/Stan.

London House Antique Centre
London House, High St. GL56 0AH. Est. 1979. Open 10-5 including Sun. (Sun. 11-5 Nov.-March). SIZE: Large. *STOCK: Furniture, paintings, watercolours, prints, Doulton Lambeth, Royal Doulton, potlids, porcelain, domestic artifacts, clocks, silver, jewellery and plate, mainly 17th-19th C, £5-£3,000.* LOC: Centre of High St. (A429). PARK: Easy. TEL: 01608 651084; website - www.london-house-antiques.co.uk. VAT: Stan/Spec.

Seaford House Antiques `LAPADA`
Seaford House, High St. GL56 0AD. (Derek and Kathy Young). CINOA. CADA. Est. 1988. Open 10-5.30, Mon. and Tues. by appointment. SIZE: Medium. *STOCK: Furniture, 18th C to Edwardian especially upholstered, £500-£5,000; English and Continental porcelain including Worcester, Coalport, Meissen, Sitzendorf, Sampson and Copeland, mirrors and paintings, 19th C, £100-£3,000.* PARK: Easy. TEL: 01608 652423; fax - same. VAT: Spec.

Simply Antiques
at Windsor House Antiques Centre, High St. GL56 0AD. (G. Ellis). Open 10-5, Tues. and Sun. 12-5. *STOCK: Visiting card cases and small period furniture, mainly 18th to early 19th C.* LOC: In large 17th C premises, adjacent town

GARY WRIGHT ANTIQUES LTD
TRADE WAREHOUSE

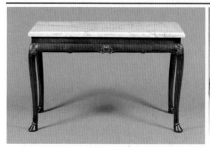  

C18th Irish Serving Table   Geo IV giltwood convex mirror   Geo III set 12 dining chairs

Over 700 pieces of good quality C18th - C19th furniture and unusual objects at trade prices

5 Fosseway Business Park, Stratford Road, Moreton-in-Marsh, Glos. GL56 9NQ

Direct train to London Paddington - 90 mins

Tel/Fax: 01608 652007   Mobile: 07831 653843
Email: info@garywrightantiques.co.uk
Website: www.garywrightantiques.co.uk

hall. PARK: Easy. TEL: 01608 650993; e-mail - info@simply-antiques.com; website - www.simply-antiques.com. SER: Finder. FAIRS: NEC; Cooper. VAT: Spec.

The Roger Widdas Gallery
High St. GL56 0AD. Est. 1977. Open 10-5, Sun. 11-4. CL: Tues. SIZE: Medium. *STOCK: 19th C English and European paintings and watercolours including Impressionist art, £2,000-£50,000; 19th C English and European town furniture, £1,000-£20,000.* PARK: Opposite - in New St. TEL: 01608 650618; fax - 01608 652301; e-mail - gallery@widdas.com; website - www.widdas.com. SER: Restorations (oil paintings).

Windsor House Antiques Centre
High St. GL56 0AD. Open 10-5, Tues. and Sun. 12-5. SIZE: 48 dealers. *STOCK: Comprehensive selection of mid-range furniture, from 1650-1914; silver, portrait miniatures, ivory, visiting card cases, French decorative items, English and European porcelain, pottery and glass, objets de vertu, caddies and boxes, brass, copper and pewter.* LOC: Large 17th C premises, adjacent town hall. PARK: Ample. TEL: 01608 650993; fax - 01858 565438; e-mail - windsorhouse@btinternet.com; website - www.windsorhouse.co.uk

Gary Wright Antiques
Unit 5, Fosseway Business Park, Stratford Rd. GL56 9NQ. Est. 1983. Open 9.30-5.30, Sun. by appointment. SIZE: Large. *STOCK: English and Continental furniture, 18th-19th C, £500-£30,000; unusual and decorative objects, 17th-20th C, £200-£4,000.* LOC: Entrance adjacent to railway bridge on north side of Moreton, on Fosseway (A429). PARK: Easy. TEL: 01608 652007; fax - same; mobile - 07831 653843; e-mail - info@garywrightantiques.co.uk; website - www.garywrightantiques.co.uk. SER: Valuations; restorations; buys at auction (furniture). VAT: Stan/Spec.

NEWENT

Jillings Antiques - Distinctive Antique Clocks   `BADA` `LAPADA`
Croft House, 17 Church St. GL18 1PU. (Doro and John Jillings). CINOA. Est. 1986. Open by appointment. *STOCK: 18th to early 19th C English and Continental clocks including bronze, ormolu, marble and boulle.* PARK: Easy. TEL: 01531 822100; fax - 01531 822666; mobile - 07973 830110; e-mail - clocks@jillings.com; website - www.jillings.com. SER: Valuations; restorations; repairs; shipping worldwide; free delivery and set up in UK. FAIRS: BADA (March); Olympia (June, Nov., Feb); New York Fall (Oct). VAT: Margin.

GLOUCESTERSHIRE

The Doll's House
Market Place. GL54 3EJ. (Miss Michal Morse). Est. 1971. Open Thurs., Fri. and Sat. 10-5, other times prior telephone call advisable. SIZE: Small. STOCK: Handmade doll's houses and miniature furniture in one twelfth scale. LOC: A40. PARK: Easy. TEL: 01451 860431; home and fax - same. SER: Replica houses and special designs to order.

Keith Harding's World of Mechanical Music
The Oak House, High St. GL54 3ET. (K. Harding FBHI and C.A.Burnett CMBHI). Est. 1961. Open 10-6 including Sun. SIZE: Large. STOCK: Clocks, musical boxes and automata. PARK: Easy. TEL: 01451 860181; fax - 01451 861133; e-mail - keith@mechanicalmusic.co.uk; website - www.mechanicalmusic.co.uk. SER: Guided tours, demonstrations, and written articles; valuations; restorations (musical boxes and clocks); buys at auction. VAT: Stan/Spec.

Robson Antiques
New Barn Farm, London Rd. GL54 3LX. Est. 1982. Open daily till late. STOCK: Furniture, from 18th C, £50-£5,000; garden artefacts. PARK: Easy. TEL: 01451 861071/861006.

Nina Zborowska
BADA

Damsels Mill, Paradise. GL6 6UD. Est. 1980. By appointment, except during exhibitions (May-June and Oct.-Nov) 11-5 including Sun. SIZE: Medium. STOCK: Modern British paintings and drawings, St Ives, Newlyn, NEAC and Bloomsbury schools, 1900-1970, £500-£40,000. LOC: From Cheltenham towards Stroud on A46, take first turning on left to Sheepscombe. PARK: Easy. TEL: 01452 812460; fax - 01452 812912; e-mail - enquiries@ninazborowska.com; website - www.ninazborowska.com. SER: Valuations; restorations. FAIRS: Olympia (Spring); 20th/21st C British Art.

Ian Hodgkins and Co. Ltd
Upper Vatch Mill, The Vatch. GL6 7JY. Open by appointment. STOCK: Antiquarian books including pre-Raphaelites and associates, the Brontës, Jane Austen; 19th C illustrated, children's art and literature books. TEL: 01453 764270; fax - 01453 755233; e-mail - i.hodgkins@dial.pipex.com; website - www. ianhodgkins.com.

Ashton Gower Antiques
LAPADA

9/9A Talbot Court, Market Square. GL54 1BQ. (C. Gower and B. Ashton). Est. 1987. Open 10-5. STOCK: English and Continental furniture, gilt mirrors and decorative accessories, 18th-20th C, £25-£5,000. LOC: Between the square and Sheep St. PARK: Nearby. TEL: 01451 870699; fax - same; e-mail - ashtongower@aol.com; website - www.antiquesweb.co.uk/ashtongower. SER: Valuations; restorations; buys at auction. VAT: Stan/Spec.

Duncan J. Baggott
LAPADA

Woolcomber House, Sheep St. GL54 1AA. CADA. Est. 1967. Open 9-5.30 or by appointment. CL: Bank Holidays. SIZE: Large. STOCK: 17th-20th C English oak, mahogany and walnut furniture, paintings, domestic metalwork and decorative items; garden statuary and ornaments. PARK: Sheep St. or Market Sq. TEL: 01451 830662; fax - 01451 832174. SER: Worldwide shipping; UK delivery. FAIRS: Exhibition Oct. annually (CADA).

Baggott Church Street Ltd
BADA

Church St. GL54 1BB. (D.J. and C.M. Baggott). CADA. Est. 1978. Open 9.30-5.30 or by appointment. SIZE: Large. STOCK: English furniture, 17th-19th C; portrait paintings, metalwork, pottery, treen and decorative items. LOC: South-west corner of market square. PARK: Market square. TEL: 01451 830370; fax - 01451 832174. SER: Annual exhibition - Oct.

Oonagh Black
LAPADA

Lower Farm House, Coln Rogers. GL54 3LA. (Mr and Mrs Victor Black). Est. 1978. Open by appointment. SIZE: 4 large rooms. STOCK: Country and French provincial furniture, textiles and related items. LOC: Just off A429 Fosseway between Cirencester and Stow-on-the-Wold. PARK: Easy. TEL: 01285 720717/720920; fax - 01285 720910; mobile - 07768 568966; e-mail - oonagh@victorblack.co.uk. FAIRS: Olympia; Harvey Decorative; Penman; NEC. VAT: Spec.

Church Street Antiques Centre
3/4 Church St. GL54 1BB. (Mrs G. E. Niner). Est. 1970. Open 9.45-5. SIZE: Medium - 18 dealers. STOCK: Furniture, 1680-1930, £50-£4,000; pottery especially Staffordshire, porcelain especially 18th C Worcester, silver, metalwork, jewellery, vintage leather, glass, children's furniture and toys. PARK: Nearby. TEL: 01451 870186. FAIRS: NEC.

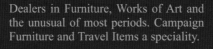

Annarella Clark Antiques

11 Park St. GL54 1AQ. Est. 1968. Open 10-5 or
by appointment. SIZE: Medium. *STOCK: Wicker
and garden, English and French country and
painted furniture, needlework, pottery, quilts and
decorative objects.* LOC: Park St. leads from
Sheep St., 1st right at lights leading into town.
PARK: Easy. TEL: 01451 830535; home - same.

Christopher Clarke Antiques Ltd LAPADA

The Fosseway. GL54 1JS. (I.D., D.S. and S.F.
Clarke). CADA. Est. 1961. Open 9.30-5.30 or by
appointment. SIZE: Large. *STOCK: Furniture
including campaign, 17th-20th C; works of art,
metalware, treen, pictures, decorative items,
animal antiques.* LOC: Corner of The Fosseway
and Sheep St. PARK: Easy. TEL: 01451 830476;
fax - 01451 830300; e-mail - cclarkeantiques@
aol.com; website - www.antiques-in-england.
com. FAIRS: Olympia (June, Nov. and Feb).

Cotswold Galleries

The Square, GL54 1AB. (Richard and Cherry
Glaisyer). CADA. FATG. Est. 1961. Open 9-5.30
or by appointment. SIZE: Large. *STOCK: Oil
paintings especially 19th-20th C landscape.*
PARK: Easy. TEL: 01451 870567; fax - 01451
870678; website - www.cotswoldgalleries.com.
SER: Restorations; framing.

The John Davies Gallery

Church St. GL54 1BB. CADA. Est. 1977. Open
9.30-1.30 and 2.30-5.30. SIZE: Large. *STOCK:
Contemporary and late period paintings; limited
edition bronzes.* PARK: In square. TEL: 01451
831698; fax - 01451 832477; e-mail -
daviesart@aol.com; website - www.the-john-
davies-gallery.co.uk. SER: Restorations and
conservation to museum standard.

Durham House Antiques Centre

Sheep St. GL54 1AA. (Alan Smith). Open 10-5,
Sun. 11-5. SIZE: 30+ dealers. PARK: Easy. TEL:
01451 870404; fax - same; e-mail -
DurhamHouseGB@aol.com. SER: Buys at
auction. FAIRS: NEC (Aug); Newark; Ardingly.
Below are listed the dealers at this centre.

Acorn Antiques

(Derek Howe and Stanley Taylor). Est. 1987. *19th
C Staffordshire figures and animals.*

DURHAM HOUSE ANTIQUES CENTRE
STOW-ON-THE-WOLD

A Quality Antiques Centre in the Heart of the Cotswolds Over 30 Well Established Trade Dealers

Monday - Saturday 10-5
Sunday 11-5
Tel/Fax: 01451 870404
email: DurhamHouseGB@aol.com

Sheep Street, STOW-ON-THE-WOLD, GL54 1AA

Ancient and Oriental Ltd
Ancient art and archaeological items from many periods, lands and cultures.

Michael Armson Antiques
Quality 18th-19th C mahogany and oak furniture, Staffordshire and metalware.

Aston Antiques
Arts and Crafts and Art Deco lighting, decanters, drinking glasses and ceramics, metalwork and furniture.

Judi Bland Antiques
Toby jugs, Staffordshire, pot lids, Prattware, bargeware, country furniture and decorative items.

Bread and Roses
19th-20th C kitchen, dairy, laundry and garden collectibles; country furniture.

Broadway Clocks
English and French carriage, bracket and mantle clocks, also wall and longcase.

Simon Clarke Antiques
Oak and mahogany furniture, pictures, prints, metalware and leather items, ceramics, glass and door furniture.

Bryan Collyer
English pottery and Staffordshire figures, corkscrews, prints and pictures, small furniture.

Crockwell Antiques
(Philip Dawes). 18th-19th C oak and mahogany furniture, longcase clocks, silver, brass and copper, ironstone china and fireplace accessories.

Lee Elliott Antiques
19th-20th C prints and pictures, specialising in rural pastimes.

Jane Fairfield
Elegant silver and plate, Continental porcelain and objets d'art.

Tony and Jane Finegan
Traditional English and French furniture and mirrors, lighting, decorative accessories including papier mâché and tole.

Marion Gregg Antiques
19th-20th C Oriental ceramics and cabinet pieces, fabrics and carvings, English furniture and accessories.

Beryl and Brian Harrison
Quality linen and lace accessories, table and bed linen.

Erna Hiscock and John Shepherd
Fine samplers and needlework, early carvings and ceramics, blue and white, country furniture and decorative items.

Dorothy Hyatt
Early English porcelain and pottery (Worcester, creamware and blue and white); 18th-19th C drinking glasses, decanters and table objects.

Corrie Jeffries Antiques
Decorative accessories, stitchery and textiles, pictures and prints, sewing ephemera, objets d' art.

Ian Kellam
English and Continental porcelain, silver and jewellery, religious objects and cabinet pieces.

Little Nells
(Helen Middleton). *Coronation commemoratives, automobilia, Staffordshire and majolica, collectibles and small interesting items.*

Mansard Antiques
(Mr and Mrs Lee Elliott). *18th-20th C oak and mahogany furniture, clocks and decorative items.*

Audrey McConnell
Silver and jewellery, picture frames, ceramics, ivory and micromosaics.

Atalanti Meyers
Arts and Crafts ceramics, pewter, small furniture.

Colin Morris
Early oak furniture and carvings, pewter, copper and brass, ceramics, religious imagery and interesting vernacular objects.

Paper Moon Books
Fine 19th-20th C bindings including poetry, prose and history; prayer books and bibles.

Pauline Parkes
Sewing ephemera, 19th-20th C mauchlineware, treen and tartanware.

Edith and Brian Prosser Antiques
18th-20th C furniture, mirrors, prints and

lighting; decorative items including glass and ceramics, metalware and objets de vertu.

Quartz and Clay
Arts and Crafts, Art Deco glass and ceramics especially Whitefriars, Clarice Cliff and Denby.

Lindsey Richardson Antiques
19th C ceramics including Staffordshire, blue and white and majolica; glass and small decorative items.

Simply Antiques
(Graham Ellis). *Visiting card cases, objects of vertu.* SER: Search and seek.

Betty Thornley Antiques
18th-19th C engravings, 19th C porcelain, candlesticks and metalware.

Times Past
(Judy Pollitt). *Needlework tools, chatelaines, small silver and objets de vertu*

Yorca Antiques
(Paul and Philippa Hughes). *Fine quality English porcelain including Derby and Worcester.*

The Fosse Gallery
The Square. GL54 1AF. Est. 1979. Open 10-5.30. SIZE: Large. *STOCK: English and Scottish painters, many RA, RSA and Royal Glasgow Institute members, including Gore, Howard, Ward, Dunstan, Spear, Weight, Morrocco, Donaldson, McClure, Haig, Devlin and Michael Scott.* LOC: Off Fosseway, A429. PARK: Easy. TEL: 01451 831319; fax - 01451 870309. SER: Valuations.

Fox Cottage Antiques
Digbeth St. GL54 1BN. (Sue London). Est. 1995. Open 10-5. SIZE: 10 dealers. *STOCK: Wide variety of general antiques including pottery and porcelain, silver and plate, metalware, prints, small furniture, country and decorative items, mainly pre 1900, £5-£500.* LOC: Left hand side at bottom of narrow street, running down from the square. PARK: Nearby. TEL: 01451 870307.

Keith Hockin Antiques BADA
The Square. GL54 1AF. CADA. Est. 1968. Open Thurs., Fri. and Sat., 10-5, other times by appointment or ring the bell. SIZE: Medium. *STOCK: Oak furniture, 1600-1750; country furniture in oak, fruitwoods, yew, 1700-1850; pewter, copper, brass, ironwork, all periods.* Not Stocked: Mahogany. PARK: Easy. TEL: 01451 831058; fax - same; e-mail - keithhockin@aol.com. SER: Buys at auction (oak, pewter, metalwork). VAT: Stan/Spec.

La Chaise Antique

Beauport, Sheep Street, Stow-on-the-Wold, Glos GL54 1AA
Tel: (01451) 830582 Mobile: (07831) 205002

Specialists in leather chairs, upholstery and suppliers of loose leather desk tops. Always available from our new Showroom at Stow-on-the-Wold after 30 years at Faringdon.

Typical example of our leather fully re-upholstered Victorian Chesterfields.

Huntington Antiques Ltd   LAPADA
Church St. GL54 1BE. (M.F. and S.P. Golding). CADA. CINOA. Resident. Est. 1974. Open 9.30-5.30 or by appointment. SIZE: Large. *STOCK: Early period and fine country furniture, metalware, treen and textiles, tapestries and works of art.* LOC: Opposite main gates to church. TEL: 01451 830842; fax - 01451 832211; e-mail - info@huntington-antiques.com; website - www.huntington-antiques.com. SER: Valuations; buys at auction. FAIRS: LAPADA. VAT: Spec.

Kenulf Fine Arts   LAPADA
Digbeth St. GL54 1BN. (E. and J. Ford). Est. 1978. Open 10-5, Sun. 12-5. SIZE: 7 rooms. *STOCK: 19th to early 20th C oils, watercolours and prints; decorative items, fine period walnut and mahogany furniture; bronzes and contemporary paintings.* LOC: Near Barclays Bank. PARK: Easy. TEL: 01451 870878; mobile - 07774 107269; e-mail - kenulf.finearts@virgin. net. SER: Valuations; restorations (oils and watercolours, period framing). FAIRS: NEC; LAPADA; Northern; Belgian. VAT: Spec.

T.M. King-Smith & Simon W. Nutter
Wraggs Row, Fosseway. GL54 1JT. Est. 1975. Open 9.30-5.30. *STOCK: 18th-19th C mahogany and oak furniture, £500-£10,000; silver, porcelain, brass and copper.* LOC: Near traffic lights opposite the Unicorn Hotel. TEL: 01451 830658. SER: Buys at auction. VAT: Spec.

La Chaise Antique   LAPADA
Beauport, Sheep St. GL54 1AA. (Roger Clark). Est. 1968. Open 9.30-5.30. CL: Sun. except by appointment. SIZE: Large. *STOCK: Chairs, pre-1860; furniture, 18th-19th C; general antiques, decorators' items, upholstered library and Victorian arm chairs (leather/fabric).* Not Stocked: Silver, porcelain and glass. PARK: Ample. TEL: 01451 830582; mobile - 07831 205002. SER: Valuations; restorations;

upholstery (leather and fabrics); table top liners. FAIRS: NEC (April, Aug., Nov.); LAPADA NEC (Jan.), London (Oct). VAT: Spec.

Roger Lamb Antiques & Works of Art
LAPADA
The Square. GL54 1AB. CADA. Open 10-5. *STOCK: 18th to early 19th C furniture especially small items, lighting, decorative accessories, oils and watercolours.* TEL: 01451 831371. SER: Search.

Malt House Antiques
The Malt House, Digbeth St. GL54 1BN. (C.P. Mortimer). Open 10-5.30 (including Sun.) and by appointment. CL: Tues. SIZE: Large. *STOCK: Fine English furniture, oak, walnut, fruitwood and mahogany, 17th-19th C; ceramics, wine related items, bottles, prints and paintings, pot-lids, collectables, treen, medical and dental items, specialist books.* LOC: Just off The Square. PARK: Easy. TEL: 01451 830592; fax - same; e-mail - Malthousestow@aol.com; website - www.malthouseantiques.co.uk.

Oriental Gallery
GL56 0QW. (Patricia Cater). Open by appointment. *STOCK: Oriental ceramics and works of art.* TEL: 01451 830944; fax - 01451 870126; e-mail - patriciacaterorg@aol.com; website - www.patriciacater-orientalart.com. FAIRS: Olympia.

Park House Antiques
Park St. GL54 1AQ. (G. and B. Sutton). Est. 1986. Open Wed.- Sat. 10-1 and 2-4.30. Nov., Dec., Jan. and May by appointment only. SIZE: Large. *STOCK: Early dolls, teddy bears, toys, Victorian linen and lace, porcelain, collectables, small furniture and pictures.* PARK: Easy. TEL: 01451 830159; home - same; e-mail - info@thetoymuseum.co.uk; website - www. thetoymuseum.co.uk. SER: Museum of dolls,

teddies, toys, textiles and collectables; teddy bears repaired; antique dolls dressed.

Antony Preston Antiques Ltd `BADA`
The Square. GL54 1AB. CADA. Est. 1965. Open 9.30-5.30 or by appointment. STOCK: 18th-19th C English and Continental furniture and objects; barometers and period lighting. TEL: 01451 831586; fax - 01451 831596. VAT: Stan/Spec.

Queens Parade Antiques Ltd `BADA`
The Square. GL54 1AB. (Sally and Antony Preston). CADA. Est. 1965. Open 9.30-5.30. SIZE: Large. STOCK: 18th-19th C furniture, papier mâché, tôle peinte, needlework and period lighting. LOC: Off Fosse Way. PARK: Easy. TEL: 01451 831586; e-mail - antony@antonypreston.com. FAIRS: Grosvenor House; BADA. VAT: Stan/Spec.

Michael Rowland Antiques
Little Elms, The Square. GL54 1AF. Est. 1991. Open 10.45-5. SIZE: Medium. *STOCK: Furniture including Welsh dressers, farmhouse, gateleg and side tables, bureaux, 17th-18th C, £500-£8,000.* PARK: Easy. TEL: 01451 870089; home - same. VAT: Spec.

Ruskin Decorative Arts
5 Talbot Court. GL54 1DP. (Anne and William Morris). CADA. Est. 1990. Open 10-1 and 2-5.30. SIZE: Small. *STOCK: Interesting and unusual decorative objects, Arts and Crafts furniture, Art Nouveau, Art Deco, glass and pottery, metalwork, 1860-1940.* LOC: Between the square and Sheep St. PARK: Nearby. TEL: 01451 832254; fax - 01451 832167; home - 01993 831880; e-mail - william.anne@ruskindecarts.co.uk. SER: Valuations. FAIRS: NEC.

Samarkand Galleries `LAPADA`
7 & 8 Brewery Yard, Sheep St. GL54 1AA. (Brian MacDonald). CADA. CINOA. FRGS. Est. 1979. Open 10-5.30, Sun. by appointment. SIZE: Medium. *STOCK: Tribal and village rugs and artefacts, 19th C, £100-£10,000; fine decorative carpets, 19th-20th C, £1,000-£10,000+; kelims, 19th-20th C, £200-£2,000; also unique contemporary rugs and carpets.* LOC: Street adjacent to Market Sq. PARK: Easy. TEL: 01451 832322; fax - same; e-mail - mac@samarkand.co.uk; website - www.samarkand.co.uk. SER: Exhibitions; valuations; restorations; cleaning. FAIRS: Hali, Olympia (June). VAT: Stan/Spec.

Arthur Seager Antiques
50 Sheep St. GL54 1AA. Est. 1977. Open Thurs., Fri. and Sat. 11-4. *STOCK: Period oak, carvings and sculpture, £500-£20,000.* TEL: 01451 831605; e-mail - stock@arthurseager.evesham.net; website - www.arthurseager.com.

Stow Antiques `LAPADA`
The Square. GL54 1AF. (Mr and Mrs J. and Bruce Hutton-Clarke). CADA. Resident. Est. 1969. Open Mon.-Sat. 10-5.30, other times by appointment. SIZE: Large. *STOCK: Furniture, mainly Georgian, £500-£30,000; decorative items, gilded mirrors, £50-£10,000.* PARK: Easy. TEL: 01451 830377; fax - 01451 870018; e-mail - hazel@stowantiques.demon.co.uk. SER: Shipping worldwide.

Styles of Stow
The Little House, Sheep St. GL54 1JS. (Mr and Mrs W.J. Styles). Est. 1981. Open 10-5.30. SIZE: Medium. *STOCK: Longcase (100+) and bracket clocks, barometers, 18th-19th C, £400-£30,000; fine furniture, 18th-19th C, £250-£15,000; oils and watercolours, 19th-20th C, £25-£20,000.* LOC: Opposite post office. PARK: Easy. TEL: 01451 830455; home and fax - same; e-mail - info@stylesofstow.co.uk; website - www.stylesofstow.co.uk. SER: Valuations; restorations; buys at auction (longcase and bracket clocks). VAT: Margin.

Talbot Court Galleries
Talbot Court. GL54 1BQ. (J.P. Trevers). CADA. IMCOS. Est. 1988. Open 9.30-1 and 1.30-5.30. SIZE: Medium. *STOCK: Prints and maps, 1580-1880, £10-£5,000.* LOC: Behind Talbot Hotel in precinct between the square and Sheep St. PARK: Nearby. TEL: 01451 832169; fax - 01451 832167. SER: Valuations; restorations; cleaning; colouring; framing; buys at auction (engravings). VAT: Stan.

The Titian Gallery `LAPADA`
Sheep St. GL54 1JS. (Ilona Johnson Gibbs). CADA. CINOA. Est. 1978. Open 10-5.30 and by appointment. SIZE: Medium. *STOCK: Fine 18th-19th C British and European oil paintings and watercolours, £1,000-£40,000.* LOC: Near The Fosseway. PARK: Adjacent and nearby. TEL: 01451 830004; fax - 01451 830126; e-mail - ilona@titiangallery.co.uk; website - www.titiangallery.co.uk. SER: Valuations; buys at auction (oils and watercolours). FAIRS: CADA exhibition. VAT: Spec.

Tudor

House

7 showrooms of

Antiques

Open Monday – Saturday

10.00am – 5.00pm

Sunday 11.00am – 4.00pm

Sheep Street, Stow-on-the-Wold, Glos., GL54 1AA
Tel/Fax: 01451 830021

Tudor House

Sheep St. GL54 1AA. (Peter Collingridge and Roy Hooper). Est. 2001. Open 10-5, Sun. 11-4. SIZE: 7 showrooms. *STOCK: Furniture, £500-£10,000; metalware, £50-£2,500; both 1700-1900. Porcelain, 1720-1920, £50-£2,500; watercolours, 1780-1940, £50-£1,000.* LOC: Turn at traffic lights from A429. PARK: At rear. TEL: 01451 830021; fax - same; mobile - 07860 581858. SER: Valuations. VAT: Spec. Below are listed the dealers trading from this address.

Mike & Shirley Allen
19th-20th C glass, porcelain and pottery; 19th C small furniture.

Ashley Antiques
Curios.

Christopher Ashton
French furniture, metalware, lighting, works of art.

Colin Brand
Clocks, porcelain, decorative furniture, militaria.

Jeremy Collingridge
Fountain pens.

Peter Collingridge
Metalware, furniture 1700-1900.

Vienneta Edwards
18th-19th C pottery, metalware, decorative and collectable items.

Maureen Gough
Traditional English antique furniture and objects.

Roy Hooper
Metalware, Arts & Crafts, Art Nouveau.

Hazel Kewley
Blue & white pottery, Staffordshire figures and animals, decorative collectables.

Atalanti Meyer
Decorative items including pewter, silver, glass and porcelain.

Tim Olney
18th to early 19th C English porcelain, especially Worcester and Newhall.

Iris Walker
Decorative furniture, objets d'art, garden furniture.

Elizabeth Watkiss
Silver, 19th C boxes, blue & white transfer printed pottery.

WYNDHAMS

1 Brewery Yard, Sheep Street, Stow-on-the-Wold, Gloucestershire
Tel/Fax: 01451 870067

Fine 18th and 19th Century English Furniture and Decorative Antiques

Vanbrugh House Antiques
Park St. GL54 1AQ. (J. and M.M. Sands). Resident. Est. 1972. Open 10-5.30 or by appointment. *STOCK: Furniture and decorative items, 17th to early 19th C; early maps, music boxes, clocks and barometers.* LOC: Opposite the Bell Inn. PARK: Easy. TEL: 01451 830797; fax - same. SER: Valuations. VAT: Stan/Spec.

Wyndhams   LAPADA
1 Brewery Yard, Sheep St. GL54 1AA. (Philip Brown and Kevin Quin). Est. 1988. Open 10-5 or by appointment. SIZE: Medium - 2 showrooms. *STOCK: Fine mid-18th to early 19th C English exotic wood furniture and barometers; decorative antiques including 19th C Chinese blue and white ceramics, boxes and caddies; brass and ceramic lampbases; late 19th to early 20th C garden watercolours and prints.* PARK: The Square. TEL: 01451 870067; fax - same; e-mail - antiques@ wyndhams.com; website - www.wyndhams.com. SER: Valuations. VAT: Spec.

TADDINGTON, Nr. Cheltenham

Architectural Heritage
Taddington Manor. GL54 5RY. (Adrian, Suzy, Alex and Adam Puddy). CADA. Est. 1978. Open 9.30-5.30, Sat. 10.30-4.30. SIZE: Large. *STOCK:*

Oak and pine period panelled rooms; stone and marble chimney pieces; stone, marble, bronze and terracotta statuary; garden ornaments, fountains, temples, well-heads, seats, urns, cisterns, sundials and summer houses. PARK: Easy. TEL: 01386 584414; fax - 01386 584236; e-mail - puddy@architectural-heritage.co.uk; website - www.architectural-heritage.co.uk. SER: Worldwide delivery; shipping; bespoke ornaments, chimneypieces and panelled rooms. FAIRS: Chelsea Flower Show. VAT: Stan.

TETBURY

The Antiques Emporium
The Old Chapel, Long St. GL8 8AA. (D. Sayers). TADA. Est. 1993. Open 10-5, Sun. 1-5. SIZE: Large - 38 dealers. *STOCK: Fruitwood and country furniture, fine oak and mahogany, clocks, china, porcelain, treen, copper and brass, jewellery, silver, kitchenalia, £1-£5,000.* Not Stocked: Reproductions. PARK: Nearby. TEL: 01666 505281; fax - 01666 505661. SER: Export. VAT: Stan/Spec.

Artique
Talboys House, Church St. GL8 8JG. (George Bristow). TADA. Open 10-6, Sun. 12-4. *STOCK: Interiors, textiles, carpets and kelims and objets*

d'art from the Orient. TEL: 01666 503597; fax - same; e-mail - george@artique.demon.co.uk.

Ball and Claw Antiques
45 Long St. GL8 8AA. (Chris Kirkland). TADA. Est. 1994. Open 10-5 and most Sundays 2-5. SIZE: Medium. *STOCK: 17th-19th C furniture, engravings, pictures, ceramics and general antiques.* PARK: Easy. TEL: 01666 502440; mobile - 07957 870423; e-mail - chris@balland claw.co.uk; website - www.ballandclaw.co.uk. SER: Finder.

Balmuir House Antiques `LAPADA`
14 Long St. GL8 8AQ. (P. Whittam). TADA. Open 9.30-5.30. SIZE: Large. *STOCK: Furniture, paintings, mirrors, 19th C, £500-£5,000.* LOC: Town centre. PARK: Easy. TEL: 01666 503822; home - same. SER: Restorations (furniture, upholstery, paintings). VAT: Spec.

The Black Sheep
51 Long St. GL8 8AA. (Oliver McErlain). Open 10.30-5, Sat. 10-5, Sun. 1-5. SIZE: Small. *STOCK: Traditional English furniture.* PARK: Easy. TEL: 01666 505026.

Breakspeare Antiques `LAPADA`
36 and 57 Long St. GL8 8AQ. (M. and S. Breakspeare). CADA. Resident. Est. 1962. Open 10-5 or by appointment. CL: Thurs. SIZE: Medium. *STOCK: English period furniture - early walnut, 1690-1740, mahogany, 1750-1835.* PARK: Own. TEL: 01666 503122; fax - same. VAT: Spec.

The Chest of Drawers
24 Long St. GL8 8AQ. (A. and P. Bristow). TADA. Resident. Est. 1969. Open Tues.-Fri. 9.30-6, Mon. by appointment. SIZE: Medium. *STOCK: Late Georgian and Regency furniture; country pieces, 17th-18th C; walnut and other woods, 18th C; pictures.* LOC: On A433. PARK: Easy. TEL: 01666 502105; home - same. VAT: Spec.

Day Antiques `BADA`
5 New Church St. GL8 8DS. CADA. TADA. Est. 1975. Open 10-5. SIZE: Medium. *STOCK: Early oak furniture and related items.* PARK: Easy. TEL: 01666 502413; fax - 01666 505894; e-mail - dayantiques@lineone.net; website - www.dayantiques.com VAT: Spec.

The Decorator Source
39a Long St. GL8 8AA. (Colin Gee). TADA. Open 10-5 or by appointment. SIZE: Large. *STOCK: French provincial furniture - armoires, farm tables, buffets; decorative and interior*

design items. PARK: Easy. TEL: 01666 505358. VAT: Stan/Spec.

Anne Fowler
59 Long St. GL8 8AA. TADA. Open Tues.-Sat. 10-1 and 2-5 or by appointment. *STOCK: Decorative, mainly French antiques, painted furniture, mirrors and lighting, 18th-20th C.* TEL: 01666 505044; fax - 01666 500256; mobile - 07968 945715; e-mail - anne@annefowler. fsnet.co.uk.

Jacqueline Hall Antiques
32 Long St. GL8 8AQ. (Jacqueline Hall). TADA. Est. 1976. Open 10-5. CL: Sun. except by appointment. SIZE: Medium. *STOCK: Furniture, painted English and Continental, mirrors, £500-£4,500; decorative items and objects, 18th-19th C.* PARK: Nearby. TEL: 01666 500093/500247; mobile - 07976 204914; e-mail - j.hall.antiques @talk21.com. SER: Valuations. FAIRS: BABAADA, Bath; Decorative Antiques, Battersea. VAT: Stan/Spec.

Hampton Gallery
8 Tetbury Upton. GL8 8LP. (P. Downey). Resident. Est. 1969. Open by appointment. SIZE: Large. *STOCK: Weapons, arms and armour, 1700-1880, £100-£25,000.* LOC: Off junction 17, M4. PARK: Easy. TEL: 01666 502971. SER: Valuations; buys at auction (arms). FAIRS: All major. VAT: Spec.

Jester Antiques
10 Church St. GL8 8JG. (Lorna Coles and Peter Bairsto). TADA. Open 10-5.30, including Sun. *STOCK: Longcase and wall clocks, also oil portraits and pictures, Oriental objects, lamps, furniture, decorative items, outside statuary and architectural.* PARK: Easy. TEL: 01666 505125; e-mail - sales@jesterantiques.co.uk; website - www.jesterantiques.co.uk. SER: Shipping; delivery. VAT: Margin.

Merlin Antiques
Shops 4 & 5 Chipping Court Shopping Mall. GL8 8ES. (Miriam and Brian Smith). Est. 1990. Open 9.30-5, Sun. by appointment. SIZE: Medium. *STOCK: Furniture, Georgian to date, £50-£2,000; collectables, glass, pictures, china, jewellery - gold, silver and costume, £2-£500.* PARK: Nearby. TEL: 01666 505008. SER: Valuations; restorations.

Bobbie Middleton
58 Long St. GL8 8AQ. CADA, TADA. Open 10-1 and 2.30-5, Sun. by appointment. *STOCK: Country house furniture, mirrors and upholstered furniture, 18th-19th C.* LOC: On corner with New

Church St. TEL: 01666 502761; e-mail - bobbiemiddleton@lineone.net. VAT: Spec.

Paul Nash Antiques `LAPADA`
14A The Green. GL8 8DN. Est. 1961. Open by appointment. *STOCK: Period furniture, decorative objects and fossils.* TEL: 01666 503707; mobile - 07785 570701. VAT: Spec.

Peter Norden Antiques `LAPADA`
61 Long St. GL8 8AA. (Peter and Jenny Norden). TADA. Est. 1960. Open 10-5.30, Sun. by appointment. SIZE: Medium. *STOCK: Early oak furniture, 16th-17th C, £250-£20,000; country furniture, 17th-19th C, £75-£10,000; early carvings, metalware, pewter, pottery, treen, 14th-19th C, £10-£10,000.* PARK: Nearby. TEL: 01666 503854; fax - 01666 505595; home - 01452 770536; e-mail - peternorden-antiques@linone.net; website - www.peter-norden-antiques.co.uk. SER: Valuations. VAT: Spec.

Not Just Antiques
2 London Rd. GL8 8JN. (Patrick and Maggie Beetholme-Smith). Resident. Est. 1960. Open 10.30-6. SIZE: Small. *STOCK: 18th-19th C Georgian furniture, mahogany, rosewood and walnut and accessories; boxes, paintings.* LOC: From Market Place, take Long St. to crossroads, premises on right-hand corner. PARK: Hampton St. TEL: 01666 500009; fax - same; mobile - 07802 895260; e-mail - notjustantiques@btopenworld.com.

Panache
32 Long St. GL8 8AQ. (Linda Biggs). TADA. Open 10-5 or by appointment. SIZE: Medium. *STOCK: French provincial and painted furniture, mirrors, chandeliers, garden and decorative accessories.* PARK: Easy. TEL: 01666 502423.

Porch House Antiques
40/42 Long St. GL8 8AQ. (Anne and Mervyn Woodburn). TADA. Est. 1977. Open 10-5. SIZE: Large. *STOCK: 17th-20th C furniture and decorative items.* LOC: Town centre. TEL: 01666 502687. VAT: Spec.

Sharland & Lewis
52 Long St. GL8 8AQ. (Ali Sharland). TADA. Open 10.30-5, Sat 10-5 or by appointment. SIZE: Medium. *STOCK: Painted furniture, textiles and decorative objects.* PARK: Easy. TEL: 01666 500354; website - www.sharland&lewis.com.

Sieff
49 Long St. GL8 8AA. TADA. Est. 1994. Open 10-5.30, Sun. by appointment. SIZE: Large. *STOCK: English and French 18th-20th C furniture and objets, £100-£10,000.* PARK: Easy. TEL: 01666 504477; fax - 01666 504478; e-mail - sieff@sieff.co.uk; website - www.sieff.co.uk. SER: Valuations; buys at auction. FAIRS: Harvey Decorative Antiques & Textile. VAT: Stan/Spec.

The Sporting Gallery
12 Church St. (B. Hulftegger). TADA. Open 10-5. SIZE: Medium. *STOCK: Period and contemporary sporting pictures, engravings, watercolours, oils and associated sporting items.* PARK: Easy. TEL: 01666 504605; e-mail - info@sporting-gallery.com.

Tetbury Gallery
18 Market Place. GL8 8DD. (Jane Maile). FATG. TADA. Open every day. *STOCK: Original and limited edition prints, from Victorian watercolours and oils to contemporary artists including Russell Flint, David Shepherd and Ben Maile.* TEL: 01666 503412.

Tetbury Old Books
4 The Chipping. GL8 8ET. TADA. Open 10-6, Sun. 11-5. *STOCK: Antiquarian and secondhand books and prints.* TEL: 01666 504330; fax - 01666 504458; e-mail - oldbooks@tetbury.co.uk.

Top Banana Antiques Mall
1 New Church St. GL8 8DS. TADA. Open 10-5.30, Sun. 2-5. SIZE: Large - 20 dealers. *STOCK: General antiques and decorative arts, £2-£15,000.* LOC: Beginning of Long St. PARK: Easy. TEL: 0871 2881102; fax - 0871 2881103; e-mail - info@topbananaantiques.com; website - www.topbananaantiques.com. SER: Packing and shipping. VAT: Stan/Spec.

Townsend Bateson
51A Long St. GL8 8AA. TADA. Est. 1995. Open 10-5. SIZE: Medium. *STOCK: Mainly French provincial and painted furniture, ceramics and interior design items.* TEL: 01666 505083. SER: Shipping. VAT: Global.

Westwood House Antiques and Beehive Antiques
29 Long St. GL8 8AA. (Richard Griffiths and Lynne Petersen). TADA. Resident. Est. 1993. Open 10-5.30 or by appointment. SIZE: Large. *STOCK: Oak, elm and ash country furniture especially dressers, dresser bases and tables, 17th-19th C; occasional French pieces; decorative country pottery.* TEL: 01666 502328; fax - same; mobile - 07774 952909; e-mail - westwoodhouseantiques@tinyworld.co.uk. VAT: Spec.

TEWKESBURY

Berkeley Antiques
132 High St. GL20 5JR. (P.S. Dennis). Open 10-5.30. CL: Thurs. pm. SIZE: Large. STOCK: *Mahogany, oak, walnut, 17th-19th C, £50-£2,000; brass, copper, silver, china and glass.* TEL: 01684 292034; fax - 01684 274264. SER: Restorations. VAT: Stan/Spec.

Gainsborough House Antiques
81 Church St. GL20 5RX. (A. and B. Hilson). Open 9.30-5. STOCK: *Furniture, 18th to early 19th C; glass, porcelain.* TEL: 01684 293072. SER: Restorations; conservation.

Tewkesbury Antiques & Collectables Centre
Tolsey Lane (by The Cross). GL20 5AE. Open 9.30-5.30, Sun. 10.30-5.30. SIZE: 10+ units. STOCK: *Furniture, rugs, porcelain, glass, textiles, pictures, kitchenalia.* LOC: Town centre. TEL: 01684 294091.

THORNBURY, Nr. Bristol

Thornbury Antiques
3A High St. BS35 2AE. (H. Hill). Est. 1993. Open 10-4.30. SIZE: Small. STOCK: *Victorian and Edwardian furniture, china and linen.* PARK: Opposite. TEL: 01454 413722. SER: Upholstery; restorations. VAT: Spec.

TODENHAM, Nr. Moreton-in-Marsh

Geoffrey Stead `BADA`
Wyatts Farm. GL56 9NY. Est. 1963. Open by appointment. STOCK: English and Continental furniture, decorative works of art and sculpture. LOC: 3 miles from Moreton-in-Marsh. PARK: Easy. TEL: 01608 650997; fax - 01608 650597; mobile - 07768 460450; e-mail - geoffreystead@geoffreystead.com. SER: Valuations. FAIRS: Olympia. VAT: Spec.

WHITTINGTON, Nr. Cheltenham

Whittington Barn Antiques
(Miss Marie Pinchin and Andrew Rogers). Resident. Est. 1982. Open by appointment only. SIZE: Medium. STOCK: *18th-19th C English and French furniture and mirrors, £100-£2,000; 20th C lighting, £100-£1,000.* LOC: A40 Cheltenham to Oxford road. PARK: Easy. TEL: 01242 820164; mobile - 07710 411501. FAIRS: Newark. VAT: Stan/Spec.

WICKWAR

Bell Passage Antiques `LAPADA`
38 High St. GL12 8NP. (Mrs D.V. Brand). Est. 1966. Open 9-5. CL: Thurs. except by appointment. STOCK: *Furniture, glass, porcelain, some pictures.* LOC: On B4060. PARK: Easy. TEL: 01454 294251; fax - same. SER: Restorations; upholstery; caning.

WINCHCOMBE

Campden Country Pine Antiques
Didbrook Fields Farm, Toddington. GL54 5PE. (Jane Kennedy). Est. 1988. Open 7 days by appointment. SIZE: Medium. STOCK: *Antique pine.* PARK: Easy. TEL: 01242 620950; e-mail - thekettle@aol.com. *Trade Only.*

The Clock Shop
11 North St. GL54 5LH. (M. Lovatt). Est. 1994. Open 10-1 and 2-4.30. CL: Mon. SIZE: Small. STOCK: *Antique and period clocks, barometers and gramophones, £100-£3,000.* TEL: 01242 604780; fax - same; website - www.clock-shop-winchcombe.co.uk SER: Valuations; restorations (clocks). VAT: Spec.

Cotswold Antiques. com
Didbrook Fields, Toddington. GL54 5PE. (Frank Kennedy). Est. 1988. Open 7 days mainly by appointment. SIZE: Small. STOCK: *English and Continental furniture, 17th-19th C.* PARK: Own. TEL: 01242 620950; e-mail - thekettle@aol.com.

Government House
St Georges House, High St. GL54 5LJ. Est. 1979. Open by appointment. STOCK: *Antique and pre-war lighting and accessories.* LOC: Village centre. PARK: Own. TEL: 01242 604562; mobile - 07970 430684. SER: Spare parts stocked; restorations (period lighting). FAIRS: Newark, Ardingly, Swinderby. VAT: Spec/Global.

In Period Antiques
Queen Anne House, High St. GL54 5LJ. (John Edgeler). Resident. Est. 1999. Open Thurs.- Sat. 9.30-5, other times by appointment. SIZE: Medium. STOCK: *Furniture, oak, mahogany and walnut, 17th -19th C; metalware, glass, ceramics and decorative items.* PARK: Easy. TEL: 01242 602319.

Prichard Antiques
16 High St. GL54 5LJ. (K.H. and D.Y. Prichard). CADA. Est. 1979. Open 9-5.30, Sun. by appointment. SIZE: Large. STOCK: *Period and decorative furniture, £10-£20,000; treen and metalwork, £5-£5,000; interesting and decorative accessories.* LOC: On B4632 Broadway to Cheltenham road. PARK: Easy. TEL: 01242 603566. VAT: Spec.

HAMPSHIRE

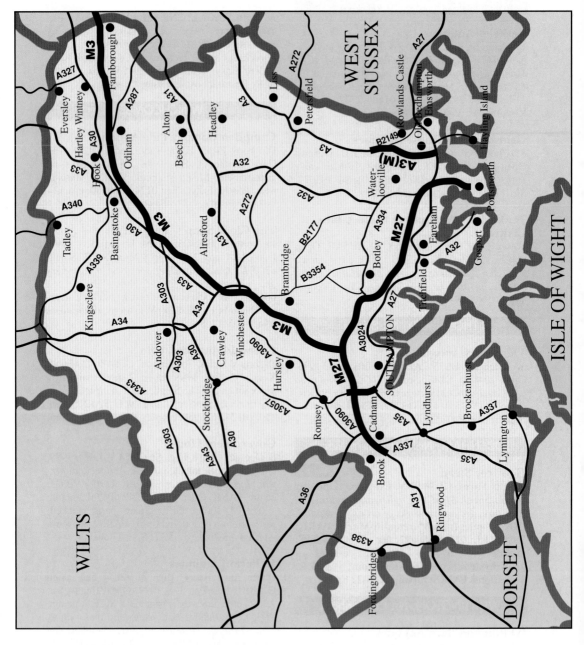

Dealers and Shops in Hampshire

Alresford	5	Crawley	1	Hook	1	Ringwood	3
Alton	1	Emsworth	5	Hursley	1	Romsey	2
Andover	1	Eversley	2	Kingsclere	1	Rowlands Castle	1
Basingstoke	1	Fareham	1	Liss	1	Southampton	5
Beech	1	Farnborough	1	Lymington	5	Stockbridge	6
Botley	1	Fordingbridge	2	Lyndhurst	2	Tadley	1
Brambridge	1	Gosport	3	Odiham	1	Titchfield	2
Brockenhurst	2	Hartley Wintney	8	Old Bedhampton	1	Waterlooville	1
Brook	1	Hayling Island	1	Petersfield	4	Winchester	13
Cadnam	1	Headley	1	Portsmouth	4		

ALRESFORD, Nr. Winchester

Artemesia
16 West St. SO24 9AT. (D.T.L. Wright). Est. 1972. Open 9.30-5. SIZE: Medium. *STOCK: English and Continental furniture, English, Continental and Oriental porcelain and works of art, £20-£6,000.* LOC: A31. PARK: Nearby. TEL: 01962 732277. SER: Valuations.

Evans and Evans   LAPADA
40 West St. SO24 9AU. (D. and N. Evans). Est. 1953. Open Fri. and Sat. or by appointment. SIZE: Medium. *STOCK: Clocks, watches, 1680-1900, £250-£50,000; musical boxes, 19th C, £500-£12,000; Regency and Victorian barometers, £200-£2,000. Stock only as listed.* LOC: A31. Shop on left going east. PARK: Easy. TEL: 01962 732170. SER: Valuations; buys at auction. VAT: Stan/Spec.

Laurence Oxley
Studio Bookshop and Gallery, 17 Broad St. SO24 9AW. (Laurence and Anthony Oxley). ABA. FATG. Est. 1951. Open 9-5. SIZE: Large. *STOCK: Antiquarian books, £5-£2,500; topographical prints, £2-£250; maps, £5-£800; watercolours, (specialising in M.Birket Foster, RWS 1825-1899), £100-£30,000.* LOC: B3046. PARK: Easy. TEL: 01962 732188 (books), 01962 732998 (pictures). SER: Valuations; restorations (oil paintings, watercolours, prints and books); framing; book-binding. FAIRS: London ABA (Chelsea). VAT: Stan.

Pineapple House Antiques
49 Broad St. SO24. (Peter Radford). Est. 1979. Open Thurs. and Fri. 11-4, Sat. 10.30-6, Sun. 11-6, other times by appointment. SIZE: Small. *STOCK: Furniture, especially dining tables, chairs, sideboards and smaller items, 18th-20th C.* PARK: Easy. TEL: 01962 736575; fax - same; mobile - 07973 254749. SER: Valuations; restorations; repairs; cabinet making.

Tudor Antiques & Fine Art Ltd
The Old Exchange, Station Rd. SO24 9JG. Est. 1985. Open 10-4, Sun. by appointment. CL: Wed. SIZE: Medium. *STOCK: 17th-19th C English, Continental and Oriental furniture and works of art; large display of authenticated Chinese furniture; dining tables, £2,000-£25,000; sets of dining chairs, £1,500-£10,000; dining room furniture, £1,000-£20,000.* LOC: Town centre. PARK: Easy and station. TEL: 01962 735345; fax - 01962 736345; mobile - 07774 908888; e-mail - e&ptudor@tudor-antiques.co.uk; website - www.tudor-antiques.co.uk. SER: Valuations;

restorations (furniture - structural, veneer and polishing).

ALTON

Appleton Eves Ltd
30 Normandy St. GU34 1BX. (Richard Eves and Errin Bale). Est. 2000. Open 10-5. SIZE: Small - 9 dealers. *STOCK: 19th-20th C silver, jewellery, pictures, china, glass and metalwork, £5-£500.* PARK: Nearby. TEL: 01420 84422; fax - same; mobile - 07747 043655; e-mail - richard.eves@ carltonhouseantiques.co.uk; website - www. appleton-eves.co.uk.

ANDOVER

Graylings Antiques
(Nick and Gail Young). Est. 1968. Open by appointment. *STOCK: Staffordshire portrait figures and animals, 1800-1890, £50-£2,500.* PARK: Easy. TEL: 01264 710077; home - same. SER: Valuations; restorations. FAIRS: NEC; Newark; Shepton Mallet.

BASINGSTOKE

Squirrel Collectors Centre
9A New St. RG21 1DF. (A.H. Stone). Est. 1981. Open 10-5.30. SIZE: Small. *STOCK: Jewellery and silver, Victorian and Edwardian, £5-£4,500; books, postcards, watches, collectors' items, smalls, china, toys and large furniture showroom.* LOC: Near traffic lights at junction with Winchester St. PARK: Nearby. TEL: 01256 464885; e-mail - ahs@squirrelsuk.fsnet.co.uk. SER: Valuations. VAT: Stan.

BEECH, Nr. Alton

Jardinique
Old Park Farm, Kings Hill. GU34 4AW. (Edward and Sarah Neish). Resident. Est. 1994. Open 10-5. CL: Sun. and Mon. and Jan. and Feb. except by appointment. SIZE: Very large. *STOCK: Garden ornaments, urns, statuary and furniture, from 17th C, £10-£5,000.* LOC: From Alton on the A339 Basingstoke road, take first left signed Beech, after 1.5 miles premises on left opposite Alton Abbey. PARK: Easy. TEL: 01420 560055; fax - 01420 560050; e-mail - Jardinique @aol.com. SER: Valuations; buys at auction (as stock). VAT: Stan/Spec.

BOTLEY, Nr. Southampton

The Furniture Trading Co
Old Mills. S03 2GB. (L. Davies). Est. 1986. Open 9-5.30, Sun. 12-4. SIZE: Medium. *STOCK:*

Antique and reproduction furniture, including painted and distressed. LOC: Off M27, exit 7. PARK: Easy. TEL: 01489 788194; fax - 01489 797337. SER: Valuations; restorations (furniture including upholstery, caning and French polishing); furniture made to order - old and new pine and painted; interior decoration. VAT: Stan.

BRAMBRIDGE, Nr. Eastleigh

Brambridge Antiques
The Barn, Bugle Farm, Highbridge Rd. SO50 6HS. (Desmond and Ann May). Est. 1982. Open 10-5. SIZE: Medium. *STOCK: Furniture, including oak and pine, late Georgian to Edwardian.* PARK: Easy. TEL: 01962 714386; home - 02380 269205. SER: Valuations; restorations (furniture including upholstery and re-leathering).

BROCKENHURST

Antiquiteas
37 Brookley Rd. SO42 7RB. (R. Wolstenholme and S. Hamilton). Resident. Est. 1996. Open 9.30-5, Sun. 10-4. SIZE: Medium. *STOCK: Furniture including pine, £50-£350; china and glass, copper and brass, £10-£100; all 19th-20th C.* LOC: Near watersplash and village post office. PARK: Easy. TEL: 01590 622120. VAT: Stan.

Squirrels
Lyndhurst Rd. SO42 7RL. (Sue Crocket). Est. 1990. Open Wed.-Sun. 10-5, until dusk in winter. *STOCK: Furniture including stripped pine, china especially blue and white, Victoriana, Art Deco, Art Nouveau, kitchenalia and gardenalia, 19th-*

20th C, to £1,000. LOC: Opposite Rose and Crown. PARK: Easy. TEL: 01590 622433,

BROOK, Nr. Cadnam

F.E.A. Briggs Ltd
Birchenwood Farm. SO43 7JA. Est. 1968. Open by appointment. SIZE: Large warehouse. *STOCK: Antique and Victorian furniture.* LOC: M27 exit 1. PARK: Easy. TEL: 023 8081 2595; e-mail - feabriggs@aol.com. SER: Restorations; valuations. VAT: Stan/Spec.

CADNAM

Buckingham's
Twin Firs, Southampton Rd. SO40 2NQ. Resident. Est. 1978. Open 9-6 or by appointment. CL: Thurs. SIZE: Large. *STOCK: Mainly pine, some period and Victorian furniture.* PARK: Easy. TEL: 023 8081 2122. VAT: Stan/Spec.

CRAWLEY, Nr. Winchester

The Pine Barn
Folly Farm. SO21. (S. Baker). Open 9-5, including Sun. *STOCK: Pine and country furniture.* TEL: 01962 776687.

EMSWORTH

Antique Bed Company
32 North St. PO10 7DG. (Ian and Judi Trewick). Est. 1993. Open 9-5.30, Wed. 9-12.30, Sat. 9-5. SIZE: Small. *STOCK: Iron and brass, brass and wooden beds, 19th C, to £1,000.* LOC: From A259 roundabout in Emsworth, turn towards station.

A.V. Becquerel, Two Panthers, bronze, signed, 25in. long. Sold for £3,680 in May 2000.

From an article entitled "Animal Sculpture" by Paul Davidson which appeared in the July/August 2002 issue of *Antique Collecting*. For more details and to subscribe see page 21.

PARK: Nearby. TEL: 01243 376074; fax - same; home - 02392 492772. SER: Restorations (beds).

Bookends
7 High St. PO10 7AQ. (Mrs Carol Waldron). Est. 1982. Open 9.30-5, Sun. 10-3. SIZE: Medium. *STOCK: Books, some antiquarian; sheet music and scores, £2-£100.* PARK: Nearby. TEL: 01243 372154; mobile - 07796 263508; e-mail - cawaldron@tinyworld.co.uk. SER: Valuations; book search.

Clockwise
10 South St. PO10 7EH. (D. Judge). AHS. GMC. Est. 1976. Open Tues.-Sat. 10-4. SIZE: Small. *STOCK: Longcase, wall, mantel, bracket and carriage clocks, 18th-19th C, £300-£12,000.* LOC: A259 off A27, head for harbour. PARK: Easy. TEL: 01243 377558; e-mail - judge@clock-wise.fsnet.co.uk; website - www.clock-wise.co.uk. SER: Valuations; restorations.

Dolphin Quay Antique Centre
Queen St. PO10 7BU. (C. and L. Creamer). Est. 1996. Open 10-5, Sun. and Bank Holidays 10-4. SIZE: Large - 30+ dealers. *STOCK: Fine English, French and country furniture, 18th C to 1939, £50-£5,000; marine antiques; clocks - bracket, mantel, longcase, £100-£5,000; wristwatches, fobs, dress watches, vintage pens, sporting apparel, luggage, conservatory and garden antiques, decorative arts, silver, jewellery, china, paintings, watercolours, prints.* PARK: Own and in square. TEL: 01243 379994.

Tiffins Antiques
12 Queen St. PO10 7BL. (Phyl Hudson). Est. 1987. Open 9.30-5. CL: Mon. and Tues. SIZE: Small. *STOCK: General antiques, oil lamps and silver.* TEL: 01243 372497; home - same.

EVERSLEY, Nr. Wokingham

Eversley Antiques
Church Lane. RG27 0PX. (H. Craven and C. Granger). Est. 1988. Open 10-5 including Sun. SIZE: Large. *STOCK: Regency, Victorian and Edwardian furniture; glass, ceramics, pictures, mirrors, silver and collectables.* LOC: A327 1.5 miles from Blackbush airport. PARK: Easy. TEL: 0118 9328518.

Colin Harris Antiques
at Eversley Antiques Centre, Church Lane. RG27 0PX. Est. 1966. Open 10-5 including Sun. *STOCK: General antiques, furniture and decorative items.* LOC: A327 1.5 miles from Blackbush airport. PARK: Easy. TEL: Home - 0118 973 2580. VAT: Spec.

FAREHAM

Elizabethans
58 High St. PO16 7BG. (E.J. Keeble). Est. 1961. Open 10-4. CL: Wed. and Fri. *STOCK: Small general antiques including furniture.* PARK: Easy. TEL: 01329 234964 (answerphone).

FARNBOROUGH

Martin and Parke LAPADA
97 Lynchford Rd. GU14 6ET. (J. Martin). Est. 1971. Open 9-5. SIZE: Large. *STOCK: Furniture, shipping goods and books.* PARK: Easy. TEL: 01252 515311. VAT: Stan.

FORDINGBRIDGE

Mark Collier BADA
24 High St. SP6 1AX. STOCK: Period and decorative antiques. Not Stocked: Coins, medals and stamps. TEL: 01425 652555; fax - 01425 656886.

Quatrefoil
Burgate. SP6 1LX. (C.D. and Mrs I. Aston). Resident. Est. 1972. Always open. SIZE: Large. *STOCK: Early oak furniture, 16th-18th C, £50-£15,000; carvings and sculpture, 13th-17th C, £20-£20,000; antiquities and coins, £50-£10,000.* LOC: On A338, adjacent Tudor Rose Inn. PARK: Easy. TEL: 01425 653309. VAT: Stan/Spec.

GOSPORT

Former Glory
49 Whitworth Rd. PO12 3AH. (Les Brannon). Est. 1987. Open 9.30-5. SIZE: Small. *STOCK: Victorian and Edwardian furniture, £120-£400.* LOC: Near town centre. PARK: Easy. TEL: 02392 504869. SER: Valuations; restorations (furniture repairs, refinishing, repolishing, traditional upholstery)

Peter Pan's Bazaar
87 Forton Rd. PO12 4TG. (S.V. Panormo). Est. 1960. CL: Mon., Tues. and Wed. *STOCK: Vintage cameras, early photographica, images, 1850-1950, £5-£1,500.* LOC: Main road into town. PARK: Easy. TEL: 02392 524254. FAIRS: Main south of England.

Peter Pan's of Gosport
87 Forton Rd. PO12 4TG. (J. McClaren). Est. 1965. CL: Mon., Tues. and Wed. *STOCK: Jewellery, dolls, toys and miniatures.* LOC: Main road into town. PARK: Easy. TEL: 02392 524254. FAIRS: Main south of England.

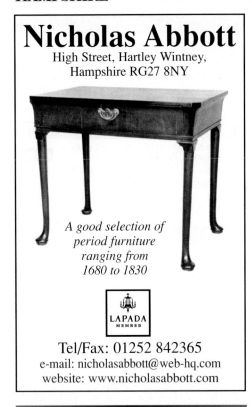

Nicholas Abbott
High Street, Hartley Wintney,
Hampshire RG27 8NY

*A good selection of
period furniture
ranging from
1680 to 1830*

LAPADA
MEMBER

Tel/Fax: 01252 842365
e-mail: nicholasabbott@web-hq.com
website: www.nicholasabbott.com

HARTLEY WINTNEY

Nicholas Abbott
LAPADA
High St. RG27 8NY. (C.N. Abbott). Est. 1962. Open 9.30-5.30 or by appointment. SIZE: Medium. *STOCK: Walnut and mahogany English furniture, 18th to early 19th C.* LOC: Village centre. PARK: Easy. TEL: 01252 842365; fax - same; e-mail - nicholasabbott@web-hq.com; website - www.nicholasabbott.com. SER: Valuations. VAT: Stan/Spec.

Anvil Antiques
The Green. RG27 8PG. (Andrew Pitter). Open 10-5. SIZE: Medium. *STOCK: General antiques.* LOC: A30. PARK: Easy. TEL: 01252 845403; mobile - 07778 934938. SER: Restorations (porcelain).

Cedar Antiques Centre Ltd
High St. RG27 8NY. (Derek and Sally Green). Est. 1998. Open 10-5.30, Sun. 11.5. SIZE: Large - 40+ dealers. *STOCK: Quality furniture, glass, porcelain and pottery, paintings, rugs, silver, collectibles from teddy bears to treen; Cornishware museum.* LOC: A30 village centre. PARK: Opposite. TEL: 01252 843222; fax - 01252 842111; e-mail - cac@cedar-antiques.com; website - www.cedar-antiques.com. SER: Restorations (furniture). VAT: Stan/Spec.

Cedar Antiques Limited
High St. RG27 8NY. (Derek and Sally Green). Est. 1964. Open 9-5.30, Sat. and Sun. 11-5. SIZE: Large. *STOCK: Fine English oak, walnut and country furniture, 17th-18th C, £50-£10,000; French provincial furniture, 1680-1780, £800-£5,000; steel and brasswork, £30-£1,000.* Not Stocked: China, glass, silver. LOC: A30. PARK: Opposite. TEL: 01252 843252; fax - 01252 842111; e-mail - ca@cedar-antiques.com; website - www.cedar-antiques.com. SER: Valuations; restorations (period furniture); interior design and furnishing. VAT: Stan/Spec.

Deva Antiques
High St. RG27 8NY. (A. Gratwick). Est. 1987. Open 9-5.30. SIZE: Large. *STOCK: 18th-19th C English mahogany and walnut furniture.* PARK: Easy. TEL: 01252 843538; 01252 842946; fax - same; e-mail - devaants@aol.com; website - www.deva-antiques.com. VAT: Stan/Spec.

David Lazarus Antiques
BADA
High St. RG27 8NS. Resident. Est. 1973. Open 9.30-5.30; some Sundays, other times by appointment. SIZE: Medium. *STOCK: 17th to early 19th C English and Continental furniture; objets d'art.* LOC: Main street. PARK: Own. TEL: 01252 842272; fax - same. VAT: Stan/Spec.

A.W. Porter and Son
High St. RG27 8NY. (M.A. and S.J. Porter). Est. 1844. Open 9.30-5, Wed. 9.30-4. *STOCK: Clocks, silver, jewellery, glass.* LOC: Opposite Lloyds Bank. TEL: 01252 842676; fax - 01252 842064; e-mail - mark@awporter.fsnet.co.uk. SER: Restorations (clocks). VAT: Stan/Spec.

Sheila Revell Antiques
at Deva, High St. RG27 8NY. Est. 1986. Open 9-5.30. *STOCK: 18th-19th C decorative objects, small furniture and collectors' items especially tea caddies and boxes.* PARK: Easy. TEL: 01252 843538.

J. MORTON LEE

FINE WATERCOLOURS

Cedar House, Bacon Lane,
Hayling Island, Hants. PO11 0DN

By appointment (023) 9246 4444
EMail: j.mortonlee@btinternet.com

A.V. Copley FIELDING p.o.w.s. 1787 - 1855
Off the Entrance to Portsmouth Harbour
Signed and dated 1834. 25.5 x 35.5 cm.

**ALSO EXHIBITING AT MAJOR
ANTIQUE FAIRS**

HAYLING ISLAND

J. Morton Lee   BADA
Cedar House, Bacon Lane. PO11 0DN.
(Commander and Mrs J. Morton Lee). Est.
1984. Open by appointment. *STOCK:
Watercolours, 18th-20th C, £50-£10,000.*
PARK: Easy. TEL: 02392 464444; mobile -
07860 810938; e-mail - j.mortonlee@
btinternet.com. SER: Valuations; buys at
auction; exhibitions in June and Dec. FAIRS:
West London (Jan); Petersfield (Feb); BADA
(March); Buxton (May); NEC (Aug);
Harrogate (Sept); Olympia (Nov). VAT:
Stan/Spec.

HEADLEY

Victorian Dreams
The Old Holme School, Village Green, Crabtree
Lane. GU35 8QH. (S. Kay). Est. 1990. Open 9-
5.30, Sun. 10-4. SIZE: Large. *STOCK: Bedsteads
including wooden, brass and iron, brass, caned
and upholstered.* PARK: Easy. TEL: 01428
717000; fax - 01428 717111; e-mail -
sales@victorian-dreams.co.uk; website -
www.victorian-dreams.co.ok. SER: Valuations;
restorations (metalwork and woodwork).

HOOK

Csaky's Antiques
RG27 0AT. Open by appointment. *STOCK: Early
English and Continental furniture; carvings,
works of art; modern art and sculpture,
specialising in Guy Taplin.* TEL: 01256 880111;
fax - 01256 880601; mobile - 07773 429831; e-
mail - csakyart@btinternet.com.

HURSLEY, Nr. Winchester

The Pine Emporium
The Old Bakery. SO21 2JY. (J. Greatrix). Est.
1993. Open 8.30-6, Sat. 9-5.30, Sun. 11-4. SIZE:
Large. *STOCK: Pine furniture, antique and
reclaimed, from 18th C; oak furniture, from 18th
C; contemporary furniture and accessories.*
LOC: 3 miles west of Winchester on A31 to
Romsey. PARK: Easy. TEL: 01962 775449; fax -
01962 775123; website - www.pine
emporium.com. SER: Valuations; restorations;
bespoke manufacture. VAT: Stan.

KINGSCLERE, Nr. Newbury

**Kingsclere Old Bookshop (Wyseby
House Books)**
2A George St. RG20 5NQ. (Dr. Tim and Mrs
Anne Oldham). PBFA. Est. 1978. Open 9-5.
SIZE: Medium. *STOCK: Old, unusual and out-
of-print books on fine art, art history,
architecture, decorative arts, design,
photography, biology, natural history, science,
horticulture and gardening; prints: all 19th-20th
C, £5-£500.* PARK: Nearby. TEL: 01635 297995;
fax - 01635 297677; e-mail - info@wyseby.co.uk;
website - www.wyseby.co.uk. SER: Valuations.
FAIRS: PBFA London. VAT: Stan.

LISS

Plestor Barn Antiques
Farnham Rd. GU33 6JQ. (T.P. and C.A.
McCarthy). Est. 1982. Open 10-5, Sat. 10-2.
SIZE: Large. *STOCK: Furniture including
upholstered, Victorian and Edwardian, shipping
goods, pine; china and glass, copper and brass.*
LOC: A325, 2 mins from A3 roundabout, near
Spread Eagle public house. TEL: 01730 893922;
mobile - 07850 539998.

LYMINGTON

Century Fine Arts
120 High St. SO41 9AQ. (S.A. and V. Roberts).
Open 9.15-5.30. SIZE: Large. *STOCK: English
furniture, English School watercolours and oil*

paintings. TEL: 01590 673532; fax - 01590 678855; website - www.centuryfinearts.co.uk. VAT: Stan/ Spec.

Lymington Antiques Centre
76 High St. SO41 9AL. (Lisa Reeves and Angela Simpson). Est. 1990. Open 10-5, Sat. 9-5. SIZE: 30 dealers. *STOCK: General antiques, books, clocks and watches, jewellery, glass.* PARK: Nearby. TEL: 01590 670934.

Barry Papworth
28 St. Thomas St. SO41 9NE. Est. 1960. Open 9-5. SIZE: Small. *STOCK: Diamond jewellery, £50-£10,000; silver, £25-£1,500; both 18th-19th C. Watches, 19th C, £50-£1,000.* LOC: A337 into town, bay window on left. TEL: 01590 676422. SER: Valuations (NAG registered); restorations. VAT: Stan/Spec.

Robert Perera Fine Art
19 St. Thomas St. SO41 9NB. (R.J.D. Perera). Open 10-1 and 2-5, Wed. 10-1, lunch-times and Sun. by appointment. SIZE: Small. *STOCK: British paintings, 19th-20th C, £100-£5,000; occasional ceramics and sculpture, 19th-20th C, £50-£1,500; paintings and etchings by W.L. Wyllie.* LOC: Top (west) end of main shopping

area. PARK: Easy. TEL: 01590 678230; fax - same; website - www.art-gallery.co.uk. SER: Framing. VAT: Margin.

Wick Antiques   LAPADA
Fairlea House, 110-112 Marsh Lane. SO41 8EE. (R.W. and Mrs. C. Wallrock). Est. 1985. Open 9-5, Sat. 10-1. SIZE: Medium. *STOCK: French and English furniture, 18th-19th C, £1,000-£15,000; small items, 19th to early 20th C, £100-£1,000.* LOC: Town outskirts. PARK: Own. TEL: 01590 677558; fax - same; home - 01590 672515; mobile - 07768 877069; e-mail - charles@ wickantiques.co.uk; website - www.wick antiques.co.uk. SER: Valuations; restorations; furniture polishing; repairs; upholstery; re-gilding; buys at auction. FAIRS: Olympia (June); LAPADA (Jan., April, Oct). VAT: Spec.

LYNDHURST

Lita Kaye of Lyndhurst
13 High St. SO43 7BB. (S. and S. Ferder). Est. 1947. Open 9.30-1 and 2.15-5. SIZE: Large. *STOCK: Furniture, clocks, 1690-1820; decorative porcelain, 19th C.* LOC: A35. PARK: 100yds. in High St. TEL: 023 8028 2337. VAT: Stan/Spec.

Lyndhurst Antiques Centre
19-21 High St. SO43 7BB. (Robert Sparks). Est. 1997. Open 10-5 including Sun. SIZE: Medium. *STOCK: Furniture and clocks, 18th to early 20th C, £50-£5,000; ceramics, 18th to mid 20th C, £5-£1,000; collectables, 20th C, £2-£200.* LOC: Main street by traffic lights. PARK: Free public car park nearby. TEL: 023 8028 4000.

ODIHAM

The Odiham Gallery   LAPADA
78 High St. RG25 1HJ. (I. Walker). Open 10-5, Sat. 10-1. *STOCK: Decorative and Oriental rugs and carpets.* PARK: Easy. TEL: 01256 703415.

OLD BEDHAMPTON

J F F Fire Brigade & Military Collectables
Ye Olde Coach House, Mill Lane. PO9 3JH. (Johnny Franklin). Resident. Est. 1982. Open by appointment. *STOCK: Brass firemen's helmets and fire related memorabilia; military, police and ambulance items including helmets, cap and collar badges, buttons, uniforms, caps, weapons, equipment, medals and brooches.* PARK: Easy. TEL: 02392 486485; e-mail - jffcollectables@ aol.com. SER: Valuations; buys at auction. FAIRS: 999 Memorabilia.

PETERSFIELD

The Barn
North Rd. GU31 4AH. (P. Gadsden). Est. 1956. Open 9-5. *STOCK: Victoriana, bric-a-brac; also large store of trade and shipping goods.* TEL: 01730 262958.

The Folly Antiques Centre
Folly Market, College St. GU31 4AD. (Red Goblet Ltd). Est. 1980. Open 9.30-5. SIZE: Small. *STOCK: Furniture, 19th-20th C, £20-£1,000; ceramics and silver, 18th-20th C, £5-£100; jewellery, 19th-20th C; pictures, general antiques and collectables.* LOC: Town centre. PARK: Opposite - Festival Hall, Heath Rd. TEL: 01730 266650.

The Petersfield Bookshop
16a Chapel St. GU32 3DS. (F. Westwood). ABA. Est. 1918. Open 9-5.30. SIZE: Large. *STOCK: Books, old and modern, £1-£500; maps and prints, 1600-1859, £1-£200; oils and watercolours, 19th C, £20-£1,000.* LOC: Chapel St. runs from the square to Station Rd. PARK: Opposite. TEL: 01730 263438; fax - 01730 269426; e-mail - sales@petersfieldbookshop.com; website - www. petersfieldbookshop.com. SER: Restorations and rebinding of old leather books; picture-framing and mount-cutting. FAIRS: London ABA. VAT: Stan.

Underwood Oak
(Dale and Ann Egerton). Est. 1998. Open by appointment. *STOCK: Oak furniture, 17th-19th C, £200-£10,000.* PARK: Easy. TEL: 01730 263972; fax - 01730 267797; website - www. underwoodoak.co.uk. SER: Valuations; search.

PORTSMOUTH

Academy Books
13 Marmion Rd., Southsea. PO5 2AT. (William Robinson). Open 9-12 and 1-5, Fri. 9-12 and 1-3.30, Sat. 9-5.30. SIZE: Medium. *STOCK: Antiquarian books, 17th C, £5-£500; pictures, prints and postcards, £1-£100; some china, £25-£25.* LOC: Near St. Jude's Church. PARK: Opposite. TEL: 02392 816632; fax/home - same. SER: Valuations; restorations (books).

A. Fleming (Southsea) Ltd
The Clock Tower, Castle Rd., Southsea. PO5 3DE. (A.J. and Mrs C. E. Fleming). Est. 1905. Open 9.30-5.30, Sat. 9.30-1 or by appointment. *STOCK: Furniture, silver, barometers, boxes and general antiques.* PARK: Easy. TEL: 02392 822934; fax - 02392 293501; e-mail - mail@ flemingsantiques.fsnet.co.uk; website - www. flemingsantiques.com. SER: Restorations. FAIRS: Local vetted. VAT: Stan/Spec.

Gray's Antique Centre
129-131 Havant Rd., Drayton. PO6 2AA. (Alexandra J. Gray). Est. 1968. Open 10-5, Sun. 12-4. CL: Wed. SIZE: Large - 10 dealers. *STOCK: English and French furniture, £200-£5,000; prints and paintings, china, collectables, £25-£3,000; all 18th-20th C.* PARK: Easy and side of shop. TEL: 02392 376379; mobile - 07752 781835. SER: Restorations (furniture and upholstery).

Oldfield Gallery
76 Elm Grove, Southsea. PO5 1LN. Est. 1970. Open 10-5. CL: Mon. SIZE: Large. *STOCK: Maps and engravings, 16th-19th C, £5-£1,000; decorative prints, 18th-20th C, £5-£1,000.* PARK: Nearby. TEL: 02392 838042; fax - 02392 838042; e-mail - oldfield_maps@compuserve. com; website - www.oldfield-antiquemaps.co.uk. SER: Valuations; framing. FAIRS: London Map Bonnington Hotel (monthly). VAT: Stan.

RINGWOOD

Millers of Chelsea Antiques Ltd   LAPADA
Netherbrook House, 86 Christchurch Rd. BH24 1DR. Est. 1897. Open Mon. 9.30-1.30, Tues.-Fri.

9.30-5, Sat. 10-3, other times by appointment. SIZE: Large. *STOCK: Furniture - English and Continental country, mahogany, gilt and military; decorative items, treen, majolica and faïence, 18th-19th C, £25-£5,000.* LOC: On B3347 towards Christchurch. PARK: Own. TEL: 01425 472062; fax - 01425 472727; e-mail - mail@millers-antiques.co.uk; website - www.millers-antiques.co.uk. SER: Restorations. FAIRS: Decorative Antiques; Wilton. VAT: Stan/Spec.

R. Morgan Antiques
90 Christchurch Rd. BH24 1DR. Est. 1984. Open Tues.-Sat. 10-5. SIZE: Small. *STOCK: Militaria and postcards.* LOC: Off A31 into Ringwood, straight over 1st roundabout, left at next roundabout, shop 150yds. on right. PARK: Easy and at rear. TEL: 01425 479400; fax - same. SER: Valuations; restorations. FAIRS: Yeovil; Woking Postcard. VAT: Stan/Spec.

Lorraine Tarrant Antiques
23 Market Place. BH24 1AN. Est. 1991. Open 10-5. CL: Mon. SIZE: Medium. *STOCK: Victorian furniture, to £1,000; china, glass, collectors items, £5-£100.* LOC: Opposite church. PARK: Easy. TEL: 01425 461123.

ROMSEY

Bell Antiques
8 Bell St. SO51 8GA. (M. and B.M. Gay). FGA. Est. 1979. Open 9.30-5.30. CL: Wed. (winter). SIZE: Large. *STOCK: Jewellery and silver, glass, pottery, porcelain, small furniture, prints and maps, mainly 19th-20th C.* LOC: Near market place. PARK: Town centre. TEL: 01794 514719. VAT: Global/Stan/Spec.

Rick Hubbard Art Deco
3 Tee Court, Bell St. SO51 8GY. Est. 1994. Open 10-3, Sat. 9-4, prior telephone call advisable. SIZE: Small. *STOCK: Clarice Cliff, Susie Cooper, Shelley, Myott, Carltonware.* PARK: Easy. TEL: 01794 513133; fax - same; mobile - 07767 267607; e-mail - rick@rickhubbard-artdeco.co.uk; website - www.rickhubbard-artdeco.co.uk. FAIRS: Alexandra Palace.

ROWLANDS CASTLE, Nr. Portsmouth

Good Day Antiques and Decor
22 The Green. PO9 6AB. (Gillian Day). Est. 1980. Open 11-5, Sun. 12-4.30. CL: Tues. and Wed. SIZE: Medium. *STOCK: Furniture, 1812-1940, £100-£1,000; porcelain and pottery, 1800-1950, £25-£500; jewellery and silver, 1840-1970, £25-£1,000; collectables, 19th-20th C, £5-£50.* LOC: Off junction 2, A3(M). PARK: Easy. TEL: 02392 412924; home - 02392 413221; e-mail -

gooddayantiques@aol.com. SER: Restorations (silver plating, gilding, engraving and porcelain).

SOUTHAMPTON

Mr. Alfred's "Old Curiosity Shop" and The Morris and Shirley Galleries
280 Shirley Rd., Shirley. SO15 3HL. Est. 1952. Open 9-6, including Sun. *STOCK: Furniture, 18th-20th C; paintings, porcelain, bronzes, brass, glass, books, silver, jewellery and general antiques.* LOC: On left of main Shirley road, 3/4 mile from Southampton central station. PARK: Own. TEL: 02380 774772. SER: Fine art dealer; valuations; auctions; curator; restorations; framing.

Amber Antiques
115 Portswood Rd., Portswood. SO17 2FX. (R. Boyle). Est. 1985. Open 10-5, Sat. 9-5, Sun. 11-3. SIZE: Large. *STOCK: Furniture, late Victorian to 1930's, £100-£1,500.* PARK: Easy. TEL: 02380 583645; fax - same. SER: Restorations; repairs; French polishing. VAT: Stan/Spec.

Meg Campbell
10 Church Lane, Highfield. SO17 1SZ. Est. 1967. Open by appointment. *STOCK: English, Scottish and Irish silver, collectors' pieces, Old Sheffield plate, portrait miniatures.* TEL: 02380 557636; fax - 02380 581070. SER: Mail order; catalogues available. VAT: Spec.

Cobwebs
78 Northam Rd. SO14 0PB. (P.R. and J.M. Boyd-Smith). Est. 1975. Open 10.30-4. CL: Wed. SIZE: Medium. *STOCK: Ocean liner memorabilia, china, silverplate, ephemera, paintings, furniture, ship fittings, 1840-1990, £5-£5,000.* LOC: Main road into city centre from the east. PARK: 20yds. TEL: 02380 227458; fax - same; website - www.cobwebs.uk.com. SER: Valuations. FAIRS: Beaulieu Boat & Auto; Ship Show, Westminster.

The Olympic Gallery
80 Northam Rd. SO14 0PB. (J.M. and P.R. Boyd-Smith). Est. 2002. Open 10.30-4. CL: Wed. SIZE: Medium. *STOCK: Prints, paintings, posters, artwork from ocean liners; ships furniture and fittings.* LOC: Main road into city from the east. PARK: Outside. TEL: 02380 227458; fax - same.

STOCKBRIDGE

Antique Eyes
Brookside, High St. SO20 6EY. (Jane and Julian Benson). Est. 1987. SIZE: Medium. *STOCK: English and Continental furniture and decorative items, china and glass, 18th-19th C, £50-£3,000.* PARK: Easy. TEL: 01264 811137; fax - 01264

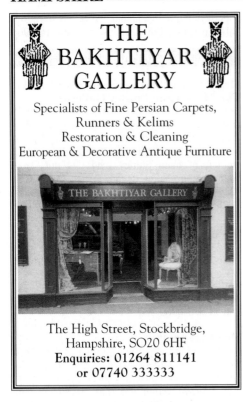

THE BAKHTIYAR GALLERY

Specialists of Fine Persian Carpets,
Runners & Kelims
Restoration & Cleaning
European & Decorative Antique Furniture

The High Street, Stockbridge,
Hampshire, SO20 6HF
**Enquiries: 01264 811141
or 07740 333333**

710447; mobile - 07747 611025; home - 01264 710389; e-mail - oldreceyes@aol.com. FAIRS: Decorative Antiques & Textile, Battersea; Little Chelsea.

T.R. Baker
at Stockbridge Antique Centre, Old London Rd. SO20 6EJ. Est. 1962. Open 10-5. CL: Wed. SIZE: Large. *STOCK: General antiques, country furniture.* LOC: On White Hart roundabout. TEL: 01264 811008; fax - same. SER: Stripping; restorations; repairs.

The Bakhtiyar Gallery
High St. SO20 6HF. (Masoud Mazaheri-Asadi). Open 10-5. SIZE: 2 floors. *STOCK: Fine English and European furniture, decorative antiques and mirrors; hand-made Persian carpets, runners, kelims, new, old and antique nomadic, village and fine city pieces.* PARK: Front of shop. TEL: 01264 811141; fax - 01264 811077; mobile - 07740 333333; e-mail - bakhtiyar@ bakhtiyar.com; website - www.bakhtiyar.com and www.thebakhtiyargallery.com. SER: Valuations; restorations (furniture and carpets). FAIRS: Annual exhibitions, Salisbury

Lane Antiques
High St. SO20 6EU. (Mrs E.K. Lane). Est. 1981.

Open 10-5. CL: Mon. SIZE: Small. *STOCK: English and Continental porcelain, 18th-20th C; silver and plate, decorative items, glass, chandeliers, lighting, small furniture, oils and watercolours; boxes, 18th-19th C.* PARK: Easy. TEL: 01264 810435; e-mail - info@laneantiques. fsnet.uk; website - www.stockbridge.org.uk.

Fizzy Warren Decorative Antiques
High St. SO20 6EY. Est. 1988. Open 10.30-5. SIZE: Medium. *STOCK: Decorative antique furniture, mirrors, chandeliers, lamps and wall lights, tapestries, small tables, chairs, china and glass, papier mache, to £2,000.* LOC: Next to Greyhound public house. PARK: Easy. TEL: 01264 811137; home - 01962 867428; mobile - 07762 201076; e-mail - brymerhouse@aol.com; website - www.stockbridge.org.uk.

The Wykeham Gallery
High St. SO20 6HE. (Mark Jerram and Gerald Dodson). Est. 1986. Open 10-5. SIZE: Medium. *STOCK: Paintings, sculpture, watercolours, 1890-1940 and contemporary, £150-£15,000.* LOC: Main street. PARK: Easy. TEL: 01264 810364; fax - 01264 810182; e-mail - enquiries@ wykehamgallery.co.uk; website - www. wykehamgallery.co.uk. SER: Valuations; restorations (paintings and works on paper); buys at auction (19th-20th C pictures). VAT: Spec.

TADLEY

Gasson Antiques and Interiors LAPADA
P O Box 7225. RG26 5IY. Open by appointment. *STOCK: Georgian, Victorian and Edwardian furniture, clocks, porcelain and decorative items.* TEL: 01189 813636; mobile - 07860 827651.

TITCHFIELD, Nr. Fareham

Alexanders
13 South St. PO14 4DL. Open Tues.-Sat. 10-5. *STOCK: General antiques including Art Nouveau and Art Deco.* PARK: Easy. TEL: 01329 315962. SER: Restorations (furniture and silver).

Gaylords
75 West St. PO14 4DG. (I. Hebbard). Est. 1970. Open 9.30-5.30. SIZE: Large. *STOCK: Furniture, from 18th C; clocks, £50-£10,000.* LOC: Off junction 9 M27. PARK: Easy. TEL: 01329 843402; home - 01329 847134. SER: Valuations. VAT: Stan/Spec.

WATERLOOVILLE

Goss and Crested China Centre and Goss Museum

62 Murray Rd. PO8 9JL. (L.J. Pine). Est. 1968. Open 9-5. SIZE: Medium. *STOCK: Goss, 1860-1930, £2-£1,000; other heraldic china, Art Deco pottery including Carlton ware, Charlotte Rhead, Chamelion, 1890-1930, £1-£1,000.* PARK: Easy. TEL: 02392 597440; fax - 02392 591975; e-mail - info@gosschinaclub.demon.co.uk; website - www.gosscrestedchina.co.uk. SER: Valuations; collections purchased; mail order catalogue; relevant books. VAT: Stan.

WINCHESTER

Bell Fine Art

67b Parchment St. SO23 8AT. (L.E. Bell). FATG. Est. 1977. Open 9.30-5.30. SIZE: Large. *STOCK: Watercolours, oils and prints, 1750-1950, £5-£10,000.* PARK: 2 spaces. TEL: 01962 860439; fax - same; home - 01962 862947; e-mail - sales@bell-fine-art.demon.co.uk. SER: Valuations; restorations (oils and watercolours); buys at auction. FAIRS: Petersfield; Surrey; Chelsea; Kensington. VAT: Spec.

Burgess Farm Antiques

39 Jewry St. SO23 8RY. (N. Spencer-Brayn). Est. 1970. Open 9-5. SIZE: Large. *STOCK: Furniture, especially pine and country, 18th-19th C, £25-£5,000; architectural items - doors, panelling, fire-places.* LOC: One way street, right turn from top of High St. or St. George, shop 100 yards on right. PARK: Easy. TEL: 01962 777546. SER: Stripping; export. VAT: Stan/Spec.

Burns and Graham

BADA

27 St. Thomas St. SO23 9HJ. (M. and G. Rollitt). Est. 1971. Open Thurs. and Fri. 9.30-5, Sat. 9.30-1 or by appointment. *STOCK: English furniture, mirrors, period decorative items, 1680-1840.* LOC: Town centre. PARK: At rear. TEL: 01962 853779; fax - same; mobile - 07771 960393. SER: Valuations. FAIRS: Olympia (Feb., June, Nov). VAT: Stan/Spec.

The Clock Workshop (Winchester)

6a Parchment St. SO23 8AT. (P. Ponsford-Jones and K.J. Hurd). BHI. AHS. Est. 1997. Open Mon.-Sat. 9-5. SIZE: Large. *STOCK: Restored longcase, wall, dial, mantel, bracket and carriage clocks, especially English, 18th-19th C, £300-£18,000; barometers, books and tools.* LOC: Central, off main pedestrian precinct, near W.H.Smiths. PARK: Easy. TEL: 01962 842331; mobiles - 07885 954302 and 07973 736155; e-mail - kjhurd@btopenworld.com; website - www.clock-work-shop.co.uk. SER: Valuations; restorations (clocks and barometers). VAT: Margin.

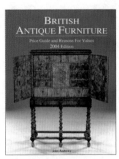
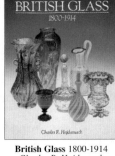
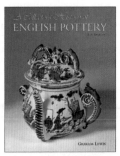
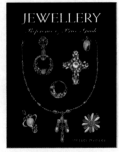
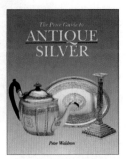

Lacewing Fine Art Gallery
28 St Thomas St. SO23 9HJ. (N. James). Open Tues.-Sat. 10-5. *STOCK: Paintings, watercolours, sculpture, Old Master drawings, 16th-20th C.* TEL: 01962 878700; fax - 01962 870583; e-mail - noeljames@lacewing.co.uk; website - www.lacewing.co.uk.

G.E. Marsh Antique Clocks Ltd **BADA**
32a The Square. SO23 9EX. BHI. AHS. Est. 1947. Open 9.30-5, Sat. 9.30-1 and 2-5. *STOCK: Clocks including longcase, bracket, Emglish, French and Continental, watches and barometers, 1680-1880.* **LOC: Near cathedral. PARK: Easy. TEL: 01962 844443; fax - same; e-mail - gem@marshclocks.co.uk; website - www.marshclocks.co.uk. SER: Valuations; restorations; commissions.**

The Pine Cellars
39 Jewry St. and 7 Upper Brook St. SO23 8RY. (N. Spencer-Brayn). Est. 1970. Open 9.30-5. SIZE: Large and warehouses. *STOCK: Pine and country furniture, 18th-19th C, £10-£5,000; painted furniture, architectural items, panelled rooms, lighting and china.* LOC: One way street, a right turn from top of High St. or St. Georges St., shop 100yds. on right. Brook St. premises - opposite Brooks Shopping Centre. PARK: Nearby. TEL: 01962 867014/777546/870102. SER: Stripping and export. VAT: Stan/Spec.

Samuels Spencers Antiques and Decorative Arts Emporium
39 Jewry St. SO23 8RY. (N.Spencer-Brayn). Open 9.30-5. SIZE: 31 dealers. *STOCK: General antiques.* LOC: One way street, right turn from top of High St. or St. George St., shop 100yds. on right. PARK: Nearby. TEL: 01962 867014/777546.

SPCK Bookshops
24 The Square. SO23 9EX. Open 9-5.30. *STOCK: Secondhand theological books.* LOC: Near cathedral. TEL: 01962 866617; fax - 01962 890312; e-mail - winchester@spck.org.uk.

Todd and Austin Antiques of Winchester
2 Andover Rd. SO23 7BS. (G. Austin). Est. 1964. Open Tues.-Fri. 9.30-5, Sat. 9.30-12.30. SIZE: Medium. *STOCK: 19th C glass, paperweights, silver, tea caddies, boxes, objets d'art and decorative items; late 18th-late 19th C pottery and porcelain, some Oriental porcelain; small furniture; hanging lamps and chandeliers.* LOC: 1 min. from Winchester Station. PARK: Easy. TEL: 01962 869824. SER: Selected range on view at Lainston House Hotel, Sparsholt, Nr Winchester; finder.

Irene S. Trudgett
3 Andover Rd. SO23 7BS. Est. 1964. Open 10-4, Thurs. and Sat. 9.30-12. SIZE: Medium. *STOCK: Cigarette cards, china including Goss, glass; pottery including Doulton, Minton, Wedgwood, Wade; militaria, silver.* LOC: Near station. PARK: Limited or nearby. TEL: 01962 854132.

Webb Fine Arts
38 Jewry St. SO23 8RY. (D.H. Webb). Est. 1955. Open 9-5, Sat. 9-1. SIZE: Large - 4 floors. *STOCK: Oil paintings and furniture.* PARK: Own. TEL: 01962 842273; website - www.webbfinearts.co.uk. SER: Valuations; restorations (oil paintings); lining and framing; buys at auction (paintings). VAT: Stan/Spec.

Winchester Furniture
20 Jewry St. SO23 8RZ. (Janice Wright). Est. 1997. Open 10-5. SIZE: Large. *STOCK: Furniture - Georgian-Edwardian, French painted and country; collectables, memorabilia, jewellery and silver, glass and ceramics.* LOC: City centre, 2 mins. from station. PARK: Adjacent. TEL: 01962 850123; fax - 01962 850345. SER: Below are some of the dealers at this centre.

David File
Clocks and furniture. TEL: Mobile - 07711 069633.

French Oak Furniture Co.
French country furniture.

The Painted Furniture Co.
French and English painted furniture. TEL: Mobile - 07977 926317.

Mark Patterson Antiques
Furniture and mirrors. TEL: 01489 878800.

Roger Thompson Antiques
Furniture and mirrors. TEL: 01962 866633.

Three Ways Pine
Old and reclaimed pine furniture. TEL: 01202 730501; fax - same; mobile - 07811 015220.

HEREFORDSHIRE

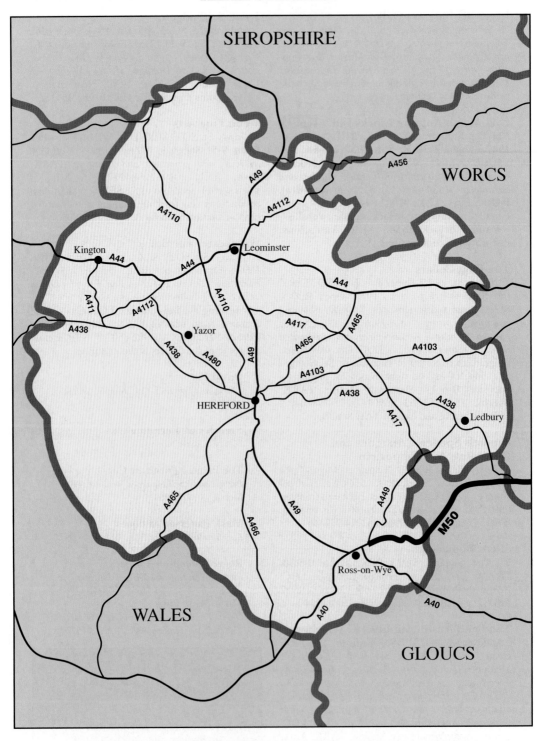

HEREFORD

I. and J.L. Brown Ltd
Whitestone Park, Whitestone. HR1 3SE. Open 9-5.30. SIZE: Large. *STOCK: Matched sets of period country chairs, English country, French provincial and reproduction furniture, decorative items.* LOC: A4103, 4 miles from Hereford towards Worcester. PARK: Easy. TEL: 01432 851991; fax - 01432 851994; e-mail - enquiries@brownantiques.com; website - www.brownantiques.com. SER: Restorations; re-rushing chairs. VAT: Stan/Spec.

Great Brampton House Antiques Ltd
LAPADA

Great Brampton House, Madley. HR2 9NA. (Lady Pidgeon). Est. 1969. Open 9-5, Sat. and Sun. by appointment. SIZE: Large. *STOCK: English and French furniture and fine art.* TEL: 01981 250244; fax - 01981 251333.

Hereford Antique Centre
128 Widemarsh St. HR4 9HN. (G.P. Smith). Est. 1991. Open 10-5, Sun. 12-5. SIZE: 30 dealers. *STOCK: General antiques and collectables.* PARK: Easy. TEL: 01432 266242. SER: Restorations; shipping.

Warings of Hereford
47 St. Owen St. HR1 2JB. Open 9-6 including Sun. *STOCK: Fine 19th C furniture, farmhouse pine; gold and silver.* TEL: 01432 276241.

KINGTON

Castle Hill Books
12 Church St. HR5 3AZ. (Peter Newman). Est. 1988. Open 10.30-1, Sat. 10.30-1 and 2-5. *STOCK: Out of print, secondhand and antiquarian books especially British topography, Herefordshire, Radnorshire, Wales, archaeology.* LOC: Off High St. PARK: Easy. TEL: 01544 231195; fax - 01544 231161; e-mail - sales@castlehillbooks.co.uk; website - www.castlehillbooks.co.uk.

LEDBURY

John Nash Antiques and Interiors
Tudor House, 17c High St. HR8 1DS. (J. Nash and L. Calleja). Est. 1972. Open 10-5.30, Sun. by appointment. SIZE: Medium. *STOCK: Mahogany, oak and walnut furniture, 18th-20th C, £300-£10,000; decorative items, fabrics and wallpapers.* TEL: 01531 635714; fax - 01531 635050; home - 01684 540432. SER: Valuations; restorations; buys at auction (furniture and silver). VAT: Stan/Spec.

Serendipity
The Tythings, Preston Court. HR8 2LL. (Mrs R. Ford). Est. 1967. Open 9-5 or by appointment. SIZE: Large. *STOCK: 17th-20th C furniture especially long dining tables, sets of chairs and four-poster beds; general antiques.* LOC: Take A449 for 3 miles from Ledbury, at roundabout turn left on B4215, premises 800yds. on left behind half-timbered house. TEL: 01531 660245/660421; e-mail - sales@serendipity-antiques.co.uk; website - www.serendipity-antiques.co.uk. SER: Restorations (furniture); buys at auction. FAIRS: Kensington; Olympia; Battersea. VAT: Stan/Spec.

Keith Smith Books
78B The Homend. HR8 1BX. PBFA. Est. 1986. Open 10-5. SIZE: Small. *STOCK: Secondhand and old books.* LOC: Main road. PARK: Easy. TEL: 01531 635336; e-mail - keith@ksbooks.demon.co.uk. SER: Valuations. FAIRS: Royal National Book, London; Churchdown Book, Gloucester.

LEOMINSTER

Barometer Shop
New St. HR6 8DP. (R. Cookson). MBHI. Est. 1965. Open 9-5, Sat. 10-4 or by appointment. *STOCK: Barometers, barographs, clocks, scientific instruments, period furniture.* LOC: Corner of A49 and Broad St. PARK: Own. TEL: 01568 613652/610200; fax - 01568 610200. SER: Valuations; restorations (workshop on the Register of the Conservation Unit of the Museums and Galleries Commission). FAIRS: County.

Chapel Walk Antique Centre
Chapel Walk, Off Burgess St. HR6 8DE. (Mark, Sarah and Lee Sidwells). Est. 1998. Open 10-5 and by appointment. SIZE: Medium. *STOCK: Furniture, 18th to early 20th C, £50-£1,500; country pine, 19th to early 20th C, £10-£1,000; cameras, 19th-20th C; Staffordshire figures, 19th C, £60-£1,000; collectables, 18th-20th C, £1-£1,000; American Indian jewellery, 20th C, £10-£800; oils and watercolours, 18th-20th C, £40-£3,000; French furniture and collectables, 18th-20th C, £50-£1,000.* LOC: Opposite main car park. PARK: Easy. TEL: 01568 613630; mobile - 07944 045467; e-mail - chapelcentre@aol.com. SER: Valuations; restorations (furniture and china). FAIRS: Peterborough Festival; Antiques in the Park; Bingley Hall.

Coltsfoot Gallery
Hatfield. HR6 0SF. (Edwin Collins). Est. 1971. SIZE: Medium. *STOCK: Sporting and wildlife*

watercolours and prints, £20-£2,000. PARK: Easy. TEL: 01568 760277. SER: Restoration and conservation of works of art on paper; mounting; framing.

Coromandel
The Pound House; Leysters. HR6 0HS. (P. Lang and B. Leigh). Resident. Open any time by appointment. *STOCK: Boxes, table cabinets and decorative items, Anglo-Indian and European Colonial, 17th-19th C, £250-£10,000.* PARK: Easy. TEL: 01568 750294; fax - 01568 750237; mobile - 07932 102756; e-mail - info@ antiqueboxes.com. SER: Restorations (ivory, tortoiseshell, horn, mother of pearl etc). VAT: Stan/Spec.

Courts Miscellany
48A Bridge St. HR6 6DZ. (George Court). Est. 1983. Open 10.30-5. *STOCK: General curios including corkscrews, social and political history, police, fire brigade and sporting items; tools, horse brasses, enamel signs - advertising, military, brewery; studio pottery and commemoratives.* TEL: 01568 612995.

Farmers Gallery
1 High St. HR6 8LZ. SIZE: 6 galleries. *STOCK: 18th-19th C furniture, paintings, prints, maps, frames, needlework, porcelain and decorative items.* LOC: Town centre. PARK: Easy. TEL: 01568 611413; fax - 01568 611141. SER: Exhibition gallery available.

Jeffery Hammond Antiques   `LAPADA`
Shaftesbury House, 38 Broad St. HR6 8BS. (J. and E. Hammond). Resident. Est. 1970. Open 9-6, Sun. by appointment. SIZE: Medium. *STOCK: Furniture and works of art, 18th to early 19th C.* LOC: Town centre. PARK: Own. TEL: 01568 614876; fax - same; mobile - 07971 289367; e-mail - enquiries@jefferyhammondantiques.co.uk; website - www.jefferyhammondantiques.co.uk. SER: Valuations; buys at auction (furniture). VAT: Stan/Spec.

Leominster Antiques Market
14 Broad St. HR6 8BS. Est. 1975. Open 10-5. SIZE: 18 units - 3 floors. *STOCK: Mahogany, oak, pine, kitchenalia, collectables, toys, glass, textiles, silver, postcards, Gaudy Welsh, fine china, pictures, jewellery, tools.* PARK: Nearby. TEL: 01568 612189.

Linden House Antiques
1 Draper's Lane. HR6 8ND. (C. Scott-Mayfield). Est. 1987. Open 10-1 and 2-5. SIZE: Large. *STOCK: Furniture, 18th C to Edwardian, £100-£10,000, pictures, 1700's to 1940's, £50-£5,000;*

silver and jewellery, porcelain and pottery, carvings, objets d'art, kitchenalia, textiles, 18th-20th C, £5-£3,000. LOC: Town centre. PARK: Easy. TEL: 01568 620350; home - 01568 612127; mobile - 07790 671722; e-mail - busca@lineone.net. SER: Valuations; restorations (re-upholstery); repairs (jewellery). FAIRS: Bingley Hall; NEC.

The Old Shoe Box
Church St. HR6. Open 10-5. *STOCK: Furniture, china, prints, watercolours and smalls.* TEL: 01568 611414. SER: Mount cutting; framing.

ROSS-ON-WYE

Baileys Home & Garden
Station Approach. HR9 7BW. (M. and S. Bailey). Est. 1978. Open 9-5. SIZE: Medium. *STOCK: Garden furniture, tools, orchard ladders, junk-style garden painted furniture, kitchenware, quilts, Welsh blankets, French and English lighting, bathrooms (including copper baths, metal washstands), fireplaces, industrial lamps, factory trolleys, machinists' stools, shoe lasts, baskets, bobbins.* LOC: Gloucester side of Ross, just off A40. PARK: Easy. TEL: 01989 563015; fax - 01989 768172; e-mail - sales@baileys-home-garden.co.uk; website - www.baileyshomeandgarden.com. VAT: Stan.

Fritz Fryer Antique Lighting
12 Brookend St. HR9 7EG. (F. Fryer and J. Graham). Est. 1981. Open 10-5.30, Sun. by appointment. SIZE: Large. *STOCK: Decorative lighting, original shades, Georgian to Art Deco.* PARK: Easy. TEL: 01989 567416; fax - 01989 566742; e-mail - ffryer@wyenet.co.uk; website - www.fritzfryer.co.uk. SER: Restorations; lighting scheme design.

W. John Griffiths Antiques
30A Brookend St. HR9 7EE. Est. 1994. Open 10-5.30. SIZE: Medium. *STOCK: Oak and mahogany town and country furniture, 17th to early 20th C, £500-£5,000; decorative objects, pictures, prints and ceramics, 18th-19th C, £20-£3,500.* PARK: Opposite. TEL: 01989 763682; mobile - 07768 606507.

Robin Lloyd Antiques
23/24 Brookend St. HR9 7EE. Est. 1970. Open 10-5. SIZE: Large - 5 showrooms. *STOCK: Country furniture, mainly long tables and early oak, longcase clocks.* LOC: 100yds. downhill from Market Hall. PARK: Nearby. TEL: 01989 562123; fax - same; website - www.robinlloyd antiques.com. SER: Export (especially to USA). VAT: Global/Spec.

Merchants House Antiques
36 High St. HR9 5HD. (N. Cockman). Est. 1969. Open 10-5. SIZE: Large. *STOCK: General antiques.* LOC: A40. TEL: 01989 563010. SER: Valuations; restorations; buys at auction. VAT: Spec.

Ross Old Book and Print Shop
51 and 52 High St. HR9 5HH. (Phil Thredder and Sarah Miller). PBFA. Est. 1984. Open Tues.-Sat. 10-5. CL: Mid-Jan. to mid-Feb. *STOCK: Antiquarian and secondhand books, prints and maps.* PARK: Behind shop. TEL: 01989 567458; fax - 01989 567861; e-mail - enquiries@ rossoldbooks.co.uk; website - www.rossold books.co.uk. SER: Worldwide postal.

Ross-on-Wye Antiques Gallery
Gloucester Rd. HR9 5BU. (Michael Aslanian). Est. 1996. Open 10.30-5, Sun. by appointment. CL: Bank Holidays. SIZE: Large. *STOCK: Wide variety of general antiques and collectables, from BC to 1950's.* LOC: Town centre. TEL: 01989 762290; fax - 01989 76229; website - www.rossantiquesgallery.com. SER: Valuations; buys at auction.

Waterfall Antiques
2 High St. HR9 5HL. (O. McCarthy). Est. 1995. Open 10-4, Wed. and Fri. 9.30-12. SIZE: Medium. *STOCK: Country pine furniture, Victorian and Edwardian; china and general antiques.* PARK: At rear. TEL: 01989 563103; mobile - 07932 105542. SER: Valuations.

YAZOR

M. and J. Russell
The Old Vicarage. HR4 7BA. Est. 1969. Usually open Fri. to Mon. and evenings, other times appointment advisable. SIZE: Medium. *STOCK: English period oak and country furniture, some garden antiques.* LOC: 7 miles west of Hereford on A480. PARK: Easy. TEL: 01981 590674. SER: Valuations. VAT: Spec. *Mainly Trade.*

HERTFORDSHIRE

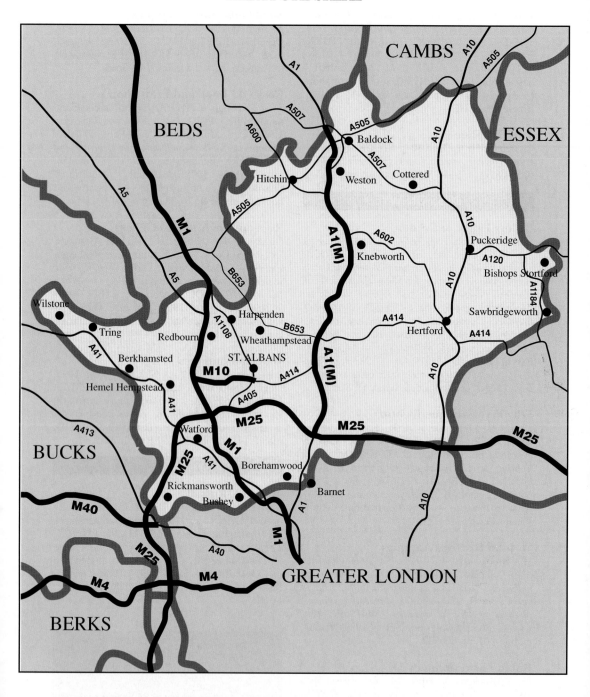

BALDOCK

The Attic
20 Whitehorse St. SG7 6QN. (P. Sheppard). Est. 1977. CL: Thurs. SIZE: Small. *STOCK: Small furniture, china, brass and copper, dolls and teddy bears, £5-£100.* LOC: 3 mins. from A1(M). PARK: Easy. TEL: 01462 893880.

Anthony Butt Antiques
7/9 Church St. SG7 5AE. Resident. Est. 1968. Open by appointment. SIZE: Small. *STOCK: English furniture, 17th-19th C, £500-£5,000; works of art and objects of interest.* Not Stocked: Bric-a-brac, shipping goods. PARK: Easy. TEL: 01462 895272. SER: Valuations. VAT: Spec.

Howards
33 Whitehorse St. SG7 6QF. (D.N. Howard). Est. 1970. Open 9.30-5.00. CL: Mon. *STOCK: Clocks, 18th-19th C, £200-£5,000.* PARK: Easy. TEL: 01462 892385. SER: Valuations; restorations; repairs. VAT: Spec.

Ralph and Bruce Moss
26 Whitehorse St. SG7 6QQ. (R.A. and B.A. Moss). Est. 1973. Open 9-6. SIZE: Large. *STOCK: Furniture, £100-£10,000; general antiques, £5-£5,000.* LOC: A505, in town centre. PARK: Own. TEL: 01462 892751. VAT: Stan/Spec.

BARNET

C. Bellinger Antiques
91 Wood St. EN5 4BX. Est. 1974. Open Thurs., Fri. and Sat. 10-4 or by appointment. SIZE: Medium. *STOCK: Furniture, silver and plate, smalls.* LOC: Opposite Ravenscroft Park. PARK: Within 100yds. TEL: 020 8449 3467. VAT: Spec.

Michael Lipitch Ltd   BADA
P O Box 3146. EN4 0BP. Est. 1959. Open by appointment. *STOCK: 18th to early 19th C English furniture, decoration and works of art.* TEL: 020 8441 4340; mobile - 07730 954347; e-mail - michaellipitch@hotmail.com. SER: Specialist advice. FAIRS: Grosvenor House. VAT: Spec.

BERKHAMSTED

Home and Colonial
134 High St. HP4 3AT. (Alison and Graeme Reid-Davies, Liz and Tony Stanton-Kipping). Est. 1997. Open 10-5.30, Sun. 11-5. CL: Wed. SIZE: Large. *STOCK: Period and country furniture, Arts and Crafts, Art Deco, decorative antiques, clocks and barometers, metalware, pictures,* *porcelain, silver, glass, jewellery, textiles and costume, antiquarian books, radios, gramophones and telephones, toys and teddy bears, fireplaces, garden antiques and lighting, £10-£10,000.* LOC: M25 junction 20; M1 junction 8. PARK: Easy. TEL: 01442 877007; e-mail - homeandcolonial@btinternet.com; website - www.homeandcolonial.co.uk. SER: Design; prop hire; antiques sourcing.

BISHOP'S STORTFORD

David Penney
Grooms Cottage, Elsenham Hall, Elsenham. CM22 6DP. BHI. Est. 1973. Strictly no visitors, no stock held on premises. *STOCK: Watches, 18th-19th C, £500-£50,000; watch movements, 18th-19th C, £50-£5,000; horological books and ephemera, 18th-20th C, £5-£15,000.* TEL: 01279 814946; fax - 01279 814962; e-mail - info@davidpenney.co.uk. SER: Valuations; restorations; specialist research; postal auction catalogue; buys at auction (watches, clocks and all technical horology). VAT: Stan/Spec. *Mail Order Only.*

The Windhill Antiquary
4 High St. CM23 2LT. (G.R. Crozier). Est. 1951. Open 10-1 and 2-4 appointment advisable. CL: Wed. pm. SIZE: Medium. *STOCK: English furniture, 18th C; carved and gilded wall mirrors, 17th-19th C.* LOC: Next to George Hotel. PARK: Up hill - first right. TEL: 01279 651587; home - 01920 821316.

BOREHAMWOOD

Barnet-Cattanach   BADA
The Old Marble Works, 18 Glenhaven Ave. WD6 1BB. Est. 1977. Open by appointment. SIZE: Small. *STOCK: 18th to early 19th C furniture and accessories.* PARK: Easy. TEL: 020 7727 0460/020 8207 6792; fax - 020 8381 5889. FAIRS: Olympia.

BUSHEY, Nr. Watford

Bushey Antiques Centre
39 High St. WD23 1BD. (Graham Lindsay). Est. 1983. Open 9.30-5.00, Sun. 10-4.00. SIZE: 14 dealers. *STOCK: Furniture, 18th-20th C; smalls, collectables, clocks, crystal and coloured glass, jewellery, lighting and pictures.* LOC: Between Stanmore, Harrow and Watford. PARK: At rear. TEL: 020 8950 5040; home - same. SER: Valuations; restorations (woodwork and furniture); framing. VAT: Spec.

Country Life Interiors
33a High St. WD3 1BD. (Peter Myers). Est.

1981. Open 10-6. SIZE: Large. *STOCK: Victorian and Edwardian, European and Scandinavian original pine, French country oak; kitchenalia, watercolours, china and Art Deco.* PARK: Easy. TEL: 020 8950 8575; fax - 020 8950 6982; e-mail - sales@countrylifeinteriors. com; website - www.countrylifeinteriors.com. VAT: Stan.

COTTERED

Wareside Antiques
SG9 9PT. (David Broxup). Est. 1983. Open by appointment. *STOCK: Victorian dining room furniture, especially extending dining tables; sets of 6, 8 and 10 Victorian dining chairs, chiffoniers, buffets etc.* TEL: 01763 281234.

HARPENDEN

Meg Andrews
Est. 1982. Open by appointment. *STOCK: Worldwide collectable, hangable and wearable antique costume and textiles including Chinese embroideries and woven fabrics, robes, shoes, hats, large hangings, Morris and Arts and Crafts embroideries and woven cloths, Paisley shawls, samplers, silkwork pictures; European costumes and textiles.* TEL: 01582 460107; home - same; fax - 01582 461112; e-mail - meg.andrews@ clara.co.uk; website - www.meg-andrews.com. SER: Valuations; advice. FAIRS: Manchester Textile Society; (March); Hammersmith Town Hall Costume and Textile. VAT: Spec.

HEMEL HEMPSTEAD

Abbey Antiques - Fine Jewellery & Silver
97 High St., Old Town. HP1 3AH. (L., E., S. and C. Eames). Est. 1962. Open 9.30-5.30. SIZE: Medium. *STOCK: Silver, plate, jewellery, £5-£5,000.* LOC: M1, junction 8, M25, junction 20, bypass main shopping centre to Old Town. PARK: Easy. TEL: 01442 264667; e-mail - simoneames@abbey.uk.com. SER: Valuations; jewellery design and repair. VAT: Stan/Global.

Cherry Antiques
101 High St. HP1 3AH. (A. and R.S. Cullen). Open 9.30-4.30. CL: Wed. pm. SIZE: Medium. *STOCK: Victorian, Edwardian and some period furniture, pine, general antiques, collectors' and decorative items, bric-a-brac, needlework tools, dolls, linens, some silver, plate, jewellery, glass, pottery, porcelain, brass, copper, some shipping items.* PARK: Easy. TEL: 01442 264358. VAT: Stan/Spec.

Off the Wall
52 High St., Old Town. HP1 3AF. (Michelle Smith). Est. 2001. Open 10-5.30, Sun. 11-4. SIZE: Small. *STOCK: Antiques and collectables, from 1830; some furniture including pine dressers and tables.* LOC: Near St. Mary's Church. PARK: Nearby. TEL: 01442 218300.

The Pine Emporium
Hilliers Garden Centre, Leighton Buzzard Rd., Piccotts End. (J. Greatrix). Open 9-5.30, Sun. 11-4. *STOCK: Pine furniture, antique and reclaimed, from 18th C; oak, from 18th C.* TEL: 01442 244644. SER: Restorations; bespoke manufacture.

HERTFORD

Beckwith and Son
St. Nicholas Hall, St. Andrew St. SG14 1HZ. (G.C. M.Gray). Est. 1904. Open 9-1 and 2-5.30. SIZE: Large. *STOCK: General antiques, furniture, silver, pottery, porcelain, prints, weapons, clocks, watches, glass.* LOC: A414/B158. PARK: Adjacent. TEL: 01992 582079; e-mail - sales@beckwithandson antiques.co.uk; website - www.beckwith andsonantiques.co.uk. SER: Valuations; restorations (fine porcelain, furniture, upholstery, silver and clocks). VAT: Spec.

Gillmark Gallery
25 Parliament Sq. SG14 1EX. (Mark Pretlove and Gill Woodhouse). Est. 1997. CL: Mon. and Thurs. pm. SIZE: Medium. *STOCK: Maps and prints, 16th-20th C, £10-£5000; secondhand books, 18th-20th C, £1-£5,000.* LOC: 15 yards from roundabout at junction of A414 and B158. PARK: Nearby. TEL: 01992 534444; fax - 01992 554734; e-mail - gillmark@btinternet.com; website - www.gillmark.com. SER: Framing, conservation, restorations, map and print colouring. VAT: Stan.

Hertford Antiques
51 St Andrew St. SG14 1HZ. (S.D. Garratt and R.F. Norris and A.G. Vingoe). Est. 1994. Open 10-5.30, Sun.11-4.30. SIZE: Large - 50+ dealers. *STOCK: Furniture, jewellery, porcelain, silver, glass, books, £5-£4,000.* LOC: Next to St Andrew's Church. PARK: Easy. TEL: 01992 504504; fax - 01992 589776; e-mail - simon@hertfordantiques.fsnet.co.uk; website - www.hertfordantiques.co.uk.

Robert Horton Antiques
13 Castle St. SG14 1ER. BWCMG. Est. 1972. Open 9-5. *STOCK: Clocks, barometers, furniture.* TEL: 01992 587546; fax - same. SER: Restorations and repairs (clock movements, cases and dials). VAT: Stan/Spec.

Tapestry Antiques
27 St. Andrew St. SG14 1HZ. (D.W. and P. Stokes). Est. 1973. Open 10-1 and 2-5, Sat. 10-5.30, Sun. by appointment. CL: Thurs. SIZE: Medium. *STOCK: Furniture, 18th-19th C, £100-£1,000; porcelain, 19th to early 20th C, £25-£500; brass and copper, 18th-19th C, £50-£300.* LOC: Near rail station. PARK: Easy and behind premises. TEL: 01992 587438. SER: Valuations.

HITCHIN

Michael Gander
10-11 Bridge St. SG5 2DE. Est. 1973. Open Mon. 3-6, Wed., Thurs. and Sat. 9-6 or by appointment. *STOCK: Period furniture, metalware, ceramics, glass, pictures.* TEL: 01462 432678; mobile - 07885 728976.

Eric T. Moore
24 Bridge St. SG5 2DF. Open 9.30-5, Sat. 9.30-5.30. SIZE: Large. *STOCK: Secondhand and antiquarian books, maps and prints.* LOC: Bottom of Tilehouse St. TEL: 01462 450497; e-mail - booksales@erictmoore.co.uk; website - www.erictmoore.co.uk. SER: Book binding and search.

**Phillips of Hitchin (Antiques) Ltd BADA
The Manor House. SG5 1JW. (J. and B. Phillips). Est. 1884. Open 9-5.30, Sat. by appointment. SIZE: Small. *STOCK: Mahogany furniture, 18th to early 19th C, £500-£20,000; reference books.* LOC: In Bancroft, main street of Hitchin. PARK: Easy. TEL: 01462 432067; fax - 01462 441368. VAT: Spec.**

Tom Salusbury Antiques
7 Nutleigh Grove. SG5 2NH. Est. 1963. Open by appointment. SIZE: Small. *STOCK: Furniture, to 1910, £100-£3,000.* LOC: 3 miles from A1, junction 8. PARK: Easy. TEL: 01462 454274; fax - same; 01462 441520. SER: Valuations; restorations (especially upholstery). VAT: Stan/Spec.

KNEBWORTH

Hamilton Billiards & Games Co.
Park Lane. SG3 6PJ. (H. Hamilton). Est. 1980. Open 9-5, weekends and evenings by appointment. SIZE: Large. *STOCK: Victorian and Edwardian billiard tables, £3,000-£18,000; 19th C convertible billiard/dining tables and accessories, £30-£5,000; indoor and outdoor games.* LOC: Near rail station. PARK: Easy. TEL: 01438 811995. SER: Valuations; restorations (billiard tables and furniture); buys at auction (as stock). VAT: Stan.

PUCKERIDGE

St. Ouen Antiques
Vintage Corner, Old Cambridge Rd. SG11 1SA. (J., J. and S.T. Blake and Mrs P.B. Francis). Est. 1918. Open 10.30-5. SIZE: Large. *STOCK: English and Continental furniture, decorative items, silver, porcelain, pottery, glass, clocks, barometers, paintings.* TEL: 01920 821336. SER: Valuations; restorations.

REDBOURN

Antique Print Shop
86 High St. AL3 7BD. (David Tilleke). AIA (Scot). Est. 1982. Open 9-4. SIZE: Small. *STOCK: Prints, all categories, 1650-1930.* PARK: Easy. TEL: 01582 794488; mobile - 07801 682268; home - 01442 397094; e-mail - antiqueprintshop@btinternet.com; website - www.antiqueprintshop.co.uk. SER: Valuations.

Bushwood Antiques `LAPADA`
Stags End Equestrian Centre, Gaddesden Lane. HP2 6HN. (Anthony Bush). CINOA. Est. 1967. Open 8.30-4, Sat. 10-4. SIZE: Large. *STOCK: 18th-19th C furniture, accessories and objects of art.* LOC: Telephone for directions. PARK: Easy. TEL: 01582 794700; fax - 01582 792299; e-mail - antiques@bushwood.co.uk; website - www. bushwood.co.uk.

J.N. Antiques
86 High St. AL3 7BD. (M. and J. Brunning). Est. 1975. Open 9-6. SIZE: Medium. *STOCK: Furniture, 18th-20th C, £5-£3,000; brass and copper, porcelain, 19th C, £5-£100; pictures, 19th-20th C.* LOC: Close to junction 8, M1. PARK: 50 yds. TEL: 01582 793603; e-mail - jnantiques@btopenworld.com. SER: Valuations. VAT: Spec.

Tim Wharton Antiques LAPADA
24 High St. AL3 7LL. Est. 1970. Open 10-5.30, Sat. 10-4. CL: Mon. and usually Thurs. *STOCK: Oak and country furniture, 17th-19th C; some mahogany, 18th to early 19th C; copper, brass, ironware and general small antiques.* LOC: On left entering village from St. Albans on A5183. PARK: Easy. TEL: 01582 794371; mobile - 07850 622880; e-mail - tim@timwharton antiques.co.uk; website - www.timwharton antiques.co.uk. VAT: Stan/Spec.

RICKMANSWORTH

Clive A. Burden Ltd
Elmcote House, The Green, Croxley Green. WD3 3HN. (Philip D. Burden). ABA. IMCOS. Est.

1966. Open by appointment. SIZE: Medium. *STOCK: Maps, 1500-1860, £5-£1,500; natural history, botanical and Vanity Fair prints, 1720-1870, £1-£1,000; antiquarian books, pre-1870, £10-£5,000.* TEL: 01923 778097/772387; fax - 01923 896520. SER: Valuations; buys at auction (as stock). VAT: Stan.

ROYSTON

Philip Dawes Antiques
37-39 Kneesworth St. SG8 5AB. Est. 1997. Open 9.30-5. SIZE: Medium. *STOCK: Oak, mahogany and pine, 18th to early 20th C, £100-£2,000; garden furniture and ornaments, £50-£500; decorative items, 19th-20th C, £25-£100.* PARK: Easy. TEL: 01763 243039. SER: Valuations; restorations (furniture including caning and upholstery); framing; buys at auction. VAT: Stan.

SAWBRIDGEWORTH

Charnwood Antiques and Arcane Antiques Centre
Unit E2 Ground Floor, The Maltings, Station Rd. CM21 9JX. (Nigel Hoy and Nicola Smith). EADA. GMC. Open 10-5, Sat. and Sun. 11-5. CL: Mon. SIZE: Large. *STOCK: Furniture, 18th C to Edwardian, £500-£8,000; European and Oriental porcelain, glass, silver and jewellery, longcase clocks, 19th C oils and watercolours.* LOC: From Harlow on A1184, turn right at first mini roundabout into Station Rd., over river bridge, first right into maltings. Shop 100 yards on left. PARK: Easy. TEL: 01279 600562; mobile -07957 551899. SER: Restorations (furniture including structural and veneer, French polishing, traditional upholstery, desk re-leathering, brass ware supplied and fitted).

The Herts and Essex Antiques Centre
The Maltings, Station Rd. CM21 9JX. Est. 1982. Open 10-5, Sat. and Sun. 10.30-5.30. SIZE: Large - over 100 dealers. *STOCK: General antiques and collectables, £1-£2,000.* LOC: Opposite B.R. station. PARK: Easy. TEL: 01279 722044; website - www.antiques-of-britain.co.uk.

Riverside Antiques Ltd
The Maltings, Station Rd. CM21 9JX. (Chris Scott and John Maynard). EADA. Est. 1998. Open 10-5 including Sun. SIZE: Large. *STOCK: General antiques, art and collectables.* PARK: Easy. TEL: 01279 600985; fax - 01279 726398. SER: Valuations; restorations.

ST. ALBANS

By George! Antiques Centre
23 George St. AL3 4ER. Open 10-5, Sun. 1-5.

SIZE: 20 dealers. *STOCK: A wide range of general antiques, jewellery and collectables.* LOC: 100yds. from Clock Tower. PARK: Internal courtyard (loading) and Christopher Place (NCP) nearby. TEL: 01727 853032. SER: Restorations.

The Clock Shop - Philip Setterfield of St. Albans
161 Victoria St. AL1 3TA. Est. 1974. Open 11-4. CL: Thurs. *STOCK: Clocks and watches.* LOC: City station bridge. TEL: 01727 856633; fax - same. SER: Restorations; repairs (clocks, watches and barometers). VAT: Stan/Spec.

Forget-me-Knot Antiques
at Over the Moon, 27 High St. AL3 4EH. (Heather Sharp). Est. 1987. Open 9.30-5.30, Sun. by appointment. *STOCK: Mainly Victorian jewellery and collectables, specializing in silver name brooches.* LOC: Opposite The Tudor Tavern. TEL: 01727 848907. SER: Valuations. VAT: Stan.

James of St Albans
11 George St. AL3 4ER. (S.N. and W. James). Est. 1957. Open 10-5, Thurs. 10-4. *STOCK: Furniture including reproduction; smalls, brass and copper; topographical maps and prints of Hertfordshire.* TEL: 01727 856996. VAT: Stan/Spec.

Magic Lanterns
at By George! Antiques Centre, 23 George St. AL3 4ES. (Josie A. Marsden). Est. 1987. Open 10-5, Thurs. 11-5, Sat. 10-5.30, Sun. 1-5. SIZE: Medium. *STOCK: Lighting - candle, gas and early electric, 1800-1950's, £35-£1,500; small furniture, prints, mirrors, china, metalware, fire accessories, 1850-1950, £25-£1,000.* LOC: Near the abbey. PARK: Multi-storey nearby. TEL: 01727 853032/865680.

Oriental Rug Gallery Ltd
42 Verulam Rd. AL3 4DQ. (R. Mathias and J. Blair). BORDA. Open 10-5.30. *STOCK: Russian, Afghan, Turkish and Persian carpets, rugs and kelims; Oriental objets d'art.* TEL: +44 (0) 1727 841046; fax - same; e-mail - rugs@orientalrug gallery.com; website - www.orientalruggallery.com.

TRING

John Bly
BADA

The Old Billiards Room, Church Yard. HP23 5MW. Est. 1891. Open Wed.-Sat. 9.30-4.30. SIZE: Large. *STOCK: English furniture.* LOC: Next to church. PARK: Easy. TEL: 01442 823030. SER: Valuations; restorations; consultancy. FAIRS: BADA; Grosvenor House; West Palm Beach.

Founders: F.G. Collins & C. Collins in 1907

Eighteenth and nineteenth century English furniture

Antiques purchased

Wheathampstead

Hertfordshire AL4 8AP England
Telephone: 01582 833111

Junction 4 on the A1(M) 5 miles

Country Clocks
3 Pendley Bridge Cottages, Tring Station. HP23 5QU. (T. Cartmell). Resident. Est. 1976. Prior telephone call advisable. SIZE: Small. *STOCK: Clocks, 18th-19th C.* LOC: One mile from A41 in village, cottage nearest canal bridge. PARK: Easy. TEL: 01442 825090. SER: Restorations (clocks); valuations.

Farrelly Antiques
The Long Barn, 50 High St. HP23 5AG. (P. Farrelly). Open 9-4. *STOCK: Furniture.* TEL: 01442 891905. SER: Restorations. VAT: Spec.

New England House Antiques
50 High St. HP23 5AG. (Jennifer and Suj Munjee). Est. 1990. Open 10.30-5. CL: Mon. SIZE: Large - 6 showrooms on 3 floors. *STOCK: Fine Georgian and Victorian furniture, £100-£10,000; paintings, glass, silver, decorative furnishings specialising in antique table lights and hand-made shades.* LOC: A41 towards Aylesbury. PARK: Next to shop. TEL: 01442 827262; home - 01462 431914; website - www.newenglandhouseantiques.co.uk. SER: Valuations; restorations (paintings, metalwork and furniture); searches undertaken. VAT: Stan/Spec.

Thwaites Fine Stringed Instruments
33 Chalk Hill, WD19 4BL. (J.H. and W.J. Pamplin and C.A. Lovell). Open 9-5, Sat. 9.30-12.30. *STOCK: Stringed instruments, from violins to double basses.* PARK: Own. TEL: 01923 232412; fax - 01923 232463; e-mail - sales@thwaites.com; website - www.thwaites.com. SER: Restorations.

Weston Antiques
Weston Barns, Hitchin Rd. (M.A. Green). Est. 1974. Open Tues.-Sat. 10.30-5.30. SIZE: Small. *STOCK: Period furniture, longcase and mantel clocks, mainly 18th-19th C.* LOC: Off B197, near junction 9 A1(M). PARK: Easy. TEL: 01462 790646; fax - 01462 680304; mobile - 07802 403800; e-mail - greencoantiques@btinternet.com; website - www.antiquesrestorers.com. SER: Valuations; restorations (furniture and clocks). VAT: Spec.

Collins Antiques (F.G. and C. Collins Ltd.)
Corner House. AL4 8AP. (S.J. and M.C. Collins). Est. 1907. Open 9-1 and 2-5. SIZE: Medium. *STOCK: Furniture - mahogany, 1730-1920, £100-£8,000; oak, 1600-1800, £50-£5,000; walnut, 1700-1740, £75-£3,000.* LOC: London, A1(M) junction 4 to B653. PARK: Easy. TEL: 01582 833111. VAT: Stan/Spec.

The Old Bakery Antiques
3 Station Rd. AL4 8BU. (Maurice Shifrin). Open 10-6, Sun. 11-4. CL: Wed. SIZE: Large. *STOCK: 19th C furniture, £500-£1,000.* PARK: Easy, own. TEL: 01582 831999; fax - 01582 831555. VAT: Stan/Spec.

Michael Armson (Antiques) Ltd
The Old Post Office, 34 Tring Rd. HP23 4PB. Est. 1970. Open 8-2. SIZE: Large. *STOCK: Furniture, 17th-19th C.* PARK: Easy. TEL: 01442 890990; fax - 01442 891167; mobile - 07860 910034; e-mail - armsonantiques@ic24.net; website - www.armsonantiques.com. FAIRS: NEC. VAT: Spec.

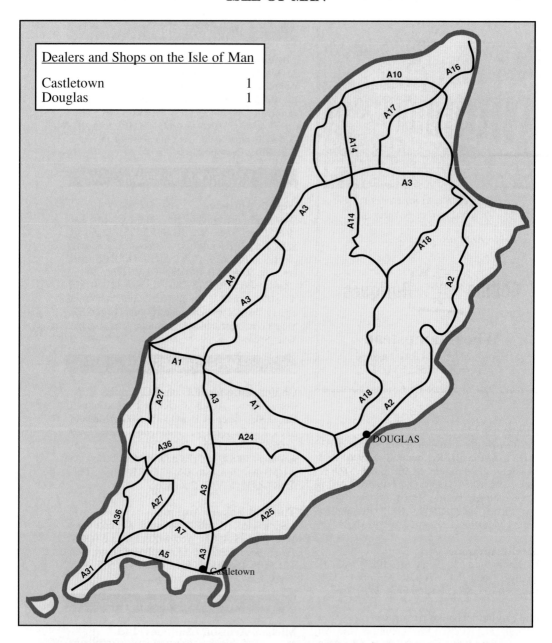

Dealers and Shops on the Isle of Man

Castletown	1
Douglas	1

CASTLETOWN

J. and H. Bell Antiques
22 Arbory St. IM9 1LJ. Est. 1965. Open Wed., Fri. and Sat. 10-5. SIZE: Medium. *STOCK: Jewellery, silver, china, early metalware, furniture, 18th-20th C, £5-£5,000.* TEL: 01624 823132/822414. VAT: Stan/Spec.

DOUGLAS

John Corrin Antiques
73 Circular Rd. IM1 1AZ. Est. 1972. Open Sat. 10-4.30 otherwise by appointment. SIZE: Medium. *STOCK: Furniture, 18th-19th C, £100-£6,000; clocks, barometers, 19th C.* LOC: From the promenade, travel up Victoria St., this becomes Prospect Hill and Circular Rd. is on left. PARK: Easy. TEL: 01624 629655; home - 01624 621382.

SILVER BOXES

ERIC DELIEB

- *Wide-ranging survey of silver boxes - their use and decoration from the sixteenth to the nineteenth centuries*

- *A very collectable area of silver*

- *The product of much original research*

"The authoritative work, which no collector should be without"
Ian Pickford

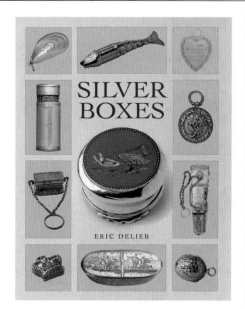

The silver box has fascinated and intrigued collectors for many centuries. It is perhaps safe to say that no other *objets de vertu* have attracted such vivid attention from maker and collector alike.

This book is a comprehensive study of the subject which concentrates on the development of the silver box in England from the sixteenth to the late nineteenth centuries. Because the interest of collectors lies not so much in the shape or type of boxes as in the wide variety of uses to which they have been put and the splendid enrichment lavished upon them, there is a penetrating analysis of the roots and derivations of ornament. The full colour illustrations show boxes with as many diverse forms and uses as possible.

The term box covers any receptacle (unless it is a vessel) whether it is a snuffbox, a pyx or a lancet case for use in phlebotomy, as long as it possesses a lid, hinged or otherwise. The usual snuffboxes and vinaigrettes appear in plenty and have been carefully selected to show the ingenuity of silver craftsmen. More importantly perhaps we find the splendid variety of 'special purpose' silver boxes: religious, dental and medical, skippet and seal, Masonic, jewel caskets, sweetmeat boxes, pomanders – there is even the unique sumptuous Henry VII 'Barber-Surgeon's case' of circa 1512 with its glowing enamels.

There is much hitherto unpublished material including pieces from private collections and articles from Livery Companies and other institutions.

11 x 8½in./279 x 216mm.
168pp.
205 col., and 120 b.&w.
1 85149 313 1
£25.00

Available from all good booksellers and direct from the publisher:
ANTIQUE COLLECTORS' CLUB
Sandy Lane, Old Martlesham, Woodbridge, Suffolk, IP12 4SD.
Tel: 01394 389950   Fax: 01394 389999
Email: sales@antique-acc.com
Website: www.antique-acc.com

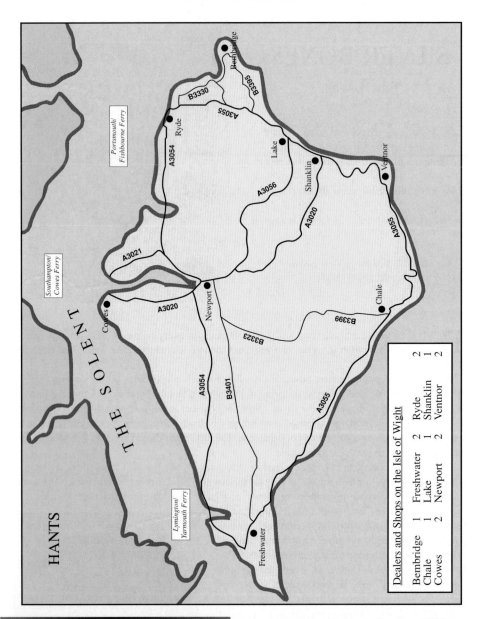

Dealers and Shops on the Isle of Wight

Bembridge	1	Freshwater	2	Ryde	2
Chale	1	Lake	1	Shanklin	1
Cowes	2	Newport	2	Ventnor	2

BEMBRIDGE

Windmill Antiques
1 Foreland Rd. PO35 5XN. (E.J. de Kort). Est. 1970. Open Wed.- Sat. 10-1 and 2.15-4. SIZE: Medium. *STOCK: Furniture, silver, porcelain, jewellery.* TEL: 01983 873666. SER: Buys at auction. VAT: Stan/Spec.

CHALE

Curios of Chale
3 Church Place. PO38 2HA. (Michael Gregory).

Est. 1983. Open 12-5 including Sun. SIZE: Large. *STOCK: Architectural items, fireplaces, £50-£500; general antiques, curios and taxidermy, £5-£500; mostly 19th C.* LOC: Off Military Rd., near Black-Gang. PARK: Easy. TEL: 01983 730230; mobile - 07811 835159. SER: Valuations.

COWES

Flagstaff Antiques
Tudor House, Bath Rd. PO31 7RH. (T.A.M. Cockram). Est. 1970. Open from 10 am. CL:

Wed. SIZE: Small. *STOCK: Jewellery, 19th-20th C, £50-£2,000; porcelain, 19th C, £25-£1,000; pictures, 19th-20th C, £10-£1,000.* LOC: 100 yards from The Parade. PARK: Easy. TEL: 01983 200138. SER: Valuations; restorations (porcelain and silver).

Royal Standard Antiques
70-72 Park Rd. PO31 7LY. (Dennis and Caroline Bradbury). Resident. Est. 1992. Open 10.30-5.30 or any time by appointment. SIZE: Medium. *STOCK: Georgian, Victorian, Edwardian and French provincial furniture, £100-£1,000+; architectural items, £20-£500; pictures, commemoratives, breweriana, £5-£500.* LOC: 5 mins. walk from hydrofoil terminus; corner of Victoria Rd. PARK: Own, behind premises. TEL: 01983 281672; home - same; e-mail - caroline@royalstandardantiques.fsbusiness.co.uk; website - www.royalstandardantiques.fsbusiness.co.uk. SER: Restorations; upholstery, caning, stained glass.

Aladdin's Cave
147/149 School Green Rd. PO40 9BB. (Mrs J. Dunn). Est. 1984. Open 9.30-4. CL: Tues.-Thurs. in winter. SIZE: Medium. *STOCK: China, collectors' items, glass, linen, old pine, furniture, memorabilia, books, 19th-20th C, £5-£500.* PARK: Easy. TEL: 01983 752934; home - 01983 753846.

Ye Olde Village Clock Shop
3 Moa Place. PO40 9DS. (Ron and Sandra Tayler). Est. 1970. Open 9.30-1 or by appointment. CL: Mon., Tues and Thurs. SIZE: Small. *STOCK: Clocks - longcase, Vienna, carriage, bracket, French and novelty, 17th-19th C, £300-£6,000; mechanical music.* PARK: Easy. TEL: 01983 754193; home - same. SER: Valuations; restorations (clocks).

Lake Antiques
Sandown Rd. PO36 9JP. (P. Burfield). Est. 1982. Open 10-4. CL: Wed. *STOCK: General antiques, Georgian and Victorian furniture, clocks.* LOC: On the main Sandown to Shanklin Road. PARK: On forecourt. TEL: 01983 406888/865005; mobile - 07710 067678.

Mike Heath Antiques
3-4 Holyrood St. PO30 5AU. (M. and B. Heath). Est. 1979. Open 9.30-5. CL: Thurs. SIZE: Medium. *STOCK: General antiques and bric-a-*

brac, *19th-20th C, £5-£500.* LOC: Off High St. PARK: Nearby. TEL: 01983 525748; home - same. SER: Restorations (copper and brass).

Lugley Street Antiques
13 Lugley St. PO30 5HD. (D.A. Newman). Est. 1986. Open 9.30-5. CL: Thurs. SIZE: Large. *STOCK: Furniture, clocks, china and collectables, late 18th to early 20th C, £5-£2,500.* LOC: Town centre. PARK: Meters. TEL: 01983 523348. SER: Valuations; restorations (furniture). VAT: Margin.

Nooks & Crannies
60 High St. PO33 2RS. (David and Sally Burnett). Est. 1985. Open 9.30-1.30 and 2.30-5. CL: Thurs. SIZE: Small. *STOCK: China, glass, collectables, some furniture, gramophones and radios, Victorian to 1950's, £1-£750.* PARK: Limited. TEL: 01983 568984; home - 01983 868261. FAIRS: Ardingly.

Victoria Antiques
Union St. PO33 2LQ. (J. Strudwick). Open 9.30-5 including Sun. CL: Mon. and Tues. *STOCK: General antiques and collectables, mainly porcelain and china.* TEL: 01983 564661; mobile - 07970 175926.

The Shanklin Gallery
67 Regent St. PO37 7AE. (Jacqueline and Terry Townsend). FATG. Est. 1992. Open 9-5. SIZE: Medium. *STOCK: Oils, watercolours, engravings, prints, maps, 17th-20th C, £10-£2,000.* LOC: Town centre near rail station. PARK: Easy. TEL: 01983 863113; e-mail - spaltown@compuserve.com. SER: Valuations; restorations (oils, watercolours and prints); framing.

Ultramarine
40B High St. PO38 1LG. (Milly Stevens). Open Wed.-Sat. 10-2. SIZE: Small. *STOCK: 19th-20th C collectables including jewellery, china, studio pottery, textiles and glass, £5-£500.* LOC: Central. PARK: Nearby. TEL: 01983 854062.

Ventnor Rare Books
32 Pier St. PO38 1SX. (Nigel and Teresa Traylen). ABA. PBFA. Est. 1989. Open 10-5. CL: Wed. *STOCK: Antiquarian and secondhand books, prints.* TEL: 01983 853706; fax - 01983 854706.

KENT

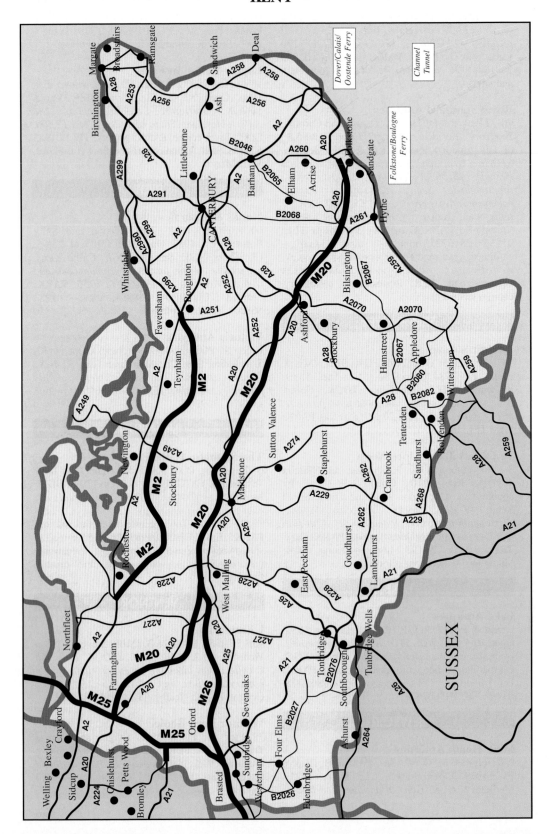

ACRISE, Nr. Folkestone

R. Kirby Antiques
Caroline Farm, Ridge Row. CT18 8JT. (R.D. and M.W. Kirby). Est. 1972. Open by appointment 7 days. *STOCK: Early period oak, 16th-18th C, and works of art.* TEL: 01303 893230; fax - 01303 891478; e-mail - rkirby@antiques8. fsnet.co.uk. SER: Valuations.

APPLEDORE, Nr. Ashford

Richard Back 2 Wood
The Old Goods Shed, Station Rd. TN26 2DF. Est. 1987. Open 9-5, Sat. 9-4, Sun. 11-4. *STOCK: Stripped and finished pine furniture.* LOC: Adjacent to station. PARK: Easy. TEL: 01233 758109; mobile - 07831 655414; home - 01233 860400; e-mail - pine@back2wood.com; website - www.back2wood.com. VAT: Stan/Margin.

Dealers and Shops in Kent

Acrise	1	Chislehurst	2	Littlebourne	1	Southborough	2
Appledore	2	Cranbrook	5	Maidstone	2	Staplehurst	1
Ash	1	Crayford	1	Margate	1	Stockbury	1
Ashford	1	Deal	5	Newington	1	Sundridge	1
Ashurst	1	East Peckham	1	Northfleet	1	Sutton Valence	1
Barham	1	Edenbridge	3	Otford	3	Tenterden	3
Beckenham	1	Elham	1	Petts Wood	1	Teynham	2
Bexley	1	Farningham	2	Ramsgate	2	Tonbridge	4
Bilsington	1	Faversham	1	Rochester	8	Tunbridge Wells	31
Birchington	3	Folkestone	2	Rolvenden	3	Welling	1
Boughton	1	Four Elms	2	Sandgate	13	West Malling	2
Brasted	12	Goudhurst	1	Sandhurst	1	Westerham	10
Broadstairs	1	Hamstreet	1	Sandwich	3	Whitstable	3
Bromley	3	Hythe	4	Sevenoaks	5	Wittersham	1
Canterbury	17	Lamberhurst	1	Sidcup	2		

ASH, Nr. Canterbury

Henry's of Ash
51 The Street. CT3 2EN. (P.H. Robinson). Est. 1988. Open 10-12 and 2-5. CL: Tues. pm and Wed. SIZE: Small. *STOCK: General antiques, linen, Victorian and Art Deco, £5-100; small furniture, £50-£500.* LOC: Main street. PARK: Outside. TEL: 01304 812600. SER: Buys at auction (small items). FAIRS: Copthorne; Bromley.

ASHFORD

County Antiques
Old Mill Cottage, Kennett Lane, Stanford North. TN25 6DG. (B. Nilson). Open by appointment. *STOCK: General antiques.* TEL: 01303 813039.

ASHURST

The Baldfaced Stag
TN3 9TE. (Mike Roberts). SALVO. Est. 1987. Open 10-5.30. CL: Mon. SIZE: Large plus barn. *STOCK: Fine period chimney pieces, garden statuary and sculptures, light fittings.* LOC: A264 between Tunbridge Wells and East Grinstead. PARK: Easy. TEL: 01892 740877; e-mail - mike@architecturalemporium.com; website - www.architecturalemporium.com. SER: Shipping. VAT: Stan/Spec.

BARHAM, Nr. Canterbury

Stablegate Antiques
CT4 6QD. (Mr and Mrs M.J. Giuntini). Est. 1989. Open 10-5.30 including Sun. SIZE: Large. *STOCK: Georgian and Victorian dining tables, chairs, sideboards, bureaux, davenports, chests of drawers; silver plate, china, clocks, jewellery, glass, objets d'art, collectables, copper, brass.* LOC: Village just off the A2 to Dover. PARK: Easy. TEL: 01227 831639; mobile - 07802 439777.

BECKENHAM

Beckenham Antiques & Collectors' Market
Public Hall, Bromley Rd. BR3. Est. 1979. Open Wed. 8.30-2. SIZE: 16 stalls. *STOCK: General antiques.* TEL: 020 8660 1369.

Pepys Antiques
9 Kelsey Park Rd. BR3 2LH. (S.P. Elton). Est. 1969. Open 10-2. CL: Wed. *STOCK: Furniture, paintings, clocks, silver, porcelain, copper, brass.* LOC: Central Beckenham. TEL: 020 8650 0994.

BEXLEY

Village Antiques
43 High St. DA5 1AB. (Mrs J.A. Wood and Mrs J. Dampier). Est. 1982. Open Wed.-Sat. 10-4.30. SIZE: Medium. *STOCK: Period and old pine furniture; ceramics, metalware and decorative items.* LOC: Opposite Station Approach. PARK: Rear of High St. TEL: 01322 528278.

BILSINGTON, Nr. Ashford

The Barn at Bislington
Swanton Lane. TN25 7JR. (Gabrielle De Giles). Open by appointment. *STOCK: Country furniture, mainly French, tables, mirrors, armoires, chairs, to £5,000.* LOC: 5 miles south of Ashford. PARK: Easy. TEL: 01233 720917; fax - 01233 720156; mobile - 07721 015263; e-mail - gabrielle@gabrielledegiles.com; website - www.gabrielledegiles.com. VAT: Spec.

BIRCHINGTON

Birchington Antiques
63 Station Rd. CT7 9RE. (Poppy and Graham Booker). Open 10-5. CL: Tues. SIZE: Small. *STOCK: Furniture, porcelain and collectables, 19th to early 20th C, £5-£1,000.* LOC: Just off A249 to Margate. PARK: Easy. TEL: 01843 842811; home - 01843 298696. SER: Re-upholstery; buys at auction.

John Chawner
36 Station Approach. CT7 9RD. Open 10.30-12.30 and 2-5. CL: Tues. *STOCK: Clocks, barometers, smalls and bureaux.* PARK: Easy. TEL: 01843 846943/843309. SER: Repairs (clocks and barometers).

Galleria Pinocchio
28 Station Approach. CT7 9RD. (Frank and Olga Tramontin). Est. 1997. Open 10-5. SIZE: Small. *STOCK: Fishing items, £10-£150; militaria, £5-£300; Victorian and Edwardian furniture and bric-a-brac, to £300; clocks, to £1,600.* LOC: Opposite station. PARK: Easy. TEL: 01843 847592; home - same; mobile - 07951 660864; e-mail - olga@galpin.fsnet.co.uk.

BOUGHTON, Nr. Faversham

Jean Collyer Antiques
194 The Street. ME13 9AL. (Mrs J.B. Collyer). Est. 1977. Open by appointment. SIZE: Small. *STOCK: Porcelain, glass, 18th to mid-19th C.* PARK: Easy. TEL: 01227 751454; home - 01227 752831. SER: Valuations.

BRASTED, Nr. Westerham

David Barrington
The Antique Shop. TN16 1JA. Est. 1947. Open 9-6. SIZE: Medium. *STOCK: Furniture, 18th C.* LOC: A25. PARK: Easy. TEL: 01959 562537. VAT: Stan/Spec.

Bigwood Antiques
High St. TN16 1JA. (S. Bigwood). Est. 1984. Open 10.30-5, Sun. 12.45-4.30. SIZE: Small. *STOCK: Furniture, 19th -20th C, £250-£4,000.* PARK: Easy. TEL: 01959 564458. SER: Restorations. VAT: Stan/Spec.

Cooper Fine Arts Ltd
Swan House, High St. TN16 1JJ. (J. Hill-Reid). Est. 1976. Open 10-6, Sun. 11-5. SIZE: Medium. *STOCK: 18th-19th C furniture, paintings and decorative.* PARK: Easy. TEL: 01959 565818. VAT: Stan/Spec.

Courtyard Antiques
High St. TN16 1JE. (H. La Trobe). Open 10-5, Sun. and Bank Holidays 12.30-4.30. SIZE: Medium. *STOCK: 19th C furniture (including extending dining tables), silver, jewellery, glass, ceramics, Tunbridge ware, watercolours, prints and objets d'art.* PARK: Easy. TEL: 01959 564483; fax - 01732 454726. SER: Restorations (furniture); French polishing; re-leathering.

Keymer Son & Co. Ltd
Swaylands Place, The Green. TN16 1JY. Est. 1977. Open 10-1 and 2.30-5. CL: Sat. SIZE: Small. *STOCK: 18th-19th C furniture, £100-£3,000.* LOC: A25. PARK: Easy. TEL: 01959 564203; fax - 01959 561138.

Roy Massingham Antiques LAPADA
The Coach House. TN16 1JJ. Est. 1968. Open by appointment. *STOCK: 18th-19th C furniture, pictures and decorative items.* LOC: 10 mins. from M25. PARK: Easy. TEL: 01959 562408; mobile - 07860 326825. VAT: Spec.

Old Bakery Antiques
High St. TN16 1JA. (Pauline Turner). Est. 1998. Open 10.30-5, Sun. 11-4.30. SIZE: Small. *STOCK: 18th to early 20th C furniture, £200-£2,000; fine period porcelain, £50-£1,000; watercolours and prints, £50-£500; copper and brass, £10-£200; mirrors, £100-£500; clocks, £250-£1,000.* PARK: Easy. TEL: 01959 564545. FAIRS: NEC; Olympia.

Old Manor House Antiques
The Green. TN16 1JL. (Jane R. Read). Est. 1983. Open Tues.-Sat. *STOCK: Clocks, barometers,*

lighting, copper and brass, mirrors, furniture and general antiques. PARK: Easy. TEL: 01959 562536.

Southdown House Antiques
High St. TN16 1JE. (Graham Stead). Est. 1982. Open 10-5. SIZE: 7 showrooms. *STOCK: Furniture, 18th C oak and 19th C mahogany and walnut; decorative items, metalware, textiles, porcelain, glass and pictures, £50-£5,000.* LOC: A25. PARK: Own. TEL: 01959 563522. SER: Restorations (furniture). VAT: Spec.

Dinah Stoodley & Celia Jennings
High St. TN16 1JE. Est. 1965. Open 10-5. SIZE: Medium. *STOCK: Oak and country furniture, 1600-1800; ceramics, 1600-1880; European woodcarving and sculpture, 1400-1700.* LOC: A25. PARK: Easy. TEL: 01959 563616; website - www.early-carving.com. FAIRS: Olympia. VAT: Spec.

Tilings Antiques
High St. TN16 1JA. (Penny Fawcett). Est. 1974. Open 10-5.30 or by appointment. SIZE: Medium. *STOCK: Furniture, decorative items, 18th-19th C, £20-£2,000.* LOC: A25 village centre. PARK: Easy. TEL: 01959 564735; mobile - 07885 103234; e-mail - penny.fawcett@object.co.uk. VAT: Stan/Spec.

W.W. Warner (Antiques) `BADA`
The Green, High St. TN16 1JL. (C.S. Jowitt). Est. 1957. Open 10-5. *STOCK: 18th-19th C English and Continental pottery, porcelain, glass, furniture.* LOC: A25. PARK: Easy. TEL: 01959 563698. SER: Valuations; restorations.

Broadstairs Antiques and Collectables
49 Belvedere Rd. CT10 1PF. (P. Edwards). Est. 1980. Open 10-4.30. CL: Wed. *STOCK: General antiques, linen, china and small furniture.* LOC: Road opposite Lloyds TSB. PARK: Easy. TEL: 01843 861965. FAIRS: Ramada Hotel, Hollingbourne; DMG.

Patric Capon `BADA`
PO Box 581. BR1 2WX. Open by appointment. *STOCK: Unusual carriage clocks, 19th C, £450-£6,000; 8-day and 2-day marine chronometers, 19th C, £850-£4,500; clocks and barometers, 18th-19th C, £400-£6,500.* TEL: 020 8467 5722; fax - 020 8295 1475. SER: Valuations; restorations.

Peter Morris
1 Station Concourse, Bromley North BR Station. BR1 4EQ. BNTA. OMRS. ANA. IBNS. BDOS. Open 10-1 and 2-6, Sat. 9-2. CL: Wed. SIZE: Medium. *STOCK: Coins, from 1660's; medals, from 1790; antiquities, Egyptian, Greek and Roman; bank notes, from 1800; all 50p to £1,000.* LOC: Inside station. PARK: Easy. TEL: 020 8313 3410; fax - 020 8466 8502; e-mail - info@petermorris.co.uk; website - www.petermorris.co.uk. SER: Valuations; buys at auction. FAIRS: BNTA Coinex; OMRS Convention; major UK and European Coin & Medal. VAT: Stan/Spec.

Past and Present
22 Plaistow Lane. BR1 3DQ. (Mrs Jan Sibley). Est. 1992. Open 9-5.30. SIZE: Small. *STOCK: General antiques and collectables including furniture and garden items.* PARK: Nearby. TEL: 0208 466 7056; home - 0208 464 0290. SER: Valuations.

Antique and Design
The Old Oast, Hollow Lane. CT1 3SA. (Steve Couchman). Est. 1988. Open 9-6, Sun. 10-4. SIZE: Large. *STOCK: Pine furniture, decorative items, 1800-1950, £5-£1,500.* LOC: M2 from London, Canterbury exit, straight at first roundabout, right at second and third roundabouts, left at second pedestrian lights, shop 500 yards. TEL: 01227 762871. SER: Restorations; buys at auction; import and export. VAT: Stan/Spec.

R. J. Baker
16 Palace St. CT1 2DZ. Est. 1979. Open 9.30-5. CL: Mon. SIZE: Small. *STOCK: Silver and jewellery, 18th-19th C, £500-£10,000; handmade modern silverware, modern jewellery.* LOC: 5 mins. from cathedral, opposite The King's School. PARK: Easy. TEL: 01227 463224. SER: Valuations; restorations; gold and silversmiths; manufacturers. VAT: Stan/Spec.

Burgate Antique Centre
10c Burgate. CT1 2HG. (V. Reeves). Est. 1986. Open 10-5. SIZE: 14 dealers. *STOCK: General antiques and collectables.* LOC: City wall overlooking cathedral gardens. TEL: 01227 456500.

Bygones Reclamation
Nackington Rd. CT4 7BA. (Bob and Sue Thorpe). SALVO. Est. 1995. Open 8-5.30, Sat. 8.30-6, Sun. 9-5. *STOCK: Victorian fireplaces, cast-iron radiators, 19th C, £200-£1,500; garden*

statuary, 18th-20th C, £300-£1,500. LOC: B2068 Hythe road, 2 miles from city centre. PARK: Own. TEL: 01227 767453; fax - 01227 762153; e-mail - bob@bygones.net and jay@bygones.net. SER: Valuations; restorations. FAIRS: Newark. VAT: Spec.

Canterbury Antiques
2 The Borough. CT1 2DR. (M.D. Patten). Est. 1993. Open 10-5. SIZE: Medium. STOCK: Clocks and barometers, china, furniture, to Victorian, £50-£10,000. PARK: Loading only and nearby. TEL: 01227 785755; fax - 01227 766222; mobile - 07711 404231.

The Canterbury Bookshop
37 Northgate. CT1 1BL. (David Miles). ABA. PBFA. Est. 1980. Open 10-5. SIZE: Medium. STOCK: Antiquarian and secondhand books, children's books, prints. PARK: Easy. TEL: 01227 464773; fax - 01227 780073. FAIRS: PBFA and major provincial; ABA; Olympia; Chelsea.

Chaucer Bookshop
6-7 Beer Cart Lane. CT1 2NY. (Sir Robert Sherston-Baker Bt). ABA. PBFA. Est. 1956. Open 10-5. STOCK: Books and prints, 18th-20th C, £5-£150; maps, 18th-19th C, £50-£250. LOC: 5 mins. walk from cathedral, via Mercery Lane and St. Margaret's St. PARK: Castle St. TEL: 01227 453912; fax - 01227 451893; e-mail - chaucerbooks@btconnect.com. SER: Valuations; buys at auction (books, maps and prints). VAT: Stan.

City Pride Ltd
72-73 Northgate. CT1 1BB. (M.D. Patten). Est. 1993. Open 10-5. SIZE: Medium. STOCK: General antiques, collectables, furniture, Victorian, 1920s, 1930s, £2-£4,000. TEL: 01227 764255; fax - 01227 766222.

Coach House Antiques Centre
2A Duck Lane, St. Radigunds. CT1 2AE. Est. 1975. Open daily. SIZE: Large. STOCK: General antiques, small furniture, ceramics, glass, linen, books, collectors' items and bygones. Not Stocked: Jewellery. PARK: Nearby. TEL: 01227 463117.

Conquest House Antiques
17 Palace St. CT1 2DZ. (C.C. Hill and D.A. Magee). Open 10-4. STOCK: 18th-19th C furniture, chandeliers and decorative items. LOC: Near cathedral. PARK: St. Radigunds. TEL: 01227 464587; fax - 01227 451375. SER: Restorations; valuations; packing and shipping; delivery.

H.S. Greenfield and Son, Gunmakers (Est. 1805)
The Shooting Grounds, Sturry Hill, Sturry. CT2 0NQ. (T.S. Greenfield). Open 9-5.30. STOCK: English sporting guns, in pairs and singles; Continental sporting guns, firearms. PARK: Own. TEL: 01227 713222. SER: Valuations; restorations (antique firearms). VAT: Stan.

Nan Leith's Brocanterbury
Errol House, 68 Stour St. CT1 2NZ. Resident. Est. 1983. Open Mon., Wed., Fri. and Sat. 1-6 or by appointment. STOCK: Art Deco, Victoriana, pressed glass, costume jewellery. LOC: Close to Heritage Museum. TEL: 01227 454519.

Michael Pearson Antiques
Est. 1977. Open by appointment. STOCK: 17th-18th C furniture including early oak and country; clocks and wood carvings. TEL: 01227 459939; e-mail - pearson12@btopenworld.com. SER: Valuations; restorations (clocks and furniture). VAT: Spec.

Pinetum
25 Oaten Hill. CT1 3HZ. (Alan Pattinson). Est. 1967. Open 9.30-5, Sat. 10-4, Sun. 11-4. SIZE: Medium. STOCK: 18th-19th C pine and country furniture, £50-£3,000. LOC: Old Dover road. PARK: Easy. TEL: 01227 780365; home - same. SER: Valuations; restorations (furniture); buys at auction (furniture).

The Saracen's Lantern
9 The Borough. CT1 2DR. (W.J. Christophers). Est. 1970. STOCK: General antiques, silver, jewellery, clocks, watches, Victorian bottles and pot-lids, prints, porcelain and pottery, plates, Royal commemoratives, post-cards, brass, copper and pewter. LOC: Near cathedral opposite King's School. PARK: At rear, by way of Northgate and St. Radigun's St. TEL: 01227 451968.

Victorian Fireplace
Thanet House, 92 Broad St. CT1 2LU. (J.J. Griffith). Est. 1980. Open 10-5.30. CL: Mon. SIZE: Medium. STOCK: Georgian to Victorian fireplaces. LOC: Town centre. PARK: Nearby. TEL: 01227 767723. SER: Restorations; fitting. VAT: Stan/Spec.

World Coins
35-36 Broad St. CT1 2LR. (David Mason). Est. 1970. Open 9.30-5. CL: Thurs. pm. SIZE: Medium. STOCK: Coins, 3rd C BC to date, to £1,000; banknotes, 1792 to date; medals, 1815-1970. LOC: Opposite car park by city wall and ring road. PARK: Easy. TEL: 01227 768887. SER: Valuations; identification and advice.

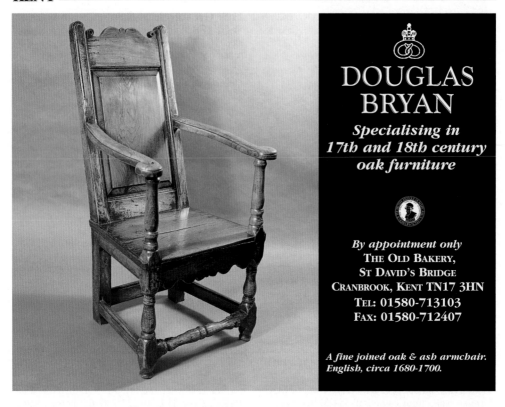

CHISLEHURST

Chislehurst Antiques `LAPADA`
7 Royal Parade. BR7 6NR. (Mrs M. Crawley).
Est. 1976. Open Mon., Fri., Sat., 10-5, Sun. 11-4.
SIZE: Large. *STOCK: Furniture, 1760-1910; lighting - oil, gas, electric, 1850-1910; mirrors, 1820-1910.* LOC: Half mile from A20, 3 miles from M25. PARK: Easy. TEL: 020 8467 1530; mobile - 07773 345266. FAIRS: Olympia; NEC. VAT: Spec.

Michael Sim
1 Royal Parade. BR7 5PG. Est. 1983. Open 9-6 including Sun. SIZE: Medium. *STOCK: English furniture, Georgian and Regency, £500-£50,000; clocks, barometers, globes and scientific instruments, £500-£50,000; Oriental works of art, £50-£5,000; portrait miniatures, £300-£5,000; animalier bronzes, £1,000-£10,000.* LOC: 50yds. from War Memorial at junction of Bromley Rd. and Centre Common Rd. PARK: Easy. TEL: 020 8467 7040; home - same; fax - 020 8857 1313. SER: Valuations; restorations; buys at auction. VAT: Spec.

CRANBROOK

Antiques at Cranbrook
19 High St. TN17 3EE. Est. 1978. Open 10-5. SIZE: 10 dealers. *STOCK: Small general antiques.* TEL: 01580 712173.

Douglas Bryan `BADA` `LAPADA`
The Old Bakery, St. David's Bridge. TN17 3HN. (Douglas and Catherine Bryan). Est. 1971. Open by appointment. SIZE: Medium.
STOCK: Mainly English oak and country furniture, 17th-18th C; woodcarvings, some metalware. **LOC: Adjacent Tanyard car park - off road towards Windmill. PARK: Adjacent. TEL: 01580 713103; fax - 01580 712407; mobile - 07774 737303. FAIRS: Olympia (Feb., June, Nov); BADA.**

Cranbrook Gallery
21B Stone St. TN17 3HF. (P.J. and N.A. Rodgers). Est. 1978. Open Tues.-Sat. 9.30-5. *STOCK: Watercolours, prints and maps, 18th-19th C.* TEL: 01580 720720; e-mail - cranbrookg@aol.com; website - www.cranbrookgallery.com. SER: Framing; restorations; picture search. VAT: Margin.

Swan Antiques

Stone St. TN17 3HF. (R. White). Est. 1982. Open Thurs., Fri. and Sat. 10-1 and 2-5 and by appointment. SIZE: Medium. *STOCK: Country furniture, 17th-19th C, from £500+; folk art and naïve paintings.* LOC: Town centre. PARK: Easy. TEL: 01580 712720; home - 01580 291864. SER: Valuations; buys at auction. FAIRS: Olympia; Battersea Decorative & Fine Art. VAT: Spec.

Vestry Antiques

3 Stone St. TN17 3HF. (Mrs Lynn Dawkins). Est. 1992. Open 9.30-5. *STOCK: 18th-19th C oak, mahogany, pine and decorative items.* LOC: Next to church. PARK: Nearby (loading and unloading only outside shop). TEL: 01580 713563. SER: Valuations.

CRAYFORD

Watling Antiques

139 Crayford Rd. DA1 4AS. Open 10-6.30. *STOCK: General antiques and shipping goods.* TEL: 01322 523620.

DEAL

J. Clarke-Hall Ltd

75 Middle St. CT14 6HN. (Sally Edgecombe). Est. 1934. Open by appointment. *STOCK: English literature especially Samuel Johnson and the 18th Century.* PARK: Easy. TEL: 01304 375467. FAIRS: Hilton, Bonnington (June). *Mail Order Only.*

Decors

67 Beach St. CT14 6HY. (N. Loftus-Potter). Est. 1973. Open 9.30-7 including Sun; in winter Fri.-Mon. or by appointment. *STOCK: Decorative items, general antiques and fabrics (including modern).* PARK: Easy. TEL: 01304 368030; fax - same; home - same; e-mail - potter@decors antiques.com; website - www.decorsantiques. com. SER: Finder; restorations.

Pretty Bizarre

170 High St. CT14 6BQ. (Philip Hartley). Open Fri. and Sat. 10-4.30 or by appointment. SIZE: Medium. *STOCK: Art Deco to 1970's ceramics and collectables.* TEL: Mobile - 07973 794537.

Quill Antiques

12 Alfred Sq. CT14 6LR. (A.J. and A.R. Young). Open 9-5.30. *STOCK: General antiques, porcelain, postcards.* TEL: 01304 375958.

Serendipity

125 High St. CT14 6BB. (M. and K. Short). Est. 1976. Open 10-1 and 2-4.30, Sat. 9.30-4.30 or by appointment. SIZE: Medium. *STOCK: Staffordshire figures, ceramics, pictures, furniture.* PARK: Easy. TEL: 01304 369165; home - 01304 366536; e-mail - dipityantiques@ aol.com. SER: Valuations; restorations (ceramics and oil paintings).

EAST PECKHAM, Nr. Tonbridge

Desmond and Amanda North

The Orchard, Hale St. TN12 5JB. Est. 1971. Open daily, appointment advisable. SIZE: Medium. *STOCK: Oriental rugs, runners, carpets and cushions, 1800-1939, £60-£3,500.* LOC: On B2015, 400yds south of roundabout at northern end of Hale Street bypass (A228). PARK: Easy. TEL: 01622 871353; home - same; fax - 01622 872998. SER: Valuations; restorations (reweaving, re-edging and patching); cleaning.

The Four Seasons, 1840s, 9½in. high. Note the characteristic sandy base.

From an article entitled "Dudson – a Family of Potters since 1800" by Audrey Dudson which appeared in the May 2002 issue of *Antique Collecting*. For more details and to subscribe see page 21.

LENNOX CATO

ANTIQUES AND WORKS OF ART

1 THE SQUARE, CHURCH STREET,
EDENBRIDGE, KENT, TN8 5BD,
ENGLAND

TELEPHONE/FAX:
+44 (0) 1732 865 988

website: www.lennoxcato.com
Email: cato@lennoxcato.com

Open: WED. - FRI. 9.30 - 5.00pm;
SAT. 10 - 4pm
or by appointment

A MEMBER OF THE
BRITISH ANTIQUE DEALERS' ASSOCIATION

Very rare 19th century block fronted mahogany bureau,
raised on the original shaped bracket feet.
Width 36ins. Depth 19½ins. Height 39ins.

EDENBRIDGE

Lennox Cato   BADA LAPADA
**1 The Square, Church St. TN8 5BD. (Lennox and
Susan Cato). Est. 1975. Open Wed.-Fr. 9.30-5.30,
Sat. 10-4 or by appointment. SIZE: Large.
STOCK: *18th-19th C English and Continental
furniture and related items, including mirrors,
lamps, paintings, ceramics.* LOC: Town centre
(B2026), next door to Chevertons. PARK:
Nearby. TEL: 01732 865988; mobile - 07836
233473; e-mail - cato@lennoxcato.com; website -
www.lennoxcato.com. SER: Valuations;
restorations. FAIRS: Olympia (Spring, Summer,
Winter); BADA (London and Harrogate). VAT:
Stan/Spec.**

Chevertons of Edenbridge Ltd   BADA LAPADA
**Taylour House, 67-73 High St. TN8 5AL. (D.
and A. Adam). CINOA. Est. 1961. Open 9-5.30.
SIZE: 25 showrooms. STOCK: *Furniture and
accessories, £500-£40,000.* LOC: From
Westerham, on B2026 to Edenbridge. PARK:
Own. TEL: 01732 863196/863358; fax - 01732
864298; e-mail - chevertons@msn.com;
website - www.chevertons.com. FAIRS:
Olympia (Feb., June, Nov); LAPADA,
(London and Birmingham). VAT: Stan/Spec.**

ELHAM, Nr. Canterbury

Elham Antiques
High St. CT4 6TB. (Julian and Linda Chambers).
Resident. Est. 1990. Open 10-5.30. CL: Mon.
SIZE: Large. *STOCK: Fireplaces, 18th-19th C,
£500-£1,000; country furniture, late 17th C to
late 19th C, £500-£1,000; trains and models,
early 20th C, £200-£600.* PARK: Easy. TEL:
01303 840085; home - 01303 840874. SER:
Valuations. VAT: Spec.

FARNINGHAM

P.T. Beasley
Forge Yard, High St. DA4 0DB. (P.T. and R.
Beasley). Est. 1964. Open every day, prior telephone
call advisable. *STOCK: English furniture, pewter,
brass, Delft and woodcarvings.* LOC: Opposite
Social Club. PARK: Easy. TEL: 01322 862453.

Farningham Pine
High St. DA4. (P. and Mrs. T.A. Dzierzek). Est.
1987. Open 10-5. CL: Wed. STOCK: *Pine
furniture, from 1830, £25-£5,000.* LOC: 1 mile
from M25, junction 3, on A20, first turn off
(A225), before Brands Hatch if heading south.
PARK: Easy. TEL: 01322 863168/863230; fax -
01322 863168. VAT: Stan/Spec.

FAVERSHAM

Squires Antiques (Faversham)
3 Jacob Yard, Preston St. ME13 8NY. (A. Squires). Est. 1985. Open 10-5. CL: Wed. and Thurs. SIZE: Large. *STOCK: General antiques.* PARK: Nearby. TEL: 01795 531503; fax - 01227 750396; e-mail - squiresantiques@aol.com.

FOLKESTONE

Alan Lord Antiques
71 Tontine St. CT20 1JR. (A.G., J.A. and R.G. Lord). Est. 1952. Open 9-5. CL: Wed. and Sat pm., other times by appointment. SIZE: Large. *STOCK: Period and Victorian furniture, china, silver. Rear warehouse - trade and shipping goods.* LOC: Road up from harbour. PARK: Easy. TEL: 01303 253674 anytime. VAT: Stan/Spec.

G. and D.I. Marrin and Sons
149 Sandgate Rd. CT20 2DA. ABA. PBFA. ILABA. Est. 1949. Open 9.30-1 and 2.30-5.30. CL: Mon. SIZE: Large. *STOCK: Maps, early engravings, topographical and sporting prints, paintings, drawings, books, engravings.* TEL: 01303 253016; fax - 01303 850956; e-mail - marrinbook@clara.co.uk; website - www.marrinbook.clara.net. SER: Restorations; framing.

FAIRS: Olympia, Chelsea Town Hall Book; Russell Hotel. VAT: Stan.

FOUR ELMS, Nr. Edenbridge

Treasures
The Cross Roads. TN8 7NH. (B. Ward-Lee). Est. 1974. Open 10-5. *STOCK: Copper, brass, glass, porcelain, silver, jewellery, linen, books, toys, pine, small furniture and collectables.* PARK: Forecourt. TEL: 01732 700363.

Yew Tree Antiques
The Cross Roads. TN8 7NH. (Mrs C. Nixon). Est. 1984. Open 10-5. SIZE: Medium. *STOCK: Porcelain and copper, 19th-20th C, £5-£500; glass, jewellery, linen, small furniture and collectables.* LOC: Off A25 - B269. PARK: Easy. TEL: 01732 700215.

GOUDHURST

Mill House Antiques
High St. Est. 1968. Open 10-5. CL: Wed pm. SIZE: Medium. *STOCK: Oak, pine country and painted furniture and associated items, 18th C to Victorian, £5-£1,000.* LOC: Off A21 on to A262, village about 3 miles. PARK: Easy. TEL: 01580 212476; home - 01580 211703. SER: Valuations.

HAMSTREET, Nr. Ashford

Woodville Antiques
The Street. TN26 2HG. (A.S. MacBean). Est. 1972. Open Tues.-Sat. 10-5.30. SIZE: Small. *STOCK: Woodworking tools, 18th-20th C; 19th C furniture, glass and pictures.* LOC: Village centre. PARK: Easy. TEL: 01233 732981; home - same; e-mail - woodvilleantique@yahoo.co.uk. SER: Valuations.

HYTHE

Malthouse Arcade
High St. CT21 5BW. (Mr and Mrs R.M. Maxtone Graham). Est. 1974. Open Fri., Sat. and Bank Holiday Mon. 9.30-5.30. SIZE: Large - 37 stalls. *STOCK: Furniture, jewellery and collectors' items.* LOC: West end of High St. PARK: 50yds. TEL: 01303 260103; home - 01304 613270.

Military History Bookshop
27 High St. CT21 5AD. (I.H. and G.M. Knight). Est. 1975. Open 10-5, Sat. 10-2. SIZE: Medium. *STOCK: Military books.* TEL: 01303 237883; fax - 01303 268149; e-mail - info@military historybooks.com; website - www.militaryhistory books.com. SER: Search.

Owlets
99 High St. CT21 5JH. Open 9-5. *STOCK: Antique and estate jewellery and silver.* TEL: 01303 230333; e-mail - alison@owlets.co.uk; website - www.owlets.co.uk.

Samovar Antiques
158 High St. CT21 5JR. (Mrs F. Rignault). Open 9.30-5, Wed. 9.30-1. *STOCK: 19th C and French provincial furniture, Oriental carpets and rugs, general antiques.* PARK: Own. TEL: 01303 264239.

LAMBERHURST

The China Locker
TN3 8HN. (G. Wilson). Est. 1973. Open by appointment. SIZE: Small. *STOCK: Prints, 18th-19th C, £5-£40.* TEL: 01892 890555. FAIRS: Local.

LITTLEBOURNE, Nr. Canterbury

Jimmy Warren Antiques
Cedar Lodge, 28 The Hill. CT3 1TA. Est. 1969. Open 10-5 including Sun. SIZE: Small. *STOCK: Decorative antiques and garden ornaments.* LOC: A257. PARK: Own. TEL: 01227 721510; e-mail - enquiries@jimmywarren.co.uk; website - www.jimmywarren.co.uk. SER: Valuations. VAT: Stan/Spec.

MAIDSTONE

Gem Antiques
10 Gabriels Hill. Est. 1969. Open 10-5. SIZE: Small. *STOCK: Clocks and barometers, £200-£10,000; jewellery, £5-£10,000.* TEL: 01622 763344. SER: Valuations; restorations; repairs.

Sutton Valence Antiques
Unit 4 Haslemere Estate, Sutton Rd. ME15 9NL. (T. and N. Mullarkey). Est. 1971. Open 9-5.30, Sun. 11-4. SIZE: Large warehouse. *STOCK: Antique and shipping furniture.* LOC: Approx. 3 miles south of Maidstone, just off A274. PARK: Easy. TEL: 01622 675332; fax - 01622 692593; e-mail - svantiques@aol.com; website - www.svantiques.co.uk. SER: Container packing and shipping; restorations; courier; buys at auction.

MARGATE

Cottage Antiques
172 Northdown Rd., Cliftonville. CT9 2RB. (D. J. and Mrs L. O. Empsley). Est. 1982. Open 10-5. CL: Wed. SIZE: Large. *STOCK: Furniture, 1700-1930; china, 1800-1950; jewellery, Victorian to Art Deco; general antiques and collectables.* PARK: Easy. TEL: 01843 298214; home - 01843 299166; mobile - 07771 542872; e-mail - davidjempsley@aol.com. SER: Valuations; restorations (furniture and china, replating).

Furniture Mart
Bath Place. CT9 2BN. (R.G. Scott). Est. 1971. CL: Wed. SIZE: Large. *STOCK: General antiques £1-£3,000; shipping goods.* LOC: Corner of Bath Place. TEL: 01843 220653. SER: Restorations; restoration materials supplied; container packing. VAT: Global/Stan.

NEWINGTON, Nr. Sittingbourne

Newington Antiques   `LAPADA`
58-60 High St. (Georgina McKinnon). Est. 1994. Open 10-5, Sun. 10-2 or by appointment. CL: Mon. and Wed. SIZE: Large. *STOCK: Furniture, late 18th to late 19th C, £500-£3,000; pre-1930 smalls, pictures, decorative items, £50-£4,000.* LOC: A2, close to A249, off junction 5, M2. PARK: Own. TEL: 01795 844448; fax - 01795 841448; website - www.antiqueskent.co.uk. SER: Valuations; restorations (furniture including upholstery, china, metal). FAIRS: Newark.

NORTHFLEET

Northfleet Hill Antiques
36 The Hill. DA11 9EX. (Mrs M. Kilby). Est.

1986. Open Mon., Tues., Fri., some Sats. 10-5 and by appointment. SIZE: Small. *STOCK: Furniture, 19th to early 20th C, £50-£800; bygones and collectables, £1-£100.* LOC: A226 near junction with B261 and B2175. PARK: Easy (behind Ye Olde Coach and Horses Inn). TEL: 01474 321521. FAIRS: Chelsea.

OTFORD

Ellenor Antiques and Tea Shop
11a High St. TN14. (Ellenor Hospice Care). Open 10-5. SIZE: Medium. *STOCK: Furniture, ceramics, glass, 18th to early 20th C, £5-£1,500.* LOC: Towards Sevenoaks, 3 miles south of junction 4, M25. PARK: Nearby. TEL: 01959 524322. SER: Items sold on donation or commission basis for hospice charity.

Mandarin Gallery - Oriental Art
The Mill Pond, 16 High St. TN14 5PQ. (J. and M.C. Liu). Est. 1984. Open 10-5. CL: Wed. SIZE: Medium. *STOCK: Chinese rosewood and lacquer furniture, 18th-19th C; jade and soap stone, ivory and wood carvings.* Not Stocked: Non-Oriental items. LOC: A225. PARK: Easy. TEL: 01959 522778; home - 01732 457399; fax - same; e-mail - mandaringallery@hotmail.com. SER: Restorations (Chinese rosewood furniture).

Otford Antiques & Collectors Centre
26-28 High St. TN15 9DF. (Mr and Mrs David Lowrie). Est. 1997. Open 10-5, Sun. 11-4. SIZE: Large. *STOCK: Furniture and collectables, to £800+.* PARK: Easy. TEL: 01959 522025; fax - 01732 883365; website - www.otfordantiques.co.uk. SER: Restorations (polishing, caning and upholstery).

PETTS WOOD, Nr. Orpington

Beehive
22 Station Sq. BR5 1NA. Est. 1994. Open 9.30-5, Sat. 9.30-4.30. SIZE: 50 dealers. *STOCK: Collectables, china, glass, jewellery and furniture, 19th-20th C, £1-£1,000.* PARK: Easy. TEL: 01689 890675. FAIRS: Bexleyheath.

RAMSGATE

Granny's Attic
2 Addington St. CT11 9JL. (Penelope J. Warn). Est. 1987. Open 10-5. CL: Thurs. pm. SIZE: Medium. *STOCK: Pre-1940's items, £2-£1,500.* LOC: Left off harbour approach road or right off Westcliffe Rd. PARK: Easy. TEL: 01843 588955; home - 01843 596288; mobile - 07773 155339. SER: Free local delivery, national and Continental delivery by arrangement.

Thanet Antiques
45 Albert St. CT11 9EX. (Mr and Mrs R. Fomison). Est. 1971. Open by appointment. SIZE: Large. *STOCK: Furniture and bric-a-brac, 18th-20th C, £1-£5,000.* LOC: From London Rd. right to seafront. With harbour on right turn first left down Addington St., then last right. PARK: Own. TEL: 01843 597336; home - 01843 597540; e-mail - fomison@aol.com; website - www.thanetantiques.co.uk.

ROCHESTER

Baggins Book Bazaar - The Largest Secondhand Bookshop in England
19 High St. ME1 1PY. Est. 1986. Open 10-6 including Sun. SIZE: Large. *STOCK: Secondhand and antiquarian books.* LOC: Next to the Guildhall Museum. PARK: Nearby. TEL: 01634 811651; fax - 01634 840591; website - www.bagginsbooks.co.uk. SER: Book search.

City Antiques Ltd
78 High St. ME1 1JY. (Bryan Ware). Est. 1987. Open 10-5. SIZE: Medium. *STOCK: Clocks - longcase, mantel and bracket, 1760-1930, £300-£4,000; Georgian to Edwardian furniture, £200-£2,500; barometers - banjo, Fitzroy, stick, aneroid and mercury, 1800-1940, £250-£2,000; silver, pocket watches and china.* LOC: Central. PARK: Nearby. TEL: 01634 841278; e-mail - wareclockmad@aol.com. SER: Valuations; restorations (clocks).

Cottage Style Antiques
24 Bill Street Rd. ME2 4RB. (W. Miskimmin). Est. 1981. Open 9.30-5.30. *STOCK: General and architectural antiques.* TEL: 01634 717623.

Field Staff & Woods
93 High St. ME1 1LX. (Jim Field, Jane Staff and John Wood). Open 10-5. SIZE: Large - 3 showrooms. *STOCK: General antiques and collectables.* LOC: Centre of High St. TEL: 01634 846144/840108.

Francis Iles
Rutland House, La Providence, High St. ME1 1LX. (The Family Iles). Est. 1960. Open 9.30-5.30. SIZE: Large. *STOCK: Over 700 works, all mediums including sculpture, mainly 20th C, £50-£10,000.* PARK: 40yds. TEL: 01634 843081; fax - 01634 846681; e-mails - advice@artycat.com; nettie@francis-iles.com; websites - www.francis-iles.com and www.artycat.com. SER: Restorations; cleaning; relining; framing. FAIRS: Affordable Art (Spring). VAT: Stan/Spec.

Kaizen International Ltd

88 High St. ME1 1JT. (Jason Hunt). Est. 1997. Open 9-5.30. SIZE: Medium. *STOCK: General antiques including antique and secondhand jewellery.* PARK: Nearby. TEL: 01634 814132; website - www.kaizenInternational.com. SER: Valuations; restorations (jewellery).

Langley Galleries

143 High St. ME1 1EL. (K.J. Cook). Est. 1978. Open 9-5. *STOCK: Prints, watercolours, oils, 19th-20th C.* TEL: 01634 811802. SER: Framing.

Memories

128 High St. ME1 1JT. (Mrs M. Bond, Mrs D. Deltufo, Mrs J. Davies and Mrs J. Birkill). Est. 1985. Open 9-5, Sun. 11-5. SIZE: Medium. *STOCK: Small furniture, £50-£500; china, £5-£75; both 1900-1950; pictures, late Victorian to Edwardian, £20-£70; collectables, bric-a-brac, linen and books.* PARK: Opposite. TEL: 01634 811044.

ROLVENDEN, Nr. Cranbrook

Falstaff Antiques

63-67 High St. TN17 4LP. (C.M. Booth). Est. 1964. Open 9-6, Sun. by appointment. SIZE: Medium. *STOCK: English furniture, £5-£700; china, metal, glass, silver, £1-£200.* Not Stocked: Paintings. LOC: On A28, 3 miles from Tenterden, 1st shop on left in village. PARK: Easy. TEL: 01580 241234. SER: Valuations. VAT: Stan/Spec.

Harriet Ann Sleigh Beds

Cherry Garden Farm, Hastings Rd. TN17 4PL. (Mrs R. Churchod). Est. 1987. Open by appointment. SIZE: Medium. *STOCK: Eastern European and Scandinavian sleigh beds; French fruitwood doubles or singles; European pine armoires, chests and cabinets; bedside lights, bedroom decorative accessories especially childrens.* PARK: Easy. TEL: 01580 243005. SER: Mattresses available to order; reproduction beds in certain styles.

J.D. and R.M. Walters

10 Regent St. TN17 4PE. Est. 1977. Open 8-6, Sat. 11-4.30 or by appointment. SIZE: Small. *STOCK: Mahogany furniture, 18th-19th C.* LOC: A28 turn left in village centre onto B2086, shop on left. PARK: Easy. TEL: 01580 241563; home - same. SER: Handmade copies of period furniture including chairs; restorations (GMC). VAT: Stan/Spec.

SANDGATE

Antique Country Furniture and Interiors

21 High St. CT20 3BD. (Gabrielle de Giles). Est. 1987. Open Tues.-Sat. 10.30-5. *STOCK: Country furniture, mainly French, 18th-20th C, to £5,000.* PARK: Behind shop. TEL: 01303 255600; fax - 01233 720156; mobile - 07721 015263; e-mail - gabrielle@gabrielledegiles.com; website - www. gabrielledegiles.com

Christopher Buck Antiques `BADA`

56-60 High St. CT20 3AP. (Christopher and Jane Buck). Est. 1983. Open 10-5. CL: Wed. SIZE: Medium. STOCK: English furniture, 18th C, £500-£30,000; decorative items, 18th-19th C, £100-£2,000. LOC: 5 mins. from junction 12, M20 and Channel Tunnel. PARK: Easy. TEL: 01303 221229; fax - 01303 221229; e-mail - cb@christopherbuck.co.uk. SER: Valuations; restorations (furniture); buys at auction. FAIRS: Olympia (June, Nov); BADA (March). VAT: Stan/Spec.

Finch Antiques

40 High St. CT20 3AP. (Robert and Sylvia Finch). Est. 1978. Open 9.30-6, Sun. 10.30-4. SIZE: Medium. *STOCK: Furniture, 1800-1920, £150-£3,000; silver plate and writing items, £5-£400.* PARK: Easy. TEL: 01303 240725. SER: Restorations (furniture, French polishing).

Michael Fitch Antiques `LAPADA`

95-99 High St. CT20 3BY. Est. 1980. Open 10-

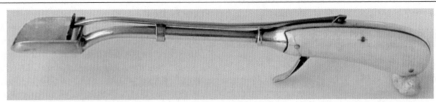

A very rare electroplated cheese scoop, the pistol-grip ivory handle with sprung trigger operating the pusher. Struck four times with the marker's mark 'HA' for Atkin Brothers, and stamped 'Registered 6th September 1870', £375. (Schredds of Portobello)

From an article entitled "Silver Stilton Cheese Scoops" by Jane Ewart which appeared in the December/January 2003 issue of *Antique Collecting*. For more details and to subscribe see page 21.

5.30, Sun. by appointment. SIZE: Large. *STOCK: Georgian, Victorian and Edwardian furniture and clocks.* PARK: Own. TEL: 01303 249600; fax - same; website - www.michaelfitchantiques.co.uk. SER: Delivery; shipping advice.

Freeman and Lloyd Antiques   BADA LAPADA

44 High St. CT20 3AP. (K. Freeman and M.R. Lloyd). CINOA. Est. 1968. Open 10-5.30, Mon., Wed. and Fri. by appointment only. SIZE: Medium. STOCK: Fine Georgian and Regency English furniture; clocks, paintings and other period items. LOC: On main coast road between Hythe and Folkestone (A259). PARK: Easy. TEL: 01303 248986; fax - 01303 241353; mobile - 07860 100073; e-mail - enquiries@freemanandlloyd.com; website - www.freemanandlloyd.com. SER: Valuations. FAIRS: Olympia (Feb., June, Nov.); BADA (March). VAT: Spec.

David Gilbert Antiques
30 High St. CT20 3AP. Est. 1975. Open 9-5. SIZE: Medium. *STOCK: Furniture, smalls, glass, 1790-1930, £5-£1,000.* LOC: A259. PARK: Easy. TEL: 01303 850491; home - 01304 812237. SER: Valuations.

Jonathan Greenwall Antiques   LAPADA
61-63 High St. CT20 3AH. Est. 1964. Open 9.30-5. SIZE: Large. *STOCK: Furniture, to 19th C; decorative items, jewellery, oils and watercolours, prints and maps, sculpture and bronzes.* LOC: Folkestone-Brighton road. PARK: Easy. TEL: 01303 248987. SER: Valuations.

David M. Lancefield Antiques   LAPADA
53 High St. CT20 3AH. Est. 1976. Open 10-6, Sun. and Bank Holidays 11-5. SIZE: Large. *STOCK: Furniture, 17th-20th C; silver, metalware, decorative items, ceramics, mainly 18th-20th C.* PARK: Own. TEL: 01303 850149; fax - same; e-mail - david@antique direct.freeserve.co.uk; website - www.davidm lancefield.co.uk. SER: Valuations; restorations.

J. Luckhurst Antiques
63 High St. CT20 3AH. Est. 1989. Open 9.30-5 and by appointment. SIZE: Small. *STOCK: Furniture - Georgian, Victorian, Edwardian and decorative; gilt mirrors, carpets.* PARK: Nearby. TEL: Home - 01303 891642; mobile - 07786 983231. SER: Valuations; restorations (period furniture). FAIRS: Newark; Ardingly.

Annette Mobbs Antiques

53 High St. CT20 3AH. Est. 1991. Open 10-6, Sun. 11-5. SIZE: Large. *STOCK: Furniture and silver, late 18th-20th C; coloured pot-lids, 19th C; drinking glasses, jewellery, prints, table lamps, decorative items, 19th-20th C.* LOC: Village centre. PARK: Easy. TEL: 01303 850149; fax - same.

Old English Oak

102 High St. CT20 3BY. (A. Martin). Est. 1997. Open 10-6. *STOCK: Oak furniture and interesting items.* PARK: Nearby. TEL: 01303 248560.

Old English Pine

100 High St. CT20 3BY. (A. Martin). Est. 1986. Open 10-6. SIZE: 15 showrooms. *STOCK: Pine furniture and interesting items.* PARK: Nearby. TEL: 01303 248560.

Brian West Antiques

Emporium, 31-33 High St. CT20 3AH. Est. 1978. Prior telephone call advisable. SIZE: Medium. *STOCK: Arts and Crafts, Art Nouveau, Aesthetic Movement, Gothic Revival and decorative Victorian and Edwardian furniture, £100-£3,000.* LOC: Village centre. PARK: Nearby - on sea front. TEL: 01303 244430; mobile - 07860 149387.

SANDHURST

Forge Antiques and Restorations

Rye Rd. TN18 5JG. (James Nesfield). Est. 1975. Open 10-1 and 2-5, Sat. 10-5, Sun. and Mon. by appointment. *STOCK: Victorian and Edwardian furniture, £100-£1,200; ceramics, 18th-20th C, £5-£1,000.* LOC: A268. PARK: Own. TEL: 01580 850308; home - 01580 850665. SER: Valuations; restorations (furniture). FAIRS: Penshurst, Ardingly, Maidstone. VAT: Spec.

SANDWICH

All Our Yesterdays & Chris Baker Gramophones

3 Cattle Market. CT13 9AE. (Sandie and Chris Baker). Est. 1994. Open 10.30-2.30, Fri. 10.30-2, Sat. 10.30-3.30, Sun. by appointment. CL: Wed. *STOCK: General antiques, gramophones and associated items, £5-£1,000.* PARK: Behind Guildhall. TEL: 01304 614756; e-mail - cbgramophones@aol.com. SER: Repairs (gramophones, phonographs, etc).

James Porter Antiques

5 Potter St. CT13 9DR. Est. 1948. Open 9.30-5.30. CL: Wed. *STOCK: Period furniture, brass

and copper.* PARK: Market St. TEL: 01304 612218.

Sandwich Fine Books

41 Strand St. CT13 9DN. (Nick McConnell). ABA. PBFA. Est. 1976. Open by appointment. SIZE: Medium. *STOCK: Leather-bound antiquarian books.* LOC: Central. PARK: Nearby. TEL: 01304 620300; fax - same; mobile - 07977 573766; e-mail - Mcconnellbooks@ aol.com; website - www.abebooks.com/home/ sandwichfinebooks. SER: Valuations. FAIRS: ABA - Olympia, Chelsea Town Hall; monthly PBFA Russell Hotel.

SEVENOAKS

Antiques & Fine Furniture

18 London Rd., Dunton Green. TN13 2UE. (C.E. West). Est. 1977. Open 10-5. SIZE: Large. *STOCK: Clocks and watches, period furniture, porcelain, glass, toys, bric-a-brac.* LOC: London road into town, opposite Whitmore's Vauxhall showroom. PARK: Easy. TEL: 01732 464346. SER: Valuations; restorations (clocks, furniture); re-upholstery, curtains and soft furnishings).

Neill Robinson Blaxill `LAPADA`

21 St. John's Hill. TN13 3NX. FBHI. Open 9-6, appointment preferred. *STOCK: Clocks, barometers, decorative items and furniture, 17th-19th C.* LOC: 1 mile from High St. PARK: Easy. TEL: 01732 454179; website - www.antiques-clocks.co.uk. SER: Valuations; restorations.

Gem Antiques

122 High St. TN13 1XA. Est. 1969. Open 10-5. SIZE: Small. *STOCK: Clocks and furniture, 17th-19th C, £500-£10,000; jewellery, 18th-20th C, £10-£10,000.* LOC: Next door to Boots. PARK: Nearby. TEL: 01732 743540. SER: Valuations; restorations (as stock). VAT: Spec.

Sargeant Antiques

26 London Rd. TN13 1AP. (D. and Miss A. Sargeant). Est. 1947. Open 9-5, Wed. 9-1, Sat. 10-5. SIZE: Medium. *STOCK: Georgian and Victorian glass and furniture, from £60; collectables; lighting including chandeliers.* LOC: Town centre. PARK: Nearby. TEL: 01732 457304; fax - 01732 457688; mobile - 07771 553632/553624. SER: Valuations; restorations (lighting).

Woven Magic `LAPADA`

3 Blighs Court. TN13 1DD. (J. Caslake). Est. 1997. Open 10-6, Sun. by appointment. *STOCK: Oriental carpets and rugs, £250-£10,000; kilim stools, £85-£550; kilim and carpet cushions, £20-

£75. TEL: 01732 469477; fax - 01732 469974. SER: Valuations; restorations; hand-cleaning; kilim stools and cushions made to order. FAIRS: Olympia (June).

SIDCUP

Memory Lane Antiques & Collectables
143 Station Rd. DA15 7AA. (Mrs Lynn Brackley). Est. 1999. Open 10-5.30, Sat. 10-5, Sun. by appointment. CL: Wed. SIZE: Small. STOCK: Furniture, china, vintage clothes, linen, reproduction lamps, £5-£1,000. LOC: Opposite station. PARK: At rear and station. TEL: 020 8300 0552; home - 020 8304 7066.

Ward Antiques
105 Main Rd. DA14 6ND. (T. and M. Ward). Est. 1981. Open 10-5, Sun. 11-2. SIZE: Large. STOCK: Fireplaces, Victorian and Edwardian furniture; £50-£1,000. LOC: Off A20. PARK: Opposite. TEL: 020 8302 2929.

SOUTHBOROUGH, Nr. Tunbridge Wells

Henry Baines BADA LAPADA
14 Church Rd. TN4 0RX. Est. 1968. Open Tues.-Fri. 10-5, Sat. 10-4.30, prior telephone call advisable. SIZE: Medium. STOCK: Early oak and country furniture especially tables and sets of chairs; French provincial furniture and decorative items. PARK: Easy. TEL: 01892 532099. VAT: Stan/Spec.

Peter Hoare Antiques
35 London Rd. TN4 0PB. Est. 1985. Open 10-5.30. CL: Mon. SIZE: Medium. STOCK: British Arts and Crafts furniture, Gothic revival, aesthetic movement, 19th-20th C design, £25-£5,000. LOC: A26. PARK: At rear. TEL: 01892 524623; fax - 01892 619776. SER: Valuations.

STAPLEHURST, Nr. Tonbridge

Staplehurst Antiques
Crampton House, High St. TN12 0AU. (Mr and Mrs Draper). Est. 1991. Open 10-4.30. CL: Mon. SIZE: Medium. STOCK: Dining furniture including sideboards and cabinets, late Victorian to 1930's, £300-£2,500; collectables, £1-£250. PARK: Easy. TEL: 01580 890424; website - www.staplehurst-antiques.co.uk. SER: Restorations (furniture). VAT: Stan/Spec.

STOCKBURY

Steppes Hill Farm Antiques BADA
The Hill Farm, South St. ME9 7RB. (W.F.A. Buck). Est. 1965. Always open, appointment

advisable. SIZE: Medium. STOCK: English porcelain, pottery, pot-lids, 18th-20th C, to £30,000; small silver; caddy spoons, wine labels, silver boxes, furniture, 18th-19th C, to £30,000. LOC: 5 mins. from M2 on A249. Enquire in village for Steppes Hill Antiques. PARK: Easy. TEL: 01795 842205. SER: Valuations; buys at auction. FAIRS: BADA; International Ceramics; Olympia (Nov). VAT: Spec.

SUNDRIDGE, Nr. Sevenoaks

Sundridge Gallery
9 Church Rd. TN14 6DT. (T. and M. Tyrer). Est. 1986. Open 10-5.30. STOCK: Watercolours and oils, 19th-20th C. LOC: Off M25, junction 5. PARK: Easy. TEL: 01959 564104. SER: Restorations. VAT: Spec

SUTTON VALENCE, Nr. Maidstone

Sutton Valence Antiques
North St. ME17 3AP. (T.,N.and J. Mullarkey and O. Marles). CINOA. Est. 1971. Open 9-5, Sat. 10-4. SIZE: Large. STOCK: Furniture, porcelain, clocks, silver, metalware, 18th-20th C. LOC: On A274 Maidstone to Tenterden Rd. PARK: Side of shop. TEL: 01622 843333; fax - 01622 843499; e-mail - svantiques@aol.com; website - www.svantiques.co.uk SER: Valuations; restorations; container packing and shipping; courier; buys at auction.

TENTERDEN

Flower House Antiques LAPADA
90 High St. TN30 6JB. (Barry Rayner and Quentin Johnson). Open 9.30-5.30, Sun. by appointment. SIZE: Medium. STOCK: English and Continental furniture, 16th to early 19th C; Oriental works of art, 16th-19th C; pictures, lighting, mirrors, objets d'art. LOC: A28. PARK: Easy and private. TEL: 01580 763764. SER: Valuations; restorations. VAT: Spec.

Gaby's Clocks and Things
140 High St. TN30 6HT. (Gaby Gunst). Est. 1972. Open 10.30-5. SIZE: Small. STOCK: Clocks - longcase and grandmother, regulator wall, English dial, bracket, mantel and skeleton, restored and guaranteed. PARK: Limited or nearby. TEL: 01580 765818. SER: Valuations; restorations (clocks).

Tenterden Antiques and Silver Vaults
66 High St. TN30 6AU. (T.J. Smith). Open 10-5 including Sun. STOCK: Clocks, silver, telephones, barometers and general antiques. PARK: Easy. TEL: 01580 765885.

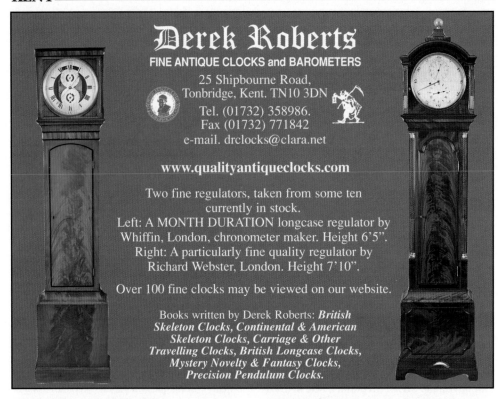
TEYNHAM, Nr. Sittingbourne

Jackson-Grant Antiques
The Old Chapel, 133 London Rd. ME9 9QJ.
(D.M. Jackson-Grant). Est. 1966. Open 10-5,
Sun. 1-5. SIZE: Large. STOCK: General
antiques, French and English furniture,
bookcases, buffets, beds, smalls, 18th C to Art
Deco, £5-£3,000. LOC: A2 between Faversham
and Sittingbourne. PARK: Easy. TEL: 01795
522027; home - same; mobile - 07831 591881; e-
mail - david.jacksongrant@bt.openworld.com;
website - www.jackson-grantantiques.co.uk.
SER: Customised tester beds available. VAT:
Stan/Spec.

Peggottys
The Old Chapel, 133 London Rd. ME9 9QJ. (B.
Smith). Est. 1999. Open 10-5, Sun. 1-5. SIZE:
Large. STOCK: Beds including wooden, half-
testers and four-posters, French, English and
Flemish, 1800-1920; Edwardian, Victorian,
Georgian, Rococo, Renaissance, Breton and
Henri 11, £750-£5,000. LOC: A2 Village centre.
PARK: Outside. TEL: 01795 522027; home -
same; website - www.peggottysbeds.co.uk.

TONBRIDGE

Barden House Antiques
1-3 Priory St. TN9 2AP. (Mrs B.D. Parsons).
Open 10-5. SIZE: 3 dealers. STOCK: General
antiques and collectables. PARK: Nearby. TEL:
01732 350142; evenings - 01732 355718.

The New Curiosity Shop
7 Tollgate Buildings, Hadlow Rd. TN9 1NX.
(Greta May). Est. 1987. Open Tues., Thurs., Fri.
and Sat. 10-5. SIZE: Small. STOCK: General
antiques and collectables including old and artist
bears, from Victorian. LOC: A26 off High St.
PARK: Adjacent. TEL: 01732 366730; e-mail -
gretamayantiques@hotmail.com. SER: Valuations;
restorations (teddy bears). FAIRS: Ramada Hotel.

Derek Roberts Fine Antique Clocks & Barometers BADA
25 Shipbourne Rd. TN10 3DN. Est. 1968. Open
9.30-5.30 or by appointment. SIZE: Large.
STOCK: Fine restored clocks, mostly £2,000-
£100,000. LOC: From Hildenborough B245 to
Tonbridge, left just before first lights, left again,
shop 50 yards on right. PARK: Easy. TEL: 01732
358986; fax - 01732 771842; e-mail - drclocks@
clara.net; website - www.qualityantiqueclocks.
com. SER: Cabinet making. VAT: Spec.

B.V.M. Somerset

Stags Head, 9 Stafford Rd. TN9 1HT. Est. 1948. Open 11-6.30. *STOCK: Clocks, £500-£5,000.* LOC: Off High St. beside castle. TEL: 01732 352017; fax - 01732 368343. SER: Valuations; restorations (cabinets, gilt and French polishing); buys at auction (longcase and bracket clocks). VAT: Stan.

TUNBRIDGE WELLS

Aaron Antiques

77 St. Johns Rd. TN4 9TT. (R.J. Goodman). Open 9-5. *STOCK: Clocks and pocket watches, paintings and prints; period and shipping furniture; English, Continental and Oriental porcelain; antiquarian books, postcards, coins and medals.* TEL: 01892 517644. VAT: Stan/Spec.

Amadeus Antiques

32 Mount Ephraim. TN3. (P.A. Davies). Open 10-5, Sun. by appointment. SIZE: Medium. *STOCK: Unusual furniture, to Art Deco, £50-£5,000; china and bric-a-brac, £25-£500; chandeliers, £100-£1,000.* LOC: Near hospital. PARK: Easy. TEL: 01892 544406; 01892 864884. SER: Valuations.

The Architectural Emporium

55 St John's Rd. TN4 9TP. (Mike Roberts and Nick Bates). SALVO. Est. 1988. Open 10-5.30. SIZE: Medium. *STOCK: Fireplaces, garden statuary, lighting, decorative salvage, Georgian to Edwardian.* LOC: A26 towards Southborough. PARK: John St. TEL: 01892 540368; website - www.architecturalemporium.com. VAT: Stan/Spec.

Beau Nash Antiques

29 Lower Walk, The Pantiles. TN2 5TD. (Nicola Rowlett and David Wrenn). Est. 1992. Open 11-5. CL: Mon. and Fri. SIZE: Medium. *STOCK: Furniture, silver, porcelain and glass, 18th-20th C.* LOC: Behind Tourist Information Centre. PARK: Pantiles. TEL: 01892 537810.

Calverley Antiques

30 Crescent Rd. TN1 2LZ. (P. A. Nimmo). Est. 1995. Open 10-5.30 including Sun. *STOCK: Furniture including European pine, 1920's oak, decorative painted and garden.* LOC: Near police station and Assembly Hall. PARK: Multi-storey next door. TEL: 01892 538254; e-mail - phil@calverleyantiques.com. FAIRS: Ardingly.

Chapel Place Antiques

9 Chapel Place. TN1 1YQ. (J. and A. Clare). Est. 1984. Open 9-6. *STOCK: Silver photo frames, antique and modern jewellery, old silver plate,* claret jugs, hand-painted Limoge boxes. LOC: Near The Pantiles. PARK: Nearby. TEL: 01892 546561.

Claremont Antiques

48 St John's Rd. TN4 9NY. (Anthony Broad). Open 10-5.30, other times by appointment. SIZE: Large + trade warehouse. *STOCK: British, French and Continental original painted pine country furniture, fruitwood farm tables, 18th-19th C; some decorative items; all £10-£5,000.* LOC: On A26 London Road, by St John's Church. PARK: Easy. TEL: 01892 511651; fax - 01892 517360; e-mail - ant@claremont antiques.com; website - www.claremontantiques.com. VAT: Stan/Spec.

Down Lane Hall Antiques

Culverden Down, St John's. TN4 9SA. (Michael Howlett). Est. 1980. Open 9-5, Sat. 10-5. SIZE: Large. *STOCK: Georgian, Victorian and Edwardian furniture; clocks and barometers.* LOC: Half mile from town centre, on A26. PARK: Easy. TEL: 01892 522440; home - 01892 522425. SER: Restorations; French polishing.

Glassdrumman Antiques

7 Union Square, The Pantiles. TN4 8HE. (Graham and Amanda Dyson Rooke). Open Tues.-Sat. 10-5.30. SIZE: Medium. *STOCK: Silver, jewellery, watches, clocks, furniture, decorative items, 18th-20th C.* PARK: Nearby. TEL: 01892 538615; fax - same. VAT: Stan/Spec.

Pamela Goodwin

11 The Pantiles. TN2 5TD. Est. 1980. Open 9.30-5, Sat. 9.30-5.30. SIZE: Medium. *STOCK: Furniture, longcase and wall clocks, mirrors, oil lamps, ceramics, silver and glass, collectibles, Tunbridgeware, music boxes, decorative items, 18th-20th C, £50-£5,000.* LOC: Central. PARK: Nearby. TEL: 01892 618200; fax - same; e-mail - mail@goodwinantiques.co.uk; website - www.goodwinantiques.co.uk.

Ivy Hale

48A St John's Rd. TN4 9NY. Est. 1988. Open 10-5.30. SIZE: Medium. *STOCK: Oak and country furniture and related decorative items, £50-£4,000.* PARK: Nearby. TEL: 01892 614004; mobile - 07788 598785; e-mail - mail@ivyhale.com. SER: Valuations; restorations.

Hall's Bookshop

20-22 Chapel Place. TN1 1YQ. Est. 1898. Open 9.30-5. *STOCK: Antiquarian and secondhand books.* TEL: 01892 527842.

Kent & Sussex Gold Refiners

7 Vale Rd. (Mr and Mrs A.C. Padley). NAG. Est. 1926. Open 9-5.30. CL: Wed. *STOCK: Antique and modern jewellery, silver and plate, £15-£100,000.* LOC: Around corner from High St. PARK: Nearby. TEL: 01892 526084; fax - 01892 543602. SER: Valuations; restorations (antique silver and jewellery). VAT: Stan/Spec.

Kentdale Antiques

Motts Farm Estate, Forge Rd., Eridge Green. TN3 9LJ. (C. Bigwood and T. Rayfield). Est. 1981. Open 9-5. CL: Sat. SIZE: Warehouse. *STOCK: Mostly mahogany and walnut furniture.* LOC: Telephone for directions. PARK: Easy. TEL: 01892 863840; fax - same; e-mail - kentdale. antiques@ukgateway.net. SER: Restorations (furniture). VAT: Stan/Spec.*Trade only.*

Mason's Antiques

49 St John's Rd. TN4 9TP. (D.J. Mason). Est. 1986. Open 11-4. *STOCK: Furniture - chairs, chests including painted, desks.* PARK: Easy. TEL: 01892 515864

Millennium Centre Antiques

58 St John's Rd. TN4 9NY. (Mr and Mrs Watson). Est. 1995. Open 10-5.30, Sat. 10-5. SIZE: Medium. *STOCK: 18th-19th C English and French furniture, £10-£2,000.* PARK: Easy and free opposite. TEL: 01892 678830; fax - same; mobile - 07946 891896; website - www. millenniumcentreantiques.co.uk. SER: Valuations; restorations (French polishing). FAIRS: Chelsea Brocante.

Howard Neville Antiques

21 The Pantiles. TN4. (H.C.C. Neville). Est. 1967. Open by appointment. SIZE: Medium. *STOCK: General antiques, furniture, sculpture and works of art, 16th-18th C.* PARK: Easy. TEL: 01892 511461; home - 01435 882409. SER: Valuations; restorations. VAT: Spec.

Old Colonial

56 St John's Rd., St John's. TN4 9NY. (Dee Martyn and Suzy Rees). Est. 1982. Open 10-5.30. SIZE: Small. *STOCK: English and French country and decorative furniture and associated smalls.* LOC: Approximately 1 mile outside Tunbridge Wells. PARK: Opposite. TEL: 01892 533993; fax - 01892 513281. VAT: Spec.

The Pantiles Antiques

31 The Pantiles. TN2 5TD. (Mrs E.M. Blackburn). Est. 1979. Open 10-5. SIZE: Medium. *STOCK: Georgian, Victorian and Edwardian furniture; 19th C porcelain, silver.* LOC: Lower Walk. PARK: Easy. TEL: 01892 531291.

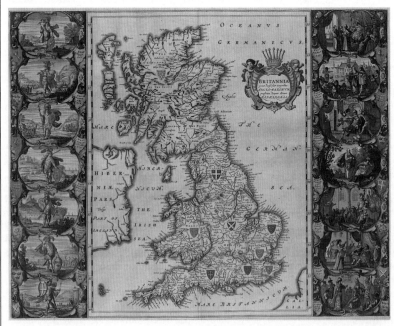

Joan Blaeu's map of Saxon Britain, 1645 (16¾in. x 21in.). Copied from a prototype Speed map but with finer design and engraving. General maps of the British Isles of this period can be £500-£2,500 and Blaeu county maps £300-£1,000.

From an article entitled "Antique County Maps" by Jonathan Potter which appeared in the September 2002 issue of *Antique Collecting*. For more details and to subscribe see page 21.

Pantiles Oriental Carpets

31A The Pantiles. TN2 5TD. (Judith Williams). Est. 1980. Open 10-5.30. CL: Wed. SIZE: Small. *STOCK: Oriental carpets, rugs, kelims and tribal artifacts.* LOC: Lower walk. PARK: Nearby. TEL: 01892 530416; fax - 01892 530416. SER: Restorations and cleaning (carpets, rugs, kelims, tapestries).

Pantiles Spa Antiques

4/5/6 Union Square, The Pantiles. TN4 8HE. (J.A. Cowpland). Est. 1979. Open 9.30-5, Sat. 9.30-5.30. SIZE: Large. *STOCK: Period and Victorian furniture especially dining tables and chairs, £200-£10,000; pictures, £50-£3,000; clocks, £100-£5,000; porcelain, £50-£2,000; silver, £50-£1,000; all 17th-19th C; dolls, bears and toys.* PARK: Nearby. TEL: 01892 541377; fax - 01435 865660; e-mail - psa.wells@ btinternet.com; website - www.antiques-tun-wells-kent.co.uk. SER: Restorations (furniture); 30 mile radius free delivery (large items). VAT: Spec.

Payne & Son (Silversmiths) Ltd

Clock House, 37 High St. TN1 1XL. (E.D., M.D. and A.E. Payne). NAG: FGA. Est. 1790. Open 9-5.30, Mon. 9.30-5.30, Sat. 9-5. SIZE: Medium. *STOCK: Jewellery, Victorian to modern; silver, Georgian to modern; Swiss watches, to modern; all £50-£10,000+.* LOC: Halfway along High St., marked by projecting clock. PARK: Limited. TEL: 01892 525874; fax - 01892 535447; e-mail - jewellers@payneandson.com; website - www. payneandson.com. SER: Valuations; restorations (jewellery, silver, watches and clocks)

Phoenix Antiques

51-53 St. John's Rd. TN4 9TP. (Peter Janes, Jane Stott and Robert Pilbeam). Est. 1982. Open 10-5.30 or by appointment. SIZE: Large. *STOCK: 18th-19th C French, English, original painted and country furniture, decorative furnishings, original gilt overmantel mirrors, garden statuary.* LOC: On A26 from A21 into town, by St. John's Church. PARK: Easy. TEL: 01892 549099; e-mail - robert.pilbeam@virgin.net. VAT: Spec.

Redleaf Gallery

1 Castle St. TN1 1XJ. (Nick Hills). Open Tues.-Sat. 10.30-5.30. *STOCK: 19th-20th C watercolours, modern British and contemporary paintings.* LOC: Off High St. PARK: Nearby. TEL: 01892 526695. VAT: Spec.

Ian Relf Antiques

132/134 Camden Rd. TN4. Open 9.30-1.30 and 2.30-5.30. *STOCK: Mainly furniture.* TEL: 01892 538362.

Sporting Antiques

10 Union House, The Pantiles. TN4 8HE. (L.A. Franklin and Mrs Pat Hayes). Est. 1996. Open 10-5.30. SIZE: Small. *STOCK: Firearms - civil and military pistols, civil, military and sporting longarms; edged weapons - swords, bayonets, daggers and knives; fishing tackle - rods, reels, gaffs and nets; marine - telescopes, binoculars, compasses, clocks, sextants; surveying - levels, scopes, theodolites, instruments; sporting - golf, football, rugby, fencing, skiing, croquet; sporting and military prints.* PARK: Nearby. TEL: 01892 522661; fax - same.

John Thompson

27 The Pantiles. TN2 5TD. Est. 1982. Open 10-1 and 2-5. SIZE: Medium. *STOCK: Furniture, late 17th to early 19th C; paintings 17th-20th C; decorative items.* Not Stocked: Jewellery, silver and militaria. PARK: Linden Road or Warwick Park. TEL: 01892 547215. VAT: Spec.

Tunbridge Wells Antiques

12 Union Sq., The Pantiles. TN4 8HE. (N.J. Harding). Est. 1980. Open 10-5. SIZE: Large. *STOCK: Antiques and collectables including silver, jewellery, Georgian, Victorian and Edwardian furniture, soft furnishings, Staffordshire figures, clocks and watches, samplers, collectables, Tunbridgeware, antique-related reference books.* PARK: Nearby. TEL: 01892 533708; e-mail - nick@staffordshirefigures.com; website - www. staffordshirefigures.com. SER: Valuations; buys at auction (Tunbridgeware) shipping. VAT: Stan/Spec.

Up Country

The Old Corn Stores, 68 St. John's Rd. TN4 9PE. (G.J. Price and C.M. Springett). Est. 1988. Open 9-5.30. SIZE: Large. *STOCK: British and European country furniture, £50-£5,000; associated decorative and interesting items, £5-£500; all 18th-19th C.* LOC: On main London road to Southborough and A21 trunk road which joins M25 and M26 at Sevenoaks intersection. PARK: Own at rear. TEL: 01892 523341; fax - 01892 530382; e-mail - mail@upcountry antiques.co.uk; website - www.upcountry antiques.co.uk. VAT: Stan.

Variety Box

16 Chapel Place. TN1 1YQ. Est. 1955. Open 9.45-5. CL: Wed. SIZE: Small. *STOCK: Tunbridge ware and sewing antiques, 19th C, £5-£300; hatpins, 20th C, £5-£100; small collectables, 18th-20th C, £5-£100.* LOC: 2 mins. from Pantiles towards High St. PARK: Limited. TEL: 01892 531868; e-mail - antiques@varietyboxantiques.com. FAIRS: Ardingly, Newark, Alexandra Palace.

The Vintage Watch Co.
The Old Pipe House, 74 High St. TN1 1YB. (F. Lawrence). Open Wed.-Sat. 10-5. *STOCK: Pre-1950's fine wrist watches, pocket watches.* TEL: 01892 616077. SER: Restorations.

WELLING

The Emporium Antiques, Collectibles & Craft Centre
138-140 Upper Wickham Lane. DA16 3DP. Est. 1999. Open Tues.-Sat. 10-5. SIZE: Medium. *STOCK: Royal Doulton, Wade, Kevin Francis, Sylvac, Beswick, Winstanley cats, Lladro, Wedgwood, £10-£300; Swarovski crystal, furniture, kitchenalia.* LOC: From Bexleyheath, right at Welling corner on High St. into Upper Wickham Lane. TEL: 020 8855 8308; fax - same; e-mail - info@theemporiumwelling.co.uk; website - www.theemporiumwelling.co.uk.

WEST MALLING

The Old Clock Shop
63 High St. ME19 6NA. (S.L. Luck). Est. 1970. Open 9-5. SIZE: Large. *STOCK: Grandfather clocks, 17th-19th C; carriage, bracket, wall clocks and barometers.* LOC: Half a mile from M20. PARK: Easy. TEL: 01732 843246; website - www.theoldclockshop.co.uk. VAT: Spec.

Rose and Crown Antiques
40 High St. ME19 6QR. (Candy and Julian Lovegrove). GMC. Est. 1995. Open Tues.-Sat. 9.30-5.30. SIZE: Medium. *STOCK: General antiques including furniture, 18th to early 20th C.* PARK: Free. TEL: 01732 872707; fax - 01732 872810; website - www.antiqueswestmalling.co.uk. SER: Restorations (furniture including French polishing and upholstery). FAIRS: NEC.

WESTERHAM

Apollo Antique Galleries   LAPADA
19 -21 Market Sq. TN16 1AN. (S.M. and R.W. Barr). Est. 1967. Open 9.30-5.30. SIZE: Large. *STOCK: Georgian, Victorian and Edwardian furniture; 19th C oils and watercolours; bronze and marble statuary; clocks, silver.* LOC: Between junctions 5 and 6 of M25, close to Gatwick Airport. PARK: Easy. TEL: 01959 562200; fax - 01959 562600; e-mail - enq@apollogalleries.com; website - www.apollogalleries.com. SER: Valuations; free delivery. FAIRS: Olympia; LAPADA. VAT: Stan/Spec.

Castle Antiques Centre
1 London Rd. TN16 1BB. (Stewart Ward Properties). Est. 1986. Open 10-5, Sun. 11-6.

SIZE: Small - 8 dealers. *STOCK: General antiques, books, linen, collectables, costume, chandeliers, cat images.* LOC: Just off town centre. PARK: Easy - nearby. TEL: 01959 562492. SER: Valuations; props for stage productions. FAIRS: Ardingly; Alexandra Palace.

The Design Gallery 1850-1950
5 The Green. TN16 1AS. (John Masters and Chrissie Painell). Est. 1993. Open Tues.-Sat. 10-5.30, Sun. 1-4, Mon. by appointment. SIZE: Medium. *STOCK: Decorative arts, 1850-1950 - Arts & Crafts, Gothic Revival, Aesthetic Movement, Art Deco, Art Nouveau furniture, ceramics, metalware, bronzes, glass, paintings, prints and etchings, books, £50-£20,000.* PARK: Easy. TEL: 01959 561234; fax - same; home - 01342 870786; mobile - 07785 503044; e-mail - sales @thedesigngallery.uk.com; website - www. thedesigngallery.uk.com. SER: Valuations; restorations (furniture, metalware and paintings).

Peter Dyke
3 The Green. TN16 1AS. Est. 1977. Open 10-5.30. SIZE: Medium. *STOCK: Furniture, 18th-19th C, £500-£10,000; paintings, 19th-20th C, £500-£1,000+; decorative objects, 19th C, £150-£1,000.* TEL: 01959 565020. SER: Valuations; buys at auction. VAT: Spec.

London House Antiques
4 Market Sq. TN16 1AW. Est. 1977. Open 10-5, Sun. by appointment. SIZE: Medium. *STOCK: Furniture, 18th-19th C, £500-£10,000; paintings, prints and engravings, 19th-20th C, £100-£2,000; English and German teddy bears and dolls, 19th-20th C, £100-£3,000; clocks and bronzes, 19th C, £300-£5,000; silver and porcelain, 19th-20th C, £50-£1,500.* LOC: Off M25, junction 6 on A25 to Westerham. PARK: Easy. TEL: 01959 564479; e-mail - londonhouseantiques@hotmail.com.

Regal Antiques   LAPADA
2 Market Sq. TN16 1AW. (T. Lawrence). Open Wed.-Sat. 11-5. *STOCK: Antique jewellery, fine paintings, portrait miniatures, porcelain.* TEL: 01959 561778. SER: Picture restorations.

Taylor-Smith Antiques
4 The Grange, High St. TN16 1AH. (Ashton Taylor-Smith). Est. 1986. Open 10-5. CL: Wed. *STOCK: Fine 18th-19th C furniture; paintings, porcelain, glass and decorative items.* PARK: Easy. TEL: 01959 563100; fax - 01959 565300; e-mail - ashton@ts-antiques.co.uk.

Taylor-Smith Books   LAPADA
2 High St. TN16 1RF. Est. 1972. Open by

appointment. *STOCK: Books by Sir Winston Churchill and related items.* PARK: Adjacent. TEL: 01959 561561; fax - 01959 561561.

Westerham Antiques Warehouse
The Old Sorting Office, Fullers Hill, London Rd. TN16 1AA. (R.W. Barr). Open 10-5.30. *STOCK: 18th-19th C furniture especially dining tables and sets of chairs.* PARK: Free. TEL: 01959 561622; fax - 01959 562986; e-mail - westhouse. antiques@virgin.net. SER: Valuations; shipping; insurance. FAIRS: NEC; Olympia (LAPADA). VAT: Spec.

Westerham House Antiques
The Old Sorting Office, Fullers Hill, London Rd. TN16 1AA. (R.W. Barr). Open 10-5.30. *STOCK: 18th-19th C English furniture, animal and figurative bronzes, oil paintings.* PARK: Easy. TEL: 01959 561622; mobile - 07885 883441; e-mail - westhouse.antiques@virgin.net. SER: Export; valuations. FAIRS: Olympia; NEC; LAPADA. VAT: Spec.

WHITSTABLE

Boulevard Antiques
139 Tankerton Rd., Tankerton. CT5 2HZ. (Mrs J. Baker). Est. 1984. Open 9.30-5. SIZE: Small. *STOCK: China, 18th-20th C, £10-£500; furniture, 19th-20th C, £50-£800; postcards, 20th C, to £30; dolls, books, 19th-20th C, £1-£500.* LOC: North side of main shopping street. PARK: Easy. TEL: 01277 273335. SER: Valuations.

Laurens Antiques
2 Harbour St. CT5 1AG. (G. A. Laurens). Est. 1965. Open 9.30-5.30. SIZE: Medium. *STOCK: Furniture, 18th-19th C, £300-£500+.* LOC: Turn off Thanet Way at Whitstable exit, straight down to one-way system in High St. PARK: Easy. TEL: 01227 261940; home - same. SER: Valuations; restorations (cabinet work); buys at auction.

Tankerton Antiques
136 Tankerton Rd. CT5 2AN. (Mrs F. Holland and Paul Wrighton). Est. 1985. Open Tues., Fri. and Sat. 10.30-5. SIZE: Medium. *STOCK: Furniture, Regency to 1930's, £50-£1,500; china, from 18th C, to £1,500; glass, Regency to 1930's, to £400; clocks and barometers, from 1800, £30-£2,500; French, English and German costume jewellery, £30-£300.* LOC: From A299 Thanet Way take A290/B2205 turn off to Whitstable. Through town and into Tankerton. Shop on right just past roundabout. TEL: 01227 266490; mobile - 07702 244064. SER: Repairs (clocks and barometers). FAIRS: Ardingly; Brunel Clock & Watch.

Tall vase signed by Reginald Haggar (as decorator), Harold Thomas (as thrower), Agnete Hoy and James Rushton. Such collaborative signed wares are not easy to find. This one, dated 1945, is in the collection of The Potteries Museum & Art Gallery, Stoke-on-Trent.

From an article entitled "Bullers Art Pottery" by Sue Taylor which appeared in the June 2003 issue of ***Antique Collecting***. For more details and to subscribe see page 21.

WITTERSHAM

Old Corner House Antiques
6 Poplar Rd. TN30 7PG. (G. and F. Shepherd). Open Wed.-Sat. 10-5 or by appointment. *STOCK: General antiques, country furniture, samplers; 18th-19th C English pottery including blue and white and creamware; watercolours, 19th to early 20th C.* PARK: Easy. TEL: 01797 270236.

LANCASHIRE

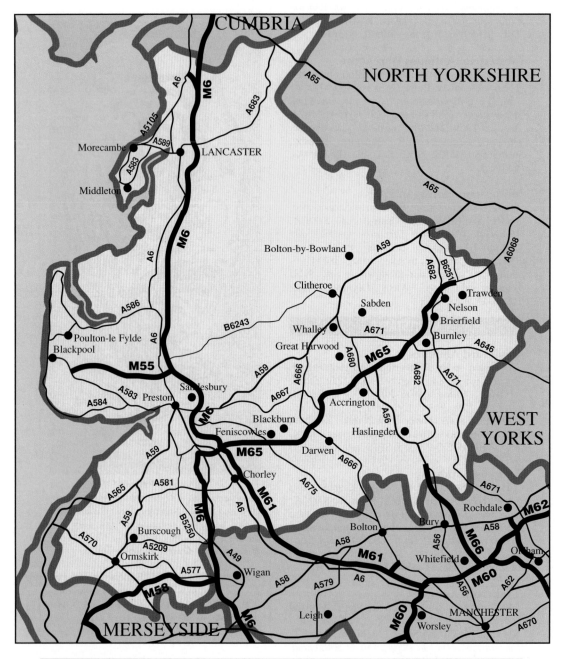

CUMBRIA

NORTH YORKSHIRE

WEST YORKS

MERSEYSIDE

Morecambe
Middleton
LANCASTER
Bolton-by-Bowland
Clitheroe
Sabden
Trawden
Nelson
Brierfield
Whalley
Burnley
Great Harwood
Poulton-le Fylde
Blackpool
Samlesbury
Preston
Accrington
Blackburn
Haslingden
Feniscowles
Darwen
Chorley
Rochdale
Burscough
Bolton
Bury
Ormskirk
Whitefield
Oldham
Wigan
Leigh
Worsley
MANCHESTER

Dealers and Shops in Lancashire

Accrington	1	Bury	1	Manchester	17	Sabden	2
Blackburn	2	Chorley	2	Middleton Village	1	Samlesbury	1
Blackpool	4	Clitheroe	4	Morecambe	2	Trawden	1
Bolton	5	Darwen	3	Nelson	1	Whalley	2
Bolton-by-Bowland		Feniscowles	1	Oldham	3	Whitefield	1
	2	Great Harwood	2	Ormskirk	2	Wigan	3
Brierfield	1	Haslingden	4	Poulton-le-Fylde	1	Worsley	1
Burnley	3	Lancaster	6	Preston	8		
Burscough	1	Leigh	1	Rochdale	1		

ACCRINGTON

The Coin and Jewellery Shop
129a Blackburn Rd. BB5 0AA. Est. 1977. Open 9.30-5. CL: Wed. *STOCK: Coins, jewellery and small antiques.* TEL: 01254 384757.

BLACKBURN

Ancient and Modern
17 New Market St. BB1 7DR. (Gail and Zachary Coles). NAG. OMRS. Est. 1943. Open 9-5.30. SIZE: Medium. *STOCK: Jewellery, Georgian to date, up to £30,000; clocks, vintage and modern watches including Rolex, Cartier, Patek; militaria and silver; diamond merchants.* LOC: Town centre, opposite side entrance of Marks & Spencer. PARK: Easy. TEL: 01254 677866/668818; fax - 01254 677866. SER: Valuations; repairs; restorations. FAIRS: Bangkok; Miami; London. VAT: Stan/Margin/ Global.

Mitchell's Antiques
76 Bolton Rd. BB2 3PZ. (S. Mitchell). Est. 1972. Open 9-5. *STOCK: General antiques, gold and silver jewellery, wrist watches.* LOC: Main road. PARK: Easy. TEL: 01254 664663.

BLACKPOOL

Ascot Antiques
106 Holmfield Rd. FY2 9RF. (J.C. Winwood). Est. 1987. Open by appointment. SIZE: Small. *STOCK: Furniture and oil paintings, Georgian to Victorian.* PARK: Easy. TEL: 01253 356383; home - same; mobile - 07816 645716. SER: Valuations.

Chard Coins
521 Lytham Rd. FY4 1RJ. Est. 1965. Open 9-5. CL: Sat. SIZE: Large. *STOCK: Paintings and furniture, English and ancient coins, gold bullion coins, jewellery and silver, £50-£20,000+.* LOC: Between Central Promenade south and Blackpool Airport main gates, 1/4 mile from airport. PARK: Easy. TEL: 01253 343081. SER: Valuations. VAT: Stan/Spec.

Ann and Peter Christian
400/402 Waterloo Rd., Marton. FY4 4BL. Est. 1978. Open 10-5.30. SIZE: Large. *STOCK: Decorative arts and reproduction lighting.* TEL: 01253 763268; website - www.20da.co.uk.

Nostalgia
95 Coronation St. FY1 4QE. (P. Jackson). Est. 1978. Open 10-4, including Sun. in summer. SIZE: Small. *STOCK: Royal commemoratives, 19th-20th C, £5-£150.* LOC: Town centre, near Winter Gardens. PARK: Easy. TEL: 01253 293251.

BOLTON

Bolton Antique Centre
96 Great Moor St. BL3 6DS. (Granville Roberts). Est. 1992. Open 10-4.30. SIZE: Large. *STOCK: General antiques and collectables.* PARK: Opposite. TEL: 01204 362694.

Drop Dial Antiques
Last Drop Village, Hospital Rd., Bromley Cross. BL7 9PZ. (I.W. and I.E. Roberts). Est. 1975. Open every afternoon except Mon. and Fri. SIZE: Medium. *STOCK: Clocks, mainly English and French, 18th-20th C, £100-£4,000; mercury barometers, 19th-20th C, paintings, silver, furniture and general antiques, £20-£2,000.* PARK: Easy. TEL: 01204 307186; home - 01257 480995. SER: Valuations; restorations (clocks and barometers). VAT: Stan/Spec.

Siri Ellis Books
The Last Drop Village, Hospital Rd., Bromley Cross. BL7 9PZ. PBFA. Est. 1998. Open 12-5, Sat. and Sun. 10-5. SIZE: Small. *STOCK: Rare and collectable childrens books, 50p to £2,000.* PARK: Easy. TEL: 01204 597511; e-mail - mail@siriellisbooks.co.uk; website - www. siriellisbooks.co.uk. FAIRS: PBFA; Buxton.

Ironchurch Antiques Centre
Blackburn Rd. BL1 8DR . (P.J. Wilkinson). Est. 1975. Open 10-5 including Sun. SIZE: Large. *STOCK: Furniture, china, glass, clocks, books, jewellery, 17th C to date, £1-£10,000.* PARK: Free nearby. TEL: 01204 383616. SER: Valuations; restorations.

G. Oakes and Son
Unit 3, Dunscar Industrial Estate, Blackburn Rd. BL7 9PQ. Est. 1958. Open 9-5 or by appointment. SIZE: Large. *STOCK: Furniture and bric-a-brac.* LOC: Off A666. PARK: Easy. TEL: 01204 309935; e-mail - ycs12@dial.pipex. com. SER: Packing and shipping; buys at auction. VAT: Stan.

BOLTON-BY-BOWLAND, Nr. Clitheroe

Farmhouse Antiques
23 Main St. BB7 4NY. (M. Howard). Est. 1980. Open Sat., Sun. and Bank Holidays 12-4.30 (Sundays only in winter) or by appointment. SIZE: Small. *STOCK: Bed and table linen, quilts, christening robes, lace, samplers, embroideries,*

bags, buttons, trimmings, beads, costume to Victorian jewellery, Victoriana, china. LOC: Off A59, past Clitheroe, through Sawley. PARK: Easy. TEL: 01200 441457/447294.

Harrop Fold Clocks (F. Robinson)
Harrop Fold, Lane Ends. BB7 4PJ. Est. 1974. Open by appointment. SIZE: Medium. *STOCK: British longcase and wall clocks, barometers, 18th-19th C, £1,000-£10,000.* LOC: Through Clitheroe to Chatburn and Grindleton. Take Slaidburn road, turn left after 3 miles. (Please telephone for more details). PARK: Own. TEL: 01200 447665; home - same; e-mail - robinson harrop@aol.com. SER: Valuations; restorations (clocks).

BRIERFIELD, Nr. Nelson

J.H. Blakey and Sons Ltd (Est. 1905)
Burnley Rd. BB9 5AD. *STOCK: Furniture, brass, copper, pewter, clocks, curios.* TEL: 01282 613593; e-mail - sales@blakeys.fsworld.co.uk. SER: Restorations. VAT: Stan.

BURNLEY

Brun Lea Antiques
3/5 Standish St. BB11 1AP. Est. 1974. Open 9.30-5.30. SIZE: Large. *STOCK: General antiques and shipping goods.* LOC: Town centre. PARK: Easy. TEL: 01282 413513; e-mail - jwaite@ freenetname.co.uk; website - www.antiques-atlas.com/brunlea/htm.

Brun Lea Antiques (J. Waite Ltd)
Unit 1, Rear Elm St. Mill, Travis St. BB10 1DG. Est. 1974. Open 8.30-5.30, Fri. and Sat. 9-4, Sun. 12-4. SIZE: Large warehouse. *STOCK: Georgian furniture to 1930's shipping goods.* PARK: Easy. TEL: 01282 413513; fax - 01282 832769; e-mail - jwaite@freenetname.co.uk; website - www. antiques-atlas.com/brunlea/htm

King's Mill Antique Centre
Unit 2 King's Mill, Queen St., Harle Syke. BB10 2HX. (Michael and Linda Heuer). Open 10-5, Thurs. 10-7, Sun. 11-5. SIZE: Large. *STOCK: Furniture and bric-a-brac, Edwardian and Victorian, £5-£1,000.* LOC: From General Hospital, follow brown tourist signs for Queen's Mill. PARK: Easy. TEL: 01282 431953; mobile - 07803 153752. SER: Export.

BURSCOUGH, Nr. Ormskirk

West Lancs. Antique Exports   **LAPADA**
Victoria Mill, Victoria St. L40 0SN. (W. and B. Griffiths). Est. 1959. Open 9-5.30, Sat. and Sun. 10-5. SIZE: Large. *STOCK: Shipping furniture.* TEL: 01704 894634; fax - 01704 894486. SER: Courier; packing and shipping. VAT: Stan.

BURY

Newtons
151 The Rock. BL9 0ND. (Newtons of Bury). Est. 1900. Open 9-5. SIZE: Small. *STOCK: General antiques, 18th-19th C, £5-£500; furniture including reproduction.* Not Stocked: Continental furniture. LOC: From Manchester through Bury town centre, shop is on left 200yds. before fire station. PARK: Opposite. TEL: 0161 764 1863; website - www.newtonsofbury.com. SER: Valuations; restorations (furniture). VAT: Stan.

CHORLEY

Antiques and Crafts Centre
Botany Bay Villages Ltd., Canal Mill, Botany Brow. PR6 9AF. Open daily including Sun. SIZE: Large - 5 floors. *STOCK: Porcelain, china and jewellery; furniture, memorabilia and curios and crafts.* LOC: Opposite junction 8, M61. PARK: Easy. TEL: 01257 261220. VAT: Stan.

Heskin Hall Antiques

Heskin Hall, Wood Lane, Heskin. PR7 5PA. (Harrison Steen Ltd). Est. 1996. Open 10-5.30 seven days. SIZE: Large - 70+ dealers. *STOCK: Wide range of general antiques.* LOC: B5250. PARK: Easy. TEL: 01257 452044; fax - 01257 450690; website - www.heskinhall.com. SER: Valuations; restorations.

Brittons - Watches and Antiques

4 King St. BB7 2EP. Est. 1970. CL: Wed. *STOCK: Jewellery and collectors' watches.* LOC: Town centre opposite main Post Office. PARK: Opposite. TEL: 01200 425555; fax - 01200 424200; website - www.brittons-watches.co.uk. SER: Valuations.

Folly Antiques

22 Moor Lane. BB7 1BE. (N.P. Medd). Est. 1967. Open 9-6, Wed. and Sun. by appointment. SIZE: Medium. *STOCK: Decorative and upholstered items, furniture, £100-£2,000; pictures, brass and objects, £5-£2,000; all 19th-20th C; garden furniture, small architectural items, 18th-20th C, £20-£2,000.* LOC: 15 miles from junction 31, M6, via A59. PARK: Opposite. TEL: 01200 429461. VAT: Stan/Spec.

Lee's Antiques

59 Whalley Rd. BB7 1EE. (P.A. Lee). *STOCK: General antiques.* TEL: 01200 424921; home - 01200 425441.

Past & Present

22 Whalley Rd. BB7 1AW. (D. and Mrs K. J. Hollings). Est. 1988. Open Sat. 10.30-5, other times by appointment. SIZE: Small. *STOCK: Victorian and Georgian cast iron fireplaces and ranges, £85-£1,500; Victorian and Edwardian wooden mantels, marble fireplaces, dog grates, coal buckets, brass and cast iron fenders; fireplace accessories, spare parts, brass and copper, small collectables.* LOC: Near town centre. PARK: Easy. TEL: 01200 428678; home - 01200 445373; mobile - 07779 478716. SER: Restorations (repairs, refurbishing, re-tiling cast iron fireplaces).

Belgrave Antique Centre

Britannia Mill, 136 Bolton Rd. (Martin and Elaine Cooney). Est. 1998. Open 9.30-5, Sun. 10-4.30. SIZE: Large - 40 dealers. *STOCK: Porcelain, pottery, glass, furniture, architectural, collectables.* LOC: Opposite India Mill. PARK: Easy. TEL: 01254 777714. SER: Valuations. FAIRS: Newark, Ardingly, Swinderby.

Grove Antiques

Hampden Mill, Springbank. (J. Cooney). Open 9-5, Sun. 10-2. *STOCK: General antiques.* TEL: 01254 777144. SER: Valuations.

K.C. Antiques   `LAPADA`

538 Bolton Rd. BB3 2JR. (K. and J. Anderton). Resident. Open 9-6, Sun. 12-5. *STOCK: Georgian, Victorian and Edwardian furniture and decorative items.* LOC: A666. PARK: Easy. TEL: 01254 772252. SER: Buys at auction. VAT: Stan/Spec.

Old Smithy

726 Preston Old Rd. BB2 5EP. (R.C. and I.R. Lynch). Est. 1967. Open 9.30-5. SIZE: Large. *STOCK: Period and Victorian fireplaces, pub and architectural items, violins and musical instruments, pictures and prints, furniture, shipping items, brass, copper.* LOC: Opposite Fieldens Arms. PARK: Own or nearby. TEL: 01254 209943/580874. SER: Valuations; restorations (wooden items); buys at auction. FAIRS: Newark, Lincs.

Benny Charlesworth's Snuff Box

51 Blackburn Rd. BB6 7DF. (N. Walsh). Est. 1984. Open 10-5. SIZE: Small. *STOCK: Furniture, china, linen, costume jewellery, teddies.* LOC: 200yds. from town centre, off A680. PARK: Next to shop. TEL: 01254 888550. FAIRS: Local.

Jean's Military Memories

32 Queen St. BB6 7QQ. (Len and Jean South). Est. 1994. Open 9-5, Sat. 9-4, other times by appointment. SIZE: Medium. *STOCK: Air weaponry, from 1880, £30-£4,000; deactivated weaponry, £100-£2,000; swords, £50-£1,000; knives, £10-£1,200.* LOC: Main road. PARK: Easy. TEL: 01254 877825; fax - same; mobile - 07713 636069; e-mail - jean.south@btinternet.com.

P.J. Brown Antiques

8 Church St. BB4 5QU. Est. 1979. Open 10-5, Sat. and Sun. by appointment. SIZE: Medium. *STOCK: Georgian, Victorian and Edwardian furniture, shipping goods, old advertising items, bottles and related items.* LOC: Town centre, off Bury Rd./Regent St. PARK: Easy. TEL: 01706 224888. VAT: Stan/Spec.

Fieldings Antiques

176, 178 and 180 Blackburn Rd. BB1 2LG. Est. 1956. Open 9-4.30, Fri. 9-4, Thurs. and other times by appointment. SIZE: Large. *STOCK: Longcase clocks, £30-£2,000; wall clocks, sets of chairs, pine, period oak, French furniture, glass, shipping goods, toys, steam engines, veteran cars, vintage and veteran motor cycles.* PARK: Easy. TEL: 01706 214254; mobile - 07973 698961; home - 01254 263358.

Holden Wood Antiques Centre

St Stephen's Church, Grane Rd. BB4 4AT. (Peter and Mary Crossley and John Ainscough). Est. 1996. Open 10-5.30 including Sun. SIZE: 35 dealers. *STOCK: Furniture, 18th-19th C, £200-£2,000; ceramics including figures, glass, 19th C, £50-£2,000.* PARK: Own. TEL: 01706 830803; e-mail - john@holdenwood.co.uk; website - www.holdenwood.co.uk. SER: Valuations; restorations.

P.W. Norgrove - Antique Clocks

38 Bury Rd. BB4 5LR. Est. 1978. Open most days, prior telephone call advisable. *STOCK: Longcase, wall, bracket and mantel clocks.* PARK: Easy. TEL: 01706 211995; mobile - 07788 164621. SER: Repair and restorations (clocks); re-caning Bergere suites and chairs.

LANCASTER

Anything Old & Military Collectables

55 Scotforth Rd. LA1 4SA. (Graham H. Chambers). Est. 1985. Open Wed.-Sat. 1.30-6, Sun. by appointment. SIZE: Medium. *STOCK: WW1 and WW2 British, Imperial German, Third Reich and Commonwealth medals, cap badges, uniforms and head dress, edged weapons and field equipment, £5-£500.* LOC: 1.5 miles south of city centre on A6. PARK: Easy. TEL: 01524 69933; home - same. SER: Valuations; full size and miniature medal mounting.

The Assembly Rooms Market

King St. LA1 1XD. Open Tues.-Sat. 10-4.30. SIZE: Several dealers. *STOCK: General antiques, period and costume jewellery, Victorian to '60's costume and retro fashion, books.* LOC: Town centre. TEL: Market Supervisor - 01524 66627; website - www.lancasterdistrictmarkets. co.uk.

G.B. Antiques Ltd

Lancaster Leisure Park, Wyresdale Rd. LA1 3LA. (Mrs G. Blackburn). Open 10-5 including Sun. SIZE: Large. 100+ dealers. *STOCK: Porcelain, glass and silver, late 19th to early 20th C; small*

furniture, Victorian to early 20th C. LOC: Off M6, junction 33 or 34. PARK: Easy. TEL: 01524 844734; fax - 01524 844735; home - 01772 861593. SER: Valuations; buys at auction. VAT: Stan/Spec.

Lancaster Leisure Park Antiques Centre

Wyresdale Rd. (on site of former Hornsea Pottery Plant). LA1 5LA. Open 10-5 including Sun. SIZE: 140 dealers. *STOCK: Wide range of general antiques and collectables.* LOC: Off M6, junction 33 or 34. PARK: Easy. TEL: 01524 844734.

Lancastrian Antiques & Co

70/72 Penny St. LA1 1XF. (S.P. and H.S. Wilkinson). Open 10-4. CL: Wed. *STOCK: Furniture, lighting, paintings, bric-a-brac.* LOC: City centre. TEL: 01524 847004.

LEIGH

Leigh Jewellery

3 Queens St. (R. Bibby). Open 9.30-5.30, Wed. 9.30-12.30. *STOCK: Jewellery.* TEL: 01942 607947/722509; mobile - 07802 833467.

MANCHESTER

A.S. Antique Galleries

26 Broad St, Salford. M6 5BY. (A. Sternshine). Est. 1975. Open Thurs., Fri. and Sat. 10-5.30 or by appointment. SIZE: Large. *STOCK: Art Nouveau and Art Deco bronzes, bronze and ivory figures, silver, glass, ceramics, furniture, jewellery, lighting and general antiques.* Not Stocked: Weapons. LOC: On A6, one mile north of Manchester city centre, next to Salford University College. PARK: Easy. TEL: 0161 737 5938; mobile - 07836 368230; fax - 0161 737 6626; e-mail - as@sternshine.demon.co.uk. SER: Valuations; restorations; commission purchasing.

Antique Fireplace Warehouse

1090 Stockport Rd, Levenshulme. M19 2SU. (D. McMullan & Son). Open 9-6, Sun. 11-5. *STOCK: Fireplaces and architectural items.* PARK: Easy. TEL: 0161 431 8075; fax - 0161 431 8084.

Antiques Village

The Old Town Hall, 965 Stockport Rd., Levenshulme. M19 3NP. Est. 1978. Open 10-5.30, Sun. 11-4. SIZE: 40+ dealers. *STOCK: Furniture and clocks, reproduction pine, fireplaces, collectables.* LOC: A6 between Manchester and Stockport. PARK: Own. TEL: 0161 256 4644; fax - same; mobile - 07976 985982. SER: Valuations; restorations; pine stripping. FAIRS: Newark.

Cathedral Jewellers
38 Thomas St. M4 1ER. (Jason Taylor). Open 9.30-5. *STOCK: Jewellery.* TEL: 0161 832 3042.

Didsbury Antiques
85 School Lane, Didsbury. M20 6WN. (Alan Willis). Est. 1982. Open 10-5. *STOCK: Ceramics, silver and furniture.* LOC: Near village centre. PARK: Easy. TEL: 0161 434 7487; home - 0161 434 6931. SER: Valuations.

Empire Exchange
1 Newton St., Piccadilly. M1 1HW. (David Ireland). Est. 1975. Open every day 9-7.30 except Christmas day. SIZE: Large. *STOCK: General small antiques including silver, pottery, clocks and watches, ephemera, autographs, football memorabilia, records, books and comics, 18th-20th C, £5-£10,000.* PARK: Easy. TEL: 0161 236 4445; fax - 0161 273 5007; home - 07931 257915. SER: Valuations. VAT: Stan/Spec.

Family Antiques
405/407 Bury New Rd., Prestwich. M25 1AA. (J. and J. Ditondo). Open daily. *STOCK: General antiques.* TEL: 0161 798 0036.

Fernlea Antiques
Failsworth Mill, Ashton Rd West, Failsworth. M35 0FD. (A.J. and Mrs B. McLaughlin). Est. 1983. Open 10-5. SIZE: Large. *STOCK: General antiques and shipping goods.* PARK: Easy. TEL: 0161 682 0589; e-mail - fernlea@i12.com; websites - www.fernleaantiques.com and www.fernleaantiques.co.uk. SER: Container packing (worldwide).

Fulda Gallery Ltd
19 Vine St., Salford. M7 3PG. (M.J. Fulda). Est. 1969. Open by appointment. *STOCK: Oil paintings, 1500-1950, £500-£30,000; watercolours, 1800-1930, £350-£10,000.* LOC: Near Salford police station off Bury New Rd. TEL: 0161 792 1962; mobile - 07836 518313. SER: Valuations; restorations; buys at auction.

Gibb's Bookshop Ltd
10 Charlotte St. M1 4FL. ABA. Est. 1926. Open 10-5. *STOCK: Books.* TEL: 0161 236 7179.

In-Situ Manchester
Talbot Mill, 44 Ellesmere St., Hulme. M15 4JY. (Laurence Green). Est. 1983. Open 10-5.30. SIZE: Large. *STOCK: Architectural items including fireplaces, doors, panelling, sanitary ware, radiators, flooring, glass, gardenware, staircasing.* TEL: 0161 839 5525; mobile - 07780 993773; e-mail - enquiries@insitumanchester.com; website - www.insitumanchester.com.

In-Situ Manchester South Architectural Antiques
Unit G4, Longford Rd., Stretford. M32 0HQ. (S. Newsham). SALVO. Open 9-5.30. *STOCK: Architectural antiques, fireplaces, radiators, flooring, stoves, doors, glass, lighting, sanitaryware.* TEL: 0161 865 2110; fax - same; e-mail - sales@insituarchitectural.com; website - www.insituarchitectural.com.

Eric J. Morten
Warburton St., Didsbury. M20 6WA. Est. 1959. Open 10-5.30. SIZE: Medium. *STOCK: Antiquarian books, 16th-20th C, £5-£5,000.* LOC: Off Wilmslow Rd., near traffic lights in Didsbury village. A34. PARK: Easy. TEL: 0161 445 7629 and 01265 277959; fax - 0161 448 1323. SER: Valuations; buys at auction (antiquarian books). FAIRS: PBFA.

R.J. O'Brien and Son Antique Ltd
Failsworth Mill, Ashton Rd. West, Failsworth. M35 0FD. Est. 1970. Open 9-5. CL: Sat. SIZE: Very large. *STOCK: Furniture, Victorian, Edwardian and 1930's; shipping goods, general antiques and pianos.* PARK: Own. TEL: 0161 688 4414; mobiles - 07850 485201 and 07710 455489; e-mail - obanantiques@btinternet.com; website - www.Antique-Exports.com. SER: Container and courier service.

Secondhand and Rare Books
1 Church St. M4 1PN. Est. 1970. Open 12-4. *STOCK: Books.* PARK: Nearby. TEL: 0161 834 5964 or 01625 861608. SER: Valuations.

St. James Antiques
STOCK: Jewellery, silver and paintings. TEL: 0161 773 4662; mobile - 07808 521671.

Village Antiques
416 Bury New Rd., Prestwich. M25 1BD. (R. Weidenbaum). Est. 1981. Open 10-5, Wed. 10-1. SIZE: Medium. *STOCK: 19th C pottery and porcelain, £5-£300; 18th C glass; small furniture; Art Deco clocks, figurines and lamps; Art Nouveau figurines.* LOC: Village centre, 2 mins. from M62. PARK: Easy - side and opposite. TEL: 0161 773 3612.

MIDDLETON VILLAGE, Nr. Morecambe

G G Antique Wholesalers Ltd
Newfield House, Middleton Rd. LA3 3PP. (G. Goulding). Est. 1967. Open any time by appointment. SIZE: Large. *STOCK: Shipping goods, £30-£5,000, English and European furniture.* LOC: On main road between Morecambe promenade and Middleton village. PARK: Easy. TEL: 01524 850757; fax - 01524 851565; e-mail - jay@ggantique-wholesalers.com; website - www.ggantique-wholesalers.com. SER: Courier; packing; 40ft containers weekly worldwide. VAT: Stan. *Trade Only.*

MORECAMBE

Tyson's Antiques
Clark St. LA4 5HT. (George, Andrew and Shirley Tyson). Est. 1952. Open Sat. 8-11.30, other times by appointment. SIZE: Large. *STOCK: Georgian, Victorian and Edwardian furniture.* PARK: Easy. TEL: 01524 416763/425235/420098; mobile - 07971 836892; website - www.tysonsantiques. freeserve.co.uk. VAT: Stan/Spec. *Trade Only.*

Luigino Vescovi
135 Balmoral Rd. LA3 1HJ. Est. 1970. Open by appointment every day. SIZE: Warehouse. *STOCK: Georgian and Victorian furniture, inlaid Edwardian and plated ware, £50-£10,000.* PARK: Easy. TEL: 01524 416732; mobile - 07860 784856. VAT: Stan/Spec/Export

NELSON

Colin Blakey Fireplaces
115 Manchester Rd. BB10 2LS. Est. 1906. Open 9.30-5, Sun. 12-3.30. SIZE: Large. *STOCK: Fireplaces and hearth furniture, paintings and prints.* LOC: Exit 12, M65. PARK: Opposite. TEL: 01282 614941; fax - 01282 698511; e-mail - cbfireplaces@hotmail.com; website - www. colinblakeyfireplaces.co.uk. SER: Manufacturers and suppliers of hand-carved marble fireplaces and hardwood mantels. VAT: Stan.

OLDHAM

Charles Howell Jeweller
2 Lord St. OL1 3EY. (N.G. Howell). NAG. Est. 1870. Open 9.15-5.15. SIZE: Small. *STOCK: Edwardian and Victorian jewellery, £25-£2,000; silver, early to mid 20th C, £40-£1,500; watches, Victorian to mid 20th C, £50-£800.* LOC: Town centre, off High St. PARK: Limited or by arrangement. TEL: 0161 624 1479. SER: Valuations; restorations (jewellery and watches); buys at auction. VAT: Stan/Spec.

Marks Jewellers and Antique Dealers

16 Waterloo St. OL1 1SQ. (B.J. and S. Marks). Est. 1969. Open 9.30-5. SIZE: Medium. *STOCK: General antiques, Victorian and Edwardian jewellery, silver and watches.* LOC: Town centre, off Yorkshire St. PARK: Nearby. TEL: 0161 624 5975; fax - same; e-mail - bmarks46@hotmail. com. SER: Valuations.

H.C. Simpson and Sons Jewellers (Oldham)Ltd

37 High St. OL1 3BA. Open 9-5.30. *STOCK: Clocks, jewellery, watches.* TEL: 0161 624 7187. SER: Restorations (clocks, watches and jewellery).

ORMSKIRK

Green Lane Antiques

Unit B20 Malthouse Business Centre, 48 Southport Rd. L39 1QR. (J. Swift). Est. 1982. Open seven days 10-4. SIZE: Large. *STOCK: Furniture - pine, mahogany and oak; longcase clocks.* PARK: Easy. TEL: 01695 580731; home - 01704 895444; mobile - 07715 371902. SER: Restorations (longcase clocks).

Alan Grice Antiques

106 Aughton St. L39 3BS. Open 10-6. *STOCK: Period furniture.* PARK: Easy. TEL: 01695 572007.

POULTON-LE-FYLDE

Ray Wade Antiques

P O Box 39. FY6 9GA. Est. 1978. Trades at fairs or by appointment. *STOCK: Decorative items, sculpture, European and Oriental works of art, paintings.* TEL: 01253 700715; fax - 01253 702342; mobile - 07836 291336; e-mail - antiques@r-wades.demon.co.uk. SER: Finder; valuations; buys for export. VAT: Stan/Spec/Global.

PRESTON

The Antique Centre

56 Garstang Rd. PR1 1NA. (Paul Allison). Est. 1966. Open 9-5.30, Sat. 9.30-5.30, Sun. 10.30-4.30. SIZE: Large, 20 dealers. *STOCK: Furniture, including French pine, Georgian-Edwardian; porcelain, silver, clocks, bric-a-brac and pictures.* PARK: Easy. TEL: 01772 882078; fax - 01772 252842; e-mail - paul@paulallison antiques.co.uk; website - www.paulallison antiques.co.uk. SER: Worldwide shipping; containers.

European Fine Arts and Antiques

10 Cannon St. PR1 3NR. (B. Beck). Est. 1970. Open 9.30-5.30. SIZE: Medium. *STOCK: Victorian paintings and furniture, to £2,000.* LOC: Town centre - Fishergate. PARK: Loading only and nearby. TEL: 01772 883886; fax - 01772 823888; e-mail - info@european-fine-arts.co.uk; website - www.european-fine-arts.co.uk. SER: Valuations; buys at auction. VAT: Stan/Spec.

Hackler's Jewellers

6b Lune St. PR1. (N.E. Oldfield). FBHI. *STOCK: Antique clocks.* TEL: 01772 258465. VAT: Stan.

Halewood and Sons

37 Friargate. PR1 2AT. ABA. PBFA. Est. 1867. CL: Thurs. pm. *STOCK: Antiquarian books and maps.* TEL: 01772 252603; e-mail - books@halewoodandsons.co.uk.

Nelson's Antiques

113 New Hall Lane. PR1 5PB. (W. and L. Nelson). Open 10-5 or by appointment. *STOCK: General antiques and collectors' items.* LOC: Half mile from junction 31, M6. PARK: Easy. TEL: 01772 794896/862066. SER: Valuations.

Preston Antique Centre

The Mill, New Hall Lane. PR1 5NX. Open 8.30-5.30, Sat.10-4, Sun. 10-5. SIZE: Large - 40+ dealers. *STOCK: General antiques, Georgian-Edwardian; shipping furniture; shipping, Dutch, Italian and French furniture; collectables and longcase clocks.* PARK: Own. TEL: 01772 794498/651548; fax - 01772 651694; e-mail - prestonantiques@talk21.com; websites - www.antiques-atlas.com/preston.htm and www.preston antiquescentre.com.

Preston Book Co

68 Friargate. PR1 2ED. (M. Halewood). Est. 1950. Open 10-5.30. *STOCK: Antiquarian books.* LOC: Town centre. PARK: Easy. TEL: 01772 252613. SER: Buys at auction.

Priory Collectables

7 Priory Lane, Penwortham. (David Howden). Est. 1988. Open 11-4, Sun. - trade by appointment. CL: Mon.and Wed. SIZE: Small. *STOCK: Cutlery and silver plate, from 1850, £5-£500; collectables including china, glass, clocks, toby jugs, Wade, Sylvac, small furniture.* LOC: Turn right at traffic lights in Penwortham into Priory Lane. PARK: Easy. TEL: 01772 752090.

ROCHDALE

Antiques and Bygones

100 Drake St. OL16 1PQ. (K. and E. Bonn). Est. 1983. Open 10-4, Sat. 10-2. CL: Mon. and Tues. SIZE: Small. *STOCK: Pottery, coins and medals, jewellery, 19th-20th C, £5-£100.* TEL: 01706 648114.

SABDEN, Nr. Clitheroe

Walter Aspinall Antiques

Pendle Antiques Centre, Union Mill, Watt St. BB7 9ED. Est. 1964. Open 9-5, Sat. and Sun. 11-4 or by appointment. SIZE: Large. *STOCK: Furniture and bric-a-brac.* LOC: On Pendle Hill between Clitheroe and Padiham. PARK: Easy. TEL: 01282 778642; fax - 01282 778643; e-mail - walter.aspinall@btinternet.com. SER: Export; packing; courier; containers; wholesale. VAT: Stan.

Pendle Antiques Centre Ltd

Union Mill, Watt St. BB7 9ED. (B. Seed and J.L. Billington). Est. 1993. Open 10-5, Sun. 11-5 (other times by appointment for Trade). SIZE: 10 dealers. *STOCK: Furniture and bric-a-brac.* LOC: Over Pendle Hill, off the A59 between Clitheroe and Padiham. TEL: 01282 776311; fax - 01282 778643; e-mail - sales@pendleantiquescentre.co.uk; website - www.pendleantiquescentre.co.uk.

SAMLESBURY, Nr. Preston

Samlesbury Hall

(Dating from 1325). Preston New Rd. PR5 0UP. (Samlesbury Hall Trust). Est. 1969. Open 11-4.30. Admission - adults £2.50, children £1. CL: Mon. and Sat. SIZE: Large. *STOCK: General collectable antiques.* LOC: Exit 31, M6 on A677 between Preston and Blackburn. PARK: Easy. TEL: 01254 812010/2229. FAIRS: Craft Exhibitions.

TRAWDEN, Nr. Colne

Jack Moore Antiques and Stained Glass

The Old Rock, Keighley Rd. BB8 8RW. (Jack Moore and Connie Hartley). Est. 1976. Open Wed.-Sat. 9-5 or by appointment. SIZE: Medium. *STOCK: Stained glass and furniture.* PARK: Easy. TEL: 01282 869478; home - same; fax - 01282 865193; mobile - 07802 331594. SER: Restoration and manufacture of stained glass; container packing; courier. VAT: Stan.

WHALLEY, Nr. Clitheroe

T. Brindle Antiques and Brindle Fine Arts Ltd   LAPADA

41 King St. BB7 9SP. Est. 1964. Open 10-4.30, Mon. and other times by appointment. *STOCK: English and Continental furniture, fine oil paintings, Japanese works of art, bronzes and porcelain.* PARK: Easy. TEL: 01254 825200. FAIRS: Olympia (June).

Edmund Davies & Son Antiques

32 King St. BB7 9SL. (E. and P. Davies). Est. 1960. Open 10-5. SIZE: Medium + trade warehouse. *STOCK: Oak and country furniture, longcase clocks, to £10,000; jewellery, to £500.* Not Stocked: Reproductions. LOC: A59 (11 miles from M6). PARK: Easy. TEL: 01254 823764. SER: Restorations (longcase clocks). VAT: Stan/Spec.

WHITEFIELD, Nr. Manchester

Henry Donn Gallery

138/142 Bury New Rd. M45 6AD. (Henry and Nicholas Donn). FATG. Est. 1954. Open 9.30-5. SIZE: Large. *STOCK: Paintings, 19th-20th C, £20-£100,000.* LOC: Off M60, junction 17 towards Bury. PARK: Own at rear. TEL: 0161 766 8819; fax - same; e-mail - donn@netlineuk. net; website - www.henrydonngallery.com. SER: Valuations; framing; restorations. VAT: Stan/Spec.

WIGAN

Colin de Rouffignac
57 Wigan Lane. WN1 2LF. BNTA. Est. 1972. Open 10-4.30. CL: Wed. *STOCK: Furniture, jewellery, oils and watercolours.* PARK: Easy. TEL: 01942 237927.

John Robinson Antiques
172-176 Manchester Rd., Higher Ince. WN2 2EA. Est. 1965. Open any time. SIZE: Large. *STOCK: General antiques.* LOC: A577 near Ince Bar. PARK: Easy. TEL: 01942 247773/241671. SER: Export packing. VAT: Stan. *Export and Trade Only.*

Wiend Books & Collectables
8-12 The Wiend. WN1 1PF. (Paul and Roslyn Morris). PBFA. Est. 1997. Open 9.30-5. CL: Tues. SIZE: 7 rooms. *STOCK: Books, £5-£80; ephemera, £1-£20; advertising items, Wade, £5-£50; all mainly 19th-20th C.* LOC: Between Market Place and Millgate. PARK: Millgate. TEL: 01942 820500; fax - same; website - www.wiendbooks.co.uk. SER: Valuations. FAIRS: Bolton Reebok Stadium; Haigh Hall; PBFA; North West Book.

WORSLEY, Nr. Manchester

Northern Clocks LAPADA
Boothsbank Farm, Leigh Rd. M28 1LL. (R.M. Love and Miss M.A. Love). Est. 1998. Open by appointment. SIZE: Large. *STOCK: Provincial longcase and bracket clocks, 18th C.* LOC: Off junction 13, M60. PARK: Easy. TEL: 0161 790 8414; home - same; fax - 0161 703 7567; e-mail - info@northernclocks.co.uk; website - www.northernclocks.co.uk. SER: Valuations; restorations. VAT: Stan.

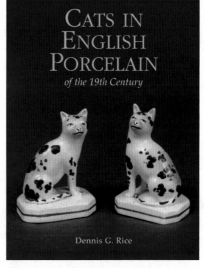

LEICESTERSHIRE

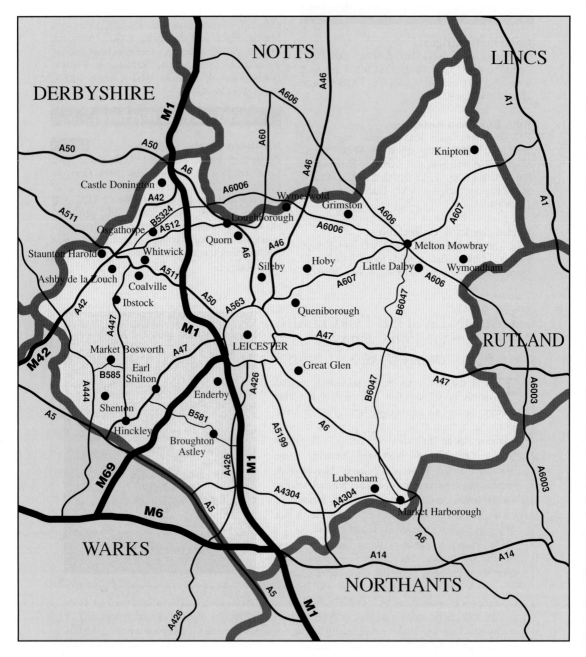

Dealers and Shops in Leicestershire

Ashby de la Zouch	1	Grimston	1	Loughborough	1	Quorn	1
Broughton Astley	1	Hinckley	1	Lubenham	2	Shenton	1
Castle Donington	1	Hoby	1	Market Bosworth	3	Sileby	1
Coalville	1	Ibstock	1	Market Harborough	3	Staunton Harold	1
Earl Shilton	1	Knipton	1	Melton Mowbray	1	Whitwick	1
Enderby	1	Leicester	9	Osgathorpe	1	Wymeswold	1
Great Glen	1	Little Dalby	1	Queniborough	1	Wymondham	1

ASHBY-DE-LA-ZOUCH

Affordable Antiques
Old Forge, North St. LE65 1HS. (Jacqueline and Brian Sidwells). Est. 1994. Open 10-5. SIZE: Small. *STOCK: Victorian pine and period furniture, china especially Bretby and Measham bargeware.* LOC: Just off Market St. opposite Leisure Centre. PARK: Opposite. TEL: 01530 413744; fax - same; mobile - 07966 424861; e-mail - j.sidwells@care4free.net; website - www. affordableantiques.co.uk. SER: Restorations; stripping (pine). FAIRS: Newark; DMG.

BROUGHTON ASTLEY, Nr. Leicester

Old Bakehouse Antiques and Gallery
10 Green Rd. LE9 6RA. (S.R. Needham). Open Thurs.-Sat. 10-6, Sun. 2-5. *STOCK: Period furniture.* PARK: Easy. TEL: 01455 282276.

CASTLE DONINGTON

The Book Shop
17 Borough St. DE74 2LP. (Michael and Margaret Fletcher). Est. 1970. Open 9-5, Sat. 9-12. CL: Wed. SIZE: Small. *STOCK: Books - aviation history, military, railway and antiquarian; pictures and prints, die cast toys.* LOC: Opposite village church. PARK: Easy. TEL: 01332 814391. SER: Valuations; restorations (book-binding); framing. FAIRS: Donington; airshows - Duxford, Waddington, Cottesmore, Cosford and Woodford, RIAT, IPMS.

COALVILLE

Keystone Antiques LAPADA
9 Ashby Rd. LE67 3LF. (I. and H. McPherson). FGA. Est. 1979. Open Thurs., Fri. and Sat. 10-5, Mon. and Tues. by appointment. SIZE: Medium. *STOCK: Jewellery, Victorian and Georgian, £25-£1,500; silver, 1700-1920, £20-£500; small collectable items, 18th-19th C, £15-£300; furniture, cranberry, needlework tools, Victorian and Georgian table glass.* LOC: A115, town centre. PARK: At rear. TEL: 01530 835966; e-mail - heathermcp@webleicester.co.uk. SER: Valuations (jewellery); gem testing.

EARL SHILTON

The Glory Hole
69 High St. LE9 7DH. (M. Crowston). Est. 1994. Open 10-5.30, Sun. 10-2. SIZE: Large. *STOCK: Victorian and Edwardian furniture, £100-£1,000; porcelain, 1860-1930's, £5-£50.* PARK: Easy.

TEL: 01455 847922; mobile - 07710 101364; e-mail - mark@thegloryhole.co.uk; website - www. thegloryhole.co.uk. SER: Valuations; restorations including door stripping; buys at auction (furniture). FAIRS: Newark; Ardingly.

ENDERBY

Ken Smith Antiques Ltd LAPADA
215-217 Leicester Rd. LE19 2BJ. (K.W.Sansom). Est. 1888. Open Mon.-Fri. 9.30-5. SIZE: Small. *STOCK: Furniture, mainly 1880-1930, £100-£1,000; clocks, smalls and bric-a-brac.* TEL: 0116 286 2341; fax - 0116 286 3230. VAT: Stan/Spec.

GREAT GLEN

Sitting Pretty
45a Main St. LE8 9GH. (Jennifer Jones-Fenleigh). Est. 1979. Open Thurs., Fri. and Sat. 10-5.30, other days by appointment. *STOCK: Upholstered furniture, 18th-20th C, £50-£1,000.* LOC: Off A6. PARK: Easy. TEL: 0116 259 3711; home - same. SER: Valuations; restorations (re-upholstery, French polishing, caning and rushing). VAT: Spec.

GRIMSTON, Nr. Melton Mowbray

Ancient & Oriental Ltd
69 Main St. LE14 3BZ. (A. Szolin). ADA. Open by appointment. SIZE: Medium. *STOCK: Ancient Egyptian, Greek, Roman, Celtic, Saxon, Pre-Columbian and medieval antiquities.* PARK: Easy. TEL: 01664 812044; fax - 01664 810087; e-mail - alex@antiquities.co.uk; website - www. antiquities.co.uk. SER: Valuations; illustrated catalogues (4 per year).

HINCKLEY

House Things Antiques
Trinity Lane, 44 Mansion St. LE10 0AU. (P.W. Robertson). Est. 1976. Open 10-6. SIZE: Small. *STOCK: Stripped pine, satinwood, oak and walnut, mainly Victorian and Edwardian, £50-£600; small collectors' items, 1860-1930s, £5-£100; cast iron fireplaces, brass and iron beds, 1890-1920's, £50-£1,000; garden items.* LOC: Inner ring road. PARK: Easy. TEL: 01455 618518; home - 01455 212797. SER: Valuations; restorations.

Magpie Antiques
126 Castle St. LE10 1DD. Est. 1982. Open 9-5. SIZE: Small. *STOCK: Oak and mahogany furniture, Regency to Edwardian; Staffordshire*

pottery and porcelain; English and Continental items and collectables. PARK: Nearby. TEL: 01455 891819; e-mail - michelle@magpie antiques.fsnet.co.uk. SER: Valuations. FAIRS: Ardingly, Newark, Swinderby, Keddlestone Hall, Peterborough, Warwick.

HOBY, Nr. Melton Mowbray

Withers of Leicester
The Old Rutland, Church Lane. LE14 3DU. (S. Frings). Est. 1860. Open 9-5.30. CL: Thurs. pm. and Sat. SIZE: Medium. STOCK: Furniture, 17th-19th C, £50-£3,000; china, 18th-19th C, £10-£300; oil paintings, 19th C, £5-£500. Not Stocked: Jewellery and coins. PARK: Easy. TEL: 01664 434803. SER: Valuations; restorations (furniture). VAT: Stan/Spec.

IBSTOCK, Nr. Leicester

Mandrake Stevenson Antiques
101 High St. LE67 6LJ. Est. 1979. Open 10-5, Sat. 10-1. CL: Wed. SIZE: Small. STOCK: Furniture, pre 1930's. PARK: Easy. TEL: 01530 260898; mobile - 07903 602022. SER: Valuations; restorations (furniture).

KNIPTON, Nr. Grantham

Anthony W. Laywood
NG32 1RF. Est. 1967. Open by appointment. SIZE: Medium. STOCK: Antiquarian books, pre-1850, £20-£8,000. LOC: 1.5 miles off the Grantham-Melton Mowbray road. PARK: Easy. TEL: 01476 870224; fax - 01476 870198; e-mail - laywood@ globalnet.co.uk. SER: Valuations; buys at auction.

LEICESTER

Boulevard Antique and Shipping Centre
63 King Richard's Rd. LE3 5QG. Open Mon.-Fri. 9-6 or any time by appointment. SIZE: Large. STOCK: Furniture including oak, mahogany and shipping; general antiques, some smalls. LOC: A46 from junction 21, M1. PARK: Own. TEL: 0116 233 8828; fax - 0116 233 8823. VAT: Stan.

Britain's Heritage
Shaftesbury Hall, 3 Holy Bones. LE1 4LJ. (Mr and Mrs J. Dennis). Est. 1980. Open 9.30-5.30, Sat. 9.30-5. SIZE: Large. STOCK: Fireplaces, 18th-20th C, £100-£25,000. LOC: Off Vaughan Way, 70 yards from Holiday Inn. PARK: Own. TEL: 0116 251 9592; fax - 0116 262 5990; e-mail - britainsheritage@tinyonline.co.uk; website - www.britainsheritage.co.uk. SER: Valuations; restorations (antique fireplaces). VAT: Stan/Spec.

Clarendon Books
144 Clarendon Park Rd. LE2 3AE. (Julian Smith). PBFA. Est. 1984. Open 10-5. SIZE: Small. STOCK: Antiquarian and second-hand books, £1-£1,000. LOC: Between London Rd. (A6) and Welford Rd. (A50), 2 miles south of city centre. PARK: Easy. TEL: 0116 270 1856; fax - 0116 270 9020; home - 0116 270 1914. SER: Valuations; restorations; repairs; binding; buys at auction (books and maps). FAIRS: London HD; PBFA.

Corry's Antiques   LAPADA
24 Francis St., Stoneygate. LE2 2BD. (Mrs E.I. Corry). Est. 1962. Open 10-5. SIZE: Medium. STOCK: Furniture, 18th-19th C, £500-£10,000; paintings, 19th C, £100-£8,000; silver, porcelain, 18th-20th C, £5-£5,000. TEL: 0116 270 3794; mobile - 07989 427411; e-mail - customer@ corrys-antiques.com; website - www.corrys-antiques.com. SER: Restorations. FAIRS: NEC; LAPADA, NEC and London. VAT: Spec.

Leicester Antiques Warehouse
Clarkes Rd., Wigston. LE18 2BG. Est. 2002. Open Tues.-Sat. 10-5, Sun. 12-5. SIZE: Large - 40 dealers. STOCK: Furniture and general antiques. LOC: B582 towards Wigston, cross railway bridge, turn immediately sharp left into Clarkes Rd., warehouse on left at end of road. PARK: Easy. TEL: 0116 288 1315; website - www.antiques-of-britain.co.uk.

Letty's Antiques
6 Rutland St. LE1 1RA. (I.H. Dubberley). Est. 1952. Open 9.30-5. CL: Thurs. Jan.-March. STOCK: Silver, jewellery, china and brass. LOC: City centre. TEL: 0116 2626435. SER: Valuations (silver and jewellery).

Oxford Street Antique Centre
16-26 Oxford St. LE1 5XU. (Paul and Linda Giles). Est. 1987. Open 10-5.30, Sat. 10-5, Sun. 2-5. SIZE: Large warehouse, 14 showrooms on 4 floors. STOCK: Victorian and Edwardian furniture, shipping goods, pine, bric-a-brac and general antiques, 19th to mid-20th C, 50p-£5,000. LOC: Inner ring road. PARK: Own. TEL: 0116 2553006; fax - 0116 2555863. SER: Container loading facilities. VAT: Stan/Spec.

The Rug Gallery
50 Montague Rd., Clarendon Park. LE2 1TH. (Dr. Roy Short). Est. 1987. Open Fri. and Sat. 10-4 or by appointment. SIZE: Medium. STOCK: Oriental rugs and kilims, early 19th to 20th C, £100-£2,000; Swat, Afghan, Indian and Chinese furniture, 18th-19th C, £50-£1,000; tribal

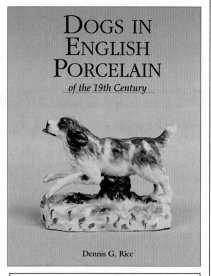
embroidery and jewellery, 19th-20th C, £10-£1,000. LOC: From London Rd. A6, take Victoria Park Rd., to Queen's Rd., then Montague Rd. PARK: Easy. TEL: 0116 2700085; fax - 0116 2700113.

West End Antiques
1 Lothair Rd., Off Aylestone Rd. LE2 7QE. Est. 1986. Open Tues.-Sat. 10-4.30. SIZE: Small. STOCK: Furniture, porcelain, silver, 19th C, £25-£1,000. PARK: Easy. TEL: 0116 244 0086. FAIRS: Castle Donington.

LITTLE DALBY, Nr. Melton Mowbray

Treedale Antiques
Little Dalby Hall, Pickwell Lane. LE14 2XB. (G.K. Warren). GMC. Est. 1972. Open 9-5, Sat. and Sun. by appointment. SIZE: Large, workshop and showroom. STOCK: Furniture including walnut, mahogany and oak, from 1680, to £3,000; portraits and paintings, tapestries and chandeliers. PARK: Own. TEL: 01664 454535; home - same. SER: Valuations; restorations (furniture).

LOUGHBOROUGH

Lowe of Loughborough
37-40 Church Gate. LE11 1UE. Est. 1846. CL: Sat. SIZE: Large. STOCK: Furniture and period upholstery from early oak, 1600 to Edwardian; mahogany, walnut, oak, £20-£8,000; clocks, bracket and longcase, £95-£2,500; porcelain, maps, copper and brass. Not Stocked: Jewellery. LOC: Opposite parish church. PARK: Own. TEL: 01509 212554/217876. SER: Upholstery; restorations; interior design. VAT: Stan/Spec.

LUBENHAM, Nr. Market Harborough

Oaktree Antiques
The Draper's House, Main St. LE16 9TF. (Gillian Abraham and John Wright). Open Wed.-Sun. 10-6. SIZE: Medium. STOCK: Town and country furniture, 17th-19th C; longcase clocks, Georgian to early Victorian; works of art. LOC: A4304. PARK: Opposite on village green. TEL: 01858 410041; mobile - 07710 205696; website - www.oaktreeantiques.co.uk. VAT: Spec.

Stevens and Son

61 Main St. LE16 9TF. (M.J. Stevens). Resident. Est. 1977. Open 10-5. *STOCK: General antiques, mainly furniture.* LOC: A427 via junction 20 M1. TEL: 01858 463521. SER: Restorations (furniture).

MARKET BOSWORTH

Bosworth Antiques

10 Main St. CV13 0JW. (John Thorp). Est. 1986. Open 10-1 and 2-5. CL: Tues. *STOCK: General antiques, 19th-20th C.* PARK: Easy. TEL: 01455 292134. SER: Valuations.

Country Pine Antiques

4 Main St. CV13 0JW. (T.W. and L.M. Richardson). Est. 1980. Open 10-5.30, Thurs. 10-3. CL: Mon. SIZE: Medium. *STOCK: Stripped pine, oak and interesting and unusual decorative items.* LOC: Off A447 in Market Place. PARK: Easy. TEL: 01455 291303.

P. Stanworth (Fine Arts)

The Grange, 2 Barton Rd. CV13 0LQ. (Mr and Mrs G. and James Stanworth). Resident. Est. 1965. Open by appointment. SIZE: Medium. *STOCK: Oil paintings and watercolours, 18th to early 20th C.* LOC: Road just off town square. PARK: Easy. TEL: 01455 291023. VAT: Spec.

MARKET HARBOROUGH

Graftons of Market Harborough

92 St Mary's Rd. LE16 7DX. (F. Ingall). Est. 1967. Open Mon., Tues., Fri. and Sat. 10-5.30, other times by appointment. *STOCK: Oils, watercolours, etchings and engravings, 18th-19th C.* PARK: Forecourt. TEL: 01858 433557. FAIRS: Royal Show.

Walter Moores and Son `LAPADA`

P O Box 5338. LE16 7WG. (Peter Moores). Est. 1925. Open by appointment. *STOCK: Georgian furniture; complementary Victorian items.* TEL: 07071 226202; fax - same; mobile - 07710 019045; e-mail - waltermoores@btinternet.com; website - www.waltermoores.co.uk. FAIRS: Most major. VAT: Spec.

J. Stamp and Sons

The Chestnuts, 15 Kettering Rd. LE16 8AN. (M. Stamp). Resident. Est. 1947. Open 8-5.30, Sat. 9-12.30 or by appointment. SIZE: Medium. *STOCK: Mahogany and oak furniture, 18th-19th C, £500-£5,000; Victorian furniture, £250-£2,500; Edwardian furniture, £100-£1,000.* LOC: A6. PARK: Easy. TEL: 01858 462524; fax -

01858 465643. SER: Valuations (furniture); restorations (furniture). VAT: Stan/Spec.

MELTON MOWBRAY

Flagstones Pine & Interiors

24 Burton St. LE13 1AF. (Julie Adcock and David Kealey). Est. 1986. Open 9.30-5.15, Sun. 10.30-3.30. CL: Mon. SIZE: Medium. *STOCK: English and European pine furniture, 18th-20th C; new and reclaimed wood reproductions, including kitchens; bespoke furniture.* PARK: Easy. TEL: 01664 566438; e-mail - flagstones pine@email.com; website - www.flagstonespine. com. SER: Restorations; stripping; waxing; re-seating (rush and cane). VAT: Stan.

OSGATHORPE, Nr. Loughborough

David E. Burrows `LAPADA`

Manor House Farm. LE12 9SY. Est. 1973. *STOCK: Pine, oak, mahogany and walnut furniture, clocks, £100-£10,000.* LOC: Junction 23, M1, turn right off Ashby road after 4.5 miles, farm next to church; or off A42. PARK: Easy. TEL: 01530 222218; mobile - 07702 059030; fax - 01530 223139; e-mail - david.burrows2@ virgin.net. VAT: Stan/Spec.

QUENIBOROUGH, Nr. Leicester

J. Green and Son

1 Coppice Lane. LE7 3DR. (R. Green). Resident. Est. 1932. Appointment advisable. SIZE: Medium. *STOCK: 18th-19th C English and Continental furniture.* LOC: Off A607 Leicester to Melton Mowbray Rd. PARK: Easy. TEL: 0116 2606682. SER: Valuations; buys at auction. VAT: Stan/Spec.

QUORN

Quorn Pine and Decoratives

The New Mills, Leicester Rd. LE12 8ES. (S. Yates and S. Parker). Est. 1982. Open 9-6, Sat. 9.30-5.30. SIZE: Large. *STOCK: Pine and country furniture.* PARK: Own. TEL: 01509 416031; website - www.quorn-pine.co.uk. SER: Stripping and restorations (pine). VAT: Stan/Spec.

SHENTON, Nr. Market Bosworth

Whitemoors Antiques and Fine Art

Mill Lane. CV13 6BZ. (D. Dolby and P. McGowan). Est. 1987. Open Mon.-Fri. 11-4, (until 5 in summer), Sat. and Sun. 11-5. SIZE: Large - 20+ unit holders. *STOCK: Furniture, £25-£2,000; smalls, £5-£200; prints and pictures,*

Victorian to early 20th C, £40-£400. LOC: A5 onto A444 towards Burton-on-Trent, first right then second left. PARK: Easy. TEL: 01455 212250; 01455 212981 (ansaphone); fax - 01455 213342.

SILEBY, Nr. Loughborough

R. A. James Antiques
Ammonite Gallery, 15a High St. LE12 7RX. *STOCK: Mainly stripped pine, general antiques.* TEL: 01509 812169; mobile - 07713 132650.

STAUNTON HAROLD

Ropers Hill Antiques
Ropers Hill Farm. LE65 1SE. (S. and R. Southworth). Est. 1974. Open by appointment. SIZE: Small. *STOCK: General antiques, silver and metalware.* LOC: On old A453. PARK: Easy. TEL: 01530 413919. SER: Valuations.

WHITWICK, Nr. Coalville

Charles Antiques
3 Market Place. LE67 5AE. (Brian Haydon). Est. 1970. Open afternoons, Sat. 10-12 and 2-4, Wed. and Sun. by appointment. CL: Mon. SIZE: Small.

STOCK: Clocks, 18th C, £25-£4,000; furniture, 19th C, £50-£1,000; china. LOC: A511. PARK: Easy. TEL: 01530 836932; home - same; mobile - 07831 204406. SER: Buys at auction. VAT: Stan/Spec.

WYMESWOLD, Nr. Loughborough

N. Bryan-Peach Antiques
30 Brook St. LE12 6TU. Resident. Est. 1977. Open by appointment. *STOCK: Clocks, barometers, 18th-19th C furniture, £50-£5,000.* PARK: Easy. TEL: 01509 880425. SER: Valuations; restorations; buys at auction. VAT: Spec.

WYMONDHAM, Nr. Melton Mowbray

Old Bakery Antiques
Main St. LE14 2AG. (Tina Bryan). Est. 1990. Open 10-5.30. CL: Thurs. SIZE: Medium. *STOCK: Cottage, garden, architectural and reclamation items including pine furniture, kitchenalia, advertising items, chimney pots, stained glass, doors and door hardware, tiles, rural and domestic bygones.* PARK: Easy. TEL: 01572 787472; home - same.

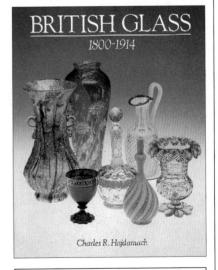

LINCOLNSHIRE

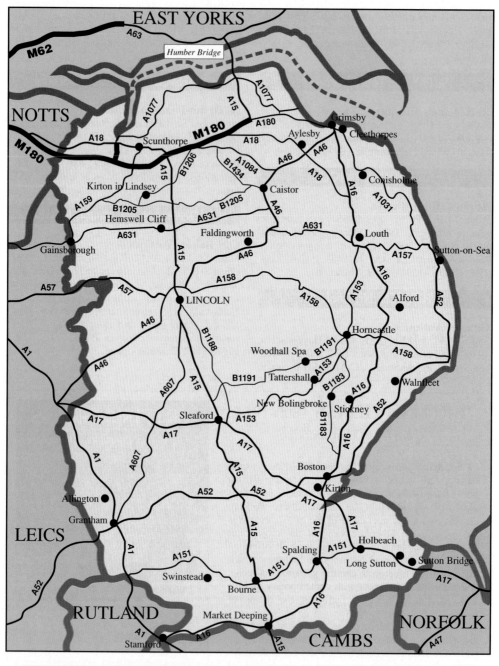

Dealers and Shops in Lincolnshire				Horncastle	9	Spalding	3
				Kirton	1	Stamford	10
				Kirton in Lindsey	1	Stickney	1
Alford	1	Conisholme	1	Lincoln	11	Sutton Bridge	3
Allington	1	Faldingworth	1	Long Sutton	1	Sutton-on-Sea	1
Aylesby	1	Gainsborough	3	Louth	1	Swinstead	1
Boston	2	Grantham	5	Market Deeping	2	Tattershall	1
Bourne	3	Grimsby	2	New Bolingbroke	1	Wainfleet	1
Caistor	1	Hemswell Cliff	5	Scunthorpe	1	Woodhall Spa	2
Cleethorpes	1	Holbeach	1	Sleaford	2		

ALFORD

Trade Antiques
5 High St. LN13 9DS. (P.E. Poole). Est. 1961.
CL: Sat. SIZE: Medium. *STOCK: General
shipping goods, clocks and watches.* PARK:
Easy. TEL: 01507 462854. *Trade Only.*

ALLINGTON, Nr. Grantham

**Garth Vincent Antique Arms and
Armour** LAPADA
The Old Manor House. NG32 2DH. Est. 1979.
Open by appointment. SIZE: Medium. *STOCK:
Militaria including firearms, swords, rapiers and
daggers; armour, 16th-19th C, £50-£15,000.*
LOC: Opposite church. PARK: Easy. TEL: 01400
281358; home - same; fax - 01400 282658;
mobile - 07785 352151; e-mail - garthvincent@
compuserve.com; website - www.guns.uk.com.
SER: Valuations; restorations; buys at auction.
FAIRS: London and major city Arms; NEC
(Aug). VAT: Spec.

AYLESBY, Nr. Grimsby

Robin Fowler (Period Clocks) LAPADA
Washing Dales, Washing Dales Lane. DN37 7LH.
Open by appointment. SIZE: Large. *STOCK:
Clocks and barometers, 17th-18th C.* PARK:
Easy. TEL: 01472 751335. SER: Restorations
(clocks and barometers). FAIRS: LAPADA;
Bailey; Galloway. VAT: Spec.

BOSTON

Pennyfarthing Antiques
1 Red Lion St. PE21 6NY. (Philip Hale). Est.
1992. Open Tues., Wed., Fri. and Sat. 10-4.30.
SIZE: Small. *STOCK: Small furniture, ceramics,
copper and brass, some silver and jewellery,
mainly 1870's to 1930's.* LOC: 100 yards from
Market Place. PARK: NCP nearby. TEL: 01205
362988; home - 01205 367246; e-mail -
pennyfarthing@onetel.net.uk; website - www.
pennyfarthingantiques.net.

**Portobello Row Antique & Collectors'
Centre**
93-95 High St. PE21. Est. 1982. Open 10-4.
SIZE: 9 dealers. *STOCK: Shipping furniture,
kitchenalia, blue and white china, 1940's-70's
clothing, bric-a-brac.* TEL: 01205 368692.

BOURNE

Antique & Secondhand Traders
The Warehouse, 39 West St. (C.A. and A.L.

Thompson). Est. 1962. Open Mon., Tues., Fri.
and Sat. 10-5 or by appointment. SIZE:
Warehouse. *STOCK: Furniture - antique,
Victorian, Edwardian, shipping, oak,
reproduction and modern, £50-£5,000.* LOC: On
A15, 8 miles from Stamford A1. PARK: Own.
TEL: 01778 394700; mobiles - Alan - 07885
694299, Clyde - 07958 941728. SER: Valuations.
FAIRS: Newark; Ardingly. VAT: Spec/Global.

Bourne Antiques & Arts
44 West St. PE10 9NX. (R.A. and Mrs J.M.
Warner). Est. 2000. Open 10-5, Sun. 11-5. CL:
Wed. SIZE: Medium - 30 dealers. *STOCK: Wide
range of general antiques including furniture,
silver, porcelain and glass, maps and prints,
jewellery, clocks, copper and brass, £5-£1,000+.*
LOC: Close to town centre. TEL: 01778 394725;
fax - same; e-mail - baanda@supanet.com;
website - www.bourneantiques.com.

The Complete Automobilist
6 Graham Hill Way. PE10 9PJ. Est. 1967. Open 9-
5. CL: Sat. *STOCK: Hard-to-get parts for older
vehicles.* TEL: 01778 426222; fax - 01778
426333; e-mail - colincrabbe@compauto.co.uk;
website - www.completeautomobilist.com. SER:
Colour catalogue available £2.

CAISTOR

Caistor Antiques
12 High St. LN7 6TX. (Susan Rutter). Est. 1982.
Open by appointment day or night. *STOCK:
Pottery, furniture, jewellery, dolls, linen, silver,
18th-20th C.* LOC: Off A46 between Grimsby
and Market Rasen. PARK: Own. TEL: 01472
851975; home - same. SER: Valuations.

CLEETHORPES

Yesterday's Antiques
86 Grimsby Rd. DN35 7DP. (Jeanette and
Norman Bishop). Resident. Est. 1983. Open 9-5,
Sun. by appointment. SIZE: Large. *STOCK:
Furniture, £50-£2,000; fireplaces, £500-£1,000;
French beds, clocks, £300-£1,200; all 19th C.*
LOC: A180 on right entering town, opposite Esso
garage. PARK: Easy. TEL: 01472
343020/504093. SER: Valuations; restorations
(polishing and stripping); repairs (clocks);
renovations (fireplaces).

CONISHOLME, Nr. Louth

A Barn Full of Brass Beds
The Farmhouse, Ashleigh Farm, Main Rd. LN11
7LS. (J.J. Tebbs). Est. 1985. Open by

appointment. SIZE: Large. *STOCK: Brass and iron beds, 1860-1910, from £250.* LOC: 10 miles N.E. of Louth. PARK: Easy. TEL: 01507 358092; e-mail - brassbeds@clara.co.uk; websites - www.brassandironbeds.co.uk and www.princess andthepea.co.uk. SER: Restorations; bespoke bases and mattresses.. VAT: Stan.

FALDINGWORTH, Nr. Market Rasen

Brownlow Antiques Centre
Lincoln Rd. LN8 3SF. (Sylvia and Alex Stephens). Est. 1994. Open Tues.-Sat. 10-5, Sun. 12-5. SIZE: Large. *STOCK: Furniture, 18th C to pre-1940, £50-£3,000; bric-a-brac, collectables, clocks, musical boxes, kitchenalia, books, from £2.* LOC: A46 towards Grimsby, 10 miles north of Lincoln. PARK: Own. TEL: 01673 885367; home - same; e-mail - info@brownlowantiques centre.co.uk; website - www.brownlowantiques centre.co.uk. SER: Restorations. FAIRS: Local.

GAINSBOROUGH

S. Carrick's Antiques and Shipping
130 Trinity St. DN21 5PD. Open 8.30-5. *STOCK: General antiques and shipping furniture.* TEL: 01427 611393/810409; mobile - 07850 470966.

Stanley Hunt Jewellers
22 Church St. DN21. (S. and R.S. Hunt). Est. 1952. Open 9-5. CL: Wed. SIZE: Medium. *STOCK: Antique jewellery.* LOC: Main street from Market Place. PARK: Easy. TEL: 01427 613051; home - same. SER: Valuations; restorations (gold, silver, clocks).

Pilgrims Antiques Centre
66 Church St. DN21 2JR. Est. 1986. CL: Mon. and Wed. SIZE: Large. *STOCK: Jewellery, miniatures, silver, silhouettes, paintings, textiles, ceramics and books, £5-£1,000; furniture, £50-£1,000.* LOC: Near Old Hall. PARK: Easy. TEL: 01427 810897. SER: Valuations. FAIRS: Newark; Birmingham.

GRANTHAM

Grantham Clocks
30 Lodge Way. NG31 8DD. (R. Conder). Resident. Est. 1987. Open by appointment. *STOCK: Clocks.* PARK: Easy. TEL: 01476 561784. SER: Restorations.

Grantham Furniture Emporium
4-6 Wharf Rd. NG31 6BA. (K. and J.E. Hamilton). Est. 1970. Open 10-4, Sun. 11-4. CL: Mon. and Wed. SIZE: Large. *STOCK: Victorian,* *Edwardian and shipping furniture, £5-£3,000.* LOC: Town centre, near Post Office. PARK: Own at rear. TEL: 01476 562967.

Harlequin Antiques
46 Swinegate. NG31 6RL. (A.R. and Mrs S.B. Marshall). Est. 1996. Open from 9. SIZE: Medium. *STOCK: Furniture and china, 19th C, £50-£1,000; collectables, 19th-20th C, £20-£200.* LOC: 100 yards from High St., opposite Blue Pig public house. PARK: Easy. TEL: 01476 563346. SER: Valuations.

Notions Antiques Centre
1 & 2a Market Place. NG31 6LQ. (Mr and Mrs L. Checkley). Est. 1984. Open 10-5, Sat. 9.30-5, Sun. 11-4. SIZE: 70+ dealers. *STOCK: Furniture, ceramics, pictures, jewellery, textiles, silver, bygone tooling, clocks, books, toys, architectural fittings, railwayana and enamel signs.* LOC: Down from Angel and Royal Hotel. PARK: Easy. TEL: 01476 563603; mobile - 07736 677978. SER: Valuations; repairs. FAIRS: Newark.

Marcus Wilkinson
The Tyme House, 1 Blue Court. NG31 6NJ. NAWCC. AHS. BHI. Est. 1935. Open 10-4.30. SIZE: Small. *STOCK: Jewellery, watches and silver, 19th C, £50-£5,000.* PARK: Nearby. TEL: 01476 560400 and 01529 413149; e-mail - marcus@timeshop.co.uk; websites - www.englishclocks.net and www.englishclocks.com. SER: Valuations; restorations (including clock and watch movements); buys at auction (rings and watches). FAIRS: USA. VAT: Spec.

GRIMSBY

Abbeygate Gallery & Antiques Centre
14 Abbeygate. DN31 1JY. (R.L. Cumming and A.F. Sanders). Est. 1998. Open 10-4. SIZE: Medium. *STOCK: Pottery and glass, militaria, coins and medals, £5-£100; small furniture, £25-£500; all 19th-20th C; 18th C porcelain.* LOC: 2 mins. from train station and Freshney Place Shopping Centre. PARK: Nearby. TEL: 01472 361129; website - www.abbeygate-antiques.co.uk. SER: Valuations; finder.

Bell Antiques
68 Harold St. DN32 7NQ. (V. Hawkey). Est. 1964. Open by appointment, telephone previous evening. SIZE: Large. *STOCK: Grandfather clocks, barometers and furniture.* Not Stocked: Reproduction. PARK: Easy. TEL: 01472 695110; home - same. FAIRS: Newark. VAT: Stan/Spec.

HEMSWELL CLIFF, Nr. Gainsborough

Astra House Antiques Centre
Old RAF Hemswell. DN21 5TL. (Michael Frith).
Est. 1987. Open 10-5 including Sun. SIZE: Large.
70 dealers. *STOCK: Wide variety of general
antiques and shipping goods, including Victorian,
Edwardian and Continental furniture and smalls.*
LOC: Near Caenby Corner Roundabout
A15/A631. PARK: Easy. TEL: 01427 668312;
fax - same; mobile - 07768 626786; e-mail -
astraantiqueshemswell@btinternet.com; website
- www.antiquecentreuk.com.

Hemswell Antique Centres
Caenby Corner Estate. DN21 5TJ. (Robert and
Jonathon Miller). Est. 1986. Open 10-5 including
Sun. SIZE: 270+ dealers. *STOCK: Period
furniture, 17th-19th C; watercolours and oils,
19th C; silver and plate, clocks, porcelain, china,
jewellery, books, prints, linen and pine.* LOC:
A15 from Lincoln then A631 towards
Gainsborough, 1 mile from roundabout, follow
signs. PARK: Easy. TEL: 01427 668389; fax -
01427 668935; e-mail - info@hemswell-
antiques.com. SER: Restorations (oak, mahogany
and pine; upholstery); delivery.

Kate
Kate House, Caenby Corner Estate. DN21 5TJ.
(Mr Shamsa). Est. 1966. Open 9-4.30, Sun. 9-2.
STOCK: Pine including reproduction. PARK:
Own. TEL: 01427 668724/668904; fax - 01427
668905.

Elaine Lonsdale Bookseller and
Bookbinder
Upper Floor, Building 2, Hemswell Antiques
Centre, Caenby Corner Estate. DN21 5TJ. (Elaine
Lonsdale). PBFA. Est. 1988. Open daily
including Sun. SIZE: Small. *STOCK:
Antiquarian and second-hand books and
ephemera.* PARK: Easy. TEL: 01484 642821;
mobile - 07710 480581; e-mail - lainelonsdale@
yahoo.co.uk. SER: Valuations; book-binding.
FAIRS: PBFA; Buxton.

Second Time Around
Hemswell Antique Centre, Caenby Corner Estate,
Gainsborough. DN21 5TJ. (G.L. Powis). Est.
1985. Open 10-5 including Sun. SIZE: Large.
*STOCK: Longcase and bracket clocks,
barometers, pre 1830, £1,650-£35,000.* LOC:
A15 from Lincoln to Caenby Corner roundabout,
left towards Gainsborough for 1 mile (A631).
PARK: Easy. TEL: 01427 668389; home - 01522
543167; mobile - 07860 679495. SER:
Restorations (clocks).

HOLBEACH, Nr. Spalding

P.J. Cassidy (Books)
1 Boston Rd. PE12 7LR. Est. 1974. Open 10-6.
SIZE: Medium. *STOCK: Books, 19th-20th C, £2-
£300; maps, prints and engravings, 17th-19th C,
£10-£500.* LOC: 1/4 mile from A17. PARK:
Nearby. TEL: 01406 426322; fax - same; e-mail -
bookscass@aol.com. SER: Valuations; framing
and mount cutting. VAT: Stan.

HORNCASTLE

G. Baker Antiques
16 South St. LN9 6DX. Est. 1974. Open 9-5,
Wed. 9-1, Sun. by appointment. SIZE: Small.
STOCK: Furniture, 18th-20th C, £10-£10,000.
LOC: A153. PARK: Easy. TEL: 01507 526553;
mobile - 07767 216264. SER: Valuations;
restorations (furniture). FAIRS: Swinderby;
Newark. VAT: Stan/Spec.

Clare Boam
22-38 North St. LN9 5DX. Est. 1977. Open 9-5,
Sun 2-4.30. SIZE: Large. *STOCK: Furniture and
bric-a-brac, 19th-20th C, to £1,000.* LOC:
Louth/Grimsby road out of town. PARK: Easy.
TEL: 01507 522381; home - same; e-mail -
clareboam@btconnect.com. VAT: Global.

Great Expectations
37-43 East St. LN9. (Clare Boam). Est. 1977.
Open 9-5, Sun. and Bank Holidays 1-4.30. SIZE:
Large. *STOCK: Wide variety of general antiques
including pine, oak, mahogany, kitchenalia,
luggage, books, china, glass, collectables, 50p to
£1,000.* LOC: A158, 100 yards from traffic lights.
PARK: At rear or in Trinity Centre. TEL: 01507
524202; home - 01507 522381; e-mail - clare
boam@btconnect.com; website - www.great
expectationshorncastle.co.uk.

Le Strange Emporium
25 Bull Ring. LN9 5HU. Open 9-5.30, Sun. 11-5.
SIZE: Large. *STOCK: Antiques and collectables.*
LOC: Town centre. PARK: Nearby. TEL: 01507
524260; fax - same.

Lindsey Court Architectural Antiques
Lindsey Court. LN9 5DH. (Lindsay White). Est.
1989. Open 10-4, Sun. by appointment. SIZE:
Medium. *STOCK: Architectural antiques,
English, French and Spanish reclamations, York
stone flagging and garden statuary, £50-£10,000.*
LOC: Behind the library. PARK: Own. TEL:
01507 527794; fax - 01507 526670; mobile -
07768 396117; e-mail - lndsy150@netscape
online.co.uk; sales@1starchitectural.co.uk;

website - www.1starchitectural.co.uk. SER: Container and shipping. FAIRS: Newark. VAT: Stan/Global.

Alan Read - Period Furniture
60 & 62 West St. LN9 5AD. Est. 1981. Open 10-4.30. CL: Mon. and Wed. except by appointment. SIZE: Large. *STOCK: 17th-19th C furniture, early oak, walnut and decorative items.* LOC: A158 Lincoln to Skegness road, at junction with B1191 Woodhall Spa road. PARK: Easy. TEL: 01507 524324; fax - 01507 525548; e-mail - alanpread@lineone.net. SER: Valuations; bespoke copies; interior design. VAT: Stan/Spec.

Seaview Antiques
Stanhope Rd. LN9 5DG. (M. Chalk and Tracey Collins). Open 9-5. SIZE: Large + warehouse. *STOCK: Victorian, Edwardian and decorative furniture; smalls, brassware, silver and plate, lamps, boxes.* LOC: A158. PARK: Easy. TEL: 01507 524524.

Laurence Shaw Antiques
77 East St. LN9 6AA. (L.D. Shaw). Est. 1971. Open 8.30-5, prior telephone call advisable. SIZE: Medium. *STOCK: Furniture, china, glass, metalware, books, collectables, general antiques, 17th-20th C.* LOC: Opposite Trinity Church. TEL: 01507 527638; e-mail - lmidwinter@aol.com. SER: Consultant; valuations. VAT: Global/Spec.

The Trinity Centre
East St. LN9 5DX. (Clare Boam). Est. 2002. Open Mon.-Fri. 9-5, Sun. and Bank Holidays 1-4.30.SIZE: Large. *STOCK: Furniture, china, glass and collectables.* LOC: In the Holy Trinity Church - Skegness road out of town. PARK: Own. TEL: 01507 525256.

Kirton Antiques   LAPADA
3 High St. PE20 1DR. (A.R. Marshall). Est. 1973. Open 8.30-5, Sat. 8.30-12 or by appointment. SIZE: Large - warehouse. *STOCK: Furniture, all periods; painted pine, chairs, decorative items, glass, metal, pottery, china, picture frames.* PARK: Own. TEL: 01205 722595; evenings - 01205 722134; fax - 01205 722895; e-mail - alan.marshall@modcomp.net. SER: Valuations. VAT: Stan.

Mr Van Hefflin
12 High St. DN21 4LU. Est. 1820. Open 10-5.

STOCK: Jewellery, curios, silver, paintings. PARK: Easy. SER: Valuations.

Annette Antiques
77 Bailgate. LN1 3AR. (Mrs A. Bhalla). Est. 1972. Open Tues.-Sat. 2-6. SIZE: Small. *STOCK: Porcelain, glass and small silver, 19th-20th C; clocks, silver flatware, watercolours, prints and drawings, 18th-20th C, £10-£500; collectables, including dolls houses, furniture and accessories.* LOC: 2 mins. from castle and cathedral. PARK: Nearby. TEL: 01522 546838; home - 01205 260219. SER: Restorations (furniture). FAIRS: Alexandra Palace.

C. and K.E. Dring
111 High St. LN5 7PY. Est. 1977. Open 10-5.30. CL: Wed. *STOCK: Victorian and Edwardian inlaid furniture; shipping goods, porcelain, clocks, musical boxes, tin-plated toys, trains and Dinkys.* PARK: Opposite. TEL: 01522 540733/792794.

Golden Goose Books
20 and 21 Steep Hill. LN2 1LT. (R. West-Skinn and Mrs A. Cockram). PBFA. Est. 1983. Open 10-5.30. SIZE: Large. *STOCK: Antiquarian and secondhand books, maps and prints.* PARK: Nearby. TEL: 01522 522589; home - 01673 878622.

Hansford at No 2 Antiques & Period Design
2 Exchequergate. LN2 1PZ. Open 10-1 and 2-5. SIZE: Large. *STOCK: Furniture and decorative items, 18th-20th C, £50-£10,000.* LOC: In square between cathedral and castle. PARK: Castle Hill. TEL: 01522 568612.

David J. Hansord & Son   BADA
6 & 7 Castle Hill. LN1 3AA. (David, John and Anne Hansord). Est. 1972. Open 10-1 and 2-5. SIZE: Large. STOCK: Furniture, clocks, barometers, works of art, 18th C, £50-£50,000. LOC: In square between cathedral and castle. PARK: Castle Hill. TEL: 01522 530044; fax - same. SER: Valuations; restorations (furniture, barometers and clocks); buys at auction. FAIRS: Olympia (June, Nov). VAT: Spec.

Harlequin Gallery and Golden Goose Globe Restorers
22 Steep Hill. LN2 1LT. (R. West-Skinn). PBFA. Est. 1962. Open 10-5.30. SIZE: Large. *STOCK: Antiquarian and secondhand books, antique*

maps and prints. TEL: 01522 522589; home - 01673 858294. SER: Restoration (globes and philosophical instruments).

Dorrian Lambert Antiques Centre
64, 65 Steep Hill. LN1 1YN. (R. Lambert). Est. 1981. Open 10-5, Sun. in summer. SIZE: Medium, 15 dealers. STOCK: Small furniture, clocks, chairs, pottery, porcelain, jewellery, books, sporting antiques, books and collectables, 18th to early 20th C. PARK: Loading only or nearby. TEL: 01522 545916; home - 01427 848686. SER: Valuations; restorations (clocks).

Mansions
5a Eastgate. LN2 1QA. (R.E. & J.A. Mance). Est. 1989. Open 10-5. STOCK: General antiques, decorative items, period lighting. TEL: 01522 513631/560271.

Rowletts of Lincoln
338 High St. LN5 7DQ. (A.H. and P.L. Rowlett). Est. 1965. Open 9-5. STOCK: Antique and secondhand jewellery. TEL: 01522 524139; fax - 01522 523427. VAT: Global/Margin.

Timepiece Repairs
43 Steep Hill. LN2 1LU. (R. Ellis). FBHI. Est. 1978. Open Sat. 10-4, other times by appointment. SIZE: Small. STOCK: Clocks and watches, 18th-20th C, £10-£8,000; barometers, 19th-20th C, £100-£1,500. LOC: Near cathedral. PARK: 100 metres. TEL: 01522 525831; home - 01522 881790. SER: Valuations; restorations (movements, dials and cases); buys at auction (horological). VAT: Stan/Spec.

James Usher and Son Ltd
incorporating John Smith & Son, 26 & 27 Guildhall St. LN1 1TR. Open 9-5.30. STOCK: Silver, jewellery. TEL: 01522 527547/523120

LONG SUTTON

The Chapel Emporium Antique Centre
London Rd. PE12. (J.A. Beck and B. Hill). Est. 1984. Open 10-5 including Sun. CL: Mon. SIZE: Large. STOCK: Furniture, 18th-19th C, £100-£5,000; collectables, 19th-20th C, 50p-£300; ephemera, 19th C, 50p-£25. LOC: Opposite playing fields. PARK: Free opposite. TEL: 01406 364808; e-mail - barbara.hill4@btopenworld. co.uk.

LOUTH

Old Maltings Antique Centre
38 Aswell St. LN11 9HP. (Norman and Margaret Coffey). Est. 1980. Open 10-4.30, Sat. 10-5, Sun.

11-4. SIZE: Large - over 40 cabinets. STOCK: Furniture including Victorian and Edwardian, collectables, ceramics, glass, jewellery. LOC: 2 mins. walk from town centre. PARK: Easy. TEL: 01507 600366; e-mail - norman@tomaclin cs.fsnet.co.uk; website - www.antiques-atlas. com. SER: Valuations; restorations; stripping (pine). FAIRS: Swinderby.

MARKET DEEPING

Market Deeping Antiques & Craft Centre
50-56 High St. PE6. (J. Strutt and C. Stubbins). Resident. Est. 1995. SIZE: Large. STOCK: General antiques, bric-a-brac and craft items. LOC: A15. PARK: Easy. TEL: 01778 380238.

Portland House Antiques
23 Church St. PE6 8AN. (G.W. Cree and V.E. Bass). Est. 1987. Open Mon.-Sat. or by appointment. SIZE: Medium. STOCK: Porcelain, glass, furniture, 18th-19th C, £100-£10,000. PARK: Easy. TEL: 01778 347129; home - same. SER: Buys at auction. VAT: Stan/Spec.

NEW BOLINGBROKE, Nr. Boston

Junktion
The Old Railway Station. (J. Rundle). Est. 1981. Open Wed., Thurs. and Sat. SIZE: Large. STOCK: Early advertising, decorative and architectural items; toys, automobilia, mechanical antiques and bygones; early slot machines, wireless, telephones, bakelite, 20th C collectables. Not Stocked: Porcelain and jewellery. LOC: B1183 Boston to Horncastle. PARK: Easy. TEL: 01205 480087/480068.

SCUNTHORPE

Antiques & Collectables & Gun Shop
Rear of 251 Ashby High St. DN16 2SQ. (J.A. Bowden). Est. 1973. Open 9-5. STOCK: Clocks, furniture, arms and collectables. TEL: 01724 865445/720606. SER: Restorations; repairs.

SLEAFORD

Mill Antiques
19A Northgate. NG34 7BH. (John Noble and A. Crabtree). Est. 1988. Open 9-5. SIZE: Medium. STOCK: General antiques including furniture, porcelain and pictures, 18th-20th C, £5-£5,500. LOC: 100 yards from market square. PARK: Loading only. TEL: 01529 413342; home - 01529 415101. SER: Valuations; restorations (furniture and porcelain).

Marcus Wilkinson

The Little Tyme House, 13 Southgate. NG34 7SU. (M. and P. Wilkinson). BHI. AHS. NAWCC. Est. 1935. Open 10-4.30. SIZE: Small. *STOCK: Jewellery, watches and silver, £50-£5,000.* LOC: High St. near River Slea. PARK: Nearby. TEL: 01529 413149 and 01476 560400; e-mail - marcus@timeshop.freeserve.co.uk. SER: Valuations; restorations (including clock and watch movements); buys at auction (rings and watches). VAT: Stan.

SPALDING

Dean's Antiques

"The Walnuts", Weston St. Mary's. PE12 6JB. (Mrs B. Dean). Est. 1969. Open daily. SIZE: Medium. *STOCK: General antiques, farm and country bygones, £2-£200.* LOC: On Spalding to Holbeach main road A151. PARK: Easy. TEL: 01406 370429.

Penman Clockcare (UK) Ltd

Unit 4 & 5 Pied Calf Yard, Sheepmarket. PE11 1BE. (Michael Strutt). BWCMG. Est. 1998. Open 9-5, Sat. 9-4. *STOCK: Clocks 18th-20th C; watches, 19th-20th C; jewellery.* LOC: In yard behind Pied Calf public house, opposite PO. PARK: Nearby. TEL: 01755 714900; 01755 840955 (ansaphone); website - www.penman clockcare.co.uk. SER: Valuations; restorations (clocks and watches).

Spalding Antiques

1 Abbey Path, The Crescent. PE11 1AY. (John Mumford). Est. 1980. Open 10-5, Thurs. 10-12 and 1.30-5, Sat. 10-4. SIZE: Medium. *STOCK: Clocks, furniture and smalls, 19th C, £10-£3,000.* LOC: Opposite Sessions House. PARK: Victoria St. TEL: 01775 713185. SER: Valuations.

STAMFORD

Norman Blackburn

Old Print Shop, 7 Red Lion Sq. PE9 2AJ. Est. 1974. Open 10-5, Tues. by appointment; CL: Mon. SIZE: Large. *STOCK: Prints in period frames - decorative, stipple and mezzotints, botanical, sporting, marine, portraits and views, pre-1860.* LOC: Top end of town. PARK: On riverside. TEL: 01780 489151; fax - same; mobile - 07714 721846; e-mail - oldprints@ normanblackburn.com; website - www.norman blackburn.com. SER: Valuations.

Dawson of Stamford Ltd

6 Red Lion Sq. PE9 2AJ. (J. Dawson). Open 9-5.30. *STOCK: Fine antique furniture, jewellery and silver.* LOC: Town centre between St. John's Church and All Saint's Church. TEL: 01780 754166. VAT: Stan/Spec.

Hunters Antiques & Interior Design

9a St. Mary's Hill. PE9 2DP. (Jill Hunter). Est. 2000. Open 9.30-5.30. SIZE: Medium. *STOCK: Period mahogany and country furniture, decorative items.* LOC: Just over town bridge, on the left. PARK: George Hotel. TEL: 01780 757946; fax - same; mobile - 07976 796969. SER: Restorations (furniture, clocks and barometers); interior design. VAT: Stan/Spec.

Graham Pickett Antiques

7 High St., St Martins. PE9 2LF. (G.R. Pickett). Est. 1990. Open 10-5.30, Sun. by appointment. SIZE: Medium. *STOCK: Furniture - country, 1650-1900, French provincial, 1700-1900, both £50-£3,000; French and English beds, 1750-1900, £350-£4,000.* LOC: From A1 north into town, on right by 1st lights opposite George Hotel. PARK: Easy. TEL: 01780 481064; home - 01780 764502; mobile - 07710 936948; e-mail - graham@pickettantiques.demon.co.uk; website - www.pickettantiques.demon.co.uk. FAIRS: Newark IACF. VAT: Stan/Spec.

Sinclair's

11/12 St. Mary's St. PE9. (J.S. Sinclair). Est. 1970. Open 9-5.30. SIZE: Large. *STOCK: Oak country furniture, 18th C, £200-£3,000; Victorian mahogany furniture, £100-£1,000; Edwardian furniture.* LOC: Near A1. PARK: George Hotel. TEL: 01780 765421. VAT: Stan/Spec.

St. George's Antiques

1 St. George's Sq. PE9 2BN. (G.H. Burns). Est. 1974. Open 9-1 and 2-4.30. CL: Sat. SIZE: Shop + trade only warehouse. *STOCK: Period and Victorian furniture, some small items.* TEL: 01780 754117; home - 01780 460456. VAT: Stan/Spec.

St. Martins Antiques Centre

23a High St., St. Martin's. PE9 2LF. (P. B. Light). Est. 1993. Open 10-5 including Sun. SIZE: 60 dealers. *STOCK: Georgian, Victorian and Edwardian furniture, country pine, Art Deco and Arts and Crafts furniture, porcelain, glass, copper, brass, clocks and watches, silver, jewellery, military books, leather and willow, paintings, prints, textiles, fireplaces, surrounds and grates, 20th C lighting and other artefacts, collectables and ephemera including Roman and Chinese.* LOC: Approx.1 mile from first exit for Stamford on A1. PARK: At rear. TEL: 01780 481158; fax - same; e-mail - peter@st-martins-antiques.co.uk; website - www.st-martins-antiques.co.uk.

Staniland (Booksellers)
4/5 St. George's St. PE9 2BJ. (V.A. and B.J. Valentine-Ketchum). PBFA. Est. 1973. Open 10-5. CL: Thurs. SIZE: Large. *STOCK: Books, mainly 19th-20th C, £1-£2,000.* LOC: High St. PARK: St. Leonard's St. TEL: 01780 755800; e-mail - stanilandbooksellers@btinternet.com.

Andrew Thomas
Old Granary, 10 North St. PE9 2YN. Est. 1970. Open 9-6. SIZE: Large. *STOCK: Pine and country furniture in original paint; ironware.* LOC: From south take old A1 through Stamford. Turn right at second set of traffic lights, warehouse on right. PARK: Opposite. TEL: 01780 762236; home - 01780 410627. VAT: Stan.

Vaughan Antiques   LAPADA
45 Broad St. PE9 1PX.. (Barry and Lindy Vaughan). Est. 1993. Open 10-5, Fri. 10-3. SIZE: Large. *STOCK: 18th-19th C furniture, decorative items, clocks, paintings, metalware, mirrors, jewellery.* PARK: Easy. TEL: 01780 765888; e-mail - vaughanantiques@aol.com. FAIRS: NEC. VAT: Spec.

STICKNEY, Nr. Boston

B and B Antiques
Main Rd. PE22 8AD. (B.J. Whittaker and J. Shooter). Open by appointment. *STOCK: General antiques.* PARK: Easy. TEL: 01205 480204.

SUTTON BRIDGE

The Antique Shop
100 Bridge Rd. PE12 9SA. (R. Gittins). Est. 1973. Open 9-5.30, Sun. 11-5. SIZE: Large - 8 showrooms. *STOCK: Victorian furniture, glass,* china, oil lamps and clocks. Not Stocked: Pine. LOC: On old A17 opposite church. PARK: Easy. TEL: 01406 350535. VAT: Spec.

Old Barn Antiques & Furnishings
48-50 Bridge Rd. PE12 9UA. (S. and Mrs T.J. Jackson). Est. 1984. Open 9-5, Sat. 10-5, Sun. 11-4. SIZE: Large + trade warehouse. *STOCK: 19th-20th C furniture - oak, mahogany, walnut, pine and upholstered.* LOC: Village centre, 200 yards from swing-bridge. PARK: Easy. TEL: 01406 359123; fax - 01406 359158; mobile - 07956 677282. SER: Shipping; storage and packing. VAT: Spec.

Old Barn Antiques Warehouse
220 New Rd. PE12 9QE. (S. and Mrs T. Jackson). Est. 1984. Open Mon.-Fri. 9-5.30 or by appointment. SIZE: Large. *STOCK: 18th-20th C furniture - shipping goods, oak - carved, pineapple, Jacobean, distressed, barley twist; mahogany, walnut and pine original, unrestored and reclaimed timber copies.* LOC: 1 mile out of village, following new road past golf course. PARK: Own. TEL: 01406 350435; fax - 01406 359158; mobile - 07956 677228; e-mail - oldbarnanti@aol.com. SER: Storage; container and export facilities. VAT: Stan/Spec. *Trade & Export Only.*

SUTTON-ON-SEA

Knicks Knacks Emporium
41 High St. LN12 2EY. (Mr and Mrs R.A. Nicholson). Est. 1983. Open 10.30-1 and 2-5, including Sun. CL: Mon. SIZE: Medium + small warehouse. *STOCK: Victorian gas lights, lights and lamps, brass and iron beds, cast-iron fireplaces, bygones, curios, tools, collectables, pottery, porcelain, Art Deco, Art Nouveau, advertising items, furniture and shipping goods, £1-£1,000.* LOC: A52. PARK: Easy. TEL: 01507 441916; fax - same; home - 01507 441657; mobile - 07977 547199; e-mail - robin@knicks knacks.com; website - www.knicksknacks.com. FAIRS: Newark.

SWINSTEAD

Robin Shield Antiques LAPADA
Tyton House, 11 Park Rd. NG33 4PH. Est. 1974. Open by appointment any time. SIZE: Medium. *STOCK: Furniture and paintings, £200-£20,000; works of art, £100-£5,000; all 17th-19th C.* PARK: Easy. TEL: 01476 550892; mobile - 07860 520391; e-mail - robinshield@fsmail.net. SER: Valuations; buys at auction. VAT: Stan/Spec.

TATTERSHALL

Wayside Antiques
Market Place. LN4 4LQ. (G. Ball). Est. 1969. Open any time by appointment. *STOCK: General antiques.* LOC: A158. PARK: Easy. TEL: 01526 342436.

WAINFLEET, Nr. Skegness

Haven Antiques
Bank House, 36 High St. PE24 4BJ. (Julie Crowson). Est. 1980. Open daily except Thurs., Sun. by appointment. SIZE: Small. *STOCK:* *General antiques, jewellery, porcelain and collectibles.* LOC: A52. PARK: Easy and opposite. TEL: 01754 880661; home - same. SER: Valuations.

WOODHALL SPA

Underwoodhall Antiques
5 The Broadway. LN10 6ST. (G. and A. Underwood). Est. 1987. Open 10-5, Sun. 1-4.30, prior telephone call advisable. SIZE: Medium. *STOCK: Furniture, £10-£1,000; porcelain and china, £5-£500; general antiques, £1-£500; pictures, £5-£500, all 1750 to date.* LOC: B1191. PARK: Easy. TEL: 01526 353815; e-mail - underwoodhall@supanet.com. SER: Framing. FAIRS: Newark.

V.O.C. Antiques LAPADA
27 Witham Rd. LN10 6RW. (D.J. and C.J. Leyland). Resident. Est. 1970. Open 9.30-5.30, Sun. 2-5. SIZE: Medium. *STOCK: 17th-19th C furniture, to £5,000; period brass and copper, pottery, porcelain and pictures.* LOC: B1191. PARK: Easy. TEL: 01526 352753; fax - same; home - same. SER: Valuations.

Minton Bridge pattern pearlware teawares, c.1805. Oval teapots and square handled cups are recorded in early sales accounts. Details of moulded handles and knobs help in attribution. Very similar shaped wares were being produced by many factories during the 1795-1810 period and this pattern was also used by Spode and Harley.

From an article entitled "Minton Printed Pottery 1796-1836" by Geoffrey Priestman which appeared in the March 2003 issue of *Antique Collecting*. For more details and to subscribe see page 21.

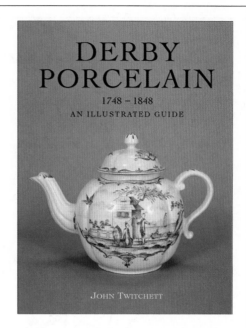

MERSEYSIDE

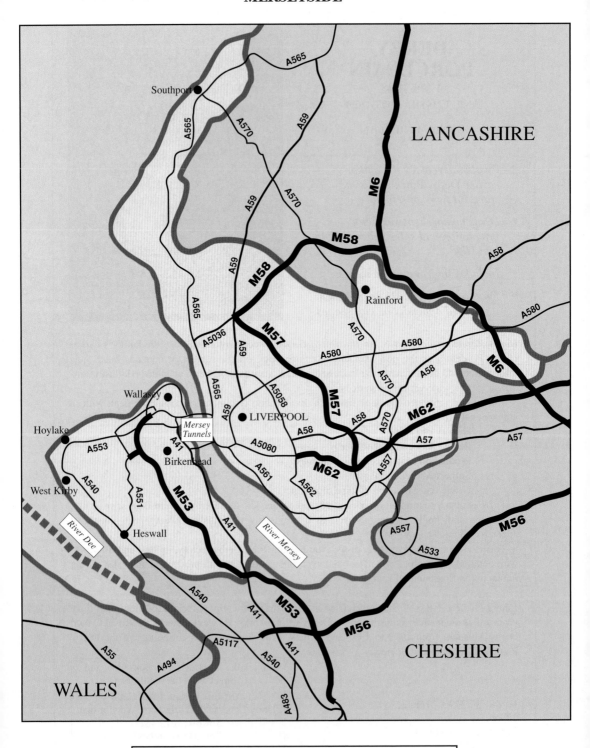

Dealers and Shops on Merseyside					
Birkenhead	2	Liverpool	10	Wallasey	3
Heswall	1	Rainford	1	West Kirby	1
Hoylake	2	Southport	12		

BIRKENHEAD

Bodhouse Antiques
379 New Chester Rd., Rock Ferry. CH42 1LB.
(G. and F.M. Antonini). Open 9-5, Sat. and Sun.
by appointment. SIZE: Large. *STOCK: Furniture,
19th C; ceramics, from 19th C; silver plate, 18th-
20th C; all £5-£1,000+; prints and pictures, 19th
C, £25-£1,000+.* PARK: Easy. TEL: 0151 644
9494; home - 0151 652 6433; mobiles - 07802
608357 and 07710 561199; e-mail - antonini@
btinternet.com. SER: Packing; courier; regular
containers to Italy and Spain. FAIRS: Newark.
VAT: Stan/Spec.

D & T Architectural Salvage
106 Church Rd., Higher Tranmere. CH42 0LJ.
(David Lyons). Est. 1998. Open Wed., Fri. and
Sat. 10-5, other times by appointment. SIZE:
Medium. *STOCK: Interior and exterior doors,
£35-£3,000; fire places, cast iron and timber
surrounds, slate marble, £200-£5,000; radiators,
£150-£1,000; flooring and architectural items.*
LOC: Town centre. TEL: 0151 670 0058; mobile
- 07970 698518. SER: Valuations; restorations.

HESWALL

C. Rosenberg
The Antique Shop, 120-122 Telegraph Rd. CH60
0AQ. Est. 1960. Open Fri. and Sat. 10-5, other
times by appointment. *STOCK: Jewellery, silver,
porcelain, objets d'art.* TEL: 0151 342 1053.

HOYLAKE

Mansell Antiques and Collectables
Mulberry House, 128-130 Market St. CH47 3BH.
(Gary Mansell and David Williamson). Open 9-
5.30, Sun. and other times by appointment. CL:
Wed. SIZE: Large. *STOCK: Furniture, pine,
china, decorative arts.* LOC: A540 in town
centre. PARK: Own. TEL: 0151 632 0892;
mobile - 07944 883021; fax - 0151 632 6137.
FAIRS: Chester Art Deco. VAT: Margin.

Kevin Whay's Clocks & Antiques
The Quadrant. CH47 2EE. LBHI. Est. 1969.
Open Fri. 10-4 and by appointment. *STOCK:
Clocks, barometers, furniture and jewellery.*
PARK: Easy. TEL: 0151 336 3432; fax - same; e-
mail - kevin@lots.uk.com. SER: Restorations
(clocks, barometers, dials and cases).

LIVERPOOL

Antique Fireplaces
43a Crosby Rd. North, Waterloo. (J. Toole). Est.

1978. Open 10-5, Sat. 10-5.30. SIZE: Medium.
*STOCK: Fireplaces, 18th-19th C, £100-£1,000+;
doors, 19th C, from £35.* PARK: Easy. TEL: 0151
949 0819. SER: Valuations; restorations. VAT:
Stan.

Boodle and Dunthorne Ltd
Boodle House, Lord St. L2 9SQ. Est. 1798. Open
9-5.30. *STOCK: Jewellery and some silver.* TEL:
0151 227 2525. VAT: Stan/Spec.

The Boydell Galleries `BADA` `LAPADA`
**(Paul Breen). Est. 1851. Open by appointment.
SIZE: Small. STOCK: English watercolours,
18th-20th C, £50-£10,000; maps and prints,
16th-19th C, £1-£2,000. LOC: Blundellsands.
PARK: Easy. TEL: 0151 932 9220; fax - 0151
924 0199; e-mail - boydellgalleries@
btinternet.com; website - www.boydell
galleries.co.uk. SER: Valuations; cleaning;
restorations; buys at auction. FAIRS:
National. VAT: Stan/Spec/ Global.**

Circa 1900
11-13 Holts Arcade, India Buildings, Water St. L2
0RR. (Wayne Colquhoun). Est. 1989. Open 10-
2.30 and 3.30-6, Sat. and Sun. by appointment.
SIZE: Small. *STOCK: Art Nouveau, classic Art
Deco, decorative and applied arts, 1860-1940,
£10-£1,000+.* LOC: 100 yards from Liver
Buildings. PARK: Easy. TEL: 0151 236 1282; fax
- same; e-mail - classicartdeco@aol.com;
website - www.classicartdeco.com. SER:
Valuations.

Edward's Jewellers
45a Whitechapel. LI 6DT. (R.A. Lewis). FGA.
Est. 1967. Open by appointment. CL: Sat. SIZE:
Small. *STOCK: Jewellery, silver and plate, 19th-
20th C, £50-£1,000.* LOC: City centre. TEL: 0151
236 2909. SER: Valuations.

Maggs Shipping Ltd
66-68 St Anne St. L3 3DY. (G. Webster). Est.
1965. Open 9-5, weekends by appointment.
*STOCK: General antiques, period and shipping
smalls, £1-£1,000.* LOC: In town centre by
Central station. PARK: Meters. TEL: 0151 207
2555; evenings - 01928 564958. SER:
Restorations; container packing, courier.

Pryors of Liverpool
110 London Rd. L3 5NL. (Mr Wilding). Est.
1876. Open 8-4. *STOCK: General antiques,
jewellery, Georgian and Victorian silver, pottery,
porcelain, coins and medals, clocks, paintings,
ivory and carvings.* LOC: 400 yards from St.
Georges Hall, Walker Art Gallery. PARK: Nearby

Pay & Display. TEL: 0151 709 1361; e-mail - pawilding@aol.com. VAT: Stan.

Ryan-Wood Antiques
102 Seel St. L1 4BL. Est. 1972. Open 10-5. CL: Some Bank Holiday weekends. SIZE: Large. *STOCK: Furniture, paintings, china, silver, curios, bric-a-brac, Victoriana, Edwardiana, Art Deco, architectural.* LOC: City centre, close to Anglican cathedral. PARK: Easy. TEL: 0151 709 7776; home/fax - 0151 709 3203; mobile - 07050 094779; e-mail - pdw@ryan-wood.freeserve.co. uk; website - www.ryan-wood.freeserve.co.uk. SER: Restorations; valuations. VAT: Stan/Spec.

Stefani Antiques
497 Smithdown Rd. L15 5AE. (T. Stefani). Est. 1969. Open 10-5. CL: Wed. SIZE: Medium. *STOCK: Furniture, to 1910, £200-£2,000; jewellery, £25-£2,000; pottery, silver, old Sheffield plate, porcelain, bronzes.* LOC: On main road, near Penny Lane. PARK: Easy. TEL: 0151 734 1933; home - 0151 733 4836; mobile - 07753 743287. SER: Valuations; restorations (furniture including French polishing and upholstery).

Swainbanks Ltd
50-56 Fox St. L3 3BQ. Open 9-5 or by appointment. CL: Sat. SIZE: Large. *STOCK: Shipping goods and general antiques.* TEL: 0151 207 9466; fax - 0151 284 9466. SER: Containers. VAT: Stan.

RAINFORD, Nr. St. Helens

Colin Stock
BADA
8 Mossborough Rd. WA11 8QN. Est. 1895. Open by appointment. STOCK: Furniture, 18th-19th C. TEL: 0174 488 2246.

SOUTHPORT

Birkdale Antiques
119a Upper Aughton Rd., Birkdale. PR8 5EX. (John Napp). Est. 1996. CL: Mon. SIZE: Small. *STOCK: English and Continental furniture, £200-£2,000.* LOC: From Lord St. West into Lulworth Rd., first left into Aughton Rd., over railway crossing into Upper Aughton Rd. PARK: Easy. TEL: 01704 550117; home - 01704 567680. SER: Valuations; restorations (furniture including polishing); buys at auction. FAIRS: Stafford, Newark, Swinderby.

C.K. Broadhurst and Co Ltd
5-7 Market St. PR8 1HD. (Laurens R. Hardman). ABA. ILAB. PBFA. Est. 1926. Open 9-5.30. SIZE: 4 floors. *STOCK: Rare books, first editions, art and architecture, collecting.* LOC: Town centre, off Lord St. by Victorian bandstand. TEL: 01704 532064/534110; fax - 01704 542009; e-mail - litereria@aol.com; website - www.ckbroadhurst.com. SER: Book search; valuations; restorations; rebinding. FAIRS: Olympia; Chelsea; some provincial.

Howard Antiques and Fine Art
Hillside Bridge, Waterloo Rd. (Howard E. Ward). Est. 2002. Open 9.30-4.45, Thurs. 1.30-5, Sat. 11-4, Sun. 11-3. SIZE: Medium. *STOCK: Victorian marquetry furniture, £500-£10,000; fine bracket and longcase clocks, 1760-1870, £3,000-£20,000; modern oil paintings, £250-£5,000; fine bronzes, 1890-1940, £250-£10,000.* LOC: 800 yards from entrance to Royal Birkdale golf club towards Liverpool. TEL: 01704 567206; mobile - 07803 013239. SER: Valuations. VAT: Stan.

Molloy's Furnishers Ltd
6-8 St. James St. PR8 5AE. (P. Molloy). Est. 1955. Open daily. SIZE: Large. *STOCK: Mahogany and oak, shipping and Edwardian furniture.* LOC: Off A570 Scarisbrick New Rd. PARK: Easy. TEL: 01704 535204; fax - 01704 548101. VAT: Stan.

John Nolan - King Street Antiques
29 King St. PR8 1LH. Est. 1972. Open Mon.-Sat. SIZE: Medium. *STOCK: Furniture and decorative items.* LOC: Town centre. PARK: Easy. TEL: 01704 540808; mobile - 07714 322252. SER: Courier; packing and shipping. VAT: Stan/Spec.

The Original British American Antiques
Kings House, 27 King St. PR8 1LH. (John Nolan). Est. 1976. Open 10-5, evenings by appointment. SIZE: Medium + warehouse. *STOCK: Export items, especially for US decorator market.* LOC: Town centre. PARK: Easy. TEL: 01704 540808; mobile - 07714 322252. SER: Courier; packing and shipping. VAT: Stan/Spec. *Trade only.*

Osiris Antiques
104 Shakespeare St. and The Royal Arcade, 131A Lord St. PR8. (C. and P. Wood). Est. 1983. Open 10.45-4.45, Sat. 11-5.15, Sun. by appointment; Royal Arcade - 11-5.30 including Sun. CL: Tues. SIZE: Small. *STOCK: Art Nouveau and Art Deco, Arts and Crafts, £10-£1,000; period clothing and accessories, 1850-1950, £5-£200; jewellery, 1880-1960, to £150.* LOC: Just out of town, off main road leading to motorway. PARK: Easy. TEL: 01704 500991; mobile - 07802

818500; home - 01704 560418. SER: Valuations; buys at auction (Art Nouveau, Art Deco); lectures given on Decorative Arts 1895-1930.

David M. Regan
25 Hoghton St. PR9 0NS. Est. 1983. Open Mon., Wed., Fri. and Sat. 10-5. SIZE: Small. *STOCK: Roman and English coins, £3-£300; post and cigarette cards, small collectables.* TEL: 01704 531266. SER: Valuations.

The Southport Antiques Centre
27/29 King St. PR8 1LH. (J. Nolan). Open 10-5. SIZE: Large, 11 rooms + warehouse. LOC: Town centre. PARK: Easy. TEL: 01704 540808; mobile - 07714 322252. Below are listed the dealers at this centre. VAT: Stan/Spec.

Antiques and Interiors

British-American Antiques
Shipping goods.

Halsall Hall Antiques
Country furniture.

King St. Antiques
General antiques.

John Nolan
Period furniture.

Pine Country Antiques
Country pine furniture.

S.M. Collectors Items
Doulton and pressed glass.

The Spinning Wheel Antiques
1 Liverpool Rd., Birkdale. PR8 4AR. (Roy and Pat Bell). Est. 1966. Open 10.30-5. CL: Tues. SIZE: Small. *STOCK: Antiques and collectables, old golf items, £5-£5,000+.* TEL: 01704 568245/567613; fax - same; e-mail - roypat@ patroy.fsnet.co.uk.

Tony and Anne Sutcliffe Antiques
130 Cemetery Rd. and warehouse - 37A Linaker St. PR8. Est. 1969. Open 8.30-5 including Sun. or by appointment. SIZE: Large. *STOCK: Shipping goods, Victorian and period furniture.* LOC: Town centre. TEL: 01704 537068; home - 01704 533465; mobile - 07860 949816/480376. SER: Containers; courier. VAT: Stan/Spec.

Weldons Jewellery and Antiques
567 Lord St. PR9 0BB. (H.W. and N.C. Weldon). Est. 1914. Open 9.30-5.30. SIZE: Medium. *STOCK: Furniture, clocks, watches, jewellery, silver, coins.* Not Stocked: Militaria. PARK: Easy.

TEL: 01704 532191; fax - 01704 500091; e-mail - weldongemsuk@aol.com. SER: Valuations; restorations. VAT: Stan/Spec.

WALLASEY

Arbiter
10 Atherton St., New Brighton. CH45 2NY. (W.D.L. Scobie and P.D. Ferrett). Resident. Est. 1983. Open Wed.-Sat. 1-5 or by appointment. *STOCK: Decorative arts, 1850-1980; base metal and treen, £20-£2,000; Oriental, ethnographic and antiquities, £40-£1,500; original prints and drawings, £80-£500.* LOC: Opposite New Brighton station. PARK: Easy. TEL: 0151 639 1159. SER: Valuations; buys at auction; consultant.

Decade Antiques & Interiors
62 Grove Rd. CH45 3HW. (A.M. Duffy). Est. 1980. Open 10-5. SIZE: Medium. *STOCK: General antiques, textiles, decorative items, Continental furniture.* LOC: From junction 1, M53 take A554 to Wallasey/New Brighton, turn right into Harrison Drive then left into Grove Rd. PARK: Easy. TEL: 0151 638 0433/639 6905; fax - 0151 638 9995. FAIRS: Antique Textile (Manchester).

Victoria Antiques/City Strippers
155-157 Brighton St. CH44 8DU. (J.M. Colyer). Est. 1978. Open 9.30-5.30. SIZE: Large. *STOCK: Furniture.* PARK: Easy. TEL: 0151 639 0080. SER: Restorations.

WEST KIRBY

Helen Horswill Antiques and Decorative Arts
62 Grange Rd. CH48 4EG. Est. 1977. Open 10-5.30. CL: Mon. and Wed. SIZE: Medium. *STOCK: Furniture, 17th-19th C; decorative items.* LOC: A540. PARK: Easy. TEL: 0151 625 2803; mobile - 07879 456244.

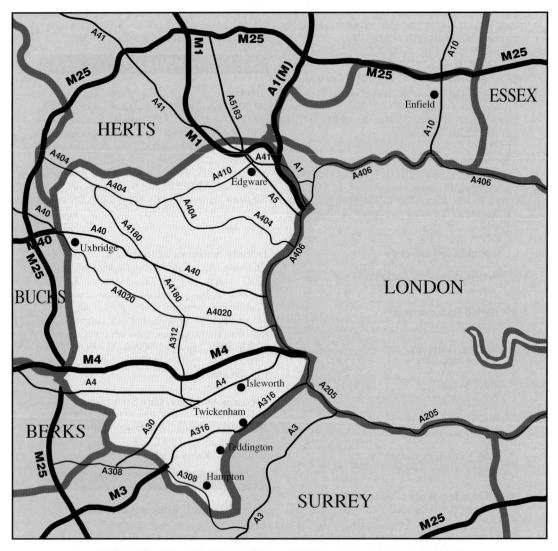

Dealers and Shops in Middlesex			
		Teddington	1
Edgware	1	Hampton	3	Twickenham	10
Enfield	2	Isleworth	1	Uxbridge	1

EDGWARE

Edgware Antiques
19 Whitchurch Lane. HA8 7JZ. (E. Schloss). Est. 1972. Open Thurs.- Sat. 10-5 or by appointment. SIZE: Medium. *STOCK: Furniture, pictures, silver and plate, brass and copper, clocks, bric-a-brac, porcelain and shipping goods.* PARK: Easy. TEL: 020 8952 1606; home - 020 8952 5924.

ENFIELD

Gallerie Veronique
66 Chase Side. EN2 6NJ. (Veronica Aslangul). Est. 1993. Open 10-3, Sat. 10-5. CL: Sun (except by appointment) and Wed. SIZE: Medium. *STOCK: Furniture including decorative, 1820-1970, £50-£1,000.* LOC: Near junction A10 and M25. PARK: Easy. TEL: 020 8342 1005; fax - 020 8342 1005; mobile - 07770 410041. SER: Restorations (French polishing and upholstery).

Period Style Lighting

8-9 Antiques Village, East Lodge Lane, Botany Bay. EN2 8AS. (Gillian and Geoff Day). Est. 1992. Open 10-5 including Sun. CL: Mon. SIZE: Medium. *STOCK: Lighting - period, Victorian and Edwardian, French and Italian chandeliers, £150-£1,000; period style wall and centre lights, Tiffany lamps, glass shades.* LOC: North London. PARK: Easy. TEL: 020 8363 9789; fax - 020 8363 2369; e-mail - sales@periodstylelighting. com. SER: Lighting design for cottages and country houses; restorations; repairs.

HAMPTON

Hunter's of Hampton

76 Station Rd. TW12 2AX. (Robin and Julia Hunter). Est. 1990. Open Mon. 10-5.30, Fri. and Sat. 10-6, other times by appointment. SIZE: Large. *STOCK: Victorian and Edwardian furniture, stripped pine, mirrors, £50-£1,500.* LOC: Off High St. and A308 close to Kempton Park Racecourse. PARK: Easy. TEL: 020 8979 5624; fax - same.

Peco

72 Station Rd. TW12 2BT. (C.D. Taylor). Est. 1969. Open 8.15-5.15. SIZE: Large. *STOCK: Doors, 18th-20th C, £75-£250; fireplaces including French and marble, 18th-19th C, £495-£5,500; stoves.* LOC: 1.5 miles from Hampton Court. Turning off Hampton Court/Sunbury Rd. PARK: Own. TEL: 020 8979 8310. SER: Restorations (marble, stained glass, cast iron fireplaces, doors); stained glass made to order. VAT: Stan.

Ian Sheridan's Bookshop

Thames Villa, 34 Thames St. TW12 2DX. Est. 1960. Open 11-5 (dusk in winter), including Sun. SIZE: Large. *STOCK: Antiquarian and secondhand books.* LOC: 1 mile from Hampton Court Palace. PARK: Riverside. TEL: 020 8979 1704.

TEDDINGTON

Chris Hollingshead

10 Linden Grove. TW11 8LT. Resident. Est. 1994. Open 9-6 by appointment only. SIZE: Small. *STOCK: Antiquarian, scarce and out-of-print books, specialising in botany, horticulture, landscape architecture and plant hunting, £10-£500.* PARK: Easy. TEL: 020 8255 4774; e-mail - c.hollingshead@btinternet.com.

TWICKENHAM

Ailsa Gallery

32 Crown Rd. (C.A. Wiltshire). Open Thurs., Fri. and Sat. 10-5, other times by appointment. SIZE: Small. *STOCK: Paintings, 19th-20th C, £200-£3,000; bronze, decorative arts, small furniture, silver and glass.* LOC: Off St. Margarets Rd., near station. PARK: Easy. TEL: 020 8891 2345; home - 020 8892 0188.

Antique Interiors

93 Crown Rd., St. Margaret's. TW1 3EX. (A. Mundy). Est. 1996. Open 10.30-5.30, Sun. by appointment. CL: Mon. SIZE: Medium. *STOCK: English and French pine, painted, country and mahogany furniture and doors, 19th C and earlier; French garden seating and tables.* LOC: Close to BR station. PARK: Easy. TEL: 020 8607 9853; e-mail - andrewmundy@onetel.net.uk. SER: Valuations; restorations; upholstery.

Anthony C. Hall

30 Staines Rd. TW2 5AH. Est. 1966. Open Mon., Tues., Thurs. and Fri. 10-5. SIZE: Medium. *STOCK: Antiquarian books.* PARK: Easy. TEL: 020 8898 2638; fax - 020 8893 8855; website - www.hallbooks.co.uk.

John Ives Bookseller

5 Normanhurst Drive, St. Margarets. TW1 1NA. PBFA. Resident. Est. 1977. Open by appointment at any time. SIZE: Medium. *STOCK: Scarce and out of print books on antiques and collecting, £1-£500.* LOC: Off St. Margarets Rd. near its junction with Chertsey Rd. PARK: Easy. TEL: 020 8892 6265; fax - 020 8744 3944; e-mail - jives@btconnect.com; website - www.ukbookworld.com/members/johnives. SER: Valuations (as stock).

Tobias Jellinek Antiques

20 Park Rd. TW1 2PX. (Mrs D.L. and T.P. Jellinek). Est. 1963. Open by appointment. SIZE: Small. *STOCK: Fine early furniture and objects, 16th-17th C or earlier, £500-£5,000+.* LOC: East of town centre near Richmond Bridge. PARK: Easy. TEL: 020 8892 6892; home - same; fax - 020 8744 9298; mobile - 07831 523 671; e-mail - toby@jellinek.com. SER: Valuations; buys at auction (as stock). VAT: Stan/Spec.

Marble Hill Gallery

70/72 Richmond Rd. TW1 3BE. (D. and L. Newson). Est. 1974. Open 10-5.30. *STOCK: English and French marble and natural stone, pine and white Adam-style mantels.* PARK: Easy. TEL: 020 8892 1488; website - www.marblehill. co.uk. VAT: Stan/Spec.

David Morley Antiques

371 Richmond Rd. TW1 2EF. (D.J. and J.M. Morley). Est. 1968. Open 10-1 and 2-5. CL: Wed. SIZE: Medium. *STOCK: General antiques, collectors' items, old toys.* Not Stocked: Large furniture. LOC: East of town centre approx. 200yds. from Richmond Bridge. PARK: In side road (adjacent to shop). TEL: 020 8892 2986.

Phelps Antiques LAPADA

133-135 St. Margarets Rd. TW1 1RG. (R.C. Phelps). Est. 1870. Open 10-5.30, Sat. 9.30-5.30, Sun. 12-4. SIZE: Large - several dealers. *STOCK: Furniture and small collectables, 1800-1920's; fireside accessories, lighting and mirrors.* LOC: Adjacent St. Margaret's station. PARK: Easy, at rear of shop. TEL: 020 8892 1778/7129; fax - 020 8892 3661; e-mail - antiques@phelps.co.uk; website - www.phelps.co.uk. SER: Restorations. VAT: Stan/Spec.

Rita Shenton

142 Percy Rd. TW2 6JG. Est. 1973. Open by appointment. SIZE: Medium. *STOCK: Clocks, watches, barometers, sundials, scientific instruments, automata and ornamental turning books, £1-£1,000.* LOC: Continuation of Whitton High St. PARK: Easy. TEL: 020 8894 6888; fax - 020 8893 8766; e-mail - rita@shentonbooks.com; website - www.shentonbooks.com. SER: Valuations; buys at auction (horological books); catalogues available. FAIRS: Midland and Brunel Clock and Watch. *International postal service.*

Twickenham Antiques Warehouse

80 Colne Rd. TW2 6QE. (A. Clubb). Est. 1985. Open 9.30-1 and 2-5, Sat. 10-4, Sun. 10-2. SIZE: Medium. *STOCK: European furniture, 1700-1920, £50-£2,000.* LOC: Off London Rd. PARK: Easy. TEL: 020 8894 5555; mobile - 07973 132847; e-mail - andclubb@aol.com; website - www.twickenhamantiques.com. SER: Valuations; restorations (French polishing, cabinet work, carving). VAT: Spec.

UXBRIDGE

Antiques Warehouse (Uxbridge)

34-35 Rockingham Rd. UB8 2TZ. (Mike, Sue and Ben Allenby and Simon Phillips). Est. 1977. Open 10-6. SIZE: Large. *STOCK: General antiques, shipping items, £1-£4,000.* PARK: Easy. TEL: 01895 256963/271012; fax - 01895 252157; e-mail - info@uxbridgeantiques.co.uk; website - www.uxbridgeantiques.co.uk. SER: Restorations; French polishing; re-upholstery; VAT: Stan/Global.

Carved walnut hall bench, English or Dutch c.1700. This type of bench is known to have been popular in Holland, but several examples survive in England. In this case the bench is carved with the arms of the Booth family. It was probably made for George Booth (1675-1758), Earl of Warrington.
DUNHAM MASSEY, NATIONAL TRUST PHOTOGRAPHIC LIBRARY/ANDREAS VON EINSIEDEL

From the book "English Furniture - from Charles II to Queen Anne 1660-1714" by Adam Bowett.

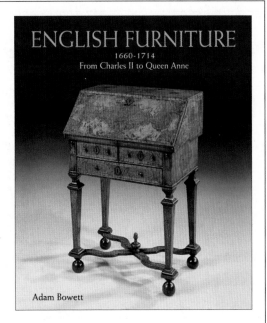

NORFOLK

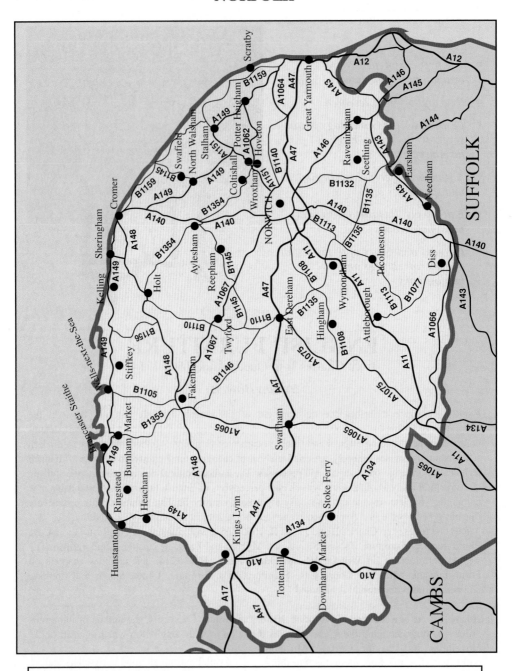

ATTLEBOROUGH

A.E. Bush and Partners
Vineyards Antiques Gallery, Leys Lane. NR17 1NE. (A.G., M.S. and J.A. Becker). Est. 1940. Open 9-1 and 2-5.30. SIZE: Large. *STOCK: Walnut and mahogany, 18th-19th C.* LOC: Town outskirts. PARK: Easy. TEL: 01953 454239/452175. SER: Restorations; wholesale antiques and export; storage; buys at auction. VAT: Stan/Spec.

AYLSHAM

Pearse Lukies
The Old Vicarage. NR11. Est. 1975. Open preferably by appointment. *STOCK: Period oak, sculpture, objects, 18th C furniture.* TEL: 01263 734137. *Trade Only.*

BRANCASTER STAITHE, Nr. King's Lynn

Staithe Antiques
Coast Rd. PE31 8BJ. (Anne and Tony Webb). Est. 1994. Open Tues.-Sun. SIZE: Small. *STOCK: 18th-19th C furniture, china, glass and pictures.* PARK: Easy. TEL: 01485 210600. SER: Restorations.

BURNHAM MARKET

The Brazen Head Bookshop & Gallery
Market Place. PE31 8HD. (David S. Kenyon). Est. 1997. Open 9.30-5.30. SIZE: Large. *STOCK: Rare, out-of-print and secondhand books; paintings, prints and ceramics.* LOC: On green, opposite PO. PARK: Easy. TEL: 01328 730700; fax - 01328 730929; e-mail - brazenheadbook@ aol.com. SER: Valuations.

M. and A. Cringle
The Old Black Horse. PE31 8HD. Est. 1965. Open 10-1 and 2-5. CL: Wed. SIZE: Medium. *STOCK: 18th to early 19th C furniture, £50-£2,000; china, glass, pottery, prints, maps, £10-£500; modern china and decorative items.* Not Stocked: Large furniture. LOC: In village centre. PARK: Easy. TEL: 01328 738456; e-mail - pmcringle@aol.com.

Hamilton Antiques
North St. PE31 8HG. (A. Hudson). Open 10-1 and 2-5. SIZE: Medium. *STOCK: Georgian furniture; porcelain, decorative items.* LOC: 20yds. from village green towards coast. PARK: Easy. TEL: 01328 738187; fax - same. VAT: Stan/Spec.

Market House
BADA
PE31 8HF. (D.H. and J. Maufe). Resident. Est. 1978. Open 10-6, but appointment advisable. SIZE: Medium. *STOCK: English furniture - walnut, mahogany, rosewood, late 17th to mid-19th C; works of art, mirrors, small decorative items.* Not Stocked: Silver, jewellery, clocks, porcelain or any reproductions. LOC: B1355, large Queen Anne house on green in village centre. PARK: Easy. TEL: 01328 738475; fax - 01328 730750. SER: Valuations; buys at auction. FAIRS: Olympia (Nov); BADA (March). VAT: Spec.

COLTISHALL

Roger Bradbury Antiques
Church St. NR12 7DJ. Est. 1967. Open by appointment. *STOCK: Cargoes - Tek Sing, Nanking, Vung Tao, Diana.* PARK: Easy. TEL: 01603 737444. SER: Valuations. VAT: Stan.

Coltishall Antiques Centre
High St. NR3 7AA. (I. Ford). Est. 1980. Open 10-4.30. SIZE: Several specialists. *STOCK: A wide variety of items including 19th C porcelain and pottery, silver and plate, copper, brass, jewellery, collectors' items, militaria, glass, bijouterie.* LOC: B1150 corner of main street. PARK: Easy. TEL: 01603 738306.

Village Clocks
9 High St. NR12 7AA. (Mike Darley). Open Mon.-Sat. *STOCK: Clocks - 18th-19th C longcase, bracket, English wall and regulators.* LOC: Main Norwich to North Walsham road. PARK: Easy. TEL: 01603 736047; fax - same; mobile - 07050 229758; website - www.village-clocks.co.uk. SER: Valuations; restorations (cases and movements).

CROMER

Bond Street Antiques
6 Bond St. and 38 Church St. NR27 9DA. (M.R.T. and J.A. Jones). NAG, FGA. Est. 1970. Open 9-1 and 2-5. SIZE: Medium. *STOCK: Jewellery, silver, porcelain, china, glass, 18th-20th C, £50-£5,000.* LOC: From Church St. bear right to Post Office, shop on opposite side on street further along. PARK: Easy. TEL: 01263 513134; home - same. SER: Valuations; repairs (jewellery); gem testing. VAT: Stan.

Books Etc.
15A Church St. NR27 9ES. (Kevin and Christine Reynor). UACC. Est. 1996. Open Easter to end Oct, 10-4 including Sun., Nov.-Easter Thurs.-Sat.

10-3.30 or by appointment. SIZE: Medium. *STOCK: Books, football programmes, memorabilia and autographs.* LOC: Town centre. PARK: Nearby. TEL: 01263 515501; e-mail - bookskcr@aol.com. SER: Valuations.

Collectors World

6 New Parade, Church St. NR27 9EP. (John and Irene Nockels). Est. 1988. Open 10-1 and 2-4, Sat. 10-1 and 2-5, Sun. 2.30-5. CL: Mon. SIZE: Small. *STOCK: Collectables, 19th-20th C, £5-£100.* LOC: Near traffic lights on Norwich road. PARK: Limited at rear. TEL: 01263 515330; home - 01263 514174. FAIRS: Norfolk Showground; Newark.

DISS

The Antiques & Collectors Centre (Diss)

3 Cobbs Yard, St Nicholas St. IP22 4LB. (Dean Cockaday and Chris Beecham). Est. 1997. Open 10-4.30. SIZE: Large. *STOCK: Royal commemoratives, 19th-20th C; Victorian to 1930's porcelain, £50-£100; modern collectables, 1930's-70's, £25-£50; rustic bygones, £20-£200; jewellery, £10-£300.* LOC: Next to Diss Ironworks, off St. Nicholas St. PARK: Easy. TEL: 01379 644472. VAT: Spec.

Diss Antiques & Interiors   LAPADA

2 & 3 Market Place. IP22 4JT. (B. Wimshurst). Est. 1973. Open 9-5. SIZE: Large. *STOCK: Furniture, barometers, clocks, jewellery, porcelain, copper, brass.* PARK: Nearby. TEL: 01379 642213; e-mail - sales@dissantiques.co.uk. SER: Repairs (furniture, jewellery and china). VAT: Stan/Spec.

DOWNHAM MARKET

Antiques & Gifts

47 Bridge St. PE38 9DW. (B. and T. Addrison). Est. 1980. Usually open 10-5. SIZE: Medium. *STOCK: Furniture - pine, oak, mahogany; brass and iron beds, bric-a-brac and smalls, Victorian to 1930.* PARK: Free nearby. TEL: 01366 387700. SER: Free local delivery.

Castle Antiques

1 Paradise Rd. PE38 9HS. (Margaret Goodwin). Est. 1987. Open 10-4.30. SIZE: Large. *STOCK: Furniture including 18th C oak coffers, £750-£950; clocks, mirrors, silver tea services, Royal Dux, Royal Worcester, cranberry glass and lamps.* LOC: Town centre. PARK: Nearby. TEL: 01366 388324; fax - same; mobile - 07946 201911.

EARSHAM, Nr. Bungay

Earsham Hall Pine

Earsham Hall. NR35 2AN. (R. Derham). Est. 1976. Open 9-5, Sun. 10.30-5. SIZE: Large. *STOCK: Pine furniture.* LOC: On Earsham to Hedenham Rd. PARK: Easy. TEL: 01986 893423; fax - 01986 895656; website - www.earshamhallpine.co.uk. SER: Containers.

EAST DEREHAM

Village Books

20A High St. NR19 1DR. (J.A.R. and J.W. James). Est. 1996. Open 9.30-4.30, Wed. 9.30-3, Sat. 9.30-5. SIZE: Medium. *STOCK: Books, 19th-20th C, £1-£150.* LOC: Just off Market Place. PARK: Nearby. TEL: 01362 853066; fax - same; e-mail - VillageBkDereham@aol.com. SER: Book binding. VAT: Stan.

FAKENHAM

Fakenham Antique Centre

Old Congregational Church, 14 Norwich Rd. NR21 8AZ. (Julie Hunt and Mandy Allen). Est. 1984. Open 10-4.30. SIZE: 27 dealers. *STOCK: Furniture, glass, ceramics, books, pens, oil lamps, kitchenalia, memorabilia, clocks, paintings and prints.* LOC: Turn off A148 at roundabout to town, at traffic lights turn up Queens Rd., left at second mini-roundabout, centre 50yds. on right opposite Godfrey DIY. PARK: Easy. TEL: 01328 862941. SER: Restorations (furniture); polishing; replacement handles; cane and rush seating repairs.

Sue Rivett Antiques and Bygones

6 Norwich Rd. NR21. (Mrs S. Rivett). Est. 1969. Open 10-1. *STOCK: General antiques and bygones.* LOC: On Norwich Rd. into Fakenham. PARK: Easy. TEL: 01328 862924; home - 01263 860462; mobile - 07778 819965. SER: Valuations.

GREAT YARMOUTH

Barry's Antiques

35 King St. NR30 2PN. Open 9.30-5. SIZE: Large. *STOCK: Jewellery, porcelain, clocks, glass, pictures.* LOC: Main shopping street. PARK: Opposite. TEL: 01493 842713. VAT: Stan/Spec.

David Ferrow

77 Howard St. South. NR30 1LN. ABA. PBFA. Est. 1940. Open 10-5. CL: Thurs. SIZE: Large. *STOCK: Books, some antiquarian maps, local*

prints, manuscripts. LOC: From London, sign before river bridge to The Docks, keep to nearside, turn left and then right to car park. PARK: Easy. TEL: 01493 843800. SER: Valuations; restorations (books and prints). VAT: Stan.

Folkes Antiques and Jewellers
74 Victoria Arcade. NR30 2NU. (Mrs J. Baldry). Est. 1946. Open 10-4. *STOCK: General antiques especially jewellery and collectables.* LOC: From A47 into town centre, shop on right of Victoria Arcade, opposite Regent Rd. to seafront. PARK: Easy. TEL: 01493 851354. SER: Valuations; repairs. FAIRS: Local collectors.

Gold and Silver Exchange
Theatre Plain. NR30 2BE. (C. Birch). Open 9.30-5.15. *STOCK: Coins, medals and secondhand jewellery.* TEL: 01493 859430.

Peter Howkins Antiques
132 King St. NR30 2PQ. Est. 1946. Open 9.30-4. *STOCK: Furniture, silver, pottery, glass, bronzes, Georgian-Edwardian.* LOC: From Norwich through town one-way system to road signposted Lowestoft which intersects King St. PARK: Easy. TEL: 01493 851180. SER: Valuations; restorations.

Peter Howkins Jewellers
135 King St. NR30 2PQ. (Peter and Valerie Howkins). NAG. Est. 1945. Open 9.30-5. SIZE: Medium. *STOCK: Jewellery, silver, crystal, porcelain, pottery, Georgian to present day.* LOC: South of Market Place. PARK: Limited and nearby. TEL: 01493 844639; fax - 01493 844857. SER: Valuations; restorations; repairs. VAT: Spec.

Wheatleys
16 Northgate St., White Horse Plain and Fullers Hill. NR30 1BA. Est. 1971. Open 9.30-5, Thurs. 9.30-1. SIZE: Large. *STOCK: Jewellery and general antiques.* LOC: 2 mins. walk from Market Place. PARK: Easy. TEL: 01493 857219. VAT: Stan.

HEACHAM, Nr. King's Lynn

Peter Robinson
Pear Tree House, 7 Lynn Rd. PE31 7HU. Est. 1880. Appointment advisable. SIZE: Small. *STOCK: Furniture, 1600-1900, £10-£5,000; china, 1750-1900, metalwork, 1700-1870; both £2-£1,000.* LOC: Shop on left on entry to village. PARK: Easy. TEL: 01485 570228. SER: Valuations; buys at auction.

HINGHAM, Nr. Norwich

Mongers
15 Market Place. NR9 4AF. (Sam and Trudie Coster). SALVO. Est. 1997. Open 9.30-5.30. SIZE: Large. *STOCK: Fireplaces, 1700-1930, £400-£900; sanitaryware, 1870-1950, £250-£1,000; Victorian and Edwardian garden antiques, £50-£500.* LOC: B1108. PARK: Easy. TEL: 01953 851868; fax - 01953 851870; e-mail - trudie@mongersofhingham.co.uk; website - www.mongersofhingham.co.uk. SER: Restorations (bath re-surfacing, fireplaces); stripping (pine). VAT: Stan/Spec.

Past & Present
16a The Fairland. NR9 4HN. (C. George). Est. 1970. Open Tues.-Sun. 10-5. SIZE: Medium. *STOCK: Furniture, £25-£1,500; smalls, 18th-19th C, £10-£500.* LOC: B1108. PARK: Easy. TEL: 01953 851471; home - 01953 851400; website - www.pastandpresentantiques.co.uk. SER: Valuations. FAIRS: Swinderby, Newark, Staffordshire. VAT: Stan.

HOLT

Baron Art
9 & 17 Chapel Yard, Albert St. NR25 6HG. (Anthony R. Baron and Michael J. Bellis). Est. 1992. Open 9.30-5.30 including Sun. SIZE: Medium. *STOCK: Paintings, 19th-20th C, £50-£5,000; prints and lithographs, 19th-20th C, £5-£500; collectables, 1830-1940, £5-£500; books and Art Deco.* PARK: Easy. TEL: 01263 713906; home - 01263 713430. SER: Valuations; buys at auction (paintings); framing. VAT: Stan/Spec.

Baskerville Bindings
3-5 Fish Hill. NR25 6BD. Open 10-5. SIZE: 10 rooms. *STOCK: Antique leatherbound books for decoration and library furnishing.* TEL: 01263 711143; fax - 01263 711153; e-mail - antique@leatherboundbooks.com; website - www.leatherboundbooks.com.

Cottage Collectables
8 Fish Hill and 3 Chapel Yard. NR25 6BD. (Philip & Linda Morris). Est. 1984. Open 10-5, Sun. 11-5. SIZE: Medium. *STOCK: Collectables, 18th-20th C, £5-£250; furniture, 18th-20th C, £50-£300; jewellery, from Victorian, £5-£50; linen.* PARK: Easy. TEL: 01263 711707/712920; e-mail - cottcoll@aol.com. SER: Valuations; restorations (furniture and ceramics); buys at auction (furniture and collectables). FAIRS: Swinderby, Peterborough, Newark and others.

Past Caring

Fine Antique linens & baby gowns
Vintage clothing

Opening times
Mon-Sat
11–5pm
Closed Thurs
& Sun

6 Chapel Yard, Holt, Norfolk NR25 6HG
Tel: 01263 713771 or 01362 683363

Anthony Fell `LAPADA`
Chester House, 47 Bull St. NR25 6HP. (A.J. and C.R. Austin-Fell). CINOA. Est. 1996. Open 9.30-1 and 2-5, prior telephone call advisable if travelling long distance. SIZE: Medium. *STOCK: English and Continental furniture, 16th-18th C, £1,000-£50,000; works of art, 16th C to contemporary, £1,000-£20,000.* LOC: Near Post Office. PARK: Easy. TEL: 01263 712712; fax - same; e-mail - afellantiques@tiscali.co.uk. SER: Valuations; restorations. FAIRS: Olympia (June, Nov). VAT: Spec.

Simon Finch Norfolk
3-5 Fish Hill. NR25 6BD. ABA. Est. 1976. Open 10-5. SIZE: 10 rooms. *STOCK: Antiquarian and secondhand books; bindings.* TEL: 01263 712650; website - www.simonfinch.com.

Heathfield Antiques & Country Pine
Candlestick Lane, Thornage Rd. NR25 6SU. (S.M. Heathfield). Est. 1990. Open 8-5. SIZE: Large. *STOCK: Pine furniture, £50-£1,500.* LOC: From Holt roundabout junction of A148/B1149, take the unmarked road, business half a mile on left hand side. PARK: Own. TEL: 01263 711609; website - www.antique-pine.net. VAT: Stan/Global.

Judy Hines of Holt - The Gallery
3 Fish Hill. NR25 6BD. Est. 1973. Open 11-5. CL: Mon. *STOCK: Modern British paintings; sculptures; British prints 1900-1980.* TEL: 01263 713000; fax - same; e-mail - judyhinesgallery@hotmail.com. SER: Framing; viewing by card index.

Holt Antique Centre
Albert Hall, Albert St. NR25. (David Attfield). Est. 1980. Open 10-5, Sat. 10-5.30 (Sun. Easter-October). SIZE: Large. *STOCK: Pine and country furniture, china, glass, lighting, silver plate and kitchenalia, jewellery, clothes, soft*

furnishings, 18th-20th C, £1-£1,500. LOC: Turn right from Chapel Yard car park, 100 yards. PARK: Easy. TEL: 01263 712097; home - 01263 860347.

Mews Antique Emporium
17B High St. Est. 1998. Open 10-5. SIZE: Large - 12 dealers. *STOCK: 18th-20th C furniture, collectables, £1-£1,000.* PARK: Nearby. TEL: 01263 713224.

Past Caring
6 Chapel Yard. NR25 6HG. (L. Mossman). Est. 1988. Open 11-5. CL: Thurs. SIZE: Medium. *STOCK: Period clothes, linen and textiles, Victorian to 1950, £5-£200; jewellery and accessories, Victorian to 1960, £5-£125.* PARK: Easy. TEL: 01263 713771; home - 01362 683363; e-mail - pstcaring@aol.com. SER: Valuations; restorations (christening gowns and some beadwork). FAIRS: Alexandra Palace.

Richard Scott Antiques
30 High St. NR25 6BH. Est. 1967. Open 10-5. CL: Thurs. SIZE: Large. *STOCK: Pottery, porcelain, glass, furniture, contemporary ceramics, oil lamps and spares, general antiques.* LOC: On A148. PARK: Easy. TEL: 01263 712479. SER: Valuations; conservation advice.

HOVETON, Nr. Wroxham

Eric Bates and Sons Ltd.
Horning Road West. NR12 8QJ. (Eric, Graham and James Bates). Est. 1973. Open 9-5. SIZE: Large. *STOCK: Victorian and Edwardian furniture.* LOC: Opposite rail station. PARK: Easy. TEL: 01603 781771; fax - 01603 781773; e-mail - furniture@ebates.fsnet.co.uk; website - www.batesfurniture.co.uk. SER: Restorations (furniture); manufacturer of period-style furniture; upholstery; container packing and shipping. VAT: Stan/Spec.

HUNSTANTON

Delawood Antiques
10 Westgate. PE36 5AL. (R.C. Woodhouse).
Resident. Est. 1975. Open Mon., Wed., Fri., Sat.
10-5 and most Sun. afternoons, other times by
chance or appointment. SIZE: Small. *STOCK:
General antiques, furniture, jewellery, collectors'
items, books, £1-£1,000.* LOC: Near town centre
and bus station. PARK: Easy. TEL: 01485
532903; home and fax - same. SER: Valuations;
commission sales.

**Le Strange Old Barns Antiques, Arts &
Craft Centre**
Golf Course Rd., Old Hunstanton. PE36 6JG. (E.
Maloney and R.M. Welier). Est. 1994. Open 10-
6, (10-5 winter), including Sun. SIZE: Large.
*STOCK: General antiques, collectables, arts and
crafts.* PARK: Easy. TEL: 01485 533402.

R.C. Woodhouse (Antiquarian Horologist)
10 Westgate. PE36 5AL. MBHI. BWCG.
Resident. Est. 1975. Open Mon., Wed., Fri, Sat.
and usually Sun. afternoons, other times by
chance or appointment. SIZE: Small. *STOCK:
Georgian, Victorian and Edwardian longcase,
dial, wall and mantel clocks; some watches and
barometers.* LOC: Near town centre and bus
station. PARK: Easy. TEL: 01485 532903; home
and fax - same. SER: Valuations; restorations
(longcase, bracket, chiming, carriage, French,
wall clocks, dials, barometers); small locks
repaired and lost keys made - postal service if
required.

KELLING, Nr. Holt

**The Old Reading Room Gallery and
Tea Room**
NR25 7EL. (B.R. Taylor). Est. 1994. Open 9.30-
4.30 including Sun. SIZE: Large. *STOCK:
Paintings and prints, wood carvings, books,
postcards and collectables.* LOC: A149 coast
road between Weybourne and Cley, at war
memorial in village. PARK: Easy. TEL: 01263
588227; home - 01263 588435. SER:
Restorations; framing. VAT: Stan/Spec.

KING'S LYNN

Tim Clayton Jewellery & Antiques
21-23 Chapel St. PE30 1EG. (Tim and Sue
Clayton). NAG. Est. 1975. Open 9-5. SIZE:
Large. *STOCK: Silver, jewellery, clocks,
furniture, china and pictures.* LOC: Town centre.
PARK: Nearby. TEL: 01553 772329; fax - 01553
776583; e-mail - timpclayton@yahoo.co.uk.

SER: Bespoke jewellery; repairs; picture framing.
VAT: Global/ Margin.

James K. Lee
Nicholson House, 29 Church St. PE30. (A.J. and
J.K. Lee). Est. 1950. Open 9-6 including Sun.
SIZE: Small. *STOCK: Furniture including desks,
chests of drawers and tables, 18th-19th C, £800-
£4,500.* LOC: In old town, through Southgates, by
mini roundabout. PARK: Easy and NCP opposite.
TEL: 01553 810681; fax - 01553 760128; home -
01553 811522. SER: Valuations; restorations
including polishing; buys at auction (furniture).

Norfolk Galleries
Railway Rd. PE30 1PF. (B. Houchen and G.R.
Cumbley). Est. 1975. Open 8.30-5.30, Sat. by
appointment. *STOCK: Victorian and Edwardian
furniture.* LOC: Main street. PARK: Nearby.
TEL: 01553 765060.

Old Curiosity Shop
25 St. James St. PE30 5DA. (Mrs R.S. Wright).
Est. 1980. Open 10.30-5, Sat. 9.30-6. SIZE:
Small. *STOCK: General collectable smalls,
glass, clothing, linen, jewellery, lighting, Art
Deco and Art Nouveau, furniture, prints, stripped
pine and paintings, pre 1930, £1-£500.* LOC: Off
Saturday market place towards London Rd.
PARK: At rear or nearby. TEL: 01553 766591.
SER: Restorations (teddy bears); repairs (clocks).
FAIRS: Alexandra Palace, Newark; local.

**The Old Granary Antiques and
Collectors Centre**
King Staithe Lane, Off Queen St. PE30 1LZ. Est.
1977. Open 10-5. *STOCK: China, coins, glass,
books, stamps, silver, jewellery, brass, copper,
postcards, linen, some furniture and general
antiques.* PARK: Easy. TEL: 01553 775509.

NEEDHAM, Nr. Harleston

**Jennifer and Raymond Norman
Antiques**
Henstead Lodge. IP20 9LA. Resident. Est. 1974.
Open by appointment. *STOCK: Clocks, 1780-
1900, £100-£5,000; longcase, 1720-1830,
£1,000-£8,000; stereoscopic views and viewers.*
LOC: A143 Harleston by-pass. At Harleston/
Needham roundabout turn towards Harleston.
Entrance to Henstead Lodge immediately on
right. PARK: Easy. TEL: 01379 855124; fax -
01379 855134; mobile - 07774 887045; e-mail -
rjn@longcase.co.uk; website - www.world
ofstereoviews.com. SER: Valuations; restorations
(longcase clocks - cases and movements); buys at
auction. VAT: Stan/Spec.

The Angel Bookshop
4 Aylsham Rd. NR28 0BH. (O.D., M.E. and W.T.E. Green). PBFA. ABA. Est. 1980. Open 9.30-5, Sat. 9.30-3.30. CL: Wed. SIZE: Medium. *STOCK: Books, 1700 to date, £3-£500.* LOC: Short walk from town centre. PARK: Nearby. TEL: 01692 404054; e-mail - angelbooks@ onetel.net.uk. SER: Valuations; buys at auction. FAIRS: East Anglia PBFA.

3A Antiques
2 and 3A Wrights Court, Elm Hill. NR3 1HQ. (Philip and Julie Milne). Est. 1983. Open 9-5. SIZE: Small. *STOCK: General antiques and collectables, curios and bric-a-brac.* LOC: City centre. TEL: 01603 667441.

Albrow and Sons Family Jewellers
10 All Saints Green. NR1 3NA. (R. Albrow). NAG Registered Valuer. Open 9.30-4.30. *STOCK: Jewellery, silver, plate, china, glass, furniture.* LOC: Opposite John Lewis'. PARK: Behind John Lewis'. TEL: 01603 622569; fax - 01603 766158. SER: Valuations; repairs.

Liz Allport-Lomax
t/a Corner Antiques. Est. 1971. *STOCK: Porcelain, glass, silver, objects de vertue, sewing accessories, small furniture and collectors items - card cases, lace bobbins, snuff boxes, scent bottles.* TEL: 01603 737631; mobile - 07747 843074: e-mail - liz.allport@lineone.net; website - www.lomaxantiques.fairs.co.uk. FAIRS: Organiser of Lomax Antiques Fairs at Langley School (May and Oct.); North Norfolk, Burnham Market (Easter); Southwold (July).

Antiques & Interiors
31-35 Elm Hill. NR3 1HG. (P.S. Russell-Davis). Est. 1976. Open 10-5. *STOCK: 19th-20th C furniture; Art Deco, Arts & Crafts and modern design; studio pottery, pictures, lighting, decorative objects.* PARK: Nearby. TEL: 01603 622695; home - 01603 632446; fax - same; e-mail - patrick.russelldavis@btopenworld.com; website - www.20ci.com and www.englishartdeco.com. SER: Restorations (furniture).

The Bank House Gallery
`LAPADA`
Newmarket Rd. NR2 2HW. (R.S.Mitchell). Resident. Est. 1979. Open by appointment. *STOCK: English oil paintings especially Norwich and Suffolk schools, 19th C, £1,000-£50,000.* LOC: On A11 between City centre and ring road.

PARK: Own. TEL: 01603 633380; e-mail - bankart.com; website - www.bankart.com. SER: Valuations; restorations. VAT: Stan/Spec.

Black Horse Antiques Centre
8-10 Wensum St. NR3 1HR. (Julie Hunt and Mandy Allen). Est. 2002. Open 10-5. CL: Bank Holidays. SIZE: 20 dealers. *STOCK: Period furniture, glassware, ceramics, silver, jewellery, paintings and prints, books, militaria, lighting, vintage cameras, ecclesiastical antiquities and stained glass, Art Deco and country pine.* LOC: Near the cathedral. PARK: Loading bay for collections only. TEL: 01603 623339; fax - same; mobiles - 07876 254173/5; e-mail - mandyallen @btconnect.co.uk. SER: Restorations (furniture including polishing and stripping, china); interior design, framing.

James Brett
`BADA`
42 St. Giles St. NR2 1LW. Est. 1870. Open 9.30-1 and 2-5, Sat. by appointment. SIZE: Large. *STOCK: Antique furniture, mahogany, walnut and oak; sculpture and metalwork.* LOC: Near City Hall. PARK: Easy. TEL: 01603 628171; fax - 01603 630245. FAIRS: Olympia. VAT: Stan/Spec.

Cloisters Antique & Collectors Fair
St. Andrew's and Blackfriars Hall, St. Andrew's Plain. NR3 1AU. (Norwich City Council). Est. 1976. Open Wed. 9-3. SIZE: 21 dealers. *STOCK: Wide range of antiques and collectables.* LOC: City centre. PARK: Easy. TEL: 01603 628477; fax - 01603 762182; bookings - 01493 750981.

Country and Eastern Ltd.
Old Skating Rink Gallery, 34-36 Bethal St. NR2 1NR. (J. Millward). Est. 1978. Open 10-5. SIZE: Very large. *STOCK: Oriental rugs, kelims and textiles; Indian and S.E. Asian antiques - furniture, objects, ceramics and metalwork.* LOC: Near The Forum. PARK: Easy. TEL: 01603 663890; fax - 01603 758108; website - www.countryandeastern. co.uk. SER: Export. VAT: Stan.

Crome Gallery and Frame Shop
34 Elm Hill. NR3 1HG. (J. Willis). UKIC. Est. 1971. Open 9.30-5. SIZE: Large. *STOCK: Watercolours, oils and prints, mainly 20th C, some 19th C; wood carvings and sculpture.* LOC: Near cathedral. PARK: Easy. TEL: 01603 622827; e-mail - jwillis@elmhillgallery.com. SER: Crome Gallery Conservation (oils, watercolours, prints, frames); framing.

Clive Dennett Coins
66 St. Benedicts St. NR2 4AR. BNTA. Est. 1970.

CL: Thurs. and lunchtime. SIZE: Small. *STOCK: Coins and medals, ancient Greek to date, £5-£5,000; jewellery, 19th-20th C; banknotes, 20th C; both £5-£1,000.* PARK: Easy. TEL: 01603 624315. SER: Valuations; buys at auction (as stock). FAIRS: London Coin; International Banknote, London; Maastricht.

The Fairhurst Gallery
Bedford St. NR2 1AR. Est. 1951. Open 9-5. CL: Sat. pm. SIZE: Medium. *STOCK: Oil paintings, £5-£5,000; watercolours, £5-£2,000, both 19th-20th C; frames, 18th-20th C; furniture, £500-£10,000.* LOC: Behind Travel Centre. TEL: 01603 614214. SER: Valuations; restorations; cleaning; framemakers. VAT: Spec.

Nicholas Fowle Antiques `BADA`
Websdale Court, Bedford St. NR2 1AR. Est. 1965. Open 9-5, Sat. 9-12. SIZE: Medium. STOCK: Furniture, £500-£10,000; works of art, £5-£1,000; both 17th-19th C. LOC: City centre pedestrian area (limited access for loading and unloading). PARK: St Andrews multi-storey. TEL: 01603 219964; fax - 01692 630378; e-mail - nfowleantiques@aol.com. SER: Valuations; restorations (furniture). VAT: Stan/Spec.

Peter J. Hadley Bookseller
29 Surrey St. NR1 3NX. ABA. Est. 1982. Open by appointment. SIZE: Small. *STOCK: Books - architecture, literature, art reference and illustrated.* LOC: City centre. PARK: Easy. TEL: 01603 663411; home - same; fax - 01603 613113; e-mail - books@hadley.co.uk; website - www.hadley.co.uk. FAIRS: Ludlow; York.

Leona Levine Silver Specialist `BADA`
35 St. Giles St. NR2 1JN. Est. 1865. Open 9.30-5. CL: Thurs. STOCK: Silver and Sheffield plate. LOC: 100 yards from City Hall. PARK: Multi-storey. TEL: 01603 628709; fax - same. SER: Valuations; engraving; restorations. VAT: Stan/Spec.

Maddermarket Antiques
18c Lower Goat Lane. NR2 1EL. (Mr and Mrs H. Tagg). NAG. Est. 1978. Open 9-5. *STOCK: Antique, secondhand and modern jewellery and silver, £10-£10,000.* PARK: St Giles multi-storey. TEL: 01603 620610; fax - same.

Mandell's Gallery `BADA`
Elm Hill. NR3 1HN. (Geoffrey and Pauline Allen). Est. 1964. Open 9-5. SIZE: Large. STOCK: Oils and watercolours, especially English and Continental works and Norwich

and Suffolk painters, 19th-20th C. **LOC: Near shopping centre, close to cathedral. PARK: Easy. TEL: 01603 626892/629180; fax - 01603 767471. SER: Conservation; framing. FAIRS: Snape. VAT: Spec.**

The Movie Shop
Antiquarian and Nostalgia Centre, 11 St. Gregory's Alley. NR2 1ER. Open 11-5. SIZE: Large. *STOCK: Books, magazines and movie ephemera; telephones, collectables and general antiques.* TEL: 01603 615239; e-mail - pete cossey@thenorwichmovieshop.com; website - www.thenorwichmovieshop.com.

Norwich Collectors Toyshop
Tombland Antique Centre, Augustine Stewart House, 14 Tombland. NR3 1HF. (S. Marshall). Est. 1985. Open 9.30-5. *STOCK: Dinky and Corgi toys, 1940-1990, £5-£150; trains and soldiers, 1910-1980, £5-£500; teddies and tin toys, 1920-1980, £5-£200.* TEL: 01603 457761. SER: Valuations. FAIRS: Sandown Park, NEC, Donington Park, Doncaster Racecourse, Norfolk Showground.

Oswald Sebley
20 Lower Goat Lane. NR2 1EL. (P.H. Knights). Est. 1895. Open 9-5.15. CL: Thurs. SIZE: Small. *STOCK: Silver, 18th-20th C, £15-£2,000; jewellery, Victorian, £10-£4,000.* LOC: 150yds. to right of City Hall, down paved street. PARK: Nearby. TEL: 01603 626504. SER: Valuations; restorations (silver and gold jewellery). VAT: Stan/Spec.

Stiffkey Bathrooms
89 Upper St. Giles St. NR2 1AB. Est. 1985. Open 10-5. *STOCK: Victorian, Edwardian and French bathroom fittings.* PARK: Easy. TEL: 01603 627850; fax - 01603 619775. SER: Mail order period bathroom accessories.

Timgems
30 Elm Hill. NR3 1HG. (Tim Snelling). Open Tues., Wed., Fri. and Sat. 11-4. SIZE: Small. *STOCK: Jewellery and silver, £10-£3,000; small objects, £10-£1,000.* PARK: Monastery Court. TEL: 01603 623296; e-mail - tim.snelling@ btinternet.com. SER: Valuations; restorations.

Tombland Antiques Centre
Augustine Steward House, 14 Tombland. NR3 1HF. (Mrs Joan Gale). Est. 1974. Open 10-5, including occasional Sun. SIZE: Large. *STOCK: Furniture, 18th-20th C, £50-£2,000; china, porcelain, antiquities, dolls, Art Deco, Art Nouveau, collectables, curios, militaria, pens,*

silver, pictures, postcards, jewellery, cranberry and other glass, toys, kitchelalia, linen. LOC: City centre, opposite cathedral. PARK: Elm Hill. TEL: 01603 619129. SER: Valuations.

The Tombland Bookshop
8 Tombland. NR3 1HF. (J.G. and A.H. Freeman). Open 9.30-5. *STOCK: Antiquarian and secondhand books.* TEL: 01603 490000; fax - 01603 760610; e-mail - tombland.bookshop@ virgin.net.

Tombland Jewellers & Silversmiths
12/13 Tombland. NR3 1HF. NAG. Est. 1972. Open 9-5, Sat. 9-4. *STOCK: English silver, flatware and jewellery, from 17th C; mustard pots, collectors' items, barometers, barographs, from 18th C.* LOC: Opposite Erpingham Gate, Norwich cathedral and Maid's Head Hotel. TEL: 01603 624914; fax - 01603 764310. SER: Valuations; restorations; export facilities. VAT: Stan/Spec.

Malcolm Turner
15 St. Giles St. NR2 1JL. Open 9-5. CL: Thurs. SIZE: Small. *STOCK: Bronzeware, coins, Oriental ceramics, silver, Staffordshire, Imari, mostly 19th C, £50-£1,000.* PARK: Nearby. TEL: 01603 627007. SER: Valuations. VAT: Stan.

POTTER HEIGHAM

Times Past Antiques
Station Rd. NR29 5AD. (P. Dellar). Open Wed.-Sun. 10-5. *STOCK: Barometers, clocks, furniture including reproduction, china, pictures, glass, collectables, bric-a-brac.* LOC: A149 village centre. PARK: Easy. TEL: 01692 670898.

RAVENINGHAM

M.D. Cannell Antiques
Castell Farm, Beccles Rd. NR14 6NU. Resident. Est. 1982. Open Fri., Sat., Sun. and Mon. 10-6 or by appointment. SIZE: Large. *STOCK: Oriental rugs, carpets, kilims, furniture, metalwork and decorative items.* LOC: On B1140. PARK: Easy. TEL: 01508 548441. VAT: Stan/Spec.

REEPHAM

Echo Antiques
Church Hill. NR10 4JW. (M. Stiefel and N. Bundock). Est. 1986. Open 10-5. CL: Thurs. SIZE: Medium. *STOCK: Furniture, 1650-1900, £10-£2,000; pine, 1800-1900, £50-£1,000; small items, 1650-1900, £10-£1,000.* Not Stocked: Jewellery. PARK: Market Sq. TEL: 01603 873291; home - 01603 872068. SER: Valuations; restorations (furniture); buys at auction.

The Beano Book, *1965, £10-£20.*

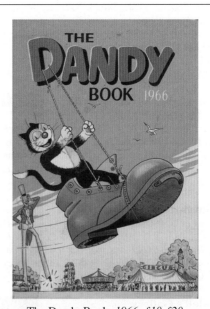

The Dandy Book, *1966, £10-£20.*

From an article entitled "Children's Annuals" by Adrian Greenwood which appeared in the December/January 2003 issue of ***Antique Collecting***. For more details and to subscribe see page 21.

RINGSTEAD, Nr. Hunstanton

Ringstead Village Antique Centre,
41 High St. PE36 5JU. (Tim and Cathy Roberts). Est. 1997. Open 8-5.30 including Sun; Tues., Wed. and Sat. 8-1. SIZE: 12 rooms including 2 courtyards. *STOCK: Furniture including pine, Edwardian and period, £50-£2,000; porcelain, curios, kitchenalia, books and magazines, paintings and prints.* LOC: 3 miles from Hunstanton. PARK: Easy. TEL: 01485 525270.

SCRATBY, Nr. Gt. Yarmouth

Keith Lawson Antique Clocks
Scratby Garden Centre, Beach Rd. NR29 3AJ. LBHI. Est. 1979. Open seven days 2-6. SIZE: Large. *STOCK: Clocks and barometers.* LOC: B1159. PARK: Easy. TEL: 01493 730950; website - www.antiqueclocks.co.uk. SER: Valuations; restorations. VAT: Stan/Spec.

SEETHING, Nr. Brooke

Country House Antiques
NR15 1AL. Est. 1979. Open by appointment. SIZE: Large trade warehouses. *STOCK: Mahogany, oak, walnut furniture, 17th-19th C;* *interesting china and porcelain.* LOC: Village centre. PARK: Easy. TEL: 01508 558144; mobile - 07860 595658. *Trade only.*

SHERINGHAM

R.L. Cook
12 Sycamore Grove. NR26 8PG. Est. 1950. Open by appointment. SIZE: Small. *STOCK: Secondhand and antiquarian books.* PARK: Easy. TEL: 01263 822050.

Dorothy's Antiques
23 Waterbank Rd. NR26 8RB. (Mrs D.E. Collier). Est. 1975. Open 11.15-4. *STOCK: Cranberry glass, Royal Worcester, Royal Dux, commemorative and other china; small furniture.* PARK: Easy. TEL: 01263 822319; home - 01263 823018.

Parriss
20 Station Rd. NR26 8RE. (J.H. Parriss). Est. 1947. Open 9-5.30. CL: Wed. SIZE: Medium. *STOCK: Jewellery, £30-£2,500; silver, £40-£2,000; clocks, £100-£3,000.* LOC: A1082, in main street. PARK: Within 150yds. TEL: 01263 822661. SER: Valuations; restorations (jewellery, silver, clocks). VAT: Stan.

The Westcliffe Gallery
2-8 Augusta St. NR26 8LA. (Richard and Sheila Parks). Resident. Est. 1979. Open 9.30-1 and 2-5.30, Sat. 9.30-5.30, Sun. 10-4. SIZE: Medium. *STOCK: Oils, watercolours and drawings, 19th-20th C, £100-£15,000; furniture.* LOC: Town centre. PARK: Easy. TEL: 01263 824320; e-mail - sparks@westcliffe.fsnet.co.uk. SER: Valuations; restorations (oils, watercolours, prints); gilding. VAT: Stan/Spec.

STALHAM

Stalham Antique Gallery   LAPADA
29 High St. NR12 9AH. (Mike Hicks). CINOA. Est. 1970. Open 9-1 and 2-5. CL: Sat pm. SIZE: Medium. *STOCK: Furniture, 17th C to 19th C; pictures, china, glass, brass.* Not Stocked: Reproductions. PARK: Easy. TEL: 01692 580636; e-mail - mbhickslink@talk21.com. SER: Valuations; restorations. FAIRS: Langley (Oct). VAT: Spec.

STIFFKEY

Stiffkey Antiques
The Old Methodist Chapel. NR23 1AJ. Est. 1976. Open 10-5 including Sun. *STOCK: Door furniture, window fittings, fireplaces and accessories, 1800-1920; carpets, bric-a-brac, bronze garden statuary and water features.* PARK: Easy. TEL: 01328 830099; door and window fittings - 01328 830690; fax - 01328 830005.

The Stiffkey Lamp Shop
Townshend Arms. NR23 1AJ. (R. Belsten and D. Mann). Est. 1976. Open 10-5 including Sun. SIZE: Medium. *STOCK: Lamps including rare, hanging, wall and table and fittings, electric, converted gas and oil, 1800-1920, £25-£2,000.* LOC: Coast road near Wells-next-the-Sea. PARK: Easy. TEL: 01328 830460; fax - 01328 830005; website - www.stiffkeylampshop.co.uk. VAT: Stan.

STOKE FERRY, Nr. King's Lynn

Farmhouse Antiques
White's Farmhouse, Barker's Drove. PE33 9TA. (P. Philpot). Resident. Est. 1969. Open by appointment. *STOCK: General antiques.* PARK: Easy. TEL: 01366 500588. SER: Restorations; furniture made to order in old timber.

SWAFFHAM

Cranglegate Antiques
Market Place. PE37 7LE. (Mrs R.D. Buckie). Resident. Est. 1965. Open Tues., Thurs. and Sat. 10-1 and 2-5.30. SIZE: Small. *STOCK: Small furniture, general antiques and collectors items, 17th-20th C.* LOC: A47. PARK: In square opposite or in passage at rear. TEL: Home - 01760 721052; e-mail - rbuckie@buckie-antiques.com; website - www.buckie-antiques.com.

SWAFIELD, Nr. North Walsham

Staithe Lodge Gallery
Staithe Lodge. NR28 0RQ. (M.C.A. Foster). Resident. Est. 1976. Open 9-5. CL: Wed. SIZE: Large. *STOCK: Watercolours, paintings and prints, 1800-1950, £50-£500; furniture including reproduction.* LOC: On B1145 at the Mundesley end of the North Walsham by-pass. PARK: Easy. TEL: 01692 402669. SER: Restorations; framing; buys at auction (mainly watercolours).

TACOLNESTON, Nr. Norwich

Freya Antiques
St. Mary's Farm, Cheneys Lane. NR16 1DB. Usually open but appointment advisable; evenings by appointment. SIZE: Large. *STOCK: General antiques, especially pine and country furniture; upholstery, secondhand and antiquarian books.* PARK: Own. TEL: 01508 489252; mobile - 07799 401067; e-mail - freyaantiques@ic24.net; websites - www.freyaantiques.co.uk and www.antiquesbarn.co.uk. SER: Valuations; restorations; re-upholstery.

TOTTENHILL, Nr. King's Lynn

Jubilee Antiques
Coach House, Whin Common Rd. PE33 0RS. (Mr and Mrs A.J. Lee). Est. 1953. Open daily including Sun. SIZE: Medium. *STOCK: Furniture especially Victorian chairs, £50-£4,000; interesting items.* LOC: Between King's Lynn and Downham Market, adjacent to A10. PARK: Easy. TEL: 01553 810681; home - same. SER: Valuations; restorations (furniture).

TWYFORD, Nr. Fakenham

Norton Antiques
NR20 5LZ. (T. and N. Hepburn). Est. 1966. Open by appointment. *STOCK: Furniture, 1680-1900, £25-£8,000; oils and watercolours, 19th to early 20th C, £25-£5,000; clocks, 18th-19th C, £50-£6,000; woodworking and craftsman's hand tools.* PARK: Easy. TEL: 01362 683331. SER: Valuations.

A souvenir rectangular toilet box with velvet greeting panel, lined with checked paper. Similar pieces were sold at seaside resorts. c.1885. (Constance King Collection)

From an article entitled "Flowers of the Sea" by Constance King which appeared in the February 2003 issue of *Antique Collecting*. For more details and to subscribe see page 21.

WELLS-NEXT-THE-SEA

Church Street Antiques
2 Church St. NR23 1JA. (Paula Ford and Lesley Ann Irons). Open 10-4 including Sun. (winter - Thurs.-Sun.), Mon. by appointment. SIZE: Small. *STOCK: Textiles, lace, costume jewellery, hat pins, kitchenalia, ephemera, collectables, £1-£500.* LOC: A149 main coast road, opposite church. PARK: Easy. TEL: 01328 711698.

Wells Antique Centre
The Old Mill, Maryland. NR23 1LY. Est. 1986. Open 10-5 (10-4 winter) including Sun. SIZE: 15 dealers. *STOCK: General antiques and collectables.* PARK: Easy. TEL: 01328 711433.

WROXHAM

T.C.S. Brooke
BADA
incorporating The Ruth Lowe Gallery of Contemporary Art, The Grange. NR12 8RX. (S.T. Brooke). Est. 1952. Open 9.30-1 and 2.15-5.30. CL: Mon. SIZE: 3 large showrooms and gallery. *STOCK: English porcelain, 18th C; furniture, mainly Georgian; silver, glass, works of art, Oriental rugs.* LOC: On main Norwich road. PARK: Easy. TEL: 01603 782644. SER: Valuations. VAT: Spec.

WYMONDHAM

Antique and Collectors Fair
Central Hall. (Gabrielle Thornhill). 1st Friday monthly 9-3.30. SIZE: 25 stalls. *STOCK:*

General antiques and collectables. TEL: 01493 750981.

King
Market Place. NR18 0AX. (M. King). Est. 1969. Open 9-4. CL: Mon., Tues. and Wed., except by appointment. SIZE: 5 Rooms. *STOCK: General antiques, furniture, copper, brass, silver, jewellery, porcelain.* PARK: Easy. TEL: 01953 604758; evenings - 01953 602427. FAIRS: Lomax.

Turret House
27 Middleton St. NR18 0AB. (Dr and Mrs D.H. Morgan). PBFA. Resident. Est. 1972. SIZE: Small. *STOCK: Antiquarian books especially science and medical; occasional scientific instruments.* LOC: Corner of Vicar St., adjacent to War Memorial. TEL: 01953 603462. SER: Buys at auction. FAIRS: London Scientific & Medical Instrument Fairs; PBFA (London and New York). VAT: Stan/Spec.

Wymondham Antique and Collectors Centre
3 Town Green. NR18 0PN. (Charles White). Est. 1987. Open 10-5 including Sun. SIZE: Large, 18 dealers. *STOCK: China including crested, Victorian to 1960's; jewellery, postcards, books, glass, toys, furniture, clocks.* PARK: Easy. TEL: 01953 604817; fax - 01603 811112; home - same; mobile - 07771 970112. SER: Valuations. FAIRS: Norwich; Swinderby; Crystal Palace; Newark; Peterborough.

NORTHAMPTONSHIRE

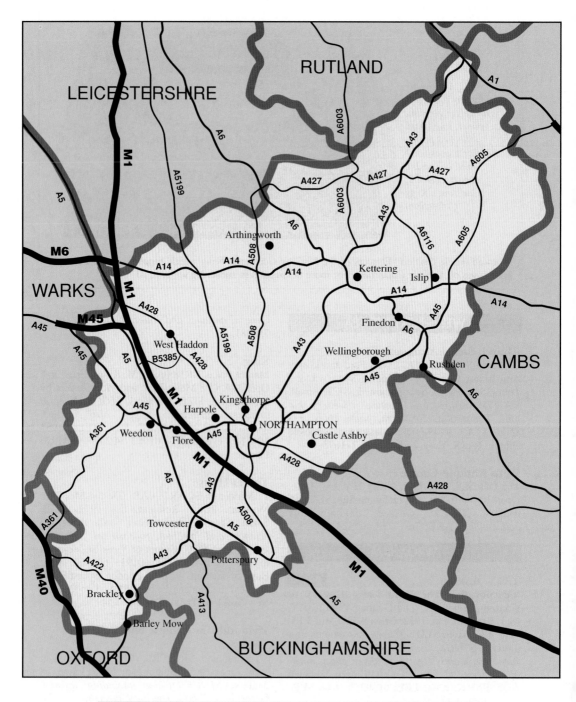

A taste of the country

Reindeer Antiques
LIMITED

17TH, 18TH AND 19TH CENTURY FINE ENGLISH FURNITURE

LAPADA
MEMBER

ESTABLISHED FOR OVER 30 YEARS

OUR NORTHANTS SHOWROOM HOUSES
ONE OF THE LARGEST AND FINEST COLLECTIONS
IN EUROPE, WHILST OUR KENSINGTON PREMISES EXTENDS
OUR UNIQUE SERVICES INTO THE HEART OF LONDON

43 Watling Street, Potterspury, Nr Towcester, Northamptonshire NN12 7QD
Telephone: 01908 542407/542200 Facsimile: 01908 542121
Internet: www.reindeerantiques.co.uk

Also at: 81 Kensington Church Street, London W8 4BG
Telephone: 020 7937 3754 Facsimile: 020 7937 7199

NORTHAMPTONSHIRE

ARTHINGWORTH, Nr. Market Harborough (Leics)

Coughton Galleries Ltd
The Old Manor. LE16 8JT. (Lady Isabel Throckmorton). Est. 1968. Open Wed., Thurs., Sat., Sun. and Bank Holidays, 10.30-5 or by appointment. SIZE: Medium. *STOCK: Modern British and Irish oil paintings and watercolours, mainly Royal academicians.* PARK: Easy. TEL: 01858 525436; fax - 01858 525535. VAT: Spec.

BARLEY MOW, Nr. Brackley

Amors of Evenley Antiques
NN13 5SB. Est. 1960. Open seven days. SIZE: Large. *STOCK: Furniture, paintings and pictures, pottery.* LOC: Period barn complex adjacent A43 4 miles junction 10 M40, towards Brackley, just over Oxfordshire border. PARK: Own. TEL: 01869 811342; e-mail - amorsof evenley@hotmail.com. SER: Valuations. *Mainly trade.*

BRACKLEY

Brackley Antique Cellar
Manor Rd. NN13. (Jim Broomfield). Est. 2000. Open 10-5 including Sun. SIZE: Large, over 100 dealers. *STOCK: Wide range of general antiques.* LOC: Below Co-op Superstore. PARK: Easy. TEL: 01280 841841; fax - 01280 841851.

Brackley Antiques
69 High St. NN13 7BW. (Mrs B.H. Nutting). Est. 1977. Open 10-6, Wed. 10-12, Sun. by appointment. SIZE: Medium. *STOCK: Furniture especially traditionally upholstered, 19th C, £50-£2,000; ceramics, 18th-20th C, £2-£400; interesting and unusual items.* LOC: A43. PARK: Easy. TEL: 01280 703362; home - same. SER: Restorations (furniture and upholstery).

Courtyard Antiques and Bazaar
Market House Courtyard. NN13 7AB. (Sir Peter G. Titterton). FIMI, FCIM. Est. 1996. Open 10-6, Sat. 10-5. SIZE: Three showrooms. *STOCK: 17th-20th C furniture and effects including Oriental.* LOC: Close to Town Hall. PARK: Easy. TEL: 01280 701218; fax/home - 01280 703631. SER: Valuations; restorations (furniture).

Peter Jackson Antiques
NN13 7AB. Open by appointment. *STOCK: Derby porcelain.* TEL: Mobile - 07702 230074. SER: Valuations; restorations.

The Old Hall Bookshop
32 Market Place. NN13 7DP. (John and Juliet Townsend). ABA. PBFA. ILAB. Est. 1977. Open 9.30-5.30, Sat. 9.30-1 and 2-5.30. SIZE: Large. *STOCK: Antiquarian, secondhand and new books and maps.* LOC: Town centre on east side of Market Place. PARK: Easy. TEL: 01280 704146; fax - 01280 705131; e-mail - books@oldhall books.com; website - www.oldhallbooks.com. SER: Search; catalogues available. FAIRS: Occasional PBFA. VAT: Stan.

Right Angle
24 Manor Rd. NN13 6AJ. (Chris and Val Pendleton). FATG. Est. 1981. Open 9.30-5.30, Sat. 9.30-4.30. CL: Wed. *STOCK: Drawings, British etchings, 1880-1940.* PARK: Opposite. TEL: 01280 702462; e-mail - chris@rightangle art.com; website - www.rightangleart.com. SER: Restorations (frames); gilding and framing.

CASTLE ASHBY

Castle Ashby Gallery
The Old Farmyard. NN7 1LF. (G.S.Wright - Fine Paintings). Est. 1987. Open 10-5 including Sun. CL: Mon. *STOCK: 19th-20th C oil paintings and watercolours, furniture and decorative furnishings.* LOC: Adjacent to Castle Ashby House. PARK: Easy. TEL: 01604 696787; fax - 01604 415055; e-mail - sales@periodhomes.net. SER: Valuations; restorations (oils). VAT: Spec.

FINEDON

Aspidistra Antiques
51 High St. NN9 5JN. (Pat and Geoff Moss). Resident. Est. 1993. Open 10-5, Sun. 11-5. SIZE: Large. *STOCK: Arts and Crafts, Art Nouveau and Art Deco metal, ceramics, plaster and furniture, £25-£1,000; general antiques, £1-£500; 1950's, 1960's, 1970's memorabilia.* LOC: Off A14 junction 10 - turn right just before roundabout in village centre. From junction 11, turn right at roundabout and immediate left. PARK: Easy. TEL: 01933 680196; mobile - 07768 071948. SER: Valuations; restorations (furniture); buys at auction. FAIRS: NEC; GMEX; Newark; Alexandra Palace.

Simon Banks Antiques
28 Church St. NN9 5NA. Est. 1984. Open every day. SIZE: Large. *STOCK: 17th-20th C furniture, £50-£5,000; glass, silver, ceramics, prints, copper, decorative and collectable items, clocks including longcase, wall and mantel.* LOC: Near church. PARK: Easy. TEL: 01933 680371; mobile - 07976 787539. SER: Valuations; search; nationwide delivery. VAT: Stan/Spec.

M.C. Chapman

LAPADA

11-25 Bell Hill. NN9 5ND. Est. 1967. Open 9-5.30, Sun. 11-5. SIZE: Large. *STOCK: Furniture, clocks, decorative items, 18th-20th C, £100-£4,000.* LOC: 400 yards off A510. PARK: Easy. TEL: 01933 681260; fax - 01933 682210. SER: Container facilities. VAT: Stan/Spec/Global.

Robert Cheney Antiques

11-13 High St. NN9 5JN. Est. 1992. Open 9-5.30, Sun. 11-4. SIZE: Medium. *STOCK: 18th-20th C furniture, china and glass, £5-£5,000.* LOC: A6. PARK: Easy. TEL: 01933 681048; home - 01933 680085. SER: Valuations.

E.K. Antiques

37 High St. NN9 5NB. (Edward Kubacki). Est. 1967. Open 9.30-5, Sun. 11-4. SIZE: Medium-several dealers. *STOCK: Furniture, china, silver, glass, pictures, needlework, clocks and decorative items, 1680-1950, £5-£8,000.* PARK: Easy. TEL: 01933 681882; home - 01933 410245. SER: Restorations (furniture); French polishing; valuations. FAIRS: Huntingdon; Kimbolton Castle.

Finedon Antiques (Centre)

11-25 Bell Hill. NN9 5ND. Est. 1973. Open 9-5.30, Sun. 11-5. SIZE: Large - 35 dealers. *STOCK: Furniture, decorative items, collectables, silver, ceramics, soft furnishings, 18th to mid-20th C.* LOC: 400 yards off A510. PARK: Easy. TEL: 01933 681260/682210; fax - 01933 682210; e-mail - sales@finedonantiques. com; website - www.finedonantiques.co.uk. SER: Search service; export facilities; nationwide delivery. VAT: Stan/Spec/Global.

FLORE, Nr. Weedon

Blockheads and Granary Antiques

The Huntershields. NN7 4LZ. (Mrs C. Madeira and Richard Sear). Est. 1968. Open 9.30-6, Sun. and other times by appointment. SIZE: Large. *STOCK: Furniture, 17th-19th C, £50-£5,000; early metalware specialist; decorative and period items, 19th C, £50-£2,000; wooden hat maker's blocks, brims and complete models.* LOC: Off M1, junction 16, into Flore, last turning on left at bollard, premises on right at bottom of lane. PARK: Easy. TEL: 01327 340718; home - same; fax - 01327 349263. FAIRS: Newark.

Christopher Jones Antiques

Flore House, The Avenue. NN7 4LZ. Est. 1977. Open 10-5, Sat. 11-4.30, Sun. by appointment. SIZE: Large. *STOCK: Period and decorative furniture, lighting, porcelain, glass and objects,* *18th-20th C.* PARK: Easy. TEL: 01327 342165; e-mail - florehouse@msn.com. SER: Interior decor advice. FAIRS: Olympia. VAT: Spec.

HARPOLE

Inglenook Antiques

23 High St. NN7 4DH. (T. and P. Havard). Est. 1971. Open 9-7. SIZE: Small. *STOCK: General antiques, £1-£500.* LOC: Main street. PARK: Easy. TEL: 01604 830007. SER: Restorations (longcase clocks).

ISLIP, Nr. Thrapston

John Roe Antiques

The Furnace Site, Kettering Rd. NN14 3JW. Est. 1968. Open 9-5.30, Sat. 10-4. *STOCK: General antiques; Continental and American shipping goods.* TEL: 01832 732937. VAT: Stan.

KETTERING

Dragon Antiques

85 Rockingham Rd. NN16 8LA. Est. 1982. Open 10-4. CL: Thurs. *STOCK: Pictures, Oriental items, militaria and general antiques.* PARK: Easy. TEL: 01536 517017. SER: Framing.

KINGSTHORPE, Nr. Northampton

Laila Gray Antiques

25 Welford Rd. NN2 8AQ. Open 9-5.30. *STOCK: Pine.* TEL: 01604 715277. SER: Waxing; stripping.

The Old Brigade

10a Harborough Rd. NN2 7AZ. (S.C.Wilson). Est. 1978. Open by appointment. SIZE: Medium. *STOCK: Military items, especially German Third Reich, 1850's to 1945, £5-£5,000.* LOC: Junction 15, M1. PARK: Easy. TEL: 01604 719389; fax - 01604 712489; website - www.theoldbrigade.co. uk. SER: Valuations; illus. catalogue (£5 + SAE). VAT: Stan/Spec.

NORTHAMPTON

F. and C.H. Cave
111 Kettering Rd. NN1 4BA. Est. 1879. Open 9-
5.30. CL: Thurs. SIZE: Large. *STOCK: Furniture
- Georgian, Victorian and decorative; general
antiques.* LOC: Near town centre, quarter mile
outside pedestrianised area. PARK: Adjoining
side streets. TEL: 01604 638278. VAT: Spec.

Michael Jones Jeweller
1 Gold St. NN1 1SA. Est. 1919. *STOCK: Silver,
gold and gem jewellery, French carriage clocks.*
TEL: 01604 632548; fax - 01604 233813;
website - www.michaeljonesjeweller.co.uk. VAT:
Margin.

Occultique
30 St Michael's Ave. NN1 4JQ. (Michael J.
Lovett). Est. 1973. Open by appointment only.
SIZE: Small. *STOCK: Books and artifacts, 50p-
£500.* TEL: 01604 627727; fax - 01604 603860;
e-mail - enquiries@occultique.co.uk; website -
www.occultique.co.uk. SER: Catalogue
available. VAT: Stan.

Penny's Antiques
83 Kettering Rd. NN1 4AW. (Mrs P. Mawby).

Est. 1976. Open Mon., Wed., Fri. and Sat. 11-4.
SIZE: Small. *STOCK: Kitchen chairs, pictures,
army badges, furniture, china, smalls, toys, glass
and brass, Victorian to 1940, £5-£100.* LOC: A43
near town centre. PARK: Easy. TEL: 01604
632429. FAIRS: Newark; Kempton Park;
Sunbury.

POTTERSPURY, Nr. Towcester

Reindeer Antiques Ltd   BADA LAPADA
43 Watling St. NN12 7QD. (John Butterworth
and Nicholas Fuller). Est. 1959. Open 9-6, Sat.,
Sun. and other times by appointment. SIZE:
Large. *STOCK: Fine English furniture, 17th-
19th C; caddies, clocks, smalls, paintings.* LOC:
A5. PARK: Own. TEL: 01908 542407/542200;
fax - 01908 542121. FAIRS: BADA. LAPADA.
VAT: Stan/Spec.

Tillmans Antiques
Wakefield Country Courtyard, Wakefield Farm.
(N.L. Tillman). Est. 1999. Open 10-5, Sat. 10-
5.30, Sun. and Bank Holiday Mon. 10-4. CL:
Mon. and Tues. SIZE: Small. *STOCK: Porcelain
and glass including cranberry, vaseline and
decorative, 19th C; silver, 18th to early 20th C;
pictures and furniture.* LOC: Off A5. PARK:
Easy. TEL: 01327 811882; home - 01327 342524;
e-mail - weedonantiques@tiscali.co.uk. FAIRS:
NEC; Silsoe; Milton Keynes; Wavendon.

RUSHDEN

Magpies
1 East Grove. NN10 0AP. (Jim and Janet Ward).
Est. 1993. Open 10-5, Nov.-Feb. 10-4, Sun. 12-4.
SIZE: Large. *STOCK: Furniture, £20-£1,000;
china, glass, kitchenalia and bric-a-brac,
postcards, clocks, 78 records, £1-£100, all 19th-
20th C.* LOC: A6 south on one-way system, first
left after passing old station. PARK: Easy. TEL:
01933 411404.

D.W. Sherwood Antiques Ltd
59 Little St. NN10 0LS. Est. 1960. Open Tues.,
Wed., Fri. and Sat. 11-5. *STOCK: General
antiques.* TEL: 01933 353265.

TOWCESTER

Clark Galleries
215 Watling St. NN12 6BX. (A. and S.D. Clark).
FBAPCR. Est. 1963. Open 9-5, Sat. 9-4. SIZE:
Medium. *STOCK: Landscape paintings, 18th-
19th C, £500-£15,000; portraits, 17th-18th C,
£500-£10,000.* LOC: M1, junction 15A, on A5.
PARK: Easy and at rear. TEL: 01327 352957;

website - www.clarkgalleries.com. SER: Valuations; restorations and re-lining (oil paintings and frames); picture hire. VAT: Stan/Spec.

Ron Green
227-239 Watling St. West. NN12 6DD. (Michael, Nicholas and Christopher Green). Est. 1952. Open 9-6, Sun. by appointment. SIZE: Large. *STOCK: English and Continental furniture, paintings and decorative items, £30-£30,000.* PARK: Easy. TEL: 01327 350387/350615; fax - 01327 350615; e-mail - ron@green227. freeserve.co.uk; website - www.rongreen antiques.com. SER: Valuations; restorations.

WEEDON

Helios & Co (Antiques)
25/27 High St. NN7 4QD. (J. Skiba and B. Walters). Est. 1976. Open 9.30-5.30, Sat. and Sun. 10-5. CL: Mon. SIZE: 20 showrooms. *STOCK: English and Continental furniture especially dining tables and sets of chairs; decorative accessories, longcase clocks and pianos.* LOC: 4 miles from junction 16, M1 towards Daventry. PARK: Easy. TEL: 01327 340264; fax - 01327 342235; e-mail - john@skiba.net. SER: Suppliers and restorers to H. M. Govt. VAT: Spec.

Rococo Antiques, Architectural Goods and Furnishings
The Former Wesleyan Chapel, Bridge St., Lower

Weedon. NN7 4PN. (N.K. Griffiths). Resident. Open 10-5, Sun. by appointment. *STOCK: Architectural goods and furnishings, general antiques.* TEL: 01327 341288; mobile - 07939 212542; e-mail - neville@nevillegriffiths.co.uk. VAT: Stan/Spec.

The Village Antique Market
62 High St. NN7 4QD. (E.A. and J.M. Saunders). Est. 1967. Open 10.30-5.15 including Sun. and Bank Holidays. SIZE: Large - 40 dealers. *STOCK: General antiques and interesting items.* LOC: Off junction 16, M1. PARK: In front yard. TEL: 01327 342015.

Weedon Antiques
23 High St. NN7 4QD. (N.L. Tillman). Est. 2000. Open 10-5, Sun. and Bank Holidays 10.30-4.30. CL: Mon. and Tues. SIZE: Medium. *STOCK: Porcelain including Royal Worcester, Coalport, Derby, Noritake, George Jones, Aynsley and Limoges; silver including Georgian, all £15-£1,000; glass including cranberry, vaseline, rummers, 17th-20th C, £15-£500; pictures, £50-£1,000; furniture, £200-£3,000.* LOC: A45, 2 miles from junction 16, M1. PARK: Easy. TEL: 01327 349777; home - 01327 342524; e-mail - weedonantiques@tiscali.co.uk. SER: Valuations. FAIRS: NEC; Milton Keynes; Wavendon.

WELLINGBOROUGH

Antiques and Bric-a-Brac Market
Market Sq. NN8 1AF. Open Tues. 9-4. SIZE: 135

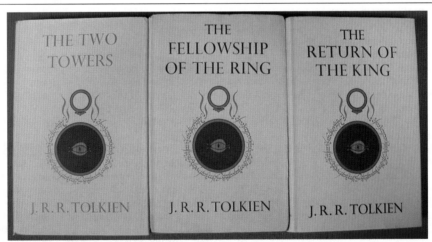

Lord of the Rings. *A good set of first editions like this is selling for huge sums. Some dealers are already saying Tolkien has reached his peak and is due for a plunge.*

From an article entitled "Antiquarian and Second-hand Books" by Adrian Greenwood which appeared in the July/August 2002 issue of ***Antique Collecting***. For more details and to subscribe see page 21.

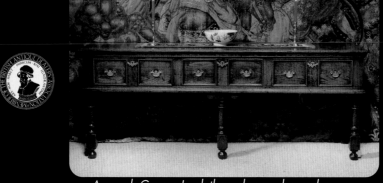
stalls. *STOCK: General antiques and collectables.* LOC: Town Centre. PARK: Easy. TEL: 01933 2317939; mobile - 07786 522407.

Park Gallery & Bookshop
16 Cannon St. NN8 5DJ. (Mrs J.A. Foster). Est. 1979. Open 10-5.30. SIZE: Medium. *STOCK: Books, maps and prints, 18th-19th C, £2-£300.* LOC: Continuation of A510 into town. PARK: Easy. TEL: 01933 222592; e-mail - judy@ parkbookshop.freeserve.co.uk. SER: Framing; book search.

Bryan Perkins Antiques
Finedon Rd. NN8 4DJ. (J., B.H. and S.C. Perkins). Est. 1971. Open 9-5. CL: Sat. pm. SIZE: Large. *STOCK: Furniture and paintings, 19th C, £200-£5,000; small items.* PARK: Easy. TEL: 01933 228812; home - 01536 790259. SER: Valuations; restorations (furniture). VAT: Spec. *Trade Only.*

WEST HADDON

Barber Antiques
8 High St. NN6 7AP. (Miss Alison Barber). Est. 1994. Open by appointment. SIZE: Medium.

STOCK: Staffordshire animals and blue and white, 19th-20th C, £50-£2,000; writing boxes, tea caddies. LOC: A428. PARK: Easy. TEL: 01788 510315; e-mail - ali@barberantiques. freeserve.co.uk; website - www.barberantiques. co.uk.

The Country Pine Shop
The Romney Building, Northampton Rd. NN6 7AS. (Ryan and Dodd). Est. 1985. Open 8-5. SIZE: Large. *STOCK: English and Continental stripped pine, £30-£1,200.* LOC: A428. TEL: 01788 510430.

Paul Hopwell Antiques   BADA LAPADA
30 High St. NN6 7AP. Est. 1974. Open 10-6, Sun. by appointment. SIZE: Large. *STOCK: 17th-18th C oak and walnut country furniture, longcase clocks, metalware: oil paintings and prints, mainly sporting and country pursuits.* LOC: A428. PARK: Easy. TEL: 01788 510636; fax - 01788 510044; e-mail - PaulHopwell@ antiqueoak.co.uk; website - www.antiqueoak. co.uk. SER: Valuations; restorations (furniture and metalware); buys at auction. VAT: Spec.

Mauchline Ware
A Collector's Guide

David Trachtenberg
and Thomas Keith

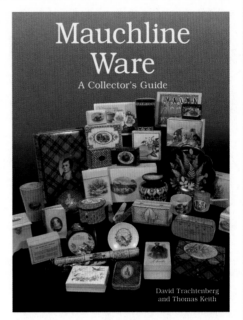

- *The most comprehensive book to be published on the subject of Mauchline Ware*

- *Profusely illustrated throughout with over 350 illustrations*

- *Contains a full list of product ranges, with price guide*

- *Describes the process of manufacture and illustrates the variety of decoration applied to the ware*

To date, very little has previously been published about this highly collectable souvenir ware which was manufactured in Scotland between 1840 and 1939. Mauchline ware is now widely collected around the world and prices are on the increase.

Now this much-needed book, *Mauchline Ware - A Collector's Guide,* documents the history and manufacture of the ware and catalogues the vast array of items which were produced in various shapes, sizes and finishes. Mauchline ware appeals to a wide span of collectors as the articles are linked to activities such as sewing, smoking, reading and writing. The important connection between Robert Burns, Scotland's national poet, and the town of Mauchline is also examined.

The book also contains a chapter on care and maintenance, as well as a price guide and a full list of product range.

David Trachtenberg owns and operates an architectural consulting firm in New York, as well as an antiques business. He is a member of the Mauchline Ware Collectors' Club and has contributed to the club's journal.

Thomas Keith works for New Dimensions Publishing Co. in New York City and is the author of various critical articles. He is also co-author of a number of plays and a volume of poetry.

11 x 8½in./279 x 216mm.
280pp.,
306 col. plates, 50 b.&w.
1 85149 392 1
£35.00

Available from all good booksellers and
direct from the publisher:
ANTIQUE COLLECTORS' CLUB
Sandy Lane, Old Martlesham, Woodbridge,
Suffolk, IP12 4SD.
Tel: 01394 389950
Fax: 01394 389999
Email: sales@antique-acc.com
Website: www.antique-acc.com

NORTHUMBERLAND

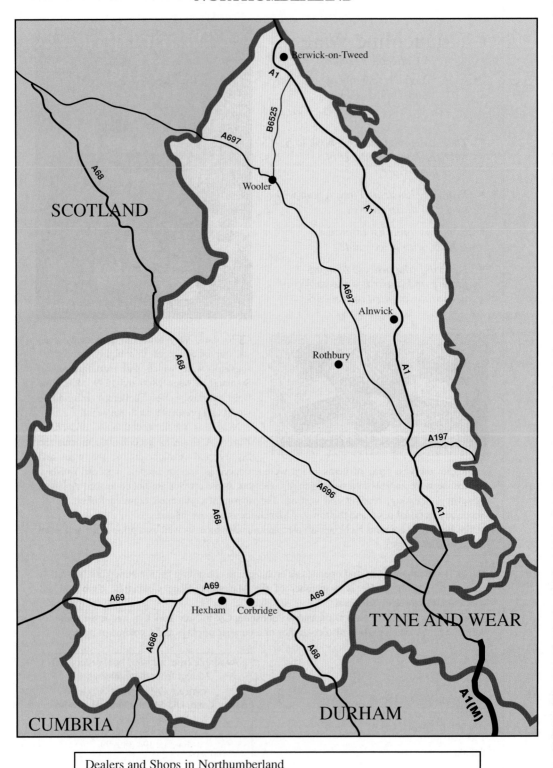

Dealers and Shops in Northumberland					
Alnwick	5	Corbridge	1	Rothbury	1
Berwick-on-Tweed	2	Hexham	7	Wooler	2

ALNWICK

G.M. Athey
Castle Corner, Narrowgate. NE66 0NP. Est. 1980. Open 8.30-4.30. SIZE: 3 floors. *STOCK: English oak and mahogany furniture, glass, china and brass, 18th-19th C.* LOC: Part of Alnwick Castle. PARK: Easy. TEL: 01665 604229; mobile - 07836 718350; e-mail - gmatheyantiques51@ fsnet.co.uk; website - www.atheysantiques.com. SER: Restorations (furniture including upholstery). FAIRS: Newark.

Bailiffgate Antique Pine
22 Bailiffgate. NE66 1LX. (S. Aston). Est. 1994. Open Thurs.-Sat. 10-4.30. SIZE: Large. *STOCK: Country pine furniture.* LOC: Opposite the castle. PARK: Easy. TEL: 01665 603616. SER: Valuations; buys at auction.

Barter Books
Alnwick Station. NE66 2NP. (Stuart & Mary Manley). IABA. Est. 1990. Open daily including Sun. SIZE: Large. *STOCK: Antiquarian books, £10-£5,000.* LOC: Off A1, on left on town approach. PARK: Easy. TEL: 01665 604888; fax - 01665 604444; e-mail - webquery@ barterbooks.co.uk; website - www.barterbooks. co.uk. SER: Valuations; book-binding and repairs.

Gordon Caris
30 Fenkle St. NE66 1HR. Open Thurs. and Fri. 10-4. *STOCK: Clocks and watches.* TEL: 01665 510820. SER: Restorations (clocks and watches).

Tamblyn
12 Bondgate Without. NE66 1PP. (Mrs S.M. Hirst and Prof. B.E. Hirst). Est. 1981. Open 10-4.30. SIZE: Medium. *STOCK: General antiques including country furniture, pottery, pictures; antiquities, glass, to 20th C, £5-£1,500.* LOC: Diagonally opposite war memorial at southern entrance to town. PARK: Easy. TEL: 01665 603024; home - same. SER: Valuations.

BERWICK-UPON-TWEED

Treasure Chest
53 West St. TD15 2DX. (Y. Scott and K. Russell). Est. 1988. Open 11-4. CL: Tues. and Thurs. SIZE: Medium. *STOCK: China, jewellery, glass, clothes, linen, silver plate and small furniture, from 1860, £1-£400.* LOC: Approximately 1 mile from A1. PARK: Easy. TEL: Home - 01289 307736/305675. SER: Restorations (china). FAIRS: Local; Newark.

Woodside Reclamation (Architectural Antiques)
Woodside, Scremerston. TD15 2SY. (Keith Allan and Lynne Gray). SALVO. Est. 1990. Open Tues.-Sat. 9-5. SIZE: Large. *STOCK: Architectural salvage including fireplaces, baths, kitchen pine, 19th C.* LOC: Adjacent A1, just south of town. PARK: Easy. TEL: 01289 331211; fax - 01289 330274; home - 01289 302658; website - www.redbaths.co.uk. SER: Restorations (stripping and finishing).

CORBRIDGE

Judith Michael
20A Watling St. NE45 5AH. (Judith Troldahl and Gillian Anderson). Est. 1970. Open 10-5. CL: Mon. SIZE: Medium. *STOCK: China, glass, silver, furniture, mirrors, light fittings and jewellery.* LOC: Just off A69. PARK: Easy. TEL: 01434 633165; fax - same. SER: Valuations.

HEXHAM

Boadens Antiques
29 and 30 Market Place. NE46 3PB. (Richard, Sandra and Chris Boaden). Est. 1948. Open 9-5. SIZE: Large. *STOCK: Furniture - antique, Victorian and secondhand, £100-£3,000; silver, paintings, jewellery, £50-£1,500; china and glass, £5-£2,000.* LOC: Opposite Hexham Abbey, off A69. PARK: Nearby. TEL: 01434 603187; fax - 01434 603474; e-mail - antiques@boadens. fsnet.co.uk. SER: Valuations. VAT: Stan/Spec.

Gordon Caris
16 Market Place. NE46 1XQ. Est. 1972. Open 9-5. CL: Thurs. *STOCK: Clocks and watches.* TEL: 01434 602106; website - www.caris-clocks.com. SER: Restorations (clocks and watches).

Hedley's of Hexham
3 St. Mary's Chare. NE46 1NQ. (P. Torday). Est. 1819. Open Mon.10-4, Tues.-Sat. 9.30-5. SIZE: Medium. *STOCK: Furniture, 18th-20th C; porcelain, silver, glass, jewellery, prints and collectables.* LOC: Off Market Place. PARK: 200 yds. TEL: 01434 602317. SER: Valuations; restorations. VAT: Stan/Spec.

Priest Popple Books
9B Priest Popple. NE46 1PF. (John B. Patterson). Est. 1997. Open 9-5. SIZE: Medium. *STOCK: Books - second-hand non-fiction, first editions, antiquarian, £5-£1,500; sheet music, LP's.* LOC: From A69 to town centre, premises top of bus station. PARK: Easy. TEL: 01434 607773; e-mail - priestpopple.books@tinyworld.co.uk. SER: Valuations; book-binding; booksearch.

EIGHTEENTH CENTURY ENGLISH
DRINKING GLASSES
AN ILLUSTRATED GUIDE

L.M. Bickerton

- *Digitally enhanced photographs*

- *A wealth of illustrations which facilitate identification of individual pieces*

- *The standard work on the subject, long out of print, and much sought after*

- *Comprehensive bibliography*

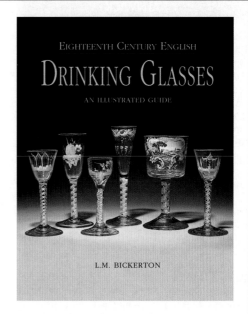

EIGHTEENTH CENTURY ENGLISH
DRINKING GLASSES
AN ILLUSTRATED GUIDE

L.M. BICKERTON

Firmly established as the standard textbook on its subject, this important work has been out of print for some time and much sought after by dealers and collectors throughout the antiquarian book trade. L.M. Bickerton's book was unique for two reasons, its wealth of illustrations and its extensive bibliography by Robert Elleray.

Interest in eighteenth century drinking glasses continues to be very strong and collectors are encouraged by the enormous variety of bowls and stems which are an eloquent testimony to the ingenuity and craftsmanship of glass-workers of the time.

In the last revision the author had extended the number of illustrations to over one thousand. This has made the book particularly valuable, since it was obviously impossible to show every minor variation' although the sheer number of examples included provided a very good representation of what collectors were likely to find. A chapter was also included giving much fuller definitions of the classes of drinking glasses, avoiding the need for constant reference to other authorities. Special coverage of baluster-stemmed and engraved glasses was also included.

Robert Elleray contributed the superb bibliography of English glass, the most detailed ever produced on the subject.

Collectors, dealers, auction houses and anyone interested in this fascinating area of the eighteenth century decorative arts will welcome this timely reprint.

11 x 8½in./279 x 216mm.
1 85149 351 4
432pp., 1,220 b.&w.
£49.50

Available from all good booksellers and
direct from the publisher:
ANTIQUE COLLECTORS' CLUB
Sandy Lane, Old Martlesham, Woodbridge,
Suffolk, IP12 4SD.
Tel: 01394 389950
Fax: 01394 389999
Email: sales@antique-acc.com
Website: www.antique-acc.com

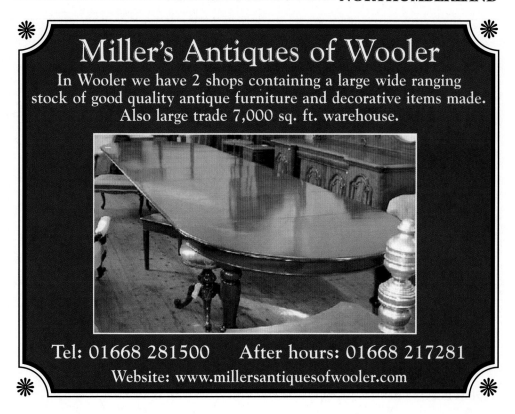
Renney Antiques
6 Rear Battle Hill. NE46 1BB. Est. 1987. Open 10-5 or by appointment. SIZE: Large. *STOCK: Decorative lighting, English and French furniture, garden, architectural and decorative items, textiles, china and glass.* LOC: Main shopping street, opposite NatWest Bank. PARK: 400 metres. TEL: 01434 607964; e-mail - renney@btconnect.com. SER: Valuations; buys at auction.

The Violin Shop
27 Hencotes. NE46 2EQ. (D. Mann). Est. 1970. Open 10-5 or by appointment. *STOCK: Violins, violas, cellos, basses and bows.* TEL: 01434 607897; e-mail - davehexviolins@aol.com; website - www.hexham-violins.co.uk. SER: Repairs; restorations; bow re-hairing; new instruments made.

ROTHBURY, Nr. Morpeth

Golfark International
5 Tollgate Crescent. NE65 7RE. (Michael Arkle). Est. 1997. *STOCK: Golf clubs and bags.* LOC: 2 mins. from centre. PARK: Easy. TEL: 01669 620487; fax/home - same; mobile - 07710 693860; e-mail - michael@golfark.freeserve. co.uk.

WOOLER

Hamish Dunn Antiques
17 High St. NE71 6BU. Est. 1986. Open 9.30-12 and 1-4.30, Thurs. 9.30-12. SIZE: Medium. *STOCK: Curios and collectables, 19th-20th C, £5-£500; antiquarian and secondhand books, 18th-20th C, £1-£200; small furniture, 19th-20th C, £15-£1,000.* LOC: Off A697. PARK: Easy. TEL: 01668 281341; home - 01668 282013. VAT: Stan/Spec.

James Miller Antiques LAPADA
1-5 Church St. NE71 6BZ. Est. 1947. Open Mon.-Fri. 9.30-5, trade anytime by appointment. SIZE: Large and warehouses. *STOCK: Georgian-Edwardian furniture and clocks.* LOC: A697. PARK: Nearby. TEL: 01668 281500; fax - 01668 282383; home - 01668 217281; website - www. millersantiquesofwooler.com. FAIRS: Newark. VAT: Stan/Spec.

NOTTINGHAMSHIRE

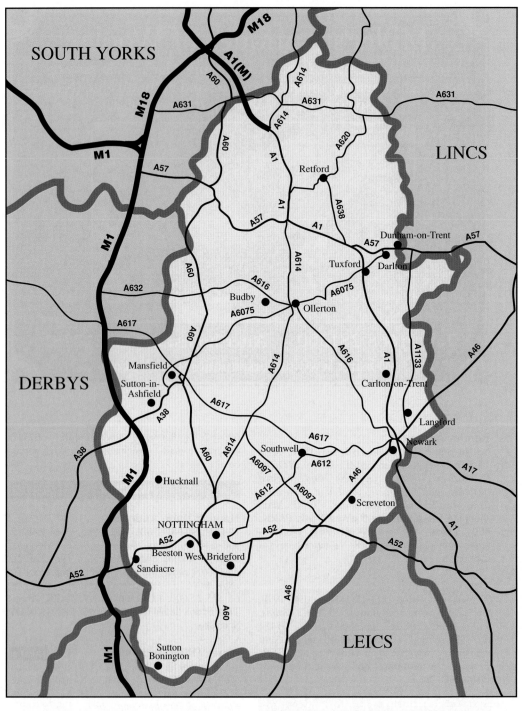

Dealers and Shops in Nottinghamshire							
Beeston	1	Hucknall	1	Ollerton	1	Sutton Bonington	1
Budby	1	Langford	1	Retford	2	Sutton-in-Ashfield	1
Carlton-on-Trent	1	Mansfield	1	Sandiacre	1	Tuxford	1
Darlton	1	Newark	9	Screveton	1	West Bridgford	3
Dunham-on-Trent	1	Nottingham	19	Southwell	2		

BEESTON

S. & E.M. Turner Violins
1-5 Lily Grove. NG9 1QL. (Steve and Liz Turner). Est. 1987. Open 9-6, Sat. 9-5. *STOCK: 18th-20th C violins, violas, cellos, basses, bows; old flutes, clarinets, concertinas, guitars, harps, oboes and saxophones.* PARK: Easy. TEL: 0115 943 0333; fax - 0115 943 0444; mobile - 07831 265272; e-mail - turnerviolins@compuserv.com. SER: Valuations; restorations.

BUDBY, Nr. Newark

Dukeries Antiques Centre
Thoresby Park. NG22 9EX. (J.A. and J.E. Coupe). Est. 1967. Open 10-5 including Sun. SIZE: Large. *STOCK: Furniture, £25-£8,000; porcelain, £10-£500; pictures, £50-£5,000; all 18th to early 20th C.* LOC: From A1 take A614 towards Nottingham to Ollerton, turn right on to A616. PARK: Easy. TEL: 01623 822252; fax - 01623 822209. SER: Valuations; restorations (furniture). VAT: Stan/Spec.

CARLTON-ON-TRENT, Nr. Newark

Tudor Rose Antiques
Yew Tree Farm. NG23 6NL. (D.H. and C. Rose). Est. 1984. Open by appointment. SIZE: Medium. *STOCK: Furniture, including oak and country, pine, mahogany and fine; interesting items, copper, brass, decorative items and soft furnishings; treen.* LOC: Off A1. PARK: Easy. TEL: 01636 821841. FAIRS: Local. VAT: Stan/Spec.

DARLTON

A.J. O'Sullivan Antiques
Whimpton House, Dunham Rd. NG22 0TA. Resident. Est. 1977. Open 9-5, Sat. 9-1. SIZE: Medium. *STOCK: Furniture, 18th-19th C, £200-£4,000: decorative items.* LOC: From A1 take A57 (Lincoln road) at Markham Moor roundabout through Darlton, premises 1/4 mile on left. PARK: Easy. TEL: 01777 228626; fax - same; e-mail - tonyos@talk21.com. SER: Valuations; restorations (furniture). FAIRS: Newark. VAT: Stan/Spec/Global.

DUNHAM-ON-TRENT

R. G. Antiques
Main St. NG22 0TY. (R.G. and D.C. Barnett). Est. 1975. Open 10-6 including Sun. SIZE: Small. *STOCK: Arms, armour and militaria, general antiques, 18th-20th C, £5-£1,000.* PARK: Easy. TEL: 01777 228312. SER: Buys at auction (arms and armour).

HUCKNALL

Ivory Gate
Curiosity Corner, 86 Watnall Rd. NG15 7JW. (B. Orridge). Est. 1975. Open 9.30-4. CL: Wed. SIZE: Large. *STOCK: Furniture, 18th-19th C, £200-£4,000; porcelain and glass, 18th-20th C, £10-£1,500.* LOC: A52 near city centre. PARK: Easy. TEL: 0115 947 3054; home - 0115 963 0789; mobile - 07799 533272; e-mail - ivorygateantique@aol.com. SER: Restorations (furniture including upholstery). FAIRS: Keddleston Hall, Lamport; Derby University.

LANGFORD, Nr. Newark

T. Baker
Langford House Farm. NG23 7RR. Est. 1966. CL: Sun. except by appointment and Sat. SIZE: Medium. *STOCK: Victoriana, period furniture and oak.* LOC: A1133. PARK: Own. TEL: 01636 704026. *Trade Only.*

MANSFIELD

Fair Deal Antiques
138 Chesterfield Rd. North. NG19 7JD. (D. Lowe). Est. 1972. Open 9.30-5.30. CL: Sat. pm. and Sun. except by appointment. SIZE: Large. *STOCK: Shipping goods, £50-£100; furniture, mainly mahogany, Victorian, £100-£1,000; period furniture, metalware and small items.* PARK: Easy. TEL: 01623 653768/512419. VAT: Stan. *Trade Only.*

NEWARK

Antiques Trade Space
Millennium House, Brunel Dr. NG24 1YP. (Trade Space Ltd). Open 9-5, Sat. 10-4.30. SIZE: 200+ dealers. *STOCK: Wide range of general antiques.* LOC: 1 mile from town centre and Newark Showground. PARK: Easy. TEL: 01636 651444; fax - 01636 651442; e-mail - info@antiquestrade space.com; website - www.antiquestrade space.com.

Castle Gate Antiques Centre
55 Castle Gate. NG24 1BE. Est. 1985. Open 9.30-5. SIZE: Large. *STOCK: Wide variety of general antiques.* LOC: A46 through town, 250yds. from castle. PARK: Easy. TEL: 01636 700076. SER: Restorations. Below are listed the dealers at this centre.

& Barrington
Fine antique and modern silver. TEL: Mobile - 07850 577724.

John Dench
Period furniture.

Dukeries Antiques
Period furniture.

Vivienne Flint
Town and country furniture.

Sinclair Antiques
Furniture, pottery, decorative items.

Village Antiques
Period furniture.

David Walsh
Early pottery.

R.R. Limb Antiques
31-35 Northgate. NG24 1HD. Open 9-6. *STOCK: General antiques and pianos.* TEL: 01636 674546.

Lombard Antiques
35 Lombard St. NG24 1XG. (Bernard J. McGrath and Ann Mason). Est. 1980. Open 10-5. CL: Sun. except during Newark Fair. SIZE: Medium. *STOCK: Collectables, 18th-19th C; longcase clocks, 18th-19th C, £2,000-£15,000; furniture, 17th to early 20th C, £50-£10,000; porcelain, jewellery, silver and antiquities.* LOC: Corner of Castlegate. PARK: Own. TEL: 01636 702296; e-mail - mcgrathbl@aol.com; website - www.quality-antique-clocks.com. SER: Valuations; restorations (clock movements, dials and cases); repairs (porcelain); buys at auction. FAIRS: Newark. VAT: Spec.

M B G Antiques, Fine Art & Jewellery
41B Castlegate. NG24 1BE. (Margaret Begley-Gray). DGA. Est. 1982. Open Wed., Fri. and Sat. 11-4. SIZE: Small. *STOCK: Jewellery, paintings, miniatures, 19th to early 20th C, to £4,000.* PARK: Nearby. TEL: 01636 650790; fax - 01636 679586; mobile - 07702 209808; e-mail - mbgantiques@mail.com. SER: Valuations; restorations (jewellery and paintings). FAIRS: NEC; Robert Bailey.

Newark Antiques Centre
Regent House, Lombard St. NG24 1XP. (Marks Tinsley). Est. 1988. Open 9.30-4.30, Sun. 11-4. SIZE: 55 units and 58 cabinets. *STOCK: Georgian, Victorian and period furniture, pottery, porcelain, glass, textiles, militaria, clocks, pictures, books, silver, antiquities, jewellery, paintings, coins, Oriental, pine, oil lamps.* LOC: Opposite bus station. PARK: Own. TEL: 01636 605504; fax - 01636 605101. SER: Upholstery; fabrics; cleaning (metal); valuations; restorations.

Newark Antiques Warehouse `LAPADA`

Old Kelham Rd. NG24 1BX. Est. 1984. Open 8.30-5.30, Sat. 9.30-4. SIZE: 30+ dealers, 80+ cabinets. *STOCK: Mainly 17th-20th C furniture and decorative items, smalls and collectables.* LOC: Just off A1. PARK: Easy. TEL: 01636 674869; fax - 01636 612933; e-mail - enquiries@newarkantiques.co.uk; website - www.newarkantiques.co.uk. SER: Valuations. FAIRS: Newark (Sundays).

No. 1 Castlegate Antiques

1-3 Castlegate. NG24 1AZ. (Christine Kavanagh). Est. 1998. Open 9.30-5, Sat. 9.30-5.30. SIZE: Large - 12 dealers. *STOCK: 18th-19th C English mahogany furniture; 17th-19th C English oak furniture and decorative objects; all £100-£5,000.* LOC: Town centre. PARK: Opposite. TEL: 01636 701877; website - www.castlegateantiques.com. SER: Valuations. VAT: Stan/Spec.

Jack Spratt Antiques

Unit 5, George St. NG24 1LU. Open 8-5.30, Sat. 8-4, Sun. 10.30-3.30. SIZE: Warehouse. *STOCK: Pine and oak.* LOC: Near station. PARK: Easy. TEL: 01636 681666/7; fax - 01636 681670. VAT: Stan.

NOTTINGHAM

Acanthus Antiques & Collectables

140 Derby Rd., Off Canning Circus. NG7 1LR. (Trak E. and Mrs Smith). Est. 1980. Open 10.30-2.30, Tues. and Thurs. 9.30-2, Sat. 12.30-4. SIZE: Small. *STOCK: Ceramics and glass, 19th-20th C, £5-£1,000; collectors' items, mainly 20th C, £5-£800; period furniture, 18th-19th C, £200-£1,500.* LOC: Derby Rd. exit from Queens Medical Centre traffic island, continue for 1 mile, shop on left. PARK: Nearby. TEL: 0115 924 3226; e-mail - trak.e.smith@btinternet.com; website - www.acanthusantiques.co.uk. SER: Valuations; restorations (furniture and ceramics); buys at auction. FAIRS: Newark, Swinderby, Donington.

Antiques across the World `LAPADA`

James Alexander Building, BR Goods Yard, London Rd./Manvers St. NG2 3AE. (A.R. Rimes). Est. 1993. Open 9-5, Sat. 10-2. SIZE: Large. *STOCK: Furniture, 18th C to Edwardian, £300-£5,000.* PARK: Easy. TEL: 0115 979 9199; fax - 0116 239 3134; home - 0116 239 3119; e-mail - tonyrimes@btinternet.com. SER: Valuations; buys at auction (furniture); finder; courier. FAIRS: Newark. VAT: Stan/Spec.

Dave Buckley Antique Exports

Nottingham Antique Centre, London Rd. NG2 3AE. Open by appointment. SIZE: Warehouse. *STOCK: Shipping furniture for USA, European and Japanese markets.* LOC: Old British Rail goods yard, off London Rd, by Hooters restaurant. PARK: Easy. TEL: 0115 9504504; e-mail - dave@nottsantiques.fsnet.co.uk. SER: Container packing; export facilities. *Trade Only.*

Castle Antiques

78 Derby Rd. NG1 5FD. Open 9.30-5. *STOCK: Maps, prints and general antiques.* TEL: 0115 947 3913.

Cathay Antiques

74 Derby Rd. NG1 5FD. (Paul Shum). Est. 1999. Open 10-5. SIZE: Large. *STOCK: Fine Oriental antiques - furniture, from Qing dynasty, £50-£2,000; porcelain, late 19th to 20th C, £30-£300; ceramics, from AD 800, £90-£2,000; wood craft, 18th-19th C, £20-£400; embroidery, 19th C, £10-£50; Tibetan furniture, 19th-20th C, £200-£700.* PARK: Easy. TEL: 01159 881216; fax - same; home - 01664 480633; mobile - 07977 282866; e-mail - paulshum8@hotmail.com. FAIRS: Local.

Collectors World

188 Wollaton Rd., Wollaton. NG8 1HJ. (M. T. Ray). Est. 1975. Open 10.30-5. CL: Mon. SIZE: Small. *STOCK: Ancient and modern coins and banknotes, 20th C cigarette and postcards, 19th C medals and accessories, all £1-£100.* LOC: Ring road at A609 Crown Island/Raleigh Island. PARK: Easy. TEL: 0115 928 0347; fax - same. SER: Valuations; buys at auction (coins and banknotes). FAIRS: Newark, Birmingham MSCF; various specialist.

The Golden Cage

99 Derby Rd., Canning Circus. NG1 5BB. (J. Pearson). Open 10-5. *STOCK: Formal wear and period clothing, from Victorian to 1970's; costume jewellery.* TEL: 0115 9411600/9476478. SER: Hire (including 20's-40's and period costume); clothes copied to order.

Granny's Attic

308 Carlton Hill, Carlton. NG4 1GD. (Mrs A. Pembleton). Open Tues., Thurs., Fri. and Sat. 9-5. *STOCK: Dolls, miniatures, general antiques and furniture.* PARK: Easy. TEL: 0115 9265204. SER: Repairs.

Harlequin Antiques

79-81 Mansfield Rd., Daybrook. NG5 6BE. (P.R. Hinchley). Est. 1992. Open 9.30-5. SIZE: Large. *STOCK: 18th-19th C pine furniture, £300-£1,200.* LOC: A60 Mansfield road, north from Nottingham. PARK: Easy. TEL: 01159 674590. SER: Valuations; restorations (oak and mahogany). VAT: Global.

D.D. and A. Ingle
380 Carlton Hill. NG4 1JA. Est. 1968. Open 9-5. SIZE: Small. *STOCK: Coins and medals, from Roman, £50-£100; jewellery and watches, £50-£1,000.* PARK: Nearby. TEL: 0115 987 3325; e-mail - ddaingle@talk21.com. SER: Valuations; restorations.

Melville Kemp Ltd   `LAPADA`
79-81 Derby Rd. NG1 5BA.. Est. 1900. Open Mon., Wed. and Fri. 10-4. SIZE: Small. *STOCK: Jewellery, Victorian; silver, Georgian and Victorian, both £5-£10,000; ornate English and Continental porcelain, Sheffield plate.* LOC: From Nottingham on main Derby Rd. PARK: Easy. TEL: 0115 941 7055; fax - 0115 941 3075. SER: Valuations; restorations (silver, china, jewellery); buys at auction. VAT: Stan/Spec.

Lights, Camera, Action UK Ltd.
6 Western Gardens, Western Boulevard, Aspley. NG8 5GP. UACC. Est. 1996. Open by appointment. SIZE: Small. *STOCK: Autographs - film, television, sport, historical; Titanic memorabilia.* LOC: Off Nutall Rd. PARK: Easy. TEL: 0115 913 1116; mobile - 0797 0342363; e-mail - nickstraw@lca.ntl-midlands.com; website - www.lca-autographs.co.uk. SER: Valuations; buys at auction. FAIRS: NEC; local.

Michael D. Long
96-98 Derby Rd. NG1 5FB. Est. 1970. Open 9.30-5, Sat. 10-4. SIZE: Large. *STOCK: Arms and armour of all ages and nations.* LOC: From city centre take main Derby Rd., shop on right. PARK: Easy. TEL: 0115 9413307/9474137; fax - 0115 9414199; e-mail - sales@michaeldlong.com; website - www. michaeldlong.com. VAT: Stan/Spec.

Luna
23 George St. NG1 3BH. (Paul Rose). Est. 1994. Open 10-5.30. SIZE: Small. *STOCK: Design items - glass, ceramics, furniture, telephones, post-war, from £5.* LOC: Near Market Sq. Hockley. PARK: Easy. TEL: 0115 924 3267; website - www.luna-online.co.uk.

Anthony Mitchell Fine Paintings
Sunnymede House, 11 Albemarle Rd., Woodthorpe. NG5 4FE. (M. Mitchell). Est. 1965. Open by appointment. *STOCK: Oil paintings, £2,000-£100,000; watercolours, £500-£30,000.* LOC: North on Nottingham ring road to junction with Mansfield road, turn right, then 3rd left. PARK: Easy. TEL: 0115 9623865; fax - same. SER: Valuations; restorations. VAT: Spec.

NSE Medal Dept.
97 Derby Rd. NG1 5BB. (Dennis Henson). Est. 1983. Open 8.30-3.30. SIZE: Medium. *STOCK: Medals, badges and coins, £5-£1,000+.* PARK: Easy. TEL: 0115 950 1882. SER: Valuations; medal mounting and framing.

S. Pembleton
306-308 Carlton Hill, Carlton. NG4 1JB. Open Tues., Thurs. and Fri. 9-5, Sat. 10-5. *STOCK: General antiques.* PARK: Easy. TEL: 0115 9265204. SER: Repairs (watches, clocks and furniture).

Top Hat Antiques
62 Derby Rd. NG1 5FD. (Top Hat Exhibitions Ltd). Est. 1978. Open 10-5. SIZE: 3 floors. *STOCK: Furniture, Georgian to Edwardian; metalware, silver, porcelain, prints, watercolours, oil paintings, glass and collectables.* LOC: A52 town centre. PARK: Meters. TEL: 0115 941 9143; website - www.tophat-antiques.co.uk. FAIRS: National Art Deco, Loughborough (organisers). VAT: Stan/Spec.

Vintage Wireless Shop
The Hewarths, Sandiacre. NG10 5NQ. (Mr Yates). Est. 1977. Open by appointment. *STOCK: Early wireless and pre-war televisions, crystal sets, horn speakers, valves, books and magazines.* PARK: Easy. TEL: 0115 9393139; fax - 0115 9490180; mobile - 07989 102976; e-mail - vintagewireless@aol.com. SER: Valuations; repairs; finder.

OLLERTON

Hamlyn Lodge
Station Rd. NG22 9BN. (N., J.S. and M.J. Barrows). Open Tues.-Sat. 10-5. SIZE: Small. *STOCK: General antiques, 18th-19th C, £100-£3,000.* LOC: Off A614. PARK: Easy. TEL: 01623 823600; website - www.hamlynlodge. co.uk. SER: Restorations (furniture).

RETFORD

Stanley Hunt Jewellers
22 The Square. DN22 6DQ. *STOCK: Jewellery.* TEL: 01777 703144.

Ranby Hall   `LAPADA`
Barnby Moor. DN22 8JQ. (Paul Wyatt). Est. 1980. Open Sat. and Sun. 10-6, other days by appointment. SIZE: Large. *STOCK: Furniture, 18th-20th C, £300-£25,000; mirrors, 19th C to 1930, £500-£15,000; oil paintings, 17th-20th C, £1,500-£10,000; garden urns and furniture, from 19th C, £500-£8,000.* LOC: Take Barnby Moor

turning off A1, travel 1/4 mile - drive to house on right. PARK: Easy. TEL: 01777 860696; fax - 01777 701317; e-mail - paul.wyatt@ranbyhall.com; website - www.ranbyhall.com. SER: Buys at auction (furniture and oils). FAIRS: DMG Newark, LAPADA; Bailey, Tatton Park; RDS Dublin. VAT: Stan/Spec.

SANDIACRE

The Glory Hole

14-16 Station Rd. NG10 5BG. (Colin and Debbie Reid). Est. 1982. Open 10-5.30. SIZE: Small. *STOCK: Victorian pine, walnut, oak and mahogany furniture; pine kitchens and fireplaces; restored fireplaces.* PARK: Nearby. TEL: 0115 9394081; fax - 0115 9394085. SER: Restorations; stripping; polishing; repairs.

SCREVETON

Red Lodge Antiques

Fosseway. (L. Bradford). Resident. Est. 1999. Open 9-5 or by appointment, Sat. and Sun. appointment only. SIZE: Large. *STOCK: Shipping furniture, 1900-1930s, £25-£1,000.* LOC: A46 approx. 10 miles from Nottingham and 5 miles from Newark. PARK: Own. TEL: 01949 20244; home - same; e-mail - redlodgeantiques@tradeexport.fsnet.co.uk. SER: Container facilites available. *Trade & Export Only.*

SOUTHWELL

Strouds (of Southwell Antiques)

3-7 Church St. NG25 0HQ. (V.N. Stroud). Est. 1972. Open 9.30-5 or by appointment. SIZE: Large. *STOCK: Furniture, clocks, metalware and decorative items, 17th-19th C, £10-£50,000.* LOC: Town centre. PARK: Easy. TEL: 01636 815001; fax - same. VAT: Stan/Spec.

Westhorpe Antiques

Old Grapes Inn, Westhorpe. (Ralph Downing). Est. 1974. Open 10-5.30, Sun. until 4 - ring bell to gain admittance. SIZE: Small. *STOCK: Furniture, mainly oak, 17th to mid 19th C, £50-£500; brass, copper and pewter, 17th to late 19th C, £10-£200; vintage fishing tackle including reels and rods, stuffed fish, sporting items, £10-£300.* LOC: 15 mins. from Newark. PARK: Easy. TEL: 01636 814095; home - same. SER: Valuations; restorations (furniture); buys at auction. FAIRS: Newark.

SUTTON BONINGTON

Goodacre Engraving

The Dial House, 120 Main St. LE12 5PF. Est. 1948.

STOCK: Longcase and bracket clock movements, parts and castings. TEL: 01509 673082, fax - same. SER: Hand engraving; movement repairs; silvering and dial repainting. VAT: Stan.

SUTTON-IN-ASHFIELD

Yesterday and Today

82 Station Rd. NG17 5HB. (John and Chris Turner). Resident. Est. 1990. Open Wed.-Sat. 9.30-5.30, Sun. 11-4. SIZE: Medium. *STOCK: Furniture, 1920's-1930's oak and walnut, £50-£500; clocks, 19th C, £100-£2,000; collectables.* LOC: 3 miles from junction 28, M1, take A38 towards Mansfield. PARK: Easy. TEL: 01623 442215; mobile - 07957 552753. FAIRS: Swinderby.

TUXFORD

Sally Mitchell's Gallery

9 Eldon St. NG22 0LB. FATG. Est. 1976. Open Tues.-Sat. 10-5, Sun. and Mon. by appointment. SIZE: Medium. *STOCK: Contemporary sporting and animal paintings, £200-£5,000; limited edition sporting and animal prints, 20th C, £20-£350.* LOC: 1 min. from A1, 14 miles north of Newark. PARK: Easy. TEL: 01777 838 234/655; e-mail - info@sallymitchell.com; website - www.sallymitchell.com. FAIRS: CLA Game and Burghley Horse Trials. VAT: Stan/Spec.

WEST BRIDGFORD

Bridgford Antiques

2A Rushworth Ave. NG2 7LF. Est. 1986. Open 10.30-5. SIZE: Small. *STOCK: General antiques, collectables, pictures, books and postcards.* LOC: Opposite County Hall. PARK: Easy. TEL: 0115 9821835; home - 0115 9817161.

Joan Cotton (Antiques)

5 Davies Rd. NG2 5JE. Est. 1969. Open 9-4.30. CL: Wed. *STOCK: General antiques, Victoriana, jewellery, silver, china, glass and bygones.* LOC: 1/2 mile along Bridgford Rd. from Trent Bridge, in town centre. PARK: On forecourt. TEL: 0115 9813043.

Portland Antiques & Curios

5 Portland Rd. NG2 6DN. (Brendan and Carole Sprakes). Est. 1999. Open Wed.-Sat. 10-5, other days by appointment. SIZE: Small. *STOCK: Furniture, £50-£750; china, £5-£150; jewellery, £10-£300; mainly 19th-20th C.* LOC: Off Melton Rd. PARK: Easy. TEL: 0115 914 2123; fax - same; home - 0115 914 8614. SER: Delivery. VAT: Stan.

OXFORDSHIRE

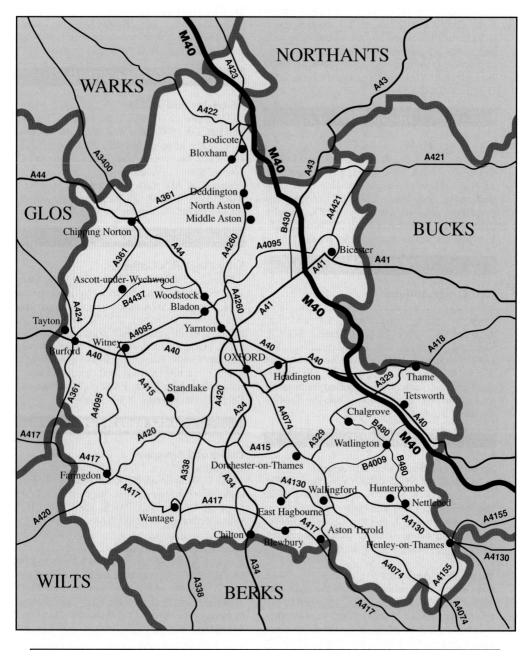

ASCOTT-UNDER-WYCHWOOD

William Antiques
Manor Farm. OX7 6AL. (Robert Gripper). Est. 1982. Open Mon.-Fri. 9-5. SIZE: Medium. *STOCK: Victorian and Georgian furniture, mainly mahogany.* LOC: A361 from Chipping Norton, turn left in town between river bridge and level crossing. PARK: Easy. TEL: 01993 831960; home - same; fax - 01993 830395; e-mail - robgripper@aol.com. SER: Valuations; restorations. VAT: Margin.

ASTON TIRROLD, Nr. Didcot

John Harrison Fine Art
Skirmers, Aston St. OX11 9DQ. (J.M.C. Harrison). TVADA. Strictly by appointment. *STOCK: Drawings and watercolours, 18th-19th C.* TEL: 01235 850260. SER: Commissions undertaken.

BICESTER

R.A. Barnes LAPADA
PO Box 82. OX25 1RA. Open by appointment. *STOCK: English, Oriental and Continental porcelain, antiques and collectables; Wedgwood, ironstone, china, glass, copper, 19th C; Bohemian and art glass, Regency, Victorian and some 18th C small furniture, primitive paintings.* TEL: 01844 237388. VAT: Stan/Spec.

BLADON, Nr. Woodstock

Park House Tearoom & Antiques
26 Park St. OX20 1RW. (H.R. and T. Thomas). Resident. Est. 1996. Open daily. SIZE: Medium. *STOCK: Furniture and decorative smalls.* LOC: On A4095 Woodstock to Witney road. PARK: Own. TEL: 01993 812817; fax - 01993 812912; e-mail - hughthomas@htshipping.com; website - www.htshipping.com. SER: Valuations; restorations; buys at auction; monthly shipping service to USA (check website for rate details).

BLEWBURY

Blewbury Antiques
London Rd. OX11 9NX. (E. Richardson). Est. 1971. Open 10-6 including weekends. CL: Tues. and Wed. *STOCK: General antiques, books, bric-a-brac, country and garden items, oil lamps and oil lamp parts.* PARK: Easy. TEL: 01235 850366.

BLOXHAM, Nr. Banbury

H.C. Dickins
High St. OX15 4LT. (P. and H.R. Dickins). Open 10-5.30, Sat. 10-1. *STOCK: 19th-20th C British sporting and landscape paintings, watercolours, drawings and prints.* TEL: 01295 721949; website - www.hcdickins.co.uk.

BODICOTE, Nr. Banbury

Blender Antiques
Cotefield Farm, Oxford Rd. OX15 4AQ. (Neil Robson). TVADA. Open Mon.-Fri. 9.30-5 or by appointment. SIZE: Large. *STOCK: English and Continental furniture, mirrors, lighting and decorative accessories.* LOC: Banbury-Oxford road, opposite Banbury Rugby Club. PARK: Own. TEL: 01295 254754; fax - 01295 276139; mobile - 07785 785447.

BURFORD

Antiques @ The George
104 High St. OX18 4QJ. (C. Oswald). Est. 1992. Open 10-5, Sun. 12-5. SIZE: Large. *STOCK: General antiques including china, furniture, textiles, silver, plate, books, glass, pictures, early 18th C to 1930's.* LOC: Main road. PARK: Around corner. TEL: 01993 823319.

Burford Antique Centre
Cheltenham Rd., At the Roundabout. OX18 4JA. (G. Viventi). Est. 1979. Open 10-6 including Sun. SIZE: Large. *STOCK: Furniture, 18th-19th C, £100-£5,000; china and pictures.* LOC: A40. PARK: Easy. TEL: 01993 823227. SER: Restorations (furniture including re-leathering).

The Burford Gallery
Classica House, High St. OX18 4QA. (B. Etheridge). Est. 1976. Open 9.30-5.30. SIZE: Medium. *STOCK: British and Continental watercolours, 18th-20th C, £40-£6,000.* LOC: 400yds. from A40 roundabout. PARK: Easy. TEL: 01993 822305; fax - 01993 824148. SER: Valuations; framing and mounting; buys at auction (watercolours). VAT: Spec.

Bygones
29 High St. OX18 4RN. (C.B. Jenkins). Est. 1986. Open 10-1 and 2-5, Sat. 10-5, Sun. 12-5. SIZE:Small. *STOCK: Prints and pictures, 1900's, £5-£50; china and glass, curios, 1880-1950, £5-£250.* LOC: A40. PARK: Easy. TEL: 01993 823588; fax - 01993 704338.

Jonathan Fyson Antiques
50 High St. OX18 4QF. (J.R. Fyson). CADA. Est. 1970. Open 9.30-1 and 2-5.30, Sat. from 10. SIZE: Medium. *STOCK: English and Continental furniture, decorative brass and steel including*

lighting and fireplace accessories; club fenders, mirrors, porcelain, table glass, jewellery. LOC: At junction of A40/A361 between Oxford and Cheltenham. PARK: Easy. TEL: 01993 823204; fax - same; home - 01367 860223; e-mail - j@fyson.co.uk. SER: Valuations. VAT: Spec.

Gateway Antiques

Cheltenham Rd., Burford Roundabout. OX18 4JA. (M.C. Ford and P. Brown). CADA. Est. 1986. Open 10-5.30 and Sun. 2-5. SIZE: Large. *STOCK: English and Continental furniture, 18th to early 20th C; decorative accessories.* LOC: On roundabout (A40) Oxford/Cheltenham road, adjacent to the Cotswold Gateway Hotel. PARK: Easy. TEL: 01993 823678/822624; fax - 01993 823857; e-mail - enquiries@gatewayantiques.co.uk; website - www.gatewayantiques.co.uk. SER: Courier (multi-lingual). VAT: Stan/Spec.

Horseshoe Antiques and Gallery

97 High St. OX18 4QA. (B. Evans). Open 9-5.30, Sun. by appointment. SIZE: Medium. *STOCK: Clocks including longcase (all fully restored); early oak and country furniture; oil paintings and watercolours; copper and brass, horse brasses.* LOC: East side of High St. PARK: Easy. TEL: 01993 823244; fax - 01993 822429. VAT: Spec.

Hubert's Antiques · LAPADA

Burford Roundabout, Cheltenham Rd. OX18 4JA. (Michael R. Hinds). Est. 1987. Open 10-5.30. SIZE: Medium. *STOCK: Furniture, £150-£15,000; oils, £50-£10,000; clocks, £250-£7,500; all 17th onwards.* LOC: A40 half way between Oxford and Cheltenham. PARK: Easy. TEL: 01993 822151; fax - same. SER: Shipping. VAT: Spec.

David Pickup · BADA

115 High St. OX18 4RG. CADA. Est. 1977. Open 9.30-1 and 2-5.30, Sat. 10-1 and 2-4. SIZE: Medium. *STOCK: Fine furniture, works of art, from £500+; decorative objects, from £100+; all late 17th to mid 20th C, specialising in Arts and Crafts.* PARK: Easy. TEL: 01993 822555. FAIRS: Olympia. VAT: Spec.

Richard Purdon Antique Carpets · BADA

158 The Hill. OX18 4QY. CADA. Est. 1959. Open 10-5. SIZE: Medium. *STOCK: Antique Eastern and European carpets, village and tribal rugs, needlework, textiles and related items.* TEL: 01993 823777; fax - 01993 823719; e-mail - rp@richardpurdon.demon.co.uk; website - www.purdon.com. SER: Valuations; restorations. FAIRS: Hali (Olympia). VAT: Stan/Spec.

Manfred Schotten Antiques

109 High St. OX18 4RG. CADA. Est. 1974. Open 9.30-5.30 or by appointment. *STOCK: Sporting antiques and library furniture.* PARK: Easy. TEL: 01993 822302; fax - 01993 822055; e-mail - antiques@schotten.com; website - www.schotten.com. SER: Restorations; trophies. FAIRS: Olympia (Spring, Summer and Winter). VAT: Stan/Margin.

Brian Sinfield Gallery

150 High St. OX18 4QU. CADA. Est. 1972. Open 10-5.30, Mon. by appointment. SIZE: Medium. *STOCK: Mainly contemporary and late 20th C paintings, watercolours and sculpture.* PARK: Easy. TEL: 01993 824464; fax - 01993 824525; e-mail - gallery@briansinfield.com; website - www.briansinfield.com. SER: 8 exhibitions annually. VAT: Spec.

The Stone Gallery

93 High St. OX18 4QA. (Mrs Phyllis M. and Simon Marshall). Est. 1918. Open 9.15-6. SIZE: Medium. *STOCK: Pre-Raphaelite and modern British pictures, 1840-1980, £120-£30,000; paperweights, from 1840, £50-£15,000; enamel boxes, from 1760, £50-£1,000; designer jewellery.* LOC: Halfway down High St. PARK: Easy. TEL: 01993 823302; fax/home - same; e-mail - mail@stonegallery.co.uk; website - www. stonegallery.co.uk. SER: Valuations (paperweights); buys at auction (pictures and paperweights). VAT: Stan/Spec.

Swan Gallery

High St. OX18 4RE. (D. Pratt). CADA. Est. 1966. Open 10-5.30. SIZE: Large. *STOCK: Country furniture in oak, yew, walnut and fruitwood, 17th-19th C, £300-£12,000; Staffordshire figures and small decorative items, 18th-20th C, £50-£800.* PARK: Easy. TEL: 01993 822244. VAT: Mainly Spec.

Wren Gallery

34 Lower High St. OX18 4RR. (S. Hall and G. Mitchell). Est. 1986. Open 10-5.30. SIZE: Medium. *STOCK: 19th-20th C watercolours and drawings.* TEL: 01993 823495. SER: Valuations; restorations (watercolours); buys at auction (watercolours). VAT: Spec.

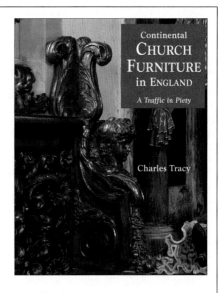

CHALGROVE, Nr. Oxford

Rupert Hitchcox Antiques

Warpsgrove Lane. OX44 7RW. (P. and R. Hitchcox). Est. 1957. Open Mon.-Sat. 10-5 (Trade), Sun. 2-5 (Trade and public). SIZE: Large - 6 barns. *STOCK: Georgian, Victorian, Edwardian and 1920's furniture*. LOC: Halfway between Oxford and Henley, just off the B480, 6 miles from junction 6 M40. PARK: Easy. TEL: 01865 890241; fax - same; e-mail - ruperts antiques@aol.com. VAT: Stan/Spec.

CHILTON, Nr. Didcot

Country Markets Antiques and Collectables

at Country Gardens Garden Centre, Newbury Rd. OX11 0QN. (G.W. Vaughan). Est. 1991. Open 10-5.30, Mon. 10.30-5.30, Sun. 10.30-4.30. SIZE: Large - 30 dealers. *STOCK: Wide variety of general antiques including furniture, books, jewellery, porcelain, militaria, cased fish and fishing tackle, £5-£5,000*. LOC: Off A34 near Harwell, 10 mins. from junction 13, M4, 20 mins. from Oxford. PARK: Easy. TEL: 01235 835125; fax - 01235 833068; e-mail - country.marketsantiques@ breathemail.net; website - www.countrymarkets. co.uk. SER: Restorations (furniture and ceramics).

CHIPPING NORTON

Antique English Windsor Chairs   BADA

9 Horse Fair. OX7 5AL. CINOA. CADA. Est. 1971. Open 10-5, prior telephone call advisable. CL: Mon. and Tues. except by appointment. *STOCK: 18th-19th C Windsor chairs, including sets.* **TEL: 01608 643322; fax - 01608 644322; e-mail - michael@antique-english-windsor-chairs.com; website - www.antique-english-windsor-chairs.com. FAIRS: BADA; Olympia (June, Nov). VAT: Stan/Spec.**

Chipping Norton Antique Centre

Ivy House, 1 Market Place and 21/44 West St. OX7 5NH. (G. Wissinger). Open 10-5.30 including Sun. SIZE: 20 dealers. *STOCK: A wide variety of smalls and furniture.* PARK: Own. TEL: 01608 644212.

Georgian House Antiques   LAPADA

21 West St. OX7 5EU. Open 9-6. *STOCK: 17th-19th C furniture and paintings.* PARK: Easy. TEL: 01608 641369. SER: Restorations. VAT: Stan.

Jonathan Howard

21 Market Place. OX7 5NA. (J.G. Howard). Est.

1979. Open by appointment or ring bell. SIZE: Small. *STOCK: Clocks - longcase, wall and carriage, 18th-19th C.* PARK: TEL: 01608 643065. SER: Valuations; restorations (movement, dials and cases).

Key Antiques

11 Horse Fair. OX7 5AL. (J. Riley). CADA. Open 10-5.30 or by appointment. CL: Mon. and Tues. SIZE: Medium. *STOCK: English period oak and country furniture, 17th-19th C; domestic metalware, pottery and associated items.* LOC: Main road. PARK: Easy. TEL: 01608 644992/643777; e-mail - key.antiques@btopen world.com; website - www.keyantiques.com. VAT: Spec.

Manchester House Antiques Centre

5a Market Place. OX7 5NA. (Mrs M. Shepherd). Est. 1997. Open 7 days 10-5. SIZE: Medium - 5 dealers. *STOCK: Wide range of general antiques including furniture, china, kitchenalia, copper and brass.* LOC: Town centre. PARK: Nearby. TEL: 01608 646412.

The Quiet Woman Antiques Centre

Southcombe. OX7 5QH. (David Belcher and Ann Marriott). Est. 1998. Open 10-6, Sat. 10-5.30, Sun. 11-4. SIZE: Large - several dealers. *STOCK: Wide variety of general antiques.* PARK: Own. TEL: 01608 646262; fax - same.

Station Mill Antiques Centre

Station Rd. OX7 5HX. (M.T. Langer). Est. 1994. Open 10-5 including Sun. SIZE: Large. *STOCK: Furniture, fine art, bric-a-brac and collectables, 17th-20th C, £2-£2,000.* LOC: Just out of town off A44 towards Moreton-in-Marsh. PARK: Easy. TEL: 01608 644563; mobile - 07092 310632; e-mail - info@stationmill.com; website - www.stationmill.com.

TRADA

21 High St. OX7 5AD. (Valerie Perkins). Est. 1978. Open 9-5. CL: Mon. SIZE: Small. *STOCK: Antiquarian maps and engravings, 1600-1900.* PARK: Nearby. TEL: 01608 644325; e-mail - val_perkins@hotmail.com. SER: Print renovation; colouring; picture frame making.

Peter Wiggins

Raffles Farm, Southcombe. OX7 5QH. Est. 1969. Usually available. *STOCK: Barometers.* LOC: 1 mile from Chipping Norton on A34. TEL: 01608 642652; home - same. SER: Valuations; restorations (barometers, clocks, automata); repairs (clocks); buys at auction.

DEDDINGTON

Castle Antiques Ltd   LAPADA
Manor Farm, Clifton. OX15 0PA. (J. and J. Vaughan). Est. 1968. Open 10-5, Sun. 10-4. SIZE: Large. *STOCK: Furniture, £25-£3,000; silver, metalware, £10-£1,000; pottery, porcelain, £10-£2,000; kitchenalia.* LOC: B4031, 6 miles from junction 10, M40. PARK: Own. TEL: 01869 338688. VAT: Stan/Spec.

Deddington Antiques Centre
Laurel House, Bull Ring, Market Sq. OX15 0TT. (Mrs B. J. Haller). TVADA. Est. 1972. Open 10-5 including Sun. SIZE: 27 dealers. *STOCK: Furniture, Georgian to 1930's, £100-£4,000; porcelain, silver, pictures, jewellery, 1700-1930, £5-£5,000; collectables, £10-£200.* LOC: Off A4260 Oxford-Banbury road at Deddington traffic lights. PARK: Easy and free. TEL: 01869 338968; fax - 01869 338916. SER: Valuations. FAIRS: TVADA.

DORCHESTER-ON-THAMES

Dorchester Antiques   LAPADA
The Barn, 3 High St. OX10 7HH. (J. and S. Hearnden). TVADA. Est. 1992. Open Tues.-Sat. 10-5. SIZE: Medium. *STOCK: Furniture including chairs and decorative country pieces, 18th-19th C.*

LOC: Opposite Abbey. PARK: Easy. TEL: 01865 341373. SER: Restorations; finder. FAIRS: TVADA.

Hallidays (Fine Antiques) Ltd   LAPADA
The Old College, High St. OX10 7HL. TVADA. CINOA. Est. 1950. Open 9-5, Sat. 10-1 and 2-4. SIZE: Large. *STOCK: 17th-19th C English and Continental furniture; 18th-19th C paintings, decorative and small items; 18th-20th C pine and marble mantelpieces, firegrates, fenders; bespoke room panelling.* LOC: 8 miles south-east of Oxford. PARK: At rear. TEL: 01865 340028/68; fax - 01865 341149; e-mail - antiques@hallidays.com; website - www.hallidays.com. FAIRS: Olympia; LAPADA, London; Gramercy Park, New York; International Antiques, Chicago. VAT: Stan/Spec.

EAST HAGBOURNE

Craig Barfoot
Tudor House. OX11 9LR. (I.C. Barfoot). Est. 1993. Open any time by appointment. SIZE: Medium. *STOCK: Longcase clocks, £3,000-£20,000; bracket and lantern clocks.* LOC: Just off A34 halfway between Oxford and Newbury. PARK: Easy. TEL: 01235 818968; home - same; mobile - 07710 858158; e-mail - craig.barfoot@tiscali.co.uk. SER: Restorations (clocks); buys at auction (clocks, English oak furniture). VAT: Spec.

E.M. Lawson and Co
Kingsholm. OX11 9LN. (W.J. and K.M. Lawson). Est. 1921. Usually open 10-5 but appointment preferred. CL: Sat. *STOCK: Antiquarian and rare books, 1500-1900.* PARK: Easy. TEL: 01235 812033. VAT: Stan.

FARINGDON

Aston Pine Antiques
16-18 London St. SN7 7AA. (P. O'Gara). Est. 1982. Open Tues.-Sat. 9-5. *STOCK: Victorian and Continental pine; Victorian fireplaces, doors and bathrooms.* TEL: 01367 243840. SER: Stripping (pine).

Oxford Architectural Antiques
16-18 London St. SN7 7AA. (M. O'Gara). Open Tues.-Sat. 9-5. *STOCK: Fireplaces, fixtures and fittings, doors.* TEL: 01367 242268; mobile - 07973 922393. SER: Packing and container. VAT: Margin.

HEADINGTON, Nr. Oxford

Barclay Antiques
107 Windmill Rd. OX3 7BT. (C. Barclay). Est. 1979. Open 10-5.30. CL: Wed. SIZE: Small. *STOCK: Porcelain, silver and jewellery, 18th-19th C, £50-£100; period lamps, 20th C, £50-£500.* PARK: Own at rear. TEL: 01865 769551. SER: Valuations.

HENLEY-ON-THAMES

Easystrip
Old Manor Farm, Bix. RG9 6BX. (R.J. Cain). Est. 1973. Open by appointment. *STOCK: Victorian doors.* LOC: A4130 right at top of dual carriageway. PARK: Easy. TEL: 01491 577289; mobile - 07785 938580. SER: Restorations (stripping).

Friday Street Antique Centre (The Ferret)
4 Friday St. RG9 1AH. (D. Etherington and C. Fentum). Est. 1985. Open 10-5.30, Sun. 12-5. SIZE: 6 dealers. *STOCK: Furniture, china, silver, books, pictures, musical instruments, unusual items.* LOC: First left after Henley bridge, then first right, business on left. PARK: Easy. TEL: 01491 574104.

Jackdaw Antiques Centres
5 Reading Rd. RG9 0AS. (Mr. and Mrs. Mayle). Est. 1998. Open 10-5.30, Sun. 12-5. *STOCK: Furniture, from Regency, £100-£2,500; china, from Victorian, £2-£200; limited edition books, £2-£50; silver, from Victorian, £15-£500.* TEL:

01491 572289; office - 01491 680954. SER: Restorations (furniture and china).

Jonkers Rare Books
24 Hart St. RG9 2AU. (Christiaan Jonkers). ABA. ILAB. PBFA. Est. 1990. Open 10-5.30. SIZE: Medium. *STOCK: Fine and rare books, 1800-1950, £50-£50,000.* LOC: Main road. PARK: Easy. TEL: 01491 576427; fax - 01491 573805; e-mail - info@jonkers.co.uk; website - www.jonkers.co.uk. SER: Valuations; buys at auction (rare books). FAIRS: Olympia.

The Barry Keene Gallery
12 Thameside. RG9 1BH. (B.M. and J.S. Keene). FATG. Est. 1971. Open 9.30-5.30 and by appointment. *STOCK: Antique and modern art, paintings, watercolours, drawings, etchings, prints and sculpture.* LOC: Junction 8/9 M4, over Henley bridge, left along riverside, 5th building on right. TEL: 01491 577119; e-mail - barrykeene @fsbdial.co.uk; website - www.barrykeene gallery.com. SER: Restorations; framing; cleaning; relining; gilding; export. VAT: Stan/Spec.

Richard J. Kingston `BADA`
95 Bell St. RG9 2BD. Open 9.30-5 or by appointment. SIZE: Medium. *STOCK: Furniture, 17th to early 19th C; silver, porcelain, glass, paintings, antiquarian and secondhand books.* PARK: Easy. TEL: 01491 574535; home - 01491 573133. SER: Restorations. FAIRS: Surrey. VAT: Stan/Spec.

The Old French Mirror Company Ltd
Nightingales, Rotherfield Greys. RG9 4QQ. (Roger and Bridget Johnson). Resident. Est. 1999. Open by appointment. SIZE: Large. *STOCK: French mirrors, 19th to early 20th C.* LOC: 3 miles from Henley-on-Thames. PARK: Easy. TEL: 01491 628080; fax - same; e-mail - bridget@frenchmirrors.co.uk; website - www. oldfrenchmirrors.com. SER: Shipping. FAIRS: Daily Telegraph House and Garden; Olympia (June); local. VAT: Spec.

Thames Oriental Rug Co
Thames Carpet Cleaners Ltd, Newtown Rd. RG9 1HG. (B. and Mrs A. Javadi-Babreh). Resident. Est. 1955. Open 9-12.30 and 1.30-5, Sat. 9-12.30. SIZE: Large. *STOCK: Oriental rugs, mid-19th C to modern.* PARK: Easy. TEL: 01491 574676/577877. SER: Valuations; restorations; cleaning. VAT: Stan.

Tudor House Antiques
49 Duke St. (David and Linda Potter). Open 10-5

including Sun. *STOCK: Furniture, garden ornaments, architectural items, brass, copper, tools, glass, china, silver and plate, 1750's to 1950's.* LOC: Town centre. PARK: Nearby. TEL: 01491 573680; home - 01189 471858. SER: Valuations.

Richard Way Bookseller

54 Friday St. RG9 1AH. (Diana Cook and Richard Way). ABA. Est. 1977. Open 10-5.30. SIZE: Small. *STOCK: Rare and secondhand books, 1600-1999, £5-£1,000.* LOC: Over Henley bridge, turn immediately left behind Angel public house, follow river, turn right, shop past Anchor public house. PARK: Easy. TEL: 01491 576663; fax - 01491 576663. SER: Valuations; restorations. VAT: Stan.

HUNTERCOMBE

The Country Seat `LAPADA`

Huntercombe Manor Barn. RG9 5RY. (Harvey Ferry and William Clegg). TVADA. Est. 1965. Open 9-5.30, Sat. 10-5, Sun. by appointment. SIZE: Large. *STOCK: Furniture - signed and designed, 1700-1970; garden and architectural/panelling; art pottery and metalwork, lighting and Whitefriars glass.* LOC: Off A4130. PARK: Easy. TEL: 01491 641349; fax - 01491 641533; e-mail - ferry&clegg@thecountryseat.com; websites - www. thecountryseat.com and www.whitefriarsglass.com. SER: Restorations; exhibitions. FAIRS: TVADA; Radley. VAT: Spec.

MIDDLE ASTON, Nr. Bicester

Cotswold Pine & Associates

The Old Poultry Farm. OX25 5QL. (R.J. Prancks). Est. 1980. Open 9-6, Sun. 10-4.30. SIZE: Large. *STOCK: Furniture, 18th-20th C.* LOC: Off A4260, 15 mins. from M40. PARK: Easy. TEL: 01869 340963. SER: Restorations; stripping; polishing; repairs. VAT: Stan/Spec.

NETTLEBED, Nr. Henley-on-Thames

Willow Antiques and the Nettlebed Antique Merchants

High St. RG9 5DA. (Willow Bicknell, Michael Plummer and Laurie Brunton). TVADA. Est. 1984. Open 10-5.30, Sun. and other times by appointment. SIZE: Large. *STOCK: Decorative, fine and unusual furniture, objects and decorations, including architectural and garden items, 17th C to 1970s, including Gothic, Aesthetic, Arts and Crafts and Art Deco.* LOC: Between Wallingford and Henley on A4074. PARK: Easy. TEL: 01491 642062/628811; mobile - 07770 554559; e-mail - willow@

nettlebedantiques.co.uk; website - www.nettlebed antiques.co.uk. SER: Finder; copy and design; advice on period design for house and garden. FAIRS: TVADA. VAT: Spec.

NORTH ASTON

Elizabeth Harvey-Lee

1 West Cottages, Middle Aston Lane. OX25 5QB. Est. 1986. Open by appointment. *STOCK: Original prints, 15th-20th C; artists' etchings, engravings, lithographs, £100-£6,000.* LOC: 6 miles from junction 10, M40, 15 miles north of Oxford. TEL: 01869 347164. SER: Illustrated catalogue available twice yearly (£20 p.a.). FAIRS: London Original Print, Royal Academy; Olympia (June, Nov); Le Salon de l'Estampe, Paris. VAT: Spec.

OXFORD

Antiques on High Ltd

85 High St. OX1 4BG. (Paul Lipson and Sally Young). TVADA. Est. 1982. Open 10-5, Sun. and Bank Holidays 11-5. SIZE: Large - 35 dealers. *STOCK: Small antiques and collectables including jewellery, silver and plate, ceramics, glass, antiquties, watches, books and coins, 17th-20th C.* LOC: Opposite Queen's Lane. PARK: St Clements, Westgate, Seacourt/Thornhill Park and Ride. TEL: 01865 251075; e-mail - antiquesonhigh@aol.com. SER: Valuations; restorations (jewellery, silver including replating). FAIRS: TVADA.

Blackwell's Rare Books

48-51 Broad St. OX1 3BQ. ABA. ILAB. PBFA. Est. 1879. Open 9-6, Tues. 9.30-6. SIZE: Large. *STOCK: Antiquarian and rare modern books.* PARK: Easy. TEL: 01865 333555; fax - 01865 794143; e-mail - rarebooks@blackwells bookshops.co.uk; website - www.rarebooks. blackwell.co.uk/. SER: Buys at auction; 3-4 catalogues annually. FAIRS: ABA (Olympia); PBFA (Oxford). VAT: Stan/Spec.

The Corner Shop

29 Walton St. OX2 6AA. (P. Hitchcox and D. Florey). Est. 1978. Open 10-5. *STOCK: Pictures, china, glass, silver, small furniture and general items.* LOC: Central north Oxford. TEL: 01865 553364.

Reginald Davis Ltd `BADA`

34 High St. OX1 4AN. Est. 1941. Open Tues.-Sat. 9-5. *STOCK: Silver, English and Continental, 17th to early 19th C; jewellery, Sheffield plate, Georgian and Victorian.* **LOC: On A40. PARK: Nearby. TEL: 01865 248347.**

SER: Valuations; restorations (silver, jewellery). VAT: Stan/Spec.

Jeremy's (Oxford Stamp Centre)
98 Cowley Rd. OX4 1JE. Open 10-12.30 and 2-5. *STOCK: Stamps and postcards.* TEL: 01865 241011; website - www.postcard.co.uk/jeremys.

Jericho Books
48 Walton St. OX2 6AD. (Frank Stringer). PBFA. Est. 1980. Open 10.30-6, Sun. 12-5. SIZE: Medium. *STOCK: Secondhand and antiquarian books.* PARK: Easy. TEL: 01865 511992; e-mail - shop@jerichobooks.com; website - www. jerichobooks.com. SER: Valuations; buys at auction (antiquarian books). FAIRS: Royal National Hotel. VAT: Stan.

Christopher Legge Oriental Carpets
25 Oakthorpe Rd., Summertown. OX2 7BD. (C.T. Legge). Est. 1970. Open 9.30-5. SIZE: Medium. *STOCK: Rugs, various sizes, 19th to early 20th C, £300-£15,000.* LOC: Near shopping parade. PARK: Easy. TEL: 01865 557572; fax - 01865 554877. SER: Valuations; restorations; re-weaving; handcleaning. VAT: Stan/Margin.

Laurie Leigh Antiques `LAPADA`
36 High St. OX1 4AN. (L. and D. Leigh). Est. 1963. Open 10.30-5.30. CL: Thurs. *STOCK: Glass and keyboard musical instruments.* TEL: 01865 244197; e-mail - laurieleigh@hotmail. com; websites - www.laurieleighantiques.com and www.davidleigh.com. SER: Restorations (keyboards). VAT: Stan/Spec.

Oriental Rug Gallery Ltd
15 Woodstock Rd. OX2 6HA. (Richard Mathias and Julian Blair). BORDA. Est. 1989. Open 10-5.30. *STOCK: Russian, Afghan, Turkish and Persian carpets, rugs and kelims; Oriental objets d'art.* TEL: +44 (0) 1865 316333; fax - same; e-mail - rugs@orientalruggallery.com; website - www.orientalruggallery.com.

Payne and Son (Goldsmiths) Ltd `BADA`
131 High St. OX1 4DH. (E.P., G.N. and J.D. Payne, P.J. Coppock, A. Salmon and D. Thornton). Est. 1790. Open weekdays 9-5. SIZE: Medium. *STOCK: British silver, antique, modern and secondhand; jewellery, all £50-£10,000+.* LOC: Town centre near Carfax traffic lights. PARK: 800yds. TEL: 01865 243787; fax - 01865 793241; e-mail - silver@payneandson.co.uk; website - www. payneandson.co.uk. SER: Restorations (English silver). FAIRS: BADA; Chelsea (Spring); Olympia (Autumn). VAT: Stan/Spec.

Sanders of Oxford Ltd
Salutation House, 104 High St. OX1 4BW. Open 10-6. SIZE: Large. *STOCK: Prints, especially Oxford; maps and Japanese woodcuts.* TEL: 01865 242590; fax - 01865 721748; e-mail - soxinfo@btclick.com; website - www.sanders ofoxford.com. SER: Restorations; framing. FAIRS: PBFA (Russell Hotel London); London Original Print. VAT: Margin/Global.

St. Clements Antiques
93 St. Clements St. OX4 1AR. (Giles Power). Est. 1998. Open 10.30-5. SIZE: Medium. *STOCK: Oak and country items, 18th-19th C, £50-£5,000; interesting curios, 18th-20th C, £5-£500.* LOC: Close to city centre, next to Magdalen Bridge. PARK: Easy, opposite. TEL: 01865 727010; home - 01865 200359. SER: Valuations. VAT: Stan/Spec.

Waterfield's
52 High St. OX1 4AS. ABA. PBFA. Est. 1973. Open 9.45-5.45. *STOCK: Antiquarian and secondhand books, all subjects, especially academic in the humanities; literature, history, philosophy, 17th-18th C English.* TEL: 01865 721809.

STANDLAKE, Nr. Witney

Manor Farm Antiques
Manor Farm. OX29 7RL. (C.W. Leveson-Gower). Est. 1964. Open daily, Sun. by appointment. SIZE: Large. *STOCK: Victorian brass and iron beds.* PARK: Easy, in farmyard. TEL: 01865 300303.

TAYNTON, Nr. Burford

Wychwood Antiques
Upper Farm Cottage. OX18 4UH. Open by appointment. *STOCK: English country furniture, Mason's Ironstone, treen, metalware and decorative items.* TEL: 01993 822860. VAT: Spec.

TETSWORTH, Nr. Thame

Quillon Antiques of Tetsworth
The Old Stores, 42a High St. OX9 7AS. (P.L. Magrath). Est. 1993. Open Tues.-Thurs. 10-5, Sat. 10-6, Sun. 12-5. SIZE: Medium. *STOCK: 17th-19th C oak and country furniture, refectory tables and coffers; armour, 15th-19th C; muskets, pistols, armourial items; big game, taxidermy, large bore sporting guns; equestrian paintings and decorative items.* LOC: A40 between exits 6 and 7, M40. PARK: Easy. TEL: 01844 281636. SER: Valuations; restorations.

The Swan at Tetsworth
High St. OX9 7AB. TVADA. Est. 1995. Open 7 days 10-6. SIZE: 40+ rooms. LOC: A40, 5 mins. from junctions 6 and 8, M40. PARK: Own large. TEL: 01844 281777; fax - 01844 281770; e-mail - antiques@theswan.co.uk. website - www.theswan.co.uk; SER: Restorations (clocks); cabinet work; gilding. Below are listed the dealers at this centre.

Deborah Abbot
Jewellery and objets d'art.

Jason Abbot
Sporting guns.

Acanthus Design
Arts & Crafts and Art Nouveau furniture and accessories.

S.J. Allison
Decorative ceramics, small furniture and silver.

Aquila Fine Art
19th to early 20th C watercolours, oils and etchings.

Beagle Antiques
Fine watercolours and oils.

David Binns
Books.

Oonagh Black
TVADA. *Continental and English furniture and associated decorative items.*

Peter Bond
Prints, watercolours. SER: Gilding.

S. Bond & Sons
Fine period furniture.

Ursula Breese
Silver, ceramics, glass and collectables.

A.J. Brown
Small furniture, silver plate and ceramics.

Ann Casey
Antique textiles, ceramics, fashion accessories and small furniture.

Caversham Antiques
Furniture and collectables.

John Chaffer
Framed antiquarian prints and maps.

Jenny Corkhill-Callin
Textiles including cushions, curtains, braids and quilts.

S. and K. Cullup
Linens and textiles.

Jacqueline Ding
Oriental antiques.

Richard and Deby Earls
Textiles, cushions, small decorative French furniture.

Sally Forster
Costume jewellery and antique accessories.

Mavis Foster-Abbott
20th C glass, specialising in Latticinio.

Framed Antiques
Collectable framed cigarette cards.

Valerie Goodchild
Furniture and decorative items.

Grate Expectations
Fireplaces, Cornish ranges, tiles, garden items and architectural salvage.

Jade Green
TVADA. *18th-19th C furniture and mirrors.*

Mary-Louise Hawkins
Fine English and Continental silver.

Hen's Teeth Antiques
(Martin Murray). TVADA. *Period furniture and decorative items.*

John Howkins Antiques
Late 18th to early 20th C furniture and decorative items.

Martin Isenberg
Period, decorative furniture, treen and ceramics.

Nigel Johnston
Furniture and clocks.

Rupert Landen Antiques
TVADA. *Georgian and Regency mahogany furniture.*

Susan Ling
Small furniture, brass and copper.

Shelagh Lister
Fine English and decorative furniture.

Rosemary Livingston
Fine silver and plate.

J. MacNaughton-Smith
TVADA. *Mainly 18th-19th C English furniture including desks, writing tables, chiffoniers, chests of drawers; small decorative items, 19th C watercolours.*

Marquetry Antiques
Chinese antiques and objets d'art.

Millroyal Antiques
Fine furniture and smalls.

Nicholas Mitchell
Unusual period furniture and smalls.

John and Gilly Mott
Art Deco furniture and collectables.

Nazaré Antiques
Antique furniture and collectables.

Old Chair Company
Upholstered furniture.

Orient Carpets
Persian rugs, kelims and textiles.

Peter Phillips
Ceramics, especially blue & white transferware; small period furniture.

Guy Roe
Period furniture and decorative items.

T.H.A. & F.M. Sharland
Frames, prints and watercolours.

Michael Soule
Fine period furniture.

Gail Spence Antiques
Small decorative, collectables and gift antiques.

Lorraine Spooner
Antique furniture and decorative items.

E. Stone Associates
Antique and secondhand jewellery. SER: Restorations.

Tartan Antiques
Objets d'art, pictures and toys.

Geoff and Coral Taylor-Robinson
French provincial furniture and decorative accessories.

Paul Templeton
Silver, jewellery and objets d'art.

Touchwood Antiques
English country furniture, especially oak; brass, door furniture, fireplaces and garden items.

Cathy Turner
Art Nouveau originals.
LAPADA

Anthony Vingoe
Glass, sporting, leather and metalware items, porcelain.

Cherry Warren
Jewellery, silver and objets d'art.

Jinny Wright
French country furniture including garden and kitchen.

Wright Associates
Jewellery, glass, silver, boxes and small furniture.

Caroline Wyatt
Fine English oak furniture, pine and silver collectables.

THAME

Rosemary and Time
42 Park St. OX9 3HR. Open 9-6. *STOCK: Clocks and barometers.* TEL: 01844 216923. SER: Valuations; restorations; old spare parts. VAT: Stan/Spec.

WALLINGFORD

de Albuquerque Antiques
12 High St. OX10 0BP. Est. 1982. Open 10-5. SIZE: Medium. *STOCK: Furniture and objects, 18th-19th C.* PARK: At rear. TEL: 01491 832322; fax - same; e-mail - janedealb@tiscali.co.uk. SER: Framing; gilding. VAT: Spec.

Toby English
10 St Mary's St. OX10 0EL. PBFA. Est. 1980. Open 9.30-5. SIZE: Medium. *STOCK: Books including art and antiques reference, 19th-20th C, £5-£1,000; prints, 19th-20th C, £20-£200; maps, 18th-19th C, £30-£1,000.* LOC: Town centre. PARK: Cattle Market. TEL: 01491 836389; fax - same; e-mail - toby@tobyenglish.com; website - www.toby english.com. SER: Valuations; restorations; buys at auction; catalogues issued. FAIRS: PBFA London.

The Lamb Arcade
83 High St. OX10 0BX. TVADA. Open 10-5, Sat. 10-5.30. *STOCK: As below plus books, crafts and ephemera.* PARK: Nearby. TEL: 01491 835166. SER: Restorations (furniture). Below are listed some of the dealers at this centre.

Alicia Antiques
(A. Collins). *China, silver, collectors' items and glassware.* TEL: 01491 1833737.

Anne Brewer Antiques
Furniture, china, jewellery. TEL: 01491 1838486.

Bright Art and Frames
Pictures. TEL: 01491 836899. SER: Framing.

Ida Chapman
French furniture and linen. TEL: 01491 835166.

Goodwood Antiques
Furniture, champagne racks and decorative items. TEL: Mobile - 07958 962272.

R. Haycraft
TEL: 01491 839622; websites - www.diva-id.com; www.iasa-online.com. DIVA (digital inventory and visual archive), artifact photography and documentation; IASA-ONLINE (International archive of stolen artifacts); restorations (furniture).

Pat Hayward
Furniture, light fittings and decorative items. TEL: 01491 824247.

Pemberton-Hall Collectables
Tin toys, motoring and aviation memorabilia, pictures, diecast and lead figures. TEL: 01491 832023.

Phoenix Antiques
Victorian parlour furniture in pine, mahogany, oak and walnut. TEL: 01491 833555.

Precious Antiques
Art Nouveau and Arts & Crafts furniture, china and glass, especially Noritake. TEL: 01491 835166.

M.M. Richmond
Oak country furniture, pewter, copper, brass, maps, treen and tools. TEL: 01865 858440.

Stag Antiques & Gallery
Jewellery, furniture, pictures, Staffordshire figures, Clarice Cliff and Belleek. TEL: 01491 834516.

Tags
(T. and A. Green). *Collectors' items, curios, dolls' house furniture, jewellery, militaria, scientific instruments and furniture.* TEL: 01491 35048.

MGJ Jewellers Ltd.
1A St. Martins St. OX10 0AQ. (Dr M.R. Jane). Est. 1971. Open 10-4.30, Sat. 10-5. SIZE: Small. *STOCK: Jewellery, Victorian and secondhand, £100-£2,500.* LOC: Town centre. PARK: Nearby. TEL: 01491 834336. VAT: Stan/Spec.

Chris and Lin O'Donnell Antiques
26 High St. OX10 0BU. Est. 1974. Open 9.30-1 and 2-5, Sat. 9.30-5.30. SIZE: Large. *STOCK: Furniture, 18th C to Edwardian, to £3,000; rugs, to £500; unusual objects, Oriental antiques, clocks, 19th C ceramics.* LOC: Into town over Wallingford Bridge, 150yds. along High St. on left-hand side. PARK: Thames St. TEL: 01491 839332. VAT: Spec.

Otter Antiques
20 High St. OX10 0BP. (P. and B. Otter). Open 9.30-5, Sun. 10.30-5. SIZE: Medium. *STOCK: Furniture, writing boxes, tea caddies, jewellery*

boxes, humidors. PARK: Easy, rear of shop. TEL: 01491 825544; website - www.otterantiques.co. uk. SER: Restorations (boxes).

Mike Ottrey Antiques
16 High St. OX10 0BP. (M.J. Ottrey). Est. 1955. Open 9.30-5.30. CL: Sat. SIZE: Large. *STOCK: Furniture, 17th-19th C; oil paintings, copper and brass, decorative and unusual items.* LOC: A429. PARK: At rear. TEL: 01491 836429. VAT: Spec.

Summers Davis Antiques Ltd `LAPADA`
Calleva House, 6 High St. OX10 0BP. (Graham Wells). CINOA. TVADA. Est. 1917. Open 9-5.30, Sat. 9-5, Sun. 11-5. SIZE: Large. *STOCK: English and Continental furniture, decorative items and objects.* Not Stocked: Silver, shipping goods. LOC: From London, shop is on left, 50yds. from Thames Bridge. PARK: Opposite, behind castellated gates. TEL: 01491 836284; fax - 01491 833443; e-mail - antiques@ summersdavis.co.uk; website - www.summers davis.co.uk. VAT: Spec.

Tooley Adams & Co
P O Box 174. OX10 0YT. (S. Luck). ABA. IMCOS. Est. 1979. Open by appointment. *STOCK: Antiquarian maps and atlases; travel and map related reference books.* TEL: 01491 838298; fax - 01491 834616; e-mail - steve@tooleys.co.uk; website - www.tooleys. co.uk. SER: Valuations; mail order. FAIRS: Worldwide; London (Bonnington Hotel); IMCOS (June); Miami (Feb); Paris (Nov). VAT: Stan.

WANTAGE

The Arbery Centre
Market Place. OX12 8AB. (Cedarstar Ltd). Est. 2000. Open 9.30-5, Sun. 11.30-5. SIZE: Large. *STOCK: Wide range of general antiques and collectables including 20th C paintings, costumes, pine and country furniture, silver, gramophones, maps, books, French furniture, brass door furniture.* TEL: 01235 769325; fax - 01235 765242.

WATLINGTON, Nr. Oxford

Cross Antiques
37 High St. OX9 5PZ. (R.A. and I.D. Crawley). Est. 1986. Open 10-6, Sun. and Wed. by appointment. SIZE: Small. *STOCK: Furniture, £100-£5,000; decorative smalls, clocks and garden items, £50-£2,000; all 1600-1900.* LOC: Off B4009 in village centre. PARK: Easy and at rear. TEL: 01491 612324; home - same.

Stephen Orton Antiques
The Antiques Warehouse, Shirburn Rd. OX49
5BZ. TVADA. Open Mon.-Fri. 9-5, other times
by appointment. SIZE: Warehouse. *STOCK:
18th-19th C furniture, some decorative items.*
LOC: 2 mins. from exit 6, M40. TEL: 01491
613752; e-mail - Orton.Antiques@virgin.net.
SER: Supply and pack containers; valuations;
restorations; buying agent. VAT: Stan/Spec.

WITNEY

Colin Greenway Antiques
90 Corn St. OX28 6BU. CADA. Resident. Est.
1975. Open 9.30-5, Sat. 10-4, Sun. by
appointment. SIZE: Large. *STOCK: Furniture,
17th-20th C; metalware, decorative and unusual
items; garden furniture.* LOC: Along High St. to
town centre, turn right, shop 400yds. on right.
PARK: Easy. TEL: 01993 705026; fax - same;
mobile - 07831 585014. VAT: Stan/Spec.

W.R. Harvey & Co (Antiques) Ltd LAPADA
86 Corn St. OX28 6BU. CADA. GMC. Open
9.30-5.30 and by appointment. SIZE: Large.
*STOCK: Fine English furniture, £500-£150,000;
clocks, mirrors, objets d'art, £250-£50,000; all*
1680-1830. LOC: 300 yards from Market Place.
PARK: Easy. TEL: 01993 706501; fax - 01993
706601; e-mail - antiques@wrharvey.co.uk;
website - www.wrharvey.co.uk. SER: Valuations;
restorations; consultancy. FAIRS: BADA;
Chelsea (March & Sept.); Olympia (June). VAT:
Stan/Spec.

Barbara Radman
Westfield House 2G Westfield Rd. OX28 1JG.
OMRS. Est. 1976. Open by appointment. SIZE:
Medium. *STOCK: Orders, medals, badges,
decorations, specialist in miniature orders,
medals and decorations of the world; military
books, police and fire brigade memorabilia,
postal history, paper money, maps and books.*
PARK: Easy and nearby. TEL: 01993 772705; fax
- same; e-mail - radman@tinyonline.co.uk. SER:
Valuations; buys at auction.

Joan Wilkins Antiques
158 Corn St. OX28 6BY. (Mrs J. Wilkins). Est.
1973. Open 10-5. *STOCK: Furniture, 18th-19th
C, £250-£3,500; 19th C glass, metalware, £10-
£1,500.* LOC: Town centre. PARK: Easy. TEL:
01993 704749. VAT: Spec.

Witney Antiques BADA LAPADA

96/100 Corn St. OX28 6BU. (L.S.A. and C.J. Jarrett and R.R. Jarrett-Scott). CADA. Est. 1962. Open 10-5, Mon. and Tues. by appointment. SIZE: Large. *STOCK: English furniture, 17th-18th C; bracket and longcase clocks, mahogany, oak and walnut, early needlework and samplers.* LOC: From Oxford on old A40 through Witney via High St., turn right at T-junction, 400yds. on right. PARK: Easy. TEL: 01993 703902/703887; fax - 01993 779852; e-mail - witneyantiques@community.co.uk; website - www.witneyantiques.com. SER: Restorations. FAIRS: BADA; Grosvenor House. VAT: Spec.

WOODSTOCK

Antiques at Heritage

6 Market Place. OX20 1TA. TVADA. Est. 1978. Open 10-1 and 2-5, Sun 1-5. SIZE: Medium. LOC: Near Town Hall. PARK: Easy. Below are listed some of the dealers selling from these premises. TEL: 01993 811332; e-mail - info@atheritage.co.uk; website - www.atheritage.co.uk.

Doreen Caudwell
Textiles and porcelain.

Diana Clark
Old and interesting books.

Francoise Daniel
Boxes, porcelain and collectables.

Liz Hall-Bakker
Art Nouveau and Deco.

Jasper Antiques
Silver and decorative items.

Diana Marcovitch
Lighting and decorative items.

Rebecca Stuart-Mobey
Furniture and glass.

Antiques of Woodstock

18/20 Market Place. OX20 1TA. (Allan James and Andrew Hennell). Est. 1975. Open 10.30-5.30, Sun. 10.30-5. SIZE: Large. *STOCK: Fine Georgian and Regency dining room furniture, long sets of period chairs, early 17th to 19th C oak and country furniture, Roman to medieval antiquities.* LOC: Opposite The Bear Hotel. PARK: Easy. TEL: 01993 811818; fax - 01993 811831. SER: Valuations; restorations; consultations; interior decor advice; buys at auction; search; commission sales. VAT: Stan.

 Witney Antiques

LSA & CJ JARRETT AND RR SCOTT
96-100 CORN STREET, WITNEY,
OXON OX28 6BU, ENGLAND.
TEL: 01993 703902. FAX: 01993 779852.
E-mail: witneyantiques@community.co.uk
Website: www.witneyantiques.com

An example from our large stock of fine British embroideries and samplers.

ANTIQUE FURNITURE, CLOCKS & TEXTILES.

Chris Baylis Country Chairs

16 Oxford St. OX20 1TS. TVADA. Est. 1977. Open Tues.-Sat. 10.30-5.30, Sun. 11-5, appointment advisable. *STOCK: English country chairs, from 1780; sets of rush seated chairs including ladder and spindle backs, Windsors, kitchen chairs and quality reproductions.* LOC: A44. PARK: Easy. TEL: 01993 813887; fax - 01993 812379; e-mail - info@realwoodfurniture.co.uk; website - www.realwoodfurniture.co.uk. VAT: Spec.

Bees Antiques

30 High St. OX20 1TG. (Jo and Jim Bateman). TVADA. Est. 1991. Open 10-1 and 1.30-5, Sun. 11-5. CL: Tues. SIZE: Small. *STOCK: Pottery, porcelain and glass, 18th-20th C, £30-£1,500; small furniture, 19th to early 20th C, £50-£2,000; metalware, 19th C, £30-£200; jewellery, 19th-20th C, £30-£1,000.* LOC: Just off A3440 Oxford/Stratford-on-Avon road, in town centre. PARK: Opposite. TEL: 01993 811062; home - 01993 771593; mobile - 07702 603419. SER: Valuations; buys at auction (as stock).

The Chair Set - Antiques

18-20 Market Place. OX20. (Allan James). Est. 1982. Open 10.30-5.30, including Sun. SIZE: Large. *STOCK: Sets of chairs, £1,000-£20,000;*

single and pairs of chairs, £200-£3,000; dining tables and accessories, £800-£15,000; all early 18th to late 19th C. LOC: Opposite Bear Hotel. PARK: Easy. TEL: 01993 811818; fax - 01428 707435. SER: Valuations; restorations (woodwork and upholstery); buys at auction (sets of chairs). VAT: Spec.

John Howard

Heritage, 6 Market Place. OX20 1TE. TVADA. CADA. Open 10-5.30. SIZE: Small. *STOCK: 18th-19th C British pottery especially rare Staffordshire animal figures, bocage figures, lustre, 18th C creamware and unusual items.* PARK: Easy. TEL: 0870 4440678; fax - same; mobile - 07831 850544; e-mail - john@ johnhoward.co.uk; website - www.antique pottery.co.uk and www.Staffordshires.com. SER: Packing; insurance service to USA. FAIRS: Olympia; BADA. VAT: Spec.

Robin Sanders and Sons

11 Market St. OX20 1SU. *STOCK: English and some French furniture, 17th-19th C; Staffordshire and Masons ironstone pottery, brass, treen and English glass pictures.* TEL: 01993 813930.

YARNTON

Yarnton Antiques Centre

Yarnton Nurseries Garden Centre, Sandy Lane. OX5 1PA. Open 10-4.30 including Sun. SIZE: 50 dealers. *STOCK: General antiques.* LOC: A44 Oxford to Woodstock road. PARK: Easy. TEL: 01865 379600.

A range of freehand-painted ornamental wares in 'multi-coloured lustres' and gold outlines: plate, matt yellow enamel in centre, pattern (7314), marked with second galleon; covered jar, 9¼in (23.5cm) high, pattern (7082), Gloria Lustre in gold; powder bowl, black foot ring, no pattern number, Gloria Lustre.

From the book "Susie Cooper - A Pioneer of Modern Design" Edited by Andrew Casey and Ann Eatwell.

Susie Cooper
A PIONEER OF MODERN DESIGN

Edited by
Andrew Casey and Ann Eatwell

- *The definitive guide to the work of this highly respected, contemporary ceramic designer*

Susie Cooper
A PIONEER OF MODERN DESIGN

Andrew Casey & Ann Eatwell

As a woman in an industry run by men, it was her ability to anticipate the mood of the day and understand market trends that enabled Susie Cooper to keep ahead of her competitors. Cooper made her name through designing for and managing her own company. This was not, however, the only way in which she was unique; she produced modern pots at affordable prices and provided customers who possessed exceptional taste, but little money, with well-designed practical and attractive pottery. Cooper's pots became symbolic of the new domestic life enjoyed by the suburban middle classes.

Her career spanned seven decades and a staggering four thousand patterns, ranging from the jazz modern colours of the Art Deco period to the Pop Art of the swinging sixties.

This centenary book outlines and discusses Susie Cooper's major achievements throughout her prolific career. It brings together the leading experts and authorities who reflect upon her life and work, as well as providing contextual contemporary evidence on the twentieth century ceramic industry as a whole. For the very first time known aspects of her life will be brought together with the unknown, including new research material and information from her family. The focus of the book is on new information and original research to add to the understanding of one of our greatest ceramic designers.

Essays incorporated in this book include 'Women Designers in Context', 'Unknown Susie Cooper', 'The Susie Cooper Style', 'Royal Connections', 'Pottery Patronage' and 'Susie Cooper and Wedgwood'.

Andrew Casey is the author of the award-winning *Twentieth Century Ceramic Designers in Britain,* also published by Antique Collectors' Club (2001). He formed the Susie Cooper Collectors' Club in 1990. He has curated several exhibitions including 'Susie Cooper Productions' for Ipswich Museums and Galleries in 1989 and 'Dynamic Designers' for Croydon Museum in 1999.

Ann Eatwell is assistant curator in the Metalwork Department of the Victoria & Albert Museum. She curated the retrospective exhibition, 'Susie Cooper Productions' and was the author of the accompanying book for the V&A Museum in 1987. She has researched and written on modern industrial ceramic production.

Available from all good booksellers and direct from the publisher:
ANTIQUE COLLECTORS' CLUB
Sandy Lane, Old Martlesham, Woodbridge, Suffolk, IP12 4SD.
Tel: 01394 389950
Fax: 01394 389999
Email: sales@antique-acc.com
Website: www.antique-acc.com

11 x 8½in./279 x 216mm.
232pp., 167 col. plates, 107 b.&w. illus
1 85149 411 1
£29.50

RUTLAND

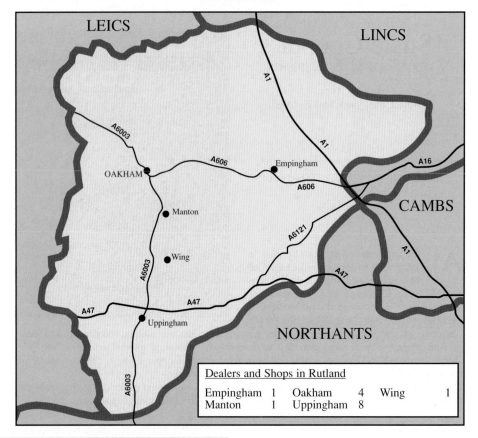

LEICS

LINCS

A1

A6003

A606 Empingham

A1

A16

OAKHAM

A606

CAMBS

Manton

A6121

A1

Wing

A6003

A47

A47 A47

A47

Uppingham

NORTHANTS

A6003

Dealers and Shops in Rutland

Empingham	1	Oakham	4	Wing	1
Manton	1	Uppingham	8		

EMPINGHAM, Nr. Oakham

Churchgate Antiques
13 Church St. LE15 8PN. (R. Wheatley). Est. 1985. Open Wed., Fri., Sat. and Sun. 12-6, other times by appointment. SIZE: Medium. *STOCK: Furniture, mainly 18th-19th C, £50-£4,000; paintings and prints, £25-£1,000; plate, 19th-20th C, £5-£300; ceramics, £5-£250; collectables, £5-£100.* LOC: Opposite church, off A606. PARK: Easy. TEL: 01780 460528.

MANTON

David Smith Antiques
Old Cottage, 20 St. Mary's Rd. LE15 8SU. Est. 1953. Open 9-5. CL: Sun., except by appointment. *STOCK: Furniture, glass, silver.* PARK: Easy. TEL: 01572 737244/737607.

OAKHAM

The Old House Gallery
13-15 Market Place. LE15 6DT. (R.A. Clarke). Est. 1979. Open 10-1 and 2-5. CL: Thurs. SIZE: Medium. *STOCK: Contemporary oil paintings,* £50-£3,500; art studio pottery, 1850-1990, £5-£500; watercolours, £25-£2,000; prints and objets d'art, £5-£500; antiquarian county maps, £15-£250; sculpture and three-dimensional works by Leach, O'Neal and Bowen. PARK: Easy. TEL: 01572 755538. SER: Valuations; restorations (oils, watercolours, prints, frames); framing.

C. Reynolds Antiques
The East Lodge, Burley Mansion House, Burley-on-the-Hill. LE15 7TE. Est. 1972. Resident. Usually available but telephone call advisable. SIZE: Large. *STOCK: Early verge watches, repeater and other unusual clocks and watches.* TEL: 01572 771551.

Swans
17 Mill St. LE15 6EA. (P.W. Jones). Est. 1988. Open 9.30-5.30, Sun. 2-5. SIZE: Large. *STOCK: French and English beds and associated furniture; 18th-19th C antiques, mainly decorative and upholstered.* LOC: 150yds. from High St. PARK: Easy. TEL: 01572 724364; fax - 01572 755094; e-mail - info@swansofoakham. co.uk; website - www.swansofoakham.co.uk. SER: Manufactures new bases and mattresses;

JOHN GARNER
51-53 High Street East, Uppingham,
Rutland, LE15 9PY

*Fine 18th & 19th Century Furniture,
Paintings, Clocks, Bronzes, Garden Statuary
Some 20th Century Furniture.*

Very large selection of period prints

Tel: **01572 823607** Fax: **01572 821654**
Website: **www.johngarnerantiques.com**

valuations; restorations; delivery (to and from France). VAT: Stan/Spec.

Treedale Antiques
10b Mill St. LE15. (G.K. Warren). GMC. Est. 1994. Open 9-5, Sun. 2-5. *STOCK: Furniture including walnut, mahogany and oak, from 1680, to £3,000; portraits, paintings, tapestries and chandeliers.* TEL: 01572 757521; home - 01664 454535. SER: Valuations; restorations (furniture).

UPPINGHAM

John Garner `LAPADA`
51-53 High St. East. LE15 9PY. FATG. Est. 1966. Open 9-5.30, Sun. 2-5, prior telephone call advisable. SIZE: 12 showrooms + warehouse. *STOCK: 18th-19th C furniture, paintings, prints, clocks, bronzes, mirrors, garden statuary, some 20th C furniture.* LOC: Just off A47, 80 yards from market place. PARK: Easy. TEL: 01572 823607; fax - 01572 821654; mobile - 07850 596556; e-mail - johngarner@aol.com; website - www.johngarnerantiques.com. SER: Valuations; restorations (furniture, paintings, prints); framing (trade); courier; export. FAIRS: Newark; Miami. VAT: Stan/Spec.

Gilberts of Uppingham
8 Ayston Rd. LE15 9RL. (M. Gilbert). Open 9.30-5, Mon. and Tues. 9.30-1 and 2-5. *STOCK: General antiques.* TEL: 01572 823486.

Goldmark Books
14 Orange St. LE15 9SQ. (Mike Goldmark). Open 9.30-5.30 and Sunday afternoons. *STOCK: Antiquarian and secondhand books.* LOC: Between Market Sq. and traffic lights. PARK: Nearby. TEL: 01572 822694.

Marc Oxley Fine Art
Resident. Est. 1981. Open by appointment. *STOCK: Original watercolours and drawings, 1700-1950, £5-£850; oils, 19th-20th C, £100-*£1,500; prints, mainly 19th C, £5-£50; maps, 17th-19th C, £10-£850.* TEL: 01572 822334; home - same; e-mail - marc@19thCwatercolours. com. SER: Valuations; restorations (oils).

T.J. Roberts
39/41 High St. East. LE15 9PY. Resident. Open 9.30-5.30. *STOCK: Furniture, porcelain and pottery, 18th-19th C; Staffordshire figures, general antiques.* PARK: Easy. TEL: 01572 821493. VAT: Stan/Spec.

Rutland Antiques Centre
Crown Passage. LE15. (Wendy Foster Grindley). Est. 1987. Open 10-5.30, Sun. 11-5. SIZE: Large. *STOCK: Wide range of general antiques, £5-£3,000.* LOC: Behind Crown Hotel, High St. PARK: Easy. TEL: 01572 824011.

Tattersall's
14b Orange St. LE15 9SQ. (J. Tattersall). Est. 1985. Open 9.30-5. CL: Mon. SIZE: Small. *STOCK: Persian rugs, 19th-20th C.* PARK: Easy, 200yds. TEL: 01572 821171; e-mail - janice_tattersall@ hotmail.com. SER: Restorations (rugs, carpets).

Woodman's House Antiques
35 High St. East. LE15 9PY. (Mr. and Mrs James Collie). Est. 1991. SIZE: Small. *STOCK: Furniture, 17th-18th C.* PARK: Easy. TEL: 01572 821799; fax - same; website - www.rutnet. co.uk/woodmans. SER: Valuations; restorations; buys at auction.

WING, Nr. Oakham

Robert Bingley Antiques
Home Farm, Church St. LE15 8RS. (Robert and Elizabeth Bingley). Open 10-5, Sun. by appointment. SIZE: Large. *STOCK: Furniture, 17th-19th C, £50-£5,000; glass, clocks, silver and plate, pictures and porcelain.* LOC: Next to church. PARK: Own. TEL: 01572 737725; mobile - 07909 585285. SER: Valuations; restorations. VAT: Spec.

SHROPSHIRE

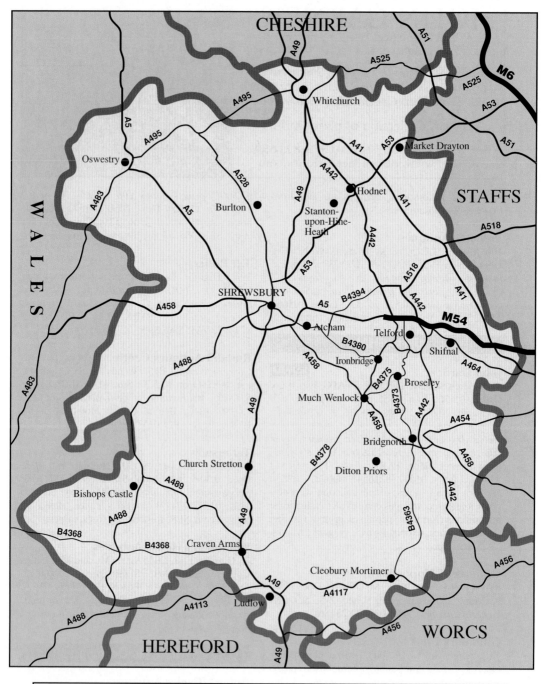

Dealers and Shops in Shropshire

Atcham	1	Craven Arms	1	Oswestry	1
Bishop's Castle	2	Ditton Priors	1	Shifnal	1
Bridgnorth	5	Hodnet	1	Shrewsbury	14
Broseley	1	Ironbridge	1	Stanton upon Hine Heath	1
Burlton	1	Ludlow	10	Telford	2
Church Stretton	3	Market Drayton	3	Whitchurch	2
Cleobury Mortimer	2	Much Wenlock	4		

ATCHAM, Nr. Shrewsbury

Mytton Antiques
Norton Cross Roads. SY4 4UH. (M.A., E.A., J.M. and S. Nares). Est. 1972. Open 9.30-5.30 or by appointment. SIZE: Medium. *STOCK: General antiques, furniture, 1700-1900, £50-£5,000; clocks, £35-£4,000; smalls, £15-£1,500.* LOC: On B5061 (the old A5) between Shrewsbury and Wellington. PARK: Own. TEL: 01952 740229 (24hrs.); fax - 01952 461154; mobiles - 07860 575639 and 07711 205503; e-mail - nares@myttonantiques.freeserve.co.uk. SER: Buys at auction; restorations: reference books supplied; restoration materials and equipment; shipping. FAIRS: NEC; Newark. VAT: Stan/Spec.

BISHOP'S CASTLE

Ark Antiques
9 Market Square. (Jill Thomas). Est. 1974. Open 10.30-4.30 and Bank Holidays. CL: Mon. and Wed. SIZE: Small. *STOCK: Oak and pine country furniture, 18th-19th C; rural tools, brass and iron beds.* PARK: Easy. TEL: Home - 01588 638608. SER: Valuations; restorations (metal and wood); buys at auction (cottage furniture and artifacts).

Decorative Antiques
47 Church St. SY9 5AD. (Evelyn Bowles and Richard Moulson). Est. 1996. Open Mon.-Sat. SIZE: Small. *STOCK: Ceramics and glass, jewellery and metalware, small furniture, 20th C, £5-£1,000.* PARK: Easy. TEL: 01588 638851; fax/home - same; e-mail - enquiries@decorative-antiques.co.uk; website - www.decorative-antiques.co.uk. SER: Valuations.

BRIDGNORTH

Bridgnorth Antiques Centre
Whitburn St. WV16 4QT. (Mrs S. Coppen and Miss G.M. Gibbons). Est. 1992. Open 10-5.30, Sun. 10.30-4.30. SIZE: Large. *STOCK: Clocks, furniture, collectables.* PARK: Easy. TEL: 01746 768055. SER: Restorations (clocks).

English Heritage
2 Whitburn St., High Town. WV16 4QN. (P.J. Wainwright). Est. 1988. Open 10-5. CL: Thurs. SIZE: Medium. *STOCK: Jewellery, silverware and general antiques, militaria, coins, collectibles, glassware.* LOC: Just off High St. PARK: Nearby. TEL: 01746 762097. VAT: Stan/Spec.

Malthouse Antiques
The Old Malthouse, 6 Underhill St. WV16 4BB. (Susan and William Mantle). Est. 1980. Open 10-6, Sun. by appointment. CL: Wed. SIZE: Medium. *STOCK: Victorian and Edwardian furniture, French beds and armoires, £100-£1,500; upholstered chairs and sofas, from 19th C, £300-£1,800; china and decorative items, 19th-20th C, £5-£150; French chandeliers.* LOC: Main road into town from Wolverhampton. PARK: Nearby. TEL: 01746 763054; fax/home - same. SER: Valuations; restorations (furniture).

Micawber Antiques
64 St. Mary's St. WV16 4DR. (N. Berthoud). Est. 1989. Open 10-5, other times by appointment. CL: Mon. and Thurs. SIZE: Medium. *STOCK: English porcelain and pottery, decorative items, £5-£500; small furniture, £100-£1,000.* LOC: 100yds. west of town hall in High St. PARK: Easy. TEL: 01746 763254; home - same.

Old Mill Antique Centre
Mill St. WV15 5AG. (D.A. and J.A. Ridgeway). Est. 1996. Open 10-5 including Sun. SIZE: Large - 90 dealers. *STOCK: Wide range of general antiques including period furniture, porcelain and silver, jewellery, prints and watercolours, collectables.* LOC: Main road. PARK: Own. TEL: 01746 768778; fax - 01746 768944; website - www.oldmill-antiques.co.uk. SER: Valuations; restorations. VAT: Stan.

BROSELEY

John Boulton Fine Art
6 Church St. TF12 5DG. Resident. Est. 1983. Open 9-5, Sun. 2-5. SIZE: Medium. *STOCK: Oils, watercolours and prints, late 19th C to contemporary, £100-£2,500.* LOC: Junction 4, M54, take A442. PARK: Easy. TEL: 01952 882860. FAIRS: Buxton; NEC; Shrewsbury; Edinburgh.

BURLTON, Nr. Shrewsbury

North Shropshire Reclamation
Wackley Lodge Farm. SY4 5TD. (A. and J. Powell). SALVO. Est. 1997. Open 7 days 9-5. SIZE: Large. *STOCK: Wide range of reclaimed materials.* LOC: A528. PARK: Easy. TEL: 01939 270719; home/fax - 01939 270895.

CHURCH STRETTON

Cardingmill Antiques
1 Burway Rd. SY6 6DL. (Mrs P. A. Benton). NHBS. Est. 1976. Open Thurs., Fri. and Sat. 11-5

or by appointment. SIZE: Medium. *STOCK: 18th-19th C longcase and wall clocks, furniture, £250-£3,000; Measham teapots, £90-£450; original horsebrasses and martingales (NHB Soc.); Victorian oil lamps with original shades, £200-£650; 18th-19th C metalware.* LOC: A49. PARK: Easy. TEL: 01694 724555; home - 01584 877880; mobile - 07802 194253; website - www.churchstretton.co.uk.

Church Stretton Books
48 High St. SY6 6BX. (Roger Toon). PBFA. Est. 1992. Open 10-5, Wed. 10-1. SIZE: Small. *STOCK: Books - mainly secondhand, some antiquarian.* LOC: Off A49 at traffic lights, after 300 yards turn left at bank, shop 150 yards on right. PARK: Nearby. TEL: 01694 724337; fax - same; e-mail - csbooks@btinternet.com. SER: Valuations. FAIRS: PBFA, Birmingham; Haydock Park.

Stretton Antiques Market
36 Sandford Ave. SY6 6BH. (T. and L. Elvins). Est. 1986. Open 9.30-5.30, Sun. and Bank Holidays 10.30-4.30. SIZE: Large - 55 dealers. *STOCK: General antiques, shipping items and collectables.* LOC: Town centre. PARK: Easy. TEL: 01694 723718.

A moulded Job Ridgway jug with Regency motifs that could have come from bronze mounts from furniture. The blue ground is painted on and simulates Wedgwood. Many factories produced similar wares but Ridgway is arguably the best. 6¼in., unmarked, 1815-20, £250-£300.

From an article entitled "Factory Fact Files" by David Battie which appeared in the March 2002 issue of *Antique Collecting*. For more details and to subscribe see page 21.

CLEOBURY MORTIMER, Nr. Kidderminster

Antique Centre
Childe Rd. DY14 8PA. Open 10-5, Sun. by appointment. SIZE: Large. *STOCK: Georgian, Victorian, Edwardian, old pine and French furniture, period beds, garden statuary and architectural items.* LOC: Between Kidderminster and Ludlow. PARK: Own. TEL: 01299 270513; fax - 01299 270513; e-mail - antiquecenter@supanet.com.

M. and M. Baldwin
24 High St. DY14 8BY. Est. 1978. Open Wed. 2-6, Fri. (Easter-Oct) and Sat. 10-1 and 2-6. SIZE: Medium. *STOCK: 19th-20th C books, to £500.* LOC: A4117. PARK: Easy. TEL: 01299 270110; fax/home - same; e-mail - books@mbaldwin. free-online.co.uk. SER: Valuations; buys at auction (books). FAIRS: Crick Boat Show; IWA National Festival. VAT: Stan.

CRAVEN ARMS

Portcullis Furniture
Ludlow Rd. SY7 9QL. (Sally Allen and John Cox). Est. 1980. Open 10-5, Sun. 10.30-4. SIZE: Large. *STOCK: Victorian, Edwardian, shipping and reproduction furniture, £5-£2,000.* LOC: A49. PARK: Easy. TEL: 01588 672263; fax - 01588 673321; home - 01588 638077. SER: Buys at auction (furniture). FAIRS: Newark; Swinderby. VAT: Stan/Global.

DITTON PRIORS

Priors Reclamation
Unit 2A Ditton Priors Industrial Estate. WV16 6SS. (Vicki Bale and Martin Foley). SALVO. Est. 1996. Open by appointment. *STOCK: Flooring and period doors, reclaimed and made to order.* PARK: Easy. TEL: 01746 712450; home - same; e-mail - vicki@priorsrec.co.uk; website - www. priorsrec.co.uk. FAIRS: Burwarton.

HODNET, Nr. Market Drayton

Hodnet Antiques
13a Shrewsbury St. TF9 3NP. (Mrs J. Scott). Est. 1976. Open Thurs. 2-5.30, other times by appointment. SIZE: Small. *STOCK: General antiques - china, glass, silver, jewellery, pictures, brass and copper, collectables and unusual decorative items, £5-£1,000; 18th-20th C furniture, £100-£5,000.* LOC: A53, Newcastle-under-Lyme to Shrewsbury road. PARK: Outside shop. TEL: Home - 01630 638591; e-mail -

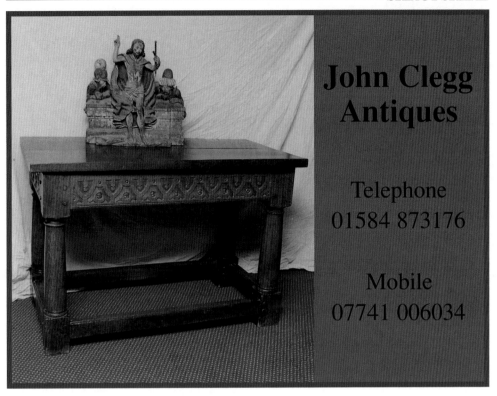

John Clegg Antiques

Telephone
01584 873176

Mobile
07741 006034

janecscott@btopenworld.com. SER: Valuations; buys at auction.

IRONBRIDGE

Tudor House Antiques
11 Tontine Hill. TF8 7AL. (Peter Whitelaw). Est. 1963. Open 10-5. *STOCK: General antiques, especially porcelain including Coalport and Caughley* . LOC: Opposite bridge. TEL: 01952 433783; e-mail - tudoriron@aol.com; website - www.tudorhouseantiques.com.

LUDLOW

Bayliss Antiques
22-24 Old St. SY8 1NP. (D., A.B. and N. Bayliss). Resident. Est. 1966. Open 10-6 or by appointment. SIZE: Medium. *STOCK: 18th-19th C furniture.* PARK: Easy. TEL: 01584 873634; fax - same. SER: Valuations. VAT: Spec.

Bebb Fine Art `LAPADA`
1 Church St. SY8 1AP. (Roger Bebb). CINOA. Est. 1978. Open 10-5.30 or by appointment. CL: Thurs. SIZE: Small. *STOCK: Oils, screen prints and lithographs including W. Kay Blacklock, John Piper, Sir Terry Frost, W. Lee-Hankey,* *Edward Bell, mainly 20th C, £200-£8,000.* LOC: Town centre. PARK: Nearby. TEL: 01584 879612; fax/home - same; e-mail - bebbfineart@ aol.com. SER: Valuations; restorations (oils).

R.G. Cave and Sons Ltd `BADA` `LAPADA`
17 Broad St. SY8 1NG. (Mrs M.C., R.G., J.R. and T.G. Cave). Resident. Est. 1962. Open 9.30-5.30. SIZE: Medium. *STOCK: Furniture, 1630-1830; clocks, barometers, metalwork, fine art and collectors' items.* LOC: Old town. PARK: Easy. TEL: 01584 873568; fax - 01584 875050. SER: Valuations. VAT: Spec.

John Clegg
12 Old St. SY8 1NP. Resident. Est. 1960. Open 8.30-5. *STOCK: Country and other period furniture, metalware and decorative items.* TEL: 01584 873176; mobile - 07741 006034.

Corve Street Antiques
141A Corve St. SY8 2PG. (Mike McAvoy and David Jones). Est. 1990. Open 10-5. SIZE: Medium. *STOCK: Oak, mahogany and pine furniture, clocks, pocket watches, china, glass, prints and pictures, £5-£5,000.* PARK: Easy. TEL: 01584 879100.

Garrard Antiques

139a Corve St. SY8 2PG. (Caroline Garrard). Est. 1985. Open 10-1 and 2-5, Sat. 10-5. SIZE: Large - 8 rooms. *STOCK: Pine and country furniture, 18th-19th C, to £3,000; French provincial furniture, 19th to early 20th C, to £900; books, linen, textiles, silver and treen, porcelain.* LOC: 200 yards below Feathers Hotel. PARK: Opposite. TEL: 01584 876727. SER: Valuations. VAT: Spec.

G. & D. Ginger Antiques

5 Corve St. SY8 1DA. Resident. Est. 1978. Open 9-5. SIZE: Large. *STOCK: 17th-18th C English and Welsh furniture, mainly oak and fruitwood, farmhouse tables, food cupboards, presses, corner cupboards, decorative and associated items.* TEL: 01584 876939; fax - 01584 876456; mobile - 07970 666437; e-mail - gdginger antiques@aol.com. VAT: Spec.

Mackenzie & Smith Furniture Restoration

4 Bull Ring. SY8 1AD. (Tim Smith). UKIC. Resident. Est. 1998. Open 9-5, Sat. 10-1. SIZE: Small. *STOCK: Oak, country and some mahogany furniture, to £1,000; smalls including door locks and fittings.* PARK: Loading and nearby. TEL: 01584 877133. SER: Restorations (17th-19th C mahogany, walnut, oak, rosewood).

Mitre House Antiques

Corve Bridge. SY8 1DY. (L. Jones). Est. 1972. Open 9-5.30. SIZE: Shop + trade warehouse. *STOCK: Clocks, pine and general antiques. Warehouse - unstripped pine and shipping goods.* TEL: 01584 872138; mobile - 07976 549013. FAIRS: Newark; Ardingly.

Valentyne Dawes Gallery

Church St. SY8 1AP. (B.S. McCreddie). Open 10-5.30. SIZE: Medium. *STOCK: Paintings, 19th-21st C, £200-£40,000; furniture, 17th-19th C, £50-£4,000; porcelain, 19th C, £5-£500.* LOC: Town centre near Buttercross. PARK: Nearby. TEL: 01584 874160; fax - 01384 455576; e-mail - sales@gallery.wyenet.co.uk; website - www. starmark.co.uk/valentyne-dawes/. SER: Valuations; restorations (oil paintings, watercolours, furniture). VAT: Spec.

MARKET DRAYTON

Arty Faherty

Honeypots Farm, Rosehill. (McNulty Wholesalers). Est. 1983. Open 11-5. *STOCK: Painted pine, mahogany; small interesting items.* PARK: Easy. TEL: 01630 639562. VAT: Stan.

Deppner Antiques
The Towers Lawn. TF9 3EB. (J. Deppner). Est. 1985. Open 9.30-5.30, Wed. 9.30-3.30, Thurs. and Sun. by appointment. SIZE: Small. *STOCK: Stripped pine, general antiques, 19th C, £20-£1,000.* LOC: From A53 towards town centre (Cheshire St.). PARK: Easy. TEL: 01630 654111. SER: Valuations. FAIRS: Newark, Ardingly.

Richard Midwinter Antiques
TF9 4EF. (Richard and Susannah Midwinter). Resident. Est. 1983. Open any time by appointment. SIZE: Medium. *STOCK: 17th-19th C town and country furniture, clocks, textiles and decorative items.* LOC: Off M6, junction 14 to Eccleshall onto High St., 4+ miles to Loggerheads, turn right towards Newcastle. TEL: 01630 673901; mobile - 07836 617361. SER: Restorations.

MUCH WENLOCK

Cruck House Antiques
23 Barrow St. TF13 6EN. (B. Roderick Smith). Est. 1985. Open 9.30-5.30. SIZE: Small. *STOCK: Silver and watercolours, 19th-20th C, £25-£300; furniture, 19th C, £50-£500; general antiques.* Not Stocked: Weapons and gold. LOC: Near the square. PARK: Easy. TEL: 01952 727165.

Raynalds Mansion
BADA
Raynalds Mansion. TF13 6AE. (John King). Resident. Est. 1970. Open Mon., Tues. and Fri. 10-2, prior telephone call advisable. SIZE: Medium. *STOCK: Period furniture and associated items, £500-£45,000.* PARK: Easy. TEL: 01952 727456; fax/home - same. FAIRS: Olympia (June). VAT: Spec.

Wenlock Fine Art
3 The Square. TF13 6LX. (P. Cotterill). Est. 1990. Open Wed.-Sat. 10-5. SIZE: Medium. *STOCK: Modern British paintings, mainly 20th C, some late 19th C.* PARK: Nearby. TEL: 01952 728232; home - 01952 252376. SER: Valuations; restorations; cleaning; mounting; framing; buys at auction (as stock). VAT: Spec.

OSWESTRY

Judith Charles Antiques & Collectables
67 Beatrice St. SY11 1QR. (C. and Mrs. J.A. Hughes). Est. 1999. Open Tues.-Fri. 9.30-3.15, Sat. 10-4. SIZE: Small. *STOCK: Small furniture, china and porcelain, Wade, Doulton, Royal Albert.* LOC: Just outside town centre. PARK: Easy. TEL: 01691 653524; fax - same; mobile - 07855 253617. SER: Valuations. FAIRS: Ellesmere.

SHIFNAL

Corner Farm Antiques
Weston Heath, Sheriffhales. TF11 8RY. (Tim Dams). GMC. Est. 1994. Open 10-5 including Sun. SIZE: Large. *STOCK: Georgian to Edwardian furniture, especially dining room extending tables and sets of chairs; longcase and wall clocks, barometers; Victorian fireplaces, lighting, soft furnishings and collectables, £5-£500.* LOC: A41 between Tong and Newport. PARK: Own large. TEL: 01952 691543; home/fax - same; website - www.antiques.uk.ws. SER: Valuations; restorations (furniture and clocks); buys at auction. VAT: Stan.

SHREWSBURY

Bear Steps Antiques
2 Bear Steps, Fish St. SY1 1UR. (John and Sally Wyatt). Open 9-5, prior telephone call advisable. SIZE: Small. *STOCK: 18th C English porcelain.* LOC: Town centre. PARK: Limited. TEL: 01743 344298; e-mail - englishporcelain@aol.com; website - www.bear-steps-antiques.co.uk. FAIRS: NEC.

Candle Lane Books
28-29 Princess St. SY1 1LW. (J. Thornhill). Est. 1974. Open 9.30-4.30. SIZE: Large. *STOCK: Antiquarian and secondhand books.* LOC: Town centre. PARK: Nearby. TEL: 01743 365301.

Juliet Chilton Antiques and Interiors
69 Wyle Cop. SY1 1UX. Open 9.30-6. SIZE: Large. *STOCK: Furniture and smalls, mainly 1700's-1920's and some reproduction.* TEL: 01743 358699; fax - same. SER: Packing and shipping.

Collectors' Place
29a Princess St., The Square. SY1 1LW. (Keith Jones). Open 10-4, Sat. 9.30-5. CL: Thurs. *STOCK: Collectables especially Prattware potlids and bottles, 1700-1900; ceramics including Wade, Beswick, Carltonware, early 20th C; Art Deco, eyebaths.* LOC: Town centre opposite Shrewsbury Antique Centre. TEL: 01743 246150; e-mail - darren.bec@virgin.net.

Deja Vu Antiques
48 High St. SY1 1ST. (I. and Mrs A. S. Jones). Open 9.30-5. SIZE: Small. *STOCK: 1920's to 1950's telephones, £50-£500; Victorian pine and walnut furniture, general antiques and reproduction items, £5-£500.* PARK: Nearby. TEL: 01743 362251; website - www.antiquephones.co.uk. SER: Restorations (telephones). FAIRS: Art Deco - Loughborough, Chester, Leeds, Warwick Hilton.

Adrian Donnelly Antique Clocks
7 The Parade, St Mary's Place. SY1 1DL. BHI. BWCG. Est. 1985. Open 10-5, Sat. 10-1. SIZE: Medium. *STOCK: Longcase and bracket clocks and barometers, 17th-19th C, £250-£12,000.* LOC: Town centre. PARK: Easy. TEL: 01743 361388; fax - same; e-mail - clockshop shrewsbury@hotmail.com. SER: Restorations (clocks and barometers). VAT: Stan/Spec.

Expressions
17 Princess St. SY1 1LP. Open 10.30-4.30. *STOCK: Art Deco originals, ceramics, furniture, jewellery, lighting, mirrors, prints.* TEL: 01743 351731.

The Little Gem
18 St. Mary's St. SY1 1ED. (M.A. Bowdler). Est. 1969. Open 9-5.30. CL: Thurs. (except Dec.). SIZE: Medium. *STOCK: Georgian and Victorian jewellery; unusual gem stones, watches; handmade jewellery.* Not Stocked: Weapons, coins, medals, furniture. LOC: Opposite St. Mary's Church along from G.P.O. PARK: In side road (St. Mary's Place) opposite shop. TEL: 01743 352085; e-mail - mbowdler@little gem.freeserve.co.uk; website - www.thelittle gem.co.uk. SER: Repairs; valuations.

Mansers Antiques
LAPADA
Coleham Head. SY3 7BJ. Est. 1944. Open 9-5. SIZE: Large. *STOCK: Furniture, 18th-20th C, £250-£50,000; silver, porcelain, glass, mirrors, decorative items, £50-£10,000.* Not Stocked: Coins, books. LOC: 150yds. from English bridge away from Town centre. PARK: Own. TEL: 01743 351120/245730; fax - 01743 271047; e-mail - mansers@theantiquedealers.com; website - www.theantiquedealers.com. SER: Valuations; restorations. VAT: Stan/Spec.

Princess Antique Centre
14a The Square. SY1. (J. Langford). Open 9.30-5. SIZE: 35 dealers. *STOCK: General antiques and collectables.* PARK: Nearby. TEL: 01743 343701.

Quayside Antiques
9 Frankwell. SY3. (Jean and Chris Winter). Open Tues. and Wed. 10-4, Fri. and Sat. 10-5. SIZE: Large. *STOCK: Victorian and Edwardian furniture, especially dining tables and sets of chairs, desks, bookcases, wardrobes.* LOC: Near Halls Saleroom. PARK: Own. TEL: 01743 360490; workshop - 01948 665838; home - 01948 830363. SER: Restorations (furniture). FAIRS: NEC.

Shrewsbury Antique Centre
15 Princess House, The Square. SY1 1JZ. (J. Langford). Est. 1978. Open 9.30-5.30. SIZE: Large - 50 dealers. *STOCK: General antiques and collectables.* LOC: Town centre just off the square. PARK: Nearby. TEL: 01743 247704.

Shrewsbury Antique Market
Frankwell Quay Warehouse. SY3 8LG. (J. Langford). Open 9.30-5. SIZE: Large - 45 units. *STOCK: General antiques and collectors' items, £1-£2,000.* LOC: Alongside Frankwell Quay car park. PARK: Easy. TEL: 01743 350916.

Tiffany Antiques
Shrewsbury Antique Centre, 15 Princess House, The Square. SY1 1JZ. (A. Wilcox). Est. 1988. Open 9.30-5.30. *STOCK: Metalware, collectables, curios, china and glass.* LOC: Town centre. PARK: Multi-storey. TEL: Home - 01270 257425; mobile - 07970 419263. SER: Buys at auction.

STANTON UPON HINE HEATH
Nr. Shrewsbury

Marcus Moore Antiques
Booley House, Booley. SY4 4LY. (M.G.J. and M.P. Moore). Est. 1980. Usually open but prior telephone call advisable. SIZE: Large. *STOCK: Oak and country furniture, late 17th to 18th C; Georgian mahogany furniture, 18th to early 19th C; all £50-£7,000; some Victorian furniture; associated items.* LOC: Half a mile north of Stanton on right. PARK: Easy. TEL: 01939 200333; website - www.marcusmoore-antiques.com. SER: Restorations (furniture); polishing; search; shipping. VAT: Stan/Spec.

TELFORD

Haygate Gallery
40 Haygate Rd., Wellington. TF1 1QT. (Mrs M. Kuznierz). Open 9-5, Sat. 9-1. CL: Wed. *STOCK: Chandeliers, lighting and decorative antiques.* LOC: One mile from junction 7, M54. PARK: Easy. TEL: 01952 248553. SER: Framing.

Brian James Antiques
Old Maltings, The Lawns, Wellington. TF1 3AF. Est. 1985. Open 9-6, Sat. 9.30-12.30, Sun. by appointment. SIZE: Large. *STOCK: Chests of drawers, Georgian to Victorian, £50-£1,500.* LOC: Off M54, junction 6. Follow signs for Telford Hospital then Wellington Centre, turn right at Red Lion. PARK: Easy. TEL: 01952 256592/243906; e-mail - bjames45@hotmail. com. SER: Restorations (inlay, veneering,

polishing); conversions; linen presses, sideboards, cabinets and chests made to order. VAT: Stan.

Age of Elegance
54 High St. SY13 1BB. (Mike and Janet Proudlove). Est. 1988. Open 10-4. CL: Wed. SIZE: Small. *STOCK: Collectables including china and glass; Victorian and Edwardian furniture.* LOC: Midway between Shrewsbury and Chester. PARK: Easy. TEL: 01948 666145; fax - same.

Dodington Antiques
7 Sherrymill Hill. SY13 1BN. (G. MacGillivray). Resident. Est. 1978. By appointment. SIZE: Large. *STOCK: Oak, fruitwood, walnut country and 18th to early 19th C mahogany furniture, longcase clocks, barometers, £10-£6,000.* LOC: On fringe of town centre. PARK: Easy. TEL: 01948 663399. SER: Buys at auction. VAT: Stan/Spec.

Bread basket of 1826 by Sibley with retailer's mark of 'Makepeace'.

(© *The Worshipful Company of Goldsmiths*)

From an article entitled "Richard Sibley I" by Ian Pickford which appeared in the April 2003 issue of ***Antique Collecting***. For more details and to subscribe see page 21.

SOMERSET

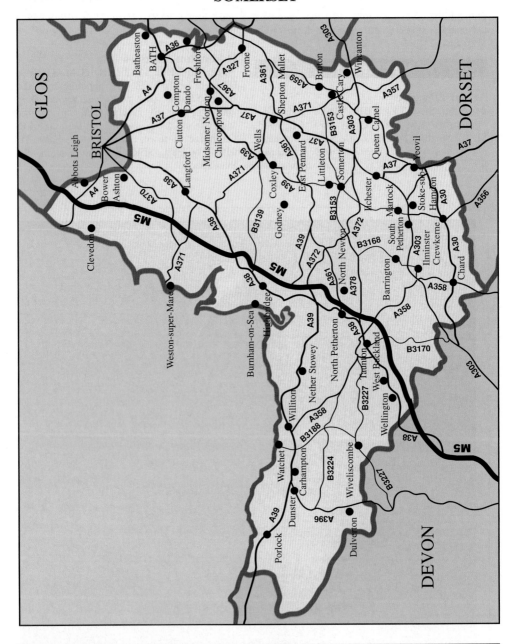

Dealers and Shops in Somerset

Abbots Leigh	1	Clutton	1	Ilminster	1	South Petherton	1
Barrington	1	Compton Dando	1	Langford	1	Stoke-sub-Hamdon	1
Bath	49	Coxley	2	Littleton	1	Taunton	5
Batheaston	1	Crewkerne	5	Martock	1	Watchet	2
Bower Ashton	1	Dulverton	4	Midsomer Norton	1	Wellington	1
Bruton	3	Dunster	1	Nether Stowey	2	Wells	3
Burnham-on-Sea	5	East Pennard	1	North Newton	1	West Buckland	1
Carhampton	1	Freshford	1	North Petherton	1	Weston-Super-Mare	3
Castle Cary	1	Frome	2	Porlock	1	Williton	2
Chard	3	Godney	1	Queen Camel	1	Wincanton	3
Chilcompton	1	Highbridge	1	Shepton Mallet	1	Wiveliscombe	3
Clevedon	3	Ilchester	1	Somerton	3	Yeovil	2

ABBOTS LEIGH, Nr. Bristol

David and Sally March Antiques `LAPADA`
Oak Wood Lodge, Stoke Leigh Woods. BS8 3QB.
(D. and S. March). Est. 1981. Open by
appointment. *STOCK: 18th to early 19th C
English porcelain especially figures, Bristol and
Plymouth.* PARK: Easy. TEL: 01275 372422; fax
- same; mobile - 07774 838376; e-mail - david.
march@lineone.net. SER: Valuations; buys at
auction (as stock). FAIRS: Olympia; LAPADA
(London and NEC); NEC; Chelsea. VAT: Spec.

BARRINGTON, Nr. Ilminster

Stuart Interiors Ltd `LAPADA`
Barrington Court. TA19 0NG. Open 9-5, Sat. 10-
5. SIZE: Large. *STOCK: Oak furniture, £100-
£10,000; accessories, £50-£2,500; both pre-
1720.* LOC: Between A303 and M5, 5 miles
north-east of Ilminster. National Trust property,
signposted in area. PARK: Easy. TEL: 01460
240349. SER: Valuations; buys at auction (early
oak furniture and accessories, interior design and
architectural items including oak panelling). VAT:
Spec.

BATH

A J Antiques
13 Broad St. BA1 5LJ. (Patrick Anketell-Jones).
Open 10-5. 30 or by appointment. *STOCK:
Furniture, Georgian to Art Deco.* LOC: City
centre. PARK: Nearby. TEL: 01225 447765.

Abbey Galleries
9 Abbey Churchyard. BA1 1LY. (R. Dickson).
NAG. NPA. Est. 1930. Open 10. 30-5. *STOCK:
Jewellery, Oriental items, 18th-19th C; silver,
18th C.* LOC: Next to the Roman Baths. TEL:
01225 460565; fax - 01225 484192. SER:
Valuations; restorations (jewellery and clocks);
buys at auction. VAT: Stan.

Adam Gallery Ltd
13 John St. BA1 2JL. (Paul and Philip Dye).
Open 9.30-5.30 or by appointment. *STOCK: 20th
C British and international paintings and prints,
especially St. Ives, Bacon, Nicholson, Francis,
Piper, Debuffet, Kandinsky, Lanyon, Moore,
Picasso, Delaunay, Hitchens, Hilton, Heron and
Scott, British contemporary, £500-£50,000.* TEL:
01225 480406; fax - same; e-mail - enquiries@
adamgallery.com; website - www.adamgallery.
com. SER: Contemporary exhibitions.

Antique Textiles & Lighting
34 Belvedere, Lansdown Rd. BA1 5BN. (Joanna
Proops). BABAADA. Open Tues. -Fri. 10-5 or by
appointment. *STOCK: Chandeliers, wall lights,
tapestries, paisleys, beadwork, fans, samplers,
bellpulls, linen and lace, tapes, ties.* LOC: 5 mins.
walk from city centre. PARK: Easy. TEL: 01225
310795; website - www.antiquetextiles.co.uk.
FAIRS: Bath.

The Antiques Warehouse
57 Walcot St. BA1 5BN. BABAADA. Est. 1991.
Open 10.30-5.30. SIZE: Medium. *STOCK: 19th
C mahogany furniture, £300-£5,000; decorative
objects, £20-£500.* LOC: From junction 18, M4
along A46 then A4, at first mini-roundabout veer
left into Walcot St. Shop 300yds on right. PARK:
Easy. TEL: 01225 444201; mobile - 07990
690240. VAT: Stan/Spec.

Arkea Antiques
10A Monmouth Place. BA1 2AX. (G.
Harmandian). Est. 1969. *STOCK: Furniture and
china.* TEL: 01225 429413/835382. SER:
Repairs (antiques); traditional French polishing;
desk leathering.

Assembly Antiques Centre
5/8 Saville Row. BA1 2QP. BABAADA. Open
10-5, Wed. 7-5. *STOCK: 18th-19th C furniture,
scent bottles and jewellery, Art Deco items, tea
caddies, boxes, pictures, lighting, Oriental
furniture, decorative effects, rare and vintage
guitars and accessories.* LOC: Rear of the
Assembly Rooms. TEL: 01225 426288; fax -
01225 426288; e-mail - lyndabrine@yahoo.co.
uk; website - www.assemblyantiquecentre.co.
uk.

Bartlett Street Antiques Centre
5-10 Bartlett St. BA1 2QZ. BABAADA. Open
9.30-5, Wed. 8-5. SIZE: 50+ dealers and 150
display cases. *STOCK: Wide range of general
antiques.* TEL: 01225 466689; stallholders -
01225 310457/446322; fax - 01225 444146; e-
mail - info@antiques-centre.co.uk; website -
www.antiques-centre.co.uk.

Bath Galleries
33 Broad St. BA1 5LP. (J. Griffiths). Open 10-
4.45. CL: Thurs. pm. SIZE: Medium. *STOCK:
Clocks, furniture, paintings, porcelain,
barometers, silver.* LOC: 50yds. from Central
Post Office. PARK: Walcot St. multi-storey,
30yds. TEL: 01225 462946. SER: Valuations;
restorations; buys at auction. VAT: Stan/Spec.

Bath Saturday Antiques Market
Walcot St. BA1 5B. (J. Whittingham). Est. 1978. Open Sat. 7-5. SIZE: 100 stalls. *STOCK: Wide variety of general antiques, £1-£4,000.* LOC: Close to Hilton Hotel. PARK: Multi-storey. TEL: Mobile - 07836 534893.

Bath Stamp and Coin Shop
Pulteney Bridge. BA2 4AY. (H. and A. Swindells). Est. 1946. Open 9.30-5.30. *STOCK: Coins - Roman, hammered, early milled, G. B. gold, silver and copper, some foreign; literature and accessories; banknotes, medals, stamps and postal history.* PARK: Laura Place; Walcot multi-storey. TEL: 01225 463073; e-mail - m.swindells @virgin.net. SER: Valuations. VAT: Stan.

George Bayntun
Manvers St. BA1 1JW. (E. W. G. Bayntun-Coward). BABAADA. Est. 1894. Open 9-1 and 2-5. 30, Sat. 9.30-1. SIZE: Large. *STOCK: Rare books. First or fine editions of English literature, standard sets, illustrated and sporting books, poetry, biography and travel, mainly in new leather bindings; antiquarian books in original bindings.* LOC: By rail and bus stations. PARK: 50 yds. by station. TEL: 01225 466000; fax - 01225 482122; e-mail - ebc@georgebayntun. com; website - www.georgebayntun.com. SER: Binding; restorations. VAT: Stan.

Bedsteads
2 Walcot Buildings, London Rd. BA1 6AD. (Mark and Nikki Ashton). BABAADA. Est. 1991. Open Tues. -Sat. 10-5. 30. *STOCK: Brass, iron and wooden bedsteads, 1840-1920, £500-£4,500; bedroom suites, 1880-1920, £2,000-£5,500.* LOC: 200 yards before traffic lights, end of London Road. TEL: 01225 339182; fax - same; home - 01275 464114. SER: Valuations; restorations (bedsteads). VAT: Stan/Spec.

Bladud House Antiques
8 Bladud Buildings. BA1 5LS. (Mrs E. Radosenska). Open 9.30-1 and 2-4.30. CL: Mon. and Thurs. *STOCK: Jewellery and small items.* TEL: 01225 462929.

Lawrence Brass
Apple Studio, Ashley. BA1 3SD. Est. 1973. Open by appointment. SIZE: Small. *STOCK: Furniture, 16th-19th C, to £50,000.* Not Stocked: Ceramics, silver, glass. LOC: A4 towards Chippenham. PARK: Easy. TEL: 01225 852222; fax - 01225 851050; website - www.lawrence brass.com. SER: Restorations (furniture, clocks and barometers). VAT: Stan/Spec.

Geoffrey Breeze
6 George St. BA1 2EH. BABAADA. Est. 1973. Open 10-5. SIZE: Large. *STOCK: Furniture - Georgian, Regency, Victorian, Arts & Crafts.* LOC: City centre. TEL: 01225 466499; fax - same; e-mail - geoffrey@geoffreybreeze.co.uk; website - www.geoffreybreeze.co.uk.

David Bridgwater
Heather Cottage, Lansdown. BA1 9BL. Est. 1984. Open by appointment. *STOCK: Architectural and garden sculpture, decorative and practical items for the period garden.* TEL: 01225 463435; e-mail - davidofbridgwater@ btinternet.com.

Camden Books
146 Walcot St. BA1 5BL. (Victor and Elizabeth Suchar). PBFA. Est. 1984. Open 10-5. *STOCK: Books - architecture, philosophy, economics, science, 18th-20th C; general, 19th-20th C.* LOC: From east on to London Rd. , then Walcot St. PARK: Easy. TEL: 01225 461606; fax - same; website - www.camdenbooks.com. SER: Valuations; buys at auction. FAIRS: Bath PBFA; London PBFA.

Brian and Caroline Craik Ltd
8 Margaret's Buildings. BA1 2LP. Est. 1963. Open 10-4. *STOCK: Decorative items, mainly 19th C; metalwork, treen, glass and pewter.* LOC: Between Royal Crescent and the Circus, off Brock St. PARK: Nearby. TEL: 01225 337161.

Mary Cruz
LAPADA
5 Broad St. BA1 5LJ. BABAADA. CINOA. Est. 1974. Open 10-6.30, Sun. by appointment. SIZE: Medium. *STOCK: 18th-19th C furniture and decorative items; 19th C and later paintings and sculpture.* PARK: Easy. TEL: 01225 334174; fax - 01225 423300. SER: Valuations; restorations; finder (Latin American Art). VAT: Stan/Spec.

D. and B. Dickinson
BADA
22 New Bond St. BA1 1BA. (S. G. , D. and N. W. Dickinson). BABAADA. Est. 1917. Open 9.30-1 and 2-5. SIZE: Small. STOCK: Jewellery, 1770-1900, £20-£2,000; silver, 1750-1900, £25-£3,000; Sheffield plate, 1770-1845, £50-£1,000. LOC: Next to Post Office. PARK: 100yds. at bottom of street, turn left then right for multi-storey. TEL: 01225 466502; website - www.dickinsonsilver.co.uk. VAT: Stan/Spec.

Frank Dux Antiques
33 Belvedere, Lansdown Rd. BA1 5HR. (F. Dux and M. Hopkins). Resident. BABAADA. Est. 1988. Open Tues. -Sat. 10-6. SIZE: Medium. *STOCK: Mainly glass, 18th-19th C English drinking glasses and decanters and later Venetian; some furniture, unusual decorative items including glass paintings.* LOC: From Broad St. up Lansdown Hill, on right 100yds. past Guinea Lane. PARK: Easy. TEL: 01225 312367; fax - same; e-mail - m.hopkins@ antique-glass.co.uk; website - www.antique-glass.co.uk.

George Gregory
Manvers St. BA1 1JW. (C.A.W. Bayntun-Coward). Est. 1845. Open 9-1 and 2-5.30, Sat. 9.30-1. SIZE: Large. *STOCK: Secondhand books, engraved views and portraits.* LOC: By rail station. PARK: By rail station. TEL: 01225 466000; fax - 01225 482122; e-mail - ebc@ georgebayntun.com; website - www.george bayntun.com.

Haliden Oriental Rug Shop
98 Walcot St. BA1 5BG. (Andrew Lloyd, Craig Bale and Owen Parry). Est. 1963. Open 10-5. SIZE: Medium. *STOCK: Caucasian, Turkish, Persian, Chinese, Afghan, Turcoman and tribal rugs and carpets, 19th C, £50-£3,000; some Oriental textiles - coats, embroideries, wall hangings, 19th C, £50-£750.* LOC: Off main London road, into town by Walcot Reclamation. PARK: Walcot St. or multi-storey. TEL: 01225 469240. SER: Valuations; cleaning; restorations; buys at auction.

Han Classical Chinese Furniture
29 Belvedere, Lansdown. BA1 5QF. (K. S. Cheung). BABAADA. Est. 2001. Open 10-4. SIZE: Small. *STOCK: Chinese furniture, paintings, vases, stone and wood carvings, £50-£5,000.* TEL: 01225 424449; fax - same; mobile - 07973 322790.

Anthony Hepworth Fine Art Dealers
1 Margarets Buildings, Brock St. BA1 2LP. Est. 1989. Open during exhibitions Wed. -Sat. 11-5 other times by appointment. *STOCK: Mainly 20th C British paintings and sculpture; African tribal art.* LOC: Off Brock St. between Royal Crescent and Circus. PARK: Brock St. TEL: 01225 447480/442917; fax - 01225 442917; mobile - 07970 480650 (during fairs only). SER: Exhibitions Bath and London. FAIRS: Olympia; 20th/21st C British Art.

Indigo
59 Walcot St. BA1 5BN. (Richard Lightbown and Marion Bender). Est. 1983. Open 10-6. SIZE: Small. *STOCK: Chinese, Indian, Japanese and Tibetan furniture and accessories, Chinese porcelain, from early 19th C, to £3,600.* LOC: 5 minutes from city centre. PARK: Easy. TEL: 01225 311795; e-mail - antiques@indigo-uk. com; website - www.indigo-uk.com

Jadis Ltd
14 and 15 Walcot Buildings, London Rd. BA1 6AD. (S. H. Creese-Parsons and N. A. Mackay). BABAADA. Est. 1970. Open 9. 30-6, Sun. by appointment. SIZE: Medium. *STOCK: English and European furniture, 18th-19th C; decorative items.* LOC: On left hand side of A4 London Rd. entering Bath. PARK: At rear. TEL: 01225 333130; fax - same; mobiles - 07768 232133 and 07879 692371; e-mails - Jadpalad@aol.com and scp.Jadis@aol.com; website - www.Jadis-Ltd. com. SER: Design service, murals and trompe l'oeil. VAT: Stan/Spec.

Kembery Antique Clocks Ltd
Bartlett Street Antique Centre, 5 Bartlett St. BA1 2QZ. (P. and E. Kembery). BABAADA. BWCMG. Est. 1993. Open 10-5. *STOCK: Longcase, bracket, mantel, wall and carriage clocks and barometers, 18th-19th C, £200-£10,000.* TEL: 0117 956 5281; website - www.kdclocks.co.uk. SER: Valuations; restorations. VAT: Spec.

Ann King

38 Belvedere, Lansdown Rd. BA1 5HR. Est. 1977. Open 10-5. SIZE: Small. *STOCK: Period clothes, 19th C to 1960; baby clothes, shawls, bead dresses, linen, lace, curtains, cushions, quilts and textiles.* PARK: Easy. TEL: 01225 336245.

Nick Kuhn

4 Miles Buildings, Off George St. BA1 2QS. Est. 1992. Usually open Sat. 10-5, other times by appointment. SIZE: Small. *STOCK: 20th C modern furniture and design, British fine art, £30-£3,000.* LOC: City centre, near Bartlett Street Antiques Centre. PARK: Nearby. TEL: 01225 425486. FAIRS: BABAADA.

Lansdown Antiques

23 Belvedere, Lansdown Rd. BA1 5ED. (Chris and Ann Kemp). BABAADA. Open 9. 30-5. 30, Sun. by appointment. *STOCK: Painted pine and country furniture, 17th-19th C; metalware, unusual and decorative items.* LOC: From A4/A46 roundabout across 2 sets of traffic lights, right at mini roundabout, right at next traffic lights, shop 350yds. on left. PARK: Easy. TEL: 01225 313417; home - same; mobile - 07801 013663; e-mail - lansdown-antiques@lineone. net. VAT: Stan/Spec.

Looking Glass of Bath

94-96 Walcot St. BA1 5BG. (Anthony Reed). Est. 1972. Open 9-6. SIZE: Medium. *STOCK: Large mirrors and picture frames, 18th-19th C, £50-£5,000; decorative prints, 18th-20th C.* PARK: Easy. TEL: 01225 461969; fax - 01225 316191; home - 01275 333595; website - www. lookinglassofbath.co.uk.SER:Valuations; restorations (re-gilding, gesso and compo work, re-silvering and bevelling glass); manufactures arched top overmantel, pier, convex and triptych mirrors; old mirror plates supplied; simulated mercury silvered mirror glass; buys at auction (mirrors and pictures). VAT: Stan/Spec.

Lopburi Art & Antiques

5 Saville Row. BA1 2QP. (Simon and Mee Ling Roper). BABAADA. Est. 1998. Open 10-5. SIZE: Large. *STOCK: 12th-19th C Buddhist art from Thailand, Cambodia and Burma, in bronze, stone and wood, £500-£35,000; 17th-19th C Tibetan painted wooden chests, £900-£7,000; Chinese furniture, carpets and Nepalese contemporary paintings.* LOC: City centre. PARK: Meters. TEL: 01225 322947; fax - same; e-mail - mail@lopburi.co.uk; website - www. lopburi.co.uk. SER: Valuations.

A bronze figure of a young woman emerging from a snail shell, unsigned, 19¾in. wide. The piece sold for £2,400 on 22nd March 2000. (Sotheby's)

From an article entitled "Art Deco Figures" by Jeremy Morrison which appeared in the December 2001/January 2002 issue of **Antique Collecting**. For more details and to subscribe see page 21.

OLD BANK ANTIQUES CENTRE
16-17 & 20 Walcot Buildings, London Road, Bath, BA1 6AD
Tel: 01225 469282/338813   Email: alexatmontague@aol.com

On the main London Road, less than half a mile from the city centre, Old Bank Antiques accommodates six well-known dealers: A.J. Antiques, Taylor-Wootten, Tinderbox, Norman Kemp, Alex Cussins and Montague Antiques. Visitors will find nine show-rooms offering a wide selection of English, continental and country furniture as well as glass, ceramics, metalwork, collectors' items and decorative objects. There is free parking at the rear, via Bedford Street.

Open Daily: 10am - 6pm. Sundays: 11am - 4pm.

E. P. Mallory and Son Ltd   `BADA`
1-4 Bridge St. and 5 Old Bond St. BA2 4AP. BABAADA. Est. 1898. Open 10-5. *STOCK: Antique and estate silver, jewellery, objets de vertu,   £50-£10,000.* TEL: (0044) 0 1225 788800; fax - (0044) 0 1225 442210; e-mail - mail@mallory-jewellers.com; website - www. mallory-jewellers.com. VAT: Stan/Spec.

Old Bank Antiques Centre
16-17 and 20 Walcot Buildings, London Rd. BA1 6AD. (A. R. Schlesinger and D. K. Moore). BABAADA. Est. 1987. Open 10-6, Sun. 11-4. SIZE: 9 showrooms. *STOCK: English, Continental and country furniture, ceramics, rugs, metalwork, interior design items.* LOC: A4 London Road, 1/2 mile from city centre near Safeway. PARK: Rear of premises, via Bedford St. TEL: 01225 469282; home - same; e-mail - alexatmontague@aol.com. SER: Valuations. Below are listed the dealers at this centre.

   A.J. Antiques
   Gene and Sally Foster
   Norman Kemp
   Montague Antiques
   Tinderbox
   Taylor Wootton

Paragon Antiques and Collectors Market
3 Bladud Buildings, The Paragon. BA1 5LS. (T. J. Clifford and Son Ltd). BABAADA. Est. 1978. Open Wed. 6. 30-3. SIZE: Large. LOC: Milsom St. /Broad St. PARK: 50yds. TEL: 01225 463715.

Patterson Liddle
10 Margaret's Buildings, Brock St. BA1 2LP. ABA. PBFA. ILAB. Open 10-5.30. *STOCK: Antiquarian books and prints especially art and architecture, illustrated and transport history, travel, English literature, maps.* PARK: Nearby. TEL: 01225 426722; fax - same; e-mail - mail@pattersonliddle.com; website - www.patterson liddle.com. SER: Transport History catalogues issued.

Quiet Street Antiques
3 Quiet St. and 14/15 John St. BA1 2JS. (K. Hastings-Spital). BABAADA. Est. 1985. Open 10-6. SIZE: Large - 8 showrooms. *STOCK: Furniture especially English mahogany, 1750-1870, £250-£12,000; objects including bronzes, caddies, boxes, mirrors, £50-£2,000; Royal Worcester porcelain, £30-£2,000; clocks including longcase, wall, bracket and carriage, 1750-1900, £150-£8,000.* LOC: 25yds. from Milsom St. PARK: Nearby. TEL: 01225 315727; fax - 01225 448300; e-mail - kerry@

MALLORY OF BATH

Fine Silver
Fine Jewellery

'Dealers in Fine Antique and Estate Jewellery, and Silver since 1898.'

1-4 BRIDGE STREET, BATH, BA2 4AP.

TELEPHONE: 01225 788800 FAX: 01225 442210

E-mail: mail@mallory-jewellers.com Website: www.mallory-jewellers.com

411

quietstreetantiques.co.uk; website - www.quiet streetantiques.co.uk. SER: Buys at auction (furniture and clocks); upholstery; free delivery 100 mile radius of Bath and weekly delivery to London. Export facilities. VAT: Spec.

Roland Gallery
33 Monmouth St. BA1 2AN. (Michael J. Pettitt). BABAADA. Est. 1982. Open Wed. and Sat. 10-5 or by appointment. SIZE: Small. *STOCK: Decorative arts, 1880-1940; silver and plate, Staffordshire figures, luggage, jewellery, unusual, decorative and novelty items, £50-£2,000.* LOC: Town city. PARK: Pay and Display. TEL: 01225 312330; mobile - 07889 723272; e-mail - the rolandgallery@aol.com. FAIRS: NEC; Sandown Park; Newark.

Sarah Russell Antiquarian Prints
5 Margaret's Buildings, Brock St. BA1 2LP. ABA. Open 10-5. *STOCK: Unusual antiquarian prints - architecture, flowers, portraits, landscapes and Bath views, many in original frames.* TEL: 01225 466335; fax - same; e-mail - bathprint@aol.com.

Michael and Jo Saffell
3 Walcot Buildings, London Rd. BA1 6AD. BABAADA. Est. 1975. Open 9. 30-5, Sat. by appointment. SIZE: Small. *STOCK: British tins and other advertising material including showcards and enamels, 1870-1939; decorative items; all £5-£5,000.* LOC: A4 - main road into city from M4. PARK: Side streets opposite. TEL: 01225 315857; fax - same; home - same; mobile - 07941 158049; e-mail - michael.saffell@virgin. net. SER: Postal. FAIRS: Newark.

Tim Snell Antiques
5 & 6 Cleveland Terrace, London Rd. BA1 5DF. BABAADA. Open 10-6 including Sun. *STOCK: Fully restored golden oak, mahogany and walnut furniture, late 19th to early 20th C.* TEL: 01225 423045.

Source
93-95 Walcot St. BA1 3SD. (Roderick I. Donaldson). Open Tues.-Sat. 10-5. *STOCK: Period architectural materials, church and bar fittings, mirrors, lighting, decorative items, metalware, ironwork and garden furniture, 20th C metal fitted kitchens.* PARK: Nearby and limited. TEL: 01225 4692000; website - www. source-antiques.co.uk. SER: Worldwide search and supply.

Susannah
25 Broad St. BA1 5LW. (Sue Holley). BABAADA. Est. 1985. Open 10-5. *STOCK: Decorative textiles and antiques.* PARK: Opposite. TEL: 01225 445069; fax - 01225 339004. FAIRS: Bath Decorative (March).

James Townshend Antiques
1 Saville Row. BA1 2QP. BABAADA. Est. 1992. Open 10-5. SIZE: Large. *STOCK: Trade furniture, china, unusual decorative items and clocks.* LOC: City centre. PARK: Easy. TEL: 01225 332290; website - www.jtownshend antiques.co.uk. SER: Delivery. VAT: Spec/Global.

Trimbridge Galleries
Trimbridge. BA1 1HD. (Mr and Mrs A. Anderson). Est. 1973. SIZE: Medium. *STOCK: Watercolours and drawings, £50-£3,000; prints and oil paintings; all 18th-20th C. Annual exhibition in November.* LOC: Just off lower end of Milsom St. PARK: Easy. TEL: 01225 466390; website - www.trimbridgegalleries.co.uk.

Vintage to Vogue
28 Milson St. BA1 1DG. (Mrs Teresa Langton). BABAADA. Est. 1995. Open Tues.-Sat. 10.30-5. *STOCK: Vintage clothing - womens, gentlemens, childrens - including hats, bags, shoes, gloves, scarves and formal wear, 1850-1950's; buttons, trimmings, costume jewellery, costume and antique lace, fashion and needlework books and magazines; all £1-£500.* LOC: In passage from Broad St. car park. PARK: Nearby. TEL: 01225 337323; website - www.vintagetovoguebath.com

Walcot Reclamation
108 Walcot St. BA1 5BG. BABAADA. Est. 1977. Open 8. 30-5. 30, Sat. 9-5. SIZE: Large. *STOCK: Architectural items - chimney pieces, ironwork, doors, fireplaces, garden statuary, period baths and fittings and traditional building materials.* PARK: Own and multi-storey nearby. TEL: 01225 444404/335532; e-mails - rick@ walcot.com and jane@reproshop.com; websites - www.walcot.com and www.reproshop.com. SER: Valuations; restorations. VAT: Stan.

BATHEASTON, Nr. Bath

Piccadilly Antiques
280 High St. BA1 7RA. BABAADA. Est. 1990. Open 9. 30-5. 30 or by appointment. SIZE: Large. *STOCK: Country, some mahogany, furniture and decorative accessories, £100-£5,000.* LOC: Off junction 17, M4 on old A4, 7 miles east of Bath. PARK: Easy. TEL: 01225 851494; fax - 01225 851120; e-mail - piccadillyantiques@ukonline. co.uk. SER: Restorations (country furniture).

FAIRS: Bath. VAT: Stan/Spec. Below are listed the dealers trading from these premises.

Robin Coleman Antiques
BABAADA. *Interesting and decorative items.* VAT: Stan/Spec.

John Davies
18th-19th C furniture and decorative items. TEL: Home - 01225 852103. VAT: Stan/Spec.

Grierson Gower
Architectural, naive and popular art, toys, models, pub and trade signs.

Mike Holt
BABAADA. *19th C decorative metalware.* VAT: Stan.

BOWER ASHTON, Nr. Bristol

Antique Four-Poster Beds
The Old Stables, Kennel Lodge Rd. BS3 2JT. (Simon and Alicia Poyntz). Est. 1973. Open Mon.-Fri. by prior appointment. SIZE: Small. *STOCK: Four-poster and French beds, bedposts.* PARK: Easy. TEL: 0117 9632563; fax - same; mobile - 07074 632563; e-mail - simonpoyntz beds@aol.com; website - www.simonpoyntz beds.com.

BRUTON

The Antique Shop
5 High St. BA10 0AB. (D. L. Gwilliam and M. J. Wren). Est. 1976. Open Thurs. -Sat. 10-5. 30 or by appointment. SIZE: Medium. *STOCK: Furniture, jewellery, silver, china, copper, brass, general collectables, decorative art and antiques, Georgian to Art Deco, £5-£4,000.* PARK: Easy. TEL: 01749 813264. SER: Repairs (clock, watch and jewellery); re-stringing pearls and beads.

Michael Lewis Gallery - Antiquarian Maps & Prints
17 High St. BA10 0AB. (Leo and Mrs J. L. Lewis). Est. 1980. Open 9. 30-5. 30 or by appointment. CL: Thurs. pm. SIZE: Large. *STOCK: Prints and maps, 18th-19th C.* LOC: A359. PARK: Nearby. TEL: 01749 813557; home - same. SER: Framing.

M. G. R. Exports
Station Rd. BA10 0EH. Est. 1980. Open Mon.-Fri. 8.30-5.30 or by appointment. SIZE: Large. *STOCK: Georgian, Victorian, Edwardian and decorative items, carved oak, barley twist and shipping goods, Continental furniture.* PARK: Easy. TEL: 01749 812460; fax - 01749 812882; e-mail - antiques@ mgr.exports.co.uk. SER: Packing and shipping.

BURNHAM-ON-SEA

Burnham Model & Collectors Shop
3 College Court, College St., TA8 1AR. (W. I. Loudon). Est. 1994. Open 9. 30-5 (including Sun. between 13th July to 31st Aug). CL: Wed. SIZE: Medium. *STOCK: Postcards, pre-1945, cigarette cards, Corgi and Dinky models, medals and banknotes, 50p-£100;* LOC: Seafront, opposite Pavilion Amusements. PARK: Opposite. TEL: 01278 780066; fax - same. SER: Valuations.

Castle Antiques
(T. C. Germain). NAG. Est. 1953. Open by appointment. SIZE: Small. *STOCK: Jewellery, silver, 18th-19th C furniture, porcelain, clocks.* TEL: 01278 785031; e-mail - castle.antiques@ virgin.net; website - www.castleantiques jewellery.com. SER: Restorations.

Colin Dyte Antiques
Vicarage Chambers, Victoria St. TA8 1AW. Est. 1950. Open 9-5 or by appointment. SIZE: Medium. *STOCK: 18th-20th furniture.* PARK: Easy. TEL: 01278 788590; fax - 01278 788604. SER: Packing; transport; documentation.

John Dyte Antiques
Vicarage Chambers, Victoria St. TA8 1AW. Est. 1970. Open 9-5.30 or by appointment. SIZE: Medium. *STOCK: Longcase clocks and 18th-20th C furniture.* TEL: 01278 788603; fax - 01278 788604; e-mail - john@johndyteantiques. fsnet.co.uk. SER: Packing; container and delivery. FAIRS: DMG; Newark. VAT: Spec.

Heape's Antiques
39 Victoria St. TA8 1AN. (Mrs M. M. Heap). Est. 1987. Open 10-1 and 2. 30-4. 30. *STOCK: Small furniture, fine arts, porcelain, glass, memorabilia.* LOC: Town centre. PARK: Easy. TEL: 01278 782131. SER: Picture framing, cleaning and restoration.

CARHAMPTON, Nr. Minehead

Chris's Crackers
Townsend Garage. (P. Marshall). Est. 1995. Open 11-5. 30 including Sun. SIZE: Large warehouses. *STOCK: Mainly 18th-19th C furniture, stripped pine, architectural antiques, iron and stone-work, general building reclamation materials and country artefacts.* LOC: A39 coast road. PARK: Easy. TEL: 01643 821873. SER: Pine stripping.

CASTLE CARY

Antiquus
West Country House, Woodcock St. BA7 7BJ. (Gerald Davison). FRSA. Est. 1962. Open Tues., Wed., Fri. and Sat. 10-5. SIZE: Small. *STOCK: Chinese porcelain and pottery, all dynasties, £25-£2,000; Chinese furniture and works of art, £75-£2,500; English furniture, 18th-20th C, £500-£2,500; English silver, 19th C, £25-£400; boxes, 18th-19th C, £100-£500; English and European pottery and porcelain, 18th-19th C, £35-£500.* PARK: Nearby. TEL: 01963 351246; mobile - 07968 810092; e-mail - gerald.davison@lineone. net; website - www.chinesemarks.com. SER: Valuations; restorations (ceramics).

CHARD

Nick Chalon Antiques
Field Bars House, Shepherds Lane. TA20 1QX. Est. 1973. Open by appointment. *STOCK: French and English country furniture, £100-£10,000.* LOC: A30. PARK: Easy. TEL: 01460 239005; e-mail - info@chezchalon.com; website - www. chezchalon.com. SER: Courier.

Chard Antique Centre
23 High St. TA20 1QF. (A. W. E. and Mrs J. Smith). Est. 1994. Open 10-5. SIZE: Medium. *STOCK: Furniture 19th C to Edwardian; pine, decorative items, pictures and collectables.* PARK: Nearby. TEL: 01460 63517.

Chez Chalon
Old Telephone Exchange, East St. TA20 1EP. (Jake Chalon). Est. 1973. Open 9-6, Sun. by appointment. *STOCK: French and English country furniture, £100-£10,000.* LOC: A30. PARK: Easy. TEL: 01460 68679; e-mail - info@chezchalon.com; website - www.chezchalon.com. SER: Restorations (trade only). VAT: Stan.

CHILCOMPTON, Nr. Bath

Billiard Room Antiques   LAPADA
The Old School, Church Lane. BA3 4HP. (Mrs J.

McKeivor). BABAADA. Est. 1992. Open by appointment. SIZE: Medium. *STOCK: Billiard, snooker and pool tables and accessories, 19th C, £100-£40,000.* PARK: Easy. TEL: 01761 232839; home and fax - same. SER: Valuations; restorations; buys at auction; search.

CLEVEDON

Beach Antiques
Adelaide House, 13 The Beach. BS21 7QU. (D. A. Coles). Est. 1970. Open Sat. and Sun. 11-5. *STOCK: Jewellery, china, brass, glass, mainly small items.* PARK: Easy. TEL: 01275 876881.

The Collector
14 The Beach. BS21 7QU. (Mrs Tina Simmonds). Est. 1993. Open 10-5, Sun. 12-5. CL: Thurs. (Jan.-Feb. open weekends only). SIZE: Small. *STOCK: Small items and collectables, from 1880, £5-£200; postcards and ephemera, 1900-1960, £1-£30; Beatrix Potter and Bunnykins figures, from 1960, £16-£300.* LOC: On sea front, near pier. PARK: Easy. TEL: 01275 875066; home - same. FAIRS: Malvern 3 Counties; Temple Meads, Brunel, Bristol.

Nostalgia
65a Hill Rd. BS21 7PD. (Mrs Wendy Moore). Est. 1985. Open Wed.-Fri. 10-1 and 2-5, Tues. 10-1 and 2-4.30, Sat. 10-1 and 2-5.30. SIZE: Medium. *STOCK: Furniture, Victorian and later, £200-£600; china and linen, 1930's and earlier, £3-£100.* PARK: Easy. TEL: 01275 342587.

CLUTTON

Ian McCarthy
Arcadian Cottage, 112 Station Rd. BS39 5RA. Resident. Est. 1958. Open by appointment. SIZE: Medium. *STOCK: Lamps - oil, gas, electric for domestic, industrial, shipping and transport usage; unusual candle lamps; copper and brassware, 17th C to 1920, £5-£2,000.* PARK: Easy and opposite. TEL: 01761 453188; fax - same; e-mail - i.mcarthy@ntlworld.com. SER: Valuations; restorations (metalware); cleaning; spares and lamp-shades.

COMPTON DANDO

Alderson **BADA**
The Old Rectory, Vicarage Lane. BS39 4LA. (C. J. R. Alderson). BABAADA. CINOA. Est. 1976. Open by appointment. *STOCK: Furniture and accessories, 17th-18th C.* TEL: 01761 490137; e-mail - kit.alderson@btopen world. com. SER: Valuations. FAIRS: BADA; Olympia. VAT: Spec.

COXLEY, Nr. Wells

Courtyard Antiques
Main Rd. BA5 1QZ. (Mr and Mrs M. J. Mitchell). Est. 1985. Open 9-5, Sun by appointment. SIZE: Medium. *STOCK: Furniture, £100-£300; smalls, £10-£50; both 19th-20th C.* TEL: 01749 679533. SER: Valuations; restorations (upholstery, cane and rush work, china and furniture).

Wells Reclamation Company
BA5 1RQ. (H. Davies). Est. 1984. Open 8. 30-5.30, Sat. 9-4. SIZE: Large. *STOCK: Architectural items, 18th-19th C.* LOC: A39 towards Glastonbury from Wells. PARK: Easy. TEL: 01749 677087. SER: Valuations. VAT: Stan.

CREWKERNE

Antiques and Country Pine
14 East St. TA18 7AG. (M. J. Wheeler). Est. 1980. Open Tues.-Sat. 10-5 or by appointment. *STOCK: Country pine and decorative items.* PARK: Own. TEL: 01460 75623.

Julian Armytage
TA18 8QG. Open by appointment. *STOCK: Fine sporting, marine and decorative prints, 18th-19th C.* TEL: 01460 73449; fax - same. VAT: Spec.

Crewkerne Antique Centre
16 Market St. TA18 7LA. (E. Blewden). Est. 1987. Open 9. 30-4. 30. SIZE: Large, 40 dealers. *STOCK: Furniture, £25-£3,000; collectables, £5-£1,000; pictures, £5-£2,000; all 18th-20th C.* LOC: A303 westward, A359 to Crewkerne, Chard road through town. PARK: Easy. TEL: 01460 77111. SER: Valuations; restorations.

Gresham Books
31 Market St. TA18 7JU. (J. and A. Hine). ABA. PBFA. Est. 1972. Open 10-5. SIZE: Medium. *STOCK: Books, 50p to £1,000.* LOC: A30. PARK: Nearby. TEL: 01460 77726; fax - 01460 52479; e-mail - jameshine@gresham-books. demon.co.uk; website - www.greshambooks.co. uk. SER: Valuations.

Hennessy
42 East St. TA18 7AG. (Carl Hennessy). Est. 1977. Open 10-5. SIZE: Large. *STOCK: Furniture - pine, country, painted and French provincial; related decorative items.* LOC: A30 from Yeovil. PARK: Easy. TEL: 01460 78600; fax - same; mobile - 07768 286455; e-mail - carl@veryold.co.uk; website - www.veryold.co. uk. VAT: Stan/ Spec.

DULVERTON

Acorn Antiques
39 High St. TA22 9DW. (P. Hounslow). Est. 1988. Open 9.30-5.30. SIZE: Medium. *STOCK: Decorative antique furniture, period and reproduction upholstery, sofas, fine art, textiles, country furniture.* LOC: Town centre. PARK: Nearby. TEL: 01398 323286; home - same. SER: Interior design.

Guy Dennler Antiques
The White Hart, 23 High St. TA22 9HB. Open 10-1 and 2-5. CL: Thurs pm. *STOCK: Fine 18th to early 19th C English furniture and decorative objects.* TEL: 01398 324300; fax - 01398 324301; e-mail - guydennler@btconnect.com.

Rothwell and Dunworth
2 Bridge St. TA22 9HJ. (Mrs C. Rothwell and M. Rothwell). ABA. Est. 1975. Open 10.30-1 and 2.15-5, including Sun. (excluding Nov-Feb). SIZE: Medium. *STOCK: Antiquarian and secondhand books especially on hunting, horses and military history.* LOC: 1st shop in village over River Barle. PARK: 100yds. TEL: 01398 323169; fax - 01398 331161; e-mail - rothwellm@aol.com. SER: Valuations.

Anthony Sampson Antiques
Holland House, Bridge St. TA22 9HJ. Est. 1968. Open 9.30-5.30, Sun. by appointment. SIZE: Medium. *STOCK: Town and country furniture, 17th to early 19th C, £500-£10,000+; porcelain, pottery, silver, glass, pictures, garden ornaments and decorative items.* LOC: Main road, prominent position near bridge. PARK: Nearby. TEL: 01398 324247; fax - 01398 324027; e-mail - anthony.sampson@virgin.net. SER: Valuations. VAT: Spec.

DUNSTER

The Crooked Window
7 High St. TA24 6SF. (Robert Ricketts). Est. 1984. SIZE: Small. *STOCK: Chinese ceramics and jade, 3000BC to 19th C, £50-£50,000; English furniture, 16th-18th C, £500-£50,000; maps and prints, 16th-18th C, £50-£2,000.* PARK: Easy. TEL: 01643 821606; home - same; mobile - 07787 722606; e-mails - icthus-fine-art@supanet.com and enquiries@antiquities.uk.com; website - www.antiquities.uk.com. SER: Valuations; lectures. FAIRS: Wilton House.

EAST PENNARD, Nr. Shepton Mallet

Pennard House Antiques LAPADA
BA4 6TP. (Martin Dearden). Resident. BABAADA.
Est. 1979. Open 9. 30-5. 30 or by appointment.
SIZE: Large. *STOCK: French and English country furniture, £300-£5,000.* LOC: From Shepton Mallet, 4 miles south off A37. One hour from Bath. PARK: Easy. TEL: 01749 860731; home - 01749 860266; fax - 01749 860732; e-mail - pennardantiques@ukonline.co.uk. SER: Valuations; restorations; export. VAT: Stan/Spec.

FRESHFORD, Nr. Bath

Janet Clarke
3 Woodside Cottages. BA2 7WJ. *STOCK: Antiquarian books on gastronomy, cookery and wine.* TEL: 01225 723186; fax - 01225 722063; e-mail - janetclarke@ukgateway.net. SER: Catalogue issued. *Mail Order Only.*

Freshfords LAPADA
High St. BA2 7WF. CINOA. Est. 1973. Open by appointment. SIZE: Large. *STOCK: English Regency furniture, 18th-19th C, £2,000-£50,000; Victorian oil paintings, £2,000-£12,000; decorative accessories, 18th-19th C, £2,000-£5,000.* LOC: 4 miles from Bath towards Warminster, just off A36. PARK: Easy. TEL: 01225 722111; fax - 01225 722991; mobile - 07720 838877; e-mail - antiques@freshfords.com; website - www.freshfords.com. SER: Valuations; restorations; buys at auction. FAIRS: Olympia; Armoury, New York. VAT: Spec.

FROME

Antiques & Country Living
43-44 Vallis Way, Badcox. BA11 3BA. (Mrs D. M. Williams). Open 9. 30-5. 30 including Sun. SIZE: Medium. *STOCK: Furniture including country, 19th-20th C, £15-£1,000; porcelain, 18th-19th C, £5-£500; books; lighting.* LOC: A362 Frome to Radstock road. PARK: Free opposite. TEL: 01373 463015; books - 01373 467125; mobile - 07808 933076.

Frome Reclamation
Station Approach. BA11 1RE. (S. J. , K. R. , R. L. and J. B. Horler). Est. 1987. Open 8-5. SIZE: Large + yard. *STOCK: Architectural reclamation.* LOC: From A361 follow signs for rail station. PARK: Easy. TEL: 01373 463919/453122; fax - 01373 453122; e-mail - info@fromerec.co.uk; website - www.fromerec.co.uk. SER: Valuations. VAT: Stan.

GODNEY, Nr. Wells

Country Brocante
Fir Tree Farm. BA5 1RZ. (Tim and Nicky Ovel). BABAADA. Est. 1993. Open by appointment. SIZE: Medium. *STOCK: 18th-19th C French farmhouse tables and early mirrors; 19th-20th C decorative lighting and chandeliers; interesting objects and furniture.* LOC: Village centre. PARK: Easy. TEL: 01458 833052; home - same; fax - 01458 835611; mobile - 07970 719708; e-mail - ovel@compuserve.com. FAIRS: Shepton Mallet; Newark. *Trade Only.*

HIGHBRIDGE

T. M. Dyte Antiques
9 Gass Close, Isleport Business Park. TA9 4JT. Open 8. 30-5. 30. CL: Sat. *STOCK: Shipping goods.* TEL: 01278 786495; e-mail - 106611.1232@compuserve. com.

ILCHESTER

Gilbert & Dale
The Old Chapel, Church St. BA22 8LN. (Roy Gilbert and Joan Dale). Est. 1965. Open 9-5.30 or by appointment. SIZE: Large. *STOCK: English and French country furniture and accessories.* LOC: Village centre on A37. PARK: Easy. TEL: 01935 840464; fax - 01935 841599; e-mail - roy@roygilbert.com.

ILMINSTER

Abingdon House Antiques
34/36 West St. TA19 9AB. (N. and E. Thompson). Est. 2001. Open 10-5 and by appointment. SIZE: Medium. *STOCK: 17th-19th C furniture and associated items.* PARK: Nearby. TEL: 01460 54659.

County Antiques
29 East St. TA19. (Mrs J. P. Barnard). Resident. Est. 1981. Usually open Sat., other times by appointment. SIZE: 4 dealers. *STOCK: 18th-19th C pottery, porcelain, metalwork, furniture and decorative antiques.* TEL: 01460 54151; home - 01460 52269; mobile - 07803 362327. SER: Upholstery.

LANGFORD, Nr. Bristol

Richard Essex Antiques
BS40 5BP. (B. R. and C. L. Essex). Est. 1969. *STOCK: General antiques from mid-18th C.* TEL: 01934 863302.

Somervale Antiques

Wing Cdr. R.G. Thomas M.B.E. R.A.F. (Ret'd)
6 Radstock Road
Midsomer Norton, Radstock, BA3 2AJ
Tel & Fax: 01761 412686 Mobile: 07885 088 022
Internet: http://www.somervaleantiquesglass.co.uk
e-mail: ronthomas@somervaleantiquesglass.co.uk

Shop open only by appointment. Resident on the premises. 24 hour telephone service. Trains to Bath met by arrangement.

Specialist in 18th and early 19th century English drinking glasses, decanters, cut and coloured, "Bristol" and "Nailsea", glass etc. Also bijouterie; scent bottles.

Member of British Antique Dealers' Association
Member of Association of Art & Antique Dealers.

LITTLETON, Nr. Somerton

Westville House Antiques
TA11 6NP. (D. and M. Stacey). Est. 1986. Open daily, Sun. by appointment. SIZE: Large. *STOCK: 18th-19th C pine, mahogany and oak furniture;* LOC: B3151 approximately 1. 5 miles north of Somerton. PARK: Own. TEL: 01458 273376; fax - same; e-mail - antique@westville. co.uk; website - www.westville.co.uk. SER: Valuations; buys at auction. VAT: Stan/Spec.

MARTOCK

Castle Reclamation
Parrett Works. TA12 6AE. (T. A. B. Dance and A. J. Wills). Est. 1986. Open daily, Sat. 10-1. SIZE: Large. *STOCK: Architectural antiques.* LOC: 2 miles off A303 between Martock and South Petherton. PARK: Easy. TEL: 01935 826483; fax - 01935 826791; website - www.castle reclamation.com. SER: Restorations (stone). FAIRS: Bath and West. VAT: Stan.

MIDSOMER NORTON, Nr. Radstock

Somervale Antiques `BADA` `LAPADA`
The Poplars, 6 Radstock Rd. BA3 2AJ. (Wing Cdr. R. G. Thomas). BABAADA. CINOA. Resident. Open by appointment. STOCK: *English drinking glasses, decanters, cut and coloured; "Bristol" and "Nailsea"glass; bijouterie; glass scent bottles, 18th to early 19th C.* **LOC: On A362. PARK: Forecourt. TEL: 01761 412686 (24hrs); fax - same; mobile - 07885 088022; e-mail - ronthomas@somervaleantiquesglass. co.uk; website - www.somervaleantiquesglass. co.uk. SER: Valuations; buys at auction; trains to Bath met by arrangement. VAT: Stan/Spec.**

NETHER STOWEY, Nr. Bridgwater

House of Antiquity
St. Mary St. TA5 1LJ. (M. S. Todd). Est. 1967. Open 10-5 or by appointment. SIZE: Medium. *STOCK: Philatelic literature, world topographical, maps, handbooks, postcards, ephemera, postal history.* LOC: A39. PARK: Easy. TEL: 01278 732426; fax - same; e-mail - mstodd@lineone.net. SER: Valuations; buys at auction. VAT: Stan.

NORTH NEWTON

Asianart. co. uk. Ltd.
Bigbere Farm, Cox Hill, TA7 0BT. (James Yarrow). Open by appointment. SIZE: Large. *STOCK: Architectural features, Chinese furniture.* LOC: Off junction 24, M5. PARK: Own. TEL: 01278 662535; website - www. asianart.co.uk. *Trade Only.*

NORTH PETHERTON

Jay's Antiques and Collectables
121A Fore St. TA6 6SA. (Mr. and Mrs Jose Alba). Est. 1982. Open 10-4. 30, Mon. 10-1. CL: Wed. *STOCK: Clocks including Victorian, mantel and wall, £50-£400; pressed and coloured glass, £15-£45; china, £10-£85.* LOC: Main st. PARK: Easy. TEL: Home - 01278 662508; mobile - 07815 734965. SER: Repairs (clocks). FAIRS: Talisman.

PORLOCK

Magpie Antiques & Collectables
High St. TA24 8PT. (Glenys Battams). Est. 1980. Opening times vary, prior telephone call advisable. SIZE: Medium. *STOCK: Jewellery and silver; 19th C glass including scent bottles, decorative objects; 18th-19th C pottery and porcelain.* LOC: Opposite Lorna Doone Hotel. PARK: Nearby. TEL: 01271 850669; fax - same; mobile - 07721 679020. SER: Valuations. FAIRS: NEC, Westonbirt, Tetbury, Newark, Westpoint, Shepton Mallet.

QUEEN CAMEL, Nr. Yeovil

Steven Ferdinando
The Old Vicarage. BA22 7NG. PBFA. Est. 1978. Open by appointment. *STOCK: Antiquarian and secondhand books.* PARK: Own. TEL: 01935 850210; e-mail - stevenferdinando@onetel. net.uk. SER: Valuations. FAIRS: Shepton Mallet.

SHEPTON MALLET

Edward Marnier Antiques
Old Bowlish House, Forum Lane, Bowlish. BA4 5JA. (E. F. Marnier). Resident. BABAADA. Est. 1989. Open 7 days, prior telephone call advisable. *STOCK: English and Continental furniture, pictures, rugs, carpets and interesting decorative objects, 17th-20th C, £5-£10,000.* LOC: Quarter mile from Shepton Mallet on A371 Wells Rd., turn right into Forum Lane. PARK: Easy. TEL: 01749 343340; mobile - 07785 110122; e-mail - emarnier@ukonline.co.uk. SER: Valuations; buys at auction. VAT: Spec.

SOMERTON

John Gardiner Antiques
Monteclefe House. TA11 7NL. Est. 1974. Appointment advisable. *STOCK: General antiques; decorative Edwardian, Georgian and quality old reproduction furnishings.* LOC: A303, close to M5. TEL: 01458 272238; fax/answerphone - 01458 274329; mobile - 07831 274427; e-mail - rpash@fsbdial.co.uk.

The London Cigarette Card Co. Ltd
West St. TA11 6NB. (I.A. and E. K. Laker, F. C. Doggett and Y. Berktay). Est. 1927. Open daily. SIZE: Medium. *STOCK: Cigarette and trade cards, 1885 to date; sets from £1.50; other cards, from 15p; frames for mounting cards and special albums.* PARK: Easy. TEL: 01458 273452; e-mail - cards@londoncigcard.co.uk; website - www.londoncigcard.co.uk. SER: Publishers of catalogues, reference books and monthly magazine; mail order; monthly auctions.

Somerton Antiques Centre
Market Place. TA11 7NB. Est. 1998. Open 10-5, Sun. by appointment. SIZE: Large - 46 dealers. *STOCK: General antiques, £5-£1,800.* PARK: Own. TEL: 01458 274423. SER: Valuations; repairs; restorations (furniture). FAIRS: Shepton Mallet.

SOUTH PETHERTON

Rostrum Antiques
The Old Flaxmill, Flaxdrayton, Drayton. TA13 5LR. BABAADA. Est. 1988. Open by appointment. SIZE: Medium. *STOCK: 18th-19th C English and Continental furniture, fine collector's boxes, objets d'art, £100-£5,000.* LOC: Near A303. PARK: Easy. TEL: 01460 249249; e-mail - rostrum.uk@virgin.net. SER: Valuations; gilding; French polishing; restorations (antique furniture and musical instruments only); replica dining tables and other furniture designed and hand-made to order; interior decoration. VAT: Spec.

STOKE-SUB-HAMDON

Wessex Antique Bedsteads
Percombe. TA14 6RD. (Jeremy Peachell). Est. 1991. Open 9-6, Sat. 10-5, Sun. and other times by appointment. SIZE: Large. *STOCK: Brass, iron and wooden bedsteads, including four-poster and half-tester, mainly Victorian and Edwardian.* LOC: Adjacent A303, north of Yeovil. PARK: Easy. TEL: 01935 829147; home - same; fax - 01935 829148; mobile - 07973 884079; e-mail - info@wessexbeds.com; website - www.wessexbeds.com. SER: Restorations (wooden and metal beds); bespoke mattresses and bases; delivery and shipping.

TAUNTON

T. J. Atkins
East Criddles Farm, Tolland, Lydeard St. Lawrence. TA4 3PW. Est. 1958. Open by appointment. SIZE: Medium. *STOCK: Porcelain and pottery including Prattware, 18th-19th C.* TEL: 01984 667310.

Cider Press Antiques Centre
58 Bridge St. TA1 1UD. (Norman D. J. Clarke and Mark W. J. Blake). Est. 1998. Open 10-5, Sun. 11-4. SIZE: Medium - 10 dealers. *STOCK: Furniture, including painted, Georgian to Victorian, £100-£1,000; jewellery, silver and plate, ceramics, glass, collectables, stamps, postcards, records and books; reclamation items.* LOC: Near town centre. PARK: Nearby. TEL: 01823 283050; fax - same; mobile - 07764 212520; home - 01823 661354. SER: Valuations; restorations (ceramics and furniture).

Selwoods
Queen Anne Cottage, Mary St. TA1 3PE. Est.

From an article entitled "Collecting Images and Symbols - Part 1: Byzantium" by Robin Peverett which appeared in the June 2002 issue of *Antique Collecting*. For more details and to subscribe see page 21.

1927. Open 9. 30-5. SIZE: Very large. *STOCK: Furniture, including Victorian and Edwardian.* PARK: Own at rear. TEL: 01823 272780.

Taunton Antiques Market - Silver Street
25/29 Silver St. TA1 3DH. (Bath Antiques Market Ltd). Est. 1978. Open Mon. 9-4 including Bank Holidays. SIZE: 100+ dealers. *STOCK: General antiques and collectables, including specialists in most fields.* LOC: 2 miles from M5, junction 25, to town centre, 100yds. from Sainsburys car park across lights. PARK: Easy - Sainsburys (town centre branch). TEL: 01823 289327; fax - same; enquiries - 020 7969 1500. SER: Valuations.

M. G. Welch Jeweller
1 Corporation St. TA1 4AJ. (Mark and Liz Welch). NAG. Est. 1985. Open 9.30-5. SIZE: Medium. *STOCK: Antique and secondhand jewellery, £100-£10,000; antique and secondhand silver, £100-£1,000; early 20th C masters including Cartier, Tiffany, Georg Jensen, Chaumet.* LOC: Town centre, corner of High St. PARK: Nearby. TEL: 01823 270456; fax - same; e-mail - sales@mgwelch.com. SER: Valuations; restorations (jewellery). VAT: Stan/Spec.

WATCHET

Clarence House Antiques
41 Swain St. TA23 0AE. Est. 1970. Open 10.30-5.30. CL: Sun. in winter. SIZE: Medium. *STOCK: General antiques, pine, brass, copper, bric-a-brac, collectables and books (including specialist and antiquarian).* PARK: Nearby. TEL: 01984 631389. VAT: Stan.

Nick Cotton Fine Art
Beachstone House, 46/47 Swain St. TA23 0AG. (Nick and Lynda Cotton). Est. 1970. Open 10-6. SIZE: Large. *STOCK: Paintings, 1850-2000; some period furniture.* PARK: Adjacent. TEL: 01984 631814; website - www.thelyndacotton gallery.co.uk. SER: Restorations; conservation; research. VAT: Spec.

WELLINGTON

Michael and Amanda Lewis Oriental Carpets and Rugs   `LAPADA`
8 North St. TA21 8LT. UKIC. Est. 1982. Open 10-1 and 2-5. 30, Mon. and weekends by appointment. SIZE: Medium. *STOCK: Oriental carpets and rugs, mainly 19th-20th C, £25-£25,000.* LOC: 1 mile from junction 26, M5. PARK: 100yds. TEL: 01823 667430; e-mail - rugmike@btopenworld.com. SER: Valuations;

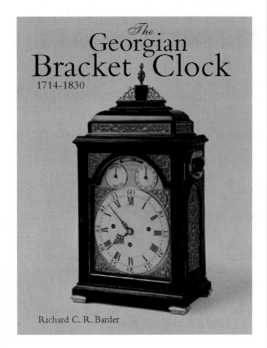

The Georgian
Bracket Clock
1714-1830

Richard C. R. Barder

Tremendous advances in clock making technology in the last decades of the seventeenth century ensured that by 1714, when George I ascended the throne, British clockmakers were acknowledged to be the best in the world. Of the many superior clocks made in England from 1714 to 1830, the majority were bracket clocks. In this definitive volume, Richard Barder, a retired dealer, shares his knowledge and admiration for these fascinating clocks with the reader.

In this superbly written book, Barder discusses case making and the specialists linked to the clock maker, the workings of the Clockmakers' Company, the development of the bracket clock in the Georgian period, notable makers, lacquer-based bracket clocks, the export trade, and the purchase, repair and restoration of bracket clocks.

The Georgian Bracket Clock has been acknowledged as the best single reference book on the subject and is essential for all dealers, collectors and students of horology.

- *An overview of the business of clock making at a time when British clock makers were acknowledged as the best in the world*

- *Presents the history of eighteenth century and early nineteenth century English bracket clocks*

- *Will appeal to the general reader, collector and specialist alike*

- *Is the best single reference on the subject*

- *A reprint of a much sought-after book*

11 x 8½in./279 x 216mm.
1 85149 158 9
236pp., 39 col., 267 b.&w.
£45.00

Available from all good booksellers and direct from the publisher:
ANTIQUE COLLECTORS' CLUB
Sandy Lane, Old Martlesham, Woodbridge, Suffolk, IP12 4SD.
Tel: 01394 389950
Fax: 01394 389999
Email: sales@antique-acc.com
Website: www.antique-acc.com

restorations; repairs; cleaning; restoration and conservation (tapestry).

WELLS

Bernard G. House
Market Place. BA5 2RF. Est. 1963. Open 9.30-5.30. SIZE: Medium. *STOCK: Barometers and scientific instruments, barographs, telescopes, tripod and hand held; furniture including miniatures and apprentice pieces, 18th-19th C; longcase and bracket clocks, metalware, decorative and architectural items.* PARK: Opposite shop. TEL: 01749 672607. SER: Repairs; restorations. VAT: Stan/Spec.

Marshalls of Wells
7 Mill St. BA5 2AS. (Trevor Marshall). Est. 1982. Open 10-5 or by appointment. SIZE: Large. *STOCK: General antiques, antique and reproduction pine, rugs and carpets.* LOC: Town centre. PARK: Easy. TEL: 01749 672489; mobile - 07092 109431; e-mail - info@marshalls-uk.com; website - www.marshalls-uk.com. SER: French polishing; pine stripping.

Sadler Street Gallery,
7a Sadler St. BA5 2RR. (Jill Swale). Est. 1993. Open 10-5. CL: Mon. *STOCK: 18th to early 20th C watercolours, oils and etchings; contemporary watercolours and oils mainly by West Country artists.* LOC: City centre. TEL: 01749 670220.

WEST BUCKLAND, Nr. Taunton

Everett Fine Art Ltd
Budleigh Studios, Budleigh. (Tim and Karen Everett). Open by appointment. *STOCK: Fine paintings and furniture, £1,000-£10,000+.* LOC: 3 miles from junction 26, M5. PARK: Easy. TEL: 01823 421710; e-mail - info@everett-art.co.uk; website - www.everett-art.co.uk. SER: Restorations; conservation (paintings and frames); framemakers. VAT: Stan/Spec.

WESTON-SUPER-MARE

D. M. Restorations
3 Laburnum Rd. BS23 3LL. (D. Pike). Open 9-5. *STOCK: Small mahogany furniture.* PARK: Easy. TEL: 01934 811120.

Sterling Books
43A Locking Rd. BS23 3DG. ABA. PBFA. ILAB. Est. 1966. Open 10-5. 30. CL: Mon. and Thurs.pm. SIZE: Large. *STOCK: Books, antiquarian and secondhand, some new; ephemera and prints.* PARK: Easy. TEL: 01934 625056; e-mail - sterling.books@talk21.com. SER: Bookbinding; picture framing.

Winter's Antiques
LAPADA
62 Severn Rd. BS23 1DT. (R. N. and E. P. Winters). Open 9-12 and 2-3.30. CL: Sat. pm. and Thurs. SIZE: Large. *STOCK: Furniture, clocks, smalls and fine art, all periods.* LOC: Off sea front. PARK: Easy. TEL: 01934 620118/814610.

WILLITON

Courtyard Antiques
Home Farm Holiday Centre, St. Audries. TA4 4DP. (Nick Wass and Liz Cain). Est. 1997. Open 9-4, Sat. 9-1, Sun. 10-4. CL: Wed. SIZE: Medium. *STOCK: English vernacular furniture - oak, elm and pine, upholstered chairs, mostly 18th-20th C, £100-£2,000.* LOC: Off the A39 at West Quantoxhead. PARK: Easy. TEL: 01984 633701; home - 01984 640314; e-mail - sales@courtyardantiques.net; website - www.courtyardantiques.net. VAT: Stan/ Spec.

Edward Venn
Unit 3, 52 Long St. TA4 4QU. Est. 1979. Open 10-5. *STOCK: Furniture, clocks.* TEL: 01984 632631. SER: Restorations (furniture, barometers and clocks).

WINCANTON

Green Dragon Antiques Centre
24 High St. BA9 9JF. (Mrs Sally Denning). Est. 1991. Open 10-5 including Sun. SIZE: 112 dealers. *STOCK: Wide variety of general antiques and collectables, £1-£1,000.* PARK: Own. TEL: 01963 34111/34702; fax - 01963 34111; website - www.greendragonantiques.com. SER: Valuations.

The Old Schoolrooms Antiques
16 Mill St. BA9 9AP. (P. L. Broomfield). Open 9-4 or by appointment. CL: Mon and Thurs. SIZE: Large. *STOCK: Georgian and Edwardian furniture, £50-£7,000+.* LOC: Left towards Bruton, left around side of post office, premises 100 yards on right. PARK: Easy. TEL: 01963 824259; mobile - 07768 726276; e-mail - old schoolrooms@aol.com. SER: Valuations; restorations (furniture). FAIRS: Newark.

Wincanton Antiques
12 High St. (Tony Kimber). Open 10-5. SIZE: Large. *STOCK: Georgian and Edwardian furniture, decorative items, £25-£7,000+.* PARK: Nearby. TEL: 01963 32223; e-mail - oldschoolrooms@aol.com. SER: Upholstery. FAIRS: Newark.

~ *The Old Schoolrooms Antiques* ~

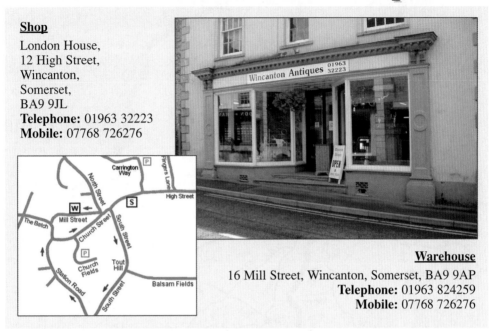

Shop

London House,
12 High Street,
Wincanton,
Somerset,
BA9 9JL
Telephone: 01963 32223
Mobile: 07768 726276

Warehouse

16 Mill Street, Wincanton, Somerset, BA9 9AP
Telephone: 01963 824259
Mobile: 07768 726276

www.oldschoolroomsantiques.com

WIVELISCOMBE

J. C. Giddings
TA4 2SN. Est. 1969. Open by appointment. SIZE: Large warehouses. *STOCK: Mainly 18th-19th C furniture, iron-work and reclamation timber.* PARK: Easy. TEL: 01984 623703. VAT: Stan. *Mainly Trade.*

Heads 'n' Tails
Bournes House, 41 Church St. TA4 2LT. (D. McKinley). Resident. Open by appointment. *STOCK: Taxidermy including Victorian cased and uncased birds, mammals and fish, £5-£2,000; decorative items, glass domes.* LOC: Opposite church. PARK: Easy. TEL: 01984 623097; fax - 01984 624445. SER: Taxidermy; restorations; commissions; hire. VAT: Spec.

Yew Tree Antiques Warehouse
Old Brewery, Golden Hill. TA4 2NA. (Nigel and Sheila Nation). Est. 1997. Open Tues. -Fri. 10-4. 30, Sat. 10-5. SIZE: Large. *STOCK: English and French furniture, mainly Victorian and Edwardian, some Georgian including French beds, armoires, buffets, chairs, tables, mirrors, pot cupboards, wash stands, over mantels, desks, piano stools, £25-£750; china, glass and pictures,*

£3-£100. PARK: Easy. TEL: 01984 623950; home - 01984 623914; mobile - 07714 266667; website - www.yewtreeantiques.co.uk.

YEOVIL

John Hamblin
Unit 6, 15 Oxford Rd., Penn Mill Trading Estate. BA21 5HR. (J. and M. A. Hamblin). Est. 1980. Open 8.30-5. CL: Sat. SIZE: Small. *STOCK: Furniture, 1750-1900, £300-£3,000.* PARK: Easy. TEL: 01935 471154; home - 01935 476673. SER: Restorations (furniture); cabinet work; French polishing. VAT: Stan.

Alan & Kathy Stacey Tea Caddies & Fine Boxes `LAPADA`
BAFRA. Resident. Est. 1989. Open any time by appointment. SIZE: Medium. *STOCK: Tea caddies and boxes, tortoiseshell, ivory, MOP, shagreen, horn, wooden, 1770-1930.* LOC: 2 miles from A303. PARK: Own. TEL: 01963 441333; home - same; fax - 01963 441330; mobile - 07810 058078; website - www. antiqueboxes.uk.com. SER: Valuations; restorations; conservation; consultancy; search; worldwide collection and delivery. FAIRS: LAPADA. VAT: Stan/Spec.

STAFFORDSHIRE

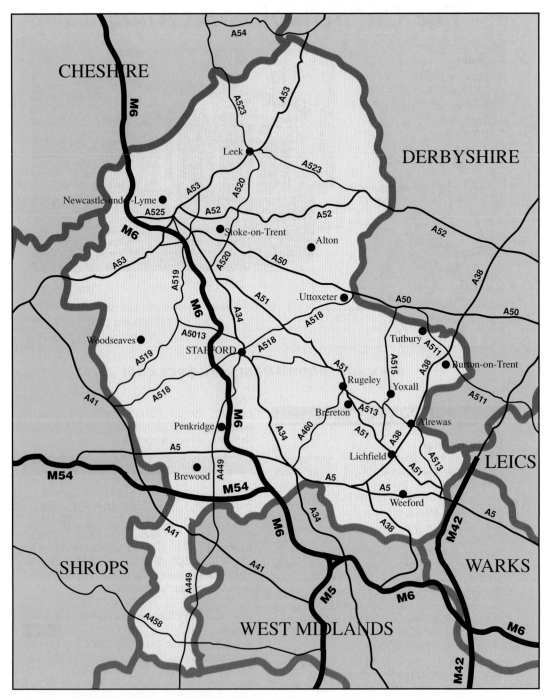

Dealers and Shops in Staffordshire

Alrewas	1	Lichfield	7	Tutbury	3
Alton	1	Newcastle-under-Lyme	2	Uttoxeter	1
Brereton	1	Penkridge	2	Weeford	1
Brewood	1	Rugeley	1	Woodseaves	1
Burton-on-Trent	3	Stafford	1	Yoxall	1
Leek	13	Stoke-on-Trent	5		

ALREWAS, Nr. Burton-on-Trent

Poley Antiques
5 Main St. DE13 7AA. (D.T. and A.G. Poley).
Est. 1977. Open Thurs. and Fri. 10-5.30, Sat. 10-
5, other times by appointment. SIZE: Small.
*STOCK: General antiques, furniture, silver,
china, glass, copper, brass.* Not Stocked: Stamps,
coins and militaria. LOC: 20yds. from A38,
between Lichfield and Burton. PARK: Own.
TEL: 01283 791151; home/fax - same; e-mail -
dennis.poley@which.net.

BRERETON, Nr. Rugeley

Rugeley Antique Centre
161/3 Main Rd. WS15 1DX. (D. and N.
Edwards). Est. 1979. Open 9-5, Sun. 12-4.30.
SIZE: Large - 40 units. *STOCK: China, glass,
pottery, pictures, furniture, pine, treen, linen and
shipping goods.* LOC: A51, one mile south of
Rugeley town, opposite Cedar Tree Hotel. PARK:
Own. TEL: 01889 577166; e-mail - info@
rugeleyantiquecentre.co.uk; website - www.
rugeleyantiquecentre.co.uk. VAT: Stan/Spec.

BREWOOD

Passiflora
25 Stafford St. ST19 9DX. (David and Paula
Whitfield). Est. 1988. Flexible opening - usually
open 10-4ish, prior telephone call advisable.
SIZE: Medium. *STOCK: General antiques,
collectables, curios, copper, brass, Mabel Lucie
Attwell corner, Victorian to 1950's, £1-£300.*
LOC: Off A5 and A449 near Gailey roundabout,
village on Shropshire Union canal. PARK: Free
opposite. TEL: 01902 851557 (answerphone);
mobile - 07711 682216; e-mails - paula.whitfield
@ukonline.co.uk and whitfield@passiflora25.
fsnet.co.uk. SER: Valuations. FAIRS: Bingley
Hall; Stafford.

BURTON-UPON-TRENT

Burton Antiques
1-2 Horninglow Rd. DE14 2PR. (C.H. Armett).
Est. 1977. Open 10-5 including Sun. SIZE: Large.
STOCK: Shipping and pine furniture. LOC:
A511. PARK: Nearby. TEL: 01283 542331. SER:
Valuations; stripping (pine); buys at auction.

M.A.J. Morris
Weavers Green, Needwood. DE13 9PQ. Est.
1993. Open by appointment only. SIZE: Small.
*STOCK: Maps, plans, charts and prints, atlases,
county histories, documents and paintings, 1550-
1950, £5-£1,000.* LOC: Telephone for directions.

PARK: Easy. TEL: 01283 575344. SER:
Valuations. VAT: Stan. *Mainly Trade.*

Justin Pinewood Ltd
The Maltings, Wharf Rd. DE14 1PZ. (S.
Silvester). Open 9-5.30, including Sun. *STOCK:
Stripped pine furniture and decorative
accessories.* TEL: 01283 510860; website -
www.justinpinewood.co.uk.

LEEK

Antiques Within Ltd
Ground Floor, Compton Mill. ST13. (R. and K.
Hicks). Est. 1992. Open 10-5.30. Sun. (Oct. to
April) 1-5.30. *STOCK: Pine, oak and mahogany,
£50-£3,000; bric-a-brac, £5-£500.* LOC: A520
towards Cheddleton, opposite Catholic church.
PARK: Easy. TEL: 01538 387848; e-mail -
antiques.within@virgin.net; website - www.
antiques-within.com. SER: Restorations; courier,
packing and shipping. FAIRS: Newark;
Swinderby. VAT: Stan.

Anvil Antiques Ltd
Cross Mills, Cross St. ST13 6BL. (J.S. Spooner
and N.M. Sullivan). Est. 1975. Open 9-5, Sat. 10-
5, Sun. 12-4. SIZE: Large. *STOCK: Stripped
pine, old and reproduction; oak, mahogany, bric-
a-brac and decorative items, architectural items.*
LOC: Ashbourne Rd., from town centre
roundabout, turn first left, Victorian mill on right.
PARK: Easy. TEL: 01538 371657. VAT: Stan.

England's Gallery
Ball Haye House, 1 Ball Haye Terr. ST13 6AP.
(F.J. and S. England). Est. 1968. Open 10-12.30
and 1.30-5.30, Mon. and other times by
appointment. SIZE: Large. *STOCK: Oils and
watercolours, 18th-19th C, £500-£10,000;
etchings, engravings, lithographs, mezzotints,
£50-£4,000.* LOC: Towards Ball Haye Green
from A523 turn at lights. PARK: Nearby. TEL:
01538 373451. SER: Valuations; restorations;
cleaning; relining; regilding; framing; mount
cutting; buys at auction (paintings). VAT: Stan.

Gemini Trading
Limes Mill, Abbotts Rd. ST13 6EY. (T.J.
Lancaster and Mrs Y.A. Goldstraw). Est. 1981.
Open Mon.-Fri. 9-5, other times by appointment.
SIZE: Large. *STOCK: Antique pine, £25-£1,500;
decorative items, £10-£200.* LOC: Turn off A53
along Abbotts Rd. before town centre. PARK:
Easy. TEL: 01538 387834; fax - 01538 399819;
e-mail - geminitrading@lineone.net. VAT: Stan.

Gilligans Antiques
59 St. Edward St. ST13 5DN. (M.T. Gilligan). Est. 1977. Open 9-5.30. *STOCK: Victorian and Edwardian furniture*. TEL: 01538 384174.

Roger Haynes - Antiques Finder
31 Compton. ST13 5NJ. Open by appointment. *STOCK: Pine, smalls and decorative items*. TEL: 01538 385161; fax - same.

Jewel Antiques
'Whitegates', 63 Basford Bridge Lane, Cheddleton. ST13 7EQ. (B. and D. Jeacott-Smith). Est. 1967. Open by appointment. *STOCK: Paintings, prints, jewellery, oil lamps, small furniture and clocks, 18th-19th C, £25-£2,000*. PARK: Easy. TEL: 01538 360744; fax - same.

Johnson's
Chorley Mill, 1 West St. ST13 8HA. (P.M. and Mrs. J.H. Johnson). Est. 1976. Open 9-5, Sat. and Sun by appointment. SIZE: Large. *STOCK: 18th-19th C English, Eastern European and French country furniture, £50-£2,000; decorative accessories, £10-£500*. PARK: Own. TEL: 01538 386745; fax - same; e-mail - johnsonantiques@btconnnect.com.

The Leek Antiques Centre (Barclay House)
4-6 Brook St. ST13 5JE. Est. 1977. Open 10.30-5, Sun. by appointment. SIZE: 3 floors - 17 showrooms. *STOCK: Extending dining tables, sets of chairs, chests of drawers, bedroom furniture, pine, pottery, watercolours and oils, upholstered furniture*. TEL: 01538 398475. SER: Valuations; restorations (furniture). FAIRS: Bowman's and West Midland, Staffordshire Showground. VAT: Stan/Spec.

Molland Antique Mirrors
2 Duke St. ST13 5LG. (John Molland). Est. 1980. Open 8-5. SIZE: Medium. *STOCK: Mirrors - gilt, painted and wooden, 19th C, £350-£4,000*. LOC: On A53 from Stoke-on-Trent, right at 1st traffic lights, shop 200 yards on left. PARK: Easy. TEL: 01538 372553; e-mail - sales@mollandmirrors.co.uk; website - www.mollandmirrors.co.uk. SER: Export packing; restorations; special commissions. FAIRS: NEC. VAT: Stan/Spec. *Mainly Trade*.

Odeon Antiques
76-78 St. Edward St. ST13 5DL. (Steve Ford). Est. 1990. Open 11-5. *STOCK: Lighting, beds, pine and general antiques*. TEL: 01538 387188; fax - same. SER: Restorations (lighting).

Page Antiques
Ground Floor, Compton Mill. ST13 5NJ. (Denis and Alma Page). Est. 1974. Open 10-5.30, Sun. 1-5 (winter only). SIZE: Medium. *STOCK: Georgian to Edwardian furniture, stripped pine and decorative items*. LOC: Town centre. PARK: Easy. TEL: Mobile - 07966 154993. SER: Courier. FAIRS: Newark; Swinderby; Buxton. VAT: Stan/Spec.

Period Features
60B St Edward St. ST13 5DL. (Lucie Storrs). Est. 2001. Open 10-5. SIZE: Small. *STOCK: Antique and reproduction hardware and ironmongery; Farrow and Ball paints and papers*. PARK: Limited. TEL: 01538 372202; e-mail - enquiries @periodfeatures.net.

LEIGH, Nr. Stoke-on-Trent

John Nicholls
Open by appointment. *STOCK: Oak furniture and related items, 17th-18th C*. TEL: 01538 702339; mobile - 07836 244024.

LICHFIELD

Mike Abrahams Books
9 Burton Old Rd., Streethay. WS13 8LJ. Est. 1975. Open by appointment. SIZE: Large. *STOCK: Books and ephemera especially Midlands topography, sport, transport, children's, illustrated, military and antiquarian, 17th C to date, £2-£1,000*. LOC: Last but one right turn A5127 Lichfield to Burton-on-Trent before road joins A38 by-pass, house on left near corner. PARK: Easy. TEL: 01543 256200; home - same. SER: Valuations. FAIRS: Stafford, Bingley Hall and Pavillion; Midland Antiquarian Book (organiser).

Cordelia and Perdy's Den Of Antiquity
53 Tamworth St. WS13 6JW. (C.R.J. and J. Mellor-Whiting). Est. 1974. Open 10-4, Sat. 10-5, Mon. and other times by appointment. SIZE: 2 rooms. *STOCK: General antiques and trade shipping goods*. PARK: Opposite. TEL: 01543 263223.

The Essence of Time
Unit 2 Curborough Hall Farm Antiques & Craft Centre, Watery Lane, Off Eastern Ave. WS13 8ES. (M.T.O. Hinton). Est. 1990. Open Wed.-Sun. 10.30-5. SIZE: Medium. *STOCK: Clocks - 30 hour and 8 day longcase, 1700-1900; Vienna regulator wall, English and French wall; mantel and novelty*. LOC: North of Lichfield. PARK: Own large. TEL: 01543 418239; home - 01902 764900; mobile - 07944 245064.

Winders
—oOo—
Fine Art and Antiques
Telephone: (01782) 712483 Mobile: 07881 652425

The market town of Newcastle, in North Staffordshire, is home to Winders, a well organised antique and fine art shop. Famous for it's Doulton, Minton and Lambeth, it is equally well known for it's 18th Century furniture. Well worth a visit, a warm welcome to be expected.

Opening Hours: 10.00 am until 5.00 pm
                        Monday to Saturday
                        Thursday by appt. only

31 Bridge Street, Newcastle-under-Lyme, Staffordshire, ST5 2RY.

James A. Jordan
7 The Corn Exchange. WS13. CMBHI. Open 9-5. *STOCK: Clocks, longcase, barometers, jewellery and small furniture.* LOC: Market Sq. city centre. PARK: Nearby. TEL: 01543 416221. SER: Restorations (clocks and chronometers).

Milestone Antiques `LAPADA`
5 Main St., Whittington. WS14 9JU. (Humphrey and Elsa Crawshaw). Resident. Est. 1988. Open Thurs.-Sat. 10-6, Sun. 11-3, other times by appointment. *STOCK: Georgian and Victorian British furniture, ceramics (especially Coalport), copper and other decorative items.* LOC: A51 Lichfield/Tamworth road, turn north at Whittington Barracks, shop 50yds. past crossroads in village centre. PARK: Easy. TEL: 01543 432248. VAT: Spec.

L. Royden Smith
Church View, Farewell Lane, Burntwood. WS7 9DP. Est. 1972. Open Sat. and Sun. 10-4 or by appointment. *STOCK: Secondhand books, general antiques, bric-a-brac.* PARK: Nearby. TEL: 01543 682217.

Brett Wilkins Ltd
Cranebrook Farm, Cranebrook Lane, Hilton. WS14 0EY. Est. 1983. Open by appointment. SIZE: Large. *STOCK: Shipping, export and French furniture.* PARK: Easy. TEL: 01543 483662; mobile - 07860 541260. FAIRS: Newark. VAT: Stan. *Export Only.*

NEWCASTLE-UNDER-LYME

Antique Forum
The Stones. ST5 2AG. Open Tues. 8-3. SIZE: 70 tables. *STOCK: General antiques.* PARK: Easy. TEL: 01278 595805.

Winder's Fine Art and Antiques
31 Bridge St. ST5 2RY. (S. Winder). Est. 1996. Open 10-5, Thurs. by appointment. SIZE: Medium. *STOCK: Furniture, oak, walnut, mahogany, 17th-19th C, £50-£10,000; longcase, mantel and wall clocks, £150-£4,000; paintings, £35-£3,000, both 18th-19th C; ceramics, especially Doulton Lambeth, and watercolours, 19th C, £15-£1,500; silver, £50-£2,000.* Not Stocked: Pine and ephemera. LOC: Close to Sainsburys and the Magistrates Courts. TEL: 01782 712483; mobile - 07881 652425. SER: Valuations; restorations; gilding; repairs (clocks). VAT: Spec.

PENKRIDGE, Nr. Stafford

Golden Oldies
1 and 5 Crown Bridge. ST19 5AA. (W.A. and M.A. Knowles). Est. 1980. Open 9.30-5.30, Mon. 9.30-1.30. *STOCK: Victorian, Edwardian and later furniture; paintings, decorative items.* LOC: 2 miles south junction 13, M6. PARK: Easy. TEL: 01785 714722. FAIRS: Newark. VAT: Global.

Inside Out (Stafford) Ltd
Coppice House, Teddesley. ST19 5RP. (H. and V. Barnes). Est. 1981. Open 10-5, Sun. 12-4. CL: Mon. SIZE: Large. *STOCK: Furniture, 1860-1940 and reproduction.* LOC: Outskirts of town. PARK: Easy. TEL: 01785 714900; home - 01785 660336. SER: Valuations; restorations. VAT: Stan.

RUGELEY

Eveline Winter
1 Wolseley Rd. WS15 2QH. (Mrs E. Winter). Est. 1962. Open Thurs.-Sat. 10.30-5 appointment advisable. SIZE: Small. *STOCK: Staffordshire figures, pre-Victorian, from £90; Victorian, £30-£500; copper, brass, glass and general antiques.* Not Stocked: Coins and weapons. LOC: Coming from Lichfield or Stafford stay on A51 and avoid town by-pass. PARK: Easy and at side of shop. TEL: 01889 583259.

STAFFORD

Windmill Antiques
9 Castle Hill, Broadeye. ST16 2QB. Est. 1990. Open 10-5. SIZE: Medium - several dealers. *STOCK: General antiques and decorative items.* LOC: Opposite Sainsbury's. PARK: Easy. TEL: 01785 228505; website - www.windmillantiques stafford.co.uk. SER: Valuations; restorations (ceramics).

STOKE-ON-TRENT

Ann's Antiques
26 Leek Rd., Stockton Brook. ST9 9MN. (Ann Byatte). Est. 1980. Open Fri. and Sat. 10-5 and by appointment. SIZE: Small. *STOCK: Victorian and Edwardian glass, porcelain, furniture, brass, copper, jewellery, paintings, pottery and unusual items; toys, rocking horses, teddies, dolls and doll's houses.* LOC: A53 main road between Hanley and Leek. PARK: Opposite. TEL: 01782 503991. SER: Valuations. VAT: Stan.

Burslem Antiques & Collectables
11 Market Place, Burslem. ST6 6AA. (D. Bradbury). Est. 1972. Open 9.30-5.30, Sun. and Bank Holidays 10-4. SIZE: Large. *STOCK: Pottery and porcelain including Minton, Doulton, Wedgwood, Worcester, Goss, Spode, Copeland, S Allcock, George Jones, Carlton, MacIntyre, Moorcroft, Moor Bros., Cauldon, Shelley, Paragon, Royal Stanley, 1750's to date.* LOC: Main road. PARK: At rear and town centre. TEL: 01782 577855; fax - 01782 577222; mobile - 07801 473524; home - 01782 710711; e-mail - info@burslemantiques.co.uk; website - www. burslemantiques.co.uk; www.burslemantiques. com. SER: Valuations; packing and shipping worldwide.

The Potteries Antique Centre Ltd
271 Waterloo Rd., Cobridge. ST6 3HR. (W. Buckley). Est. 1972. Open 9-5.30. SIZE: Large + trade and export warehouse. *STOCK: Pottery and porcelain including Doulton, Moorcroft, Beswick, Wedgwood, Coalport, Shelley, 19th and especially 20th C British; collectors' items, silver plate, clocks, brass, jewellery, pictures, furniture, 18th-20th C, £1-£5,000.* LOC: Off M6, junction 15 or 16 on to A500, follow signs for Festival Park or Potteries Shopping Centre. PARK: Easy. TEL: 01782 201455; fax - 01782 201518; 01782 286622 (auctions); e-mail - info@potteries antiquecentre.com; website - www.potteries antiquecentre.com. SER: Valuations; export facilities - supply and packing; buys at auction (pottery and collectors' items); pottery auctions held on site. FAIRS: Newark. VAT: Stan/Spec.

The Pottery Buying Centre
535 Etruria Rd., Basford. ST4 6HT. (Paul Hume). Est. 1989. Open 10-4. SIZE: 2 floors. *STOCK: Pottery and porcelain, 19th-20th C; collectables, 20th C; furniture, 18th-20th C; all £10-£1,000.* PARK: Easy. TEL: 01782 635453; home - same. SER: Valuations; restorations.

Top of the Hill (Ceramic Search)
12/14/14a Nile St., Burslem. ST6 2AF. (A. and J. Phillips). Est. 1980. Open 9.30-5, Sun. by appointment. SIZE: Large. *STOCK: Ceramics, antique and collectable, £50-£100; curios, antique and reproduction furniture, £50-£1,000.* LOC: Follow Royal Doulton signs from A500, premises opposite factory shop. PARK: Easy. TEL: 01782 834506; fax - same; e-mail - info@ ceramicsearch.co.uk; website - www.ceramic search.co.uk. SER: Valuations; restorations (ceramics); buys at auction (ceramics). FAIRS: Doulton.

TUTBURY, Nr. Burton-on-Trent

R.A. James - The Clock Shop
1 High St. DE13 9LP. (Rob and Alison James). MBHI. Est. 1988. Open 10-5. SIZE: Medium. *STOCK: Longcase, bracket and wall clocks, £500-£10,000.* LOC: 2 miles from A38/A50 junction. PARK: Easy. TEL: 01283 814596; fax - 01283 814594; website - www.antique-clocks-watches.co.uk. SER: Valuations; restorations (clocks). VAT: Stan/Spec.

Old Chapel Antique & Collectables Centre
High St. DE13 9LP. (Roger Clarke). OCS. Est. 1996. Open 10-5 including Sun., other times by appointment. SIZE: Large. *STOCK: China, glass, furniture.* PARK: Easy. TEL: 01283 815255; mobile - 07774 238775; e-mail - rocla@supanet.com. SER: Mail order. FAIRS: Swinderby.

Tutbury Mill Antiques Centre
Tutbury Mill Mews, Lower High St. DE13 9LU. Open 10.30-5.30, Sun. 12-5. SIZE: Large. *STOCK: General antiques including collectables, china and pine, from 18th C, £10-£2,500.* PARK: Easy. TEL: 01283 520074. SER: Valuations. VAT: Stan/Spec.

UTTOXETER

White House Antiques
50-52 Bridge St. ST14 8AP. (Christopher White). Est. 1983. Open 10-4.30. CL: Mon. SIZE: Medium. *STOCK: Victorian and Edwardian furniture, £100-£500; Beswick pottery, £10-£700; Beatrix Potter figures, £15-£450.* LOC: Next to Wheatsheaf public house, on Market Sq. PARK: Nearby. TEL: 01889 569344; home/fax - 01889 500380. SER: Valuations; restorations (pottery); buys at auction (Beswick, furniture).

WEEFORD, Nr. Lichfield

Blackbrook Antiques Village
London Rd. WS14 0PS. Open Tues.-Sun. 10-5.30. SIZE: 6 large showrooms. *STOCK: Architectural antiques including fireplaces, lighting, garden statuary, stained glass, furniture.* LOC: A38. PARK: Own. TEL: 01543 481450; fax - same. SER: Delivery and installation. VAT: Margin.

WOODSEAVES

AD Antiques
P O Box 1623. ST20 0SF. (Alison Davey). Open by appointment. *STOCK: British Art pottery, Arts and Crafts, Art Nouveau, Art Deco, £50-£2,000.*

TEL: 01785 284815; mobile - 07939 508171; e-mail - alison@adantiques.freeserve.co.uk; website - www.adantiques.com. SER: Valuations; buys at auction; mail order through website. FAIRS: NEC; Bingley Hall; Gaydon; Penmans Chester; Bailey's; GMEX; SECC. VAT: Spec.

YOXALL, Nr. Burton-on-Trent

H.W. Heron and Son Ltd `LAPADA`
The Antique Shop, 1 King St. DE13 8NF. (H.N.M., J. and P.D. Heron). Est. 1949. Open 9-6, Sat. 9-5.30, Sun. 2-6, Bank Holidays 10.30-5.30. SIZE: Medium. *STOCK: 18th-19th C furniture, ceramics and decorative items.* LOC: A515 village centre, opposite church. PARK: Easy. TEL: 01543 472266; home - same; fax - 01543 473800; e-mail - shop@hwheronantiques.com; website - www.hwheronantiques.com. SER: Valuations. VAT: Spec.

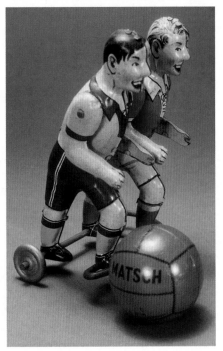

Football is always popular with boys and this unusual toy would have been attractive. Made in West Germany after the last war, it would sell for about £200. (Jane Vandell Associates)

From an article entitled "Tin Toys" by Andrew Edwards which appeared in the May 2003 issue of **Antique Collecting**. For more details and to subscribe see page 21.

SUFFOLK

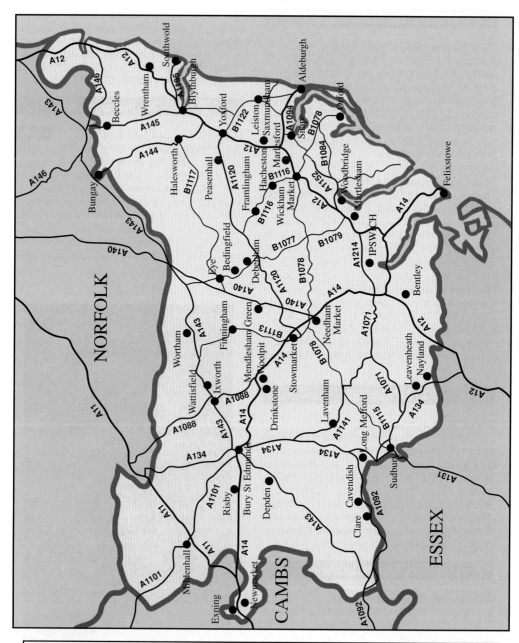

Dealers and Shops in Suffolk

Aldeburgh	2	Exning	1	Long Melford	16	Snape	1
Beccles	4	Eye	3	Marlesford	1	Southwold	5
Bedingfield	1	Felixstowe	1	Martlesham	2	Stowmarket	1
Bentley	1	Finningham	1	Mendlesham Green	1	Sudbury	3
Blythburgh	1	Framlingham	6	Mildenhall	1	Wattisfield	1
Bungay	4	Hacheston	1	Nayland	1	Wickham Market	2
Bury St. Edmunds	2	Halesworth	1	Needham Market	3	Woodbridge	10
Cavendish	1	Ipswich	9	Newmarket	2	Woolpit	1
Clare	4	Ixworth	1	Orford	1	Wortham	1
Debenham	5	Lavenham	4	Peasenhall	1	Wrentham	2
Depden	1	Leavenheath	1	Risby	1	Yoxford	2
Drinkstone	1	Leiston	2	Saxmundham	1		

HAMILTON ANTIQUES

5 Church Street, Woodbridge,
Suffolk IP12 1DH

Tel: (01394) 387222
Fax: (01394) 383832

E-mail: enquiries@hamiltonantiques.co.uk
Website: www.hamiltonantiques.co.uk

Members of LAPADA, The Association of Art and Antique Dealers, Rosemary and Hamilton Ferguson have been trading in Woodbridge since 1977. They have restored this superb 15th century building in Church Street to provide an imposing backcloth for a range of beautiful furniture.

The furniture includes pieces from the Edwardian, Victorian, William IV & Georgian period in mahogany, walnut, rosewood and occasionally oak. The furniture ranges from lovely inlaid items, smaller decorative pieces, sets of chairs, to larger items such as dining tables.

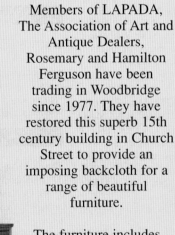

ALDEBURGH

Mole Hall Antiques
102 High St. IP15 5AB. (Peter Weaver). Est. 1976. Open 10-5, Sun. by appointment. SIZE: Small. *STOCK: Paintings, prints, unusual decorative items and country furniture.* PARK: Easy. TEL: 01728 452361; home - same.

Thompson's Gallery
175 High St. IP15 5AN. (J. and S. Thompson). Est. 1982. Open 10-5 or by appointment. SIZE: Large. *STOCK: 19th-20th C paintings; contemporary paintings and sculptures.* PARK: Easy. TEL: 01728 453743; e-mail - john@ thompsonsgallery.co.uk; website - www. thompsonsgallery.co.uk. VAT: Spec.

BECCLES

Besleys Books
4 Blyburgate. NR34 9TA. (P.A. and P.F. Besley). ABA. PBFA. Est. 1978. Open 9.30-1 and 2-5. CL: Wed. SIZE: Medium. *STOCK: Books, 50p-£1,000; prints, £7-£50; maps, £3-£100; all 17th-20th C.* LOC: Town centre. PARK: Nearby. TEL: 01502 715762; home - 01502 675649; e-mail - piers@besleysbooks.demon.co.uk; website - www.besleysbooks.demon.co.uk. SER: Valuations; restorations (book binding); buys at auction (books). FAIRS: Various ABA and PBFA.

Blyburgate Antiques
27-29 Blyburgate. NR34 9TB. (Mrs K. Lee). Resident. Est. 1997. Open 10-4.30. CL: Mon. and Wed. SIZE: Small. *STOCK: 19th-20th C china, jewellery, furniture and metalware, £5-£1,000.* PARK: Rainbow supermarket at rear. TEL: 01502 711174; fax/home - same. SER: Valuations; restorations (china). FAIRS: Alexandra Palace; Newmarket.

Fauconberges
8 Smallgate. NR34 9AD. (Richard D. Howard and Richard J. Crozier). Est. 1977. Open 10-5. SIZE: Large. *STOCK: Furniture, 1700-1900; pictures, clocks, glass, porcelain, silver.* LOC: Town centre. PARK: Easy. TEL: 01502 716147. SER: Valuations; delivery. FAIRS: Lomax, Langley (Autumn and Spring); Southwold; Burnham Market.

Saltgate Antiques
11 Saltgate. NR34 9AN. (A.M. Ratcliffe). Resident. Est. 1971. Open 10-5. CL: Wed. pm. SIZE: Medium. *STOCK: Furniture, 17th-19th C, £100-£4,500; clocks, collectors' items, brass, copper, Staffordshire figures, paintings and prints,* *19th C bric-a-brac, £5-£300.* LOC: Town centre opposite bus station. PARK: Easy. TEL: 01502 712776; e-mail - saltgate@macunlimited. net.

BEDINGFIELD, Nr. Eye

The Olde Red Lion
The Street. IP23 7LQ. Est. 1973. Open by appointment. *STOCK: Furniture and general antiques.* LOC: 3 miles from Eye, 2 miles from Debenham. TEL: 01728 628491. SER: Restorations (furniture, oil paintings, ceramics, snuff boxes, wood carvings).

BENTLEY, Nr. Ipswich

P. Dawson Furniture Restorers
Unit O, Dodnash Priory Farm. IP9 2DF. Est. 1996. Open 8-6, Sun. by appointment. SIZE: Small. *STOCK: Furniture, 17th-20th C, £50-£3,000.* LOC: Take Bentley turning off the A12 outside Ipswich, 1st right into Bergholt road, then 2nd left and follow the road round to farm estate. PARK: Easy. TEL: 01473 311947; e-mail - Paul @Dawson21.freeserve.co.uk. SER: Restorations (furniture).

BLYTHBURGH, Nr. Halesworth

E.T. Webster
Westwood Lodge. IP19 9NB. Open by appointment. SIZE: Large. *STOCK: Ancient oak beams, oak ceilings, panelling, quality reproduction oak furniture, doors, mullioned windows, oak framed barns.* TEL: 01502 478539.

BUNGAY

Black Dog Antiques
51 Earsham St. NR35 2PB. (K. Button). Est. 1986. Open seven days a week. *STOCK: General antiques including oak, mahogany and pine, china, linen and collectables, antiquities, Saxon and Roman, £1-£1000.* LOC: Opposite Post Office. PARK: Easy. TEL: 01986 895554. SER: Valuations.

Cork Brick Antiques
6 Earsham St. NR35 1AG. (G. and K. Skipper). Open 10.30-5.30. CL: Mon. *STOCK: Country and decorative antiques; architectural decoration.* PARK: Easy. TEL: 01986 894873; home - 01502 712646.

Friend or Faux
28 Earsham St. NR35 1AQ. (Kim Sisson and Jane Cudlipp). Resident. Est. 1993. Open Fri. and Sat. 10-5.30 (prior telephone call advisable on Fri.),

other days by appointment. *STOCK: Porcelain, 1800-1900, £50-£400; lighting, late 1800's to 1950, £100-£500; Victorian watercolours, £100-£200.* PARK: Nearby. TEL: 01986 896170; fax - 01502 714246. SER: Restorations (painted furniture, gilded pieces, porcelain).

One Step Back
4a Earsham St. NR35 1AQ. (Ian and Diane Wells). Est. 1970. Open 10-5. CL: Wed. SIZE: Medium. *STOCK: Furniture, from 17th C; porcelain and rugs, from 18th C; both £50-£3,000.* TEL: 01986 896626; home - 01508 550988. SER: Valuations; restorations. FAIRS: Halesworth, Bungay, Norwich.

BURY ST. EDMUNDS

The Enchanted Aviary
Lapwings, Rushbrooke Lane. IP33 2RS. (C.C. Frost). Est. 1970. Open by appointment. *STOCK: Cased and uncased mounted birds, animals and fish, mostly late Victorian, £15-£800.* PARK: Easy. TEL: 01284 725430. SER: Restorations.

Winston Mac (Silversmith)
65 St. John's St. IP33 1SJ. (E.W. McKnight). Est. 1978. Open 9-5. CL: Sun. except by appointment, and Sat. SIZE: Small. *STOCK: Silver tea services, creamers, salts, sugar casters, candlesticks, flatware.* PARK: Easy. TEL: 01284 767910. SER: Restorations (silver and plating). VAT: Stan/Spec.

CAVENDISH

Cavendish Rose Antiques
High St. CO10 8AF. (T. Patterson). Est. 1972. Open 10.30-5. SIZE: Large. *STOCK: Furniture, 18th-19th C mahogany, £150-£5,000.* PARK: Easy. TEL: 01787 282133. VAT: Spec.

CLARE, Nr. Sudbury

Robin Butler
The Old Bank House, Market Hill. CO10 8NN. Est. 1963. Open by appointment. SIZE: Large. *STOCK: Furniture, 18th-19th C, £200-£20,000; silver, 18th C, £80-£8,000; glass, 18th C, £20-£5,000; wine associated antiques, 17th-20th C, £50-£5,000.* LOC: Town centre. PARK: Easy. TEL: 01787 279111; e-mail - robin.butler@ btconnect.com. SER: Valuations. VAT: Spec.

Clare Antique Warehouse
The Mill, Malting Lane. CO10 8NW. Est. 1989. Open 9.30-5, Sun. 1-5. SIZE: Large - over 80 dealers. *STOCK: 17th-20th C furniture, textiles,*

pictures, porcelain, glass, silver, decorative items. LOC: 100yds. from High St. Follow signs for Clare Castle, Country Park. PARK: Easy. TEL: 01787 278449. SER: Valuations; restorations. VAT: Stan/Spec.

F.D. Salter Antiques
1-2 Church St. CO10 8NN. Est. 1959. Open 9-5. CL: Wed. pm. SIZE: Medium. *STOCK: 18th to early 19th C English furniture, porcelain and glass.* LOC: A1092. PARK: Easy. TEL: 01787 277693. SER: Valuations; restorations (furniture). FAIRS: West London. VAT: Stan/Spec.

Trinders' Fine Tools
Malting Lane. CO10 8NW. (P. and R. Trinder). PBFA. Est. 1975. Open 10-1 and 2-5, Wed. and Sat. 10-12, prior telephone call advisable. SIZE: Medium. *STOCK: Hand tools for craftsmen, engineers and collectors, woodworking and metalworking books including furniture reference and clocks, other art and antiques reference books.* PARK: Easy. TEL: 01787 277130; home - same; fax - 01787 277677; e-mail - peter@trindersfinetools. co.uk; website - www.trindersfinetools.co.uk/.

DEBENHAM

Edward Bigden Antiques
48 High St. IP14 6QW. Est. 2001. Open Sat. 10-5.30 or by appointment. SIZE: Small. *STOCK: Fine paintings, drawings and sculpture, 16th-21st C; fine furniture, 17th to early 19th C.* LOC: Opposite church. PARK: Easy. TEL: 01728 862065; home - same; fax - 01728 862066; mobile - 07876 745228; e-mail - edwardbigden. antiques@virgin.net; website - www.edward bigdenantiques.com.

Debenham Antiques
73 High St. IP14 6QS. Est. 1969. Open 9.15-5.30. SIZE: Large. *STOCK: 17th-19th C furniture and paintings, £50-£10,000.* PARK: Easy. TEL: 01728 860707; fax - 01728 860333. VAT: Stan/Spec.

Josh Antiques
2a Chancery Lane. IP14. (John W. Etheridge). Est. 1990. Usually open seven days 9.30-3.30, some days until 4.30. SIZE: Small. *STOCK: Oil lamps, Victorian to 1950's, £20-£200; pictures, £5-£150; metalware, china, glass, £2-100; cigarette and phone cards; kitchenalia, fire related items.* LOC: Just off High St. PARK: Easy. TEL: 01728 861680; home - same; e-mail - joshantiques@bushinternet.com. SER: Valuations.

Quercus
4 High St. IP14 6QH. (Peter Horsman and Bill

Bristow-Jones). Resident. Est. 1972. Open by appointment. SIZE: Medium. *STOCK: Oak furniture, 17th-18th C, £1,000-£5,000*. PARK: Easy. TEL: 01728 860262; home - same. SER: Valuations; restorations (17th C oak furniture). VAT: Spec.

The Suffolk Table Company
21 High St. IP14 6QL. (D. and Mrs A. Bew). Est. 1992. Open 10-6. SIZE: Medium. *STOCK: Furniture especially country tables, 18th to date, £250-£3,500*. PARK: Easy. TEL: 01728 861102; home - same; fax - 01728 861689; mobile - 07961 977070; e-mail - jbew220@aol.com. SER: Restorations (furniture). FAIRS: Newark; Ardingly.

DEPDEN, Nr. Bury St. Edmunds

Coblands Farm Antiques
Bury Rd. IP29 4BT. (Mrs Janet Harding). Open 10-5.30, Sun. 2-5. SIZE: Large. *STOCK: Antique pine and other furniture, especially wing chairs and sofas, £5-£2,000*. LOC: A143 between Haverhill and Bury St. Edmunds. PARK: Easy. TEL: 01440 820007; home - same; fax - 01440 821165. SER: Restorations (upholstery).

DRINKSTONE, Nr. Bury St. Edmunds

Denzil Grant Antiques   BADA   LAPADA
Drinkstone House. IP30 9TG. Est. 1979. Open any time by appointment. *STOCK: Furniture, especially French farm tables, 16th to early 19th C*. LOC: Off A14 between Bury St. Edmunds and Ipswich. PARK: Easy. TEL: 01449 736576; fax - 01449 737679; e-mail - denzil@ fish.co.uk; website - www.denzilgrant.com.

EXNING, Nr. Newmarket

Exning Antiques & Interiors
14-16 Oxford St. CB8 7EW. (Geoffrey Tabbron). Est. 1982. Open 9-5. SIZE: Medium. *STOCK: Period lighting, gasoliers and electroliers, table and standing lamps; drapes and decorative items.* PARK: Easy. TEL: 01638 600015; fax - 01638 600073; home - 01638 602337. SER: Restorations, conversions, cleaning and re-wiring.

EYE

Bramley Antiques
4 Broad St. 1P23 7AF. (C. Grater). Open Wed.and Sat. 9.30-5, other times by appointment. SIZE: Medium. *STOCK: Furniture, £20-£5,000; glass, £5-£500; boxes, pictures, general antiques, all 18th to early 20th C*. LOC: Town centre. PARK: Easy. TEL: 01379 871386. SER: Valuations; restorations.

English and Continental Antiques
1 Broad St. IP23. (Steve Harmer). Est. 1977. Open 10-5. CL: Mon. SIZE: Medium. *STOCK: Furniture, 17th-19th C, £50-£10,000*. PARK: Easy. TEL: 01379 871199; e-mail - stevenECA@ aol.com. SER: Restorations; upholstery.

Laburnum Cottage Antiques
Laburnum Cottage, 2 Broad St. IP23 7AF. (S. Grater). Resident. Est. 1978. Open Wed.-Sat. 9.30-5, other times by appointment. SIZE: Small. *STOCK: Porcelain and glass, £5-£250; silver and plate, £30-£100; linen, jewellery, £2.50-£100; all 18th-20th C*. LOC: Facing the Town Hall. PARK: Easy. TEL: 01379 871386. SER: Valuations.

FELIXSTOWE

John McCulloch Antiques
1a Hamilton Rd. IP11 7HN. Open 10-4.30. CL: Wed. *STOCK: Furniture, copper, brass, pictures, clocks and bric-a-brac.* LOC: Main street, sea front end at top of Bent Hill. PARK: Around corner. TEL: 01394 283126.

Tea & Antiques
109 High Rd. East. IP11 9PS. (D. George). Est. 1999. Open Thurs.-Sun. and Bank Holidays 10-5. SIZE: Small. *STOCK: General antiques and collectables, bygones and furniture, £5-£500*. LOC: Main road to Felistowe ferry. PARK: Easy. TEL: 01394 277789; e-mail - david.george25@ btopenworld.com/crossroads.

FINNINGHAM

Abington Books
Primrose Cottage, Westhorpe Rd. IP14 4TW. (J. Haldane). Est. 1971. Open by appointment. SIZE: Small. *STOCK: Books on Oriental rugs, from 1877, £1-£5,000; books on classical tapestries, from 17th C, £1-£3,000*. LOC: At bottom of private drive, about 150m. west of intersection with B1113. PARK: Easy. TEL: 01449 780303; fax - 01449 780202. SER: Valuations; book binding.

FRAMLINGHAM

Bed Bazaar
The Old Station, Station Rd. IP13 9EE. (B.J. Goodbrey). GMC. Est. 1980. Open 10-5, Sun. and Bank Holidays, 11-4. SIZE: Large. *STOCK: Wooden and metal bedsteads.* PARK: Own. TEL: 01728 723756; fax - 01728 724626; e-mail - bedbazaar@aol.com. SER: Restorations (beds); Sleeping Partners - mattresses and bases made-to-measure. VAT: Stan/Spec.

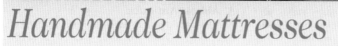

Dix-Sept
17 Station Rd. IP13. (S. Goodbrey and M. Cluzan). Est. 1996. Open Sat. 10-1 and 2-5, other times by appointment. *STOCK: French furniture and decoration, pottery, garden furniture, mirrors and textiles.* LOC: On approach road from A12. PARK: Easy. TEL: 01728 621505; fax - 01728 724884. FAIRS: Newark. VAT: Global.

Goodbreys
29 Double St. IP13 9BN. (R. and M. Goodbrey). Est. 1965. Open Sat. 9-5.30, other times by appointment. SIZE: Large. *STOCK: Decorative items including sleighbeds, upholstery, Biedermeier, simulated bamboo, painted cupboards, garden furniture, country pieces; pottery, glass, textiles, mirrors, bric-a-brac.* LOC: Up Church St. towards Framlingham Castle, opposite church gates turn right into Double St. PARK: Easy. TEL: 01728 621191; fax - 01728 724626. SER: Restorations. FAIRS: Newark. VAT: Mainly Spec. *Mainly Trade.*

Grannies
8 and 8a Market Hill. IP13 9AN. (K.C. Weston). Est. 1999. Open summer 7 days 9.30-5; winter - closed Sun. and Wed pm. SIZE: Small. *STOCK: China, glass, treen, jewellery and silver, pictures, small furniture, textiles, brass and copper, toys.* PARK: Easy. TEL: 01728 724987; home - 01473 735540. SER: Valuations.

Honeycombe Antiques
8 Market Hill. IP13 9AN. (K. Honeycombe). Est. 1997. Open 9.30-5, Sun. during summer and special events. SIZE: Small. *STOCK: Silver, Georgian to 1950, £10-£1,000; furniture - small tables, chairs, plant stands, mainly Georgian-Victorian, £30-£600; ceramics, glass and pictures, £10-£300.* LOC: Market Sq. PARK: Nearby. TEL: 01728 622011; mobile - 07789 482849; e-mail - kfh@honeycombeantiques. co.uk. SER: Valuations.

The Theatre Antiques Centre
10 Church St. IP13 9BH. (W. Darby). Est. 1988. Open 9.30-5.30. SIZE: Large. *STOCK: Furniture, 18th C, £500-£1,000; French country, 18th-19th C, £500-£1,000; country pine, 19th C, £100-£500; objets d'art, £50-£100.* TEL: 01728 621069; home - 01986 798012. SER: Valuations; restorations. VAT: Spec.

HACHESTON, Nr. Wickham Market

Joyce Hardy Pine and Country Furniture
IP13 0DS. Resident. Open 9.30-5.30, Sun. 10-12. *STOCK: Pine - dressers, corner cupboards, butcher's blocks, old French farmhouse tables, old Breakdown wardrobes.* LOC: B1116, Framlingham Rd. PARK: Easy. TEL: 01728 746485.

HALESWORTH

P & R Antiques Ltd
Fairstead Farm Buildings, Wash Lane, Spexhall. IP19 0RF. (Pauline and Robert Lewis). Est. 1997. Open by appointment. SIZE: Large. *STOCK: Chests of drawers, £900-£3,000; dining and drawing room furniture, £500-£4,000; all 18th-19th C.* LOC: From A12, take Halesworth turning, through town, turn left into Wissett Road, then right after half mile into Wash Lane, farm is half mile on right. PARK: Easy. TEL: 01986 873232; home - same; fax - 01986 874682; e-mail - pauline@prantiques.com; website - www. prantiques.com. SER: Worldwide delivery. FAIRS: Snape. VAT: Spec.

IPSWICH

A. Abbott Antiques
757 Woodbridge Rd. IP4 4NE. (C. Lillistone). Est. 1965. Open 10.30-5. CL: Wed. SIZE: Medium. *STOCK: Small items, especially clocks and jewellery; Victorian, Edwardian and*

shipping furniture, £5-£5,000. PARK: Easy. TEL: 01473 728900; fax - same; mobile - 07771 533413; e-mail - abbott_antiques@hotmail.com. FAIRS: Newark; Ardingly. VAT: Global.

Tony Adams Wireless & Bygones Shop
175 Spring Rd. IP4 5NG. Open Fri. and Sat., 9.30-12.30. *STOCK: Bygones, especially wireless sets; toy trains, cameras.*

Claude Cox at College Gateway Bookshop
3 Silent St. IP1 1TF. (Anthony Cox). ABA. PBFA. Est. 1944. Open Wed.-Sat. 10-5. SIZE: Medium. *STOCK: Books, from 1470; some local maps and prints.* LOC: Leave inner ring road at Novotel double roundabout, turn into St. Peters St. PARK: Cromwell Square and Buttermarket Centre. TEL: 01473 254776; fax - same; e-mail - books@claudecox.co.uk; website - www. claudecox.co.uk. SER: Valuations; restorations (rebinding); buys at auction; catalogue available.

The Edwardian Shop
556 Spring Rd. IP4 4NT. Est. 1979. Open 9-5. *STOCK: Victorian, Edwardian and 1920's shipping goods, £10-£400.* LOC: Half-mile from hospital. PARK: Own. TEL: 01473 716576.

Hubbard Antiques
16-18 St. Margarets Green. IP4 2BS. Est. 1964. Open 10-5.30 and by appointment. SIZE: Large. *STOCK: Furniture and decorative items, 18th-19th C.* PARK: Easy. TEL: 01473 226033/233034; fax - 01473 253639. SER: Valuations; restorations. VAT: Stan/Spec. *Trade & Export.*

Maud's Attic
25 St. Peter's St. IP1 1XF. (Wendy Childs). Est. 1996. Open Tues.-Sat. 10-5. SIZE: Small *STOCK: General antiques, collectables and reproduction including porcelain, lamps, glass, jewellery, furniture, linen and mirrors.* LOC: Town centre. PARK: Easy. TEL: 01473 221057; fax - 01473 221056; e-mail - maudsattic@ btconnect.com. SER: Valuations.

Merchant House Antiques & Interiors
27-29 St. Peter's St. IP1 1XF. (Graham and Wendy Childs). Est. 1999. Open Tues.-Sat. 10-5. SIZE: Small. *STOCK: Furniture including pine, mahogany and oak, fire surrounds and inserts, garden ornaments and furniture, lighting and mirrors, copper and brass.* LOC: Town centre. PARK: Easy. TEL: 01473 221054; fax - 01473 221056; mobile - 07768 068575.

Orwell Furniture For Life
Halifax Mill, 427 Wherstead Rd. IP2 8LH. (M. Weiner). Open 8.30-5.30, Sat. 8.30-4. *STOCK: Pine.* TEL: 01473 680091. SER: Restorations; stripping; pine furniture and kitchens made to order from old wood; manufacturers of bespoke furniture in oak, maple, cherry, painted etc.

Thompson's
418 Norwich Rd. IP1 5DX. (D. Thompson). Est. 1977. Open 9-5. CL: Sun. except by appointment. SIZE: Medium. *STOCK: Furniture, mainly late Victorian and shipping, 1870 to date, £10-£3,000.* LOC: 1 mile from town centre, on corner at traffic lights next to railway bridge. PARK: Own, at side of premises. TEL: 01473 747793; fax - same; e-mail - sales@thompsons-furniture.com; website - www.thompsons-furniture.com. SER: Valuations; buys at auction (shipping items). VAT: Stan/Spec.

Caspar Pfaff, Augsburg: a South German silver mounted ebony and ebonised 'altar' clock, basically c.1660, 23in. high.

(Christie's Images)

From an article entitled "Renaissance Clocks" by Richard Garnier which appeared in the April 2002 issue of ***Antique Collecting***. For more details and to subscribe see page 21.

IXWORTH, Nr. Bury St. Edmunds

E.W. Cousins and Son　　　LAPADA
27 High St. and The Old School. IP31 2HJ.
(E.J.A., J.E. and R.W. Cousins). Est. 1920. CL:
Sat. pm. SIZE: Large and warehouse. *STOCK:
General antiques, 18th-19th C, £50-£6,000;
shipping items.* LOC: A143. PARK: Easy. TEL:
01359 230254; fax - 01359 232370; e-mail -
john@ewcousins.co.uk; website - www.
ewcousins.co.uk. SER: Valuations; restorations.
VAT: Stan/Spec.

LAVENHAM, Nr. Sudbury

R.G. Archer (Books)
7 Water St. CO10 9RW. Est. 1970. Open 10-5
including Sun. CL: Wed. *STOCK: Antiquarian
and secondhand books.* TEL: 01787 247229.
SER: Search.

J. and J. Baker
12-14 Water St. and 3a High St. CO10 9RW. (C.J.
and Mrs B.A.J. Baker). Est. 1960. Open 10-1 and 2-
5.30. SIZE: Medium. *STOCK: Oak and mahogany
furniture, 1680-1900, £100-£10,000; oils and
watercolours, 19th C, £150-£5,000; English
porcelain and metalware, 18th-19th C, £20-£1,000;
collectors' items, £20-£1,000.* LOC: Below Swan
Hotel at T junction of A1141 and B1071. PARK:
Easy. TEL: 01787 247610. VAT: Stan/Spec.

One Bell
46 High St. CO10 9PY. (J.F. and M.A. Tinworth).
Open 11-4.30, Sat. 10.30-5, Sun. 11-5. CL: Wed.
and Thurs. SIZE: Small. *STOCK: Militaria and
collectables.* LOC: A134. PARK: Easy. TEL:
01787 248206; home - same.

**The Timbers Antique & Collectables
Centre**
High St. CO1 9PY. (Tom and Jeni White).
Resident. Est. 1996. Open every day. SIZE:
Medium. *STOCK: Smalls and furniture, £5-£500.*
PARK: Easy. TEL: 01787 247218; website -
www.timbersantiques.com.

LEAVENHEATH

Clock House
Locks Lane. CO6 4PF. (A.G. Smeeth). Est. 1983.
Open by appointment. SIZE: Small. *STOCK:
English clocks, 17th to early 19th C, £1,500-
£6,000; French and English clocks, Victorian and
Edwardian, £300-£2,000.* PARK: Easy. TEL:
01206 262187; home - same. SER: Valuations;
restorations (clocks and furniture); buys at
auction (clocks and furniture).

LEISTON

Leiston Trading Post
17 High St. IP16 4EL. (L.K. Smith). Est. 1967. Open 10-1 and 2-5, other times by appointment. CL: Wed. pm. SIZE: Large. *STOCK: Bric-a-brac, Victoriana, Victorian and Edwardian furniture, collectables.* LOC: 4 miles from Aldeburgh, Snape, and Saxmundham. PARK: Easy. TEL: 01728 830081; home - 01728 831488; e-mail - lisa@renaultsuffolk.co.uk; website - www.leiston tradingpost.co.uk. SER: Valuations. VAT: Stan.

Warrens Antiques Warehouse
High St. IP16 4EL. (J.R. Warren). Est. 1980. CL: Wed. and Sat. pm. except by appointment. SIZE: Medium. *STOCK: Furniture, Georgian, Victorian, Edwardian and shipping oak, £20-£2,000.* LOC: Off High St., driveway beside Geaters Florists. PARK: Easy. TEL: 01728 831414; home - same; mobile - 07989 865598. SER: Valuations; restorations (furniture). FAIRS: Newark; Ardingly. VAT: Stan/Spec.

LONG MELFORD

Aerial House Antiques & Collectables
Hall St. CO10 9JR. (William A. Hodge and Antonio Garrido-Jimenez). Est. 2002. Open

Tues.-Sat. 10-1.30 and 2.30-5.30, Sun. 11-4. SIZE: Small. *STOCK: General smalls and collectables including small furniture and pictures.* PARK: Easy. TEL: 01787 315540.

Sandy Cooke Antiques
Hall St. CO10 9JQ. Est. 1982. Open Fri., Sat. and Mon. 10-5. SIZE: Large. *STOCK: Furniture, 17th to early 19th C, £500-£40,000.* Not Stocked: Silver and glass. LOC: A134. PARK: Easy. TEL: 01787 378265; fax - 01284 830935; mobile - 07860 206787; e-mail - sandycooke@english furniture.co.uk; website - www.englishfurniture. co.uk. SER: Valuations; restorations; buys at auction (furniture). VAT: Stan/Spec.

Country Antiques
10 Westgate St. CO10 9DS. (Mr and Mrs G. Pink). Est. 1984. Open 11-5. CL: Mon. and Thurs. SIZE: Small. *STOCK: Objects, metalware and small furniture, £50-£2,000; unusual objects, £50-£500; watercolours and prints, 18th-19th C, £100-£2,000.* LOC: Outskirts of village, on Clare road. PARK: Easy. TEL: 01787 310617; fax - same; e-mail - countrypink@supanet.com; website - www.countrypink.co.uk.

Curtis Antiques
Ringers Yard, Hall St. CO10 9JF. Est. 1993. Open

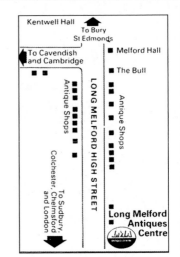

Mon., Thurs., Fri. and Sat. 9-6. SIZE: Small. *STOCK: Lalique, £400-£3,000; 17th C English oak, 18th C English mahogany; unusual items.* PARK: Easy. TEL: 01787 319991; mobile - 07787 551481; e-mail - curtisantiques@yahoo. co.uk. SER: Valuations; restorations.

Long Melford Antiques Centre
Chapel Maltings. CO10 9HX. (Baroness V. von Dahlen). Est. 1984. Open 9.30-5.30 or by appointment. SIZE: Large - 42 dealers. *STOCK: Furniture - oak, Georgian, Edwardian and Victorian; silver, china, glass, clocks and decorators' items.* LOC: A134, Sudbury end of village. TEL: 01787 379287. SER: Packing and shipping. VAT: Stan/Spec.

Alexander Lyall Antiques
Belmont House, Hall St. CO10 9JF. (A.J. Lyall). Est. 1977. Open 10-5.30. SIZE: Medium. *STOCK: Furniture, 18th-19th C.* LOC: A134 opposite Crown Hotel. PARK: Easy. TEL: 01787 375434; home - same; website - www.lyallantiques.com. SER: Restorations (furniture); buys at auction (English furniture). VAT: Stan/Spec.

Magpie Antiques
Hall St. CO10 9JT. (Mrs P. Coll). Est. 1985. Open

10.30-1 and 2.15-5, Sat. 11-5. CL: Mon. and Wed. SIZE: Small. *STOCK: Smalls including hand-painted china; furniture, Victorian and stripped pine.* LOC: Main street. PARK: Easy. TEL: 01787 310581; home - same.

Patrick Marney
The Gate House, Melford Hall. CO10 9AA. Est. 1964. Open by appointment. SIZE: Small. *STOCK: Fine barometers, 18th-19th C, £1,000-£5,000; pocket aneroids, 19th C, £150-£1,000; scientific instruments, 18th-19th C, £250-£2,000; all fully restored.* LOC: A134. PARK: Easy. TEL: 01787 880533; e-mail - patrick.marney@ virgin.net. SER: Valuations; restorations (mercury barometers). VAT: Stan.

Melford Antique Warehouse
Hall St. CO10 9JG. (D. Edwards, J. Tanner and P. Scholz). Open 9.30-5, Sun. 1-5. SIZE: 150 dealers exhibiting. *STOCK: 18th-20th C furniture and decorative items.* PARK: Easy. TEL: 01787 379638; e-mail - patrick@worldwideantiques. co.uk; website - www.antiques-access-agency. com.

Noel Mercer Antiques
Aurora House, Hall St. CO10 9RJ. Est. 1990.

Open 10-5 or by appointment. SIZE: Large. *STOCK: Early oak, walnut and country furniture, including refectory and gateleg tables, sets of chairs and dressers; works of art, £500-£30,000.* LOC: Centre of Hall St. PARK: Easy. TEL: 01787 311882. SER: Valuations; restorations. VAT: Stan/Spec.

The Persian Carpet Studio
The Old White Hart. CO10 9HX. (Sara Barber). Est. 1990. Open 10-5.30. SIZE: Medium. *STOCK: Antique and decorative Oriental carpets and rugs, from 1860, from £50.* LOC: Sudbury end of Long Melford. PARK: Own. TEL: 01787 882214; fax - 01787 882213; e-mail - sarabarber @persian-carpet-studio.net; website - www. persian-carpet-studio.net. SER: Valuations; repairs and hand-cleaning (Oriental rugs); buys at auction (Oriental carpets, rugs and textiles). Exhibitions held. VAT: Stan/Spec.

Seabrook Antiques
Hall St. CO10 9JG. (J. Tanner). Est. 1965. Open 9.30-5.30. SIZE: Large - 10 showroms. *STOCK: Furniture, £500-£15,000; objects, £100-£2,000; both 17th-18th C.* LOC: A134 near Bull Hotel. PARK: Easy. TEL: 01787 375787; fax - same; home - 01787 311788. SER: Valuations; restorations (17th-18th C furniture); buys at auction (17th-18th C furniture). FAIRS: International. VAT: Spec.

Suthburgh Antiques
Red House, Hall St. CO10 9JQ. (R.P. Alston). Est. 1977. Open by appointment. SIZE: Medium. *STOCK: Furniture, 17th C oak, 18th C walnut and mahogany, £500-£15,000; portraits, 17th-19th C, £2,000-£10,000; Georgian barometers and clocks, £400-£15,000; small collectors' items, boxes, glass, brass, copper, oak carvings and panels, £50-£600; English county maps and prints, £40-£500. Not Stocked: Victorian furniture and later items.* LOC: Opposite Bull Hotel. PARK: Easy. TEL: 01787 374818; fax - same; home - same. SER: Valuations; restorations (furniture, barometers); buys at auction. VAT: Stan/Spec.

Trident Antiques
LAPADA
2 Foundry House, Hall St. CO10 9JR. (Thomas McGlynn). Est. 1989. Open 10-5.30, Sat. 10-6, Sun. by appointment. SIZE: Medium. *STOCK: Oak furniture, 17th C, £250-£10,000; barometers, 19th C, £450-£2,500; paintings, 17th-18th C, £2,000-£6,000; objects including bottles, spoons and carvings, 17th-18th C, £100-£600.* LOC: Next to Cock and Bell Inn. PARK: Easy. TEL: 01787 883388; fax - 01787 378850; home - 01787 371867; e-mail - tridentoak@aol.

com. SER: Valuations; restorations (early English oak); buys at auction (oak furniture). FAIRS: LAPADA (NEC and London). VAT: Spec.

Village Clocks
Little St. Mary's. CO10 9LQ. (J.C. Massey). Est. 1975. Open 10-5, Sat. 9.30-5. CL: Wed. SIZE: Small. *STOCK: Clocks - longcase, bracket, wall and mantel, 18th-19th C, £500-£5,000+; carriage, 19th C, £500-£2,000+.* PARK: Easy. TEL: 01787 375896; website - www.villageclocks.net. SER: Valuations; restorations (as stock); buys at auction (clocks). FAIRS: Uxbridge Horological, Brunel University. VAT: Spec.

Vintage Pine
Hall St. CO10 9JL. (Nikki Hamilton and Irene Fielding). Est. 1999. Open 10-5. CL: Mon. SIZE: Medium. *STOCK: Victorian stripped pine, brass and copper, china and country implements.* PARK: Easy. TEL: 01787 377523; home - 01787 247771.

MARLESFORD

Antiques Warehouse (incorporating The Woodbridge Trading Co.)
The Old Mill, Main Rd. IP13 0AG. (John M. Ball). Est. 1979. Open 8-4.30, Sat. 10-4.30, Sun. 11-4.30. SIZE: Large. *STOCK: Furniture including fine country, 18th-20th C, £50-£5,000; mirrors and decorative items, 18th-20th C, £10-£2,000.* LOC: A12, 7 miles north of Woodbridge. PARK: Easy. TEL: 01728 747438; fax - 01728 747627; home - 01394 382426. SER: Valuations; buys at auction.

MARTLESHAM, Nr. Woodbridge

Martlesham Antiques
The Thatched Roadhouse. IP12 4RJ. (R.F. Frost). Est. 1973. Open Mon.-Fri., Sat. and Sun. by appointment. SIZE: Large. *STOCK: Furniture and decorative items, 17th-20th C, £25-£3,000.* LOC: A1214 opposite Red Lion public house. PARK: Own. TEL: 01394 386732; fax - 01394 382959.

John Read Antiques
29 Lark Rise, Martlesham Heath. IP5 3SA. Est. 1992. By appointment. *STOCK: Pre 1840 Staffordshire figures, animals and English pottery, including Delft, salt glaze, creamware and pearlware, coloured glazed, underglazed (Pratt) and enamel decoration, 1750-1840, £100-£8,000.* LOC: A12 Ipswich bypass, opposite BT tower. PARK: Easy. TEL: 01473 624897; home - same. SER: Valuations; restorations (as stock). FAIRS: Chelsea; NEC.

MENDLESHAM GREEN

Frank Collins Antiques
Green Farm. IP14 5RE. Open by appointment. *STOCK: Furniture, mainly mahogany and oak, 17th-18th C; decorative works of art.* TEL: 01449 766135; mobile - 07802 492153.

MILDENHALL

Mildenhall Antique Furniture
10 North Terrace. IP28 7AA. (Gary Bunker). Est. 1979. Open Tues.-Sat. 11-5. SIZE: Large. *STOCK: Victorian and 1920's oak furniture.* LOC: Near fire station, opposite Jet garage. PARK: Own at rear. TEL: Mobile - 07885 662106; e-mail - moc1oak@aol.com. SER: Packing and shipping.

NAYLAND

Maria Cass Interiors
15 High St. CO6 4JF. (Mrs B. M. Stevens). Resident. Est. 1998. Open Tues.-Fri. 10-3, Sat. 9-1, Sun. by appointment. SIZE: Small. *STOCK: 18th-19th C furniture; clocks and pocket watches; mirrors, glass, china and porcelain; rare and out of print books; picture gallery.* LOC: Village centre, on A134 towards Sudbury. PARK: Easy. TEL: 01206 263929; fax - same. SER: Restorations including upholstery. FAIRS: Newark.

NEEDHAM MARKET

Roy Arnold
77 High St. IP6 8AN. Est. 1974. Open 10-5.30, appointment advisable, Sun. by appointment. SIZE: Medium. *STOCK: Woodworkers' and craftsmen's tools; scientific instruments; books - new, secondhand and antiquarian - on tools and trades, trade catalogues; all £10-£5,000.* LOC: Off A14, centre of High St. PARK: Easy. TEL: 01449 720110; fax - 01449 722498; e-mail - ra@royarnold.com; website - www.royarnold.com. VAT: Stan.

The Old Town Hall Antique Centre
High St. IP6 8AL. (S. and R. Abbott). Est. 1980. Open 10-5. SIZE: Several dealers. *STOCK: General antiques and collectables.* PARK: Easy. TEL: 01449 720773.

The Tool Shop   `LAPADA`
78 High St. IP6 8AW. (Tony Murland and Mike Hancock). Est. 1988. Open 10-5. SIZE: Small. *STOCK: Antique and usable woodworking tools, from 19th C.* PARK: Easy. TEL: 01449 722992; fax - 01449 722683; e-mail - tony@antiquetools.

co.uk; website - www.antiquetools.co.uk. SER: Valuations; buys at auction; tool auctions held. FAIRS: All major Woodworking Shows, Woodmex, Axminster, Harrogate. VAT: Stan.

NEWMARKET

Jemima Godfrey
5 Rous Rd. CB8 8DH. (Miss A. Lanham and R.G. Thurston). Est. 1968. Open Thurs. and Fri. 10-1 and 2-4.30. SIZE: Small. *STOCK: Small antiques, jewellery and linen, 19th C.* LOC: Just off High St., near clock tower. PARK: Easy. TEL: 01638 663584.

R.E. and G.B. Way
Brettons, Burrough Green. CB8 9NA. (Gregory Way). ABA. PBFA. Est. 1964. Open 8.30-5 appointment advisable. *STOCK: Antiquarian and secondhand books on shooting, fishing, horses, racing and hunting and small general section.* TEL: 01638 507217; fax - 01638 508058; e-mail - greg@waybooks.demon.co.uk.

ORFORD

Castle Antiques
Market Sq. IP12 2LH. (S. Simpkin). Est. 1969. Open daily including Sun. 11-4.30. SIZE: Medium. *STOCK: Furniture, general small antiques, bric-a-brac, glass, china, clocks.* PARK: Easy. TEL: 01394 450100; website - www.castle-antiques.co.uk.

PEASENHALL, Nr. Saxmundham

Peasenhall Art and Antiques Gallery
The Street. IP17 2HJ. (A. and M. Wickins). Resident. Est. 1972. Open every day. *STOCK: 19th to early 20th C watercolours and oils; some furniture; walking sticks.* PARK: Easy. TEL: 01728 660224; home - same. SER: Restorations (oils, watercolours, furniture). FAIRS: Snape.

RISBY, Nr. Bury St. Edmunds

The Risby Barn
IP28 6QU. (R. and S. Martin). Est. 1986. Open 9-5.30, Sun. and Bank Holidays 10-5. SIZE: 24 dealers. *STOCK: Furniture, porcelain, metalware, tools, pine, Art Deco, oil lamps.* LOC: Just off A14 west of Bury St. Edmunds. PARK: Own. TEL: 01284 811126; fax - 01284 810783; website - www.risbybarn.co.uk.

SAXMUNDHAM

Michael Lewis
Hill Cottage, 6 Church Hill, Sternfield. IP17 1RS.

Open by appointment. *STOCK: Pine and country furniture, British and Irish, 18th-19th C, £100-£6,500.* TEL: 020 7359 7733; 01728 604776.

Snape Antiques and Collectors Centre

Snape Maltings. IP17 1SR. Est. 1992. Open 7 days 10-5 or until dusk in winter. SIZE: 40 dealers. *STOCK: Antiques and collectables, especially smalls - cutlery, pens, sewing, silver, jewellery, ceramics from 18th C, Doulton, Deco, Studio, glass, maps, prints, paintings, textiles, country, decorative and useful furniture, stamps, costume jewellery.* LOC: Next to the Concert Hall. PARK: Easy. TEL: 01728 688038.

Cannonbury

Bridgefoot Corner, Reydon. IP18 6NF. (D. Brinsmead). Est. 1975. Open 10-5, Sun. 11-4. SIZE: Medium. *STOCK: General antiques and furniture, 1800-1950's, £5-£500+.* LOC: A1095 to Southwold from A12. PARK: Easy. TEL: 01502 722133. SER: Valuations; restorations; buys at auction. FAIRS: Newark; Stoneleigh.

Farleigh House Antiques

Basement, 39 High St. IP18 6AB. (Sharon Munday). Est. 1996. Open 10-5, Sun. by appointment. CL: Wed. SIZE: Small. *STOCK: Porcelain - Lowestoft, Worcester, etc; glass and silver, jewellery, coins, medals, militaria, brass, copper and antiquities, decorative furniture.* PARK: Easy. TEL: 01502 722630; e-mail - sharon@farleighhouse.fsnet.co.uk; website - www.antiquesinsouthwold.com.

Puritan Values at the Dome

The Dome Art and Antiques Centre, Southwold Business Centre, St. Edmunds Rd. IP18 6BZ. (A.F. Geering). Resident. Est. 1984. Open 10-6, Sun. 11-5. SIZE: Large. *STOCK: Arts and Crafts, Gothic Revival, Aesthetic, decorative arts and Art Nouveau, £50-£20,000.* PARK: Easy. TEL: 01502 722211; mobile - 07966 371676; e-mail - sales@ puritanvalues.com; website - www.puritanvalues. com. SER: Valuations; restorations. FAIRS: Earls Court; Newark; NEC; Scottish Exhibition Centre. VAT: Stan/Spec.

T. Schotte Antiques

The Old Bakehouse, Black Mill Rd. IP18 6AQ. (T. and J. Schotte). Open 10-1 and 2-4. CL: Wed. SIZE: Small. *STOCK: Small furniture, £25-£500; decorative objects, £5-£250; both 18th-19th C. Unusual collectables, £5-£100.* LOC: Turn right

at the King's Head, then first left. TEL: 01502 722083. FAIRS: Long Melford monthly; Adams, Horticultural Hall, London.

S. J. Webster-Speakman

Open by appointment. *STOCK: English furniture, clocks, Staffordshire pottery, general antiques.* **TEL: 01502 722252. SER: Valuations; restorations (clocks, furniture and ceramics). FAIRS: Various.**

Trench Puzzles

Three Cow Green, Bacton. IP14 4HJ. (Kevin Holmes). Est. 1984. Open by appointment. *STOCK: Antique, old jigsaw and mechanical puzzles.* PARK: Limited. TEL: 01449 781178. SER: Mail order; search.

Napier House Antiques

Church St. CO10 6BJ. (Veronica McGregor). Est. 1977. Open 10-4.30 and by appointment. SIZE: Large. *STOCK: 18th-19th C mahogany furniture, especially larger items - linen presses, wardrobes, desks, bureaux, bookcases, dining tables, sideboards, wing chairs, £350-£5,000.* PARK: Easy. TEL: 01787 375280; fax - 01787 478757. SER: Free UK delivery.

Neate Militaria & Antiques

P O Box 3794, Preston St Mary. CO10 9PX. (Gary C. Neate). OMRS, OMSA, MMSSA. MCCofC. Open Mon.-Fri. 9-6. *STOCK: Orders, decorations and medals of the world, £5-£15,000.* TEL: 01787 248168; fax - 01787 248363; e-mail - gary@neatemedals.co.uk; website - www.neate medals.co.uk. SER: Valuations; 4 catalogues p.a. FAIRS: Brittania Medal; Aldershot Medal & Militaria; OMRS Convention. VAT: Spec. *Mail order only.*

Sitting Pretty Antiques

16 Friars St. CO10 2AA. (Darren Barrs). Est. 1982. Open 9.30-12.45 and 1.45-5 or by appointment. SIZE: Large. *STOCK: Re-upholstered period furniture, small tables and mirrors, 18th C to 1930, £50-£2,000.* LOC: Through market square, branch left at bottom fork. PARK: Further down street. TEL: 01787 880908. SER: Valuations; restorations; re-upholstery; buys at auction.

Peppers Period Pieces

Park Farm, The Street. IP22 1NT. (M.E. Pepper).

Est. 1975. Open by appointment. *STOCK:
Furniture, oak, elm, yew, fruitwood, mahogany,
16th-19th C; English domestic implements in
brass, copper, lead, tin, iron, pewter and treen,
16th to early 20th C; some pottery and porcelain,
bygones and collectables, late 19th to early 20th
C.* Not Stocked: Reproductions. LOC: Village
centre A143. PARK: TEL: 01359 250606; fax -
same. SER: Valuations; repairs and polishing.

WICKHAM MARKET

Ashe Antiques Warehouse
The Old Engine Shed, Station Rd., Campsea Ashe.
IP13. (Graham Laffling). Est. 1986. Open 10-5
including Sun. SIZE: Large. *STOCK: Furniture,
18th-20th C, £100-£5,000; collectables, pictures
and prints, 19th C, £50-£500.* LOC: 1.5 miles from
A12 Wickham Market by-pass, signposted Orford
and Tunstall. PARK: Easy. TEL: 01473 747255;
01394 460490. SER: Valuations; restorations
(ceramics); repairs (furniture); re-polishing;
upholstery; buys at auction. FAIRS: Newark.

Roy Webb
179 & 181 High St. IP13 0RQ. Open Mon.,
Thurs. and Sat. 10-6 or by appointment. *STOCK:
Furniture, 18th-19th C; clocks.* TEL: 01728
746077; home - 01394 382697. VAT: Stan.

WOODBRIDGE

Church Street Centre
6E Church St. IP12 1DH. (M. Brown). Est. 1994.
Open 10-5, Sat. 10-5.30. SIZE: Medium. *STOCK:
18th-19th C general antiques; 20th C collectables,
jewellery, silver, pictures and linen.* LOC: Town
centre, just off Thoroughfare, next to Barclays
Bank. PARK: Nearby. TEL: 01394 388887.

David Gibbins Antiques `BADA`
**The White House, 14 Market Hill. IP12 4LU. Est.
1964. Open by appointment. *STOCK: English
furniture, late 16th to early 19th C, £300-£40,000;
English pottery and porcelain, metalwork.* PARK:
Own in Theatre St. TEL: 01394 383531; fax -
same; home - 01394 382685; mobile - 07702
306914; e-mail - david@gibbinsantiques.co.uk;
website - www.gibbinsantiques.co.uk. SER:
Valuations; buys at auction. FAIRS: BADA;
Harrogate (Spring & Autumn). VAT: Spec.**

Hamilton Antiques `LAPADA`
5 Church St. IP12 1DH. (H.T. and R.E. Ferguson).
Est. 1976. Open 8.30-5, Sat. 10-5. *STOCK: Furniture
- mahogany and walnut, especially inlaid, rosewood
and some oak; prints.* TEL: 01394 387222; fax -
01394 383832; e-mail - enquiries@hamiltonantiques.

co.uk; website - www.hamiltonantiques.co.uk. SER:
Restorations; polishing. VAT: Stan/Spec.

Anthony Hurst Antiques
13 Church St. IP12 1DS. (C.G.B. Hurst). Est.
1957. Open 9.30-1 and 2-5.30. CL: Wed. and Sat.
pm. SIZE: Large. *STOCK: English furniture, oak,
walnut and mahogany, 1600-1900, £100-£5,000.*
PARK: Easy. TEL: 01394 382500. SER:
Valuations; restorations (furniture); buys at
auction. VAT: Stan/Spec.

R.A and S.M. Lambert and Son
The Bull Ride, 70A New St. IP12 1DX. Open
9.30-1 and 2-5. SIZE: Large. *STOCK: 19th-20th
C furniture.* TEL: 01394 382380.

Edward Manson (Clocks)
8 Market Hill. IP12 4LU. Open 10-5.30, Wed. 10-
1. *STOCK: Clocks.* TEL: 01394 380235; e-mail -
edwardmanson@hotmail.com. SER: Restorations
(clocks); dial painting.

Melton Antiques
Kingdom Hall, Melton Rd., Melton. IP12 1NZ.
(A. Harvey-Jones). Est. 1975. Open 9.30-5. CL:
Wed. SIZE: Small. *STOCK: Silver, collector's
items, £5-£500; decorative items and furniture,
£15-£500; both 18th-19th C; Victoriana and
general antiques, 19th C, £5-£500; sewing items.*
LOC: On right hand-side coming from
Woodbridge. PARK: Outside shop. TEL: 01394
386232. FAIRS: Sandown Park. VAT: Global.

Sarah Meysey-Thompson Antiques
10 Church St. IP12 1DH. Est. 1962. Open 10-4
some days, by appointment any time. SIZE:
Medium. *STOCK: Small furniture, late 18th to early
20th C; china, glass, and decorative items.* PARK:
Easy. TEL: 01394 382144. FAIRS: Decorative
Antiques & Textile, London. VAT: Spec.

Isobel Rhodes
10-12 Market Hill. IP12 4LU. *STOCK: Furniture,
oak, country, mahogany; brassware.* PARK:
Easy. TEL: 01394 382763. VAT: Spec.

Woodbridge Pine & Collectables
6 Market Hill. IP12. (S. Tallowin). Est. 1996.
Open 10-5. SIZE: Small. *STOCK: Smalls items,
collectables, £5-£100.* PARK: Easy. TEL: 01394
383831. SER: Valuations.

WOOLPIT, Nr. Bury St. Edmunds

J.C. Heather
The Old Crown. IP30 9SA. Est. 1946. Open 9-8
including Sun. SIZE: Medium. *STOCK:*

Suffolk House Antiques
Early oak and country furniture and works of art

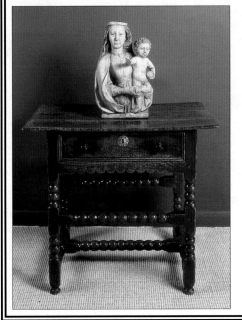

Situated just off the A12 in the middle of the village of Yoxford, Suffolk House Antiques has extensive showrooms on two floors with parking available right outside the shop.

Stock usually includes a range of dressers, gateleg and refectory tables, cupboards, chests of drawers, sets of chairs and smaller pieces of furniture. In addition there are always good examples of early ceramics, especially delftware, early carvings and metalware.

Hours of business are
10 am - 1 pm - 2.15 pm - 5.15 pm
Closed Wednesdays and Sundays,
or by appointment.

Suffolk House Antiques, High Street,
Yoxford, Suffolk IP17 3EP.
Telephone/Fax: 01728 668122
E-mail:
andrew.singleton@suffolk-house-antiques.co.uk
Website: www.suffolk-house-antiques.co.uk

Furniture, 18th-19th C, £20-£1,000. Not Stocked: China. LOC: Near centre of village on right. PARK: Easy. TEL: 01359 240297; e-mail - oldcrown@lineone.net. SER: Restorations. VAT: Stan/Spec.

WORTHAM, Nr. Eye

The Falcon Gallery
Honeypot Farm. IP22 1PW. (N. Smith). Est. 1974. Open by appointment. SIZE: Small. *STOCK: Watercolours and oils especially animal paintings and primitives, 19th C.* LOC: South side of A143 in village centre, overlooking village green, 4 miles west of Diss. PARK: Easy. TEL: 01379 783312; fax - same; e-mail - falcongallery@talk21.com. SER: Valuations; restorations (oils, watercolours); framing.

WRENTHAM, Nr. Beccles

Bly Valley Antiques
The Old Reading Rooms, 7 High St. NR34 7HD. Open 11-5 including Sun. *STOCK: 18th-19th C furniture, ceramics, silver and plate, pictures, objets d'art.* TEL: 01502 675376.

Wren House Antiques
1 High St. NR34 7HD. (Valerie and Tony Kemp).

Open Thurs.-Sat. 10.30-5, Sun. 11-4 or by appointment. SIZE: Medium. *STOCK: Furniture, china and collectables.* LOC: A12 village centre, Fiveways junction. TEL: 01502 675276.

YOXFORD

Red House Antiques
The Red House, Old High Rd. IP17 3HW. (J. and Mrs M. Trotter). Est. 1987. Open Fri. and Sat. 9.30-5, other times by appointment. *STOCK: 18th to early 19th C ceramics, £20-£1,000; late 19th to early 20th C watercolours, £50-£400.* LOC: Off either A1120 or A12, opposite churchyard. PARK: Easy. TEL: 01728 668615. SER: Valuations. FAIRS: Snape.

Suffolk House Antiques `BADA`
High St. IP17 3EP. (A. Singleton). Est. 1990. Open 10-1 and 2.15-5.15. CL: Wed. SIZE: Large. *STOCK: 17th-18th C oak and country furniture, works of art, paintings, delftware and metalware.* LOC: A1120, just off A12. PARK: Easy. TEL: 01728 668122; fax - same; mobile - 07860 521583; e-mail - andrew.singleton@ suffolk-house-antiques.co.uk; website - www. suffolk-house-antiques.co.uk. FAIRS: BADA; Snape.

SURREY

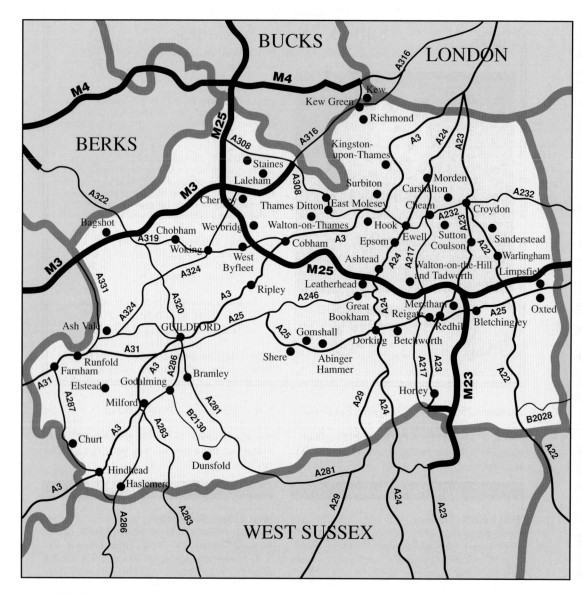

Dealers and Shops in Surrey

Abinger Hammer	2	Dorking	26	Kew	1	Runfold	1
Ash Vale	1	Dunsfold	1	Kew Green	1	Sanderstead	1
Ashtead	2	East Molesey	6	Kingston-upon-		Shere	2
Bagshot	1	Elstead	1	Thames	3	Staines	2
Betchworth	1	Epsom	1	Laleham	1	Surbiton	4
Bletchingley	3	Ewell	1	Leatherhead	1	Sutton	1
Bramley	2	Farnham	8	Limpsfield	1	Thames Ditton	1
Carshalton	2	Godalming	3	Merstham	2	Walton-on-Thames	2
Cheam	1	Gomshall	2	Milford	2	Walton-on-the-Hill	
Chertsey	2	Great Bookham	2	Morden	1	and Tadworth	1
Chobham	2	Guildford	5	Oxted	2	Warlingham	1
Churt	1	Haslemere	4	Redhill	1	West Byfleet	1
Cobham	2	Hindhead	3	Reigate	5	Weybridge	8
Coulsdon	2	Hook	1	Richmond	12	Woking	2
Croydon	2	Horley	1	Ripley	6		

ABINGER HAMMER

Abinger Bazaar
Guildford Rd. RH5 6SA. Est. 1978. Open Sat.
and Sun. 12-5 or by appointment. SIZE: Medium.
*STOCK: Antiques, collectables, books and bric-
a-brac.* LOC: A25 next to Drake's on the Pond
Restaurant. PARK: By shop or nearby. TEL:
01306 887003; mobile - 07740 484116. SER:
Finder.

Stirling Antiques
Aberdeen House. RH5 6RY. (V.S. Burrell). Est.
1968. Open 9.30-6.30. CL: Thurs. *STOCK:
Stained glass, furniture, copper, brass, jewellery,
silver, curios, dolls.* PARK: Easy. TEL: 01306
730706; fax - 01306 731575. VAT: Stan.

ASH VALE, Nr. Aldershot (Hants)

House of Christian
5-7 Vale Rd. GU12 5HH. (A. Bail). Est. 1978.
Open 10-4, Sat. 12-3. SIZE: Medium. *STOCK:
Pine, 19th-20th C, £30-£1,500; some mahogany,
oak, 19th-20th C.* LOC: On B3411 between Ash
and Ash Vale. From Ash Wharf over canal
bridge, shop (bright green) on left on hill. PARK:
Easy - opposite. TEL: 01252 314478. SER:
Valuations; restorations (including waxing and
staining); stockists of Briwax and Liberon
products.

ASHTEAD

Bumbles
90 The Street. KT21 1AW. (Barbara Kay). Est.
1992. Open 10.30-5.30. *STOCK: Coins and
cigarette cards.* PARK: Easy. TEL: 01372
276219. SER: Restorations (furniture including
upholstery); oil lamp spare parts.

Temptations
88 The Street. KT21 1AW. (Pauline Watson).
FGA, NAG. Open 10-5. *STOCK: Jewellery and
silver.* LOC: Main street. PARK: Easy. TEL:
01372 277713. SER: NAG registered valuer;
security photography; lecturer. VAT: Stan/Spec.

BAGSHOT

Country Antiques
Pantiles, 20 London Rd. GU19 5HN. (S.
Sommers and C. Martin). Est. 1990. Open 10-5
including Sun. SIZE: Large. *STOCK: Victorian
and Edwardian, some Georgian, furniture, £50-
£3,000; china and glass, collectables including
lace and prints, Victorian to 1930's, £2-£100.*
LOC: A30. PARK: Easy. TEL: 01276 489499.

BETCHWORTH, Nr. Dorking

Stoneycroft Farm `LAPADA`
Chalkpit Lane, Reigate Rd. RH3 7EY. (J.G.
Elias). Est. 1970. Open 8-5.30, Sat. 10.30-5.
SIZE: Large. *STOCK: Large oak and country
furniture, library bookcases, dining tables and
chairs, special writing furniture.* LOC: North of
A25. PARK: Own, TEL: 01737 845215; e-mail -
dorking desks@aol.com; website - www.desk.uk.
com. SER: Search; shipping.

BLETCHINGLEY

Cider House Galleries Ltd `LAPADA`
Norfolk House, 80 High St. RH1 4PA. (T.
Roberts). Est. 1967. Open 10-5.30. CL: Sat. pm.
and Sun. except by appointment. SIZE: Large.
STOCK: Paintings, 17th-20th C, from £450.
LOC: A25, behind Lawrence Auctioneers. PARK:
Own. TEL: 01883 742198; fax - 01883 744014;
e-mail - tony.roberts@virgin.net; website - www.
ciderhousegalleries.com. SER: Valuations.
FAIRS: Olympia. VAT: Stan/Spec.

John Anthony Antiques
71 High St. RH1 4LJ. (J.A. and N. Hart).
Resident. Est. 1973. Open by appointment.
STOCK: 18th to early 19th C furniture. LOC:
A25 between Redhill and Godstone. PARK: Easy.
TEL: 01883 743197; fax - 01883 742108. VAT:
Spec/Margin.

Post House Antiques
32 High St. RH1 4PE. (P. and V. Bradley). Open
daily, Sun. by appointment. *STOCK: Antique
lighting, fenders, mirrors.* LOC: A25. PARK:
Easy. TEL: 01883 743317; website - www.
antiquelightinguk.co.uk. VAT: Stan/Spec.

BRAMLEY, Nr. Guildford

Memories
High St. GU5 0HB. (P. Kelsey). Est. 1984. Open
10-5. SIZE: Small - 7 dealers. *STOCK: Victorian
and Edwardian furniture, china and glass, silver,
linen and lace, collectables and bygones,
kitchenalia, stripped pine furniture, Art Deco.*
LOC: South of Guildford on A281. PARK: Easy.
TEL: 01483 892205.

The Old Works
24 High St. GU5 0HB. (A. Sutherland). Est.
1994. Open 9-5.30, Sat. 9.30-5, Sun. 10.30-4.
SIZE: Medium. *STOCK: Furniture including
chests of drawers, wardrobes, tables, cupboards,
dressers, coffers, chairs, bookcases, Georgian to
Victorian, £100-£1,000.* LOC: A281. PARK:

Opposite. TEL: 01483 894648; home - same. SER: Restorations (carpentry).

CARSHALTON

Carshalton Antique Galleries
5 High St. SM5 3AP. (B.A. Gough). Est. 1968. Open 9-4. CL: Wed. SIZE: Large. *STOCK: General antiques, furniture, clocks, glass, china, pictures.* LOC: Carshalton Ponds. PARK: Nearby. TEL: 020 8647 5664; home - 01306 887187. VAT: Stan/Spec.

Cherub Antiques
312 Carshalton Rd. SM5 3QB. (M. Wisdom). Open 9-5.30, Sat. 10-6. *STOCK: Pine and general antiques.* TEL: 020 8643 0028. VAT: Spec.

Collectors Corner
3 The Square. SM5 3BN. (A.J. and B.M. Wilton). Est. 1975. Open 11.30-3.30, Sat. 10-5.30. CL: Wed. SIZE: Small. *STOCK: Collectors items, china, glass, 1780-1980, £50-£500; stamps, coins, medals, postcards, 19th-20th C, £5-£250.* LOC: Carshalton Ponds. PARK: Easy. TEL: 020 8669 7377. SER: Valuations; restorations.

CHEAM

Village Antiques
16 Malden Rd. SM3 8QF. (Rebecca Fownes and Sandy Jenner). Resident. Est. 1986. Open 11-5. CL: Thurs. SIZE: Medium. *STOCK: General antiques including furniture, lighting and smalls, 19th-20th C, £5-£1,000.* LOC: 10 mins. off A3 towards Worcester Park. PARK: Easy. TEL: 020 8644 8567. FAIRS: Kempton Racecourse.

CHERTSEY

Chertsey Antiques
10 Windsor St. KT16 8AS. (Leandro Ulisse). Open 8-5. SIZE: Medium. *STOCK: Furniture, jewellery, glass, pottery and porcelain, silver, silver plate, pictures, kitchenalia, memorabilia, books, linen, clocks.* PARK: Easy. TEL: 01932 563313; fax - 01753 685538; e-mail - antiques@ ulisse.co.uk. SER: Local free delivery.

D'Eyncourt
21 Windsor St. KT16 8AY. (Mr and Mrs Davies). Est. 1968. Open 10-5.15, Sat. 7-5.30, Sun. 11-5. SIZE: Medium. *STOCK: Furniture, Victorian to Art Deco, £50-£1,500; china, £5-£250; lighting and fireplaces, Victorian to present day, £25-£500.* PARK: Easy and Guildford St. TEL: 01932 563411; e-mail - deyncourt@bushinternet.com.

SER: Valuations; restorations. FAIRS: London Photograph (Bonnington Hotel, Southampton Row). VAT: Stan.

CHOBHAM

Greengrass Antiques   `LAPADA`
Hookstone Farm, Hookstone Lane, West End. GU24 9QP. (D. Greengrass). Est. 1970. Open by appointment. *STOCK: Decorative items; furniture, 19th C; works of art; shipping goods.* PARK: Easy. TEL: 01276 857582; fax - 01276 855289; mobile - 07860 399686. VAT: Spec/Global.

Mimbridge Antiques Centre
Mimbridge Garden Centre, Station Rd. GU24. (F.C.M. Scott). Est. 1998. Open 10-5 including Sun. SIZE: Medium. *STOCK: Collectors' items, furniture, prints, watercolours, maps, books and garden antiques, 18th-20th C, £5-£2,500.* LOC: Main road. PARK: Easy. TEL: 01276 855736; mobile - 07771 862284. SER: Consultants. FAIRS: Kempton.

CHURT, Nr. Farnham

Churt Curiosity Shop
Crossways. GU10 2JE. (Mrs G. Gregory). Est. 1996. Open Tues., Thurs., Fri. and Sat. 10.15-4.15. SIZE: Small. *STOCK: Pottery, porcelain and collectables, Victorian and Edwardian furniture.* LOC: A287 Farnham to Hindhead road. PARK: Easy. TEL: 01428 714096.

COBHAM

Village Antiques
38 Portsmouth Rd. KT11 1HZ. (N. Tsangari & Son). Resident. Est. 1965. Open 10-6, Sat. and Sun. by appointment. SIZE: Small. *STOCK: Oil paintings, watercolours, chairs, brass, wood, mainly 19th C.* LOC: Just off A3. PARK: Easy. TEL: 01932 589841. SER: Restorations (oil paintings). VAT: Stan.

COULSDON

Decodream
233 Chipstead Valley Rd. CR5 3BY. Open by appointment. *STOCK: Pottery - Clarice Cliff, Shorter, Shelley, Foley, F. and C. Rhead and Carlton ware.* LOC: Off junction 7, M25. PARK: Free. TEL: 020 8668 5534.

D. Potashnick Antiques
7 Stoats Nest Parade, 73 Stoats Nest Rd. CR5 2JJ. Est. 1974. Open 9-5.30, Sat. 9-12 or by appointment. *STOCK: Furniture.* LOC: Close to

M23/M25. PARK: Easy. TEL: 020 8660 8403. SER: Restorations (furniture).

CROYDON

Oscar Dahling Antiques
87 Cherry Orchard Rd. CR0 6BE. (Oscar Dahling and Liz Lancaster). Est. 1988. Open Tues., Wed., Thurs. 10.30-6, Sat. 10.30-4.30, other times by appointment. SIZE: Medium. *STOCK: Furniture, £50-£2,500; ceramics, £10-£250; jewellery and costume, £10-£500; all 18th-20th C.* LOC: First left after leaving East Croydon B.R. station. shop 300 yards, near Grouse and Claret public house. PARK: Easy. TEL: 020 8681 8090; home - same; e-mail - oscar.dahling@virgin.net. SER: Valuations; restorations.

The Whitgift Galleries
77 South End. CR0 1BF. (Mrs S. Simmons). FATG. Est. 1945. Open 10-5. CL: Wed. SIZE: Small. *STOCK: 20th C paintings.* LOC: South of town centre. PARK: Own in Aberdeen Road. TEL: 020 8688 0990; fax - 020 8760 0522; e-mail - info@whitgiftgalleries.co.uk; website - www.whitgiftgalleries.co.uk. SER: Restorations; conservation, framing. VAT: Spec.

DORKING

Adams Room Antiques   LAPADA
50/52 West St. RH4 1BU. Est. 1971. Open 10-5 including Sun. SIZE: Large. *STOCK: 18th-19th C English and French furniture especially dining; decorative Regency and objects.* TEL: 01306 887076; fax - 01306 881029. SER: Export orders arranged. VAT: Spec.

Antique Clocks by Patrick Thomas
62A West St. RH4 1BS. Est. 1992. Open 9.30-5.30, Sun. 11-4. SIZE: Medium. *STOCK: Clocks, 18th-19th C, £50-£5,000; optical antiques, 19th-20th C, £50-£3,000; sporting memorabilia, 19th-20th C, £50-£1,000.* PARK: Easy. TEL: 01306 743661; fax - same; e-mail - clockman@fsmail.net; website - www.antiqueclockshop.co.uk. SER: Valuations; restorations (clock and furniture). VAT: Spec.

Arkell Antiques Ltd
64-65 West St. RH4 1BS. (Nicholas Arkell and Margaret Monk). Est. 1982. Open 10-5. SIZE: Large. *STOCK: Georgian furniture, dining tables, chairs, Edwardian satinwood, £500-£50,000.* TEL: 01306 742152; fax - same; mobile - 07973 819783; e-mail - nick@arkellantiques.co.uk; website - www.arkellantiques.com. FAIRS: Claridges (April); LAPADA (Oct); Guildford (Oct).

Austin Antiques
11 West St. RH4 1BL. (Peter and Helen Austin). Est. 1972. Open 10-5, Sat. 10-5.30. SIZE: Large. *STOCK: 18th-19th C mahogany, rosewood and walnut, £250-£7,000; garden furniture and statuary, £25-£3,000; smalls, £10-£2,000; paintings, £25-£5,000.* LOC: Opposite church. PARK: Opposite. TEL: 01306 888288; mobile - 07971 856306. SER: Valuations; restorations (furniture).

G. D. Blay Antiques   BADA
56 West St. RH4 1BS. Open 10-5 and by appointment. CL: Mon. SIZE: Medium. *STOCK: Fine 18th to early 19th C furniture, £500-£50,000.* TEL: 01306 743398; mobile - 07785 767718. FAIRS: Olympia (summer, winter); BADA Chelsea (spring). VAT: Spec.

J. and M. Coombes
44 West St. RH4 1BU. Est. 1965. Open 9-5, Sun. 11-4. *STOCK: General antiques.* TEL: 01306 885479. VAT: Stan.

Ross Dodsworth Antiques Ltd   LAPADA
The Malthouse, 49 West St. RH4 1BU. Open 10-5, Sat. 10-5.30, other times by appointment. SIZE: Medium. *STOCK: 18th-19th town furniture - mahogany, rosewood and walnut; giltwood mirrors, £200-£20,000.* PARK: Public behind shop. TEL: 01306 886169; mobile - 07768 066432; e-mail - rossdodsworth@aol.com; website - www.rossdodsworthantiques.com. FAIRS: NEC.

Dolphin Square Antiques
42 West St. RH4 1BU. (Mr and Mrs N. James). Est. 1995. Open 10-5.30. *STOCK: Furniture, clocks, china and glass, bronzes, Staffordshire, 17th to early 20th C, £50-£15,000.* LOC: Western end of High St. PARK: Nearby. TEL: 01306 887901. SER: Valuations; shipping.

Dorking Desk Shop   LAPADA
41 West St. RH4 1BU. (J.G. Elias). Est. 1969. Open 8-1 and 2-5.30, Sat. 10.30-1 and 2-5. SIZE: Large. *STOCK: Desks, especially partners, cylinder bureaux, davenports, kneehole and pedestal, 18th to mid-20th C, £100-£60,000.* PARK: Nearby. TEL: 01306 883327; fax - 01306 875363; e-mail - dorkingdesks@aol.com; website - www.desk.uk.com. VAT: Stan/Spec.

Dorking House Antiques
17/18 West St. RH4 1BS. (Mrs G.D. Emburey). Est. 1989. Open 10-5. SIZE: 30 dealers. *STOCK: Period and pine furniture, silver, porcelain, longcase, wall and table clocks, jewellery, copper*

and brass, pictures and prints, decorative and collectors' items. LOC: Continuation of High St. into one-way system. PARK: Opposite. TEL: 01306 740915. SER: Restorations.

Great Grooms of Dorking
50/52 West Street. RH4 1BU. Open 9.30-5.30, Sun. 10-4. *STOCK: Wide variety of general antiques.* TEL: 01306 887076; fax - 01306 881029; e-mail - antiques@hampshires.co.uk; website - www.great-grooms.co.uk

Hampshires of Dorking
50-52 West St. RH4 1BU. Open 9.30-5.30, Sun. 10-4. SIZE: 12 rooms. *STOCK: Fine English walnut, mahogany, rosewood and satinwood furniture, 18th-19th C, £500-£70,000; fine art, silver, glass, porcelain, rugs, carpets, jewellery, scientific and medical instruments.* PARK: Own. TEL: 01306 887076; fax/ansaphone - 01306 881029; e-mail - michael@hampshires.co.uk; website - www.hampshires.co.uk. VAT: Spec.

Harman's Antiques `LAPADA`
19 West St. RH4 1QH. (Paul and Nicholas Harman). Est. 1956. Open 10-5. SIZE: Large. *STOCK: English mahogany and walnut furniture including tables and chairs, linen presses, sideboards, bookcases, 18th-19th C, £100-£15,000; Moorcroft and lamps.* PARK: Nearby. TEL: 01306 743330; home - same; fax - 01306 742593; e-mail - antiques@harmans-antiques.co.uk; website - www.harmans-antiques.co.uk. SER: Restorations; polishing; repairs; upholstery; valuations. VAT: Stan/Spec.

Holmwood Antiques
Norfolk Rd., South Holmwood. RH5 4LA. (R. Dewdney). Open 9-6.30, evenings and weekends by appointment. *STOCK: Georgian and Victorian furniture.* TEL: 01306 888174/888468.

The Howard Gallery `LAPADA`
5 West St. RH4 1BL. (Felicity Howard). Est. 1997. Open Wed.-Sat. 11-5, Mon. and Tues. by appointment. SIZE: Medium. *STOCK: Oak, mahogany and walnut furniture, 1680-1750, walnut marquetry, Regency, satinwood, some Gothic Revival, £700-£7,000; Continental porcelain mainly figure groups, 19th C.* PARK: Nearby. TEL: 01306 880022; fax/home - 01273 857478; e-mail - howard.gallery@virgin.net; website - www.thehowardgallery.co.uk. SER: Valuations; restorations (period furniture and upholstery).

King's Court Galleries
54 West St. RH4 1BS. (Mrs J. Joel). Open 9.30-

5.30. *STOCK: Antique maps, engravings, decorative and sporting prints.* TEL: 01306 881757; website - www.kingscourtgalleries.co.uk. SER: Framing.

Malthouse Antiques
49 West St. RH4 1BU. (Ross Dodsworth and Colin Waters). Open 10-5, Sat. 10-5.30. SIZE: Large. *STOCK: 18th-19th C mahogany, rosewood and walnut, 17th-19th C oak and country, £100-£20,000; giltwood mirrors, 18th-19th C, £300-£10,000.* PARK: Pay and display behind shop. TEL: 01306 886169. VAT: Spec.

Mayfair Antiques
43 West St. RH4 1BU. Est. 1963. Open 9-1 and 2-5. SIZE: Large. *STOCK: Furniture, mainly 18th-19th C, to £500+.* LOC: Opposite Junction Rd. PARK: Nearby. TEL: 01306 885007. VAT: Spec.

Norfolk House Galleries
48 West St. RH4 1BU. Open 10-5. *STOCK: 18th-19th C furniture, especially dining tables and sets of chairs.* TEL: 01306 881028.

Pilgrims Antique Centre
7 West St. RH4 1BL. Est. 1974. Open 10-5.30. SIZE: 10 dealers. *STOCK: Furniture, 18th to early 20th C, glass, books, barometers, Art Deco and Nouveau, paintings, smalls, copper and brass, silver.* LOC: A25 through town, just off High St. PARK: Easy. TEL: 01306 875028.

Elaine Saunderson Antiques `BADA`
18/18a Church St. RH4 1DW. (Mrs E.C. Saunderson). Est. 1988. Open 10-1 and 2-5.30, Sat. 9.30-6, other times by appointment. SIZE:

Medium. *STOCK: Furniture, late 18th to early 19th C, £1,000-£25,000; decorative items.* Not Stocked: Silver and jewellery. LOC: Turn left into North St. at end of West St. one-way. 100yds. up North St., opposite junction with Church St. PARK: Easy. TEL: 01306 881231; fax - 01306 502120; mobile - 07836 597485. SER: Valuations; restorations (furniture). VAT: Spec.

Scotts of Dorking
70 High St. RH4 1AY. Open 9-5.15. SIZE: Medium. *STOCK: Jewellery.* LOC: Opposite Boots chemist. PARK: Behind shop. TEL: 01306 880790.

Temptations, Antique Jewellery & Silver
4 Old King's Head Court. RH4 1AR. FGA, NAG. Est. 1960. Open 9.30-5. SIZE: Small. *STOCK: Jewellery and silver especially Victorian.* LOC: Off 11 High St. at the top of West St. PARK: Behind shop in North St. TEL: 01306 885452. SER: NAG registered valuer; lecturer; photographer. VAT: Stan/Spec.

Victoria and Edward Antiques Centre
61 West St. RH4 1BS. Est. 1972. Open 9.30-5.30. SIZE: Medium - 28 dealers. *STOCK: General antiques.* PARK: Nearby. TEL: 01306 889645.

The Vinery
55 West St. RH4 1BS. (Pauline Schwarz and Cindy King). Resident. Est. 1980. Open 10.30-5, other times by appointment. SIZE: Medium. *STOCK: Mahogany and walnut furniture, 18th-19th C, £500-£10,000; small Edwardian inlaid furniture and display cabinets, £300-£3,000; French furniture, late 19th to early 20th C, £500-£2,500; upholstery.* LOC: Town centre. PARK: West St. TEL: 01306 743440; fax - same. SER: Valuations; restorations (polishing, repairs, upholstery). VAT: Margin.

West Street Antiques
63 West St. RH4 1BS. (J.G. Spooner, R.A. Ratner and P.J. Spooner). Est. 1980. Open 9.30-1 and 2.15-5.30. SIZE: Medium. *STOCK: Furniture, 17th to early 20th C, £500-£15,000; arms and armour, 17th-19th C, £500-£30,000; brass and copper, ceramics, paintings and collectors' items.* Not Stocked: Jewellery and carpets. LOC: A25, one-way system. PARK: Nearby. TEL: 01306 883487; fax - same; home - 01306 730182 or 01372 452877; e-mail - weststant@aol.com; website - www.antiquearmsandarmour.com. VAT: Spec.

The Westcott Gallery
4 Guildford Rd., Westcott. RH4 3NR. (Anthony Wakefield). Open 9-5, Sat. 10-5 (exhibitions only). *STOCK: Specialist in contemporary paintings and ceramics by Surrey artists.* TEL: 01306 876261; fax - 01306 740770; e-mail - westcottgallery@cs.com; website - www. westcottgallery.co.uk.

DUNSFOLD, Nr. Godalming

Antique Buildings Ltd
GU8 4NP. (Peter Barker). Resident. Est. 1975. Open daily, Sat. and Sun. by appointment. SIZE: Large. *STOCK: Oak timbers, 17th C, £25-£1,000; architectural items, 15th-18th C, £25-£500; barn frames, 17th C, £2,000-£50,000.* LOC: From Sun public house 500 yards down Alfold road, row of white posts on left hand side, premises up tarmac drive between last two. PARK: Easy. TEL: 01483 200477; fax - 01483 200752. SER: Valuations; restorations (ancient oak framed buildings); buys at auction (buildings and architectural items). VAT: Stan.

EAST MOLESEY

Elizabeth R. Antiques
39 Bridge Rd., Hampton Court. KT8 9ER. Est. 1988. Open 10-4.30, Sun. 11-3.30. SIZE: Large. *STOCK: Furniture, 19th C and Art Deco, £500-£2,000; silver, 18th-20th C, £75-£300; toys, 20th C, £35-£600; jewellery, 19th-20th C, £40-£700; porcelain, 18th-19th C; Art Deco, Arts and Crafts porcelain and glass.* PARK: Easy. TEL: 020 8979 4004; fax - same. SER: Valuations; restorations (French polishing and waxing); repairs (clock, glass and china). FAIRS: Sandown; Alexandra Palace.

Hampton Court Emporium
52-54 Bridge Rd., Hampton Court. KT8 9HA. Est. 1992. Open 10-5.30, Sun 11-6. SIZE: Medium. *STOCK: Furniture, paintings, silver, jewellery, mirrors, books, clocks, brass and copper, objets d'art, lamps, china and porcelain, collector's cameras, Art Deco.* PARK: Palace Rd. station. TEL: 020 8941 8876; e-mail - info@ hamptoncourtemporium.com; website - www. hamptoncourtemporium.com. SER: Valuations; restorations.

Hampton Court Palace Antiques
16 Bridge Rd., Hampton Court. KT8 9HA. Est. 1969. Open 10-6 including Sun. SIZE: Medium. *STOCK: Decorative furniture, oils, watercolours, prints, 18th-19th C, £35-£6,000.* PARK: Easy. TEL: 020 8941 2212. SER: Export facilities; valuations; restorations (furniture and art).

Journeyman Antiques Centre

77 Bridge Rd., Hampton Court. KT8 9HH. (Stuart James). Open 10.30-5.30. SIZE: 10 dealers. *STOCK: 18th to early 20th C furniture, silver, ceramics, glass, prints, jewellery and decorative antiques.* LOC: Turn down Creek Rd., opposite Hampton Court station, into Bridge Rd. TEL: 020 8979 7954; e-mail - journeymanac@ aol.co.uk.

Nostradamus II

53 Bridge Rd., Hampton Court. KT8 9HA. (Heather Ferri). Est. 1998. Open 10-5.30, Sun. 11-6. CL: Mon. SIZE: Medium. *STOCK: Furniture, 18th-19th C; Art Deco, £25-£1,000; Victorian jewellery and silver, £100-£1,000; brass, lighting, cameras.* LOC: 5 mins. walk from Hampton Court rail station, 10 mins from the Palace. PARK: Easy. TEL: 020 8783 0595. SER: Valuations; restorations. VAT: Stan.

A.F.J. Turner Antiques

144A Bridge Rd. KT8 9HW. Est. 1992. Open Sat. 10-2, other times by appointment. SIZE: Small. *STOCK: Victorian and Edwardian natural history and taxidermy and associated curiosities, pre 1945, £10-£10,000.* LOC: Near Hampton Court Palace. PARK: In road opposite. TEL: Mobile - 07770 880960.

ELSTEAD

Honeypot Antiques

Milford Rd. GU8 6HP. (C. Martin, R. Turvey, A. Carney, J. Isenman and J. Ford). Est. 1996. Open 10-5, Sun.11-5. SIZE: Medium. *STOCK: Furniture, 17th-20th C, £50-£2,000; books, 17th-20th C, £5-£1,000; tools, silver, glass, £5-£1,000; china, pictures, 17th-20th C, £5-£1,000; coins and postcards, £2-£100.* LOC: Main road. PARK: Easy. TEL: 01252 703614; e-mail - brianpmartin @msn.com. SER: Valuations; restorations.

EPSOM

Vandeleur Antiquarian Books

6 Seaforth Gdns. KT19 0NR. (E.H. Bryant). PBFA. Est. 1971. Open by appointment. *STOCK: Antiquarian and secondhand books on all subjects; prints including rowing, and maps; Indian Mogul-style paintings.* TEL: 020 8393 7752; fax - same. SER: Valuations; subject lists quoted on request. FAIRS: Various book. VAT: Stan.

EWELL

J.W. McKenzie

12 Stoneleigh Park Rd. KT19 0QT. Est. 1971.

Appointment advisable. *STOCK: Old and new books and memorabilia on cricket.* TEL: 020 8393 7700; e-mail - jwmck@netcomuk.co.uk; website - www.mckenzie-cricket.co.uk.

FARNHAM

Annie's Antiques

1 Ridgway Parade, Frensham Rd. GU9 8UZ. Est. 1982. Open 9.30-5.30, Fri. 10.30-5.30, Sun. by appointment. SIZE: Medium. *STOCK: Furniture, bric-a-brac, jewellery, 19th to early 20th C, £5-£1,000; general antiques.* LOC: 1 mile out of Farnham on A287 towards Hindhead. PARK: Easy. TEL: 01252 713447; home - 01252 723217.

The Antiques Warehouse

Badshot Farm, St George's Rd., Runfold. GU9 9HR. (Hilary Burroughs). Est. 1995. Open 10-5.30, including Sun. SIZE: Large - 2 barns, 30 dealers. *STOCK: Furniture, 18th C to 1940's, £75-£10,000; china, glass, silver, jewellery, paintings, prints and interesting collectables, 18th C to 1960's, £5-£500.* LOC: A31 from Farnham towards Guildford, 1st exit (signed Runfold), left at end of slip road towards Badshot Lea, premises 200 yards on left. PARK: Own large. TEL: 01252 317590; fax - 01252 879751; website - www.w3b-ink.com/antiqueswarehouse. SER: Restorations (furniture); shipping.

Bourne Mill Antiques

39-43 Guildford Rd. GU9 9PY. Est. 1960. Open 10-5.30 including Sun. SIZE: Large - 83 dealers. *STOCK: Antique and reproduction furniture in oak, walnut, mahogany, yew and pine; china, glass, pictures, jewellery, fireplaces, beds, kitchenalia, bespoke furniture, collectors' items, books, bric-a-brac; garden ornaments, furniture and buildings.* PARK: Own. TEL: 01252 716663. SER: Shipping.

Casque and Gauntlet Militaria

55/59 Badshot Lea Rd., Badshot Lea. GU9 9LP. (R. Colt). Est. 1957. Open 11-5. SIZE: Large. *STOCK: Militaria, arms, armour.* LOC: A324 Aldershot to Farnham road. PARK: Easy. TEL: 01252 320745; fax - same. SER: Restorations (metals); re-gilding.

Christopher's Antiques

Sandford Lodge, 39a West St. GU9 7DX. (Mr and Mrs C.M. Booth). Resident. Est. 1972. Open 8-1 and 2-5.30, weekends by appointment. SIZE: Large. *STOCK: Fruitwood country and mahogany furniture, 18th-19th C; walnut furniture, 17th-18th C.* LOC: From Guildford on the A31, turn right at second roundabout. PARK:

Easy. TEL: 01252 713794; fax - 01252 713266; e-mail - cbooth7956@aol.com. SER: Valuations; restorations (furniture). VAT: Stan/Spec.

Heytesbury Antiques   **BADA   LAPADA**
P.O. Box 222. GU10 5HN. (Ivor and Sally Ingall). Est. 1974. Open by appointment. SIZE: Medium. *STOCK: 18th-19th C Continental and English furniture, statuary, bronzes and decorative items, £1,000-£15,000.* TEL: 01252 850893; fax - 01252 850828; mobile - 07836 675727. FAIRS: Olympia; Decorative Antiques & Textile. VAT: Spec.

Maltings Monthly Market
Bridge Sq. GU9 7QR. (Farnham Maltings). Est. 1969. First Sat. monthly. SIZE: 200+ stalls. *STOCK: 60% of the dealers sell a wide variety of antiques, postcards, bric-a-brac and collectables.* LOC: Follow signs to Wagon Yard car park, Maltings over footbridge. TEL: Stalls - 01252 717434; fax - 01252 718177; e-mail - FarnMalt@aol.com; website - www.farnham maltings.com.

Karel Weijand Fine Oriental Carpets
BADA   LAPADA
Lion and Lamb Courtyard. GU9 7LL. Est. 1975. Open 9.30-5.30. SIZE: Large. *STOCK: Fine antique and contemporary Oriental rugs and carpets, from £150.* LOC: Off West St. PARK: Easy. TEL: 01252 726215; e-mail - carpets@karelweijand.com. SER: Valuations; restorations; cleaning. FAIRS: BADA; LAPADA. VAT: Stan/Spec.

GODALMING

The Antique Shop
72 Ockford Rd. GU7 1RF. (G. Jones). Open 10.30-4.30, Sat. 11-5. SIZE: 6 dealers. *STOCK: General antiques including furniture, light fittings.* PARK: Opposite. TEL: 01483 414428. FAIRS: Clandon.

Heath-Bullocks   **BADA**
8 Meadrow. GU7 3HN. (Roger, Mary and Charlotte Heath-Bullock). Est. 1926. Open 10-4 (winter), 10-5 (summer), by appointment. SIZE: Large. *STOCK: English and Continental furniture.* LOC: A3100. From Guildford on the left side approaching Godalming. PARK: Own. TEL: 01483 422562; fax - 01483 426077; e-mail - heathbullocks@aol.com; websites - www.heath-bullocks.com and www.Antiques Care.com. SER: Valuations; restorations. FAIRS: BADA; Buxton; Surrey.

Priory Antiques
29 Church St. GU7 1EL. (P. Rotchell). Open 10-4. CL: Wed. *STOCK: General antiques.* TEL: 01483 421804.

GOMSHALL, Nr. Guildford

The Coach House Antiques
60 Station Rd. GU5 9NP. (P.W. and L. Reeves). Resident. Est. 1985. Open 9-5.30, Sun. 12-5. SIZE: Medium. *STOCK: Longcase clocks, 1780 to 19th C, £4,000-£20,000; furniture, 1790 to late 19th C, £1,000-£20,000.* LOC: Between Guildford and Dorking on the Shere by-pass. PARK: Easy. TEL: 01483 203838; fax - 01483 202999; e-mail - coach_house.antiques@virgin.net; website - www.coachhouseantiques.com. SER: Valuations; restorations (clocks and furniture); buys at auction (as stock). FAIRS: Guildford. VAT: Spec.

The Studio
Station Rd. GU5 9LQ. (Mrs M. Ellenger). Est. 1985. Open 12-5, Sat. and Sun. 10.30-5. SIZE: Small. *STOCK: General antiques.* LOC: A25 midway between Guildford and Dorking. PARK: Easy. TEL: 01483 202449. SER: Valuations. VAT: Stan.

GREAT BOOKHAM, Nr. Leatherhead

Roger A. Davis Antiquarian Horologist
19 Dorking Rd. KT23 4PU. BWCG. Est. 1971. Open Tues., Thurs. and Sat. 9.30-12.30 and 2-5, other times by appointment. SIZE: Small. *STOCK: Clocks, 18th-19th C, £150-£5,000.* LOC: From Leatherhead A246 to centre of village, turn left at sign for Polesden Lacey, shop 1/4 mile along Dorking Rd. PARK: Easy. TEL: 01372 457655; home - 01372 453167. SER: Valuations; restorations (mechanical and case work).

Memory Lane Antiques
30 Church Rd. KT23 3PW. (J. Westwood). Est. 1984. Open 10-5. CL: Wed. *STOCK: Toys and general antiques, pre-1920, £5-£1,000.* PARK: Easy. TEL: 01372 459908.

GUILDFORD

Cry for the Moon
17 Tunsgate. GU1 3QT. (Jonathan Owen and Harry Diamond). Est. 1977. Open 9.30-5.30. SIZE: Medium. *STOCK: Mainly jewellery, £30-£50,000; silver and objets d'art.* TEL: 01483 306600. SER: Valuations; repairs; jewellery commissions undertaken. VAT: Stan/Margin.

Denning Antiques
1 Chapel St. GU1 3UA. Est. 1986. Open 10-5. *STOCK: Silver, jewellery, lace, linen, and collectors' items.* LOC: Off High St. PARK: Nearby. TEL: 01483 539595.

Horological Workshops   **BADA**
204 Worplesdon Rd. GU2 9UY. (M.D. Tooke). Est. 1968. Open Tues.-Fri. 8.30-5.30, Sat. 9-12.30 or by appointment. SIZE: Large. *STOCK: Clocks, watches, barometers.* PARK: Easy. TEL: 01483 576496; fax - 01483 452212; e-mail - enquiries@horologicalworkshops. com; website - www.horologicalworkshops. com. SER: Restorations; collection and delivery.

Oriental Rug Gallery
230 Upper High St. GU1 3JD. (R. Mathias and J. Blair). Est. 1989. Open 10-5.30. *STOCK: Russian, Afghan, Turkish and Persian carpets, rugs and kelims; Oriental objets d'art.* TEL: + 4 (0) 1483 457600; fax - same; e-mail - rugs@ orientalruggallery.com; website - www.oriental ruggallery.com.

Pew Corner
Artington Manor Farm, Old Portsmouth Rd. GU3 1LP. (D. Bouldin, N. Alpe and M. Groes). Est. 1990. Open 10-5, Sun. 10.30-4.30. SIZE: Large. *STOCK: Church furnishings - pews, 1850-1950, £200-£1,500; chairs, 1900-1960, £25-£50; pulpits, altars, screens, bishops' chairs, fonts, stained glass (mainly Victorian).* LOC: 1 mile town centre. PARK: Easy. TEL: 01482 533337; fax - 01483 535554; e-mail - sales@pewcorner. co.uk; website - www.pewcorner.co.uk. SER: Bespoke oak furniture - dining sets, sideboards, coffee tables and bookshelves.

HASLEMERE

Haslemere Antique Market
1A Causewayside, High St. GU27 2JZ. Est. 1990. Open 9.30-5. SIZE: Large. *STOCK: Wide variety of general antiques.* LOC: Off High St. (A286). PARK: Easy. TEL: 01428 643959. SER: Valuations; restorations; buys at auction.

Serendipity Antiques & Crafts
7 Petworth Rd. GU27 2JB. (E.J. Moore). Est. 1995. Open 10-5, Sun. 10.30-4. SIZE: Medium. *STOCK: Furniture, £400-£2,000, books, £20-£100, both 19th C; china, late 19th to early 20th C, glass, silver, metalware, clocks, £5-£1,000.* LOC: East at base of High St. 100 yards on right.

PARK: High St. TEL: 01428 642682. SER: Restorations (clocks).

Surrey Clock Centre
3 Lower St. GU27 2NY. (J.P. Ingrams and S. Haw). Est. 1962. Open 9-1 and 2-5. SIZE: Large. *STOCK: Clocks and barometers.* PARK: Easy. TEL: 01428 651313. SER: Restorations; hand-made parts; shipping orders; clocks made to order. VAT: Stan/Spec.

Wood's Wharf Antiques Bazaar
56 High St. GU27 2LA. (C.M. Lunnon). SIZE: 12 dealers. *STOCK: A wide selection of antiques.* PARK: Nearby. TEL: 01428 642125; fax - same.

HINDHEAD

Albany Antiques Ltd
8-10 London Rd. GU26 6AF. (T. Winstanley). Est. 1965. Open 9-6. CL: Sun. except by appointment. *STOCK: Furniture, 17th-18th C, £20-£400; china including Chinese, £5-£400; metalware, £7-£50; both 18th-19th C.* Not Stocked: Silver. LOC: A3. PARK: Easy. TEL: 01428 605528. VAT: Stan/Spec.

M. J. Bowdery   BADA
12 London Rd. GU26 6AF. Est. 1970. Always available, prior telephone call advisable. SIZE: Medium. *STOCK: Furniture, 18th-19th C.* LOC: A3. PARK: Own. TEL: 01428 606376; mobile - 07774 821444. SER: Valuations. FAIRS: Buxton; Guildford; Petersfield. VAT: Spec.

Drummonds Architectural Antiques
The Kirkpatrick Buildings, 25 London Rd. GU26 6AB. SALVO. Est. 1988. Open 9-6. SIZE: Large. *STOCK: Architectural and decorative antiques, garden statuary and furniture, period bathrooms.* LOC: West side of A3, 50 yards north of traffic lights. PARK: Own. TEL: 01428 609444; fax - 01428 609445; e-mail - sales@drummonds-arch.co.uk; website - www.drummonds-arch.co.uk. SER: Restorations (stonework and gates); handmade cast iron baths and fittings, cast iron conservatories; vitreous re-enamelling of baths. VAT: Stan/Spec.

HOOK, Nr. Chessington

A. E. Booth & Son
300 Hook Rd. KT9 1NY. (Mrs Ann Booth and Paul Day). Est. 1934. Open 9-5 by appointment. *STOCK: Furniture, 1700-1900, to £2,000; porcelain, £20-£200.* LOC: A243 towards A3. PARK: Own. TEL: 020 8397 7675; fax - same;

e-mail - aebrestore@talk21.com. SER: Restorations (furniture including polishing); repairs; upholstery.

HORLEY

Surrey Antiques
3 Central Parade, Massetts Rd. RH6 7PP. (Michael Bradnum). Est. 1990. Open 10-5. SIZE: Medium. *STOCK: China, pottery and glass, furniture, pictures, mirrors, collectables, 19th-20th C.* LOC: On left by traffic lights, almost opposite police station. PARK: Public behind shop. TEL: 01293 775522. FAIRS: Ardingly; Copthorne; Effingham Park Hotel.

KEW

Lloyds of Kew
9 Mortlake Terrace. TW9 3DT. (C. Patterson). Open 10.30-6. *STOCK: Out-of-print and antiquarian books including gardening, film, childrens.* LOC: Junction of Kew and Mortlake Roads, 10 minutes walk from Kew Gardens Station (District line). PARK: Easy. TEL: 020 8940 2512; fax - same; mobile - 07941 592141; e-mail - books@lloydsofkew.co.uk; website - www.loydsofkew.co.uk. SER:Quarterly catalogues.

KEW GREEN

Andrew Davis
6 Mortlake Terrace. TW9 3DT. (Andrew and Glynis Davis). Resident. Est. 1969. Most days by appointment. *STOCK: Mainly pictures - oil, watercolours and prints, 18th-20th C; decorative and functional items including furniture, ceramics, glass, clocks, garden and architectural items, £10-£5,000.* LOC: South end of Kew Green. PARK: Side road or Kew Green. TEL: 020 8948 4911. SER: Valuations.

KINGSTON-UPON-THAMES

Glencorse Antiques   LAPADA
321 Richmond Rd., Ham Parade, Ham Common. KT2 5QU. (M. Igel and B.S. Prydal). Est. 1983. Open 10-5.30. *STOCK: 18th-19th C furniture; traditional modern British art, oils and watercolours, 20th-21st C.* PARK: Own. TEL: 020 8541 0871 and 020 7229 6770.

Glydon and Guess Ltd
14 Apple Market. KT1 1JE. NAG; GMC. Est. 1940. Open 9.30-5. *STOCK: Jewellery, small silver, £100-£5,000.* LOC: Town centre. TEL: 020 8546 3758. SER: Valuations; restorations.

Kingston Antique Market

29-31 Old London Rd. KT2 6ND. Est. 1995. Open 9.30-6, Thurs. 9.30-7, Sun. 10-6. SIZE: 100 dealers. *STOCK: General antiques including period furniture, porcelain, collectables and jewellery.* LOC: Off Clarence St. PARK: Easy. TEL: 020 8549 2004; e-mail - webmaster@ antiquesmarket.co.uk; website - www.antique market.co.uk.

LALEHAM, Nr. Staines

Laleham Antiques

23 Shepperton Rd. TW18 1SE. (E. Potter). Est. 1970. Open 10.30-5. SIZE: Medium. *STOCK: Furniture, porcelain, mirrors, antique lighting, silver, general and trade antiques.* LOC: B376. PARK: Easy. TEL: 01784 450353.

LEATHERHEAD

Alan's Antiques

1-3 Church St. KT22 8DN. (Michael Laikin). Est. 1960. Open 9-5.30. CL: Wed. SIZE: Medium. *STOCK: Furniture, £200+, porcelain, £100-£300, silver, £100+, all late 19th to early 20th C.* LOC: Town centre. PARK: Opposite. TEL: 01372 360646; e-mail - michael.laikin@virgin.net. SER: Valuations; restorations (porcelain). FAIRS: Sandown Park; Epsom Racecourse. VAT: Stan/Spec.

LIMPSFIELD

Limpsfield Watercolours

High St. RH8 0DT. (Mrs C. Reason). FATG. Est. 1985. Open Mon.-Thurs. 10.30-5, Sat. 9.30-4. SIZE: Small. *STOCK: Watercolours, £15-£5,000; prints and etchings, £5-£200; all 1850-1940 and contemporary.* Not Stocked: Oils. LOC: From junction 6 M25 follow A25 towards Westerham, village is left on B269. PARK: Easy. TEL: 01883 717010; website - www.limpsfieldwatercolours. com. SER: Valuations; restoration and cleaning of watercolours, prints and oils; framing including conservation. VAT: Spec.

MERSTHAM

Elm House Antiques

3 High St. RH1 3BA. (Robert Black). Est. 1995. Open 10.30-5.30. SIZE: Medium. *STOCK: Georgian to Edwardian town and country furniture, mahogany, oak and decorative items, £50-£5,000; country furniture, pine, kitchenalia, decorative items, textiles, £5-£500; brass and copper, £5-£100; period cabinet fittings.* LOC: A23 just past beginning of M23. PARK: Own.

TEL: 01737 643983. SER: Valuations; restorations (textiles, boxes, inlay, gesso work, furniture including French polishing, upholstery).

Geoffrey Van-Hay Antiques

The Old Smithy, 7 High St. RH1 3BA. Open 9-5. SIZE: Medium. *STOCK: 18th-19th C furniture, £500-£1,000.* PARK: Easy. TEL: 01737 645131; fax - same. SER: Valuations; restorations. VAT: Spec.

MILFORD, Nr. Godalming

Michael Andrews Antiques

Portsmouth Rd. GU8 5AU. Est. 1974. Open daily, Thurs. and Sun. by appointment. SIZE: Medium. *STOCK: Furniture, 18th-19th C.* LOC: Corner of Cherry Tree Rd. (on traffic lights, from A3 slip road to Petworth). PARK: Own. TEL: 01483 420765; home - same.

E. Bailey

Portsmouth Rd. GU8 5DR. (Eric Bailey). Est. 1979. Open 9-5. CL: Thurs. SIZE: Small. *STOCK: Furniture and tools, from Victorian, £5-£100; china, £5-£25.* LOC: Main road. PARK: Easy. TEL: 01483 422943.

MORDEN

A. Burton-Garbett

35 The Green. SM4 4HJ. Est. 1959. Open by appointment. Prospective clients met (at either Morden or Wimbledon tube station) by car. *STOCK: Books on Latin American and Caribbean travel, arts and antiquities.* TEL: 020 8540 2367; fax - 020 8540 4594. SER: Buys at auction (books, pictures, fine arts, ethnographica). VAT: Stan.

OXTED

Secondhand Bookshop

56 Station Rd. West. RH8 9EU. (David Neal). Est. 1985. Open 10-5. SIZE: Small. *STOCK: Books, 18th C to present day, £1-£500.* LOC: Adjacent to station. PARK: Safeway immediately behind shop. TEL: 01883 715755; home - 01883 723131. SER: Valuations; buys at auction (books). FAIRS: Book - in south-east. VAT: Stan.

Wagstaffs

Books in the Basement, 80-84 Station Rd. East. RH8 0PG. (David Neal). Est. 1985. Open 9.30-5, Sat 10-4. SIZE: Medium. *STOCK: 20th C books, £1-£100.* LOC: Opposite Station Parade. PARK: Nearby. TEL: 01883 717183; home - 01883 723131. SER: Valuations; buys at auction. VAT: Stan.

REDHILL

F.G. Lawrence and Sons
89 Brighton Rd. RH1 6PS. (Chris Lawrence). Est. 1891. Open 9-5, Sat. 9-1. SIZE: Large. *STOCK: 1920's, Edwardian, Victorian, Georgian and reproduction furniture.* LOC: On A23. PARK: Own. TEL: 01737 764196; fax - 01737 240446; e-mail - catherine.lawrence@btinternet.com. SER: Valuations. FAIRS: Newark. VAT: Stan.

REIGATE

Bourne Gallery Ltd   LAPADA
31/33 Lesbourne Rd. RH2 7JS. (J. Robertson, Ian and Linda Read). Est. 1970. Open 10-1 and 2-5. CL: Mon. SIZE: Large. *STOCK: 19th-20th C oils and watercolours, £250-£25,000; contemporary works, £250-£2,500.* PARK: Easy. TEL: 01737 241614; e-mail - bournegallery@aol.com; website - www.bournegallery.com. FAIRS: Olympia; Chelsea. VAT: Spec.

The Gallery   LAPADA
3/5 Church St. RH2 0AA. (Jeffrey S. Cohen). Open 10-6. SIZE: Medium. *STOCK: 19th-20th C oil paintings and watercolours, especially Modern British artists post 1850, £250-£25,000; Georgian, Regency and 19th C furniture including Sheraton revival, £500-£25,000.* LOC: Town centre. PARK: Easy and opposite. TEL: 01737 242813; fax - 01737 362819; e-mail - the.gallery@virgin.net; website - www.the gallery.uk.com. SER: Valuations; restorations (paintings and furniture). VAT: Stan/Spec.

Bertram Noller (Reigate)
14a London Rd. RH2 9HY. (A.M. Noller). Est. 1970. Open Tues., Thurs., Sat. 9.30-1 and 2-5.30. SIZE: Small. *STOCK: Collectors' items, furniture, grates, fenders, mantels, copper, brass, glass, pewter, £1-£500.* LOC: West side of one-way traffic system. Opposite Upper West St. car park. PARK: Opposite. TEL: 01737 242548. SER: Valuations; restorations (furniture, clocks, bronzes, brass and copper, marble).

Reigate Galleries
45a Bell St. RH2 7AQ. (J.S. Morrish). PBFA. Est. 1958. Open 9-5.30, Wed. 9-1. SIZE: Large. *STOCK: Old prints, engravings, antiquarian books.* PARK: Opposite. TEL: 01737 246055. SER: Picture framing. VAT: Stan.

M. & M. White Antique & Reproduction Centre
57 High St. RH2 9AE. Est. 1993. Open 10-5.30. SIZE: Medium. *STOCK: Mahogany, £100-* £2,500, *pine*, £60-£1,500, *both 18th C; reproduction*, 1920-1970, £40-£1,000. PARK: Easy. TEL: 01737 222331; fax - 01737 215702. FAIRS: Newark; Ardingly; Kempton Park. VAT: Spec.

RICHMOND

Antique Mart
72-74 Hill Rise. TW10 6UB. (G. Katz). Open Thurs., Fri. and Sat. 10-6, Sun. 1-6, other times by appointment. *STOCK: French and English decorative furniture, oils and watercolours, 19th-20th C.* TEL: 020 8940 6942; fax - 020 8715 4668; mobile - 07775 626423; e-mail - george katz@blueyonder.co.uk. SER: Buys at auction. VAT: Stan/Spec.

The Gooday Gallery
14 Richmond Hill. TW10 6QX. (Debbie Gooday). Est. 1971. Open Thurs.-Sat. 11-5 or any time by appointment. SIZE: Medium. *STOCK: Decorative and applied design, 1880-1980, Arts and Crafts, Art Nouveau, Art Deco, furniture, pictures, ceramics, metalwork, jewellery; African and oceanic tribal artefacts; 1950's and 1960's designer items, all £100-£5,000.* LOC: 100yds. from Richmond Bridge. PARK: Easy. TEL: 020 8940 8652; mobile - 07710 124540; e-mail - Goodaygallery@aol.com. SER: Valuations; buys at auction.

Roland Goslett Gallery
139 Kew Rd. TW9 2PN. Est. 1974. Open Thurs. and Fri. 10-6, Sat. 10-2 or by appointment. SIZE: Medium. *STOCK: English watercolours and oil paintings, 19th to early 20th C, £100-£5,000.* PARK: Meters. TEL: 020 8940 4009. SER: Valuations; restorations (oils, watercolours and frames); framing. VAT: Spec.

Hill Rise Antiques   LAPADA
26 Hill Rise. TW10 6UA. (P. Hinde and D. Milewski). Est. 1978. Open 10.30-5.30, Sun. 2.30-5.30. CL: Wed. SIZE: Large. *STOCK: 18th-19th C walnut and mahogany furniture, £100-£10,000; silver and plate, mirrors, boxes and glassware.* LOC: 1 mile from A316 (M3). PARK: At rear by arrangement. TEL: 020 8332 2941; home - same; e-mail - antiques@hillrisehouse. com. VAT: Stan/Spec.

Horton   LAPADA
2 Paved Court, The Green. TW9 1LZ. (D. Horton). FGA. *STOCK: Jewellery and silver, 18th-20th C, £500-£5,000.* TEL: 020 8332 1775; fax - 020 8332 1994; website - www.horton london.co.uk.

Lionel Jacobs
12-14 Brewers Lane. TW9 1HH. Est. 1982. Open 9-5. *STOCK: Silver and jewellery.* TEL: 020 8940 8069.

Robin Kennedy
P.O Box 265. TW9 1UB. Est. 1971. Open by appointment. *STOCK: Japanese prints, £50-£5,000.* TEL: 020 8940 5346; fax - same; e-mail - robin@japaneseprints.co.uk; website - www.japaneseprints.co.uk. FAIRS: Arts of Pacific Asia (New York, San Francisco, Santa Monica).

F. and T. Lawson Antiques
13 Hill Rise. TW10 6UQ. Resident. Est. 1965. Open 10-5.30, Sat. 10-5. CL: Wed. and Sun. am. SIZE: Medium. *STOCK: Furniture, 1680-1870; paintings and watercolours; both £30-£1,500; clocks, 1650-1930, £50-£2,000; bric-a-brac, £5-£300.* LOC: Near Richmond Bridge at bottom of Hill Rise on the river side, overlooking river. PARK: Limited and further up Hill Rise. TEL: 020 8940 0461. SER: Valuations; buys at auction.

Marryat   `LAPADA`
88 Sheen Rd. TW9 1AJ. (Marryat (Richmond) Ltd.). Est. 1990. Open 10-5.30. SIZE: Large. *STOCK: English and Continental furniture, watercolours and oils, £150-£5,000; porcelain, pottery, glass, silver, objets and decorative antiques, £10-£1,000; all 18th-19th C.* LOC: Follow M3/A316 towards Richmond, first left

into Church Rd. then left again. Close to underground station. PARK: Easy. TEL: 020 8332 0262. SER: Restorations. VAT: Stan/Spec.

Palmer Galleries
10 Paved Court. TW9 1LZ. (C.D. and V.J. Palmer). Est. 1984. Open 10-5. SIZE: Medium. *STOCK: Prints, watercolours and engravings, 19th-20th C, £50-£1,000.* PARK: Richmond Green. TEL: 020 8948 2668; e-mail - david@palmer-galleries.co.uk; website - www.palmer galleries.co.uk. VAT: Stan.

Town & Country Decorative
24 Hill Rise. TW10 6UA. Open 10.30-5.30, Sun. 2-5. *STOCK: Decorative antiques.* TEL: 020 8948 4638.

Vellantiques
127 Kew Rd. TW9 2PN. (Saviour Vellan). Open 10-6. SIZE: Medium. *STOCK: Furniture, gold and silver, porcelain, paintings and curios, £50-£3,000.* TEL: 020 8940 5392; fax - same; mobile - 07960 897075. SER: Valuations. FAIRS: Ardingly.

RIPLEY

J. Hartley Antiques Ltd   `LAPADA`
186 High St. GU23 6BB. Est. 1949. Open 8.45-5.45, Sat. 9.45-4.45. *STOCK: Queen Anne, Georgian and Edwardian furniture.* TEL: 01483 224318. VAT: Stan.

Detail of a Tumbling Block patchwork cover, c.1890. (Quilters' Guild of the British Isles)

From an article entitled "Quilts and Patchwork" by Diana Woolfe which appeared in the September 2002 issue of ***Antique Collecting***. For more details and to subscribe see page 21.

The Lamp Gallery

Talbot Walk Antique Centre, Talbot Hotel, High St. GU23 6BB. (Graham Jones). Est. 1979. Open 10-5, Sun. and Bank Holidays 11-4. SIZE: Small. *STOCK: Interior lighting including Arts and Crafts, Art Nouveau and Art Deco, 1860-1940.* PARK: Rear of hotel. TEL: 01483 211724; fax - same. SER: Valuations.

Sage Antiques and Interiors   LAPADA

High St. GU23 6BB. (H. and C. Sage). GMC. Est. 1971. Open 9.30-5.30. SIZE: Large. *STOCK: Furniture, mahogany, oak, walnut, 1600-1900, £150-£8,000; oil paintings, £100-£5,000; watercolours, £50-£1,000, china, £2-£500, all 18th-19th C; silver, Sheffield plate, brass, pewter, decorative items, 18th-19th C, £50-£1,000.* LOC: Village centre, on main road. PARK: Easy. TEL: 01483 224396; fax - 01483 211996. SER: Restorations (furniture, pictures); interior furnishing. VAT: Stan.

Sweerts de Landas   BADA

Dunsborough Park, Newark Lane. GU23 6AL. (A.J.H. and A.C. Sweerts de Landas). SALCO. Est. 1979. Open by appointment. SIZE: Large. *STOCK: Garden ornaments and statuary, 17th-20th C, £500-£250,000.* LOC: From High St. turn into Newark Lane (between estate agent and Suzuki garage), continue 400 yards, through archway on right, follow drive to gate. PARK: Easy. TEL: 01483 225366; home - same. SER: Valuations; restorations (stone, lead, cast iron, marble); buys at auction (as stock). FAIRS: Olympia; Grosvenor House. VAT: Stan/Spec.

Talbot Walk Antique Centre

The Talbot Hotel, High St. GU23 6BB. (I. Picken). Est. 1999. Open 10-5, Sun. 11-4. SIZE: Large - 40 dealers. *STOCK: English furniture, 1750-1930, £50-£5,000+; glass and ceramics, 1800-1940, £10-£3,000+; lighting, 1850-1940, £50-£2,000+; general antiques including mirrors and clocks, £10-£1,000+.* LOC: 1 mile south of A3/M25, junction 10, take the B2215 to Ripley, 400yds on left after entering village. PARK: Own at rear. TEL: 01483 211724; fax - same. VAT: Stan/Spec. Below are listed some of the dealers at this centre.

Argyll Antiques

(K. Deszberg). *Victorian furniture, Oriental ceramics and objects.*

R. Arnot

19th to early 20th C English furniture, clocks and Doulton.

Jane Aspinall

English furniture, 1800-1920; upholstery, lighting and decorative items.

Richard Barnes

Silver.

C. Catt

Furniture and works of art.

J. and M. Coombes

Oak furniture, 1700-1920.

P. Crowder

Prints and maps.

Debretts Antiques

17th-18th C brass.

Every Cloud

Decorative antiques and jewellery.

Foxhole Antiques

(J. Rourke). *Decorative French country furniture and objects.*

Deidre Geer

Decorative French provincial antiques and mirrors.

Goldsworth Books and Prints

(B. Hartles). *Early topographical books.*

D. Harman

Kitchenalia and oak.

Heirloom Restorations

(Hazel Bigwood). *Victorian and Edwardian furniture.*

Nick Hill

19th C furniture and works of art.

V. Jenkins

Country furniture, brass and fireside accessories.

The Lamp Gallery

(Graham Jones). *Interior lighting, 1860-1940 including Arts & Crafts and Art Deco.*

H. Loveland

19th C European ceramics.

G. and L. Rudder

Gustavian and Beidermeier furniture, Copenhagen porcelain.

Max and Marie Stallick

Decorative antiques including glass, lamps, metalwork and pewter.

Richard Tinson

18th to early 20th C glass.

Anthony Welling Antiques BADA
Broadway Barn, High St. GU23 6AQ. Est. 1970. Open 9.30-1 and 2-5. Sun. and evenings by appointment. SIZE: Large. *STOCK: English oak, 17th-18th C, £250-£8,000; country furniture, 18th C, £200-£6,000; brass, copper, pewter, 18th C, £100-£750.* Not Stocked: Glass, china, silver. LOC: Turn off A3 at Ripley, shop in village centre on service road. PARK: Easy. TEL: 01483 225384; fax - same. SER: Restoration (furniture). VAT: Spec.

RUNFOLD, Nr. Farnham

The Packhouse
Hewetts Kilns, Tongham Rd. GU10 1PQ. (P. Hewett). Est. 1991. Open 10.30-5.30 including Sun. SIZE: Large. *STOCK: Furniture including period, 1930's and country pine; garden statuary, architectural items.* LOC: Off A31 (Hogs Back). PARK: Easy. TEL: 01252 781010; fax - 01252 783876.

SANDERSTEAD

Raymond Slack FRSA & Shirley Warren
CR2 9DQ. *STOCK: Reference books on glass collecting.* TEL: 020 8657 1751. FAIRS: Birmingham and Woking Glass. *Mail Order.*

SHERE, Nr. Guildford

Helena's Collectables
Shops 1 and 2, Middle St. GU5 9HF. (Mrs K. White and Mrs H. Lee). Est. 1995. Open 9.30-4.30, Sat. 10-4.30, Sun. 11-4. SIZE: Medium. *STOCK: Royal Doulton, from 1930's, £100-£2,500; Beswick, from 1950's, from £50+; Walt Disney classics, Border Fine Art, Bunnykins and Beatrix Potter, Royal Crown Derby.* LOC: A24. PARK: Behind sports ground. TEL: 01483 203039; fax - same; e-mail - helen@collectables. demon.co.uk; website - www.collectables. demon.co.uk. SER: Valuations; restorations; search; buys at auction. FAIRS: DMG. VAT: Stan.

Shere Antiques Centre
Middle St. GU5 9HL. (Jean Watson). Est. 1986. Open 10-5, Sat. and Sun. 11-5. SIZE: 4 large showrooms. *STOCK: Mid-Georgian, Victorian and Edwardian clocks, silver, copper, brass, English and Continental porcelain, maps and prints, pens, watches; Victorian garden tools and associated items.* LOC: A25 - between Dorking and Guildford. PARK: Easy. TEL: 01483 202846; fax - 01483 830761; e-mail - jean.watson@shere antiques.com; website - www.shereantiques.com. SER: Restorations; collection and delivery. VAT: Stan/Spec.

STAINES

K.W. Dunster Antiques

23 Church St. TW18 4EN. (Keith and Cynthia Dunster). Est. 1972. Open 9-4.30. CL: Thurs. SIZE: Medium. *STOCK: Clocks, furniture, general antiques, interior decor, jewellery, nautical items.* PARK: Easy. TEL: 01784 453297; fax - 01784 483146; e-mail - kdunsterantiques@ aol.com. SER: Valuations. VAT: Stan/Spec.

Clive Rogers Oriental Rugs

PO Box 234. TVADA. PADA. Est. 1974. Open by appointment. SIZE: Medium. *STOCK: Oriental rugs, carpets, textiles; Near and Central Asian and Islamic works of art.* LOC: On B376, 15 mins. from Heathrow Airport. PARK: Own. TEL: 01784 481177/481100; fax - 01784 481144; mobile - 07747 114757; e-mail - info@orient-rug.com; website - www.orient-rug.com. SER: Valuations; restorations (as stock); historical analysis commission agents; buys at auction. FAIRS: TVADA; ICOC; Hali; San Francisco. VAT: Stan/Spec.

SURBITON

Cockrell Antiques

278 Ewell Rd. KT6 7AG. (Sheila and Peter Cockrell). Resident. Est. 1982. Open most Fri., Sat., Sun. and evenings, prior telephone call advisable. SIZE: Medium. *STOCK: Furniture including Art Deco, from 18th C, £50-£3,000+; decorative items, £50-£500.* LOC: Off A3 at Tolworth Tower on A240. PARK: Easy. TEL: 020 8390 8290; home - same; e-mail - antiques@ cockrell.co.uk; website - www.cockrell.co.uk. FAIRS: DMG; Kempton Park. VAT: Stan/Spec.

Maple Antiques

4 Maple Rd. KT6 4AB. (Geoff and Lynda Morris). Resident. Est. 1965. Open every day except Tues. am and Thurs. am. SIZE: Medium. *STOCK: Pine, oak, mahogany, lights and mirrors, garden statuary and urns, cast iron benches, 19th-20th C, £25-£1,000.* PARK: Easy. TEL: 020 8399 6718. SER: Valuations. FAIRS: Ardingly.

A group of daring Art Deco cut glass vases by Webb Corbett, all 1930s, designers unknown. (Broadfield House Glass Museum)

From an article entitled "Pre-War 20th Century British Cut Glass" by Andy McConnell which appeared in the November 2002 issue of ***Antique Collecting***. For more details and to subscribe see page 21.

B. M. and E. Newlove

139-141 Ewell Rd. KT6 6AL. Est. 1958. Open 9.30-5.30, Sat. by appointment. CL: Wed. SIZE: Medium and store. *STOCK: Furniture especially early oak and Georgian mahogany, 17th-19th C, £500-£10,000; china, 18th-19th C, £75-£200; paintings, all periods, £50-£2,000; longcase clocks, Georgian barometers.* Not Stocked: Pot-lids, fairings. LOC: Down Kingston by-pass at Tolworth underpass, turn right into Tolworth Broadway, then into Ewell Rd., shop 1 mile. PARK: Easy. TEL: 020 8399 8857. SER: Gilding. VAT: Stan/Spec.

Laurence Tauber Antiques

131 Ewell Rd. KT6 6AL. Open 10-5. CL: Wed. pm. *STOCK: General antiques, especially for Trade.* PARK: Easy. TEL: 020 8390 0020; mobile - 07710 443293. VAT: Stan/Spec.

SUTTON

S. Warrender and Co

4 and 6 Cheam Rd. SM1 1SR. (F.R. Warrender). Est. 1953. Open 9-5.30. CL: Wed. SIZE: Medium. *STOCK: Jewellery, 1790 to date, £10-£1,500; silver, 1762 to date, £10-£1,000; carriage clocks, 1860-1900, £115-£800.* TEL: 020 8643 4381. SER: Valuations; restorations (jewellery, silver, quality clocks). VAT: Stan.

THAMES DITTON

Clifford and Roger Dade

Boldre House, Weston Green. KT7 0JP. Resident. Est. 1937. Open 9.30-6. SIZE: Large. *STOCK: Mahogany furniture, 18th to early 19th C, £500-£5,000.* LOC: A309 between Esher and Hampton Court, near Sandown Park Racecourse. PARK: Outside shop. TEL: 020 8398 6293; fax - same; mobiles - 07766 080096 and 07932 158949. VAT: Spec.

WALTON-ON-THAMES

Antique Church Furnishings

Rivernook Farm, Sunnyside. KT12 2ET. (L. Skilling and S. Williams). Est. 1989. Open Mon.-Fri. 10-6. SIZE: Large. *STOCK: Church chairs and pews, £10-£750; altar tables and screens, pulpits, lecterns, reredos, pine and architectural items, £20-£2,000; all late 19th C to early 20th C.* LOC: Between A3050 and River Thames. PARK: Easy. TEL: 01932 252736; fax - same; website - www.churchantiques.com. SER: Valuations; buys at auction (church fixtures and furnishings, stained glass). VAT: Stan/Spec.

Susan Becker

LAPADA

P O Box 160. KT12 3HJ. (S. Becker Fleming). Est. 1959. Open by appointment. *STOCK: English (especially Royal Worcester) and Continental porcelain, 18th-20th C, £200-£25,000; glass and fine objects.* LOC: 10 mins. A3, M25, M4. PARK: Easy. TEL: 01932 227820. SER: Valuations. VAT: Spec.

WALTON-ON-THE-HILL AND TADWORTH

Ian Caldwell

LAPADA

9a Tadworth Green, Dorking Rd. KT20 5SQ. Est. 1978. Open 10-5. CL: Wed. SIZE: Medium. *STOCK: Oak, walnut and mahogany furniture especially Georgian.* LOC: 2 miles from M25, 1/4 mile from A217 on B2032 in Dorking direction. PARK: Easy. TEL: 01737 813969; e-mail - caldwell.antiques@virgin.net; website - www.freespace.virgin.net/caldwell.antiques. SER: Valuations; restorations. VAT: Stan/Spec.

WARLINGHAM

Trengove

397 Limpsfield Rd, The Green. CR6 9LA. (Brian Trengrove). Est. 1890. Open by appointment. SIZE: Small. *STOCK: General antiques, pictures.* PARK: Easy. TEL: 01883 624422.

WEST BYFLEET

Academy Billiard Company

5 Camphill Industrial Estate. KT14 6EW. (R.W. Donnachie). Est. 1975. Open any time by appointment. SIZE: Large warehouse and showroom. *STOCK: Period and antique billiard/snooker tables, all sizes, 1830-1920; combined billiard/dining tables, period accessories including other games-room equipment and lighting.* LOC: On A245, 2 miles from M25/A3 junction. PARK: Easy. TEL: 01932 352067; fax - 01932 353904; mobile - 07860 523757; e-mail - academygames@fsbdial.co.uk; website - www.games-room.com. SER: Valuations; restorations; removals; structural advice. VAT: Stan/Spec.

WEYBRIDGE

Brocante

120 Oatlands Drive, Oatlands Village. KT13 9HL. (Barry Dean and Ray Gwilliams). Est. 1988. Open 10-5.30, Sun. 10-5. CL: Mon. and Wed. SIZE: Small. *STOCK: Furniture, 19th C, £300-£1,500; porcelain, 19th C, £10-£250; Sheffield plate, 18th-19th C, £10-£300.* PARK: Easy. TEL: 01932 857807; home - 01932 345524.

SER: Valuations. FAIRS: Oatlands Park Hotel; Seven Hills Hilton, Cobham.

Church House Antiques

42 Church St. KT13 8DP. (M.I. Foster). Est. 1886. Open Thurs., Fri., Sat. 10-5.30. SIZE: Medium. *STOCK: Furniture, 18th-19th C, £95-£7,000; jewellery, 18th-19th C, some modern, £30-£5,000; pictures, silver, plate, decorative items.* Not Stocked: Coins and stamps. PARK: Behind library. TEL: 01932 842190. VAT: Stan/Spec.

The Clock Shop Weybridge

64 Church St. KT13 8DL. Est. 1970. Open 10-6. CL: Wed. SIZE: Medium. *STOCK: Clocks, 1685-1900, from £500; French carriage clocks, from £300.* LOC: Opposite HSBC bank on corner. PARK: Easy. TEL: 01932 840407/855503. SER: Valuations; restorations (clocks). VAT: Stan/Spec.

Edward Cross - Fine Paintings

128 Oatlands Drive. KT13 9HL. Est. 1973. Open Fri. 10-3, Sat. 10-12.30. SIZE: Medium. *STOCK: Fine paintings and bronzes, 19th-20th C, £500-£30,000.* LOC: A3050. PARK: Opposite. TEL: 01932 851093. SER: Valuations; restorations (watercolours and oil paintings); buys at auction (pictures). VAT: Spec.

Nostradamus Antiques

43 Church St. KT13 8DG. Open 10.30-5. *STOCK: Georgian and Victorian furniture, Art Deco, Victorian jewellery, silver, books.* TEL: 01932 820521. VAT: Spec.

Not Just Silver

16 York Rd. KT13 9DT. (Mrs S. Hughes). BJA. NAG. Est. 1969. Open 9.30-6, Sun. by appointment. *STOCK: Silver, Georgian to modern.* LOC: Opposite car park, just off Queens Rd. PARK: Opposite. TEL: 01932 842468; fax - 01932 830054; mobile - 07774 298151; e-mail - info@not-just-silver.com. SER: Valuations; repairs; silver plating.

Village Antiques

39 St Mary's Rd., Oatlands Village. KT13 9PT. (B. Mulvany). Est. 1976. Open 10-4.30. CL: Wed. SIZE: Small. *STOCK: Furniture, small silver and china, 19th-20th C, £50-£1,000.* LOC: Off Oatlands Drive. PARK: Easy. TEL: 01932 846554. SER: Valuations; restorations; French polishing; small furniture repairs. FAIRS: Ardingly.

Willow Gallery

BADA LAPADA

75 Queens Rd. KT13 9UQ. (Andrew and Jean Stevens and Alick Forrester). Est. 1987. Open 10-6, Sun. by appointment. SIZE: Large. *STOCK: British and European oil paintings, 19th C, £3,000-£200,000.* LOC: Near town centre. PARK: Easy and nearby. TEL: 01932 846095/6; e-mail - enquiries@thewillow gallery.com; website - www.thewillowgallery. com. SER: Valuations; restorations; conservation; framing; catalogue available. FAIRS: BADA; LAPADA; New York; Olympia. VAT: Spec.

WOKING

Aspidistra Antiques

Wych Hill. GU22 0EU. (Mrs P. Caswell). Open 10-4.30, Sun. 11-4. SIZE: Medium. *STOCK: Furniture, 19th C to Art Deco, £100-£3,000; china and glass, 18th C to Art Deco, £50-£1,000; silver and jewellery, 19th C to Art Deco, £50-£1,500.* LOC: Just off A320 Guildford-Woking road. PARK: Easy. TEL: 01483 771117; fax - same; website - www.aspidistra-antiques.co.uk. SER: Restorations.

Keith Baker

42 Arnold Rd. GU21 5JU. (K.R. Baker). Open Wed.-Sat. 9-4.30. *STOCK: General antiques.* PARK: Easy. TEL: 01483 767425.

Porcelain figure of a cat, Meissen, c.1741-45, Saltram, Devon. (National Trust Photographic Library/Andreas von Einsiedel)

From an article entitled "Looking After Antiques" by Frances Halahan which appeared in the June 2003 issue of *Antique Collecting*. For more details and to subscribe see page 21.

SUSSEX EAST

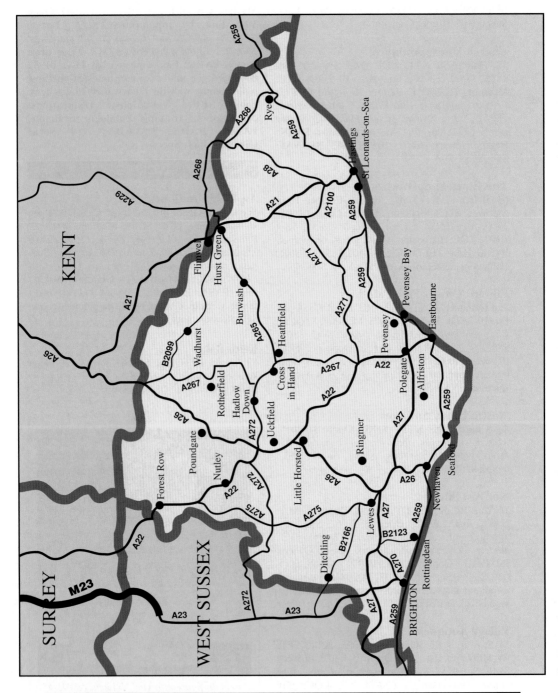

Dealers and Shops in East Sussex

Alfriston	1	Forest Row	1	Newhaven	1	Rotherfield	1
Brighton	43	Hadlow Down	1	Nutley	1	Rottingdean	1
Burwash	1	Hastings	6	Pevensey	1	Rye	7
Cross in Hand	1	Heathfield	1	Pevensey Bay	1	Seaford	3
Ditchling	1	Hurst Green	2	Polegate	3	St. Leonards-on-Sea	7
Eastbourne	14	Lewes	13	Poundgate	1	Uckfield	1
Flimwell	1	Little Horsted	1	Ringmer	1	Wadhurst	2

ALFRISTON

Alfriston Antiques
The Square. BN26 5UD. (J. Tourell). Est. 1967. Open Wed.-Sat. 11-5, Sun. 2.30-4.30. SIZE: Small. *STOCK: Collectors' items, vinaigrettes, snuff boxes, caddy spoons, silver, plate, carriage and other clocks, jewellery, paintings, pot-lids, copper, brass, books.* PARK: Easy. TEL: 01323 870498; fax - same. VAT: Stan/Spec.

BRIGHTON

Alexandria Antiques
3 Hanover Place, Lewes Rd. BN2 2SD. (A.H. Ahmed). Est. 1978. Open 9.30-6, Sat. by appointment. SIZE: 9 showrooms. *STOCK: Georgian and Victorian furniture; Oriental and European porcelain; oil and watercolour paintings; Oriental carpets, objets d'art.* PARK: Own. TEL: 01273 688793; fax - same. FAIRS: Ardingly; Newark; Sandown.

Alexandria Antiques
33 Upper North St. BN1 3FG. (A.H. Ahmed). Open 9.30-6, Sat. by appointment. *STOCK: Georgian and Victorian furniture, Oriental and European porcelain; oil and watercolour paintings; Oriental carpets, objets d'art.* TEL: 01273 328072. FAIRS: Ardingly.

Antiques et cetera
190 Portland Rd., Hove. BN3 5QN. (Ken Bomzer). Est. 1994. Open 10-3, Sat. 10-1. SIZE: Medium. *STOCK: Porcelain, £20-£1,000; glassware, £10-£500; small furniture, £50-£2,000; 50's costume, silver and gold jewellery, £5-£2,000; watercolours, prints and oils, £20-£500; silver and plate, £10-£500, 18th C to date; 18th-19th C Japanese and Chinese vases, bowls and collectables.* LOC: 1 mile from Portslade station. PARK: Easy. TEL: 01273 746159; mobile - 07747 666343; e-mail - antiques.etcetera @btinternet.com. SER: Valuations; restorations (porcelain, jewellery). FAIRS: Ardingly.

Art Deco Etc
73 Upper Gloucester Rd. BN1 3LQ. (John Clark). Est. 1979. Open by appointment. SIZE: Medium. *STOCK: Pottery, especially Poole; Scandinavian ceramics and glass; glass, lighting, mirrors, pictures and collectors' items, Art Deco, Art Nouveau, Arts and Crafts, 1950's, £5-£2,000.* LOC: From Brighton station down Queens Rd., first on right. PARK: Easy. TEL: 01273 329268; mobile - 07971 268302; e-mail - johnclark@artdecoetc.co.uk. SER: Valuations. FAIRS: Art Deco, Battersea; Alexandra Palace; Ardingly; Newark.

Ashton's Antiques
1-3 Clyde Rd., Preston Circus. BN1 4NN. (R. Ashton). Open 10-4. CL: Wed. SIZE: 4 showrooms. *STOCK: Victorian and Edwardian furniture, upholstery and decorative items.* TEL: 01273 605253; fax - same. VAT: Stan/Spec.

Brighton Architectural Salvage
33-34 Gloucester Rd. BN1 4AQ. (R.L. Legendre). Open Tues.-Sat. 10-5. *STOCK: Restored architectural items including pine furniture; fireplaces and surrounds - marble, pine, mahogany, cast-iron, Victorian tiled and cast inserts and over-mantels; doors, stained glass, panelling; cast-iron balcony and street railings, gas coal fires, light fittings; garden seats and ornaments, reclaimed flooring.* TEL: 01273 681656.

Brighton Flea Market
31A Upper St. James's St. BN2 1JN. (A. Wilkinson). Est. 1990. Open seven days. SIZE: Large. *STOCK: Bric-a-brac, furniture and collectables, 19th-20th C, £5-£1,000.* LOC: 50 yards from coast road, Kemp Town. TEL: 01273 624006; e-mail - arwilkinsn@aol.com.

Brighton Lanes Antique Centre
12 Meeting House Lane. BN1 1HB. (Peter Brynin). Est. 1967. Open 10-5.30, Sun. 12-4. SIZE: Medium. *STOCK: Furniture, clocks, silver, glass, jewellery, lighting, pens, porcelain, watches and bronzes.* LOC: North entrance to The Lanes. PARK: Loading and nearby. TEL: 01273 823121; fax - 01273 726328; e-mail - peter@brightonlanes-antiquecentre.co.uk; website - www.brightonlanes-antiquecentre. co.uk. SER: Valuations; shipping.

Tony Broadfoot
39 Upper Gardner St. BN1 4AN. Est. 1985. Open 9-5.30. SIZE: Large. *STOCK: Furniture, from 17th C.* LOC: Off North Rd. PARK: Easy. TEL: 01273 695457. SER: Restorations.

C.A.R.S. (Classic Automobilia & Regalia Specialists)
4-4a Chapel Terrace Mews, Kemp Town. BN2 1HU. (G.G. Weiner). Est. 1976. Open 10-6 by appointment only. *STOCK: Collectors' car badges, mascots and associated automobilia and related motoring memorabilia; children's pedal cars, electric cars, collectors' veteran and vintage pedal cars, 1930's-1970's.* PARK: Easy. TEL: 01273 622722 (office hours); 01273 601960; fax - same; e-mail - cars@kemptown-brighton.freeserve.co.uk; website - www.carsof brighton.co.uk; website for The Pedal Car

Collectors' Club - www.barcc.co.uk and www.brmmbrmm.com/pedalcars. SER: SAE for catalogue/price list . FAIRS: NEC; Alexandra Palace; Ardingly; Brighton Classic Car.

Campbell Wilson

1 Brunswick Sq., Hove. BN3 1EG. (Neil Wilson). Est. 1996. Open by appointment. *STOCK: Paintings especially Pre-Raphaelite and Romantic British, 1845-1903; modern British, to 1945.* LOC: On seafront. TEL: 01273 777087; website - www.campbell-wilson.demon.co.uk. SER: Buys at auction (Victorian and Modern British paintings). FAIRS: Olympia; Watercolours and Drawings; Antiques for Everyone (Glasgow).

Harry Diamond and Son

9 Union St., The Lanes. BN1 1HA. (H. and C. Diamond). Est. 1937. Open 10-4.30. *STOCK: Diamond jewellery, £500-£15,000.* Not Stocked: Coins, furniture. TEL: 01273 329696. VAT: Stan/Spec.

Faques Gallery

29 Upper St James's St., BN2 1JN. Est. 1962. Open 10-5.30. SIZE: Large. *STOCK: Reproduction oil paintings.* LOC: Kemp Town area. PARK: Side roads. TEL: 01273 624432; fax - 01273 683692. VAT: Stan.

Paul Goble Jewellers

44 Meeting House Lane, The Lanes. BN1 1HB. NAG. Est. 1965. Open 9-5.30, Sat. 9-6, Sun. 10-6. *STOCK: Jewellery, watches, silver, pictures and prints, teddy bears and dolls.* TEL: 01273 202801; fax - 01273 202736; e-mail - paulgoble @btinternet.com. SER: Trade/export; valuations. FAIRS: KM Antiques; Sandown Park. VAT: Stan/Margin.

Douglas Hall Ltd

23 Meeting House Lane. BN1 1HB. (K.J. Longthorne). Est. 1968. Open 9.30-5. *STOCK: Silver, jewellery.* TEL: 01273 325323. VAT: Stan.

Hallmark Jewellers

4 Union St., The Lanes. BN1 1HA. (J. Hersheson). Est. 1966. Open 9-5. SIZE: Small. *STOCK: Diamond and gem set jewellery; antique and modern silver.* TEL: 01273 725477; fax - same. VAT: Stan/Spec.

Heritage Antiques   `BADA` `LAPADA`

P O Box 2974. BN1 3QG. (Anjula Daniel). CINOA. Est. 1975. Open by appointment. SIZE: Large. *STOCK: Metalware, £50-£5,000; interesting and decorative items.* PARK: Easy.

TEL: 01273 326850; fax - same; e-mail - ahd@ heritage-antiques.com; website - www. heritage-antiques.com. FAIRS: Olympia. VAT: Stan/Spec.

Dudley Hume   `LAPADA`

46 Upper North St. BN1 3FH. Est. 1973. CL: Sat. pm. and Sun., except by appointment. SIZE: Medium. *STOCK: Period and Victorian furniture, metal, light fittings, decorative items.* LOC: Parallel to the Western Rd., one block to the north. TEL: 01273 323461; fax - 01273 240422; e-mail - dudley@dudleyhume.co.uk. FAIRS: Olympia (June); LAPADA (Oct.). VAT: Stan/Spec.

International Interiors

69 New Church Rd., Hove. BN3 2BB. Est. 1985. Open 10-5.30. SIZE: Medium. *STOCK: General antiques, Victorian, Georgian, French reproduction, especially mirrors.* PARK: Easy. TEL: 01273 770045. VAT: Stan.

Jezebel

14 Prince Albert St. BN1 1HE. (Amanda Davis). Est. 1989. Open 11-5.30, Sun. by appointment. SIZE: Medium. *STOCK: Art Deco ceramics, furniture, lighting, chrome, collectables including Bakelite jewellery, £20-£2,000.* LOC: Just off Ship St. near the Lanes. PARK: Easy. TEL: 01273 206091; fax - same; home - 01273 675616. SER: Valuations; restorations; buys at auction (Art Deco/Nouveau). FAIRS: Newark.

The Lanes Armoury

26 Meeting House Lane, The Lanes. BN1 1HB. (Mark and David Hawkins). Est. 1972. Open 10-5.15. *STOCK: Militaria, arms, armour and books, from 500BC to WWII.* PARK: By arrangement. TEL: 01273 321357; website - www.thelanesarmoury. co.uk.

Leoframes

70 North Rd. BN1 1YD. (S. Round). Open 9-5.30. *STOCK: Prints and maps.* TEL: 01273 695862. SER: Restorations; framing.

Harry Mason

P O Box 687, Hove. BN3 6JY. Est. 1954. Open by appointment. *STOCK: Silver and plate, 18th-20th C; jewellery, 19th-20th C.* TEL: 01273 500330; fax - 01273 553300; e-mail - mason@fastnet.co. uk. SER: Valuations; restorations (silver and jewellery); buys at auction (as stock); buyers of scrap silver and gold. FAIRS: Sunday London Hotel. VAT: Stan/Spec.

PATRICK MOORHEAD ANTIQUES

THE SOUTH OF ENGLAND'S LARGEST
QUALITY ANTIQUE WAREHOUSE 30,000 SQ FT

50 Minutes mainline from London Victoria Station
2 minutes from Brighton Station
20 Minutes London Gatwick Airport
(collection service available)

Extensive stock of quality 18th, 19th & 20th Century English and Continental Antiques

Open Monday to Friday
9.30 to 5.30 or by appointment

76 Church Street,
corner of Spring Gardens Brighton
BN1 1RL

Tel: 01273 779696
E.Mail:
patrick.moorhead@virgin.net

Patrick Moorhead Antiques
Spring Gardens, 76 Church St. BN1 1RL. (Patrick and Heather Moorhead). Est. 1984. Open 9.30-5.30, Sat. and other times by appointment. SIZE: Large trade warehouse + showrooms at 15B Prince Albert St. *STOCK: Victorian, Georgian and Continental furniture; Oriental, Continental and English porcelain, clocks, pictures, decorative objects and bronzes.* PARK: Easy. TEL: 01273 779696; fax - 01273 220196; e-mail - patrick.moorhead@virgin.net. SER: Collection from local station and Gatwick airport.

Michael Norman Antiques Ltd `BADA`
4 Frederick Place. BN1 4EA. (Michael P. Keehan). Est. 1965. Open 9-1 and 2-5.30, other times by appointment. *STOCK: English furniture.* PARK: Own. TEL: 01273 329253 or 01273 326712; fax - 01273 206556; e-mail - antiques@michaelnorman.com; website - www.michaelnorman.com. VAT: Spec.

The North Laine Antiques Market, incorporating Alan Fitchett Antiques
5-5A Upper Gardner St. BN1 4AN. (Alan and Heidi Fitchett). Est. 1969. Open 10-5.30, Sat. 9-5.30, Sun. 10-4. SIZE: Large. *STOCK: Furniture, 18th-20th C, £50-£10,000; works of*

art, silver, ceramics, books, jewellery, paintings, prints, collectables, £1-£2,000. LOC: North Laine (station area). PARK: Easy. TEL: 01273 600894; fax - same. SER: Valuations; restorations.

Oasis Antiques
39 Kensington Gdns. BN1 4AL. (I. and A. Stevenson). Est. 1970. Open 10-5.30, Mon. 11-5, Sat. 8-5.30. SIZE: Medium. *STOCK: Lighting and furniture, to 1970, £1-£5,000; European and Oriental items including bronzes, art glass, period clothes, linen and lace, gramophones, radios, telephones, collectable modern design, Art Nouveau, Art Deco.* LOC: Off North Rd. from rail station, centre of North Laines. PARK: Nearby. TEL: 01273 683885. SER: Restorations (radios, telephones, furniture, metals); polishing.

Odin Antiques
43 Preston St. BN1 2HP. (Audun Sjovold). Resident. Est. 1981. Open 10.30-5.30. SIZE: Medium. *STOCK: Furniture, 18th-19th C; telescopes, scientific instruments, 19th-20th C, £500-£1,500; maritime instruments, 19th-20th C, £500-£1,000.* LOC: Off Kings Rd. (seafront) near West Pier. PARK: Regency Sq. TEL: 01273 732738; home - same. VAT: Stan/Spec.

Colin Page Antiquarian Books

36 Duke St. BN1 1AG. (John Loska). Est. 1969. Open 9.30-5.30. *STOCK: Antiquarian and secondhand books, especially topography, travel, natural history, illustrated and leather bindings, 16th-20th C, £1-£30,000.* LOC: Town centre. PARK: Multi-storey nearby. TEL: 01273 325954.

Brian Page Antiques

18 Regent Arcade, East St. BN1 1HR. Open 10-5.30. *STOCK: Oriental antiques, 3000 BC to 20th C.* LOC: Adjacent to Town Hall. TEL: 01273 723956; fax - 01273 719228; e-mail - brianpageantiques@btinternet.com; website - www.yakimono.co.uk. VAT: Spec.

Dermot and Jill Palmer Antiques

7-8 Union St., The Lanes. BN1 1HA. Resident. Est. 1968. Open 9-6, Sun. by appointment. SIZE: Large + warehouse. *STOCK: French and English furniture, objects, pictures, mirrors, screens, garden furniture and ornamental pieces, textiles, £50-£5,000.* PARK: NCP. TEL: 01273 328669 (2 lines); fax - 01273 777641; e-mails - info@martinkidman.com and jillpalmermacunlimited.net. FAIRS: Olympia; Decorative Antiques & Textile. VAT: Stan/Spec.

Sue Pearson

18 Brighton Square, The Lanes. BN1 1HD. Est. 1982. Open 10-5 including Sun. SIZE: Large. *STOCK: Antique dolls, teddy bears, dolls' house miniatures.* PARK: NCP. TEL: 01273 329247. SER: Valuations; restorations; buys at auction (dolls and bears). FAIRS: Major London Doll and Bear. VAT: Stan/Spec.

Ben Ponting Antiques

53 Upper North St. BN1 3FH. Open 9.30-5.30. CL: Sat. *STOCK: Furniture, 18th-19th C.* TEL: 01273 329409. VAT: Spec.

Pure Design Classics

20-21 Chatham Place, Off Seven Dials. BN1 3TN. (Rachel Gander). Est. 2002. Open Tues.-Sat. 10-6. SIZE: Medium. *STOCK: Furniture including Verner Panton, Arné Jacobsen, Eames, Robin Day, 1950-1980, £50-£1,500+; ceramics, fabrics and glass, 1940-1980, £20-£300; lighting, 1940-1980.* LOC: 5 minutes north of Churchill Sq., off Seven Dials roundabout. PARK: Easy. TEL: 01273 735331; fax - 01273 734229; mobile - 07808 003547; home - 01273 494665; e-mail - info@pure2k.com; website - www.pure2k.com. SER: Valuations; buys at auction

Recollections

1a Sydney St., North Laine. BN1 4EN. (B. Bagley). Est. 1973. Open Tues., Thurs., Fri. and Sat. 10.30-4.30. SIZE: Small. *STOCK: Antique and reproduction firebaskets, firebacks, fenders, scuttles, firetools in sets or loose, spark guards, architectural salvage items, décor pieces.* LOC: From rail station down Trafalgar St., last turning on right. PARK: Opposite in Belmont St. TEL: 01273 681517. SER: Metal polishing; repairs.

Savery Antiques

257 Ditchling Rd., (Fiveways). BN1 6JH. (A. and M. Savery). Resident. Est. 1968. Open Mon. 10.30-5, Thurs.-Sat. 9.30-5. *STOCK: China, glass, metalware and collectables.* LOC: Near HSBC Bank. TEL: 01273 564899. FAIRS: Ardingly; Sandown Park.

S.L. Simmons

22 Meeting House Lane, The Lanes. BN1 1HB. NAG. Est. 1948. Open 9.30-5.30. *STOCK: Jewellery and silver, 19th C.* TEL: 01273 327949. VAT: Stan.

Sleeping Beauty Antique Beds

212 Church Rd., Hove. BN3 2DT. (Mrs Flechas). Est. 2003. Open 10-5. SIZE: Medium. *STOCK: Brass, iron and French wooden beds, 19th C, £500-£3,500.* LOC: Continuation of Western Rd. PARK: Nearby. TEL: 01273 735035; home - same; e-mail - info@antiquebeds.com; website - www.antiquebeds.com. SER: Valuations; restorations; buys at auction (beds).

Wardrobe

51 Upper North St. BN1 3FH. (Clive Parks and Philip Parfitt). Est. 1984. Open Wed.-Sat. 10-5, other times by appointment. SIZE: Medium. *STOCK: Vintage clothing, '20's to '30's, £300-£1,200; Art Deco plastics/ Bakelite, 20's-40's, £20-£100; Art Deco furniture, £400-£800.* PARK: On street - vouchers. TEL: 01273 202201; fax - same. FAIRS: Alexandra Palace; Sandown Park; Royal Horticultural Hall, Vincent Square.

E. and B. White

43 & 47 Upper North St. BN1 3FH. Est. 1962. Open 9.30-5. CL: Sat. pm. SIZE: Medium. *STOCK: Country furniture and decorative items, £50-£2,000.* LOC: Upper North St. runs parallel to and north of Western Rd. (main shopping street). TEL: 01273 328706; fax - 01273 207035. VAT: Spec.

Wilkinsons

23 New Rd. BN1 1UF. (Rosalind and Alan Wilkinson). Est. 1985. Open 10-5.30, Sun. 12-4. SIZE: Medium. *STOCK: Furniture, lighting, decorative accessories and collectables, 18th-20th*

C, £10-£5,000. LOC: Near the Theatre Royal. PARK: NCP in Church St. TEL: 01273 676303; fax - same; e-mail - arwilkinsn.@aol.com.

The Witch Ball
48 Meeting House Lane. BN1 1HB. (Mrs Gina Daniels). Est. 1967. Open 10.30-6. *STOCK: 18th-19th C topographical and decorative engravings; 16th-19th C maps.* PARK: Nearby. TEL: 01273 326618. SER: Finder; framing. VAT: Stan/Spec.

Yellow Lantern Antiques Ltd   LAPADA
34 & 34B Holland Rd., Hove. BN3 1JL. (B.R. and E.A. Higgins). Est. 1950. Open 10-1 and 2.15-5.30, Sat. 10-4. SIZE: Medium. *STOCK: Mainly English furniture, £200-£10,000; French and English clocks; both to 1850; bronzes, 19th C, £100-£5,000; Continental porcelain, 1820-1860, £50-£1,000.* LOC: From Brighton seafront to Hove, turn right after parade of Regency houses, shop 100yds. on left past traffic lights. PARK: Easy. TEL: 01273 771572; fax - 01273 455476; mobile - 07860 342976. SER: Valuations; restorations; buys at auction. FAIRS: Buxton; Harrogate; NEC; Olympia; Chester. VAT: Spec.

BURWASH, Nr. Etchingham

Chateaubriand Antiques Centre
High St. TN19 7ES. (Nick and Davina Morgan). Open 10-5.30, Sun. 12-5.30. SIZE: 8 dealers. *STOCK: Linen, furniture, glass, paintings, smalls, books and maps.* LOC: A265. PARK: Nearby. TEL: 01435 882535; e-mail - davina@chateaubriand.co.uk. SER: Shipping.

CROSS IN HAND, Nr. Heathfield

Colonial Times
Lewes Rd. TN21 0TA. (A.P. Skinner). Est. 1979. Open 10-5. SIZE: Medium + 3 barns. *STOCK: Colonial furniture, Victorian and Edwardian, £50-£2,500; clocks, Edwardian, £40-£125; Chinese antique furniture.* LOC: A267 from Tunbridge Wells to Eastbourne, opposite Esso garage. PARK: Easy. TEL: 01435 866442; home/fax - 01435 862962; e-mail - enquiries@ colonial-times.com; website - www.colonial-times.com. FAIRS: Newark. VAT: Stan.

DITCHLING

Dycheling Antiques
34 High St. BN6 8TA. (E.A. Hudson). Est. 1977. Open 10.30-5. CL: Mon. and Wed. SIZE: Large - shop and showroom. *STOCK: Georgian, Victorian and Edwardian furniture, especially dining and armchairs, £25-£5,000.* LOC: Off

A23 on A273-B2112 north of Brighton. PARK: Easy. TEL: 01273 842929; home - same; fax - 01273 841929; mobile - 07885 456341; website - www.antiquechairmatching.com. VAT: Spec.

EASTBOURNE

W. Bruford
11/13 Cornfield Rd. BN21 3NA. Est. 1883. Open 9.30-5.15. SIZE: Medium. *STOCK: Jewellery, Victorian, late Georgian; some silver, clocks (bracket and carriage).* Not Stocked: China, glass, brass, pewter, furniture. TEL: 01323 725452. SER: Valuations; restorations (clocks and silver). VAT: Stan/Spec.

Camilla's Bookshop
57 Grove Rd. BN21 4TX. (C. Francombe and S. Broad). Est. 1976. Open 10-5.30. SIZE: Large, 3 floors. *STOCK: Books including antiquarian, art, antiques and collectables, naval, military, aviation, technical, needlework, broadcasting, literature, biography and history.* LOC: Next to police station, 5 mins. from rail station. PARK: Nearby. TEL: 01323 736001; e-mail - c@millasbooks.fsnet.co.uk. SER: Valuations; postal service; own book tokens.

John Cowderoy Antiques   LAPADA
The Clock and Musical Box Centre, 42 South St. BN21 4XB. (D.J. and R.A. Cowderoy). GMC. Est. 1973. Open 8.30-5. CL: Wed. pm. SIZE: Large. *STOCK: Clocks, musical boxes, furniture, porcelain, silver and plate, jewellery, copper, brass.* LOC: 150yds. from town hall. PARK: Easy. TEL: 01323 720058; website - www. cowderoyantiques.co.uk. SER: Restorations (clocks, barometers, music boxes and furniture). VAT: Stan/Margin.

Crest Collectables
54 Grove Rd. BN21 4UD. (C. Powell). Open 10-6. *STOCK: General antiques and collectables.* TEL: 01323 721185.

John Day of Eastbourne Fine Art
9 Meads St. BN20 7QY. Est. 1964. Open during exhibitions 9.30-1 and 2-5, otherwise by appointment. SIZE: Medium. *STOCK: English, especially East Anglian, and Continental paintings and watercolours, 19th C.* LOC: Meads village, west end of Eastbourne. PARK: Easy. TEL: 01323 725634; mobile - 07960 274139. SER: Restorations; framing (oils and watercolours).

Roderick Dew
10 Furness Rd. BN21 4EZ. Est. 1971. Open by appointment. *STOCK: Antiquarian books,*

especially on art and antiques. LOC: Town centre. PARK: Easy. TEL: 01323 720239. SER: Search; catalogues available.

Eastbourne Antiques Market
80 Seaside. BN22 7QP. Est. 1969. Open 10-5.30, Sat. 10-5. SIZE: Large - 30+ stalls. *STOCK: A wide selection of general antiques and collectables.* PARK: Easy. TEL: 01323 642233.

Elliott and Scholz Antiques
12 Willingdon Rd. BN21 1TH. (C.R. Elliott and K.V. Scholz). Est. 1981. Open 9.30-4.30, Wed. and Sat. 9.30-1. SIZE: Small. *STOCK: Small furniture, £100-£500; clocks, £20-£300; bric-a-brac, £10-£100; all 19th-20th C.* LOC: A22. PARK: Easy. TEL: 01323 732200. SER: Valuations.

Enterprise Collectors Market
The Enterprise Centre, Station Parade. BN21 1BE. Est. 1989. Open 9.30-5. SIZE: Medium. *STOCK: Wide range of general antiques and collectables.* LOC: Next to rail station. PARK: Easy. TEL: 01323 732690. SER: Valuations.

A. & T. Gibbard
30 South St. BN21 4XB. PBFA. Est. 1993. Open 9.30-5.30. SIZE: Large. *STOCK: Secondhand and antiquarian books, 16th-20th C, £1-£1,000.* LOC: 200yds. east of Town Hall. TEL: 01323 734128. SER: Valuations. VAT: Stan.

The Old Town Antiques Centre
52 Ocklynge Rd. BN21 1PR. (V. Franklin). Est. 1990. Open 10-5. SIZE: Medium. *STOCK: General antiques.* LOC: East Dean coast road. PARK: Easy. TEL: 01323 416016. FAIRS: Ardingly.

Timothy Partridge Antiques
46 Ocklynge Rd. BN21 1PP. Open 10-1. *STOCK: Victorian, Edwardian and 1920's furniture.* LOC: In old town, near St. Mary's Church. PARK: Easy. TEL: 01323 638731.

Pharoahs Antiques
28 South St. Little Chelsea. BN21 4XB. (W. and J. Pharoah). Est. 1973. Open 10-5. SIZE: Medium. 14 stallholders. *STOCK: Wide range of antiques including jewellery, pine, kitchenalia, china, curios, lace, linen, Victorian furniture, original light fittings and lamps.* LOC: Near Town Hall. PARK: Easy. TEL: 01323 738655; e-mail - williampharoah@hotmail.com. FAIRS: Ardingly; Brighton.

Stewart Gallery
25 Grove Rd. BN21 4TT. (Gallery Laraine Ltd.).

Est. 1970. Open 9-5.30. SIZE: Large. *STOCK: Paintings and ceramics, 19th-20th C, £5-£25,000.* LOC: Next to library, 150yds. from station. PARK: Easy. TEL: 01323 729588; fax - 01424 772828; e-mail - stewart.gallery@virgin.net. SER: Valuations; restorations (paintings and frames). VAT: Stan/Spec.

Graham Lower
Stonecrouch Farmhouse. TN5 7QB. (Graham and Penny Lower). Est. 1972. Open by appointment. SIZE: Small. *STOCK: English and Continental 17th-18th C oak furniture.* LOC: A21. PARK: Own. TEL: 01580 879535. SER: Valuations. VAT: Spec.

Brookes-Smith Antiques
16 Hartfield Rd. RH18 5HE. (Richard and Kate Brookes-Smith). Est. 1980. Open Tues.-Sat. 9.30-5.30. CL: Wed.pm. *STOCK: Fine furniture, objects, works of art, silver and glass, £50-£20,000.* LOC: 3 miles south of East Grinstead on A22, left at roundabout down Hartfield Rd. PARK: Behind shop. TEL: 01342 826622; fax - 01342 826634; e-mail - ric@brookes-smith.com. SER: Valuations.

HADLOW DOWN, Nr. Uckfield

Hadlow Down Antiques
Hastingford Farm, School Lane. TN22 4DY. (Adrian Butler). Est. 1989. Open 10-5, Sun. 2-5, Wed. by appointment. SIZE: Large. *STOCK: General and decorative antiques, country and formal furniture, 17th C to date, £25-£2,500; English and French decorative accessories, £5-£500.* LOC: 2 mins. down School Lane from A272 in village. PARK: Easy. TEL: 01825 830707; home - same; mobile - 07730 332331. SER: Valuations; restorations (furniture); courier. FAIRS: Ardingly DMG.

HASTINGS

Coach House Antiques
42 George St. TN34 3EA. (R.J. Luck). Est. 1972. Open 10-5 including Sun. SIZE: Medium. *STOCK: Longcase clocks, 18th-19th C, £1,000+; furniture, 19th C, £100+; collectables including Dinky toys, trains, dolls' houses.* PARK: Nearby. TEL: 01424 461849. SER: Valuations; restorations (clocks and furniture); buys at auction (clocks and furniture). VAT: Spec.

George Street Antiques Centre
47 George St. TN34 3EA. (F. Stanley and H. Stallybrass). Est. 1969. Open 10-5, Sun. and winter 11-4. SIZE: Medium - 10 dealers. *STOCK: Small items, 19th-20th C, £5-£500.* LOC: In old town, parallel to seafront. PARK: Seafront. TEL: 01424 429339; home - 01424 813526/428105.

Howes Bookshop
Trinity Hall, Braybrooke Terrace. TN34 1HQ. (Miles Bartley). ABA. PBFA. Est. 1920. Open Mon.-Fri. 9.30-1 and 2-5. *STOCK: Antiquarian and academic books in literature, history, arts, bibliography.* LOC: Near rail station. PARK: Own. TEL: 01424 423437; fax - 01424 460620; e-mail - rarebooks@howes.co.uk. FAIRS: ABA; PBFA.

Nakota Curios
12 Courthouse St. TN35 3AU. (D.H. Brant). Est. 1964. Open 10.30-1 and 2-5. SIZE: Medium. *STOCK: General trade items, decorative china, Victoriana, jewellery, pictures, lighting.* Not Stocked: Coins, medals. PARK: Easy. TEL: 01424 438900.

J. Radcliffe
5 Claremont. TN34 1HA. Open 10-1 and 2-5. CL: Wed. pm. *STOCK: General antiques, trade goods.* TEL: 01424 426361.

Spice
Samphire House, 75 High St., Old Town. TN34 3EL. (S. Dix). Open by appointment. *STOCK: Early furniture and decorative items.* TEL: Mobile - 07710 209556.

HEATHFIELD

Forty One Antiques
41 High St. Open 9.30-4.30. *STOCK: General antiques.* TEL: 01435 863656/813553.

HURST GREEN

Delmar Antiques
77 London Rd. TN19 7PN. (Harry and Sara Nicol). Est. 1973. Open 10-6, Sun. by appointment. CL: Mon. *STOCK: Fine furniture, paintings and antiquarian books, 17th-18th C.* LOC: A21 between Tunbridge Wells and Hastings. PARK: Own. TEL: 01580 860345; fax - 01580 860099. SER: Restorations.

Lawson Antiques Limited
Silver Hill Farm, Silver Hill. TN19 7PU. (M.P. Baldwin). Est. 1735. Open 10-5 including Sun. SIZE: Large. *STOCK: Furniture, pictures, collectables, £5-£5,000.* LOC: North end of High St. PARK: Public at rear. TEL: 01580 860177.

LEWES

Bow Windows Book Shop
175 High St. BN7 1YE. (A. and J. Shelley). ABA. PBFA. Est. 1964. Open 9.30-5. SIZE: Large. *STOCK: Books including natural history, English literature, travel, topography.* LOC: Off A27. TEL: 01273 480780; fax - 01273 486686; e-mail - rarebooks@bowwindows.com. FAIRS: ABA.

Church-Hill Antiques Centre
6 Station St. BN7 2DA. (S. Miller and S. Ramm). Est. 1970. Open 9.30-5. SIZE: 60 stalls and cabinets. *STOCK: Wide range of general antiques including furniture, china, silver, jewellery, clocks, lighting, paintings and decorative items.* LOC: From rail station, in town centre. PARK: Easy, own. TEL: 01273 474842; fax - 01273 846797; e-mail - churchhilllewes@aol.com; website - www.church-hill-antiques.com. VAT: Stan.

Cliffe Antiques Centre
47 Cliffe High St. BN7 2AN. Est. 1984. Open 9.30-5. SIZE: Medium - 16 dealers. *STOCK: General antiques, £5-£1,000.* LOC: Follow town centre signs, turning left 200 yards past Safeways. PARK: Easy. TEL: 01273 473266.

A. & Y. Cumming
84 High St. BN7 1XN. ABA. Est. 1976. Open 10-5, Sat. 10-5.30. *STOCK: Antiquarian and out of print books.* TEL: 01273 472319; fax - 01273 486364; e-mail - a.y.cumming@ukgateway.net. SER: Buys at auction. FAIRS: Chelsea; Olympia.

The Emporium Antique Centre
42 Cliffe High St. BN7 2AN. (Doyle and Madigan). Est. 1990. Open 9.30-5, Sun. 12-4. SIZE: 55 dealers. *STOCK: Furniture, pictures, clocks, collectables, books, jewellery, Art Nouveau and Deco, decorative arts, vintage and collector's toys.* TEL: 01273 486866.

The Fifteenth Century Bookshop
99/100 High St. BN7 1XH. (Mrs S. Mirabaud). PBFA. Est. 1938. Open 10-5.30. Sun. 10.30-4. *STOCK: Antiquarian and general secondhand books, especially children's and illustrated; prints, teddies and china.* LOC: At top of cobbled lane. PARK: Opposite. TEL: 01273 474160. SER: Postal.

Griffin & Mace Antiques
27 Station St. BN7 2DB. (Martin and Caroline Easton). Est. 1973. Open 10-4. SIZE: Small. *STOCK: Mainly English, wood brass and sporting items, metalware, leather-bound books 1700-1900; taxidermy.* LOC: Near station and town hall. PARK: Station. TEL: 01273 475476; fax - same; mobile - 07770 950698; e-mail -

A relief-moulded jug clearly marked with the full maker's name 'BRADBURY, MASON & BRADBURY' along with their address 'CROWN POTTERY'. (Dreweatt Neate)

From an article entitled "Staffordshire Potters - Puzzles and Problems" by Dick Henrywood which appeared in the March 2003 issue of **Antique Collecting**. For more details and to subscribe see page 21.

griffinandmace@tiscali.co.uk. SER: Valuations. FAIRS: Victoria Horticultural Halls; NEC.

Lewes Antique Centre
20 Cliffe High St. BN7 2AH. (Jamie Pettit). Est. 1968. Open 9.30-5, Sun. 12-4. SIZE: Large - 125 stallholders. *STOCK: Furniture, china, copper and metalware, glass, clocks, architectural salvage, books and collectables.* LOC: A27 from Brighton, 2nd roundabout into Lewes, end of tunnel turn left, then next left, next right into Phoenix car park. 100m. walk to Cliffe High St. PARK: Easy. TEL: 01273 476148. SER: Shipping; stripping; restorations; valuations.

Lewes Clock Shop
5 North St. BN7 2PA. (W.F. Bruce). Est. 1982. Open 10-4. CL: Wed. SIZE: Medium. *STOCK: Clocks.* PARK: Nearby. TEL: 01273 473123; fax - same. SER: Valuations; restorations.

Lewes Flea Market
14a Market St. BN7 2NB. Est. 1995. Open daily including Sun. SIZE: Large. *STOCK: Bric-a-brac, furniture, collectables, 18th-20th C, £5-£1,000.* LOC: 50 metres north of monument. PARK: Nearby. TEL: 01273 480328.

Pastorale Antiques
15 Malling St. BN7 2RA. (O. Soucek). Est. 1984. Open 9.30-6 or by appointment. SIZE: Large. *STOCK: Pine and European country furniture, Georgian and Victorian mahogany and decorative items and garden items.* TEL: 01273 473259; home - 01435 863044; fax - 01273 473259; e-mail - pastorale@btinternet.com; website - www. pastorale.cz. SER: Delivery (Europe).

Potter Antiques
1 Lansdown Place. BN7 2JT. (Victor Potter and Jeffrey Short). GADAR. Est. 1963. *STOCK: Furniture, to Victorian; objets d'art.* PARK: Easy. TEL: 01273 487671; fax - 01273 330143; mobile - 07768 274461; e-mail - enquiries@potter antiques.com; website - www.potterantiques. com. SER: Valuations; restorations (furniture and architectural woodwork).

Southdown Antiques
48 Cliffe High St. BN7 2AN. (Miss P.I. and K.A.Foster). Est. 1969. Open by appointment. SIZE: Medium. *STOCK: Small antiques, especially 18th-19th C English, Continental and Oriental porcelain, objets d'art, works of art, glass, papier mâché trays, silver plate, £50-£350,000; reproduction and interior decor items.* LOC: A27. One-way street north. PARK: Easy. TEL: 01273 472439. VAT: Stan/Spec.

LITTLE HORSTED, Nr. Uckfield

Pianos Galore
Worth Farm. TN22 5TT. Est. 1922. Open 9-5, Sun. 10-12. SIZE: Large. *STOCK: Pianos, upright and grands especially Steinway and Bechstein grands, £250-£20,000; also piano stools.* LOC: From A22 Uckfield by-pass take A26 at Little Horsted roundabout. After 1 mile, opposite Wicklands Residential Home, turn right (opposite piano sign), down lane. PARK: Easy. TEL: 01825 750567; fax - 01825 750566. SER: Valuations; restorations (piano repolishing and reconditioning); buys at auction (pianos). VAT: Margin/Stan.

NEWHAVEN

Newhaven Flea Market
28 South Way. BN9 9LA. (J. Mayne). Est. 1971. Open every day 10-5.30 except 25th Dec. *STOCK: Victoriana, Edwardian, bric-a-brac.* TEL: 01273 517207/516065.

NUTLEY

Nutley Antiques
Libra House, High St. TN22 3NF. (Liza Hall). Open 10-5, Sun. and Bank Holidays 1.30-5. SIZE: Small. *STOCK: Country and cottage furniture, £10-£1,000; decorative items, £1-£400; prints, oils, watercolours, £5-£500; all 19th C to 1930.* LOC: A22 between East Grinstead and Uckfield. PARK: Easy. TEL: 01825 713220. VAT: Stan.

PEVENSEY

The Old Mint House
High St. BN24 5LF. (J.C. and A.J. Nicholson). Est. 1903. Open 9-5.30, Sat. 10.30-4.30, otherwise by appointment. SIZE: Large + export warehouse. *STOCK: Furniture - Georgian, Victorian, Edwardian; porcelain, clocks, barometers and decorative items, 18th C-1920's, £50-£10,000.* LOC: A27, 1 mile from Eastbourne. PARK: Easy. TEL: 01323 762337; fax - same; e-mail - antiques@minthouse.co.uk; website - www.minthouse.co.uk. SER: London trains met at local station (Polegate). VAT: Stan/Spec.

PEVENSEY BAY

Murray Brown
The Studio, Norman Rd. BN24 6JE. (G. Murray-Brown). Open by appointment. *STOCK: Paintings and prints.* TEL: 01323 764298. SER: Valuations; restorations; cleaning; conservation.

POLEGATE

Graham Price Antiques Ltd
Applestore, Chaucer Industrial Estate. BN26 6JF. Est. 1979. Open 9-5. SIZE: Large. *STOCK: Mainly furniture - country, decorative, French, Irish, painted, some formal and shipping.* LOC: Between Hastings and Brighton on A27. TEL: 01323 487167; fax - 01323 483904; website - www.grahampriceantiques.co.uk. SER: Export; packing and shipping; courier; restorations.

E. Stacy-Marks Limited   BADA LAPADA
The Flint Rooms, P O Box 808. BN26 5ST. Est. 1889. SIZE: Large. STOCK: Paintings, English, Dutch and Continental schools, 18th-20th C. TEL: 01323 482156; fax - 01323 482513. VAT: Stan.

Summer Antiques
87 High St. BN26 6AE. (R. Millis). Est. 1992. Open 9-5, Sat. 9-12. SIZE: Small. *STOCK: General antiques including silver, china, furniture, brass and copper.* LOC: 250 yards from station. PARK: Easy. TEL: 01323 483834; mobile - 07762 309870. SER: Valuations. FAIRS: Ardingly.

POUNDGATE, Nr. Crowborough

Nicholas Bowlby
Owl House, TN22 4DE. Est. 1981. Open by appointment. SIZE: Medium. *STOCK: 19th-20th C watercolours, contemporary paintings and sculpture, £200-£20,000.* TEL: 01892 667809; e-mail - nicholasbowlby@hotmail.com: website - www.nicholasbowlby.co.uk SER: Valuations; restorations; buys at auction (watercolours and drawings). VAT: Spec.

RINGMER, Nr. Lewes

Bob Hoare - Pine Antiques
Averys Nursery, Uckfield Rd. BN8 5RU. (Bob and Rose Hoare). Open 9-5, Sun. 10-4. SIZE: Large. *STOCK: Country furniture.* LOC: A26. PARK: Own. TEL: 01273 814181; fax - 01273 814714; e-mail - bob@antiquebob.demon.co.uk; website - www.antiquebob.demon.co.uk.

ROTHERFIELD

Forge Interiors
South St. TN6 3LN. (Douglas Masham). Est. 1998. Open Tues.-Sat. 10-1 and 2-5. SIZE: Small. *STOCK: Asian and English antiques and decorative items, furniture, pictures and lighting; Japanese wedding kimonos.* PARK: Easy. TEL: 01892 853000; home/fax - 01892 853122; e-mail - asiandecor@forgeinteriors.com; website - www.forgeinteriors.com. SER: Restorations (re-caning).

ROTTINGDEAN

Trade Wind
15A Little Crescent. BN2 7GF. (R. Morley Smith). Est. 1974. Open by appointment. *STOCK: Caddy and sifter spoons, wine labels and other interesting items, including coloured glass, Bristol blue, green and amethyst; early 18th-19th C white glass including folded foot and engraved items, 1710-1830.* TEL: 01273 301177.

RYE

Bragge and Sons
Landgate House. TN31 7LH. (J.R. Bragge). Est. 1840. Open 9-5. CL: Tues. and Sat. am. *STOCK: 18th C English furniture and works of art.* LOC: Entrance to town - Landgate. TEL: 01797 223358. SER: Valuations; restorations.

Chapter & Verse Booksellers
105 High St. TN31 7JE. (Spencer J. Rogers). Est. 1990. Open Tues. to Sun. 10-5. SIZE: Medium. *STOCK: Rare and antiquarian books - single items to large collections, £50-£25,000.* PARK: Loading only or nearby. TEL: 01797 222692; mobile - 07970 386905; e-mail - chapterandverse @btconnect.com. SER: Valuations; search.

Cheyne House
108 High St. TN31 7JE. (Sue and Keith Marshall). Est. 1996. Open 10-5, Sun. 11-5. CL: Tues. SIZE: Small. *STOCK: Tea caddies, writing slopes, vanity boxes and jewellery, Georgian and Victorian, £150-£500; small furniture, Georgian and Victorian, £200-£2,000; ink-stands, mirrors, candlesticks, Victorian and Edwardian, £80-£300.* PARK: Limited and nearby. TEL: 01797 222612; e-mail - cheynehouse@ryeantiques.fsnet.co.uk.

East Street Antiques
Apothecary House, 1 East St. TN31 7JY. (Mr and Mrs Bloomfield). Est. 1988. Open 10.30-5 including Sun. SIZE: Medium. *STOCK: Furniture, 18th-19th C, £500-£5,000.* LOC: Just off High St. PARK: Easy. TEL: 01797 229266; home - 01797 229157. SER: Buys at auction. FAIRS: Newark; Ardingly; NEC; Battersea Decorative.

Herbert Gordon Gasson
The Lion Galleries, Lion St. TN31 7LB. (T.J. Booth). Est. 1909. Open 10-5, Tues. and Sun. by appointment. SIZE: Large. *STOCK: 17th-19th C oak, walnut and mahogany furniture; decorative items.* Not Stocked: Silver and glass. PARK: Easy.

VICTORIAN CHINA
FAIRINGS
THE COLLECTORS' GUIDE

Derek H. Jordan

- *A brand new guide, covering the period 1850 to 1914*
- *The only book currently available on the subject*
- *Features over 400 colour illustrations*
- *Covers the history of fairings as well as values, repairs and fakes*

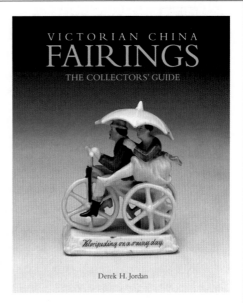

Fairings were definitely made for the huge English Fair market. The word "fair" comes from the Latin feria meaning holiday, a great day for the masses, a chance to catch up on gossip, fashions, new ideas and generally to have a good time and perhaps buy or win a small china ornament. Today we call these small German ornaments of the Victorian/ Edwardian period "fairings".

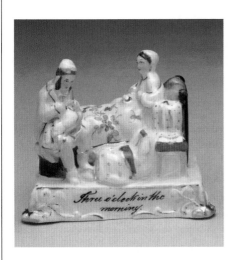

This comprehensive work is the definitive guide for the novice and experienced collector of fairings, covering the history, values, repairs and fakes, with over 400 beautiful photographs in colour. These photographs are all indexed for quick, easy reference as to identification and value. The only book available on the subject, *Victorian China Fairings – The Collectors' Guide* is an absolute must-have reference for collectors, auctioneers and dealers.

Derek H. Jordan has been a keen collector of fairings for twelve years and owns the foremost collection of pieces in the world. He was a founder member of The Fairings Collectors' Society.

11 x 8½in./279 x 216mm.
176pp., 450 col.
1 85149 446 4
£35.00

Available from all good booksellers and direct from the publisher:
ANTIQUE COLLECTORS' CLUB
Sandy Lane, Old Martlesham, Woodbridge, Suffolk, IP12 4SD.
Tel: 01394 389950   Fax: 01394 389999
Email: sales@antique-acc.com
Website: www.antique-acc.com

TEL: 01797 222208; e-mail - hggassonantiques@hotmail.com. SER: Restorations. VAT: Spec.

Ann Lingard - Rope Walk Antiques LAPADA
18-22 Rope Walk. TN31 7NA. Est. 1972. Open 9-1 and 2-5, Sat. 10-1 and 2-5. SIZE: Large. *STOCK: English antique pine furniture and accessories; kitchen shop; garden tools and accessories.* Not Stocked: Jewellery, silver and plate. PARK: Own and public next door. TEL: 01797 223486; fax - 01797 224700; e-mail - ann-lingard@ropewalkantiques.freeserve.co.uk. FAIRS: Ardingly. VAT: Stan/Global.

Wish Barn Antiques
Wish St. TN31 7DA. (Joe Dearden and Robert Wheeler). Est. 1993. Open 10-5 including Sun. SIZE: Medium. *STOCK: 19th C furniture including oak, mahogany and pine, £50-£1,500; silver plate.* LOC: Just off A259. PARK: Easy. TEL: 01797 226797; home - 01580 881485.

SEAFORD

The Courtyard Antiques Market
15 High St. BN25 1PD. (Mrs V.E. Finch). Open 9-5, Wed. 9-1. SIZE: Medium - 13 dealers. *STOCK: General antiques and collectables.* TEL: 01323 892091.

The Old House
15/17 High St. BN25 1PD. (S.M. Barrett). Est. 1928. Open 9-5, Wed. 9-1. SIZE: Large. *STOCK: 18th-20th C furniture, china and glass, £5-£5,000.* LOC: Near rail station. PARK: Opposite in Pelham Yard. TEL: 01323 892091/893795. SER: Valuations; restorations (furniture); shippers. VAT: Stan/Spec.

Seaford's "Barn Collectors' Market" and Studio Bookshop
The Barn, Church Lane. BN25 1HL. Est. 1967. Open 9.30-5. SIZE: Several dealers. *STOCK: Collectables, ephemera, books, post and cigarette cards.* LOC: Off High St. TEL: 01323 890010.

ST. LEONARDS-ON-SEA

Aarquebus Antiques
37 & 46 Norman Rd. TN38 0EJ. (Mr and Mrs G. Jukes). Resident. Est. 1957. Open 9.30-5, Sat. 9.30-1. SIZE: Medium. *STOCK: Furniture, 18th C, £500-£1,000; shipping goods, Victorian to 1930, £5-£500; glass, gold and silver, 18th-19th C, £5-£1,000.* LOC: Take A2100 to St. Leonards-on-Sea, turn right after main P.O. PARK: Easy. TEL: 01424 433267. SER: Valuations.

Bexhill Antiques
78 Norman Rd. TN38. (Mrs Kim Abbott). Est.

1986. Open 10-5. CL: Wed. *STOCK: General antiques.* TEL: 01424 200220; fax - 01424 225103; home - 01424 731430; mobile - 07702 006982; e-mail - klfarrant@aol.com. SER: Shipping arranged. VAT: Stan.

The Book Jungle
24 North St. TN38 0EX. (M. Gowen). Est. 1988. Open 10-5. CL: Wed. SIZE: Medium. *STOCK: Secondhand books.* LOC: Just off seafront. PARK: Nearby. TEL: 01424 421187.

Gensing Antiques
70 Norman Rd. TN38 0EJ. (Peter Cawson). Open normal shop hours and by appointment. *STOCK: General antiques especially early Chinese furniture and other Oriental items.* TEL: 01424 424145/714981.

The Hastings Antique Centre
59-61 Norman Rd. TN38 0EG. (R.J. Amstad). Open 10-5.30, Sun. by appointment. SIZE: Large. TEL: 01424 428561. Below are listed some of the dealers at this centre.

R.J. Amstad
Furniture.

Fred Bourne
French decorative antiques.

Pascal Bourne
French furniture.

Jenny Brown
Decorative wares.

Bruno Antiques
French furniture.

P. Few
Decorative French items.

K. Gumbrell
Decorative items.

Bridget Howett
Decorative items.

Clare Kinloch
Dolls.

G. Mennis
Sporting, leather goods.

Mick Neale
Oak.

Robert Paul Antiques
Furniture and shipping goods.

Pat Robbins
Furniture.

Glen and Linda Simmonds
French interiors.

Swallow Interiors

Monarch Antiques
371 Bexhill Rd. TN38 8AJ. (J.H. King). Est. 1983. Open Mon.-Fri. 8.30-5 or by appointment. SIZE: Warehouse. *STOCK: General furniture, especially 1930's oak furniture for the Japanese, Korean, American and European markets.* LOC: A259. PARK: Own. TEL: 01424 204141; fax - 01424 204142; home - 01424 214158/720821; mobiles - 07802 217842/213081 and 07809 027930; e-mail - monarch.antiques@virgin.net; website - www.monarch-antiques.co.uk. SER: Packing and shipping; courier; restorations. FAIRS: Newark.

John H. Yorke Antiques
Filsham Farmhouse, 111 Harley Shute Rd. TN38 8BY. Est. 40 years. Open 9-5.30. SIZE: Large. *STOCK: Furniture for trade, export and shipping.* PARK: Easy. TEL: 01424 433109; fax - 01424 461061; e-mail - filshamfarmhouse@ talk21.com; website - www.filshamfarmhouse.co. uk. VAT: Stan.

UCKFIELD

Ringles Cross Antiques
Ringles Cross. TN22 1HF. (J. Dunford). Resident. Est. 1965. Open 10-5 or by appointment. *STOCK: English furniture, mainly oak and country, 17th-18th C; accessories.* LOC: 1 mile north of Uckfield. PARK: Own. TEL: 01825 762909.

WADHURST

Baskerville Books
Angels Barn, Claphatch Farm, Wards Lane. TN5 7LH. Est. 1982. Open 10-5. SIZE: Small. *STOCK: Antiquarian and secondhand books; small collectible antiques, occasional period and shipping furniture.* TEL: 01892 526776; mobile - 07775 602526. SER: Valuations.

Park View Antiques
High St., Durgates. TN5 6DE. (B. Ross). Est. 1985. Open 10-4. CL: Wed. except by appointment. SIZE: Medium. *STOCK: Pine, oak and country furniture, 17th-19th C, £100-£1,500; decorative items, 1930's, £25-£150; iron and metalware, 17th-19th C, £25-£250.* LOC: On B2099 Frant-Hurst Green road. PARK: Easy. TEL: 01892 783630; fax - 01892 740264; home - 01892 740264; website - www.parkviewantiques. co.uk. SER: Valuations; restorations (furniture).

SUSSEX WEST

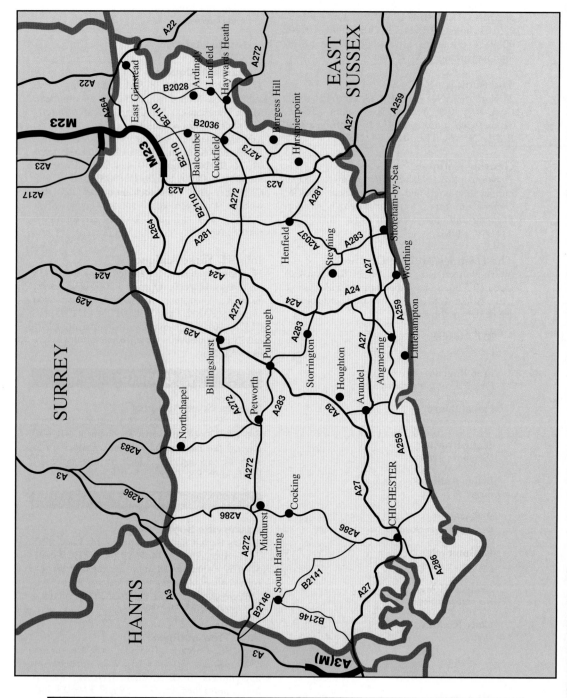

Dealers and Shops in West Sussex							
Angmering	1	Chichester	12	Houghton	1	Petworth	32
Ardingly	1	Cocking	1	Hurstpierpoint	2	Pulborough	2
Arundel	11	Cuckfield	2	Lindfield	3	Shoreham-by-Sea	1
Balcombe	1	East Grinstead	1	Littlehampton	2	South Harting	1
Billingshurst	4	Haywards Heath	1	Midhurst	2	Steyning	1
Burgess Hill	2	Henfield	2	Northchapel	1	Storrington	1
						Worthing	5

ANGMERING

Bygones
The Square. BN16 4EQ. (R.A. and Mrs L.R. Whittaker). Est. 1965. Open Tues. and Thurs. 10-1 and 2.15-5, Sat. 10-12. SIZE: Medium. *STOCK: Furniture, £50-£2,500; china, £5-£750; silver, £10-£250; linen, £5-£75; all 1790-1940.* LOC: A280. PARK: Easy. TEL: 01903 786152; home - same. SER: Valuations; buys at auction (furniture).

ARDINGLY

Rocking Horse Antique Market
16 High St. RH17 6TD. (Peter and Mrs Joy Livett). Est. 1982. Open 9.30-5.30, Sun. 10-5.30 (winter until 5 every day). SIZE: Small. *STOCK: General antiques.* PARK: Rear of village hall. TEL: 01444 892205. FAIRS: Ardingly.

ARUNDEL

Antiquities
5/7 Tarrant St. BN18 9DG. (Ian and Christina Fenwick). Est. 1990. Open 10-5, other times by appointment. SIZE: Large + displayed warehouses. *STOCK: Decorative and unusual - including 19th C English and French furniture, mahogany and fruitwood, painted items, Staffordshire, majolica, metalware, French mirrors, pond yachts, luggage, garden and architectural items.* LOC: Just off town square. PARK: Nearby. TEL: 01903 884355; fax - same; e-mail - antiquities@btconnect.com. SER: Shipping. VAT: Stan/Spec.

Arundel Clocks
Lasseters Corner, High St. BN18 9AE. (F.M. Henderson). Open 9.30-1 and 2-5. *STOCK: Clocks - longcase, £1,500-£6,000; dial, £300-£4,000; mantel and bracket, £250-£5,000; carriage, £200-£2,000.* LOC: Corner of High St. and Mill Lane. PARK: Easy. TEL: 01903 884525. SER: Valuations; restorations (dials, movements and cases). VAT: Spec.

Baynton-Williams
1st Floor, 37A High St. BN18 9AG. (R.H. and S.C. Baynton-Williams). Est. 1946. Open 10-6. *STOCK: Maps, views, sporting, marine and decorative prints.* PARK: Nearby. TEL: 01903 883588; fax - same; e-mail - gallery@baynton-williams.freeserve.co.uk; website - www.baynton-williams.com. SER: Valuations; cataloguing. VAT: Stan/Spec.

Faringdon Gallery
27 Tarrant St. BN18 9DG. (Mr and Mrs G.E. Lott).

Est. 1970. Open Wed.-Sun. 10.30-5, Mon. and Tues. by appointment. SIZE: Small. *STOCK: Water colours and etchings, late 19th C to contemporary, £150-£4,000.* LOC: From A27, first right down High St. hill. PARK: 100 yards at rear. TEL: 01903 882047; home - 01243 554572; e-mail - gelott@dircon.co.uk. SER: Valuations; restorations; buys at auction (watercolours and etchings).

Nineveh House
The Old Chapel Antiques and Collector's Centre, Tarrant St. BN18 9DG. Open 10-5, Sun. 11-5. SIZE: Large - 12 dealers. *STOCK: Wide range of general antiques including Edwardian and Victorian, country and pine furniture, jewellery and silver, paintings and prints, china and glass, luggage and Oriental rugs.* LOC: Off A27 and A29 into town then second left off High St. PARK: Own forecourt. TEL: 01903 884307.

Nostalgia
Unit 5 Old Printing Works Arcade, Tarrant St. BN18 9JH. (Lynn Williams). Est. 1995. Open Wed.-Sun. 10-5. SIZE: Small. *STOCK: Ceramics - Art Deco, Shelley, Carlton Ware, Royal Winton, Clarice Cliff, Susie Cooper, Charlotte Rhead, Burleigh Ware, 1950's Homemaker, Midwinter, 1960's Poole.* LOC: Just off main shopping street. PARK: Nearby. TEL: 01903 884546; mobile - 07711 242494.

The Old Cornstore Antiques
31 High St. BN18 9AG. (Tamborne Ltd). Est. 1982. Open 10-5, Sun. 11-5. SIZE: Large - 30 dealers. *STOCK: Wide range of general antiques, £10-£5,000.* PARK: Easy. TEL: 01903 885456. SER: Valuations. FAIRS: NEC.

Sporting Times Gone By
The Clubhouse, Unit C, 2A Fitzalan Rd. BN18 9JS. (Martin Beeney). Est. 1988. Open 10-5 by appointment, including Sun. SIZE: Large. *STOCK: Interior design items - bamboo, leather, advertising, unusual items.* PARK: Easy. TEL: 01903 885656; fax - same; mobile - 07976 942059. SER: Restorations. FAIRS: Shepton Mallet; Newark.

Spencer Swaffer `LAPADA`
30 High St. BN18 9AB. Est. 1974. Open 9-6, other times by appointment. SIZE: Large. *STOCK: Quirky decorative and traditional items, English, French, brown and painted furniture, dinner services, chandeliers, lighting, marble tables, iron low tables, bamboo, shop fittings, majolica, garden furniture.* PARK: Easy. TEL: 01903 882132; fax - 01903 884564; website - www.spencerswaffer.com. VAT: Stan/Spec.

479

Through the Lens
6 The Old Printing Works, Tarrant St. BN18 9JH. (Tim Nicholls). Est. 1989. Open 10-5. SIZE: Small. *STOCK: Wooden and brass cameras and related items; magic lanterns and slides; stereo including cards; cameras, to 1980's; movie and slide equipment, accessories and books.* PARK: Nearby. TEL: Mobile - 07759 174935. SER: Restorations (wood and brass). FAIRS: Major camera.

The Walking Stick Shop
8/9 The Old Printing Works, Tarrant St. BN18 9JH. (S. Thompson). Est. 1981. Open 8.30-5.30, Wed. 8.30-1, Sun. pm. by appointment. SIZE: Large. *STOCK: Walking sticks and canes, 1620 to date, £10-£2,000.* LOC: Off High St. PARK: Easy. TEL: 01903 883796; home - 01903 882713; fax - 01903 884491; e-mail - stuart. walkingsticks@btinternet.com; websites - www. walkingsticks.uk.com and www.walkingstick shop.co.uk. SER: Valuations; buys at auction (canes). VAT: Stan.

BALCOMBE

Woodall and Emery Ltd
Haywards Heath Rd. RH17 6PG. Est. 1884. Open 10-5. *STOCK: Chandeliers, wall brackets, table lights.* PARK: Easy. TEL: 01444 811608. SER: Restorations (including re-wiring). VAT: Stan.

BILLINGSHURST

Michael Wakelin and Helen Linfield
BADA LAPADA

P.O Box 48. RH14 0YZ. Est. 1968. Open any time by appointment. *STOCK: Fine English and Continental formal and country furniture - walnut, fruitwoods, faded mahogany and other exotic woods; early brass, bronze, iron and steel; wood carvings, treen, needlework, naïve pictures and lighting.* PARK: Easy. TEL: 01403 700004; fax - 01403 701173; e-mail - wakelin_linfield @lineone.net. SER: Shipping; valuations. FAIRS: Olympia; BADA; LAPADA; Chelsea. VAT: Stan/Spec.

BURGESS HILL

British Antique Replicas
School Close, Queen Elizabeth Ave. RH15 9RX. Est. 1963. Open 9-5.30. SIZE: Large. *STOCK: Furniture, £100-£20,000.* LOC: 3 miles west A23. PARK: Easy. TEL: 01444 245577. SER: Bespoke furniture. VAT: Stan.

Recollect Dolls Hospital
17 Junction Rd. RH15 0HR. (P. Jago). Est. 1970.

Open 10-4. CL: Mon. and Sat. *STOCK: Dolls and supplies, doll restoration materials.* TEL: 01444 871052; e-mail - dollshopuk@aol.com. SER: Restorations (dolls); catalogues available (£3 stamps).

CHICHESTER

Almshouses Arcade
19 The Hornet. PO19 4JL. (Mrs V. Barnet). Est. 1983. Open 9.30-4.30. LOC: 200yds. from Cattle Market at eastern end of city. On one-way system (A286) just before traffic lights at Market Ave. PARK: Easy. TEL: 01243 528089. Below are listed the dealers at these premises.

Antics
(P. German). *General antiques and collectables.*

Autodrome
Motoring, tin plate and ephemera. TEL: 01243 778126.

R .K. Barnett
Antiques and collectables, furniture. TEL: 01243 528089.

Collectors Corner
Small collectables and antiques. TEL: 01243 778126

Decographic
Toys, wirelesses, cameras, gramophones. TEL: 01243 787391.

The Delightful Muddle
Unit 3. (Mrs Marjorie Storey). *China, glass, objets d'art, Victorian and Edwardian, £1-£100; linen, general antiques and bric-a-brac, cutlery, £3-£65.*

East Side Records
Records. TEL: 01243 782786.

Yesteryears
(J.A. Cook). *Lighting (oil), general antiques and collectables.* TEL: 01243 771994.

Antiques & Bygones
24 The Old Butter Market, North St. PO19 1LO. (Mrs Maureen Haydon). Est. 1975. Open Tues.-Sat. 9.30-4. SIZE: Small. *STOCK: General collector's items, mainly porcelain and glass, Doulton, Beswick, small furniture.* LOC: City centre precinct opposite Woolworth's. TEL: 01243 788071. SER: Valuations.

Canon Gate Bookshop
28 South St. PO19 1EL. (Philip and Wendy Pegler). Est. 1980. Open 10.30-5. SIZE: Small. *STOCK: Books, mainly 19th-20th C, £1-£1,000.* LOC: Town centre. PARK: Nearby. TEL: 01243

778477; e-mail - philip@canongate.fsbusiness. co.uk. SER: Valuations.

Chichester Antiques Centre
46-48 The Hornet. PO19 4JG. (Mike Carter). Est. 1994. Open 10-5, Sun. 11-4. SIZE: 50 stalls. *STOCK: General antiques and collectables, 50p to £10,000*. LOC: M27, A27 east of town centre. PARK: Loading only and nearby. TEL: 01243 530100; website - www.antiqueschichester.com. SER: Restorations (clocks).

Chichester Gallery
8 The Hornet. PO19 4JG. (Tom and Mary McHale). Est. 1988. Open Tues., Wed. and Fri. 10-4. SIZE: 5 rooms. *STOCK: Victorian oils, watercolours, etchings and engravings, £250-£7,000*. PARK: Nearby. TEL: 01243 779821. SER: Cleaning; restorations; commission sales; inventories; valuations.

Frensham House Antiques
Hunston. PO20 6NX. (J. and M. Riley). Est. 1966. Open 9-6. *STOCK: English furniture, 1700-1830, £500-£6,000; clocks, paintings, copper.* LOC: One mile south of Chichester by-pass on B2145. PARK: Easy. TEL: 01243 782660.

Gems Antiques
39 West St. PO19 1RP. Open 10-1 and 2.30-5.30. CL: Mon. *STOCK: Period furniture, Staffordshire and porcelain figures, glass and pictures.* PARK: Easy. TEL: 01243 786173.

Peter Hancock Antiques
40-41 West St. PO19 1RP. Articles on coins. Est. 1950. Open 10.30-1 and 2.30-5.30. CL: Mon. SIZE: Medium. *STOCK: Silver, jewellery, porcelain, furniture, £20-£2,000; pictures, glass, clocks, books, £5-£500; all 18th-19th C; enthnographica, Art Nouveau, Art Deco, 19th-20th C, £5-£500.* LOC: From Chichester Cross, 17 doors past cathedral. PARK: Easy. TEL: 01243 786173. SER: Valuations; repairs. VAT: Stan/Spec.

Heritage Antiques
84 St. Pancras. PO19 7NL. (D.R. Grover). Est. 1987. Open 9.30-5. *STOCK: Furniture and decorative items.* TEL: 01243 783796.

Rathbone Law
59 North St. PO19 1NB. (Mr and Mrs R. Law). NAG. Est. 1902. Open 9.30-5. CL: Some Mon. *STOCK: Victorian and Edwardian fine jewellery, silver, designer pieces in gold and silver, objets d'art, fine gems.* PARK: Nearby. TEL: 01243 787881; e-mail - info@rathbonelaw.com; website - www.rathbonelaw.com. SER: Valuations.

W.D. Priddy Antiques
Unit 6 Terminus Mill, Terminus Rd. PO19 2UN. Open 10-5, Sun. 11-4 or by appointment. SIZE: Large. *STOCK: Oak, mahogany, walnut and pine furniture, mid-19th C to pre-war and shipping, £20-£6,000.* LOC: Runs off A27 Chichester bypass. PARK: Easy. TEL: 01243 783960; fax - same; e-mail - bill@priddyantiques.fsnet.co.uk; website - www.priddyantiques.co.uk. VAT: Stan/ Spec.

St. Pancras Antiques
150 St. Pancras. PO19 1SH. (R.F. and M. Willatt). Est. 1980. Open 9.30-1 and 2-5. CL: Thurs. pm. SIZE: Small. *STOCK: Arms and armour, militaria, medals, documents, uniforms and maps, 1600-1914, £5-£3,000; china, pottery and ceramics, 1800-1930, £2-£500; small furniture, 17th-19th C, £20-£1,000; coins, ancient to date.* Not Stocked: Silver and carpets. TEL: 01243 787645. SER: Valuations; restorations (arms and armour); buys at auction (militaria).

COCKING, Nr. Midhurst

The Victorian Brass Bedstead Company
Hoe Copse. GU29 0HL. (David Woolley). Resident. Est. 1970. Open by appointment. SIZE: Large. *STOCK: Victorian and Edwardian brass and iron bedsteads, bases and mattresses, 19th-20th C, £300-£3,500.* LOC: Right behind village Post Office, 3/4 mile left turning to Hoe Copse. PARK: Easy. TEL: 01730 812287; e-mail - toria@netcomuk.co.uk; website - www. vbbeds.com. SER: Valuations; restorations (brass and iron bedsteads). VAT: Stan.

CUCKFIELD

David Foord-Brown Antiques   BADA
LAPADA

High St. RH17 5JU. (David Foord-Brown and Sean Barry). Est. 1988. Open 10-5.30. SIZE: Medium. STOCK: Furniture, 1750-1880, £500-£25,000; decorative objects. Not Stocked: Country furniture. LOC: A272. PARK: Easy. TEL: 01444 414418. FAIRS: BADA.

Richard Usher Antiques
23 South St. RH17 5LB. Est. 1978. Open 10-5, other times by appointment. CL: Wed. pm. and Sat. pm. SIZE: Medium. *STOCK: Furniture, 17th-19th C, £50-£3,000; decorative items.* LOC: A272. PARK: Easy. TEL: 01444 451699. SER: Valuations; restorations.

A fine George II period walnut lowboy of superb colour and patination, retaining its original brass handles. Circa 1740.

Height: 71cm. (28in.)
Width: 80cm. (31½in.)
Depth: 48cm. (19in.)

Ashcombe Coach House
ANTIQUES

PO Box 2527, Henfield, West Sussex, BN5 9SU
Tel: (01273) 491630   Fax: (01403) 713366   Mobile: (07803) 180098
e-mail: anglocont@applied.tech.com

LAPADA
MEMBER

EAST GRINSTEAD

The Antique Print Shop
11 Middle Row. RH19 3AX. (A.A.W. Daszewski and Mrs A.C. Keddie). Est. 1988. Open Wed.-Sat. 10-5. SIZE: Small. *STOCK: Prints, pre-1880, £10-£200; maps, especially British county, 1500-1870, £20-£5,000.* LOC: On island in middle High St., opposite St. Swithins Church. PARK: Lewes Rd. TEL: 01342 410501; fax - 01342 410795. SER: Restorations; framing. FAIRS: Park Lane Hotel, London (Sundays); West London Antiques (Penman). VAT: Stan.

HAYWARDS HEATH

Roundabout Antiques Centre
7 Commercial Sq. RH16 1DW. (Angie Craik). Est. 1993. Open 10-5. CL: Mon. SIZE: Medium. *STOCK: Ceramics, glass and silver, jewellery, £50-£1,000; furniture, £50-£2,000; all 19th-20th C. Musical instruments, 20th C, £50-£2,000.* LOC: Across roundabout from rail station. PARK: On forecourt. TEL: 01273 835926/01444 417654.

HENFIELD

Alexander Antiques
Post House, Small Dole. BN5 9XE. (Mrs J.A. Goodinge). Est. 1971. CL: Sun. except by appointment. SIZE: Medium. *STOCK: Country furniture, brass, copper, pewter, samplers, small collectors' and decorative items, treen.* LOC: A2037. PARK: Easy. TEL: 01273 493121; home - same. VAT: Stan/Spec.

Ashcombe Coach House   BADA LAPADA
P O Box 2527. CINOA. Est. 1954. Open by appointment only. *STOCK: Furniture and objects, 17th to early 19th C.* PARK: Own. TEL: 01273 491630; fax - 01403 713366; mobile - 07803 180098. FAIRS: Olympia; BADA.

HOUGHTON, Nr. Arundel

Stable Antiques at Houghton
The Old Church, Main Rd. BN18 9LW. (Ian. J. Wadey). Est. 1993. Open Tues.-Sat. 11-4. *STOCK: General antiques and furniture, £20-£1,000.* LOC: B2139 between Storrington and Arundel. PARK: Own. TEL: 01798 839555; 01903 740555; fax - same; website - www.stableantiques.co.uk.

HURSTPIERPOINT

The Clock Shop
34-36 High St. BN6 9RG. Open 9-6 including Sun., or by appointment. *STOCK: 18th-19th longcase, table and wall clocks.* PARK: Easy. TEL: 01273 832081; mobile - 07860 230888. SER: Restorations (clocks and furniture).

Julian Antiques
124 High St. BN6 9PX. (Julian and Carol Ingram). Est. 1964. Open by appointment. *STOCK: French 19th C mirrors, fireplaces, fenders, furniture.* PARK: Easy. TEL: 01273 832145. FAIRS: Olympia (June).

LINDFIELD

Lindfield Galleries - David Adam `BADA`
62 High St. RH16 2HL. Est. 1972. Open Tues.-Sat. 9.30-5.00. SIZE: Large. *STOCK: Antique and contemporary Oriental carpets and rugs.* PARK: Easy. TEL: 01444 483817; fax - 01444 484682; e-mail - david@lindfieldgalleries. fsnet.co.uk; website - www.orientaland antiquerugs.com. SER: Restorations; cleaning. VAT: Stan/Spec.

Spongs Antiques Centre
102 High St. RH16 2HS. (Ashley and Karen Richardson). Est. 1999. Open 10-5, Sun. 2-5. SIZE: Medium. *STOCK: Porcelain and pottery, 18th-20th C, £10-£2000; oak, pine and mahogany furniture, 17th-20th C, £50-£1,000; silver, 17th-20th C, £30-£500.* PARK: Nearby. TEL: 01444 487566; e-mail - spongs80@ hotmail.com; website - www.spongsantiques centre.co.uk. SER: Valuations.

Stable Antiques
98A High St. RH16 2HP. (Adrian Hoyle). Est. 1987. Open 10-5.30. Sun. 12.30-5.30. SIZE: Large. *STOCK: Regency, and mahogany Victorian furniture, including extending tables, bookcases, and chests of drawers; pine and country furniture.* LOC: Off A272 on B2028, 2 miles south of Ardingly. PARK: Easy and free. TEL: 01444 483662; mobile - 07768 900331; e-mail - adrianhoyle@msn.com. SER: Valuations. VAT: Spec.

LITTLEHAMPTON

Joan's Antiques
1 New Rd. BN17 5AX. (J. Walkden and M. Hill). Est. 1976. Open Thurs.-Sat. 10.30-4.30. SIZE: Small. *STOCK: China and collectables, Victorian to 1930's, £5-£100.* LOC: From Woolworths, Surrey St, keep left and turn into New Road. PARK: Easy. TEL: 01903 722422; home - 01903 784495. FAIRS: Goodwood.

Magic of Quimper
Faux Cottage, 4A Selborne Rd. BN17 5NN. (Kay Meader). Usually available by appointment. *STOCK: Over 200 pieces of Quimper faience, Desvres and other French faience.* LOC: Telephone for directions. PARK: Easy. TEL: 01903 714261; e-mail - magic.quimper@virgin. net.

MIDHURST

Churchill Clocks
Rumbolds Hill. GU29 9BZ. (W.P. and Dr. E. Tyrrell). Open 9-5, Wed. 9-1. *STOCK: Clocks and furniture.* LOC: Main street. TEL: 01730 81389; website - www.churchillclocks.co.uk. SER: Restorations (clocks).

NORTHCHAPEL, Nr. Petworth

Callingham Antiques
GU28 9HL. Est. 1979. Open 9.30-5.30. CL: Wed. SIZE: Medium. *STOCK: Furniture, 1700-1900, £10-£10,000.* LOC: London Road 5 miles north of Petworth. PARK: Easy. TEL: 01428 707379; e-mail - antiques@callinghamfreeserve.co.uk. SER: Valuations; restorations.

PETWORTH

Angel Antiques

Church St. GU28 0AD. (Nick and Barbara Swanson). PAADA. Open 10-5.30, Sun. by appointment. SIZE: Medium. *STOCK: English and French 17th-19th C country furniture, ceramics, pictures and decorative items, £50-£15,000.* LOC: Opposite Petworth House and war memorial. TEL: 01798 343306; fax - 01798 342665; e-mail - swansonantiques@aol.com; website - www.angel-antiques.co.uk. VAT: Spec.

Antiquated   LAPADA

10 New St. GU28 0AS. (Vicki Emery). PAADA. Est. 1989. Open 10-5.30 or by appointment. *STOCK: 18th-19th C original painted furniture, decorative items, garden furniture; 19th C rocking horses.* TEL: 01798 344011; fax - same.

Baskerville Antiques   BADA

Saddlers House, Saddlers Row. GU28 0AN. (A. and B. Baskerville). Est. 1978. Open Tues.-Sat. 10-6 or by appointment. SIZE: Medium. *STOCK: English clocks and barometers, £1,000-£40,000; decorative items and instruments, £500-£10,000; all 17th-19th C.* LOC: Town centre. PARK: Public, adjoining shop. TEL: 01798 342067; home - same; fax - 01798 343956; e-mail - brianbaskerville@ aol.com. VAT: Spec.

John Bird

High St. GU28 0AU. PAADA. Open 10.15-5.15. SIZE: Medium. *STOCK: Furniture - country, pine, oak, fruitwood, mahogany, painted, architectural, garden and upholstered.* PARK: Easy. TEL: 01798 343250/865143; mobile - 07970 683949; e-mail - bird.puttnam@virgin.net. VAT: Spec.

Bradley's Past & Present

21 High St. GU28 0AU. (M. and A. Bradley). Est. 1975. CL: Mon. SIZE: Small. *STOCK: Furniture, 19th-20th C, £50-£500; china and decorative items, £5-£100; metalware, phonographs, gramophones and records.* PARK: Nearby. TEL: 01798 343533. SER: Restorations; repairs.

Brownrigg

10A New St. GU28 0AS. (George Perez Martin and Julian Muggeridge). PAADA. Est. 1999. Open 10-5.30, Sun. by appointment. *STOCK: General antiques including Continental furniture, 13th C to 1920's; lighting, luggage, ceramics, decorative items.* PARK: Easy. TEL: 01798 344321; fax - same; home - 01798 343304; e-mail - info@ brownrigg-interiors.com; website - www. brownrigg-interiors.com. SER: Interior design.

The Canon Gallery   BADA   LAPADA

New St. GU28 0AS. (Jeremy Green and James Fergusson). PAADA. Est. 1987. Open 10-1 and 2-5.30. SIZE: Medium. *STOCK: Oils and watercolours, 18th-20th C, £500-£100,000.* LOC: Main road. PARK: Easy. TEL: 01798 344422; e-mail - canongallery@btinternet. com. SER: Valuations; restorations. FAIRS: World of Watercolours; NEC; Harrogate; Olympia; New York; BADA. VAT: Spec.

Ronald G. Chambers Fine Antiques
                                  LAPADA

Market Sq. GU28 0AH. (Ronald G. Chambers and Jacqueline F. Tudor). CINOA. PAADA. Est. 1985. Open 10-5.30, Sun. 10-4.30. SIZE: 5 showrooms. *STOCK: Fine 18th-19th C furniture and objets d'art.* PARK: Free. TEL: 01798 342305; fax - 01798 342724; mobile - 07932 161968; e-mail - Jackie@ronaldchambers.com; website - www.ronaldchambers.com. SER: Search; valuations; shipping; storage.

J. Du Cros Antiques

1 Pound St. GU28 0DX. (J. and P. Du Cros). PAADA. Est. 1982. Open 10-5.30, sometimes closed Wed. pm. SIZE: Medium. *STOCK: English furniture, 1660-1900, £100-£5,000; treen, metalware, some glass.* LOC: Corner of Sadlers Row. PARK: Nearby. TEL: 01798 342071. VAT: Stan/Spec.

Elliott's

88A New St. GU28 0AS. PAADA. Est. 1990. Open Thurs., Fri. and Sat. 10-5. *STOCK: 18th-20th C furniture, fine art and decorative items.* TEL: 01798 343408.

Richard Gardner Antiques   LAPADA

Swan House, Market Sq. GU28 0AN. (Richard and Janice Gardner). PAADA. Resident. Est. 1992. Open 10-5.30 including Sun. SIZE: Large. *STOCK: Fine period furniture and works of art, up to £75,000; English and Continental porcelain, Victorian Staffordshire figures, bronzes, silver, paintings, 17th-19th C; associated items.* PARK: 50 yards. TEL: 01798 343411/344463; website - www.richard gardnerantiques.co.uk. VAT: Spec.

John Giles   LAPADA

High St. GU28 0AU. Est. 1980. Open 10-5.30. SIZE: Medium. *STOCK: Furniture - formal, painted and country, £300-£5,000; lamps, mirrors, objects and pottery.* PARK: Easy and free nearby. TEL: 01798 342136; mobile - 07770 873689; e-mail - gilesandhart@btinternet.com. FAIRS: : Olympia (June).

Granville Antiques `BADA`
5 High St. GU28 0AU. (I.E.G. Miller). CINOA. Est. 1979. Open 10-5.30 or by appointment. *STOCK: Period furniture, mainly pre-1840, £50-£15,000; accessories and pictures.* PARK: Easy. TEL: 01798 342312; mobile - 07966 279761. SER: Valuations; restorations (furniture). FAIRS: BADA. VAT: Spec.

William Hockley Antiques `LAPADA`
East St. GU28 0AB. (D. and V. Thrower). PAADA. Est. 1974. Open 10-5.30. *STOCK: Fine 18th to early 19th C furniture and decorative items, fabrics, carpets and related items.* PARK: Easy. TEL: 01798 343172; 01403 701917. SER: Interior design. VAT: Stan/Spec.

John's Corner
Allsorts, Lombard St. GU28 0AH. (J. and G. Mason). Est. 1991. Open 10-4.30. SIZE: Small. *STOCK: Ivory, netsuke, okimono, sporting prints, 19th to early 20th C, £100-£1,000+.* PARK: Nearby. TEL: 01798 343270; home - 01798 342258; e-mail - john's@corner99.freeserve. co.uk.

Philip Maggs Antiques
19 East St. GU28 0AB. (Philip and Wendy Maggs). PAADA. Est. 1988. Open 10-5. SIZE: Small. *STOCK: Eclectic European furniture, lighting, decorative antiques, 19th to early 20th C.* PARK: Easy. TEL: 01798 343993; e-mail - info@pmaggsantiques.com; website - www. pmaggsantiques.com.

Marston House
Lombard St. GU28 0AG. Open 10.30-5.30 including Sun. SIZE: Medium. *STOCK: English furniture, 1750-1920, £500-£50,000; English porcelain including Royal Worcester, glass and other wine related items.* LOC: Just off main square. PARK: Nearby. TEL: 01798 344111; fax - same; e-mail - marstonhouseantiques@ ukonline.co.uk. SER: Valuations; restorations (furniture). FAIRS: NEC.

Muttonchop Manuscripts
The Playhouse Gallery, Lombard St. GU28 0AG. (Roger S. Clarke). PBFA; PAADA. Est. 1992. Open Tues.-Fri. 10-4, Sat. 10-5. SIZE: Small. *STOCK: Non-fiction antiquarian books, 15th- 19th C; collectable, collectors and antiques reference books; maps, prints and ephemera; fiction classic sets and bindings.* LOC: Cobbled street from Market Square. PARK: Free nearby. TEL: 01798 344471; fax - same; e-mail - rogmutton@aol.com; website - www.mrmutton chops.com. SER: Valuations; restorations

(bookbinding). FAIRS: PBFA - Haywards Heath and Fontwell Park.

Octavia Antiques
East St. GU28 0AB. (Aline Bell). PAADA. Est. 1973. Open 10.30-5.30. CL: Fri. SIZE: Small. *STOCK: Decorative items - blue and white china, lamps, mirrors, chairs, small sofas, mainly 19th C.* PARK: Easy. TEL: 01798 342771.

Old Bank House
Market Sq. GU28 0AH. (Bruce Wheeler Antiques and Anthony Graham Antiques). PAADA. Open 10-5. SIZE: Medium. *STOCK: English and Continental furniture and objects, 1800-1940.* TEL: 01798 344176; mobiles - 07970 616434 and 07803 596410. FAIRS: Olympia.

Oliver Charles Antiques
Lombard St. GU28 0AG. (Allan and Deborah Gardner). PAADA. Est. 1987. Open 10-5.30 (including Sun. from April to Sept) or by appointment. SIZE: Medium. *STOCK: Georgian, Regency and selected French furniture, 1700- 1850, £1,000-£25,000; Victorian paintings, £750- £100,000.* LOC: Opposite church. PARK: Easy. TEL: 01798 344443; fax - 01798 343916; e-mail - olivercharles1@aol.com; website - www.oliver charles.co.uk. SER: Valuations.

Persian Carpet Gallery of Petworth
Church St. GU28 0AD. (Dr. Ali Mandegaran). PAADA. Est. 1974. Open 9.30-5. *STOCK: Old and new Persian, Turkish, Indian, Pakistani and Afghan rugs and carpets.* LOC: A272. PARK: Nearby. TEL: 01798 343344; fax - 01798 342673; e-mail - pcg1973@yahoo.co.uk. SER: Valuations; restorations; hand cleaning; insurance claims.

Petworth Antique Centre
East St. GU28 0AB. (D.M. Rayment). PAADA. Est. 1967. Open 10-5.30. SIZE: Large - 36 dealers. *STOCK: General antiques, books, furniture, brass, copper, pictures, textiles.* LOC: Near church. PARK: Adjoining. TEL: 01798 342073; fax - 01798 344566; e-mail - info@ petworthantiquecentre.co.uk; website - www. petworthantiquecentre.co.uk. VAT: Stan/Spec.

Annette Puttnam
2 Leppards High St. GU28 0AU. PAADA. Open 10-5.15. *STOCK: Furniture - country, pine, oak, fruitwood, mahogany, painted, architectural, garden and upholstery.* TEL: 01798 343933; mobile - 07973 421070; e-mail - bird.puttnam@ virgin.net. FAIRS: Olympia (June, Nov., Feb). VAT: Spec.

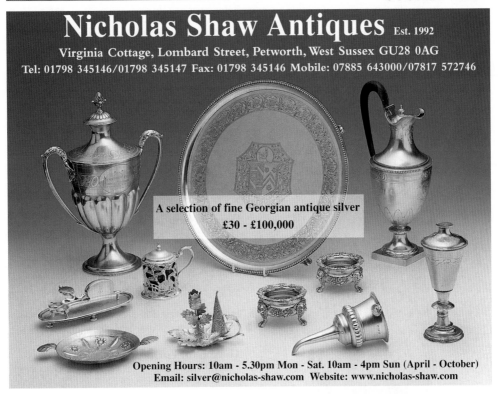
Red Lion Antiques   LAPADA

New St. GU28 0AS. (Rod Wilson). PAADA. Est. 1981. Open 10-5.30 and by appointment. SIZE: Large. *STOCK: Antiques for the country home, oak, walnut and pine furniture, 17th-19th C, £100-£20,000.* LOC: Town centre. PARK: Easy. TEL: 01798 344485; fax - 01798 344439; e-mail - rod@redlion-antiques.com; website - www.redlion-antiques.com. VAT: Spec.

Riverbank

High St. GU28 0AU. (Linda Burke-White). PAADA. Open 10-5.30. *STOCK: Antiques for the house and garden.* TEL: 01798 344401; fax - 01798 343135.

Roughshed

Pound St. GU28 0DX. (Kirstine St John Best). PAADA. Est. 1990. Open 10-5. SIZE: Small. *STOCK: French and English painted furniture, 19th-20th C, to £1,000; upholstered footstools and chairs, to £795; garden furniture, from £40; cushions, eiderdowns, lamps, lighting, French and English enamelware; bathroom cabinets and towel rails.* LOC: Towards Midhurst road from town square. PARK: Nearby. TEL: 01798 344446; mobile - 07970 599464; website - www.roughshed.co.uk. SER: Interiors consultancy.

Ruddy Antiques

6 High St. GU28 0AU. (Robin and Paula Ruddy). PAADA. Est. 1994. Open 10.30-5 or by appointment. SIZE: Medium. *STOCK: Eclectic Continental and English furniture, 18th-19th C.* TEL: 01798 344622; e-mail - ruddy.antiques@virgin.net.

Nicholas Shaw Antiques   BADA   LAPADA

Virginia Cottage, Lombard St. GU28 0AG. CINOA. PAADA. Est. 1992. Open 10-5.30, Sun. 12-4. SIZE: Small. *STOCK: Fine and rare English, Scottish and Irish silver, 16th to mid 20th C, £30-£50,000.* LOC: Town centre. PARK: Nearby. TEL: 01798 345146/345147; fax - 01798 345146; mobiles - 07885 643000 and 07817 572746; e-mail - silver@nicholas-shaw.com; website - www.nicholas-shaw.com. SER: Valuations; restorations. FAIRS: BADA; Olympia; Harrogate; NEC; LAPADA.

Tudor Rose Antiques

East St. GU28 0AG. (Mrs E.J. Lee). PAADA. Est. 2001. Open 10-5.15, Sun. 11-4.15. SIZE: Large. *STOCK: General antiques.* TEL: 01798 344309; mobile - 07980 927331; e-mail - info@tudor-rose-antiques.co.uk; website - www.tudor-rose-antiques.co.uk.

A heroic figure of Scottish history in statue form at the Bonhams sale. The 19th century stone likeness of Robert the Bruce coaxed £8,500 from a patriot.

From an article entitled "Auction Report - The Scottish Sale" by Christopher Wight which appeared in the October 2002 issue of **Antique Collecting**. For more details and to subscribe see page 21.

J.C. Tutt Antiques
Angel St. GU28 0BQ. Open 10-5. CL: Some Mon. SIZE: Large. *STOCK: Mahogany and country furniture and accessories.* PARK: Nearby. TEL: 01798 343221.

T.G. Wilkinson Antiques Ltd.
Market Sq. GU28 0AH. (Tony Wilkinson). Est. 1973. Open 10-5.30. SIZE: Medium. *STOCK: English furniture - mahogany, rosewood and walnut, 1720-1840; mirrors and pictures; all £100-£45,000.* PARK: Nearby. TEL: 01798 343638.

PULBOROUGH

Georgia Antiques
LAPADA

The Barn, Broomershill Farm. RH20 2HZ. (Georgia Hicks). CINOA. Est. 1979. Open by appointment. SIZE: Medium. *STOCK: English furniture, pictures and fine art, 18th-19th C; decorative lighting, 19th C.* PARK: Easy. TEL: 01798 872348; fax - 01798 875200; e-mail - georgia@georgia-antiques.com; website - www.georgia-antiques.com. VAT: Spec.

Thakeham Furniture
Marehill Rd. RH20 2DY. (T. and B. Chavasse). Est. 1988. Open Mon.-Fri. 9-5. SIZE: Medium. *STOCK: 18th-19th C English furniture, £100-£8,000; clocks.* LOC: 1 mile east of Pulborough next to White Horse Inn on A283. PARK: Easy. TEL: 01798 872006; mobile - 07803 086828. SER: Restorations (furniture). VAT: Spec.

SHOREHAM-BY-SEA

Rodney Arthur Classics
Unit 5 Riverbank Business Centre, Old Shoreham Rd. BN43 5FL. (Rodney Oliver). Est. 1979. Open 9.30-5, Sat. and Sun. by appointment. SIZE: Large. *STOCK: Furniture, 1800-1920, £100-£2,500.* LOC: From A27 take A283 exit near Shoreham Airport, then south towards sea, shop opposite Swiss Cottage pub. TEL: 01273 441606; fax - 01273 441977. SER: Restorations; French polishing. VAT: Stan/Spec.

SOUTH HARTING, Nr. Petersfield

Julia Holmes Antique Maps and Prints
South Gardens Cottage. GU31 5QJ. FATG. Est. 1961. Open by appointment. SIZE: Medium. *STOCK: Maps, mainly British Isles, 1600-1850, £25-£2,000; prints, especially sporting, to £500.* LOC: End of main street, on the Chichester road. PARK: Opposite. TEL: 01730 825040; e-mail - juliaandroger@beeb.net; website - www.juliamaps.co.uk. SER: Valuations; restorations;

cleaning; colouring maps and prints; framing; buys at auction; catalogues. FAIRS: Local and major sporting events.

STEYNING

David R. Fileman
Squirrels, Bayards. BN44 3AA. Open daily. *STOCK: Table glass, £20-£1,000; chandeliers, candelabra, £500-£20,000; all 18th-19th C. Collectors' items, 17th-19th C, £25-£2,000; paperweights, 19th C, £50-£5,000.* LOC: A283 to north of Steyning village. TEL: 01903 813229. SER: Valuations; restorations (chandeliers and candelabra). VAT: Stan/Spec.

STORRINGTON

Stable Antiques
46 West St. RH20 4EE. (Ian J. Wadey). Est. 1993. Open 10-6 including Sun. SIZE: Large. *STOCK: General antiques, furniture and bric-a-brac, £1-£1,000.* LOC: A283 west of A24 towards Pulborough, just before Amberley turn. PARK: Easy. TEL: 01903 740555; fax - 01903 740441; website - www.stableantiques.co.uk.

WORTHING

Acorn Antiques
91 Rowlands Rd. BN11 3JX. (Henry Nicholls). Est. 1992. Open 9-5.30, Mon. and Wed. 9-4. SIZE: Small. *STOCK: Furniture, china and porcelain, 18th-20th C.* LOC: Off Heene Road near seafront. PARK: Easy. TEL: 01903 216926. SER: Restorations; polishing. FAIRS: Ardingly; Goodwood.

Chloe Antiques
61 Brighton Rd. BN11 3EE. (Mrs D. Peters). Est. 1960. Open 10-12.30 and 1.30-4.30. CL: Wed. SIZE: Small. *STOCK: General antiques, jewellery, china, glass, bric-a-brac.* LOC: From Brighton, on main road just past Beach House Park on corner. PARK: Opposite. TEL: 01903 202697.

Corner Antiques
9/10 Havercroft Buildings, North St. BN11 1DY. (R.A. Mihok). Est. 1992. Open 10-5. SIZE: Small. *STOCK: Pine and country furniture, 19th C, £200-£500; objets d'art, 50p-£150, furniture, £100-£1,000; all 19th-20th C.* LOC: Top end of High St. turn right at the roundabout. PARK: Loading only, otherwise Connaught NCP. TEL: 01903 537669; fax - 01903 206881. SER: Restorations (furniture including French polishing, upholstering and repairs); buys at auction.

Robert Warner Antiques Ltd
1-13 South Farm Rd. BN14 7AB. Est. 1940. CL: Wed. pm. SIZE: Large. *STOCK: Furniture.* TEL: 01903 232710; fax - 01903 217515; website - www.rewarner.co.uk. VAT: Stan.

Wilsons Antiques `LAPADA`
45-47 New Broadway, Tarring Rd. BN11 4HS. (F. and K.P. Wilson). Est. 1936. Open 10-5, Sat. 10-1. SIZE: Large. *STOCK: Period furniture, 18th-19th C, £100-£10,000; Edwardian furniture, £50-£4,000; decorative items, 19th C, £10-£750; watercolours and oil paintings, 19th-20th C.* Not Stocked: Pine. PARK: Easy. TEL: 01903 202059; fax - 01903 206300; mobile - 07778 813395; e-mail - Frank@Wilsons-Antiques.com; website - www.wilsons-antiques.com. SER: Valuations. FAIRS: Olympia (June); Goodwood House; NEC. VAT: Stan/Spec/Global.

Tessa Newcomb (b.1955), 'Country Flowers', oil on board, 11in. x 24in. (David Messum Fine Art)

From an article entitled "Painters and Sculptors of East Anglia" by Geoffrey Munn which appeared in the February 2003 issue of *Antique Collecting*. For more details and to subscribe see page 21.

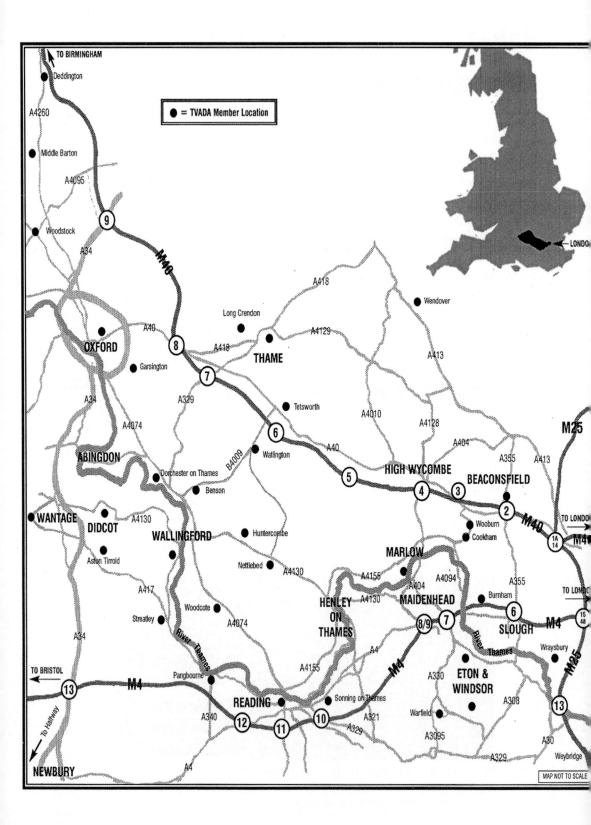

490

Thames Valley
Antique Dealers Association

Representing some 250 member dealers

In this historic and beautiful area of the Thames Valley you will find a wide variety of antiques and decorative items – appealing to the connoisseur, collector, decorator and homemaker.

Medieval and Georgian buildings are host to many of the antique dealers' shops and centres, so why not combine your search for antiques with an historical tour.

T.V.A.D.A.

Look out for the black & gold TVADA Logo sign (Tamesis, the Roman God of the Thames), hanging in the window or on the door, you can always be sure of a warm welcome inside and often refreshments too!

Our Associate Members can help you with restoration, conservation and decorating advice. Our members are experienced in dealing with customers worldwide and will help with advice on packing, shipping, and insurance.

Twice a year – in the Spring and Autumn we hold award winning Fairs and provide an opportunity to sample the quality and range of items available from TVADA members.

The Thames Valley is conveniently situated, from central London most TVADA members can be reached within one hour by road. Trains and buses serve the area well. Heathrow airport is only 8 miles from our nearest dealer, and the M4, M25 and M40 motorways provide easy accessibility. We are pleased to offer a courier service to guide you round the area.

Visit our Website **www.tvada.co.uk** for information, e-mail **antiques@tvada.co.uk** or telephone the TVADA office for more information.

The Secretary, TVADA, The Old College, Queen Street
Dorchester on Thames, Oxon OX10 7HL. Tel/Fax: 01865 341639

THAMES VALLEY
ANTIQUE DEALERS ASSOCIATION

T.V.A.D.A.

Representing over 250 Dealers
with wide ranging stocks

For further details, please contact:
Thames Valley Antique Dealers' Association
The Old College, Queen Street, Dorchester-on-Thames
Oxon OX10 7HL.
Tel/Fax: 01865 341639
e-mail: antiques@tvada.co.uk
website: www.tvada.co.uk

ASTON TIRROLD, Nr. Didcot

John Harrison Fine Art
Skirmers, Aston St. OX11 9DQ. (J.M.C. Harrison). TVADA. Strictly by appointment. *STOCK: Drawings and watercolours, 18th-19th C*. TEL: 01235 850260. SER: Commissions undertaken.

BEACONSFIELD

Period Furniture Showrooms
49 London End. HP9 2HW. (R.E.W. Hearne and N.J. Hearne). TVADA. Est. 1965. Open Mon.-Sat. 9-5.30. SIZE: Large. *STOCK: Furniture, 1700-1900, £50-£5,000*. LOC: A40 Beaconsfield Old Town. PARK: Own. TEL: 01494 674112; fax - 01494 681046; e-mail - sales@periodfurniture. net; website - www.periodfurniture.net. SER: Restorations (furniture). VAT: Stan/Spec.

BODICOTE, Nr. Banbury

Blender Antiques
Cotefield Farm, Oxford Rd. OX15 4AQ. (Neil Robson). TVADA. Open Mon.-Fri. 9.30-5 or by appointment. SIZE: Large. *STOCK: English and Continental furniture, mirrors, lighting and decorative accessories*. LOC: Banbury-Oxford road, opposite Banbury Rugby Club. PARK: Own. TEL: 01295 254754; fax - 01295 276139; mobile - 07785 785447.

CAVERSHAM, Nr. Reading

The Clock Workshop　　　LAPADA
17 Prospect St. RG4 8JB. (J. M. Yealland) FBHI. TVADA. CINOA. Est. 1980. Open 9.30-5.30, Sat. 10-1. SIZE: Small. *STOCK: Clocks, late 17th to late 19th C, £350-£60,000; barometers, 18th-19th C, £500-£12,000*. LOC: Prospect St. is the beginning of main Reading to Henley road. PARK: Behind shop in North St. TEL: 0118 9470741; e-mail - theclockworkshop@supanet. com. SER: Valuations; restorations (clocks, barometers, chronometers, barographs); buys at auction. FAIRS: TVADA; LAPADA; Olympia. VAT: Stan/Spec.

COOKHAM RISE

Cookham Antiques
35 Station Parade. SL6 9BR. (Gary Lloyd Wallis). TVADA. Est. 1990. Open daily including Sun. SIZE: Large. *STOCK: Furniture including bookcases, desks, chests of drawers, 18th-20th C, £50-£1,000*. PARK: Easy and at rear. TEL: 01628 523224; mobile - 07778 020536. SER: Valuations; restorations.

DEDDINGTON

Deddington Antiques Centre
Laurel House, Bull Ring, Market Sq. OX15 0TT. (Mrs B. J. Haller). TVADA. Est. 1972. Open 10-5 including Sun. SIZE: 27 dealers. *STOCK: Furniture, Georgian to 1930's, £100-£4,000; porcelain, silver, pictures, jewellery, 1700-1930, £5-£5,000; collectables, £10-£200*. LOC: Off A4260 Oxford-Banbury road at Deddington traffic lights. PARK: Easy and free. TEL: 01869 338968; fax - 01869 338916. SER: Valuations. FAIRS: TVADA.

DORCHESTER-ON-THAMES

Dorchester Antiques　　　LAPADA
The Barn, 3 High St. OX10 7HH. (J. and S. Hearnden). TVADA. Est. 1992. Open Tues.-Sat. 10-5. SIZE: Medium. *STOCK: Furniture including chairs and decorative country pieces, 18th-19th C*. LOC: Opposite Abbey. PARK: Easy. TEL: 01865 341373. SER: Restorations; finder. FAIRS: TVADA.

Hallidays (Fine Antiques) Ltd　　　LAPADA
The Old College, High St. OX10 7HL. TVADA. CINOA. Est. 1950. Open 9-5, Sat. 10-1 and 2-4. SIZE: Large. *STOCK: 17th-19th C English and Continental furniture; 18th-19th C paintings, decorative and small items; 18th-20th C pine and marble mantelpieces, firegrates, fenders; bespoke room panelling*. LOC: 8 miles south-east of Oxford. PARK: At rear. TEL: 01865 340028/68; fax - 01865 341149; e-mail - antiques@ hallidays.com; website - www.hallidays.com. FAIRS: Olympia; LAPADA, London; Gramercy Park, New York; International Antiques, Chicago. VAT: Stan/Spec.

HALFWAY, Nr. Newbury

Alan Walker　　　BADA
Halfway Manor. RG20 8NR. TVADA. Est. 1987. Open by appointment. SIZE: Large. *STOCK: Fine barometers and weather instruments*. LOC: 4 miles west of Newbury on A4. PARK: Easy. TEL: 01488 657670; mobile - 07770 728397; website - www.alanwalker-barometers. com. SER: Restorations.

HUNTERCOMBE

The Country Seat　　　LAPADA
Huntercombe Manor Barn. RG9 5RY. (Harvey Ferry and William Clegg). TVADA. Est. 1965. Open 9-5.30, Sat. 10-5, Sun. by appointment. SIZE: Large. *STOCK: Furniture - signed and*

493

designed, 1700-1970; garden and architectural/panelling; art pottery and metalwork, lighting and Whitefriars glass. LOC: Off A4130. PARK: Easy. TEL: 01491 641349; fax - 01491 641533; e-mail - ferry&clegg@the countryseat.com; websites - www.thecountry seat.com and www.whitefriarsglass.com. SER: Restorations; exhibitions. FAIRS: TVADA; Radley. VAT: Spec.

NETTLEBED, Nr. Henley-on-Thames

Willow Antiques and the Nettlebed Antique Merchants

High St. RG9 5DA. (Willow Bicknell, Michael Plummer and Laurie Brunton). TVADA. Est. 1984. Open 10-5.30, Sun. and other times by appointment. SIZE: Large. STOCK: Decorative, fine and unusual furniture, objects and decorations, including architectural and garden items, 17th C to 1970s, including Gothic, Aesthetic, Arts and Crafts and Art Deco. LOC: Between Wallingford and Henley on A4074. PARK: Easy. TEL: 01491 642062/628811; mobile - 07770 554559; e-mail - willow@ nettlebedantiques.co.uk; website - www. nettlebedantiques.co.uk. SER: Finder; copy and design; advice on period design for house and garden. FAIRS: TVADA. VAT: Spec.

OXFORD

Antiques on High Ltd

85 High St. OX1 4BG. (Paul Lipson and Sally Young). TVADA. Est. 1982. Open 10-5, Sun. and Bank Holidays 11-5. SIZE: Large - 35 dealers. STOCK: Small antiques and collectables including jewellery, silver and plate, ceramics, glass, antiquities, watches, books and coins, 17th-20th C. LOC: Opposite Queen's Lane. PARK: St Clements, Westgate, Seacourt/Thornhill Park and Ride. TEL: 01865 251075; e-mail - antiquesonhigh@aol.com. SER: Valuations; restorations (jewellery, silver including replating). FAIRS: TVADA.

PANGBOURNE

Rita Butler

4 Station Rd. RG8 7AN. TVADA. Est. 1999. Open Tues.-Sat. 10-5. SIZE: 2 floors. STOCK: General antiques including small furniture especially oak; early 19th C to early 20th C ceramics especially Art Deco; glass, early 1800s; silver. PARK: Opposite. TEL: 01189 845522; mobile - 07752 936327; e-mail - rbutler@ amserve.com. FAIRS: TVADA; Thames; Silhouette; Jay.

READING

Rupert Landen Antiques

Church Farm, Reading Rd., Woodcote. RG8 0QX. TVADA. Open 9-5, Sat. 10-3. CL: Mon. STOCK: Late 18th to early 19th C furniture. TEL: 01491 682396; mobile - 07974 732472.

SONNING-ON-THAMES

Cavendish Fine Arts   BADA

The Dower House. RG4 6UL. (Janet Middlemiss and Guy Hazel). TVADA. Est. 1972. Open by appointment. STOCK: Fine Queen Anne and English Georgian furniture, glass and porcelain. LOC: 5 mins. from M4. TEL: 01189 691904; mobile - 07831 295575; e-mail - janet@cavendishfinearts.com; website - www.cavendishfinearts.com. SER: Valuations; shipping; interior decoration. FAIRS: Olympia; Chelsea; BADA; TVADA. VAT: Stan/Spec.

TESWORTH, Nr. Thame

The Swan at Tetsworth

High St. OX9 7AB. TVADA. Est. 1995. Open 7 days 10-6. SIZE: 40+ rooms. LOC: A40, 5 mins. from junctions 6 and 8, M40. PARK: Own large. TEL: 01844 281777; fax - 01844 281770; website - www.theswan.co.uk; e-mail - antiques @theswan.co.uk. SER: Restorations (clocks); cabinet work; gilding.

WALLINGFORD

The Lamb Arcade

83 High St. OX10 0BX. TVADA. Open 10-5, Sat. 10-5.30. STOCK: As below plus books, crafts and ephemera. PARK: Nearby. TEL: 01491 835166. SER: Restorations (furniture).

Summers Davis Antiques Ltd **LAPADA**
Calleva House, 6 High St. OX10 0BP. (Graham
Wells). CINOA. TVADA. Est. 1917. Open 9-
5.30, Sat. 9-5, Sun. 11-5. SIZE: Large. *STOCK:
English and Continental furniture, decorative
items and objects.* Not Stocked: Silver, shipping
goods. LOC: From London, shop is on left,
50yds. from Thames Bridge. PARK: Opposite,
behind castellated gates. TEL: 01491 836284; fax
- 01491 833443; e-mail - antiques@
summersdavis.co.uk; website - www.summers
davis.co.uk. VAT: Spec.

WARFIELD

Moss End Antique Centre
Moss End Garden Centre. RG12 6EJ. TVADA.
Est. 1988. Open 10.30-5. CL: Mon. SIZE: Large
- 25 dealers. *STOCK: General antiques and
collectables.* LOC: A3095. PARK: Own. TEL:
01344 861942; website - www.mossendantiques.
co.uk. FAIRS: TVADA (Spring and Autumn).

WATLINGTON

Stephen Orton Antiques
The Antiques Warehouse, Shirburn Rd. OX49
5BZ. TVADA. Open Mon.-Fri. 9-5, other times
by appointment. SIZE: Warehouse. *STOCK:
18th-19th C furniture, some decorative items.*
LOC: 2 mins. from exit 6, M40. TEL: 01491
613752; e-mail - Orton.Antiques@virgin.net.
SER: Supply and pack containers; valuations;
restorations; buying agent. VAT: Stan/Spec.

WENDOVER

Sally Turner Antiques **LAPADA**
Hogarth House, High St. HP22 6DU. TVADA.
Open 10-5. CL: Wed. and Sun. except Dec. SIZE:
7 showrooms + barn. *STOCK: Decorative and
period furniture, general antiques and jewellery.*
PARK: Own. TEL: 01296 624402; fax - same;
mobile - 07860 201718.

WINDSOR & ETON

Marcelline Herald Antiques **LAPADA**
41 High St., Eton. SL4 6BD. TVADA. Est. 1993.
Open Tues.,Thurs., Fri. and Sat. 10-5, other days
by appointment. SIZE: Medium. *STOCK:
Furniture, £500-£15,000; mirrors, pelmets and
screens, £200-£2,500; ceramics, lamps and
prints, £50-£1,000; all 18th to early 19th C.*
PARK: Loading and nearby. TEL: 01753 833924;
fax - 0118 971 4683; home - same. FAIRS:
TVADA; Decorative Antiques & Textile. VAT:
Spec.

Peter J. Martin **LAPADA**
40 High St., Eton. SL4 6BD. (Peter J. Martin &
Son). TVADA. Est. 1963. Open 9-1 and 2-5. CL:
Sun. SIZE: Large and warehouse. *STOCK:
Period, Victorian and decorative furniture and
furnishings, £50-£20,000; metalware, £10-£500,
all from 1800.* PARK: 50yds. opposite. TEL:
01753 864901; home - 01753 863987; e-mail -
pjmartin.antiques@btopenworld.com; website -
www.pjmartin-antiques.co.uk. SER: Restorations;
shipping arranged; buys at auction. VAT:
Stan/Spec.

WOODSTOCK

Antiques at Heritage
6 Market Place. OX20 1TA. TVADA. Est. 1978.
Open 10-1 and 2-5, Sun 1-5. SIZE: Medium.
LOC: Near Town Hall. PARK: Easy. TEL: 01993
811332; e-mail - info@atheritage.co.uk; website -
www.atheritage.co.uk.

Chris Baylis Country Chairs
16 Oxford St. OX20 1TS. TVADA. Est. 1977. Open
Tues.-Sat. 10.30-5.30, Sun. 11-5, appointment
advisable. *STOCK: English country chairs, from
1780; sets of rush seated chairs including ladder
and spindle backs, Windsors, kitchen chairs and
quality reproductions.* LOC: A44. PARK: Easy.
TEL: 01993 813887; fax - 01993 812379; e-mail -
info@realwoodfurniture. co.uk; website -
www.realwoodfurniture.co.uk. VAT: Spec.

Bees Antiques
30 High St. OX20 1TG. (Jo and Jim Bateman).
TVADA. Est. 1991. Open 10-1 and 1.30-5, Sun.
11-5. CL: Tues. SIZE: Small. *STOCK: Pottery,
porcelain and glass, 18th-20th C, £30-£1,500;
small furniture, 19th to early 20th C, £50-£2,000;
metalware, 19th C, £30-£200; jewellery, 19th-
20th C, £30-£1,000.* LOC: Just off A3440
Oxford/Stratford-on-Avon road, in town centre.
PARK: Opposite. TEL: 01993 811062; home -
01993 771593; mobile - 07702 603419. SER:
Valuations; buys at auction (as stock).

John Howard **BADA**
**Heritage, 6 Market Place. OX20 1TE. TVADA.
CADA. Open 10-5.30. SIZE: Small. *STOCK:
18th-19th C British pottery especially rare
Staffordshire animal figures, bocage figures,
lustre, 18th C creamware and unusual items.*
PARK: Easy. TEL: 0870 4440678; fax - same;
mobile - 07831 850544; e-mail - john@
johnhoward.co.uk; website - www.antique
pottery.co.uk and www.Staffordshires.com.
SER: Packing; insurance service to USA.
FAIRS: Olympia; BADA. VAT: Spec.**

TYNE AND WEAR

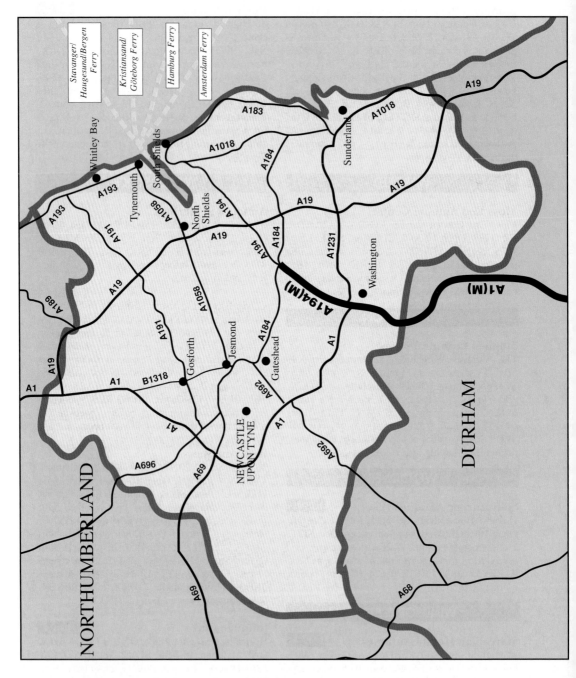

Dealers and Shops in Tyne and Wear				
			Sunderland	1
Gateshead	1	Newcastle-upon-Tyne 8	Tynemouth	4
Gosforth	2	North Shields 1	Washington	2
Jesmond	6	South Shields 1	Whitley Bay	3

GATESHEAD

Sovereign Antiques
35 The Boulevard, Antique Village, Metrocentre. NE11 9YN. Open Mon.-Wed. 10-8, Thurs. 10-9, Sat. 9-6. *STOCK: Fine antique and modern jewellery, diamonds, silver, prints and maps.* TEL: 0191 460 9604; fax - 0191 460 7600.

GOSFORTH, Nr. Newcastle-upon-Tyne

Anna Harrison Fine Antiques `LAPADA`
Harewood House, 49 Great North Rd. NE3 2HH. Est. 1976. Open 9-5. SIZE: Large. *STOCK: English furniture, porcelain, oils and watercolours.* LOC: On B1318 3 miles north of city centre, near Regent Centre. PARK: Forecourt. TEL: 0191 284 3202. SER: Valuations; restorations. VAT: Stan/Spec.

MacDonald Fine Art
6 Ashburton Rd. NE3 4XN. (T. and C. MacDonald). Est. 1976. Open 10-1 and 2.30-5.30. CL: Wed. SIZE: Medium. *STOCK: Watercolours and oils, mainly north-eastern artists, English and Scottish, 18th-20th C.* LOC: 1 mile west of A1. PARK: Easy. TEL: 0191 284 4214; home - 0191 285 6188. SER: Valuations; restorations (watercolours and oils); framing; buys at auction (watercolours and oils).

JESMOND, Nr. Newcastle-upon-Tyne

Cradlewell Antiques
4 Churchill Gardens. NE2 1LD. (Steve Bardy). Est. 1979. Open Thurs.-Sat. 11-5, Tues. and Wed. by appointment. SIZE: Medium. *STOCK: Small furniture, lighting, Art Nouveau, Art Deco, 20th C modern design, £50-£500; ceramics, bakelite telephones, £20-£200.* LOC: Left off A1058 coast road to shops at lights just before Cradlewell bypass. PARK: Easy. TEL: 0191 212 1500; mobile - 07966 246101.

Little Theatre Antiques Centre
75-79 Fern Ave. NE2 2RA. (Louise Bennett and John Bell). Est. 1994. Open 10-5.30. SIZE: Large. *STOCK: Victorian and Edwardian British furniture, £200-£3,000; north-east England pressed glass, 1860-1930, £20-£250; French furniture 1900's, £500-£2,000; ceramics, 1880-1990.* LOC: Follow city centre motorway to Jesmond exit, north up Osborne Rd. then right into Fern Ave. PARK: Own. TEL: 0191 209 4321; fax - 0191 209 4320; mobile - 07951 035038; website - www.littletheatreantiques.co.uk. SER: Restorations (furniture).

Shiners, Snobs Knobs
81 Fern Avenue, NE2 2RA. (B. and A. Lawson). SALVO. Est. 1983. Open 10-5. SIZE: Large. *STOCK: Fireplaces, door furniture, pine and vestibule doors, lighting, fenders.* LOC: Near city centre next to Little Theatre Antiques Centre. PARK: Easy. TEL: 0191 281 6474; fax - 0191 281 9041. SER: Fireplace fitting

A.C. Silver
at Graham Smith Antiques, 83 Fern Avenue. NE2 2RA. (Andrew Campbell). Est. 1980. Open 10-5. *STOCK: Silver, 17th-20th C, £50-£15,000; silver plate, 19th-20th C, £50-£1,000.* PARK: Easy. TEL: 0191 281 5065; mobile - 07836 286218. SER: Valuations. VAT: Stan/Spec.

Graham Smith Antiques `LAPADA`
83 Fern Avenue. NE2 2RA. Est. 1999. Open 10-5. SIZE: Large. *STOCK: Furniture, 18th-20th C, £50-£8,000; works of art, 18th-19th C, £100-£2,000; smalls, 18th-20th C, £10-£2,000.* LOC: Follow signs to Fern Avenue Antiques Village off Osborne Rd. PARK: Easy. TEL: 0191 281 5065; mobile - 07836 251873. SER: Valuations. FAIRS: Newark. VAT: Stan/Spec.

Turnburrys
257 Jesmond Rd. NE2 1LB. Est. 1995. Open 9-6, Sun. 12-3. SIZE: Large. *STOCK: Period, antique and bespoke fireplaces; original and bespoke vestibule doors: radiators, Victorian to 1920's, £100-£500; over mantel mirrors.* LOC: Off Cradlewell by-pass, next to Jesmond Dene. PARK: Easy. TEL: 0191 281 1770; fax - 0191 240 2569; website - www.turnburrys.co.uk. SER: Valuations; restorations (doors, furniture and fireplaces). FAIRS: Traditional Homes & Period Living, London. VAT: Stan.

NEWCASTLE-UPON-TYNE

Corbitt Stamps Ltd
5 Mosley St. NE1 1YE. (David McMonagle). PTS: BNTA: ASDA (New York). Est. 1962. Open 9-5, Sat. 9.30-4. *STOCK: Worldwide stamps, some coins and medals, post and cigarette cards, bank notes.* LOC: Near Tyne bridge. PARK: Opposite. TEL: 0191 232 7268; fax - 0191 261 4130; e-mail - info@corbitts.com; website - www.corbitts.com. SER: Valuations; regular stamp and coin auctions.

Davidson's The Jewellers Ltd
94 and 96 Grey St. NE1 6AG. (Anthony and Helen Davidson). NAG. Est. 1898. Open 9-5.30. *STOCK: Jewellery, silver.* TEL: 0191 232 2551/232 2895; fax - 0191 232 0714.

Dog Leap Antiques
61 Side. NE1 3JE. Est. 1950. Open 9.15-1 and 2-5, Sat. 9.30-1. SIZE: Small. *STOCK: Antique engravings and reproduction prints.* LOC: Bottom of Dean St. PARK: Easy. TEL: 0191 232 7269.

Owen Humble
Clayton House, Walbottle Rd., Lemington. NE15 9RU. Est. 1958. Open 10-5, Sat. 10-4. SIZE: Large and warehouse. *STOCK: Furniture, general antiques.* PARK: Easy. TEL: 0191 267 7220; fax - 0191 267 3377; e-mail - antiques@owenhumble.com. SER: Restorations. VAT: Stan/Spec.

Intercoin
103 Clayton St. NE1 5PZ. Open 9-4.30. *STOCK: Coins and items of numismatic interest; jewellery, silver.* LOC: City centre. TEL: 0191 232 2064.

Steve Johnson Medals & Militaria
PO Box 1SP. NE99 1SP. *STOCK: Medals and militaria.* TEL: Fax - 01207 547073; e-mail - steve@wwmeinc.com; website - www.wwmeinc.com. *Mail Order and Online.*

Newcastle Antique Centre
2nd Floor, 142 Northumberland St. NE1 7DQ. (L. Ingham, D. King and C. Parkin). Est. 1972. Open 10-5. SIZE: Small. *STOCK: Art Deco, Arts & Crafts, Art Nouveau, Maling, militaria, stamps, coins and postcards; railway items, tinplate, watches, Georgian and Victorian silver, glass, gold, silver, jewellery; football memorabilia.* LOC: Opposite Haymarket Metro. PARK: NCP nearby. TEL: 0191 232 9832; mobile - 07885 060155; website - www.time-antiques.co.uk. SER: Valuations; restorations (china and jewellery); repairs (clocks). FAIRS: Newark; NEC; Swinderby; Edinburgh.

R.D. Steedman
9 Grey St. NE1 6EE. ABA. Est. 1907. Open 9-5. CL: Sat. pm. *STOCK: Rare and secondhand books.* LOC: Central. TEL: 0191 232 6561. FAIRS: Olympia Book.

NORTH SHIELDS

Keel Row Books
11 Fenwick Terrace. NE29 0LU. (Bob and Brenda Cook). Est. 1980. Open 10-4.30, Sun. 11-4. CL: Wed. SIZE: Medium. *STOCK: Books - military, cinema, theatre, local history, art, railways, children's, topography, sci-fi, crime fiction, Penguin aircraft, maritime, some antiquarian, £1-£1,000.* PARK: Nearby. TEL: 0191 296 0664; home - 0191 287 3914. SER: Valuations; restorations.

This Charles II bowl and cover (London 1681, maker's mark GC) is a good example of what some English goldsmiths were capable of before the arrival of the Huguenots. Note the use of cut-card work. (Sotheby's)

From an article entitled "'Huguenot' Silver in England 1685-1730" by Ian Pickford which appeared in the May 2002 issue of *Antique Collecting*. For more details and to subscribe see page 21.

SOUTH SHIELDS

The Curiosity Shop
16 Frederick St. NE33 5EA. (G.D. Davies). Est. 1969. CL: Wed. SIZE: Large. *STOCK: General antiques, paintings, jewellery, furniture, Royal Doulton.* PARK: Free. TEL: 0191 456 5560; fax - 0191 427 7597. FAIRS: Newark.

SUNDERLAND

Peter Smith Antiques LAPADA
12-14 Borough Rd. SR1 1EP. Est. 1968. Open 9.30-4.30, Sat. 10-1, other times by appointment. SIZE: Warehouse. *STOCK: Georgian, Victorian, Edwardian longcase clocks, shipping goods, £5-£15,000.* LOC: 10 miles from A1(M); towards docks/Hendon from town centre. PARK: Easy. TEL: 0191 567 3537/567 7842; fax - 0191 514 2286; home - 0191 514 0008; e-mail - petersmithantiques@btinternet.co.uk; website - www.petersmithantiques.com. SER: Valuations; restorations; some shipping; containers packed; buys at auction. VAT: Stan/Spec.

TYNEMOUTH

Curio Corner
Unit 5/6 The Land of Green Ginger, Front St. NE30 4BP. (S. Welton). Est. 1988. Open 10.30-4.30. SIZE: Medium. *STOCK: Period furniture including Dutch oak and English.* TEL: 0191 296 3316; fax - 0191 296 3319; mobile - 07831 339906; website - www.curiocorner.co.uk.

L.O.G.G. Lights
Unit 3 The Land of Green Ginger, Front St. NE30 4BP. (S. Smyth). Est. 2001. Open 10.30-4.30. SIZE: Medium. *STOCK: Crystal chandeliers; brass, china.* TEL: 0191 296 3316; fax - 0191 296 3319; mobile - 07831 339906.

Ian Sharp Antiques Ltd. LAPADA
23 Front St. NE30 4DX. Est. 1988. Open 10-1 and 1.30-5.30 or by appointment. SIZE: Small. *STOCK: Furniture, 19th to early 20th C; British pottery including northern especially Maling and Sunderland lustreware, 18th to early 20th C.* PARK: Easy. TEL: 0191 296 0656; fax - same; e-mail - iansharp@sharpantiques.demon.co.uk; website - www.sharpantiques.demon.co.uk. FAIRS: Newark. VAT: Global/Spec.

Tynemouth Architectural Salvage
Correction House, 28 Tynemouth Rd. NE30 4AA. (Robin S. Archer). Est. 1998. Open 10-6, Fri. and Sat. 10-5. SIZE: Large. *STOCK: Antique bathrooms - cast-iron roll top baths with ball and claw feet, English and French pedestal basins, taps, showers, curtain rails, high and low level cisterns, toilets, bathroom accessories; cast-iron radiators, fires, wooden, stone, marble and slate surrounds, doors and door furniture, pews, panelling; cinema seats, coats of arms, staircases.* LOC: Short walk from Tynemouth. PARK: Easy. TEL: 0191 296 6070; fax - 0191 296 6097; e-mail - robin@tynarcsal.demon.co.uk; website - www.tynemoutharchitectural salvage.com. SER: Restorations.

WASHINGTON

Harold J. Carr Antiques
Field House, Rickleton. NE38 9HQ. Est. 1970. Open by appointment. *STOCK: General antiques and furniture.* TEL: 0191 388 6442. SER: Shippers.

Grate Expectations (Fireplaces)
Unit 9, Lee Close, Pattinson North Industrial Estate. NE38 8QF. (Geoffrey Moore). Est. 1983. Open 9-5. SIZE: Large. *STOCK: Fireplaces, £95-£2,000; fireplace accessories, £10-£125; both 19th C.* LOC: Close to A1 and A19. PARK: Easy. TEL: 0191 416 0609. SER: Restorations (cast-iron refurbishment, repair and welding). VAT: Stan.

WHITLEY BAY

Northumbria Pine
54 Whitley Rd. NE26 2NF. (C. and V. Dowland). Est. 1979. Open 9.15-4.30. SIZE: Small. *STOCK: Stripped, reclaimed, reproduction and made to order pine items.* LOC: Cullercoats end of Whitley Rd. behind sea front. PARK: Easy. TEL: 0191 252 4550; website - www.northumbria-pine.co.uk. SER: Free local delivery; restorations (table tops). VAT: Stan.

Olivers Bookshop
48A Whitley Rd. NE26 2NF. (J. Oliver). Est. 1986. Open 11-5. CL: Tues. and Wed. SIZE: Medium. *STOCK: Antiquarian and secondhand books, 50p to £500.* PARK: Easy. TEL: 0191 251 3552. SER: Valuations. FAIRS: Tynemouth Book.

Treasure Chest
2 and 4 Norham Rd. NE26 2SB. Est. 1974. Open 10.30-1 and 2-4. CL: Wed. and Thurs. SIZE: Small. *STOCK: General antiques.* LOC: Just off main shopping area of Park View, leading to Monkseaton rail station. PARK: Easy. TEL: 0191 251 2052.

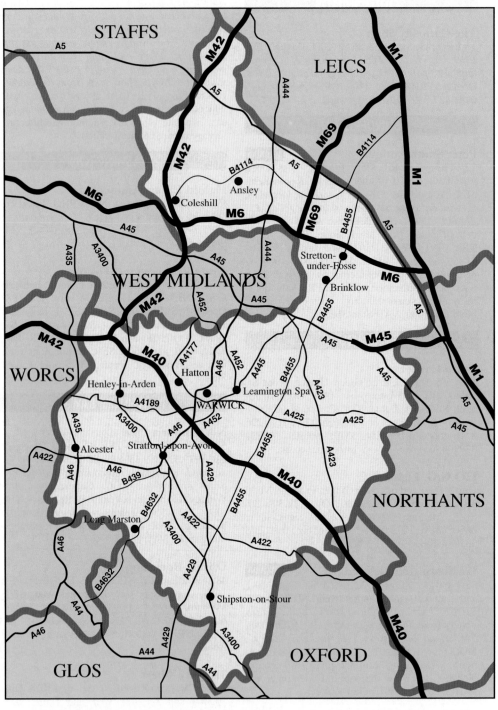

Dealers and Shops in Warwickshire					
Alcester	2	Hatton	1	Shipston-on-Stour	3
Ansley	1	Henley-in-Arden	2	Stratford-upon-Avon	9
Brinklow	1	Leamington Spa	4	Stretton-on-Fosse	1
Coleshill	1	Long Marston	1	Warwick	18

ALCESTER

High St. Antiques
11A High St. B49 5AE. (V.F.S. and J.F. Baldwin). Est. 1979. Open Fri. 12-5 and Sat. 10-5 or by appointment. SIZE: Small. *STOCK: Glass and china, 18th-20th C, £5-£200; postcards and Art Deco china.* LOC: On left-hand side near church coming from Stratford-on-Avon road. PARK: Rear of High St. TEL: 01789 764009; fax - 01789 766325. SER: Valuations.

Malthouse Antiques Centre
Market Place. B49 5AE. (J. and P. Allcock). Est. 1982. Open 10-5, Sun. 1-4. SIZE: Large. *STOCK: Furniture, china, silver, collectables and objets d'art, 18th-20th C, £1-£2,000.* LOC: Adjacent to town car park. TEL: 01789 764032.

ANSLEY, Nr. Nuneaton

Granary Antiques
Hoar Park Craft Centre. CV10 0QU. (G. Stockdale). Est. 1987. Open 10-5 including Sun. CL: Mon. except Bank Holidays. SIZE: Medium. *STOCK: Furniture, china, glass, books and collectables.* PARK: Easy. TEL: 02476 395551. SER: Restorations. FAIRS: Newark.

BRINKLOW, Nr. Rugby

The Victorian Ironmonger
The Old Garage, 70 Broad St. CV23 0LN. (Marlene and Dave Thompson). SALVO. Est. 1993. Open Fri. and Sat. 10-5, Sun. 11-3. SIZE: Medium. *STOCK: Door furniture, 17th to early 20th C, £2-£500; fireplaces, 19th C, £150-£1,500; architectural items, 17th to early 20th C, £25-£2,000.* PARK: Easy. TEL: 01788 832292; home - same; website - www.thevictorian ironmonger.co. uk.

COLESHILL

Coleshill Antiques and Interiors Ltd
12 and 14 High St. B46 1AZ. (A.J. Webster). Est. 1958. Open Tues.-Fri. 9.30-5 or by appointment. SIZE: Large. *STOCK: Continental porcelain, furniture, jewellery, silver and decorative items.* LOC: 1 mile from NEC. PARK: Easy. TEL: 01675 467416; fax - 01675 462931; e-mail - enq@coleshillantiques.com; website - www. coleshillantiques.com. SER: Valuations; restorations; repairs; interior design. VAT: Stan/Spec.

HATTON, Nr. Warwick

The Stables Antique Centre
Hatton Country World, Dark Lane. CV35 8XA. (John and Margaret Colledge). Est. 1990. Open 10-5 including Sun. SIZE: Large - 25 units. *STOCK: Furniture, 18th-19th C, £50-£3,000; china, 19th-20th C, £5-£200; clocks, 18th-19th C, £200-£4,000; linen, glass, brass and copper, paintings and prints, jukeboxes, radios, gramophones, kitchenalia and jewellery.* LOC: Just off A4177 Solihull-Warwick road, 5 mins. from junction 15, M40. PARK: Own. TEL: 01926 842405. SER: Valuations.

HENLEY-IN-ARDEN

Arden Gallery
B95 5AN. (G.B. Horton). Est. 1963. Open 1-6. CL: Sat. SIZE: Medium. *STOCK: Victorian oil paintings, £20-£1,000; watercolours, all periods, to £1,500; portrait miniatures.* LOC: A3400. PARK: Easy. TEL: 01564 792520. VAT: Spec.

Henley Antiques Centre
92 High St. B95 5BY. (Mrs Rosie Montague and Mrs Gill Rayson). Est. 2001. Open 10.30-5, Sun and Bank Holidays 11-4. SIZE: Large. *STOCK: Furniture, porcelain and collectables, 19th to early 20th C, £20-£2,000; art gallery.* LOC: Behind bakery at pedestrian crossing lights. PARK: Easy. TEL: 01564 795979; mobile - 07950 324262. SER: Valuations. FAIRS: NEC.

LEAMINGTON SPA

David & Karol Hooper Antiques
The Elephant House, 38-40 Morton St. CV32 5SY. Open by appointment. *STOCK: General antiques, fairground, circus and unusual items.* TEL: 01926 429679; mobiles - 07831 241284 and 07775 850219.

King's Cottage Antiques `LAPADA`
4 Windsor St. CV32 5EB. (G. and A. Jackson). Est. 1993. Open 9-5. SIZE: Medium. *STOCK: Early oak and country furniture, 16th-18th C.* TEL: 01926 422927.

The Light Gallery
36 Regent St. CV32 5EG. (Gary Jones). Est. 1988. Open 9.30-5.30, Sat. 9-6. SIZE: Medium. *STOCK: Lighting and especially glass shades, 19th to early 20th C, £25-£2,500; reproduction period-style lighting, shades and components, £2-£1,000.* LOC: Town centre. PARK: Easy. TEL: 01926 422421. SER: Valuations. VAT: Stan.

The Old Pine House
16 Warwick St. CV32 5LL. (Keith Platt and Marion Grindley). Est. 1982. Open Tues.-Fri. 10-5.30, Sat. 9-5. SIZE: Medium. *STOCK: Victorian stripped pine, English and European, £20-£1,000.* PARK: Easy. TEL: 01926 470477; fax - same.

LONG MARSTON, Nr. Stratford-upon-Avon

Barn Antiques Centre
Station Rd. CV37 8RB. (Bev and Graham Simpson). Est. 1978. Open Mon.-Fri. 10-5, Sun. 12-6. SIZE: Large - 50+ dealers. *STOCK: Georgian, Victorian, Edwardian and later furniture, collectables, silver, porcelain, china, kitchenalia, fireplaces, linen, pictures, 18th C to 1950, £5-£2,000.* LOC: Approx. 5 miles from Stratford. PARK: Opposite. TEL: 01789 721399; fax - 01789 721390; e-mail - info@barnantique. co.uk; website - www.barnantique.co.uk.

SHIPSTON-ON-STOUR

Fine-Lines (Fine Art)   LAPADA
The Old Rectory Lodge, West St. CV36 4HD. (L.W. and R.M. Guthrie). Est. 1975. Open every day by appointment. SIZE: Medium. *STOCK: British and European watercolours, pastels, drawings and selected oils, from 1850, £300-£20,000.* LOC: 2 mins. from town centre. PARK: Easy and nearby. TEL: 01608 662323 (answerphone); e-mail - enquiries@fine-lines fineart.co.uk; website - www.finelinesfineart. co.uk. SER: Valuations; advice (restoration and framing). VAT: Spec.

Pine and Things
Portobello Farm, Campden Rd. CV36 4PY. (Richard Wood). Est. 1991. Open 9-5. SIZE: Large - 6 showrooms. *STOCK: Pine, 18th-19th C, £50-£2,000.* LOC: A429. PARK: Easy. TEL: 01608 663849; home - same; website - www.pinethings.co.uk. VAT: Stan/Spec.

Time in Hand
11 Church St. CV36 4AP. (F.R. Bennett). Est. 1979. Open 9-1 and 2-5.30 or by appointment. SIZE: Large. *STOCK: Longcase, carriage and wall clocks, barometers.* LOC: Opposite church on main road. PARK: Free - Banbury Road. TEL: 01608 662578; e-mail - timeinhand@ shipstononstour.fsnet.co.uk. SER: Restorations (clocks, watches, barometers and mechanical instruments).

STRATFORD-UPON-AVON

Arbour Antiques Ltd
Poet's Arbour, Sheep St. CV37 6EF. (R.J. Wigington). Est. 1952. Open 9-5, Sat. by appointment. *STOCK: Arms and armour.* LOC: From town centre towards theatre and river, behind Lamb's Café through archway at right. TEL: 01789 293453. VAT: Spec.

Burman Antiques
34 College St. CV37 6BW. (J. and J. Burman Holtom). Est. 1973. Open by appointment. *STOCK: Ruskin ware, pot-lids, fishing tackle.* TEL: 01789 295164. SER: Restorations (clocks).

Thomas Crapper & Co
The Stable Yard, Alscot Park. CV37 8BL. (S.P.J. Kirby). SALVO. Est. 1985. Open Mon.-Fri. 9.30-5. SIZE: Medium. *STOCK: Restored antique bathroom fittings - roll-top baths, brass and nickel taps, canopy shower baths, plain and decorated basins, WCs and seats; hand-made replicas.* PARK: Easy. TEL: 01789 450522; fax - 01789 450523; e-mail - wc@thomas-crapper.com; website - www.thomas-crapper.com. SER: Valuations; restorations (bathroom fittings).

Howards Jewellers
44a Wood St. CV37 6JG. (Howards of Stratford Ltd). NAG. Est. 1985. Open 9.30-5.30. *STOCK: Jewellery, silver, objets d'art, 19th C.* LOC: Town centre. PARK: Nearby. TEL: 01789 205404. SER: Valuations; restorations (as stock). VAT: Stan/Spec.

George Pragnell Ltd
5 & 6 Wood St. CV37 6JA. (Jeremy Pragnall). NAG. Open 9.15-5.30. SIZE: Large. *STOCK: Fine jewellery, silver, clocks and watches.* LOC: Town centre. PARK: Nearby. TEL: 01789 267072; fax - 01789 415131; e-mail - enquiries@ pragnell.co.uk; website - www.pragnell.co.uk. SER: Valuations; repairs; remodelling. FAIRS: NEC. VAT: Stan/Spec.

Stratford Antique Centre
60 Ely St. CV37 6LN. (N. Sims). Open 10-5.30 including Sun. SIZE: 50 dealers. *STOCK: General antiques.* TEL: 01789 204180.

The Stratford Antiques and Interiors Centre Ltd
Dodwell Industrial Park, Evesham Rd. CV37 9ST. (Andrew and Suszanna Kerr). Est. 1980. Open 10-5 including Sun., evenings by appointment. SIZE: 25+ dealers. *STOCK:*

Georgian, Victorian, Edwardian and shipping furniture, £100-£10,000; china and smalls, 19th-20th C, £5-£2,000; reclaimed pine, £50-£10,000. LOC: B439. PARK: Easy. TEL: 01789 297729; fax - 01789 297710; website - www. stratfordantiques.co.uk. SER: Valuations; restorations. FAIRS: Newark; Ardingly; NEC.

The Stratford Bookshop
45A Rother St. CV37 6LT. (J. and S. Hill). PBFA. Est. 1993. Open 10-6. SIZE: Medium. *STOCK: Secondhand and out-of-print books.* LOC: From island in town centre follow Wood St., left into Rother St., shop on corner of Ely St. PARK: Easy. TEL: 01789 298362; e-mail - stratfordbshop@aol.com. FAIRS: PBFA (Stratford, Monmouth).

Robert Vaughan
20 Chapel St. CV37 6EP. (C.M. Vaughan). ABA. Est. 1953. Open 9.30-5.30. SIZE: Medium. *STOCK: Antiquarian and out-of-print books, maps and prints.* LOC: Town centre. PARK: Easy. TEL: 01789 205312. SER: Valuations; buys at auction (books). VAT: Stan.

STRETTON-ON-FOSSE

Astley House - Fine Art   LAPADA
The Old School. GL56 9SA. (David, Nanette and Caradoc Glaisyer). CADA. CINOA. Est. 1973. Open by appointment. SIZE: Large. *STOCK: Large decorative oil paintings, 19th-21st C.* LOC: Village centre. PARK: Easy. TEL: 01608 650601; fax - 01608 651777; e-mail - astart333@aol.com; website - www.art-uk.com. SER: Exhibitions; mailing list. VAT: Spec.

WARWICK

Duncan M. Allsop
68 Smith St. CV34 4HS. ABA. Est. 1965. Open 9.30-5.30. SIZE: Medium. *STOCK: Antiquarian and modern books.* LOC: East Gate, opposite Roebuck Inn. PARK: Nearby. TEL: 01926 493266; fax - same; mobile - 07770 895924. FAIRS: Royal National Hotel.

Apollo Antiques Ltd   LAPADA
The Saltisford, Birmingham Rd. CV34 4TD. (R.H. Mynott). Est. 1968. Open 9.30-5.30, Sat. 9.30-12.30. SIZE: Large. *STOCK: English furniture, 18th-19th C; Continental and gothic revival furniture, sculpture, paintings, Arts and Crafts and decorative items.* PARK: Easy. TEL: 01926 494746; fax - 01926 401477; e-mail - mynott@apolloantiques.com; website - www. apolloantiques.com. VAT: Stan/Spec

Patrick and Gillian Morley Antiques

Antique Furniture and Works of Art
Always something rare and
unusual in stock
62, WEST STREET, WARWICK, CV34 6AW

Tel: (01926) 494464 (Shop)

Brantwood Antiques & Collectables
St Mary's Chambers, Church St. CV34 4AB.
(Gillian Jackson). Est. 1999. Open afternoons and
Sat. 11-5. CL: Fri. SIZE: Small. *STOCK:
Furniture, mirrors, clocks, objets d'art, frames,
soft furnishings, writing slopes, boxes, fireside
items, mainly 19th to early 20th C, to £2,000.*
LOC: Just off High St. PARK: Nearby. TEL:
01926 403733; home - 01926 777941.

William J. Casey Antiques   LAPADA
9 High St. CV34. (William and Pat Casey). Est.
1970. Open 10-5, Sun. by appointment. SIZE:
Large. *STOCK: Furniture, 18th-20th C, £750-
£7,500.* LOC: Town Centre. PARK: Nearby. TEL:
01926 499199; home - 01562 777507. VAT: Spec.

ART BOOK SERVICES

Art Book Services is a division of the
Antique Collectors' Club through which
we can supply specially selected titles from
other publishers, together with the standard
works of reference published by the
Antique Collectors' Club.

A free catalogue containing sections on
Jewellery, Art, Paintings, Furniture,
Interiors, Decorative Arts, Collectables,
Ceramics, Clocks, Watches, Glass, Textiles,
Fashion, Carpets, Rugs, Silver, Gold and
Metalwork, can be obtained from:–

**Art Book Services
Sandy Lane, Old Martlesham,
Woodbridge, Suffolk, IP12 4SD
Tel: 01394 389977
Fax: 01394 389999
Email: sales@antique-acc.com**

Castle Antiques
24 Swan St. CV34 4BJ. (Julia Reynolds). Est.
1979. Open 10-5, Sun. by appointment. SIZE:
Medium. *STOCK: China including Shelley, linen,
silver, jewellery, furniture, 19th to early 20th C,
£100-£3,000.* LOC: Town centre. PARK: Easy -
at rear. TEL: 01926 401511; fax - 01926 492469.
SER: Restorations (ceramics). FAIRS: Heritage
Museum, Gaydon. VAT: Spec.

Entente Cordiale
9 High St. CV34. Open 10-5, Sun. by
appointment. *STOCK: English and French items.*
LOC: Town centre. PARK: Nearby. TEL: 01926
499199.

John Goodwin and Sons
20-22 High St. CV34 4AP. Open 9.30-5.30.
SIZE: Shop (+ warehouse on request - 20 mins.
away) . *STOCK: Furniture, clocks, ceramics, oil
paintings, collectables.* TEL: 01926 853332.
SER: Restorations (furniture).

Russell Lane Antiques
2-4 High St. CV34 4AP. (R.G.H. Lane). Open 10-
5. *STOCK: Fine jewellery and silver.* TEL: 01926
494494.

Patrick and Gillian Morley Antiques
                                    LAPADA
62 West St. CV34 6AW. Est. 1968. Open Tues.-
Fri. 10-5 or by appointment. SIZE: Large.
*STOCK: Furniture, 17th to late 19th C; unusual
and decorative items, sculpture, carvings; all
£250-£100,000.* PARK: Easy. TEL: 01926
494464; home - 01926 854191; e-mail - morley
antiques@tinyworld.co.uk. SER: Valuations; buys
at auction. VAT: Spec.

Christopher Peters Antiques
28 West St. CV34 6AN. (Christopher and Jill
Peters). Est. 1987. Open 10-5, other times by
appointment. SIZE: Shop + workshop and barns.

STOCK: Country antiques, original painted furniture, decorative items; 18th C French provincial furniture. LOC: Off M40, junction 15. TEL: 01926 494106; fax - 02476 303300; website - www.christopherpetersantiques.co.uk. SER: Design and installation of original unfitted kitchens; French polishing, restorations; repairs. VAT: Stan/Spec.

James Reeve
at Quinneys of Warwick, 9 Church St. CV34 4AB. (J.C. and D.J. Reeve). Est. 1865. Open 9.30-5.30. CL: Sat. pm. STOCK: Furniture, mahogany, oak, and rosewood, 17th-18th C, £80-£30,000; furniture, 19th C, £50-£10,000; glass, copper, brass, pewter, china. LOC: Town centre. PARK: Easy. TEL: 01926 498113. SER: Restorations; re-polishing. VAT: Stan/Spec.

Don Spencer Antiques
36a Market Place. CV34 4SH. Est. 1963. Open 10-5. SIZE: Large. STOCK: Desks, 1800-1930, £500-£10,000; bookcases, 1800-1920, £500-£3,000. LOC: Beneath Vintage Antiques Cetnre. PARK: Easy. TEL: 01926 499857/407989; fax - 01564 775470; home - same; website - www.antique-desks.co.uk. SER: Free UK delivery. VAT: Stan/Spec.

Summersons
172 Emscote Rd. CV34 5QN. (Peter Lightfoot). BHI. Est. 1969. Open 10-5, Sat. 10-1. SIZE: Small. STOCK: Clocks and barometers. LOC: A445 Leamington Spa road. PARK: Free. TEL: 01926 400630; fax - same; mobile - 07770 300695; e-mail - clocks@summersons.com; website - www.summersons.com. SER: Restorations; repairs; materials and parts. VAT: Spec.

Tango Art Deco & Antiques
46 Brook St. CV34 4BL. (Jenny and Martin Wills). Open Thurs., Fri. and Sat. 10-5. SIZE: Medium. STOCK: Art Deco and other furniture and accessories, pottery including Clarice Cliff, £20-£2,000. LOC: Town centre. PARK: Free nearby. TEL: 01926 496999; home/fax - 0121 704 4969; e-mail - info@tango-artdeco.co.uk; website - www.tango-artdeco.co.uk. VAT: Spec.

Vintage Antiques Centre
36 Market Place. CV34 4SH. (Peter Sellors). Est. 1977. Open 10-5.30, Sun. 11.30-4.30. SIZE: 15 dealers + cabinets. STOCK: Ceramics, glass, collectables and small furniture, 19th-20th C. PARK: Easy. TEL: 01926 491527; e-mail - vintage@globalnet.co.uk. FAIRS: NEC; National Glass.

The Warwick Antique Centre
20-22 High St. CV34 4AP. Est. 1973. Open 10-5. SIZE: 25 dealers. STOCK: Porcelain, silver and plate, jewellery, coins, militaria, books, furniture, stamps, metalware, toys, collectables, postcards, glass. TEL: 01926 491382/495704.

Warwick Antiques Warehouse
Unit 7 Cape Road Industrial Estate, Cattell Rd. CV34 4JN. (Andrew Boylin Antiques, Apollo Antiques and Gary Wright Antiques). Open 9-5.30 or by appointment. SIZE: Large. STOCK: Eclectic furniture, 17th-20th C; works of art and smalls. PARK: Easy. TEL: 01926 498849; fax - same; e-mail - aboylin1@tiscali.co.uk. SER: Valuations.

West Rock Antiques
19 West Rock, Birmingham Rd., The Saltisford. CV34 4SG. (Christina Goodson). Est. 1974. Open 9.30-5.30, Sat. 10-4. SIZE: Medium. STOCK: Furniture, £200-£5,000, decorative items, £5-£500; both 19th C; general antiques, to 1940, £50-£100. PARK: At rear. TEL: 01926 411175; fax - 01926 411176. SER: Valuations.

WEST MIDLANDS

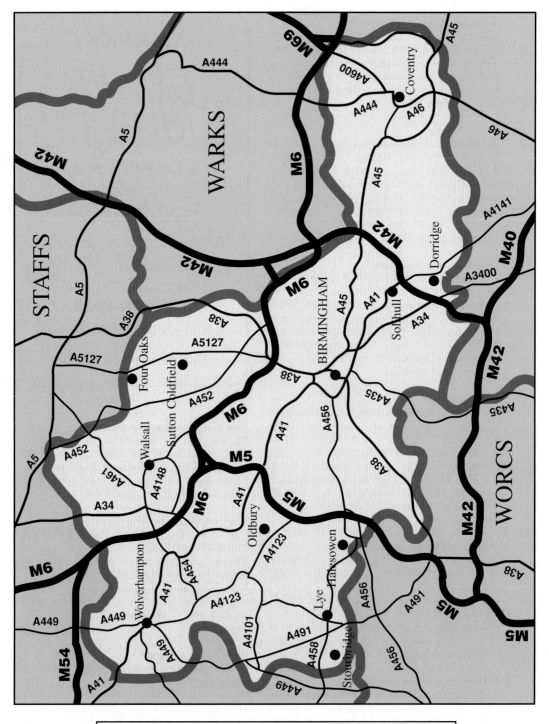

Dealers and Shops in the West Midlands					
Birmingham	19	Halesowen	2	Stourbridge	3
Coventry	3	Lye	2	Sutton Coldfield	2
Dorridge	1	Oldbury	1	Walsall	2
Four Oaks	1	Solihull	3	Wolverhampton	9

BIRMINGHAM

Peter Asbury Antiques
Greenfield House Farm, 6 Hales Lane, Smethwick, Warley. B67 6RS. (Mrs Susan Asbury). Est. 1986. Open 9.30-5. *STOCK: General antiques.* PARK: Limited. TEL: 0121 558 0579. SER: Repairs (doll, teddy bears).

Paul Baxter
B47 6LS. Open by appointment. *STOCK: Oriental ceramics and general antiques.* TEL: 01564 824920.

The Birmingham Antique Centre
1403-1407 Pershore Rd., Stirchley. B30 2JR. Est. 1960. Open 9-5.30, Sun. 10-5. *STOCK: General antiques, collectables, shipping furniture, trade display cabinets.* TEL: 0121 459 4587/689 6565.

Carleton Gallery
91 Vivian Rd., Harborne. B17 0DR. (D. Dunnett). Est. 1986. Open 9-5.30, Wed. 9-1. *STOCK: Maps and prints.* TEL: 0121 427 2487; e-mail - artworld@ukonline.co.uk.

Chesterfield Antiques
181 Gravelly Lane. B23 5SG. (Mara Cirjanic). Est. 1977. Open 9.30-5.30. *STOCK: General antiques and fine art.* TEL: 0121 373 3876.

Peter Clark Antiques   LAPADA
36 St. Mary's Row, Moseley. B13 8JG. Open 9-5.30. SIZE: Medium. *STOCK: Furniture, mid-17th C to early 20th C, £175-£2,500.* LOC: Centre of Moseley. PARK: At rear. TEL: 0121 449 8245. SER: Valuations; restorations (furniture). VAT: Stan/Spec.

R. Collyer
185 New Rd., Rubery. B45 9JP. Est. 1947. Open 9-5.30. *STOCK: Secondhand jewellery.* LOC: 1 mile from junction 4, M5. PARK: Free. TEL: 0121 453 2332. SER: Valuations; restorations.

Cross's Curios
928 Pershore Rd., Selly Park. B29 7PY. (John and Valerie Cross). Est. 1972. Open Thurs., Fri. and Sat. 10-6, other times by appointment. SIZE: Small. *STOCK: Old toys, juvenalia, dolls, tinplate, teddies, furniture, china, jewellery and collectables.* LOC: From city centre, take Pershore Rd., shop just past Pebble Mill on left. PARK: Easy. TEL: 0121 415 4866. SER: Valuations; buys at auction.

Dolly Mixtures
B68 0AU. Est. 1979. Open by appointment. *STOCK: Dolls and teddies.* TEL: 0121 422 6959. SER: Restorations.

Maurice Fellows
21 Vyse St., Hockley. B18 6LE. *STOCK: Objets d'art, jewellery.* TEL: 0121 554 0211. SER: Valuations; restorations.

Format of Birmingham Ltd
18 Bennetts Hill. B2 5QJ. (G. Charman and D. Vice). Open 9.30-5. CL: Sat. *STOCK: Coins, medals.* PARK: New St. station. TEL: 0121 643 2058. VAT: Stan/Spec.

A.W. Hone and Son Oriental Carpets
1486 Stratford Rd., Hall Green. B28 9ET. (Ian Hone). BORDA. Est. 1949. Open 9.30-5.30, Sun. 11-4. SIZE: Medium. *STOCK: Persian rugs and carpets, late 19th C to date.* LOC: A34 south of city on Robin Hood Island. PARK: Own forecourt. TEL: 0121 744 1001; fax - same; website - www.honerugs.co. SER: Valuations; restorations; finder. VAT: Stan.

Rex Johnson and Sons
8 Corporation St. B2 4RN. (D. Johnson). Open 9.15-5.15. *STOCK: Gold, silver, jewellery, porcelain and glass.* TEL: 0121 643 9674.

F. Meeks & Co
197 Warstone Lane, Hockley. B18. (M.L. and S.R. Durham). Open 9-5, Sat. 9-12. *STOCK: Clocks especially longcase, mantel and wall; vintage wrist watches and antique pocket watches; all £100-£10,000.* TEL: 0121 236 9058. SER: Valuations; restorations (clocks); clock and watch parts supplied. VAT: Stan/Spec.

Moseley Emporium
116 Alcester Rd., Moseley. B13 3EF. (G. Dorney). Est. 1982. Open 10-6. SIZE: Medium. *STOCK: Georgian to 1930's furniture, £75-£3,800.* PARK: Easy. TEL: 0121 449 3441; mobile - 07973 156902. SER: Restorations (stripping, polishing, finishing furniture). FAIRS: Newark.

Piccadilly Jewellers
105 New St. B2 4HD. (R. and R. Johnson). Open 10-5. *STOCK: Jewellery, silver and objects.* TEL: 0121 643 5791.

David Temperley Fine and Antiquarian Books
19 Rotton Park Rd., Edgbaston. B16 9JH. (D. and R.A. Temperley). Resident. Est. 1967. Open 9.30-5.30 by appointment. SIZE: Small. *STOCK: Fine antiquarian and rare books, 16th-20th C*

especially fine bindings, illustrated and private press; fine colour plate books - natural history, costume, travel; British topography and atlases; children's books, especially moveable and pop-up; early and rare English and European playing cards. LOC: 150 yards off Hagley Rd. (A456) and under 2 miles from city centre. 4 miles junction 3, M5. PARK: Easy. TEL: 0121 454 0135; fax - 0121 454 1124. SER: Valuations; restorations (book binding and paper); buys at auction (antiquarian books).

Warley Antique Centre
146 Pottery Rd., Warley Woods. B68 9HD. (Angela Hamilton). Open six days. SIZE: 70 cabinets and 4 furniture showrooms. *STOCK: General antiques, furnishings and collectables including Ruskin, Worcester, Doulton, clocks, silver, mainly 19th-20th C.* LOC: Off the A456 or A4123, junctions 2/3, M5. PARK: Easy. TEL: 0121 434 3813; mobile - 07702 976759.

The Windmill Gallery
c/o Snell & Prideaux Ltd., 6 Ernest St., Holloway Head. B1 1NS. (M. and C. Ashton). Est. 1985. Open 9-5.30, Sat. and Sun. by appointment. SIZE: Medium. *STOCK: Watercolours and drawings, 18th-20th C, £100-£3,000+.* LOC: City centre. PARK: Easy. TEL: 0121 622 3986; fax - 0121 666 6630. SER: Valuations; restorations; mounting, framing. VAT: Spec.

COVENTRY

Antiques Adventure
Rugby Rd., Binley Woods. CV3 2AW. (N. and J. Green). Est. 1969. Open 10-5 including Sun. (winter 10-4.30). SIZE: Large. *STOCK: Georgian, Victorian, Edwardian, contemporary, 1950's and 1960's furniture and effects.* LOC: Just off A46 eastern bypass, entrance off A428 Rugby road. PARK: Easy. TEL: 02476 453878; fax - 02476 445847; e-mail - sales@antiques adventure.com; website - www.antiques adventure.com. SER: Delivery (UK); shipping advice. VAT: Global/Spec/Stan.

Corner Cottage Antiques at Antiques Adventure
Rugby Rd, Binley Woods. CV3 2AW. (J. and B. Roberts). Est. 1969. Open 10-5 including Sun. *STOCK: 18th-20th C furniture, silver, porcelain, glass, brass and copper, general antiques.* PARK: Easy. TEL: Home - 01455 282583; e-mail - bobandjill@btinternet.com. VAT: Global/ Stan/Spec.

Luckmans Antiques
40 Far Gosford St. CV1 5DW. (David Auker).

Est. 1977. Open 9.30-4.15. CL: Mon. SIZE: Small. *STOCK: Bric-a-brac, books, vinyl records.* PARK: Easy. TEL: 02476 223842.

DORRIDGE, Nr. Solihull

Dorridge Antiques & Collectables
7 Forest Court. (Colleen Swift). Est. 1995. Open 11-6. SIZE: 2 floors. *STOCK: Furniture, ceramics, silver, militaria, paintings and prints, glass, general antiques and collectables.* LOC: Between Birmingham and Stratford, 10 mins. from NEC. PARK: Free. TEL: 01564 779336; home - 01564 779768.

FOUR OAKS, Nr. Sutton Coldfield

M. Allen Watch and Clockmaker
76A Walsall Rd. B74 4QY. (M.A. Allen). Est. 1969. Open 9-5.30, Sun. by appointment. SIZE: Small. *STOCK: Vintage wristwatches - Omega, Longines, Girard, Perregaux and Jaeger le Coultre; clocks - Vienna regulators, 1820-1880, mantel and wall clocks.* LOC: By Sutton Park, close to television mast. PARK: Easy. TEL: 0121 308 6117; home - 0121 308 8134. SER: Valuations; restorations (clocks and watches). VAT: Stan/Spec.

HALESOWEN

S.R. Furnishing and Antiques
Unit 1, Eagle Trading Estate, Stourbridge Rd. B63 3UA. (S. Willder). Est. 1975. *STOCK: General antiques and shipping furniture.* TEL: Mobile - 07860 820221.

Tudor House Antiques
68 Long Lane. B62 9LS. (D. Taylor). Open 9.30-5.30. *STOCK: Doors, fireplaces, pine including kitchens and furniture.* TEL: 0121 561 5563.

LYE, Nr. Stourbridge

Lye Antique Furnishings
206 High St. DY9 8JY. (P. Smith). Est. 1979. Open 9-5. SIZE: Medium. *STOCK: Furniture, china, glass, metalware, jewellery and collectors' items.* PARK: Easy. TEL: 01384 897513; mobile - 07976 765142. SER: Valuations.

OLDBURY

The Glory Hole
431 Moat Rd., B68 8EJ. (Colin Dickens). Est. 1985. Open 9.30-5.30, Tues. 12-5.30, Sat.10-5.30. SIZE: Small. *STOCK: Furniture, 19th-20th C, £50-£100; china, 20th C, £5-£100.* PARK:

Easy. TEL: 0121 544 1888; home - 0121 561 3573. SER: Valuations. FAIRS: Malvern Showground, Peterborough Festival, Norwich Sports Centre.

SOLIHULL

Renaissance
18 Marshall Lake Rd., Shirley. B90 4PL. (S.K. Macrow). GMC. Est. 1981. Open 9-5. SIZE: Small. *STOCK: General antiques.* LOC: Near Stratford Rd. TEL: 0121 745 5140. SER: Restorations (repairs, re-upholstery and polishing).

Tilleys Antiques
B91 2ES. (S.A. Alpren). GADAR. Est. 1970. Open by appointment. *STOCK: British glass, Oriental pottery, porcelain, shipping goods; silver, 19th C; Worcester.* TEL: 0121 704 1813. SER: Valuations; restorations (jewellery, silver); repairs (clocks and watches).

Yoxall Antiques
68 Yoxall Rd. B90 3RP. (Raul Burrows). Est. 1986. Open 9.30-5. SIZE: Medium. *STOCK: Georgian and Regency furniture including mahogany, walnut and rosewood; clocks and barometers, glass and china; desk stands, tea caddies, figures.* LOC: Just outside town centre. PARK: Easy. TEL: 0121 744 1744; mobile - 07860 168078; e-mail - sales@yoxallantiques. co.uk; website - www.yoxallantiques.co.uk. SER: Valuations; restorations (furniture). FAIRS: NEC.

STOURBRIDGE

Oldswinford Gallery
106 Hagley Rd., Oldswinford. DY8 1QU. (A.R. Harris). Open 9.30-5. CL: Mon. and Sat. p.m. *STOCK: 18th-20th C oil paintings, watercolours, antiquarian prints and maps.* TEL: 01384 395577. SER: Restorations; framing.

Regency Antique Trading Ltd.
116 Stourbridge Rd. DY9 7BU. (D. Bevan). Open 9.30-5. SIZE: 2 floors. *STOCK: General antiques and collectables, fireplaces and pine.* PARK: Free. TEL: 01384 868778; fax - 01384 825466; e-mail - regencytradingltd@blueyonder.co.uk; website - www.regency-antiques.co.uk. SER: Stripping; container shipping; fireplaces and kitchens from reclaimed pine.

Retro
48 Worcester St. DY8 1AS. (M. McHugo). Open 9.30-5. *STOCK: Furniture and architectural items.* TEL: 01384 442065.

SUTTON COLDFIELD

Thomas Coulborn and Sons   `BADA`
Vesey Manor, 64 Birmingham Rd. B72 1QP. (P. Coulborn and Sons). Est. 1939. Open 9.15-5.30 (1hr. lunch). SIZE: Large. *STOCK: General antiques, 1600-1830; fine English and Continental furniture, 17th-18th C; paintings and clocks.* LOC: 3 miles from Spaghetti Junction. From Birmingham A5127 through Erdington, premises on main road opposite cinema. PARK: Easy. TEL: 0121 354 3974; fax - 0121 354 4614; e-mail - art@coulborn.com; website - www.coulborn.com. SER: Valuations; restorations (furniture and paintings); buys on commission. VAT: Spec.

Driffold Gallery
78 Birmingham Rd. B72 1QR. (David Gilbert). Est. 1974. Open 10.30-6. SIZE: Medium. *STOCK: Oil paintings and watercolours, 19th C to contemporary.* LOC: Town centre approach. PARK: Own. TEL: 0121 355 5433. SER: Valuations; restorations.

WALSALL

The Doghouse (Antiques)
309 Bloxwich Rd. WS2 7BD. (John and Kate Rutter). Est. 1971. Open 9-5.30, Sun. (Oct.-March) 2-5.30. SIZE: Large. *STOCK: General antiques, fireplaces, architectural items.* LOC: B4210. PARK: At rear. TEL: 01922 630829; fax - 01922 631236; website - www.doghouse antiques.co.uk. VAT: Stan/Spec.

L.P. Antiques (Mids) Ltd
The Old Brewery, Short Acre St. WS2 8HW. (Pierre Farouz). Est. 1982. Open daily, Sun. by appointment. SIZE: Warehouse. *STOCK: French, Spanish and Continental including French and Spanish decorative furniture - armoires, buffets, beds, mirrors, tables; reproduction French tables, chairs and small items; wrought and cast iron.* LOC: Junction 10, M6, A454 towards town centre, left on A34 towards Cannock. PARK: Own. TEL: 01922 746764; fax - 01922 611316; e-mail - pierre.farouz@virgin.net; websites - www.lpantiques.net and www.something french.net. FAIRS: Swinderby. VAT: Stan.

WOLVERHAMPTON

Antiquities
75-76 Dudley Rd. Est. 1968. Open 10-6. *STOCK: General antiques.* TEL: 01902 459800.

Doveridge House Antiques

P O Box 1856. WV3 9XH. (Cdr. Harry and Mrs. Jean Bain). CINOA. Est. 1967. Open by appointment. *STOCK: 17th-19th C English and Continental furniture, fine art, clocks, decorative artifacts.* TEL: 01902 312211. SER: Valuations; restorations (furniture and oils); interior design; export. FAIRS: Advisers to NEC Antiques for Everyone.

Lamb Antique Fine Arts & Crafts Originals

77 Fancourt Ave., Penn. WV4 4HZ. (Beris and Cheryl Lamb). Est. 1982. Open by appointment. *STOCK: Pre-Raphaelites, Art Nouveau, Arts & Crafts furniture, metalware, glass, jewellery, fabrics, mirrors and prints, 1860-1920.* PARK: Easy. TEL: 01902 338510; home - same; mobile - 07850 406907; e-mail - berislamb.artscrafts @blueyonder.co.uk; website - www.antiques-originals.com. FAIRS: NEC LAPADA; Bowman.

Hoi An Hoard ceramics. (Left to right) Two jarlets, £68/£85; fish dish, £850; wine cup, £90; frog water dropper, £480. (Robert McPherson)

From an article entitled "Shipwreck Ceramics" by Patricia Hunter which appeared in the March 2002 issue of *Antique Collecting*. For more details and to subscribe see page 21.

Martin-Quick Antiques

LAPADA

Unit E2, Long Lane, Cosford. TF11 8PJ. (C.R. Quick). Est. 1965. Open every day by appointment or by chance. SIZE: Large. *STOCK: Furniture, English and French, including upholstered and country, 18th-19th C; shipping goods.* LOC: 1 mile from junction 3, M54. PARK: Easy. TEL: 01902 754703; home - 01902 752908; mobile - 07774 124859; e-mail - cqantiques@aol.com. SER: Packing and shipping. FAIRS: Newark. VAT: Stan/Spec.

Newhampton Road Antiques

184/184A Newhampton Rd. East, Whitmoreans. WV1 4PQ. (Robert and Linda Hill). Est. 1982. Open 10-3.30. SIZE: Small. *STOCK: General antiques and collectables, Victorian and Edwardian, £50-£1,500.* LOC: From A449 left at Wolverhampton football ground. PARK: Easy. TEL: 01902 712583. SER: Valuations. FAIRS: Newark, Swinderby.

No 9 Antiques

9 Upper Green, Tettenhall. WV6 8QQ. Open 10-5.30. CL: Mon. and Tues. SIZE: Medium. *STOCK: Furniture, 18th-19th C, £200-£1,000; ceramics, silver and prints, 19th C, £25-£500; works of art, £25-£100.* LOC: Corner of the Green. PARK: Easy. TEL: 01902 755333.

The Red Shop

7 Hollybush Lane, Penn. (B. Savage). Open 9.30-5.30. *STOCK: Furniture including pine.* TEL: 01902 342915.

Martin Taylor Antiques

LAPADA

140b and 323 Tettenhall Rd. WV6 0BQ. Est. 1976. Open 8.30-5.30, Sat. 9.30-4. SIZE: Large + showroom. *STOCK: Furniture, mainly 1800-1930, for the UK, USA, Japanese and Italian markets, £50-£10,000.* LOC: One mile from town centre on A41. PARK: Easy. TEL: 01902 751166; showroom - 01902 751122; fax - 01902 746502; mobile - 07836 636524; home - 01785 284539; e-mail - enquiries@mtaylor-antiques.co.uk; website - www.mtaylor-antiques.co.uk. SER: Restorations; French polishing. VAT: Stan/Spec

Wolverhampton Antiques and Collectors Market

Basement of Retail Market, Salop St. WV3 0SF. Est. 1984. Open 9-4. CL: Mon. and Thurs. SIZE: 20 units. *STOCK: China, glass, jewellery, militaria, books and comics, linen, football memorabilia, 19th-20th C, £5-£1,000.* LOC: Wolverhampton ring road, exit Chapel Ash island, market signposted. PARK: Easy - Peel St. and Pitt St. TEL: 01902 555212.

WILTSHIRE

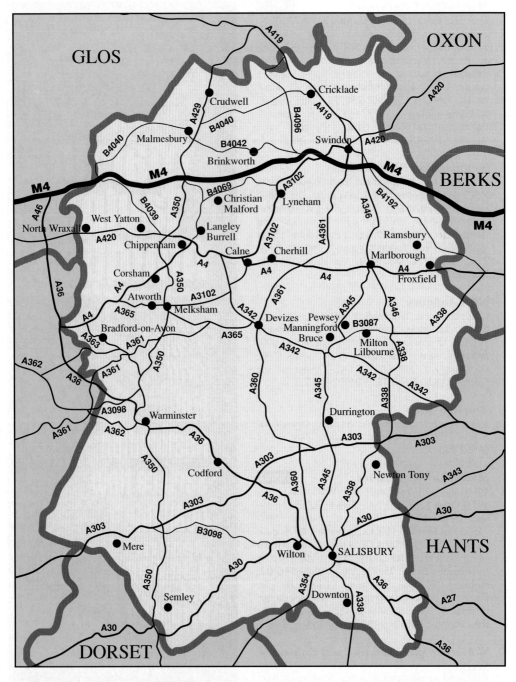

Dealers and Shops in Wiltshire

		Lyneham	1	Pewsey	1
Atworth	1	Corsham	1	Malmesbury	3	Ramsbury	2
Bradford-on-Avon	6	Cricklade	1	Manningford Bruce	1	Salisbury	14
Brinkworth	1	Crudwell	1	Marlborough	9	Semley	1
Calne	3	Devizes	3	Melksham	3	Swindon	4
Cherhill	1	Downton	1	Mere	1	Warminster	8
Chippenham	1	Durrington	1	Milton Lilbourne	1	West Yatton	1
Christian Malford	1	Froxfield	1	Newton Tony	1	Wilton	4
Codford	1	Langley Burrell	1	North Wraxall	1		

HARLEY ANTIQUES

LARGEST COLLECTION OF SELECTED ANTIQUES & DECORATIVE OBJECTS IN THE WEST COUNTRY

Full colour brochure sent on request
(Export enquiries only)

THE COMEDY
CHRISTIAN MALFORD
NR. CHIPPENHAM
WILTSHIRE SN15 4BS

TEL: 01249 720112
FAX: 01249 720553
4 MILES M4 EXIT 17
RESIDENT ON PREMISES

ATWORTH, Nr. Melksham

Peter Campbell Antiques
59 Bath Rd. SN12 8JY. (P.R. Campbell). Est. 1976. Open 10-5, Sun. and Mon. by appointment. SIZE: Medium. *STOCK: General antiques and decorative items, 18th-19th C.* Not Stocked: Silver and jewellery. LOC: Between Bath and Melksham on A365. PARK: Easy. TEL: 01225 709742; home - same. VAT: Stan/Spec.

BRADFORD-ON-AVON

Asylum House Antiques
5 Mount Pleasant. BA15 1SJ. (Peter and Maggie Jacobs). Resident. BABAADA. Est. 1986. Open by appointment. SIZE: Small. *STOCK: English and Irish drinking glasses, decanters and table glass, Georgian and Regency, £50-£2,000; decorative gilt mirrors, 18th-19th C, £500-£3,000.* LOC: Off A363 from Bath. PARK: Easy. TEL: 01225 866043; e-mail - info@asylum-antiqueglass.co.uk; website - www.antiqueglasses.biz. SER: Valuations. FAIRS: NEC; Glass Collectors' (National Motorcyle Museum). VAT: Stan/Spec.

Avon Antiques `BADA`
25, 26 and 27 Market St. BA15 1LL. (V. and A. Jenkins BA). BABAADA. Est. 1963. Open 9.45-5.30, Sun. by appointment. SIZE: Large. **STOCK: English and some Continental furniture, 1600-1880; metalwork, treen, clocks, barometers, some textiles, painted furniture, naive pictures.** LOC: A363, main street of town. PARK: Ask at shop for key to private parking opposite. TEL: 01225 862052; fax - 01225 868763; e-mail - enquiries@avon-antiques.co.uk; website - www.avon-antiques.co.uk. FAIRS: Grosvenor House; Olympia (winter). VAT: Spec.

Andrew Dando `BADA` `LAPADA`
34 Market St. BA15 1LL. (A.P. and J.M. Dando). BABAADA. Est. 1915. Open Tues.-Sat. 10-5 or by appointment. SIZE: Medium. *STOCK: English (including Staffordshire), Continental and Oriental porcelain and pottery, 17th to mid-19th C; local topographical and decorative antique prints.* LOC: Town centre. PARK: Nearby. TEL: 01225 865444; e-mail - andrew@andrewdando.co.uk; website - www.andrewdando.co.uk. SER: Valuations. FAIRS: BADA. VAT: Stan/Spec.

Mac Humble Antiques `BADA`
7-9 Woolley St. BA15 1AD. (W. Mc. A. and B.J. Humble). BABAADA. Est. 1979. Open 9.30-

BRADFORD ON AVON

Probably the best town for period antique furniture outside London

AVON ANTIQUES

Established 1963

25-26-27 MARKET STREET, BRADFORD ON AVON, WILTSHIRE BA15 1LL
TELEPHONE: (01225) 862052   ANDREW & VIBEKE JENKINS
www.avon-antiques.co.uk

MAC HUMBLE ANTIQUES

EST. 1979

18th & 19th Century Furniture, Metalware, Treen and Needlework.
Decorative items. Valuations & Restorations.

7-9 Woolley Street, Bradford-on-Avon, Wiltshire BA15 1AD

Telephone: (01225) 866329 Facsimile: (01225) 866329
E-mail: mac.humble@virgin.net

MOXHAMS ANTIQUES

Roger, Jill and Nicholas Bichard   Est. 1967

One of the largest stocks of good period furniture and accessories outside London: collectors and dealers welcome

17, 23 & 24 Silver Street, Bradford on Avon, Wiltshire BA15 1JZ
Tel: (01225) 862789 Fax: (01225) 867844 Home: (01380) 828677
E-mail: jill@moxhams-antiques.demon.co.uk

Trevor Waddington OBE

ANTIQUE CLOCKS

★ Offering quality antique clocks, restored and fully guaranteed   ★ Showroom open by appointment   ★ Stock details on request/website

5 TROWBRIDGE RD., BRADFORD ON AVON
Tel: 01225 862351
www.antiques-uk.co.uk/waddington

ANDREW DANDO

ESTABLISHED 1915

18th & EARLY 19th CENTURY POTTERY & PORCELAIN
LOCAL & DECORATIVE ANTIQUE MAPS & ENGRAVINGS

34 MARKET STREET, BRADFORD ON AVON, WILTSHIRE, BA15 1LL
TELEPHONE: 01225 865444
www.andrewdando.co.uk

An excellent place to stop for lunch with good pubs, cafes and restaurants in the centre of this beautiful Wiltshire town.

5.30, Sat. 9.30-1. SIZE: Medium. *STOCK: 17th-19th C oak, mahogany, fruitwoods, metalware, treen, samplers, silkwork pictures, decorative objects.* PARK: Nearby. TEL: 01225 866329; fax - same; e-mail - mac.humble@virgin.net; website - www.machumbleantiques.co.uk. SER: Valuations; restorations. FAIRS: BADA (March); Olympia (Nov). VAT: Stan/Spec.

Moxhams Antiques · LAPADA

17, 23 and 24 Silver St. BA15 1JZ. (R., J. and N. Bichard). BABAADA. Est. 1967. Open 9-5.30 or by appointment. SIZE: Large. *STOCK: English and Continental furniture, clocks, 1650-1850; European and Oriental pottery and porcelain, 1700-1850; decorative items, 1600-1900, all £50-£50,000.* LOC: Near town centre on B3107 towards Melksham. PARK: Own, at rear. TEL: 01225 862789; fax - 01225 867844; home - 01380 828677/01225 755026; e-mail - jill@moxhams-antiques.demon.co.uk. SER: Restorations. FAIRS: Olympia (June, Nov). VAT: Spec.

Trevor Waddington Antique Clocks

5 Trowbridge Rd. BA15 1EE. MBHI. BABAADA. Est. 1996. Strictly by appointment. SIZE: Small. *STOCK: 18th-19th C clocks - longcase, £3,000-£25,000; wall, £1,500-£3,500; carriage, bracket and mantel, £1,000-£9,000.* LOC: Quarter mile south of town bridge on A363. PARK: Easy. TEL: 01225 862351; home/fax - same; website - www.antiques-uk.co.uk/waddington. SER: Valuations; restorations (BADA/West Dean Dip. conservator).

BRINKWORTH, Nr. Malmesbury

North Wilts Exporters

Farm Hill House. SN15 5AJ. (M. Thornbury). Est. 1972. Open Mon.-Sat. or by appointment. *STOCK: Imported Continental pine, 18th-19th C; shipping goods.* LOC: Off M4, junction 16 Malmesbury road. TEL: 01666 510876; mobile - 07836 260730; e-mail - mike@northwilts.demon.co.uk; website - www.northwiltsantique exporters.com. SER: Valuations; shipping; import and export. VAT: Stan/Global.

CALNE

Calne Antiques

London Rd. SN11 0AB. (M. Blackford). GMC. Est. 1981. Open 10-5 seven days. *STOCK: Antique pine and country furniture, Victorian to 1930's; mahogany, oak and walnut.* LOC: A4, next to White Hart Hotel. PARK: Own. TEL: 01249 816311; fax - same. SER: Furniture made to order; free-standing kitchens.

Clive Farahar and Sophie Dupré - Rare Books, Autographs and Manuscripts

Horsebrook House, 15 The Green. SN11 8DQ. ABA. ILAB. PADA. UACC. Manuscript Society. Est. 1980. Open by appointment. SIZE: Medium. *STOCK: Rare books on voyages and travels, autograph letters and manuscripts, 15th-20th C, £5-£5,000+.* LOC: Off A4 in town centre. PARK: Easy. TEL: 01249 821121; fax - 01249 821202; e-mail - post@farahardupre.co.uk; website - www.farahardupre.co.uk. SER: Valuations; buys at auction (as stock). FAIRS: Universal Autograph Collectors' Club; Olympia (June). VAT: Stan.

Hilmarton Manor Press

Hilmarton Manor. SN11 8SB. (H. Baile de Laperriere). Est. 1967. Open 9-6. SIZE: Medium. *STOCK: New, out-of-print and antiquarian art related books including fine, applied, dictionaries and reference.* LOC: 3 miles from Calne on A3102 towards Swindon. PARK: Easy. TEL: 01249 760208; fax - 01249 760379. SER: Buys at auction.

CHERHILL, Nr. Calne

P.A. Oxley Antique Clocks and Barometers · LAPADA

The Old Rectory, Main Rd. SN11 8UX. BABAADA. Est. 1971. Open 9.30-5, other times by appointment. CL: Wed. SIZE: Large. *STOCK: Longcase, bracket, carriage clocks and barometers, 17th-19th C, £500-£30,000.* LOC: A4, not in village. PARK: Easy. TEL: 01249 816227; fax - 01249 821285; e-mail - info@paoxley.com; website - www.british-antiqueclocks.com. VAT: Spec.

CHIPPENHAM

Cross Hayes Antiques · LAPADA

Unit 6 Westbrook Farm, Draycot Cerne. SN15 5LH. (D. Brooks). Est. 1975. Open Mon.-Fri. 9-5 by appointment. SIZE: Warehouse. *STOCK: Furniture, 1850-1930, Victorian, Edwardian and shipping oak.* LOC: Off M4, junction 17 on B4122. PARK: Own. TEL: 01249 720033; fax - same; home - 01666 822062; e-mail - david@crosshayes.co.uk. website - www.crosshayes.co.uk; SER: Packing and shipping; courier (UK and France). VAT: Stan/Spec.

CHRISTIAN MALFORD, Nr. Chippenham

Harley Antiques

The Comedy. SN15 4BS. (G.J. Harley). Est. 1959. Open 9-6 including Sun. or later by appointment.

P.A. Oxley

Antique Clocks & Barometers
Established 1971

The Old Rectory · Cherhill · Near Calne
Wiltshire SN11 8UX
Telephone (01249) 816227 Fax (01249) 821285
Visit our Web site - Full stock & prices
www.british-antiqueclocks.com
E-mail: info@paoxley.com

Established in 1971, P.A. Oxley is one of the largest quality antique clock and barometer dealers in the U.K. Current stock includes over 30 quality restored **longcase clocks** ranging in price from £3,500 to £30,000. In addition we have a fine selection of **bracket clocks, carriage clocks** and **barometers**.

We do not exhibit at antique fairs, and therefore our extensive stock can only be viewed at our large showrooms on the main A4 London to Bath road at Cherhill or on our website address shown above.

Full shipping facilities are available to any country in the world. U.K. customers are provided with a free delivery and setting up service combined with a twelve month guarantee.

If your desire is for a genuine antique clock or barometer then please visit us at Cherhill where you can examine our large stock and discuss your exact requirement. If time is short and you cannot visit us we will send you a selection of colour photographs from which you can buy with confidence.

Hours of opening are 9.30-5.00 every day except Wednesday. Sunday and evening appointments can easily be arranged. We look forward to welcoming you to our establishment.

The Association of Art and Antique Dealers

SIZE: Large. *STOCK: Furniture, 18th-19th C, £250-£6,000; decorative objects, £30-£8,000.* LOC: B4069, 4 miles off M4, junction 17. PARK: Own. TEL: 01249 720112; home - same; fax - 01249 720553; e-mail - thecomedy.wilts@ ukonline.co.uk. SER: Colour brochure available (export only). VAT: Stan. *Trade Only.*

CODFORD, Nr. Warminster

Tina's Antiques
75 High St. BA12 0ND. (T.A. Alder). Open 9-6, Sat. 9-1. *STOCK: General antiques.* TEL: 01985 850828.

CORSHAM

Matthew Eden
Pickwick End. SN13 0JB. Resident. Est. 1951. SIZE: Large. *STOCK: Country house furniture and garden items, 17th-19th C.* LOC: A4 between Chippenham and Bath. TEL: 01249 713335; fax - 01249 713644. SER: Shipping. FAIRS: Chelsea Flower Show. VAT: Spec.

CRICKLADE, Nr. Swindon

Edred A.F. Gwilliam
Candletree House, Bath Rd. SN6 6AX. Est. 1976. Open by appointment. SIZE: Medium. *STOCK: Arms and armour, swords, pistols, long guns, £50-£20,000+.* PARK: Easy. TEL: 01793 750241; fax - 01793 750359. SER: Valuations; buys at auction. FAIRS: Major arms. VAT: Stan/Spec.

CRUDWELL

Philip A. Ruttleigh Antiques incorporating Crudwell Furniture
Odd Penny Farm. SN16 9SJ. Est. 1990. Open 9-5 and by appointment. CL: Sat. SIZE: Small. *STOCK: Furniture including pine in the paint, and decorative items, £10-£2,000.* LOC: Next to RAF Kemble on A429, 5 minutes from Cirencester, 15 mins. from junction 17, M4. PARK: Easy. TEL: 01285 770970; website - www.crudwellfurniture.co.uk. SER: Furniture restoration, including stripping; bead blasting for architectural antiques.

DEVIZES

Cross Keys Jewellers
The Ginnel, Market Pl. SN10 1HN. (D. and D. Pullen). Est. 1967. Open 9-5. *STOCK: Jewellery, silver.* LOC: Alley adjacent Nationwide Building Society. PARK: Easy. TEL: 01380 726293. SER: Valuations; repairs; restringing (pearls). VAT: Stan.

St Mary's Chapel Antiques
Northgate St. SN10 1JL. (Richard Sankey). BABAADA. Est. 1971. Open 10-6, Wed. by appointment. SIZE: Large. *STOCK: Original painted and Continental furniture, decorative accessories, garden items.* LOC: Just off market square. PARK: Easy. TEL: 01380 721399; e-mail - richard@rsankey.freeserve.co.uk; website - www.st-marys-chapel-antiques.org.uk. SER: Restorations. FAIRS: BABAADA.

Upstairs, Downstairs
40 Market Place. SN10 3DL. (J. Coom). Est. 1997. Open 9.30-4.30 including Bank Holidays, Sun. 9.30-3. CL: Wed. SIZE: Large. *STOCK: Oak, mahogany and pine furniture, toys, dolls and teddies, prints, postcards, records, silver.* PARK: Easy. TEL: 01380 730266; fax - 01380 739352; home - 01380 724892; mobile - 07974 074220; e-mail - devizesantiques@amserve. com. SER: Valuations; restorations (dolls). FAIRS: Newark, Ardingly, Kensington, Carmarthen, NEC, Westpoint.

DOWNTON, Nr. Salisbury

Mesh Antiques Ltd.
1 The Headlands. SP5 3HH. (Roger Bishop and David Venables). Est. 1993. Open 10-4 including Sun. SIZE: Large. *STOCK: Wide selection of general antiques and collectables.* LOC: A338. PARK: Easy. TEL: 01725 513380; e-mail - meshantiques@aol.com. SER: Valuations; restorations.

DURRINGTON

Cannon Militaria
21 Bulford Rd. SP4 8DL. (Len Webb). Est. 1990. Open Thurs. and Fri. 9.30-5, Sat. 9.30-1. SIZE: Small. *STOCK: Military collectables, £1-£2,000.* PARK: Easy. TEL: 01980 655099; home - 01980 653082; e-mail - leonard.webb@tiscali.co.uk. SER: Valuations. FAIRS: Mark Carter Militaria.

FROXFIELD, Nr. Marlborough

Blanchard   LAPADA
Bath Rd. SN8 3LD. Est. 1940. Open 9.30-5.30. SIZE: Large. *STOCK: 18th-20th C antiques and decorative pieces including garden furniture.* PARK: Easy. TEL: 01488 680666; fax - 01488 680668. FAIRS: Olympia (June).

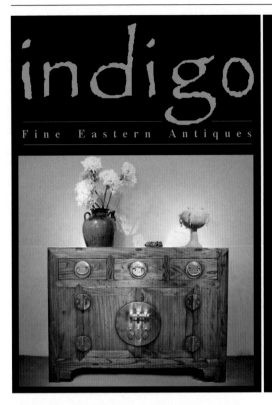
LANGLEY BURRELL, Nr. Chippenham

Harriet Fairfax Fireplaces and General Antiques
Langley Green. SN15 4LL. Open by appointment. *STOCK: China, glass, dolls, furniture, fabrics and needlework; architectural items and fittings, brass and iron knobs, knockers; fireplaces, pine and iron, 1780-1950.* TEL: 01249 652030. SER: Design consultancy.

LYNEHAM , Nr. Chippenham

Pillars Antiques
10 The Banks. SN15 4NS. (K. Clifford). Resident. Est. 1986. Open 10-5, including Sun. CL: Wed. and Thurs. SIZE: Large. *STOCK: Victorian and Edwardian pine, shipping oak.* LOC: B4069 Chippenham road, 1 mile from village. PARK: Easy. TEL: 01249 890632; home - same. VAT: Global.

MALMESBURY

Antiques - Rene Nicholls
56 High St. SN16 9AT. (Mrs R. Nicholls). Est. 1980. Open 10-5.30, Sun. by appointment. SIZE: Small. *STOCK: English pottery and porcelain, 18th to early 19th C, £50-£900; small furniture.* PARK: Opposite. TEL: 01666 823089; home - same.

Andrew Britten Antiques
48 High St. SN16 9AT. (T.M. Tyler and T.A. Freeman). Est. 1975. Open 9.30-5. SIZE: Medium. *STOCK: Furniture, decorative brass, wood, glass and porcelain items, £15-£500.* PARK: Opposite. TEL: 01666 823376; fax - 01666 825563. VAT: Spec.

Lyon Oliver Antiques
Laynes House, Oaksey. SN16 9SE. TADA. Open by appointment. *STOCK: English and Irish country house furniture, large mirrors, upholstery and decorative sculpture.* TEL: 01666 577603; e-mail - lyon@lyon-oliver.demon.co.uk. FAIRS: Olympia.

MANNINGFORD BRUCE

Indigo
Dairy Barn. SN9 6JW. (Richard Lightbown and Marion Bender). Est. 1982. Open 10-5, Sat. 10-4. SIZE: Large. *STOCK: Furniture and architectural items, accessories, Indian, Chinese, Japanese and Tibetan, from early 19th C, to £3,600.* LOC: A345 2 miles from Pewsey. PARK: Forecourt. TEL: 01672 564722; fax - 01672 564733; mobile - 07799 602417; e-mail - antiques@indigo-uk.com; website - www.indigo-uk.com. VAT: Stan.

Bowmoore Gallery
4 London Rd. SN8 1PH. Est. 1968. Open 10-6, Sun. 11-5. *STOCK: 20th C oil paintings and watercolours, small collectables, interior design and garden items.* LOC: A4. PARK: Easy. TEL: 01672 513593; mobile - 07818 054448; e-mail - bowmoore@aol.com. SER: Framing and restorations.

Brocante Antiques Centre
6 London Rd. SN8 1PH. (Robert Stenhouse and Peter Randall). Est. 1986. Open 10-5. SIZE: Large. *STOCK: Furniture including French, £50-£1,500; ceramics including Staffordshire, £5-£1,000; all 18th-20th C; collectables.* LOC: A4 entering Marlborough. PARK: Easy. TEL: 01672 516512; fax - same. SER: Valuations; restorations (furniture). VAT: Global.

William Cook (Marlborough) `LAPADA`
High Trees House, Savernake Forest. SN8 4NE. (W.J. Cook). BAFRA. Est. 1963. Open by appointment. SIZE: Medium. *STOCK: Furniture, 18th to early 19th C; objets d'art, 18th-19th C.* LOC: 1.5 miles from Marlborough on A346 towards Burbage. PARK: Easy. TEL: 01672 513017; fax - 01672 514455. SER: Valuations; restorations (furniture including polishing and gilding); buys at auction (furniture). FAIRS: Olympia; Harrogate; Claridges; Chester; Tatton Park. VAT: Stan/Spec.

Katharine House Gallery
Katharine House, The Parade. SN8 1NE. (C.C. Gange). Est. 1983. Open 10-5.30. SIZE: Medium. *STOCK: Furniture, 18th-19th C, £200-£2,000; decorative items, £100-£1,000; Chinese, Roman and Greek antiquities, 2000BC-1000AD, £100-£1,000; 20th C British paintings and prints, £10-£1,000; books, £5-£500.* PARK: Easy. TEL: 01672 514040; home - same. VAT: Stan/Spec.

Robert Kime Antiques
P O Box 454. SN8 3UR . Est. 1968. Open by appointment. *STOCK: Decorative, period furniture.* TEL: 01264 73126; e-mail - mail@robertkime.com. VAT: Spec.

The Marlborough Parade Antique Centre
The Parade. SN8 1NE. (T. Page). Est. 1985. Open 10-5 including Sun. SIZE: 57 dealers. *STOCK: Good quality furniture, paintings, silver, porcelain, glass, clocks, jewellery, copper, brass and pewter, £5-£5,000.* LOC: Adjacent A4 in town centre. PARK: Easy. TEL: 01672 515331. SER: Valuations; restorations (furniture, porcelain, copper, brass). VAT: Spec.

A Chalice bowl decorated with the Fairy Gondola pattern (Z5360), from the Fairyland Lustre range, from about 1920. Diameter 10½in. (Trustees of the Wedgwood Museum, Barlaston, Staffordshire, England)

From an article entitled "In Fairyland All Things Are Possible" by Andrew Casey which appeared in the December 2001/January 2002 issue of *Antique Collecting*. For more details and to subscribe see page 21.

Paul Martin Antiques

4 Kingsbury St. SN8 1HU. Open 10-5.30, Sun. by appointment. *STOCK: Country vernacular, mainly English, table treen, metalware, clocks, Welsh dressers, court cupboards, settles - bacon, curved and box; tables, Thames Valley and Windsor chairs, all 17th to early 19th C; decorative items - rushlight candlesticks, trivets, inglenook toasters, bible boxes, spice and food cupboards.* TEL: 01672 511188; fax - same. SER: Valuations; restorations; sourcing; reference book library.

The Military Parade Bookshop

The Parade. SN8 1NE. (G. and P. Kent). *STOCK: Military history books especially regimental histories and the World Wars.* LOC: Next to The Lamb. TEL: 01672 515470; fax - 01980 630150; e-mail - enquiry@militaryparadebooks.com; website - www.militaryparadebooks.com.

Annmarie Turner Antiques

22 Salisbury Rd. SN8 4AD. Resident. Est. 1960. Open 10-6, Sun. by appointment. SIZE: Small. *STOCK: British oak, fruitwood, pine and primitive country furniture, £50-£1,500; treen and kitchenalia, £5-£100; allied decorative items and the unusual, £20-£500, 17th C to 1920's.* Not

Stocked: Mahogany, jewellery, silver, reproduction. LOC: Left side of first roundabout approaching town from Hungerford on A4. PARK: Easy and at rear. TEL: 01672 515396; home - same. SER: Valuations. VAT: Spec.

MELKSHAM

Dann Antiques Ltd

Unit 1, Avonside Enterprise Park, New Broughton Rd. SN12 8BS. (G. Low). BABAADA. Est. 1983. Open 9-5.30, Sat. 9-1. SIZE: Large. *STOCK: 18th-19th C English furniture; French and decorative pieces, lighting, fenders, mirrors, pottery, porcelain.* PARK: Own. TEL: 01225 707329; fax - 01225 790120; e-mail - 113665.1341@compuserve.com; website - www.dannantiques.com. SER: Restorations. VAT: Stan/Spec.

Alan Jaffray

16 Market Place. SN12 6EX. BABAADA. Est. 1956. Open Mon.-Fri. 9-5. SIZE: Large. *STOCK: Furniture and smalls, 18th-19th C, £50-£2,000.* LOC: Main Bath to Devizes Road. PARK: On premises. TEL: 01225 702269; fax - 01225 790413; e-mail - jaffray.antiques@talk21.com. VAT: Stan/Spec.

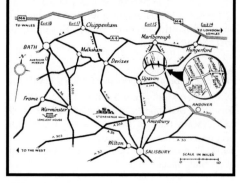
King Street Curios
8 King St. SN12 6HD. Est. 1991. SIZE: 20 units. *STOCK: China, discontinued Denby, USSR, glass, jewellery, Art Deco, kitchenalia, furniture.* LOC: A350. PARK: Own at rear. TEL: 01225 790623. FAIRS: Oasis, Swindon; Neeld Hall, Chippenham; Templemeads (Brunel), Bristol.

MERE, Nr. Warminster

Louis Stanton `BADA`
P O Box 2839. BA12 6BY. (L.R. and S.A. Stanton). CINOA. Est. 1965. Open by appointment. *STOCK: Early English oak furniture, medieval sculpture and works of art, metalware, unusual decorative items.* TEL: 01747 860747; fax - same. SER: Valuations; buys at auction.

MILTON LILBOURNE, Nr. Pewsey

Rupert Gentle Antiques `BADA`
The Manor House. SN9 5LQ. Est. 1954. Open 9.15-6. SIZE: Medium. *STOCK: English and Continental domestic metalwork, 1650-1850; treen, decorative objects, needlework and domestic accessories.* LOC: From Hungerford on A4 take A338 for Pewsey. PARK: Easy. TEL: 01672 563344; fax - 01672 563563. SER: Valuations; buys at auction. VAT: Stan/Spec.

NORTH WRAXALL, Nr. Chippenham

Delomosne and Son Ltd `BADA`
Court Close. SN14 7AD. (T.N.M. Osborne and M.C.F. Mortimer). BABAADA. Articles on chandeliers, glass and porcelain. Est. 1905. Open Mon.-Fri. 9.30-5.30, other times by appointment. SIZE: Large. *STOCK: English and Irish glass, pre-1830, £20-£20,000; glass chandeliers, English and European porcelain, needlework, papier mâché and treen.* LOC: Off A420 between Bath and Chippenham. PARK: Easy. TEL: 01225 891505; fax - 01225 891907; website - www.delomosne.co.uk. SER: Valuations; buys at auction. FAIRS: International Ceramic; Winter Olympia. VAT: Spec.

PEWSEY

Time Restored & Co
18-20 High St. SN9 5AQ. (J. H. Bowler-Reed and D.I. Rider). Est. 1975. Open 10-6. SIZE: Small. *STOCK: Clocks, barometers and musical boxes.* LOC: Village centre. PARK: Free at rear of premises. TEL: 01672 563544. SER: Valuations; restorations.

RAMSBURY, Nr. Marlborough

Heraldry Today
Parliament Piece. SN8 2QH. (Mrs Rosemary Pinches). ABA. ILAB. Est. 1954. Open 9.30-4.30. CL: Sat. SIZE: Medium. *STOCK: Heraldic and genealogical books and manuscripts, £3-£10,000.* PARK: Own. TEL: 01672 520617; fax - 01672 520183; e-mail - heraldry@heraldrytoday.co.uk; website - www.heraldrytoday.co.uk. SER: Book search; catalogues.

Inglenook Antiques
59 High St. SN8 2QN. (Dennis White). Est. 1969. Open 10-1 and 2-5, prior telephone call advisable. CL: Mon. and Wed. except by appointment. SIZE: Small. *STOCK: Oil lamps, £50-£850; clocks, barometers and spare parts, £150-£4,000; some furniture.* LOC: 3 miles from A4 between Hungerford and Marlborough. PARK: Easy. TEL: 01672 520261; home - same. SER: Restorations (longcase clock movements only).

SALISBURY

21st Century Antics
13 Brown St. SP1 1HE. (David, Geraldine, Jonathan and Benjamin Scott). Est. 1988. Open 9-5.30. SIZE: Large. *STOCK: Furniture, Georgian to date, £30-£3,000; small collectables, £2-£250.* PARK: Own. TEL: 01722 337421; fax - same; e-mail - Dave.21stcenturyantics@virgin.net; website - www.21stcenturyantics.co.uk.

Antique and Collectors Market
37 Catherine St. SP1 2DH. (Peter Beck). Est. 1977. Open 10-5. SIZE: Large. *STOCK: Silver, plate, china, glass, toys, books, prints, pens, furniture, Art Deco, antiquities.* LOC: City centre. PARK: Nearby. TEL: 01722 326033/338487; website - www.salisburyantiques.com. SER: Silver plating; repairs.

The Avonbridge Antiques and Collectors Market
United Reformed Church Hall, Fisherton St. SP2 7RG. Open Tues. 9-3.30. SIZE: 15 dealers. *STOCK: General antiques.* TEL: 01202 669061.

The Barn Book Supply
88 Crane St. SP1 2QD. (J. and J. Head). Est. 1958. Open 9.30-5. CL: Sat. *STOCK: Antiquarian books on angling, shooting, horses, deerstalking.* TEL: 01722 327767; fax - 01722 339888.

Exhibited at the Royal Academy in 1875, 'The Old Rampart at Sundown', a 40in. x 62in., canvas by Thomas George Cooper (1836-1901). (Bonhams)

From an article entitled "19th Century Paintings" by Anthony J. Lester which appeared in the June 2002 issue of *Antique Collecting*. For more details and to subscribe see page 21.

Boston Antiques
223 Wilton Rd. and warehouse at Wilton. SP2
7JY. Est. 1964. Open by appointment any time.
SIZE: Small. *STOCK: Fine rare world furniture,
16th-19th C.* PARK: Opposite. TEL: 01722
322682; 08702 417452; e-mail - derek@strange
corp.com. VAT: Stan/Spec.

Robert Bradley Antiques
71 Brown St. SP1 2BA. Est. 1970. Open 9.30-
5.30. CL: Sat. *STOCK: Furniture, 17th-18th C;
decorative items.* TEL: 01722 333677; fax -
01722 339922. VAT: Spec.

Ronald Carr
6 St. Francis Rd. SP1 3QS. (R.G. Carr). Est.
1983. Open by appointment. SIZE: Small.
*STOCK: Modern British etchings, wood
engravings and colour wood cuts, £5-£1,000.*
LOC: 1 mile north of city on A345. PARK: Easy.
TEL: 01722 328892; home - same. SER: Buys at
auction.

Castle Galleries
81 Castle St. SP1 3SP. (John C. Lodge). Est.
1971. Open 9-4.30, Sat. 9-1. CL: Mon. and Wed.
STOCK: General antiques, coins and medals.
PARK: Easy. TEL: 01722 333734; mobile -
07890 225059; e-mail - john.lodge1@tesco.net.
SER: Medal mounting.

Edward Hurst Antiques
The Garden Room, Netherhampton. SP2 8PU.
Est. 1983. Open by appointment. SIZE: Medium.
*STOCK: English furniture and associated works
of art, 1650-1820.* LOC: Just west of Salisbury.
PARK: Easy. TEL: 01722 743042; mobile -
07768 255557. FAIRS: Olympia (June, Winter,
Spring). VAT: Spec.

Myriad
48-54 Milford St. SP1 2BP. (Karen Montlake and
Stuart Hardy). Est. 1982. Open 9.30-5, Sat. 10-5,
other times by appointment. SIZE: Large.
*STOCK: Georgian mahogany, oak and pine -
chairs, corner cupboards, wardrobes, dressers,
tables, chests of drawers, coffers; Victorian
mahogany, pine and fruitwood - chests of
drawers, wardrobes, chairs, dressing tables and
dressing chests, boxes, kitchen and dining tables.*
LOC: Near town centre. PARK: Culver St. TEL:
01722 413595; fax - 01722 416395; home -
01722 718203; mobile - 07796 175624; e-mail -
karen@myriad-antiques.co.uk; website - www.
myriad-antiques.co.uk. SER: Restorations
(furniture); free collection/delivery (30 mile
radius).

Salisbury Antiques Warehouse Ltd
LAPADA
94 Wilton Rd. SP2 7JJ. (R.W. and Mrs C.
Wallrock). Est. 1964. Open 9-5.30, Fri. 9-5, Sat.10-
4, Sun. by appointment. SIZE: Large. *STOCK:
18th-19th C English and Continental furniture,
decorative works of art, clocks and pictures,
£1,000-£15,000; small items, £100-£1,000.* LOC:
A36 Warminster-Southampton road. PARK: Easy.
TEL: 01722 410634; fax - 01722 410635; mobile -
07768 877069; home - 01590 672515. SER:
Restorations (gilding). VAT: Stan/Spec.

Mike Scott Repair & Restoration
Five Bells Workshop, St. Edmunds, Church St.
SP1 1EF. Est. 1993. Open 9-5.30, Sun. 11-4.
SIZE: Small. *STOCK: Country furniture
including Windsor arm chairs, 18th to early 20th
C, £50-£1,000.* PARK: Easy. TEL: 01722
505955. SER: Restorations (furniture).

William Sheppee
Old Sarum Airfield. SP4 6DZ. (W. Hiley and J.
Hedges). Est. 1988. Open Mon.-Fri. by appointment
only. SIZE: Large. *STOCK: Indian and Chinese
antiques and antique replica mirrors.* PARK: Easy.
TEL: 01722 334454; fax - 01722 337754; e-mail -
sales@williamsheppee.com. VAT: Stan. *Trade Only.*

Chris Wadge Clocks
83 Fisherton St. SP2 7ST. (Patrick Wadge). Open
9-4. CL: Mon. *STOCK: Clocks and spare parts
for 400 day clocks.* TEL: 01722 334467; e-mail -
cwclocks@aol.com. SER: 400 day clock
specialist; repairs (antique/mechanical clocks).

SEMLEY

Dairy House Antiques
Station Rd. SP7 9AN. (A. Stevenson). Est. 1998.
Open 9-5. SIZE: Large. *STOCK: Furniture,
paintings, decorative items, 1600-1960.* LOC:
Just off the A350, 2 miles north of Shaftesbury.
PARK: Easy. TEL: 01747 853317. SER:
Valuations. VAT: Spec.

SWINDON

Penny Farthing Antiques Arcade
Victoria Centre, 138/9 Victoria Rd., Old Town.
SN1 3BU. (Ann Farthing). Est. 1999. Open 10-5.
SIZE: Large. *STOCK: Furniture, silver,
porcelain, watches, clocks.* LOC: On left on hill
between Old Town and college. PARK: Prospect
Place. TEL: 01793 536668. VAT: Stan.

Sambourne House Antiques Ltd
50-51 The Arcade, Brunel Shopping Centre. SN1

1LL. (T. and Mrs K. Cove). Est. 1984. Open 10-5, Sun. 10-4. SIZE: Large. *STOCK: Restored 19th C pine, £120-£2,000; reclaimed 19th C pine, £50-£1,500; reproduction smalls, £2-£90.* LOC: 1.5 miles off junction 16, M4, towards Swindon. PARK: Easy. TEL: 01793 610855; fax - same. SER: Stripping; specialist pine importer. VAT: Stan/Global.

Allan Smith Antique Clocks
162 Beechcroft Rd., Upper Stratton. SN2 7QE. Est. 1988. Open any time by appointment. SIZE: Large. *STOCK: 50-60 longcase clocks including automata, moonphase, painted dial, brass dial, 30 hour, 8 day, London and provincial, £1,950-£39,500; occasionally stick and banjo barometers, mantel, wall, bracket, Vienna and lantern clocks.* LOC: Near Bakers Arms Inn. PARK: Own. TEL: 01793 822977; fax - same; mobile - 07778 834342; e-mail - allansmith clocks@lineone.net: website - www.allansmith antiqueclocks.co.uk. VAT: Spec.

Victoria Bookshop
30 Wood St., Old Town. SN1 4AB. (S. Austin). Est. 1965. Open 9.30-5. SIZE: Large. *STOCK: Books, most subjects, old postcards.* LOC: Middle of Old Town shopping area. PARK: Nearby. TEL: 01793 527364.

WARMINSTER

Cassidy's Antiques
7 Silver St. BA12 8PS. (M. Cassidy). BABAADA. Est. 1989. Open 9-5, Sat. 10-5. SIZE: Medium. *STOCK: Furniture, 17th-19th C, £200-£1,500.* PARK: Easy. TEL: 01985 213313; e-mail - matcas@supanet.com; website - www.cassidyantiques.com. SER: Restorations (furniture and cabinet making).

Choice Antiques
4 Silver St. BA12 8PS. (Avril Bailey). Open 10-5.30. SIZE: Medium. *STOCK: General antiques and decorative items, 18th-19th C, £25-£2,000.* PARK: Easy. TEL: 01985 218924. VAT: Stan/Spec.

European Accent
11 Silver St. BA12 8PS. (Steve and Claire Green). BABAADA. Est. 2000. Open 10-5, Sat. 10-4. SIZE: Small. *STOCK: Decorative furniture and accessories mainly from central and eastern Europe - painted armoires, marriage chests, food cupboards, 1890-1920, £200-£1,000; small items, £50-£200; plate racks, hanging cupboards, spice drawers, bowls and plates, tablecloths and linens, 1900-1950, £50-£100.* LOC: Towards Frome, near obelisk. PARK: Easy. TEL: 01985 219736;

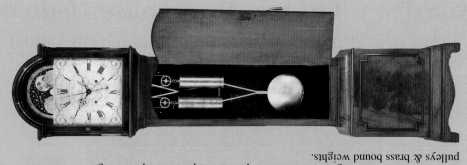

Scott Fecit detail showing double rhomboid pendulum, pierced 4 spoke weight pulleys & brass bound weights.

Allan Smith

LONGCASE CLOCKS

'Amity Cottage' 162 Beechcroft Road
Upper Stratton, Swindon, Wiltshire SN2 7QE

PHONE/FAX: (01793) 822977 • MOBILE: 07778 834342

INTERNET ON LINE CATALOGUE:
www.allansmithantiqueclocks.co.uk
Open any day or evening by appointment

I try to maintain stocks which are decorative, unusual, of good quality, proportions and originality. I can usually offer automata, moonphase, painted dial, brass dial, 30-hour, 8-day, London and provincial examples in oak, mahogany, lacquer, walnut and marquetry. From circa 1700 to circa 1840. All properly and sympathetically restored to very high standards. 50+ good examples usually in stock.

Worldwide shipping
Clockfinder service
Insurance valuations
Fine clocks always wanted
12 Months Written Guarantee

FREE UK DELIVERY & SETTING UP

Less than 10 minutes from M4 junction 15 or Swindon bus and rail stations - can collect.

Scott Fecit, small late 18 C 8 day flame mahogany longcase clock with silvered & engraved brass dial, brass insert canted receded corners to hood, centre sweep seconds, centre sweep date, dead beat escapement, moonphases to arch, and double rhomboid pendulum. 80¾" (205cms)

home/fax - 01749 813932; mobile - 07977 496762; e-mail - enquiries@europeanaccent. co.uk; website - www.europeanaccent.co.uk. FAIRS: Newark.

Isabella Antiques
3 Silver St. BA12 8PS. (B.W. Semke). BABAADA. Est. 1990. Open 10-5. SIZE: Medium. *STOCK: Furniture, late 18th C to late 19th C, £100-£5,000; boxes and mirrors, 19th C, £50-£1,000.* LOC: Main road. PARK: Easy. TEL: 01985 218933; e-mail - IsabellaAntiques@ aol.com. SER: Buys at auction (furniture). VAT: Spec.

Maxfield House Antiques
Maxfield House, 16 Silver St. BA12 8PS. (Martyn and Rosemary Reynolds). BABAADA. Est. 1992. Open 10-5 or by appointment. SIZE: Small. *STOCK: Mainly English oak and mahogany, 18th-20th C; town and country furniture; pictures and decorative objects; all £50-£2,000.* LOC: Main Bath road leading into Silver St. PARK: Easy. TEL: 01985 212121; home - same; mobile - 07703 877196; e-mail - maxfield@x-router.com; website - www. maxfield-antiques.com.

Obelisk Antiques
LAPADA
2 Silver St. BA12 8PS. (P. Tanswell). BABAADA. Open 10-1 and 2-5.30. SIZE: Large. *STOCK: English and Continental furniture, 18th-19th C; decorative items, objets d'art.* PARK: Easy. TEL: 01985 846646; fax - 01985 219901; e-mail - all@obeliskantiques.com. VAT: Spec.

Warminster Antiques Centre
6 Silver St. BA12 8PT. (Peter Walton). BABAADA. Est. 1970. Open 10-5. SIZE: 15 dealers. *STOCK: Furniture, home embellishments, textiles, silver, jewellery, collectors' items.* PARK: Easy. TEL: 01985 847269; fax - 01985 211778; mobile - 07860 584193. FAIRS: Newark.

K. and A. Welch
1A Church St. BA12 8PG. Est. 1967. Open 8-6, Sat. 9-1. SIZE: Large. *STOCK: Shipping furniture, 18th-19th C, £10-£2,000.* LOC: A36 west end of town. PARK: Own. TEL: 01985 214687; home - 01985 213433. VAT: Stan/Spec.

Heirloom & Howard Limited
Manor Farm. SN14 7EU. (D.S. Howard). BABAADA. Est. 1972. Open 10-5.30, Sat. 11-5 or by appointment. SIZE: Medium. *STOCK:*

Porcelain mainly Chinese armorial and export, 18th C, £100-£5,000; heraldic items, 18th-19th C, £10-£1,000; portrait engravings, 17th-19th C, £10-£50. LOC: 10 miles from Bath, 1/4 mile off A420 Chippenham/Bristol road. Transport from Chippenham station (4 miles) if required. PARK: Own. TEL: 01249 783038; fax - 01249 783039. SER: Valuations; buys at auction (Chinese porcelain). VAT: Spec.

Bay Tree Antiques
26 North St. SP2 0HJ. Open 9-5.30 or by appointment. SIZE: Medium. *STOCK: General antiques, specialising in period English furniture.* TEL: 01722 743392.

Hingstons of Wilton
36 North St. SP2 0HJ. Est. 1976. Open 9-5, Sat. 10-4. SIZE: Large. *STOCK: 18th-20th C furniture, clocks, pictures and objects.* PARK: Easy. TEL: 01722 742263; home - 01722 714742; mobile - 07887 870569; website - www.hingstons-antiques.co.uk.

Carol Musselwhite Antiques
6 West St. SP2 0DF. Est. 1990. Open 10-5. CL: Mon. and Jan. SIZE: Medium. *STOCK: Porcelain and pottery especially discontinued Denby, pre 1980, linen and lace, £1-£300.* LOC: Village centre. PARK: 30 metres. TEL: 01722 742573.

A.J. Romain and Sons
The Old House, 11 and 13 North St. SP2 0HA. Est. 1954. Open 9-5. CL: Wed. pm. *STOCK: Furniture, mainly 17th-18th C; early oak, walnut and marquetry; clocks, copper, brass and miscellanea.* PARK: At rear. TEL: 01722 743350. VAT: Stan/Spec.

WORCESTERSHIRE

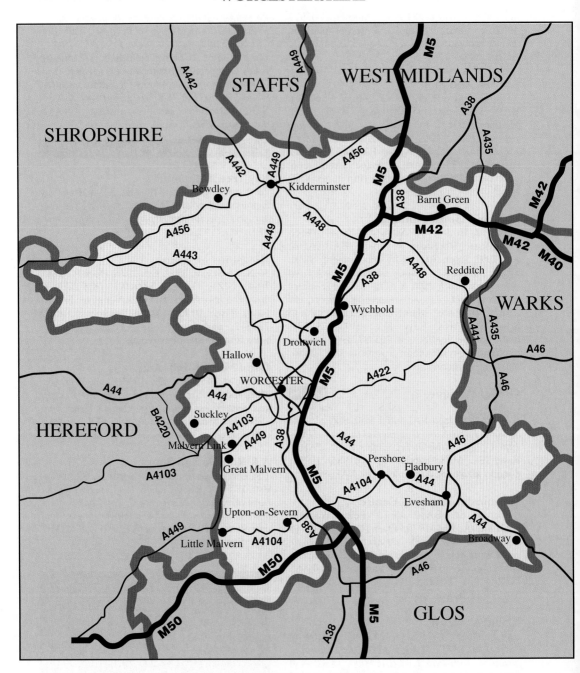

Dealers and Shops in Worcestershire

Barnt Green	1	Great Malvern	8	Redditch	1
Bewdley	2	Hallow	1	Suckley	1
Broadway	8	Kidderminster	2	Upton-upon-Severn	1
Droitwich	2	Little Malvern	2	Worcester	12
Evesham	2	Malvern Link	2	Wychbold	1
Fladbury	1	Pershore	4		

BARNT GREEN, Nr. Birmingham

Barnt Green Antiques
93 Hewell Rd. B45 8NL. (N. Slater). BAFRA. Est. 1965. Open 9-5.30. SIZE: Medium. *STOCK: Furniture, 17th-19th C, £100-£5,000.* PARK: Easy. TEL: 0121 445 4942. SER: Restorations (furniture, gilt frames, clocks and oils). VAT: Stan/Spec.

BEWDLEY

Bewdley Antiques
62A Load St. DY12 2AP. Est. 1999. Open 7 days. SIZE: Small. *STOCK: 25 cabinets displaying 19th-20th C collectables and decorative furniture.* LOC: A456 town centre. PARK: Easy. TEL: 01299 405636.

Gerard Guy Antiques
24 Kidderminster Rd. DY12 1AG. (C.G. and P.G. Mason). Est. 1990. Open 11-5, Sun. 12-4. SIZE: Medium. *STOCK: Victorian and stripped pine furniture, £250-£450.* LOC: Old A456, just outside town centre. PARK: Easy. TEL: 01299 400032; home - same. SER: Restorations (stripping, refinishing, repairs and upholstery).

BROADWAY

Broadway Dolls and Bears
76 High St. WR12 7AJ. (Janice Longhi). Open Tues.-Sat. 10-5. *STOCK: Antique and modern artist's dolls and teddy bears.* TEL: 01386 858323. SER: Teddy bear museum; restorations (bears and dolls).

Stephen Cook Antiques `LAPADA`
58 High St. WR12 7DP. Est. 1987. Open 10-5.30. SIZE: Large. *STOCK: 17th-18th C oak, walnut and mahogany, treen and paintings.* PARK: Easy. TEL: 01386 854716; fax - 01386 859360; mobile - 07973 814656; e-mail - stephen@scook antiques.com; website - www.scookantiques.com. SER: Valuations; restorations (cabinet and polishing furniture).

Fenwick and Fenwick Antiques
88-90 High St. WR12 7AJ. (George and Jane Fenwick). CADA. Est. 1980. Open 10-6 and by appointment. SIZE: Large. *STOCK: Furniture, oak, mahogany and walnut, 17th to early 19th C; samplers, boxes, treen, Tunbridgeware, Delft, decorative items and corkscrews.* PARK: Outside and own by arrangement. TEL: 01386 853227; after hours - 01386 841724; fax - 01386 858504. VAT: Spec.

Richard Hagen
Yew Tree House. WR12 7DT. Est. 1972. Open 9.30-5.30, Sun. by appointment. *STOCK: 20th C oils, watercolours and bronzes.* TEL: 01386 853624/858561; fax - 01386 852172; e-mail - fineart@richardhagen.com; website - www. richardhagen.com. VAT: Spec.

Haynes Fine Art of Broadway `BADA` `LAPADA`
Picton House Galleries, 42 High St. WR12 7DT. (A.C. Haynes). CADA. Open 9-6. SIZE: Large - 12 showrooms. *STOCK: Over 2000 British and European 16th-21st C oil paintings and watercolours.* LOC: From Lygon Arms, 100 yards up High St. on left. PARK: Easy. TEL: 01386 852649; fax - 01386 858187; e-mail - enquiries@haynes-fine-art.co.uk; website - www.haynesfineart.com. SER: Valuations; restorations; framing; catalogue available (£10). VAT: Spec.

Howards of Broadway
27a High St. WR12 7DP. (Robert Light). Est. 1989. Open 9.30-5.30. SIZE: Small. *STOCK: Jewellery, 1750 to modern; silver, 1700 to modern; both £20-£5,000; objects of vertu, 1700-1900, £50-£500.* PARK: Easy and nearby. TEL: 01386 858924; e-mail - robert.light@talk21.com. SER: Valuations; restorations. VAT: Stan/Spec.

H.W. Keil Ltd `BADA`
Tudor House. WR12 7DP. CADA. Est. 1925. Open 9.15-12.45 and 2.15-5.30. SIZE: Large. *STOCK: Walnut, oak, mahogany and rosewood furniture; early pewter, brass and copper, tapestry, glass and works of art, 17th-18th C.* LOC: By village clock. TEL: 01386 852408; fax - 01386 852069. VAT: Spec.

John Noott Galleries `BADA` `LAPADA`
28 High St., 14 Cotswold Court, and at The Lygon Arms, High St. WR12 7AA. (John, Pamela and Amanda Noott). CADA. Est. 1972. Open 9.30-1 and 2-5. SIZE: Large. *STOCK: Paintings, watercolours and bronzes, 19th C to Contemporary.* PARK: Easy. TEL: 01386 854868/858969; fax - 01386 854919. SER: Valuations; restorations; framing. VAT: Stan/Spec.

DROITWICH

Robert Belcher Antiques
128 Worcester Rd. WR9 8AN. (Robert & Wendy Belcher). Est. 1986. Open 9.30-5.30, Sun. by appointment. CL: Mon. SIZE: Large. *STOCK: Furniture, 18th-19th C, £500-£10,000; ceramics,*

*silver, glass, paintings and prints, 19th-20th C,
£50-£1,000*. PARK: Easy. TEL: 01905 772320.
SER: Valuations; restorations; picture framing.
FAIRS: NEC. VAT: Spec.

Grant Books
The Coach House, New Rd., Cutnall Green. WR9
0PQ. Est. 1971. Open 9-5 or by appointment. CL:
Sat. SIZE: Small. *STOCK: Books, prints,
pictures, clubs, golfiana, £5-£1,000*. LOC: A442
Droitwich to Kidderminster road. PARK: Easy.
TEL: 01299 851588; fax - 01299 851446; e-mail
- golf@grantbooks.co.uk; website - www.
golfbooks-memorabilia.com.

EVESHAM

Bookworms of Evesham
81 Port St. WR11 6AF. (T.J. Sims). PBFA. Est.
1999. Open 10-5, Mon. by appointment. SIZE:
Small. *STOCK: Books - Gloucestershire and
Worcestershire, 19th-20th C, £5-£1,200; John
Moore, 20th C, £5-£75; general books, 19th-20th
C, from 50p*. PARK: Behind premises. TEL:
01386 45509; fax - same. SER: Valuations;
restorations; buys at auction. FAIRS: PBFA -
Bath, Cheltenham, Cirencester; Churchdown.
VAT: Stan.

Magpie Jewellers and Antiques and
Magpie Arms & Armour
Manchester House 1 High St. WR11 4DA. (R.J.
and E.R. Bunn). Est. 1975. Open 9-5.30. SIZE:
Large. *STOCK: Silver, jewellery, furniture,
general antiques, arms and armour, books,
stamps and coins*. TEL: 01386 41631.

FLADBURY

The Hayloft Antique Centre
Craycombe Farm, Evesham Rd. WR10 2QS.
(Mrs. Susan Pryse-Jones). Est. 1994. Open 7 days
- summer 10.30-5, winter 10.30-4. SIZE: 10
dealers. *STOCK: Furniture - oak, mahogany, elm,
stripped pine; collectables, Victorian paintings
and prints, jet jewellery, reproduction pine, linen
and textiles, mirrors and books*. LOC: Just
outside village. PARK: Easy. TEL: 01386
861166; home - 01684 563926; fax - same;
mobile - 07715 283723; e-mail - sci@fsmail.net.
SER: Restorations (furniture stripping, French
polishing and repairs).

GREAT MALVERN

Carlton Antiques
43 Worcester Rd. WR14 4RB. (Dave Roberts).
Open 10-5. *STOCK: Edwardian postcards and
cigarette cards; Victorian and Edwardian
furniture, stripped pine; oil paintings,
watercolours and prints*. TEL: 01684 573092; e-
mail - dave@carlton-antiques.com; website -
www.carlton-antiques.com. SER: Valuations.

Foley Furniture
Foley Bank. WR14. (Dave Roberts). *STOCK:
Furniture - shipping, modern and old; postcards,
cigarette cards, books, pictures, sheet music and
general collectables*. LOC: Rear of 12A
Worcester Rd. TEL: 01684 891255; website -
www.carlton-antiques.com.

Great Malvern Antiques
Salisbury House, 6 Abbey Rd. WR14 3HG.
(Leonard Sutton and Robert J. Rice). Est. 1984.
Open by appointment. SIZE: Large. *STOCK:
Decorative furniture and objects, 1800-1940*.
LOC: Near theatres. PARK: Easy. TEL: 01684
575490; home - same; e-mail - gmantiques@
dial.pipex.com. SER: Valuations. FAIRS:
Decorative Antiques & Textile, Bath Decorative
Antiques. VAT: Stan/Spec. *Trade Only.*

Malvern Bookshop
7 Abbey Rd. WR14 3ES. (Howard and Julie
Hudson). Est. 1953. Open 10-5. SIZE: 5 rooms.
*STOCK: Antiquarian, secondhand books and
remainders*. LOC: By priory church steps. PARK:
Short stay on road above. TEL: 01684 575915;
e-mail - browse@malvern-bookshop.co.uk.

Malvern Studios
56 Cowleigh Rd. WR14 1QD. (L.M. Hall).
BAFRA. Open 9-5.15, Fri. and Sat. 9-4.45. CL:
Wed. *STOCK: Period, Edwardian painted and
inlaid furniture, general furnishings*. TEL: 01684
574913; fax - 01684 569475. SER: Restorations;
woodcarving; polishing; interior design. VAT:
Stan/Spec.

Miscellany Antiques
20 Cowleigh Rd. WR14 1QD. (Ray and Liz
Hunaban). Resident. Est. 1974. SIZE: Medium +
trade warehouse. *STOCK: Victorian, Edwardian
and Georgian furniture, including shipping
goods, £300-£20,000; some porcelain, silver,
bronzes and jewellery*. LOC: B4219 to Bromyard.
PARK: Own. TEL: 01684 566671; fax - 01684
560562; mobile - 07836 507954; e-mail -
liz.hunaban@virgin.net. SER: Valuations. VAT:
Stan/Spec.

Promenade Antiques
41 Worcester Rd. WR14 4RB. (Mark Selvester).
Open 10-5, Sun. 12-5. CL: Tues. *STOCK:
General antiques including Victorian and*

Edwardian furniture, bric-a-brac and books. TEL: 01684 566876.

Whitmore
Teynham Lodge, Chase Rd., Upper Colwall. WR13 6DT. (John and Stella Whitmore). BNTA. Est. 1965. *STOCK: British and foreign coins, 1700-1950; trade tokens, 1650-1900; commemorative medallions, 1600-1950; all £1-£500.* TEL: 01684 540651; 01684 541417; e-mail - teynhaml@aol.com. *Postal Only.*

HALLOW, Nr. Worcester

Antique Map and Print Gallery
April Cottage, Main Rd. WR2 6LS. (M. A. and G.P. Nichols). Open by appointment. *STOCK: Antiquarian maps, prints and books, Baxter and Le Blond prints.* LOC: Approx. 4 miles from Worcester on the Tenbury Wells Rd. PARK: Easy. TEL: 01905 641300; e-mail - antiquemap@aol.com; website - www.ampgworcester.com. SER: Greetings cards reproduced from original prints.

KIDDERMINSTER

The Antique Centre
5-8 Lion St. DY10 1PT. (Vivien Bentley). Est. 1980. Open 10-5. SIZE: Large. *STOCK: Furniture, early 18th C to 1930's, £10-£2,000; collectables, to 1930's, £1-£1,000; Victorian, Edwardian and reproduction fireplaces; jewellery and silver.* LOC: Off Bromsgrove St. PARK: Easy. TEL: 01562 740389; fax - same; mobile - 07980 300660. SER: Valuations; restorations (furniture); door stripping; repairs (jewellery); commissions.

B.B.M. Coins.
1st. Floor, 9 & 10 Lion St. DY10 1PT. (W.V. and A. Crook). Est. 1977. Open Wed., Thurs. and Fri. 10-2. SIZE: Medium. *STOCK: Coins, £5-£1,000; coin and stamp accessories.* LOC: Adjacent Youth Centre, off ring road. PARK: Easy. TEL: 01562 744118/515007; fax - 01562 829444. SER: Valuations. VAT: Stan/Spec/Global.

LITTLE MALVERN

St. James Antiques
De Lys Wells Rd. WR14 4JL. (H. Van Wyngaarden). Est. 1991. Open 10-5 or by appointment. *STOCK: Continental and English pine furniture, lighting and rugs.* PARK: Easy. TEL: 01684 563404. VAT: Stan.

MALVERN LINK

Kimber & Son
6 Lower Howsell Rd. WR14 1EF. (E.M. and M.E. Kimber). Est. 1956. Open 9-5.30, Sat. 9-1. *STOCK: 18th-20th C antiques for English, Continental and American markets.* TEL: 01684 574339; home - 01684 572000; mobile - 07814 960713. FAIRS: Newark. VAT: Stan/Spec.

Malvern Link Antiques Centre
154 Worcester Rd. WR14 1AA. (Trevor Guiver, Roger Hales, Paul Shaw, Kimber & Son). Open 10-5.30, Sun. 11-5. SIZE: Large. *STOCK: General furnishings and beds, 19th to early 20th C, £100-£2,000; collectables, china, £5-£100; fireplaces.* LOC: A449 entering Malvern Link. PARK: Easy. TEL: 01684 575750; home - 01684 575904/572491. SER: Restorations; French polishing; buys at auction. VAT: Stan/Spec.

Timeless Beds
Lower Quest Hills Rd. WR14 1RP. (S.D. Forrest). Est. 1992. Open 10-5, Sat. 10-4. SIZE: Small. *STOCK: Restored bedsteads, 1840's to 1910; hand-made mattresses, upholstered bases and bed linen.* PARK: Easy. TEL: 01684 561380; fax - same; mobile - 07932 007403; e-mail - info@timelessbeds.co.uk; website - www.timelessbeds.co.uk. SER: Valuations; restorations.

PERSHORE

The Drawing Room - Interiors & Antiques
9 Bridge St. WR10 1AJ. (Janet Davie). IDS. Est. 1980. Open 9.30-5, Sat. 9.30-1. CL: Thurs. SIZE: Medium. *STOCK: Decorative pieces including antique and reproduction furniture, lighting, mirrors, framed prints and engravings, £50-£20,000.* PARK: Easy (in main square or opposite). TEL: 01386 555747; fax - 01386 555071. SER: Valuations; interior design. VAT: Stan/Spec.

Hansen Chard Antiques
126 High St. WR10 1EA. (P.W. Ridler). BSc LBHI. Est. 1984. Open Tues., Wed., Fri. and Sat. 10-4 or by appointment. SIZE: Large. *STOCK: Clocks, barometers, models, tools, books, antique and secondhand, £5-£10,000.* LOC: On A44. PARK: Easy. TEL: 01386 553423; home - same. SER: Valuations; restorations (as stock); buys at auction (as stock). FAIRS: Brunel, Midlands, Haydock Park; Balderton Clock. VAT: Spec.

Lion Antiques
12 Bridge St. WR10 1AT. (Rachel D. Gowing). Est. 1995. Open Tues., Wed., Fri. and Sat. 9.30-4.30. SIZE: Medium. *STOCK: Mirrors, 19th to early 20th C, French and English overmantels; French, Italian and English chandeliers, mainly early 20th C; table lamps, furniture including pine and upholstered, from 18th C to late Victorian; torchieres, marble stands, busts.* PARK: Broad St. TEL: 01386 555688; mobile - 07816 834481; e-mail - armma@talk21.com. SER: Restorations (cane and rush work, frames, paint stripping); lampshades made.

S.W. Antiques
Abbey Showrooms, Newlands. WR10 1BP. (A.M. Whiteside). Est. 1978. Open 9-5. SIZE: Large. *STOCK: 19th-20th C furniture including beds and bedroom furniture, to £4,000.* Not Stocked: Jewellery, small items. LOC: 2 mins. from Abbey. PARK: Own. TEL: 01386 555580; fax - 01386 556205; website - www.sw-antiques.co.uk. VAT: Stan/Spec.

REDDITCH

Angel Antiques
211 Mount Pleasant, Southcrest. B97 4JG. (Carol Manners). Est. 1982. Open 10-3.30, Wed. 10-1.30, Sat. 9.30-5. SIZE: Small. *STOCK: Georgian, Victorian and Edwardian furniture and collectables, £5-£1,000.* PARK: Easy. TEL: 01527 545844; mobile - 07855 162542. SER: Valuations; restorations.

Lower House Fine Antiques
Lower House, Far Moor Lane, Winyates Green. B98 0QX. (Mrs J.B. Hudson). Est. 1987. Usually open but prior telephone call advisable. SIZE: Small. *STOCK: Furniture, 17th to early 20th C, £100-£4,000; silver and plate, 18th to early 20th C, £10-£1,000; oil lamps, 19th C, £50-£500.* Not Stocked: Pine furniture. LOC: 3 miles due east

Redditch town centre and half a mile from Coventry Highway island, close to A435. PARK: Own. TEL: 01527 525117; home - same; e-mail - LWSE.antiques@Tesco.net. SER: Valuations; restorations (including porcelain).

SUCKLEY

Holloways
Lower Court. WR6 5DE. (Edward and Diana Holloway). Open 9-5, Sun. in summer. SIZE: Large. *STOCK: Garden ornaments and furniture, £20-£5,000.* LOC: A44 from Worcester towards Leominster, left at Knightwick, 3 miles, situated in front of village church. PARK: Easy. TEL: 01886 884665; website - www.holloways.co.uk. SER: Valuations; restorations; buys at auction. VAT: Stan/Spec.

UPTON-UPON-SEVERN

The Highway Gallery
40 Old St. WR8 0HW. (J. Daniell). Est. 1969. Open 10.30-5 but appointment advisable. CL: Thurs. and Mon. SIZE: Small. *STOCK: Oils, watercolours, 19th-20th C, £100-£10,000.* LOC: 100yds. from crossroads towards Malvern. PARK: Easy. TEL: 01684 592645; home - 01684 592909; fax - 01684 592909; e-mail - mr.daniell@ukonline.co.uk. SER: Valuations; restorations; relining; cleaning; buys at auction (pictures).

WORCESTER

Antique Warehouse
Rear of 74 Droitwich Rd, Barbourne. WR3 8BW. (D. Venn). Open 9-5, Sat. 10-4.30. *STOCK: General antiques, shipping, restored pine and satin walnut, Victorian doors and fireplaces.* PARK: Easy. TEL: 01905 27493. SER: Stripping (wood and metalwork).

Antiques and Curios
50 Upper Tything. WR1 1JZ. (Brian W. Inett). Est. 1981. Open 9.30-5.30. SIZE: Large - 6 dealers on three floors. *STOCK: 18th to early 20th C furniture, oak, mahogany, walnut, especially Victorian and Edwardian desks, dining and bedroom, decorative and upholstered, furnishings, mirrors, pictures, clocks, curios, treen, objets d'art.* LOC: From Birmingham A38 into Worcester on right-hand side. PARK: Easy. TEL: 01905 25412/764547. SER: Restorations; re-polishing; upholstery; valuations.

The Barber's Clock
37 Droitwich Rd. WR3 7LG. (Graham Gopsill). Est. 1990. Open 9-5, Mon. 10-5, Sun. 1-4. SIZE: Medium. *STOCK: Clocks, 19th C to Art Deco, £35-£1,000; gramophones and phonographs, 20th C, £250-£475+.* PARK: Own. TEL: 01905 29022; home - 01905 779011; e-mail - graham@ barbersclock37.fsnet.com. SER: Valuations; restorations (clocks and gramophones).

Bygones by the Cathedral   `LAPADA`
Cathedral Sq. WR1. (Gabrielle Doherty Bullock). FGA. DGA. Est. 1946. Open 9.30-5.30, Sat. 9.30-1 and 2-5.30. SIZE: Medium. *STOCK: Furniture, 17th-19th C; silver, Sheffield plate, jewellery, paintings, glass; English and Continental pottery and porcelain especially Royal Worcester.* LOC: Adjacent main entrance to cathedral. TEL: 01905 25388. VAT: Spec.

Bygones of Worcester   `LAPADA`
55 Sidbury. WR1 2HU. (Gabrielle Bullock). FGA. Est. 1946. Open 9.30-1 and 2-5.30. *STOCK: 17th-20th C walnut, oak, mahogany and exotic wood furniture, brass and copper, oil paintings, porcelain, pottery and glass and decorative objects.* LOC: Opposite car park near approach to cathedral. PARK: Opposite. TEL: 01905 23132. VAT: Stan/Spec.

Gray's Antiques
29 The Tything. WR1 1JL. (David Gray). Open 8.30-5.30. *STOCK: General antiques, soft furnishings, chandeliers.* TEL: 01905 724456; fax - 01905 723433; e-mail - enqs@grays-interiors.com.

Gray's Interiors
35 The Tything. WR1 1JL. Open 8.30-5.30. *STOCK: Chandeliers, chairs, sofas, soft furnishings.* PARK: Limited. TEL: 01905 21209; e-mail - enqs@grays-interiors.com.

Heirlooms
46 Upper Tything. WR1 1JZ. (D. Tarran and L.

Rumford). Open 9.30-4.30. *STOCK: General antiques, objets d'art, Royal Worcester porcelain and prints.* TEL: 01905 23332.

Sarah Hodge
Peachley Manor, Hallow Lane, Lower Broadheath. WR2 6QL. Resident. Est. 1985. Open daily including Sun. SIZE: Large. *STOCK: General antiques, country bygones, pine and kitchenalia.* LOC: Off B4204, 3 miles N.W. Worcester. PARK: Easy. TEL: 01905 640255.

Juro Antiques
Bromyard Rd., Whitbourne. WR6 5SF. (Roy Hughes and Judy George). Open 9-1 and 2-5. *STOCK: Cider mills, stone troughs, staddle stones, fountains, statuary, vintage farm machinery, bronzes, mill wheels and unusual items.* LOC: A44. PARK: Easy. TEL: 01886 821261; fax - same; e-mail - info@juro.co.uk; website - www.juro.co.uk. FAIRS: Spring and Autumn Garden, Malvern; Royal Show, Stoneleigh.

M. Lees and Sons   `LAPADA`
Tower House, Severn St. WR1 2NB. Resident. Est. 1955. Open 9.15-5.15, Sat. by appointment. CL: Thurs. pm. SIZE: Medium. *STOCK: Furniture, 1780-1880; porcelain, 1750-1920; mirrors, Oriental and decorative.* LOC: At southern end of Worcester cathedral adjacent to Edgar Tower; near Royal Worcester Porcelain Museum and factory. PARK: Easy. TEL: 01905 26620; mobile - 07860 826218. VAT: Stan/Spec.

Worcester Antiques Centre
15 Reindeer Court, Mealcheapen St. WR1 4DF. (Stephen Zacaroli). Est. 1992. Open 10-5. *STOCK: Pottery and porcelain, 1750-1950, £10-£4,000; silver, 1750-1940, £10-£5,000; jewellery, 1800-1940, £5-£5,000; furniture, 1650-1930, £50-£10,000.* PARK: Loading only or 50 yards. TEL: 01905 610680/1; e-mail - worcesantiques@ aol.com. SER: Valuations; restorations (furniture, ceramics and metalware). FAIRS: NEC (April., Aug. and Nov); East Berkshire (May and Oct).

WYCHBOLD

D & J Lines Antiques
Papermill Lane. WR9 0DE. (Derek and Jill Lines). Open by appointment. SIZE: Medium. *STOCK: Oak and country furniture, 17th-18th C, £500-£8,000; metalware, 18th-19th C, £50-£500; Persian carpets, 19th-20th C, £50-£1,000; pearls, diamond set jewellery.* TEL: 01527 861282. SER: Valuations; restorations; desk re-leathering.

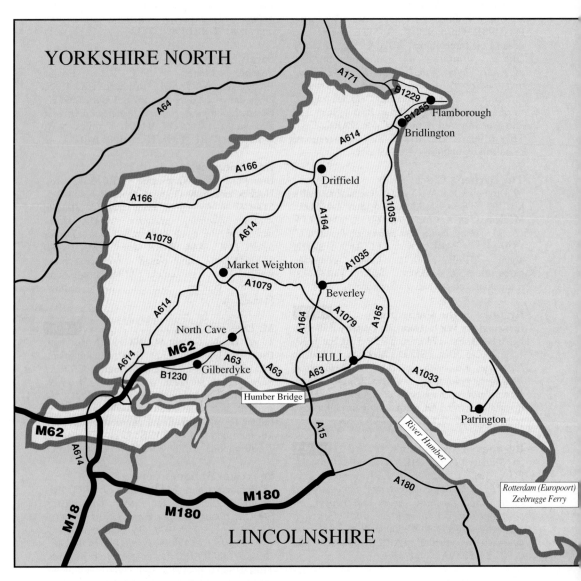

Dealers and Shops in Yorkshire East

Beverley	7	Flamborough	1	Market Weighton	3
Bridlington	4	Gilberdyke	1	North Cave	1
Driffield	3	Hull	7	Patrington	1

BEVERLEY

Karen Guest Antiques
24 Saturday Market Place. HU17. NAG registered Valuer and Jeweller. HRD Dip. of Diamond Grading. Open 9.15-5. SIZE: Medium. *STOCK: Jewellery and silver, 18th-20th C, £50-£20,000.* PARK: Easy. TEL: 01482 882334; fax - same. SER: Valuations; restorations. VAT: Stan/Spec.

David Hakeney Antiques
P O Box 171. HU17 8GX. Est. 1970. Open by appointment. *STOCK: Porcelain, silver, clocks and watches, 19th C and Edwardian furniture, decorative items.* TEL: 01482 677006; mobile - 07860 507774. FAIRS: NEC (April, Aug. and Dec); Newark; Harrogate.

Hawley Antiques
LAPADA
5 North Bar Within. HU17 8AP. Est. 1966. Open 10-4, Sat. 9.30-5. SIZE: Medium. *STOCK: General antiques, furniture, pottery, porcelain, glass, oil paintings, watercolours, silver.* LOC: Town centre. TEL: 01482 868193; mobile - 07850 225805; e-mail - john@hawleys.info; website - www.hawleys.info. SER: Restorations (fine furniture); valuations; buys at auction. FAIRS: Newark. VAT: Stan/Spec.

St Crispin Antique Centre
11 Butcher Row. HU17 0AA. (Chris Fowler and Jill Northgraves). Est. 1971.Open 10-5, Sun. 10.30-4. SIZE: 70+ dealers. *STOCK: Ceramics, glass and furniture.* TEL: 01482 869583. SER: Valuations.

James H. Starkey Galleries
49 Highgate. HU17 0DN. Est. 1968. Open 9.30-4.30, Sat. by appointment. SIZE: Medium. *STOCK: Oil paintings, 16th-19th C; drawings and watercolours, 17th-19th C.* LOC: Opposite Minster. PARK: Easy. TEL: 01482 881179; fax - 01482 861644. SER: Valuations; restorations (paintings); buys at auction. VAT: Stan/Spec.

Time and Motion
1 Beckside. HU17 0PB. (Peter A. Lancaster). FBHI. Est. 1977. Open 10-5. CL: Thurs. SIZE: Medium. *STOCK: English longcase clocks, 18th-19th C, £1,500-£8,000; English, German and French mantel and wall clocks, 19th C, £300-£3,500; aneroid and mercurial barometers, 18th-19th C, £150-£3,000.* LOC: 1 mile from town centre and Minster, 300 yards from Army Museum of Transport. PARK: Easy. TEL: 01482 881574; home - same. SER: Valuations; restorations (clocks and barometers). VAT: Stan/Spec.

Vicar Lane Antique Centre
The Old Granary, Vicar Lane, North Bar Within. HU17 8DF. (Chris Fowler and Jill Northgraves). Est. 2002. Open 10-5, Sun. 10.30-5. SIZE: Large, 20+ dealers. *STOCK: Date-lined (1910) furniture and small items.* TEL: 01482 888088. SER: Valuations.

BRIDLINGTON

C.J. and A.J. Dixon Ltd
1st Floor, 23 Prospect St. YO15 2AE. Est. 1969. Open 9.30-5. SIZE: Large. *STOCK: British war medals and decorations.* LOC: Town centre. PARK: Easy. TEL: 01262 676877/603348; fax - 01262 606600; e-mail - chris@dixonsmedals.co.uk; website - www.dixonsmedals.com. SER: Valuations; renovations. VAT: Stan/Spec.

The Georgian Rooms
56 High St., Old Town. YO16 4QA. (David Rothwell and Diane Davison). Est. 1999. Open 10-5. SIZE: 10 showrooms. *STOCK: Wide range of general antiques and collectables, Georgian to modern, £1-£13,000.* PARK: Free nearby. TEL: 01262 608600. SER: Restorations.

Priory Antiques
47-49 High St. YO16 4PR. (P.R. Rogerson). Est. 1979. Open Tues. and Fri. 10-5, Sat. 10-12. SIZE: Large. *STOCK: Georgian and Victorian furniture.* TEL: 01262 601365.

Sedman Antiques
106 Cardigan Rd. YO15 3LR. (R.H.S. and M.A. Sedman). Est. 1971. Open 10-5.30, Sun. by appointment. *STOCK: General antiques, period and shipping furniture, Oriental porcelain, Victorian collectors' items.* TEL: 01262 675671.

The Antique Pine & Country Furniture Shop

58A Middle St. North. YO25 6SU. (D. A. Smith). Est. 1977. Open 9.30-5.30, Sat. 9.30-5, Sun. by appointment. SIZE: Medium + warehouse. *STOCK: Furniture including pine and country, 18th to early 20th C, £50-£2,000; furniture designed and made to order, from £50+.* LOC: Main street. PARK: Easy. TEL: 01377 256321; home - same; e-mail - dave@pine-on-line.com; website - www.pine-on-line.com. SER: Restorations.

The Crested China Co

Highfield, Windmill Hill. YO25 5EF. (D. Taylor). Est. 1978. Open by appointment. *STOCK: Goss and crested china.* PARK: Easy. TEL: 01377 257042 (24 hr.); e-mail - dt@thecrestedchinacompany.com; website - www.thecrestedchinacompany.com. SER: Sales catalogues. FAIRS: Goss.

Karen Guest Antiques

80A Middle St. South. YO25 7QE. NAG. HRD Diploma of Diamond Grading. Est. 1989. Open 9.30-5. SIZE: Small. *STOCK: Jewellery and silver, 18th-20th C, £50-£5,000.* TEL: 01377 241467; website - www.michaelphilips.com. SER: Valuations; restorations. VAT: Stan/Spec.

Lesley Berry Antiques

The Manor House. YO15 1PD. (Mrs L Berry). Resident. Est. 1972. Open 9.30-5.30, other times by appointment. SIZE: Small. *STOCK: Furniture, silver, jewellery, amber, Whitby jet, oils, watercolours, prints, copper, brass, textiles, fountain pens, secondhand and antiquarian books on-line.* Not Stocked: Shipping goods. LOC: On corner of Tower St. and Lighthouse Rd. PARK: Easy. TEL: 01262 850943; e-mail - lb@flamboroughmanor.co.uk; website - www. flamboroughmanor.co.uk. SER: Buys at auction.

Lewis E. Hickson FBHI

Antiquarian Horologist, Sober Hill Farm. HU15 2TB. Est. 1965. Open by appointment. SIZE: Small. *STOCK: Longcase, bracket clocks, barometers and instruments.* TEL: 01430 449113. SER: Restorations; repairs.

Grannie's Parlour

33 Anlaby Rd. HU1 2PG. (A. and Mrs. N. Pye). Est. 1974. Open 11-5. CL: Thurs. *STOCK: General antiques, ephemera, Victoriana, dolls, toys, kitchenalia.* LOC: Near rail and bus station. PARK: Nearby. TEL: 01482 228258; home - 01482 341020.

Grannie's Treasures

1st Floor, 33 Anlaby Rd. HU1 2PG. (Mrs N. Pye). Est. 1974. Open 11-5. CL:Thurs. *STOCK: Advertising items, dolls prams, toys, small furniture, china and pre-1940s clothing.* LOC: Near rail and bus station. PARK: Nearby. TEL: 01482 228258; home - 01482 341020.

Hull Antique Centre

Anderson Wharf, Wincolmlee. HU2 8AH. (Melvin Anderson). Est. 1975. Open 9-5, Sat. and Sun. 10-4. SIZE: Large. *STOCK: Furniture, period, Victorian and Edwardian, 17th to early 20th C, £50-£3,000.* LOC: From M64 take Clive Sullivan Way. PARK: Easy. TEL: 01482 609958. SER: Valuations. FAIRS: Newark, Swinderby, York, Ardingly, Harrogate, Birmingham. VAT: Stan/Spec.

Imperial Antiques

397 Hessle Rd. HU3 4EH. (M. Langton). Est. 1982. Open 9-5.30. *STOCK: British stripped pine furniture, antique, old and reproduction.* PARK: Easy. TEL: 01482 327439. FAIRS: Newark, Ardingly. VAT: Stan.

Kevin Marshall's Antiques Warehouse

17-20A Wilton St., Holderness Rd. HU8 7LG. Est. 1981. Open 10-5 including Sun. SIZE: Large. *STOCK: Bathroom ware, architectural items, fires, lighting, furniture and reproductions, 19th C, £5-£5,000.* LOC: 1st right off Dansom Lane South. PARK: Easy. TEL: 01482 326559; fax - same; e-mail - kevinmarshall@antiquewarehouse.karoo. co.uk. SER: Valuations; restorations; boardroom tables made to order. VAT: Stan/Spec.

Pine-Apple Antiques

321-327 Beverley Rd. HU5 1LD. (Diane C. Todd). Est. 1981. Open 9-5.30, Sun. 11-4. SIZE: Large. *STOCK: Pine furniture, bathrooms, kitchens, curios, gifts and jewellery, mirrors, pictures and clocks, archtectural items, fireplaces, lighting including reproduction.* PARK: Easy. TEL: 01482 441384; fax - 01482 441073; mobile - 07860 874480; e-mail - diane@pine-apple.co.uk; website - www.pine-apple.co.uk.

Sandringham Antiques

64a Beverley Rd. HU5 1NE. (P. Allison). Est. 1968. *STOCK: General antiques.* TEL: 01482 847653/320874.

MARKET WEIGHTON, Nr. York

Garforth Gallery
57 Market Place. YO43 3AJ. Est. 1956. Open 10.30-4. CL: Thurs. SIZE: Small. *STOCK: Paintings, prints, maps, clocks, jewellery, silver, some porcelain, £20-£600.* LOC: Main road in town centre. TEL: 01430 803173. SER: Valuations; restorations.

Houghton Hall Antiques
Cliffe/North Cave Rd. YO43 3RE. (M.E. Watson). Est. 1965. Open daily 8-4, Sun. 11-4. SIZE: Large. *STOCK: Furniture, 17th-19th C, £5-£8,000; china, 19th C, £1-£600; paintings and prints, £20-£1,000; objets d'art.* Not Stocked: Coins, guns. LOC: Turn right on new by-pass from York (left coming from Beverley), 3/4 mile, signposted North Cave - sign on entrance. PARK: Easy. TEL: 01430 873234. SER: Valuations; restorations (furniture); buys at auction. FAIRS: New York. VAT: Stan/Spec.

Mount Pleasant Antiques Centre
46 Cliffe Rd. YO43 3BP. (Linda and John Sirrs). Est. 1974. Open 9.30-5 including Sun. SIZE: Large. *STOCK: Victorian furniture including large dining tables, bureaux, display cabinets, £200-£4,500; clocks, £60-£1,800; side and tilt top tables, silver, pottery and porcelain, jewellery, copper and books.* LOC: A1079 Market Weighton by-pass. PARK: Easy. TEL: 01430 872872; home - same. SER: Restorations (furniture); cabinet making.

NORTH CAVE

Penny Farthing Antiques
Albion House, 18 Westgate. (C.E. Dennett). Est. 1987. Open by appointment only. SIZE: Medium. *STOCK: 19th-20th C furniture, Victorian brass and iron bedsteads, £25-£2,000; linen, textiles and samplers, 18th-20th C, £5-£500; general collectables, china and glass, 19th-20th C, £5-£500.* LOC: Main road (B1230). PARK: Easy. TEL: 01430 422958; mobile - 07980 624583. SER: Valuations; buys at auction. FAIRS: Newark.

PATRINGTON

Clyde Antiques
12 Market Place. HU12 0RB. (S. M. Nettleton). Est. 1978. Open 10-5. CL: Sun., Mon. and Wed. except by appointment. SIZE: Medium. *STOCK: General antiques.* PARK: Easy. TEL: 01964 630650; home - 01964 612471. SER: Valuations. VAT: Stan.

Somewhat unusual is this watch by Nicole, Nielsen & Co that bears their own name, made even more unusual by the survival of the original leather-covered box containing spare glass and mainspring. Gold openface case hallmarked 1887, casemaker EN (Emil Nielsen). 49mm diameter. Post 1884, three-quarter plate lever movement. Watch worth between £400 and £800 depending on condition. Add at least £350 for an original box.

From an article entitled "Nicole, Nielsen & Co - the Makers' Makers" by David Penney which appeared in the April 2002 issue of ***Antique Collecting***. For more details and to subscribe see page 21.

YORKSHIRE NORTH

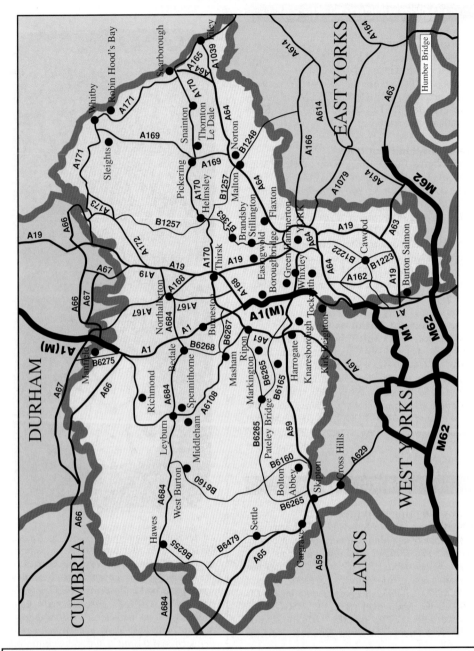

BEDALE

Bennett's Antiques & Collectables

7 Market Place. DL8 1ED. (Paul and Kim Bennett). Est. 1996. Open 9-5, Sun. by appointment. SIZE: Large. *STOCK: Furniture, 18th to early 20th C, £200-£15,000; fine art, 19th to early 20th C, £100-£6,000; clocks, 19th to early 20th C, £200-£4,000; collectables, 19th-20th C, £50-£2,000; local works of art, 20th C, £100-£1,000.* LOC: Off A1. PARK: Easy and free. TEL: 01677 427900; fax - 01677 426858; mobile - 07711 054219; e-mail - info@bennetts. uk.com; website - www.bennetts.uk.com. SER: Restorations; clock repairs; exhibitions of Yorkshire artists; worldwide shipping; weekly deliveries (London and the South). VAT: Spec.

BOLTON ABBEY, Nr. Skipton

Grove Rare Books

The Old Post Office. BD23 6EX. (Andrew and Janet Sharpe). ABA. PBFA. Est. 1984. Open Tues.-Sat. 10-5. SIZE: Medium. *STOCK: Antiquarian books and maps; topographical and sporting prints.* LOC: 1 mile from A59. PARK: At rear. TEL: 01756 710717; fax - 01756 711098; e-mail - antiquarian@groverarebooks.co.uk; website - www.groverarebooks.co.uk. SER: Valuations; restorations; buys at auction (as stock).

BOROUGHBRIDGE

St. James House Antiques

St. James Sq. YO51 9AR. (J.D. Wilson). Est. 1989. Open 9-5.30, prior telephone call advisable. SIZE: Small. *STOCK: Period and later furniture, brass, copper and china.* LOC: Town centre. PARK: Own. TEL: 01423 322508; home - same; fax - 01423 326690; mobile - 07720 544926. SER: Valuations; restorations; upholstery.

R.S. Wilson and Sons

PO Box 41. YO51 9WY. Est. 1917. Open by appointment only. SIZE: Small. *STOCK: 17th-19th C furniture and accessories.* TEL: 01423 322417; fax - same; mobile - 07711 794801.

BRANDSBY

L.L. Ward and Son

Bar House. YO61 4RQ. (R.Ward). Est. 1970. Open 8.30-5. *STOCK: Antique pine.* PARK: Easy. TEL: 01347 888651

BURNESTON, Nr. Bedale

W. Greenwood (Fine Art)

Oak Dene, Church Wynd. DL8 2JE. Est. 1978. Open by appointment. SIZE: Small. *STOCK: Paintings and watercolours, 19th-20th C, £100-£5,000; frames, £20-£500; mirrors.* LOC: Take B6285 left off A1 northbound, house 1/4 mile on right. PARK: Easy. TEL: 01677 424830; home - 01677 423217; mobile - 07885 175279. SER: Valuations; restorations (paintings and frames); framing.

BURTON SALMON

Old Hall Antiques

Hall Farm, Main St. LS25 5JS. (J.T. and S.G. Fenteman). Resident. Open Tues.-Sun. 10-5, Mon. by appointment, SIZE: Large. *STOCK: Early oak, from 1600; country furniture in oak, elm, yew and fruitwoods; pewter, brass, and copper; period metalware; works of art.* LOC: 3 miles from junction 33 M62(A1) just off A162. PARK: Easy. TEL: 01977 607778; home - 01977 672052; fax - 01977 678261. SER: Buys at auction (early oak). VAT: Spec.

CAWOOD, Nr. Selby

Cawood Antiques

Sherburn St. YO8 3SS. (J.E. Gilham). Est. 1986. Open 9-4. *STOCK: Weapons, medals, golfing memorabilia and collectors' items.* PARK: Easy. TEL: 01757 268533; e-mail - john@gilham40. freeserve.co.uk.

CROSS HILLS, Nr. Keighley

Heathcote Antiques

Skipton Rd. Junction. BD20 7DS. (M. Webster). Resident. Est. 1979. Open 10-5.30, Sun. 12.30-4.30. CL: Mon. and Tues. SIZE: Very large showroom + trade warehouse. *STOCK: Furniture, clocks, barometers, unstripped English pine, pottery, porcelain, brass and metal wares.* PARK: Own. TEL: 01535 635250; fax - 01535 637205; mobile - 07836 259640.

EASINGWOLD

Milestone Antiques

Farnley House, 101 Long St. YO61 3HY. (A.B. and S.J. Streetley). Est. 1982. Open daily, Sun. by appointment. SIZE: Medium. *STOCK: Mahogany and oak furniture especially dining tables, upholstered armchairs and sofas; longcase and wall clocks; all 18th to early 20th C.* LOC: Old A19, village centre. PARK: Easy.

TEL: 01347 821608; home - same; e-mail - milestoneantiques-easingwold@fsmail.net. SER: Valuations. VAT: Stan/Spec.

Old Flames
30 Long St. YO61 3HT. (P. Lynas and J.J. Thompson). Est. 1988. Open 10-5. SIZE: Medium. *STOCK: Fireplaces, 18th-19th C, £100-£4,000; lighting, 19th C, £100-£5,000; architectural items, 18th-19th C, £50-£2,000.* PARK: Easy. TEL: 01347 821188; website - www.oldflames.co.uk. SER: Valuations. FAIRS: Newark. VAT: Stan/Spec.

Mrs B.A.S. Reynolds
42 Long St. YO61 3HT. *STOCK: General antiques, Victorian.* TEL: 01347 821078.

Vale Antiques
Mooracres, North Moor. YO61 3NB. (J.M., C.M. and D.N. Leach). Est. 1986. Open 9-5. SIZE: Small. *STOCK: Furniture, 18th-20th C, £20-£1,500; china, brass and copper, £5-£100; prints and paintings, £15-£100.* LOC: Outskirts, just off Thirsk Rd. PARK: Easy. TEL: 01347 821298; home/fax - same; e-mail - valeantiques@moor acres.co.uk; website - www.mooracres.co.uk. SER: Restorations (furniture repair and re-polishing).

The White House Antiques & Architectural Reclamation
Thirsk Rd. YO61 3NF. (G. Hood). Resident. Est. 1960. Usually open but prior telephone call advisable. *STOCK: Rural and domestic bygones, stone troughs, architectural reclamation and garden ornaments.* LOC: 1 mile north of Easingwold, 200 yards from northern junction of bypass (A19). PARK: Easy. TEL: 01347 821479; e-mail - info@grahamhood.co.uk.

FILEY

Cairncross and Sons
31 Bellevue St. YO14 9HU. (G. Cairncross). Open 9.30-12.45 and 2-4.30. CL: Wed. pm. *STOCK: Medals, uniforms, insignia, cap badges, general militaria.* Not Stocked: Weapons. TEL: 01723 513287; e-mail - george@cairnxson. freeserve.co.uk; website - www.cairnxson. freeserve.co.uk.

FLAXTON, Nr. York

Elm Tree Antiques
YO60 7RJ. (R. and J. Jackson). Est. 1975. Open 9-5, (winter - 4.30) Sun. 10-5 (winter - Sat. and Sun. 10-4). SIZE: Large. *STOCK: Furniture, 17th C to Edwardian; small items, £5-£5,000, Staffordshire figures.* LOC: 1 mile off A64. PARK: Easy. TEL: 01904 468462; home - same; website - www.elmtreeantiques.co.uk. SER: Valuations; restorations (cabinet making, polishing and upholstery). FAIRS: Newark.

Flaxton Antique Gardens
Glebe Farm. YO60 7RU. (Tim and Heather Richardson). SALVO. Est. 1992. Open summer 10-4 including Sun. Winter by appointment. CL: Tues. SIZE: Large. *STOCK: Stone troughs, staddle stones, sundials, bird baths, urns, pedestals; statues - lead, stone, reconstituted stone; chimney pots, agricultural implements, cartwheels, Victorian edging tiles, old terracotta oil jars from Morocco, Portugal and Greece.* PARK: Easy. TEL: 01904 468468; fax - same; e-mail - flaxtonantgdns@aol.com; website - www.salvo.co.uk/dealers/flaxton. SER: Valuations. FAIRS: Harrogate Flower Show.

GARGRAVE, Nr. Skipton

Antiques at Forge Cottage
22A High St. BD23 3RB. Est. 1979. Open Wed.-Sat. 10-5. *STOCK: Pottery and porcelain.* LOC: A65. PARK: Easy. TEL: 01756 748272; mobile - 07860 525579; e-mail - philina@carrol.fsnet.co. uk. SER: Restorations; valuations. FAIRS: NEC; GMEX; Newark. VAT: Spec.

Bernard Dickinson
Estate Yard, West St. BD23 3PH . (H.H. and A.E. Mardall). Resident. Est. 1958. Open 9-5.30 or by appointment. *STOCK: Early English furniture.* LOC: Just off A65 Skipton-Settle road. PARK: Easy. TEL: 01756 748257. VAT: Spec.

Gargrave Gallery
48 High St. BD23 3RB. (B. Herrington). Est. 1975. Appointment advisable. *STOCK: General antiques, oak, mahogany, metal, paintings, 18th to early 20th C.* LOC: A65. PARK: Easy. TEL: 01756 749641.

R.N. Myers and Son `BADA`
Endsleigh House, High St. BD23 3LX. (Jean M. and Simon M. Myers). Est. 1890. Open 9-5.30 or by appointment except Sun. SIZE: Medium. *STOCK: Furniture, oak, mahogany, 17th to early 19th C; pottery, porcelain and metalware.* Not Stocked: Victoriana, weapons, coins, jewellery. LOC: A65. Skipton-Settle road. PARK: Behind shop and opposite. TEL: 01756 749587. SER: Valuations. VAT: Spec.

GREEN HAMMERTON, Nr. York

The Main Pine Co
Grangewood, The Green. YO26 8BQ. (C. and K.M.Main). Est. 1976. Open 9-5. SIZE: Large. *STOCK: Pine furniture, 18th-19th C, £100-£1,500; reproductions from reclaimed pine.* LOC: Just off A59. PARK: Easy. TEL: 01423 330451; home - 01423 331078; fax - 01423 331278; e-mail - sales@mainpinecompany.com; website - www.mainpinecompany.com. SER: Export; containers packed. VAT: Stan.

HARROGATE

Nigel Adamson
Flat 1, 19 Park View. HG1 5LY . (N.J.G. Adamson). Est. 1863. Open by appointment. *STOCK: Furniture, 17th to early 19th C; porcelain, Chinese, English and Continental .* TEL: 01423 528924; mobile - 07957 686493. SER: Valuations; restorations (furniture and porcelain). VAT: Spec.

Armstrong   BADA LAPADA
10-11 Montpellier Parade. HG1 2TJ. (M.A. Armstrong). Est. 1983. Open 10-5.30. SIZE: Medium. *STOCK: Fine English furniture, 18th to early 19th C; glasses and works of art, 18th C.* PARK: Easy. TEL: 01423 506843. FAIRS: Olympia (June, Nov). VAT: Spec.

Bryan Bowden
Oakleigh, 1 Spacey View, Leeds Rd., Pannal. HG3 1LQ. (Bryan and Elizabeth Bowden). Est. 1969. Open by appointment. SIZE: Small. *STOCK: English pottery and porcelain, 1750-1850; small Georgian furniture.* LOC: 2.5 miles south of Harrogate on Leeds road. PARK: Easy. TEL: 01423 870007; home - same. SER:

Valuations; restorations (pottery and porcelain); buys at auction (English pottery and porcelain). FAIRS: Northern; Buxton. VAT: Spec.

Country Oak Antiques
Yorkshire Country Wines, The Mill, Glasshouses. HG3 5QH. (Richard Brown). Est. 1980. Open Wed.-Sun. 11.30-4.30, (reduced hours Jan. and Feb) - most times by appointment. SIZE: Medium. *STOCK: Oak and country furniture, 17th-19th C, £50-£5,000.* LOC: 1/4 mile from crossroads of B6165. PARK: Easy. TEL: 01423 711947; fax - same; home - 01423 711223; e-mail - riversidecellars@aol.com; website - www.countryoakantiques.co.uk.

Derbyshire Antiques Ltd
27 Montpellier Parade. HG1 2TG. (R.C. Derbyshire). Est. 1960. Open 10-5.30. SIZE: Medium. *STOCK: Early oak and walnut, 16th-18th C; Georgian furniture to 1820; decorative items.* TEL: 01423 503115/564242; fax - 01423 709762.; website - www.thepewtershop.co.uk. VAT: Spec.

Dragon Antiques
10 Dragon Rd. HG1 5DF. (P.F. Broadbelt). Resident. Est. 1954. Open 11-6. Always available. SIZE: Small. *STOCK: Victorian art glass, art pottery, British and foreign postcards.* LOC: 5 mins. from town centre, opposite Dragon Rd. car park. PARK: Easy. TEL: 01423 562037.

Garth Antiques   LAPADA
16 Montpellier Parade. HG1 2TG. (J. and I. Chapman). Est. 1978. Open 10-5.30. SIZE: Large. *STOCK: Furniture, 18th-19th C, £500-£7,000; oils and watercolours, £200-£5,000.* PARK: Easy and nearby. TEL: 01423 530573. SER: Restorations; upholstery. VAT: Stan/Spec.

THE GINNEL
ANTIQUES CENTRE
HARROGATE

THE RED HOUSE
ANTIQUES CENTRE
YORK

50 specialist dealers with datelines stock in each centre
(see listings under Harrogate and York)

The Ginnel
Off Parliament St. (Opp. Debenhams)
HARROGATE 01423 508857

The Red House
Duncombe Place (100 yds. Minster)
YORK 01904 637000

The Ginnel Antiques Centre

The Ginnel. HG1 2RB. (Pauline Stephenson). Est. 1986. Open 9.30-5.30. SIZE: Large. *STOCK: All date-lined and vetted - see individual entries.* LOC: Off Parliament St. opposite Debenhams. PARK: Nearby. TEL: 01423 508857; website - www.ginnel.co.uk and www.ginnel.com. SER: Courier. Below are listed the specialist dealers at this centre.

Appleton Antiques
19th-20th pottery including Carlton, Moorcroft, Linthorpe, Poole and crested china; drinking glasses, paintings, small furniture.

Art-iques & Design
Silver especially Georg Jenson.

Fiona Aston
Objets d'art including porcelain and miniatures.

Automotive Art
Eastern antiquities.

M. Bedi
Fine 19th C furniture and paintings.

Brackmoor Antiques
Silver, porcelain and objets d'art.

Murray Burgess
Collectables and sporting memorabilia especially golf.

J.E. Chew
19th to early 20th C silver and plate.

The Clock Inn
(R.K. Mayes). Clocks. SER: Repairs; restorations.

D. Cocking
19th to early 20th C oil paintings and watercolours.

Cook's Cottage Antiques
Furniture and collectables.

Mary Cooper
Antique costumes and textiles, to 1929, including lace, fans, shawls, linen, quilts, samplers, wool and beadwork.

Cornmill Antiques
19th to early 20th C china, especially Royal Doulton.

Cornucopia
Jewellery and coins.

Drop Dial Antiques
Clocks and furniture.

Christine Edwards
18th-19th C porcelain.

G. Ford & Sons Ltd. (I.G.F. Thomson)
18th-19th C mahogany and country furniture.

Jeffrey and Pauline Glass
Porcelain and glass, objets d'art, 19th to early 20th C.

Emilia Greenwood
Jewellery.

R. Himsworth
Silver and jewellery.

Historic Gems
Jewellery.

Holyome
Porcelain especially Belleek.

James & Morton Fine Art & Antiques
19th C furniture, oil paintings and watercolours.

S. Judge
20th C pottery and porcelain including Shelley, Doulton, Bretby, Charlotte Rhead, Moorcroft.

G. Kendall
Furniture and collectables.

Kismet
Art Deco Jewellery.

542

Ian. P. Legard
18th-19th C silver.

Brian Loomes
Longcase clocks, small period furniture.

Sheila Morgan
Victorian collectables.

Octavia Antiques
1920's, 1930's pottery and porcelain.

Odyssey Antiquities
Ancient artifacts and coins.

Parker Gallery
19th to early 20th C oils and watercolours, £100-£3,000.

Paul Raine
19th C silver.

Graham Reed Fine Art
19th C porcelain, mirrors and pictures.

G. Rhodes
19th C furniture and objets d'art.

G.M. Ritchie
Porcelain, copper and brass, linen.

Rose Fine Art
19th to early 20th C prints and engravings.

Alan Sharp
English pottery and porcelain, 1750-1850.

John Tee
Oriental rugs.

Time Antiques
Porcelain and jewellery.

C.E. Tweedale
Victorian and Edwardian pottery.

Ann Wilkinson
Silver, porcelain and jewellery.

Eileen Wilson
Victorian and Edwardian jewellery; Arts and Crafts furniture.

Michael Green Pine & Country Antiques
Library House, Regent Parade. HG1 5AN. Est. 1976. Open 8.30-5.30, Sat. 8.45-4, Sun. by appointment. SIZE: Medium. *STOCK: Oak, mahogany and pine furniture, from 17th C, £5-£3,000; treen, kitchenalia and collectors treasures.* LOC: Overlooking the Stray. PARK: Easy. TEL: 01423 560452. SER: Valuations; restorations; stripping. VAT: Stan/Spec.

Havelocks
13-17 Westmoreland St. HG1 5AY. (Philip Adam). Est. 1989. Open 10-5 including Sun. SIZE: Large. *STOCK: Original pine, oak, general antique furniture.* LOC: A59 towards Skipton, turn left into Westmoreland St. PARK: Free. TEL: 01423 506721. SER: Valuations; restorations; stripping and finishing.

Carlton Hollis Ltd
10 Montpellier Mews. HG1 2TQ. (Paul and Beverley Hollis). Est. 1952. Open 10-5. *STOCK: Antique silver and jewellery.* TEL: 01423 500216; fax - 01423 500283; mobile - 07711 188565; e-mail - carltonhollis@aol.com. SER: Valuations; restorations.

London House Oriental Rugs and Carpets
9 Montpellier Parade. HG1 2TJ. Est. 1981. Open 10-5. SIZE: Medium. *STOCK: Persian, Turkish, Indian, Tibetan, Nepalese and Afghan rugs and carpets, 19th-20th C, £25-£5,000; kelims and camel bags, 19th-20th C, £25-£2,000.* LOC: Town centre on The Stray. PARK: Easy. TEL: 01423 567167; home - 01937 845123. SER: Valuations; restorations (handmade rugs). VAT: Stan.

David Love `BADA`
10 Royal Parade. HG1 2SZ. Est. 1969. Open 9-1 and 2-5.30. SIZE: Large. *STOCK: Furniture, English, 17th-19th C; pottery and porcelain, English and Continental; decorative items, all periods.* LOC: Opposite Pump Room Museum. PARK: Easy. TEL: 01423 565797/525567. SER: Valuations; buys at auction. VAT: Stan/Spec.

Charles Lumb and Sons Ltd `BADA`
2 Montpellier Gardens. HG1 2TF. (F. and A.R. Lumb). Est. 1920. Open 10-1 and 2-6. SIZE: Medium. *STOCK: Furniture, 17th to early 19th C; metalware, period accessories.* PARK: 20yds. immediately opposite. TEL: 01423 503776; home - 01423 863281; fax - 01423 530074. VAT: Spec.

McTague of Harrogate
17/19 Cheltenham Mount. HG1 1DW. (P. McTague). Open 11-5. CL: Mon. SIZE: Medium. *STOCK: Prints, watercolours, some oil paintings, mainly 18th to early 20th C.* LOC: From Conference Centre on Kings Rd., go up Cheltenham Parade and turn first left. PARK: Easy. TEL: 01423 567086; fax - 01423 564539. VAT: Stan/Spec.

Montpellier Mews Antique Market
Montpellier St. HG1 2TG. Open 10-5. SIZE: Various dealers. *STOCK: General antiques - porcelain, jewellery, furniture, paintings, interior decor, golf memorabilia, linen, glass and silver.* LOC: Behind Weatherells Antiques. TEL: 01423 530484.

Ogden of Harrogate Ltd `BADA`
38 James St. HG1 1RQ. (G.M. Ogden). Est. 1893. Open 9.15-5. SIZE: Large. STOCK: Jewellery, English silver and plate. LOC: Town centre. PARK: Easy. TEL: 01423 504123; fax - 01423 522283; e-mail - sales@ogden-of-harrogate.co.uk; website - www.ogden-of-harrogate.co.uk. SER: Repairs; restorations; valuations. VAT: Stan/Spec.

Paraphernalia
38A Cold Bath Rd. HG2 0NA. (Peter F. Hacker). Est. 1986. Open 10-5. SIZE: Medium. *STOCK: Wallplates, crested and commemorative china, cutlery, glass including carnival, Mauchlineware, bric-a-brac, small furniture.* PARK: Easy. TEL: Evenings - 01423 567968. SER: Free local delivery. FAIRS: Newark.

Paul M. Peters Antiques `LAPADA`
15a Bower Rd. HG1 1BE. Est. 1967. Open 10-5. CL: Sat. SIZE: Medium. *STOCK: Chinese and Japanese ceramics and works of art, 17th-19th C; European ceramics and glass, 18th-19th C; European metalware, scientific instruments and unusual objects.* LOC: Town centre, at bottom of Station Parade. PARK: Easy. TEL: 01423 560118. SER: Valuations. VAT: Stan/Spec.

Elaine Phillips Antiques Ltd `BADA`
1 and 2 Royal Parade. HG1 2SZ. (Colin, Elaine and Louise Phillips). Est. 1968. Open 9.30-5.30, other times by appointment. SIZE: Large. STOCK: Oak furniture, 1600-1800; country furniture, 1700-1840; some mahogany, 18th to early 19th C; period metalwork and decoration. LOC: Opposite Crown Hotel, Montpellier Quarter. PARK: Nearby. TEL: 01423 569745. FAIRS: Harrogate (Spring, Autumn). VAT: Spec.

Shieling Antiques
5 Montpellier Mews. HG1 2TQ. (Mrs. Irene Meyler). Est. 1982. Open 10-5. SIZE: Small. *STOCK: Victorian and Edwardian dairy and kitchen treen and artifacts, £20-£250; Victorian pine and country furniture, £50-£2,500; butchers' blocks on pine stands, 1940-1970, £500-£2,000; brass and copper, Georgian to Edwardian, £20-£400.* PARK: Easy. TEL: 01423 521884; home - 01423 541189; e-mail - john.meyler@cwctv.net.

Smith's (The Rink) Ltd
Dragon Rd. HG1 5DR. Est. 1906. Open 9-5.30, Sun. 11-4.30. SIZE: Large. *STOCK: General antiques, 1750-1820, £150; Victoriana, 1830-1900, £50.* LOC: From Leeds, right at Prince of Wales roundabout, left at next roundabout, 1/2 mile on Skipton Rd., left into Dragon Rd. PARK: Easy. TEL: 01423 567890. VAT: Stan/Spec.

Sutcliffe Galleries `BADA`
5 Royal Parade. HG1 2SZ. Est. 1947. Open 10-5. STOCK: Paintings, 19th C. LOC: Opposite Crown Hotel. TEL: 01423 562976; fax - 01423 528729; website - www.sutcliffegalleries.co.uk. SER: Valuations; restorations; framing. FAIRS: Harrogate. VAT: Spec.

Thorntons of Harrogate `LAPADA`
1 Montpellier Gdns. HG1 2TF. (R.H. and R.J. Thornton). Est. 1971. Open 9.30-5.30. SIZE: Medium. *STOCK: 17th-19th C furniture, metalware, clocks, paintings, porcelain, scientific instruments.* PARK: Easy. TEL: 01423 504118; fax - 01423 528400; e-mail - info@harrogateantiques.com; website - www.harrogateantiques.com. SER: Valuations. FAIRS: Harrogate (Spring). VAT: Spec.

Walker Galleries Ltd `BADA` `LAPADA`
6 Montpellier Gdns. HG1 2TF. Est. 1972. Open 9.30-1 and 2-5.30. SIZE: Medium. STOCK: Oil paintings and watercolours, 18th C furniture. TEL: 01423 567933; fax - 01423 536664; e-mail - wgltd@aol.com; websites - www.walker galleries.com and www.walkerfineart.co.uk. SER: Valuations; restorations; framing. FAIRS: BADA, London; Harrogate: Olympia. VAT: Spec.

Weatherell's of Harrogate Antiques and Fine Arts `LAPADA`
29 Montpellier Parade. HG1 2TG. Open 9-5.30. SIZE: Large. *STOCK: Period and fine decorative furniture.* TEL: 01423 507810/ 525004; fax - 01423 520005.

Chris Wilde Antiques `LAPADA`
134 King's Rd.HG1 5HY. (C.B. Wilde). Est. 1996. Open 10-5 or by appointment. SIZE: Large. *STOCK: Furniture, 1680-1920, £300-£10,000; longcase clocks, 1720-1920, £500-£10,000; ceramics, glass and pictures.* LOC: North side of town. PARK: Easy. TEL: 01423 525855; mobile - 07831 543268; e-mail - chris@harrogate.com; website - www.antiques.harrogate.com. SER: Valuations. VAT: Stan/Spec.

HAWES

Cellar Antiques
Bridge St. DL8 3QL. (Ian Milton Iveson). Est. 1987. Open 10-5, Sun. 11-5. SIZE: Medium. *STOCK: 17th-19th C oak and country furniture, longcase clocks, metalware and pottery.* LOC: Near bridge. PARK: Rear of shop. TEL: 01969 667224; home - 01969 667132. SER: Valuations.

Sturman's Antiques   `LAPADA`
Main St. DL8 3QW. Open 10-5 including Sun. *STOCK: Georgian and Victorian furniture; porcelain, silver plate, paintings; longcase, wall and mantel clocks.* PARK: Opposite. TEL: 01969 667742; fax - same. VAT: Spec.

HELMSLEY

E. Stacy-Marks Limited   `LAPADA`
10 Castlegate. YO62 5AB. Est. 1889. *STOCK: Paintings, English, Dutch and Continental schools, 18th-20th C.* TEL: 01439 771950; fax - 01439 771859.

Westway Pine
Carlton Lane. YO62 5HB. (J. and J. Dzierzek). Est. 1987. Open 9-5, Sat. 10-5, Sun. 1-5. CL: Tues. SIZE: Medium. *STOCK: Pine furniture, 19th C, £20-£2,000.* LOC: From A170 from Scarborough, first right into town, first left, then left again 100m. PARK: Easy. TEL: 01439 771399/771401; e-mail - westway.pine@btopenworld.com; website - www.westwaypine.co.uk. SER: Valuations; restorations (pine).

York Cottage Antiques   `LAPADA`
7 Church St. YO62 5AD. (G. and E.M. Thornley). Est. 1976. Open Fri. and Sat. 10-4 or by appointment. *STOCK: Early oak and country furniture; 18th-19th C metalware.* LOC: Opposite church. PARK: Adjacent. TEL: 01439 770833; home - same.

KIRK DEIGHTON, Nr. Wetherby

Elden Antiques
23 Ashdale View. LS22 4DS. (E. and D. Broadley). Est. 1970. Open 9-6, Sat. 12-5.30. SIZE: Medium. *STOCK: General antiques including furniture.* LOC: Main road between Wetherby and Knaresborough. PARK: Easy. TEL: 01937 584770; home - same; e-mail - elden.antiques@virgin.net.

KNARESBOROUGH

Robert Aagaard & Co
Frogmire House, Stockwell Rd. HG5 0JP. Est. 1961. Open 9-5, Sat. 10-4. SIZE: Medium. *STOCK: Chimney pieces, marble fire surrounds, fire baskets and cast iron interiors.* LOC: Town centre. PARK: Own. TEL: 01423 864805. VAT: Stan.

Bowkett
9 Abbey Rd. HG5 8HY. (E.S. Starkie). Resident. Est. 1919. Open 9-6. SIZE: Medium. *STOCK: Chairs, small furniture, brass, copper, pot-lids, Goss, books.* LOC: By the river at the lower road bridge. PARK: Easy. TEL: 01423 866112. SER: Restorations (upholstery and small furniture).

Early Oak
8 High St. HG5 0ES. (A.D. Gora). Est. 1995. Open by appointment. SIZE: Medium. *STOCK: Oak and country furniture, 17th-18th C, £100-£10,000; longcase clocks, £1,000-£3,000; metalware including copper and pewter, 17th-19th C, £30-£500.* PARK: Own. TEL: 01423 861845; e-mail - info@earlyoak.co.uk; website - www.earlyoak.co.uk.

Omar (Harrogate) Ltd
21 Boroughbridge Rd. HG5. Est. 1946. Open by appointment. *STOCK: Persian, Turkish, Caucasian rugs and carpets.* PARK: Easy. TEL: 01423 863199; fax - same. SER: Cleaning; restorations. VAT: Stan.

Bracelet with brooch, c.1925-30, Raymond Templier (French, 1891-1968). (© Virginia Museum of Fine Arts, Richmond)

From an article entitled "Art Deco at the Victoria and Albert Museum" by John Andrews which appeared in the May 2003 issue of *Antique Collecting*. For more details and to subscribe see page 21.

John Thompson Antiques `LAPADA`
Swadforth House, Gracious St. HG5 8DT. Est. 1968. *STOCK: 18th-19th C furniture and related decorative objects.* PARK: Easy. TEL: 01423 864698. FAIRS: Olympia. VAT: Spec.

LEYBURN

Thirkill Antiques
Newlands, Worton. DL8 3ET. Est. 1963. *STOCK: Musicals, pottery, porcelain, small furniture, 18th-19th C.* PARK: Easy. TEL: 01969 650725. SER: Restorations.

LYTHE, Nr. Whitby

Lythe Cottage Antiques
High St. (Mrs Lynne Robinson). *STOCK: Victorian, Edwardian, early oak and country cottage furniture.* LOC: Three miles from Whitby towards Staithes. PARK: Easy. TEL: Mobile - 07961 828679. SER: Valuations.

MALTON

Magpie Antiques
9-13 The Shambles. YO17 7LZ. (E.L. and G.M. Warren). Est. 1972. Open 10-4. CL: Thurs. SIZE: Small. *STOCK: General antiques and collectables, 19th-20th C, £5-£50; kitchenalia, £5-£100; some furniture.* LOC: Town centre, near Cattle Market. PARK: Nearby. TEL: 01653 691880; home - 01653 658335; mobile - 07801 854636. FAIRS: Newark; York Racecourse.

MANFIELD, Nr. Darlington

Joan and David White
Lucy Cross Cottage. DL2 2RJ. Est. 1975. Open by appointment. *STOCK: Georgian, Victorian and export furniture.* LOC: B6275, Scotch Corner to Piercebridge road, on left 3 miles after leaving A1. PARK: Easy. TEL: 01325 374303; mobile - 07779 206036. VAT: Stan/Spec.

MARKINGTON, Nr. Harrogate

Daleside Antiques
Hinks Hall Lane. HG3 3NU. Est. 1978. Open 8-5, Sat. and Sun. by appointment. *STOCK: Pine furniture, decorative items, architectural features and fittings, 18th-19th C, £50-£3,500; Georgian mahogany furniture; Victorian shop fittings.* TEL: 01765 677888; fax - 01765 677886; e-mail - sales@daleside.net; website - www.daleside.net. SER: Containers; restorations. VAT: Stan.

MASHAM, Nr. Ripon

Aura Antiques
1-3 Silver St. HG4 4DX. (R. and R. Sutcliffe). Est. 1985. Open 9.30-4.30, Sun. by appointment. SIZE: Medium. *STOCK: Furniture especially period mahogany dining furniture, 18th to mid-19th C, £50-£5,000; metalware - brass and copper, fenders, £5-£250; china, glass, silver and decorative objects, £5-£1,000; all 18th-19th C.* LOC: Corner of Market Sq. PARK: Easy. TEL: 01765 689315; home - 01765 658192; e-mail - Robert@aura-antiques.co.uk; website - www. aura-antiques.co.uk. SER: Valuations; UK delivery. VAT: Spec.

MIDDLEHAM, Nr. Leyburn

Castle Antiques Centre
34 Market Pl. DL8 4NP. (Derek and Joanne Jarvill). Est. 1994. Open 10-5.30 including Sun., Tues by appointment. SIZE: Medium (5 rooms). *STOCK: Georgian, Victorian and Edwardian furniture, pottery, porcelain, glass, clocks, metalware, silver, jewellery, general antiques and collectables.* LOC: Town centre. PARK: Easy. TEL: 01969 624655.

Middleham Antiques
The Corner Shop, Kirkgate. DL8 4PF. (Mike Pitman). Est. 1984. Open 10-5.30 most days, Wed. by appointment, prior telephone call advisable. *STOCK: Pre 1830 oak and country furniture, longcase clocks, curios, ceramics, pewter, Delftware, £20-£7,000.* PARK: Easy. TEL: 01969 622982; fax - same; e-mail - middlehamantique@aol.com; website - www. antiques.middlehamonline.com.

NORTHALLERTON

Collectors Corner
145/6 High St. DL7 8SL. (J. Wetherill). Est. 1972. Open 10-4 or by appointment. CL: Thurs. *STOCK: General antiques, collectors' items.* LOC: Opposite GPO. TEL: 01609 777623; home - 01609 775199.

NORTON, Nr. Malton

Northern Antiques Company
2 Parliament St., Scarborough Rd. YO17 9HE. (Sara Ashby-Arnold). Est. 1991. Open 9-1 and 2-5, Sat. 9.30-12.30, Sun. and evenings by appointment. SIZE: Medium. *STOCK: Country oak furniture, from 17th C, £200-£2,000; pine, Georgian to Victorian, to £1,000; upholstered sofas and chairs, cast-iron and wooden beds,*

BRIAN LOOMES

Specialist dealer in antique British clocks. Internationally recognised authority and author of numerous books on antique clocks. Large stock of longcase clocks with a number of lantern clocks and bracket clocks.

Restoration work undertaken

EST'D 37 YEARS (2003)

Resident on premises. Available six days a week but strictly by prior telephone appointment.

Copies of my current books always in stock.

CALF HAUGH FARMHOUSE, PATELEY BRIDGE, NORTH YORKS.
Tel: (01423) 711163.

(On B6265 Pateley-Grassington road.)

www.brianloomes.com

decorative items and prints, from 19th C, to £800; some contemporary interior design items. LOC: From Malton town centre on old Scarborough Rd., through Norton, shop on right above Aga shop. PARK: Easy. TEL: 01653 697520.

PATELEY BRIDGE

Brian Loomes
Calf Haugh Farm. HG3 5HW. (Brian and Joy Loomes). (Author of clock reference books). Est. 1966. Open strictly by appointment. SIZE: Medium. *STOCK: British clocks especially longcase, wall, bracket and lantern, pre-1840, £2,000-£20,000.* Not Stocked: Foreign clocks. LOC: From Pateley Bridge, first private lane on left on Grassington Rd. (B6265). PARK: Own. TEL: 01423 711163; e-mail - clocks@ brianloomes.com; website - www.brianloomes. com. VAT: Spec.

PICKERING

Country Collector
11-12 Birdgate. YO18 7AL. (G. and M. Berney). Est. 1991. Open 10-5. CL: Wed. SIZE: Small. *STOCK: Ceramics, including blue and white and Art Deco pottery, and collectables, 1800-1940, £10-£1,000.* LOC: Top of the Market Place, at

crossroads of A169 and A170. PARK: Eastgate. TEL: 01751 477481. SER: Valuations; buys at auction (ceramics). VAT: Stan.

Pickering Antique Centre
Southgate. YO18 8BL. (Tina and Jim Vance). Est. 1972. Open 10-5. SIZE: Large. *STOCK: Bedsteads, from 1840, £150-£1,500; Victorian and Edwardian furniture, from £50; longcase clocks, from 1800, £1,000-£5,000; dolls, £100-£3,000; pictures and prints, pottery and porcelain, books, costume, collectables, glass, mantel clocks, jewellery, silver and plate.* LOC: Next to traffic lights on A170 Helmsley road. PARK: Own at rear. TEL: 01751 477210; fax - same; mobile - 07747 067146; e-mail - sales@ pickantiques.freeserve.co.uk; website - www. pickeringantiquecentre.co.uk. SER: Valuations; restorations (metalware including bedsteads, furniture).

C.H. Reynolds Antiques
The Old Curiosity Shop, 122 Eastgate. YO18 7DW. Est. 1947. Open 9.30-5.30, Sun. by appointment. *STOCK: General antiques.* LOC: A170. PARK: Free, outside shop. TEL: 01751 472785.

RICHMOND

York House (Antiques)
York House, 60 Market Place. DL10 4JQ. (Christine Swift). Est. 1986. Open 9.30-5.30, Sun. 12-4. SIZE: Medium. *STOCK: Furniture, mainly Victorian and Edwardian, £500-£1,000; china, lamps, figures, Victorian to 1930s, £20-£500; kitchenalia, garden artifacts, French and English fires and fireplaces, Victorian and later, to £800.* PARK: Loading bay or nearby. TEL: 01748 850338; fax - same; home - 01748 850126; mobile - 07711 307045.

RIPON

Milton Holgate   BADA
P O Box 77. HG4 3XX. Est. 1972. Open by appointment. *STOCK: Fine English furniture and accessories, 17th-19th C.* TEL: 01765 620225.

Hornsey's of Ripon
3 Kirkgate. HG4 1PA. (Bruce, Susan and Daniel Hornsey). Est. 1976. Open 9-5.30. SIZE: Small. *STOCK: Textiles, bric-a-brac, rare and secondhand books.* PARK: Market Square. TEL: 01765 602878; fax - 01765 601692; e-mail - daniel@rarebooks.freeserve.co.uk.

Sigma Antiques and Fine Art

The Old Opera House, Water Skellgate. HG4 1BH. (D. Thomson). Est. 1963. Open 10.30-5, other times by appointment. SIZE: Large. *STOCK: 17th-20th C furniture, furnishing items, pottery, porcelain, objets d'art, paintings, jewellery and collectors' items.* LOC: Near town centre. PARK: Nearby. TEL: 01765 603163; fax - same; e-mail - sigmaantiques@aol.com. SER: Restorations (furniture); repairs (jewellery and silver); valuations. VAT: Spec.

Skellgate Curios

2 Low Skellgate. HG4 1BE. (J.I. Wain and P.S. Gyte). Est. 1974. Open 11-5. CL: Wed. *STOCK: Furniture, decorative antiques, period jewellery, silver, brass, copper and collectors items.* TEL: 01765 601290; home - 01765 635336/635332.

ROBIN HOOD'S BAY

John Gilbert Antiques

King St. YO22 4SH. Est. 1990. Open Sat. 10-1 and 2-5, Sun. 11-4, other days by appointment. SIZE: Small. *STOCK: Country furniture, 18th-19th C, £100-£1,000; oak furniture from 1650, £250-£1,500; Victorian furniture, £50-£1,000; treen, £5-£150.* LOC: At bottom of old village, between Bay and Dolphin Hotels. PARK: Top of hill. TEL: Home - 01947 880528. SER: Valuations; restorations (furniture).

SCARBOROUGH

Hanover Antiques & Collectables

33 St Nicolas Cliff. YO11 2ES. (R.E. and P.J. Baldwin). Est. 1976. Open 10-4. CL: Wed. pm. *STOCK: Small collectables, medals, badges, militaria, toys, 50p-£500.* LOC: Close to Grand Hotel. PARK: Nearby. TEL: 01723 374175.

Shuttleworths

7 Victoria Rd. YO11 1SB. (L.R. Shuttleworth). Open 10-4. CL: Wed. *STOCK: General antiques.* TEL: 01723 366278.

SETTLE

Mary Milnthorpe and Daughters Antique Shop

Market Place. BD24 9DX. (Judith Milnthorpe). Est. 1958. Open 9.30-5. CL: Wed. SIZE: Small. *STOCK: Antique and 19th C jewellery and English silver.* LOC: Opposite Town Hall. PARK: Easy. TEL: 01729 822331. VAT: Stan/Spec.

Nanbooks

Roundabout, 41 Duke St. BD24 9DJ. (J.L. and N.M. Midgley). Resident. Est. 1955. Open Tues., Fri. and Sat. 11-12.30 and 2-5.30. CL: Nov.-Feb. SIZE: Small. *STOCK: English pottery, porcelain including Oriental, glass, general small antiques, 17th-19th C, to £500.* Not Stocked: Jewellery. LOC: A65. PARK: Easy. TEL: 01729 823324; e-mail - midglui@aol.com.

Anderson Slater Antiques

6 Duke St. BD24 7DW. (K.C.Slater). Est. 1962. Open 10-1 and 2-5. CL: Wed. SIZE: Medium. *STOCK: Furniture, 18th-19th C, £200-£4,000; porcelain, 18th-19th C, £25-£500; pictures, 19th-20th C, £200-£1,500.* LOC: Main street out of Market Place. PARK: Nearby. TEL: 01729 822051. SER: Valuations; restorations (furniture and porcelain); buys at auction. VAT: Stan/Spec.

E. Thistlethwaite

The Antique Shop, Market Sq. BD24 9EF. Est. 1972. Open 9-5. CL: Wed. SIZE: Medium. *STOCK: Country furniture and metalware, 18th-19th C.* LOC: Town centre, A65. PARK: Forecourt. TEL: 01729 822460. VAT: Stan/Spec.

SKIPTON

Adamson Armoury

Otley Rd. BD23 1ET. (J.K. Adamson). Est. 1975. Open by appointment. SIZE: Medium. *STOCK: Weapons, 17th-19th C, £10-£1,000.* LOC: A65, 200yds. from town centre. PARK: At rear. TEL: 01756 791355. SER: Valuations. FAIRS: London.

Cherub Antiques

2 Albert St. BD23 1JD. (Mrs G. and Mrs V. Hutchinson). Est. 1997. Open 10.30-4.30, Sun. and Bank Holidays 12-4. CL: Tues. SIZE: Medium. *STOCK: Ceramics, especially Shelley, £2-£400; small furniture, textiles including linen, small silver, brass and copper, kitchenalia; all 19th-20th C.* LOC: Off Coach St. which joins High St. PARK: Easy. TEL: 01756 700899; mobile - 07899 996571; e-mail - enquiries@ cherubantiques.co.uk; website - www.cherub antiques.co.uk. SER: Valuations.

Corn Mill Antiques

High Corn Mill, Chapel Hill. BD23 1NL. (Mrs M. Hawkridge). Est. 1984. Open 10-4. CL: Tues. and Wed. SIZE: Medium. *STOCK: Oak, mahogany and walnut furniture, £300-£2,000; porcelain, silver plate, prints, pictures, brass and copper, £20-£500; all Georgian to 1920's.* Not Stocked: Jewellery, gold and silver. LOC: From town centre take Grassington Rd. Chapel Hill is first right. PARK: Easy. TEL: 01756 792440; home - 01729 830489. SER: Valuations. VAT: Spec.

Manor Barn

Providence Mill, The Old Foundry Yard, Cross St. BD23 2AE. (Manor Barn Furniture Ltd). Est. 1972. Open 9-5. *STOCK: Pine, 17th-19th C and reproduction; oak.* PARK: Easy. TEL: 01756 798584; fax - 01756 798536. VAT: Stan/Spec.

Skipton Antiques Centre

The Old Foundry, Cavendish St. BD23 2AB. (Andrew Tapsell). Est. 1994. Open 10.30-4.30, Sun. 11-4. SIZE: Large - 30 dealers. *STOCK: Wide range of general antiques and collectables, Georgian to Art Deco, £5-£1,500.* LOC: West side of town off A59. PARK: Loading and nearby. TEL: 01756 797667.

SLEIGHTS, Nr. Whitby

Eskdale Antiques

164 Coach Rd. YO22 4BH. (Philip Smith). Est. 1978. Open 9-5.30 including Sun. SIZE: Medium. *STOCK: Pine furniture and farm bygones, 19th-20th C, £50-£500.* LOC: Main Pickering road. PARK: Easy. TEL: 01947 810297; home - same. SER: Valuations; buys at auction.

SNAINTON, Nr. Scarborough

Antony, David & Ann Shackleton

19 & 72 High St. YO13 9AE. Resident. Est. 1984. Open every day. SIZE: Medium. *STOCK: Longcase clocks, Victorian rocking horses, Georgian and Victorian furniture, collectables, £1-£3,500.* LOC: A170, equidistant Scarborough and Pickering. PARK: Easy. TEL: 01723 859577/850172. SER: Restorations (furniture, longcase clocks, rocking horses).

SPENNITHORNE, Nr. Leyburn

N.J. and C.S. Dodsworth

Thorney Hall. DL8 5PW. Est. 1973. Open by appointment. SIZE: Medium. *STOCK: Furniture, clocks and small items, 17th-19th C.* LOC: Off A684. TEL: 01969 622277. VAT: Margin.

STILLINGTON

Pond Cottage Antiques

Brandsby Rd. YO61 1NY. (C.M. and D. Thurstans). Resident. Est. 1970. Open seven days 9-5. SIZE: Medium. *STOCK: Pine, kitchenalia, country furniture, treen, metalware, brass, copper.* LOC: B1363 York to Helmsley road. PARK: Own. TEL: 01347 810796. SER: Re-polishing. VAT: Global.

Rose Fine Art and Antiques

Fox Inn Farm, Easingwold Rd. YO61 1LS. (Mr and Mrs S. Rose). Est. 1984. Open by appointment. *STOCK: Pictures, 18th to early 20th C, £5-£2,000.* PARK: Easy. TEL: 01347 810554. SER: Valuations; restorations (pictures). *Trade Only.*

THIRSK

Classic Rocking Horses

from Windmill Antiques. (B. and J. Tildesley). Est. 1980. Open by appointment. *STOCK: Restored antique rocking horses and authentic replicas of Victorian rocking horses, £1,500-£5,000.* TEL: 01845 501330; fax - 01845 501700; e-mail - info@classicrockinghorses.co.uk; website - www.classicrockinghorses.co.uk.

Kirkgate Fine Art & Conservation

The Studio, 3 Gillings Yard. YO7 1SY. (Richard Bennett). BAPCR. UKIC. Est. 1979. Open by appointment. SIZE: Small. *STOCK: Oil paintings, £50-£2,000; watercolours, £50-£500; both 19th to mid-20th C.* LOC: Joins Market Place. PARK: Nearby. TEL: 01845 524085; home - same; e-mail - reb@vetscapes.fsnet.co.uk; website - www. kirkgateconservation.co.uk. SER: Restorations (oil paintings and framing); buys at auction.

Millgate Pine & Antiques

12 Millgate. YO7 1AA. (T.D. and M. Parvin). FSB. Est. 1990. Open 10-5. SIZE: Large + warehouse. *STOCK: English and European pine especially doors.* PARK: Nearby. TEL: 01845 523878; e-mail - babs.jenkins@btinternet.com. SER: Repairs; stripping; restorations.

Potterton Books   LAPADA

The Old Rectory, Sessay. YO7 3LZ. (Clare Jameson). Est. 1980. Open 9-5. SIZE: Large. *STOCK: Classic reference works on art, architecture, interior design, antiques and collecting.* PARK: Easy. TEL: 01845 501218; fax - 01845 501439; website - www.pottertonbooks. co.uk. SER: Book search; catalogues. FAIRS: London; Frankfurt; Paris; New York; Milan; Dubai.

THORNTON-LE-DALE

Cobweb Books

1 Pickering Rd. YO18 7LG. (Robin and Sue Buckler). Est. 1982. Open every day 10-5 June-Oct. CL: Mon. or Tues. in winter. SIZE: Medium. *STOCK: Books - leather bindings, illustrated, modern first editions, literature, military, poetry, history.* PARK: Nearby. TEL: 01751 476638; home - 01751 474402; e-mail - sales@cobwebbooks. co.uk; website - www.cobwebbooks.co.uk.

TOCKWITH, Nr. York

Tomlinsons
LAPADA

Moorside. YO26 7QG. Est. 1977. Open, trade only, Mon-Fri. 8-4.30 or by appointment. Club members - Sat. 9-4.30 and Sun. 10-4. SIZE: Large. *STOCK: Furniture, £10-£20,000; clocks, porcelain, silver plate and decorative items, £10-£5,000.* LOC: A1 Wetherby take B1224 towards York. After 3 miles turn left on to Rudgate. At end of this road turn left, business 200m on left. PARK: Easy. TEL: 01423 358833; fax - 01423 358188; e-mail - sales@tomlinson.demon.co.uk; website - www.antique-furniture.co.uk. SER: Export; restorations; container packing, desk leathering. VAT: Stan/Spec.

WEST BURTON, Nr. Leyburn

The Old Smithy
DL8 4JL. (Bill Woodbridge, Lynn Watkinson, Pete and Elaine Dobbing). Est. 2000. Open 10-4, prior telephone call advisable for winter opening. SIZE: Small. *STOCK: General antiques, silver and jewellery, collectables, £5-£300; clocks and small furniture, £50-£1,000; all 18th-20th C.* LOC: Between Leyburn and Hawes, take Kettlewell road. PARK: Easy. TEL: 01969 663224; fax - same; mobile - 07881 985555. SER: Valuations; buys at auction. *Trade Only.*

WHITBY

Age of Jazz
85 Church St. YO22 4BH. (P.A. Smith). Est. 1983. Open 10.30-12.30 and 1-5 (Sat. and Sun. only Nov. to Mar.). SIZE: Medium. *STOCK: Clarice Cliff, £100-£750.* LOC: A174. PARK: Nearby. TEL: 01947 600512. SER: Valuations; buys at auction (Clarice Cliff).

The Bazaar
7 Skinner St. YO21 3AH. (F.A. Doyle). Est. 1970. Open 10.30-5.30. *STOCK: Jewellery, furniture, general antiques and collectables, 19th C.* LOC: Town centre. TEL: 01947 602281.

'Bobbins' Wool, Crafts, Antiques
Wesley Hall, Church St. YO22 4DE. (D. and P. Hoyle). Open 10-5 including Sun. SIZE: Small. *STOCK: General antiques especially oil lamps, bric-a-brac, kitchenalia, 19th-20th C.* LOC: Between Market Place and steps to Abbey on cobbled East Side. PARK: Nearby (part of Church St. is pedestrianised). TEL: 01947 600585 (answerphone). SER: Repairs and spares (oil lamps). VAT: Stan.

Caedmon House
14 Station Sq. YO21 1DU. (E.M. Stanforth). Est. 1977. Open 12-4.30. SIZE: Medium. *STOCK: General, mainly small, antiques including jewellery, dolls, Disney and china, especially Dresden, to £1,200.* PARK: Easy. TEL: 01947 602120; home - 01947 603930. SER: Valuations; restorations (china); repairs (jewellery). VAT: Stan/Spec.

Coach House Antiques
75 Coach Rd., Sleights. YO22 5BT. (C.J. Rea). Resident. Est. 1973. Open Sat. from 10 and by appointment. SIZE: Small. *STOCK: Furniture, especially oak and country; metalware, paintings, pottery, textiles, unusual and decorative items.* LOC: On A169, 3 miles south west of Whitby. PARK: Easy, opposite. TEL: 01947 810313.

WHIXLEY

Garth Antiques
LAPADA

The Old School, Franks Lane. YO26 8AP. (I. and J. Chapman). Est. 1978. Open Tues-Sat. 10-5. SIZE: Medium. *STOCK: Furniture, 18th-19th C, £50-£3,000; brass and copper, 19th C, £1-£500; oils and watercolours, £5-£3,000.* LOC: A59, turn towards Whixley at the Cattle/Whixley junction, then left opposite The Anchor into old village, next to Village Hall. PARK: Easy. TEL: 01423 331055; fax - 01423 331733. SER: Restorations; upholstery. VAT: Stan/Spec.

YORK

Antiques Centre York
Allenby House, 41 Stonegate. YO1 8AW. (David Waggott). Est. 1996. Open seven days 9-6. SIZE: Large. *STOCK: Wide range of general antiques, from £1-£7,000.* LOC: In pedestrianised thoroughfare between mister and main shopping area. PARK: Nearby. TEL: 01904 635888; fax - 01904 676342. VAT: Stan.

Barbican Bookshop
24 Fossgate. YO1 9TA. PBFA. Est. 1961. Open 9.15-5.30. SIZE: Large. *STOCK: Books - antiquarian, secondhand and new.* LOC: City centre. PARK: Multi-storey nearby. TEL: 01904 653643; fax - 01904 653643; e-mail - mail@barbicanbookshop.co.uk; website - www.barbicanbookshop.co.uk. SER:Mail order. FAIRS: PBFA. VAT: Stan.

Bishopsgate Antiques
23/24 Bishopsgate St. YO2 1JH. (R. Wetherill). Est. 1965. Open 9.15-6. *STOCK: General antiques.* TEL: 01904 623893; fax - 01904 626511.

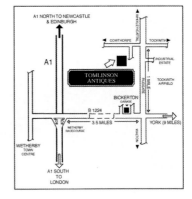

Barbara Cattle

BADA

45 Stonegate. YO1 8AW. Open 9-5.30. *STOCK: Jewellery and silver, Georgian to date.* **TEL: 01904 623862. SER: Valuations; repairs; restorations.**

Cavendish Antiques & Collectors Centre

44 Stonegate. YO1 8AS. (Debbie and Mark Smith). Est. 1996. Open seven days 9-6. SIZE: Large. *STOCK: Wide range of general antiques, £1-£7,000.* LOC: In pedestrianised thoroughfare between Minster and main shopping area. PARK: Nearby. TEL: 01904 621666; fax - 01904 675747. VAT: Stan.

Coulter Galleries

Open by appointment. *STOCK: Watercolours and oils, pre-1900; frames.* TEL: 07850 665144; fax - 01904 792285; e-mail - rober.coulter@btinternet. com.

Jack Duncan Books

36 Fossgate. YO1 9TF. Est. 1982. Open 10.30-5.30. SIZE: Large. *STOCK: Literary sets in leather and cloth bindings, antiquarian and later.* LOC: City centre. PARK: Nearby. TEL: 01904 641389; fax - 01904 672184.

Ruth Ford Antiques

39 Fossgate. YO1 9TF. Est. 1976. Open 11.30-4.30. CL: Wed. SIZE: Small. *STOCK: 18th-19th C country furniture, pine, treen and collectables, £5-£1,000.* LOC: Near Merchant Adventurers Hall. PARK: Nearby. TEL: Home - 01904 632864.

The French House (Antiques) Ltd.

74 Micklegate. YO1 6LF. (S.B. and M.J. Hazell). Est. 1995. Open 9.30-5.30. SIZE: Large. *STOCK: Wooden beds, 18th-19th C, £900-£2,500; gilt mirrors, 19th C, £300-£2,000; lighting, 19th-20th C, £200-£1,000; all French.* LOC: Main entry to city from A64. PARK: Side streets. TEL: 01904 624465; fax - 01904 629965. SER: Restorations (cabinet making, upholstery, French polishing, painting). VAT: Margin.

Golden Memories of York

14 Newgate. YO1 7LA. (M.S. and D.J. Smith). NAG. Est. 1991. Open 9-5.30. SIZE: Small. *STOCK: Antique and secondhand jewellery and silver, £5-£6,000.* LOC: Adjacent York market, off Parliament St. PARK: Multi-storey. TEL: 01904 655883; fax - 01904 623925; e-mail - golden memories@compuserve.com. SER: Repairs; valuations. VAT: Stan/Spec/Global Margin.

When new the wooden cased version of the Bush TV22 cost more than the Bakelite set – it is now worth around £50.

Classic 1950s 9-inch screen TV – the Bush TV22. The Bakelite cabinet makes this set more desirable. £200–£300.

From an article entitled "Here's Looking at You! Collecting Television Technology" by Steve Harris which appeared in the November 2002 issue of *Antique Collecting*. For more details and to subscribe see page 21.

Harpers Jewellers

2-6 Minster Gates. YO1 7HL. (J. Saffer and N. Wiseman). Open 9-5.30. SIZE: Small. *STOCK: Vintage watches, from 1900, especially unusual, quirky and very rare - Omega, Longines, Eterna specialising in Heuer and military pieces.* LOC: Near the Minster. PARK: Mary Gate. TEL: 01904 632634; fax - 01904 673370; e-mail - harpers York@btopenworld.com; website - www.vintage-watches.co.uk. SER: Valuations; restorations (watches).

Minster Gate Bookshop

8 Minster Gates. YO1 7HL. (N. Wallace). PBFA. Est. 1970. Open 9.30-5.30. SIZE: Large. *STOCK: Antiquarian and secondhand books; old maps and prints.* LOC: Opposite south door of Minster. PARK: Nearby. TEL: 01904 621812; fax - 01904 622960; e-mail - rarebooks@minstergatebooks. co.uk. SER: Valuations; restorations; book finding.

Robert Morrison and Son   `BADA`

Trentholme House, 131 The Mount. YO24 1DU. (C. and P. Morrison). Est. 1870. Open 9-5, Sat. 9-3. SIZE: Large. *STOCK: English furniture, 1700-1900; porcelain and clocks.* LOC: Near racecourse, one mile from city centre on Leeds Rd. From A1, take A64 to outskirts of York, then take A1036 York west road. PARK: Easy. TEL: 01904 655394; email - info@york-antiques.com; website - www.york-antiques.com. VAT: Stan/Spec.

Janette Ray Rare and Out of Print Books

8 Bootham. YO30 7BL. PBFA. ABA. Est. 1987. Open Fri. and Sat. 9.30-5.30 or by appointment. SIZE: Small. *STOCK: Out of print books on design, architecture and gardens.* LOC: City centre. PARK: Opposite. TEL: 01904 623088; fax - 01904 620814; e-mail - books@janetteray. co.uk; website - www.janetteray.co.uk. SER: Valuations; catalogues issued; finder. FAIRS: ABA Olympia.

The Red House Antiques Centre

Duncombe Place. (Ginnel Antiques Centres - P. Stephenson). Open Mon.-Sat. 9.30-6, (June-Sept. 9.30-8), Sun. 10.30-5.30. LOC: 200 yards from Minster. TEL: 01904 637000; e-mail - enquiries@redhouseyork.co.uk; website - www.redhouseyork.co.uk. SER: Packing and shipping; arts and antiques lectures. Below are listed the specialist dealers at this centre.

Algar Antiques
General 19th and 20th C antiques.

Antiquai
19th C ceramics and glass.

Appleton Antiques
19th-20th C pottery including Moorcroft, Carlton, Linthorpe and crested china.

Arcaize
19th C pressed glass.

Fiona Aston
19th C porcelain, silver and objets d'art.

Automotive Art
Chinese antiquities.

Margaret Bedi
18th-19th C furniture, oil paintings and watercolours.

Bootham Antiques
19th C silver, porcelain, glass and curios.

Brackmoor Antiques
Silver.

Bygones
Jewellery and dolls.

J.E. Chew
Silver.

Cookes Cottage Antiques
19th C furniture and paintings.

G. Gardiner
19th C ceramics.

Graham and Dianne
Militaria.

Harpers
Watches.

R. Hetherington
19th-20th C glass.

Robert M. Himsworth
Fine York and provincial silver.

Hogarth Antiques
Silver, plate, porcelain and treen.

Laurel Bank Antiques
Georgian, Victorian and Edwardian furniture, longcase, wall and mantel clocks.

Lycurgus Glass
19th-20th C decorative art glass and mirrors.

Stella Mar Antiques
19th C furniture and furnishings, porcelain, metalware, treen and objets d'art.

Maurice and Linda
Silver and military badges.

Olivia Meyler
Jewellery and Russian artefacts.

John Moor
Ancient art and antiques.

Needful Things
Silver, ceramics, north east glass, Davidsons.

Nichola
General antiques.

F. O'Flynn
Antique prints, maps and books.

S. Ogley
General antiques.

Past and Present
Buttons, badges, costume accessories, lace and costume jewellery.

Anne Powell
18th-19th C ceramics, Tunbridgeware and silver.

Prenelle Antiques
Ivory, marble, objets d'art.

Alan Price
17th-18th C oak furniture, brass and copper.

P.W. Raine
Silver, pewter, metalware and ceramics.

G. Rhodes
19th C furniture and paintings.

Rose Fine Art
19th C prints and maps.

E. Schwetje
Silver and glassware.

Small Fish Antiques
19th C furniture, mirrors, glass, pottery, toys, advertising materials and ephemera.

Ruby Snowden
19th C ceramics.

L. Spooner
Luggage and leather goods.

Station Road Antiques
Silver and jewellery.

Topaz Antiques
Victorian and Edwardian jewellery.

C.E. Tweedale
Victorian and Edwardian pottery and porcelain.

Upstairs-Downstairs
Kitchenalia, garden tools and bygones.

Paul Wheeler
Glass, pottery, porcelain and metalware.

Willow and Urn
American jewellery.

Wold Antiques
18th-19th C ceramics.

Gwen Wood
Belleek.

Jack Yarwood
18th-19th C wood, metalware and objets d'art.

J. Smith
47 The Shambles. YO1 7LX. BNTA. Est. 1963. Open 9.30-4.30. SIZE: Small. *STOCK: Numismatic items, £5-£1,000; British stamps, £1-£350.* LOC: City centre. TEL: 01904 654769; fax - 01904 677988. VAT: Stan/Spec.

Ken Spelman
70 Micklegate. YO1 6LF. (Peter Miller and Tony Fothergill). ABA. PBFA. Est. 1948. Open 9-5.30. SIZE: Large. *STOCK: Secondhand and antiquarian books especially fine arts and literature, 50p-£10,000.* LOC: City centre. PARK: Easy. TEL: 01904 624414; fax - 01904 626276; e-mail - rarebooks@kenspelman.com; website - www.kenspelman.com. SER: Valuations; buys at auction (books); catalogues issued. FAIRS: Bath, Oxford, York, Harrogate, Cambridge, Edinburgh and London PBFA and ABA. VAT: Spec.

St. John Antiques
26 Lord Mayor's Walk. YO31 7HA. (R. and N. Bell). Est. 1985. Open Sat. 10-5 or anytime by appointment. *STOCK: Victorian stripped pine, curios, blue and white pottery.* LOC: Near Minster. PARK: At rear. TEL: 01904 644263. SER: Stripping and finishing.

York Antiques Centre
2a Lendal. YO1 8AA. Open 10-5. SIZE: 25 dealers. *STOCK: Antiques and collectable items, 18th-20th C.* LOC: Opposite the museum gardens. PARK: Easy. TEL: 01904 641445/641582.

TIARAS
A History of Splendour

Geoffrey C. Munn

- *The majority of photographs and related material are illustrated here for the first time and gathered from private collections over three decades*

- *The photographs include those of tiaras from many Royal collections including three designed by Prince Albert for Queen Victoria*

- *Archive photographs from Boucheron and Cartier show jewels of great originality which have now been dismantled*

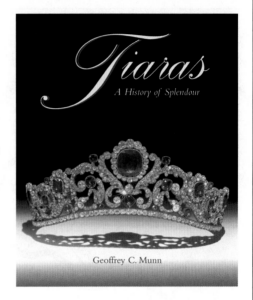

Tiaras have always inspired a great fascination and the most beautiful and influential women have been painted, photographed and admired whilst wearing them. Even in the twenty-first century they are still worn and continue to inspire special poise and elegance.

This lavishly illustrated book includes new photographs of a variety of Royal tiaras together with those of French and Russian Imperial provenances. Geoffrey Munn has been granted special access to the photographic archives of many famous jewellers, including Cartier, Boucheron and Fabergé, for his research. Other makers include Castellani, Fouquet, Garrard, Giuliano, Lalique, and Tiffany.

Many of these stunning tiaras also have great historical significance and their provenance is explained fully by the author, a specialist in jewellery and metalwork.

Among the contemporary pieces illustrated are tiaras belonging to Jamie Lee Curtis, Vivienne Westwood, Elton John and Madonna, made by Slim Barratt, Galliano and Versace.

Geoffrey Munn is the Managing Director of Wartski Ltd, prestigious antique dealers in London specialising in European precious metalwork. He is co-author of *Pre-Raphaelite to Arts and Crafts Jewellery* and author of both *Castellani and Giuliano – Revivalist Jewellers of the 19th Century* and *The Triumph of Love - Jewellery 1530-1930*. He is also the jewellery specialist on the BBC's *Antiques Roadshow*.

"…beautifully written and magnificently produced… For anyone interested in social history, it's as good a read as you are likely to have this year." **Daily Telegraph**

11¼ x 9¼in./285 x 240mm.
432pp., 250 col., & 170 b.&w. illus.
1 85149 375 1
£45.00

Available from all good booksellers and direct from the publisher:
ANTIQUE COLLECTORS' CLUB
Sandy Lane, Old Martlesham, Woodbridge, Suffolk, IP12 4SD.
Tel: 01394 389950   Fax: 01394 389999
Email: sales@antique-acc.com
Website: www.antique-acc.com

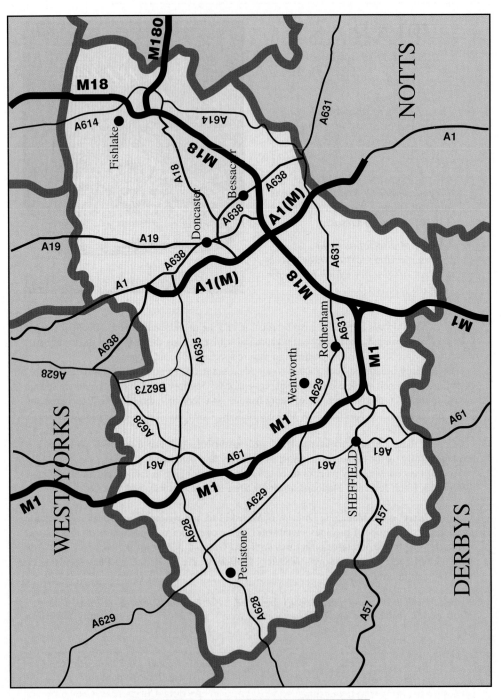

Dealers and Shops in South Yorkshire			
Bessacarr	1	Rotherham	4
Doncaster	1	Sheffield	19
Fishlake	1	Wentworth	1
Penistone	1		

BESSACARR, Nr. Doncaster

Keith Stones Grandfather Clocks
5 Ellers Drive. DN4 7DL. Est. 1988. Open by appointment. SIZE: Small. *STOCK: Grandfather clocks, especially painted dials 30 hour and 8 day movements, Georgian to early 19th C, £1,250-£3,750.* LOC: Take A638 Bawtry road off racecourse roundabout, through traffic lights after 3/4 mile, take second right into Ellers Rd. then second left. PARK: Easy. TEL: 01302 535258; home - same; website - www.kstones.fsnet.co.uk. SER: Valuations.

DONCASTER

Doncaster Sales and Exchange
20 Copley Rd. DN1 2PF. Open 9.30-5. CL: Thurs. *STOCK: General small antiques.* TEL: 01302 344857. VAT: Stan.

FISHLAKE

Fishlake Antiques
Pinfold Lane. DN7 5LA. Resident. Est. 1972. Open Sun. 1-5 and by appointment. SIZE: Medium. *STOCK: Rural furniture especially stripped pine; clocks including longcase and wall clocks, Victorian to mid-19th C, £30-£2,000; smalls, £3-£70.* LOC: Off A63. PARK: Own. TEL: 01302 841411.

PENISTONE, Nr. Sheffield

Penistone Pine and Antiques
Units 2 and 3 Penistone Court, Sheffield Rd. S36 6HP. Est. 1984. Open 9-5. SIZE: Large. *STOCK: Stripped and finished pine, 1800-1920.* PARK: Easy. TEL: 01226 370018; home - 01226 791330; mobile - 07985 652960. SER: Restorations.

ROTHERHAM

Roger Appleyard Ltd   LAPADA
Fitzwilliam Rd., Eastwood Trading Estate. S65 1SL. Open 8-5, Sat. 8-12. SIZE: Large. *STOCK: General antiques, £5-£10,000.* LOC: A630. PARK: Easy. TEL: 01709 367670/377770; fax - 01709 829395; e-mail - apple.antiques@dial.pipex.com. SER: Packing and shipping. VAT: Stan/Spec. *Trade Only.*

Foster's Antique Centre
Foster's Garden Centre, Doncaster Rd., Thrybergh. S65 4BE. (The Foster Family). Est. 1996. Open 10-4.30, Sun. 11-5. SIZE: 20 dealers. *STOCK: Wide range of general antiques and collectables including furniture, jewellery,*

Rockingham china. LOC: A630 between Rotherham and Doncaster. PARK: Own large. TEL: 01709 850337; fax - 01709 851905.

Holly Farm Antiques
Holly Farm, Harley Rd., Harley. S62 7UD. (Trevor and Linda Hardwick). Resident. Est. 1988. Open Sat. and Sun. 10-5, other days by appointment. SIZE: Small. *STOCK: Rockingham porcelain, 1830-1842, from £80; porcelain, pottery, clocks and watches, lamps, glass, silver, furniture.* LOC: B6090 quarter mile off A6135 Sheffield to Barnsley, between junctions 35/36 M1. PARK: Own. TEL: 01226 744077; home - same. SER: Valuations; buys at auction.

Philip Turnor Antiques
94a Broad St., Parkgate. Est. 1980. Open 9-5, Sat. 10-4. *STOCK: Shipping furniture including oak, 1880-1940.* LOC: Main road. PARK: Easy. TEL: 01709 524640; e-mail - philipsfurniture@turnorfreeserve.co.uk. SER: Export (Japan and USA). FAIRS: Swinderby.

SHEFFIELD

Acorn Antiques
298-300 Abbeydale Rd. S7 1FL. (R.C. and B.C. Priest). Est. 1984. Open 10-5. SIZE: Medium. *STOCK: Furniture, 19th-20th C, £20-£500; bronzes, sculptural and unusual items.* LOC: A625 to Bakewell. PARK: Easy. TEL: 0114 255 5348; home - same.

Barmouth Court Antiques Centre
Unit 2 Barmouth Rd., Off Abbeydale Rd. S7 2DH. Open 10-5, Sun. 11-4. SIZE: 50 dealers on 2 floors. *STOCK: General antiques and collectables.* TEL: 0114 255 2711; fax - 0114 258 2672.

Beech House
361 Abbeydale Rd. S7 1FS. (J.M. and A.J. Beech). Est. 1996. Open 10-5. CL: Thurs. SIZE: Small. *STOCK: Pine furniture, £100-£2,500; art and ceramics inmcluding contemporary, £50-£5,000.* LOC: 1 mile from city centre. PARK: Easy. TEL: 0114 250 1004; fax - same; mobile - 07970 196126. SER: Furniture made to order from reclaimed pine.

Chapel Antiques Centre
99 Broadfield Rd. S8 0XH. Open 10-5, Sun. and Bank Holidays 11-5. SIZE: 20+ dealers. *STOCK: Furniture, textiles and accessories.* LOC: From city centre, 1 mile along A61 Chesterfield Rd., turn right. PARK: Easy. TEL: 0114 258 8288; fax - same; website - www.antiquesinsheffield.com. SER: Upholstery; paint effects.

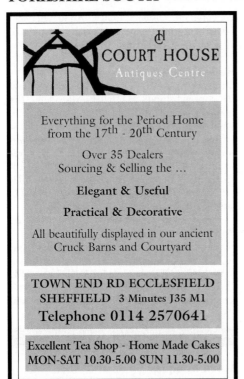

Court House Antique Centre
2-6 Town End Rd., Ecclesfield. S35 9YY. (J.P. & K.E. Owram). Open 10.30-5, Sun. 11.30-5. SIZE: Large - 35+ dealers. *STOCK: Town and country furniture, French bedroom furniture, antiquarian maps, decorative items, ceramics, glass, clocks, barometers, kitchenalia, books, silver, jewellery, lighting, mirrors, collectables, £5-£5,000.* LOC: 2 miles from M1, junction 35. Down hill, bear left into Nether Lane, through lights to church, turn left 250 yards on right. PARK: Easy. TEL: 0114 257 0641.

Dovetail Antiques
336 Abbeydale Rd. S7 1FN. (D.W. Beedle). Est. 1980. Open 9.30-4.30. SIZE: Medium. *STOCK: Georgian, Victorian and Edwardian mahogany, walnut, oak and pine furniture.* PARK: Easy. TEL: 0114 2551554; mobile - 07801 278257. SER: Restorations.

Dronfield Antiques
375-377 Abbeydale Rd. S7 1FS. (H.J. Greaves). Est. 1968. Open 10.30-5.30. CL: Thurs. except by appointment. SIZE: Large + warehouses. *STOCK: Trade and shipping goods, Victoriana, glass, china.* LOC: A621, 1 mile south of city centre. PARK: Easy. TEL: 0114 2550172/2581821; home and fax - 0114 2556024. SER: Container packing facilities. VAT: Stan.

F S Antiques
Court House Antiques Centre, 2-6 Town End Rd., Ecclesfield. S35 9YY. Open 10.30-5, Sun. 11.30-4.30. SIZE: Small. *STOCK: Longcase, wall and mantel clocks, £150-£3,000.* LOC: 2 miles from M1, junction 35. PARK: Easy. TEL: 0114 25 70641; home - 01226 382805; mobile - 07949 399481; e-mail - antique@clocksforall.f9.co.uk; website - www.antiqueclocksforall.co.uk. SER: Restorations.

Alan Hill Books
Unit 4, Meersbrook Works, Valley Rd. S8 9FT. Est. 1980. Open 10-5. *STOCK: Antiquarian books, maps and prints.* TEL: 0114 255 6242; e-mail - alanhillbooks@supanet.com.

Kelly Lighting
679 Ecclesall Rd. S11 8TG. (Frank R. Kelly). Est. 1982. Open Fri. 9-5, Sat. 10.30-5, other days by appointment. SIZE: Small. *STOCK: Lighting - ceiling, wall, table and floor, Edwardian and Victorian, £160-£10,000.* LOC: Half mile from Sheffield Parkway End. PARK: Easy. TEL: 0114 267 8500; fax - 0114 268 3242; e-mail - sales@kellyantiquelighting.co.uk; website - www.kellyantiquelighting.co.uk. SER: Restorations (polishing, lacquering, re-wiring).

Langtons Antiques & Collectables
443 London Rd./Courtyard, 100 Guernsey Rd., Heeley Bottom. S2 4HJ. (Langton Family). Est. 1999. Open 10-5. Sun. 10.30-4.30. SIZE: Large, 70+ dealers. *STOCK: Furniture, architectural items, military, china, porcelain, jewellery, clocks, Art Deco, from 1850, £5-£3,000.* LOC: M1, exit 33, A61 to city centre. PARK: Easy. TEL: 0114 258 1791. FAIRS: Newark. VAT: Stan.

Nichols Antique Centre
The Nichols Building, Shalesmoor. S3 8UJ. (T. and M. Vickers). Est. 1994. Open 10-5, Sat. and Sun. 10.30-4.30. SIZE: Large. *STOCK: Ceramics, fine furniture, clocks and collectables, mainly 19th-20th C, £50-£3,000.* LOC: A61, half mile from city centre. PARK: Easy. TEL: 0114 281 2811; fax - 0114 281 2812. SER: Valuations; restorations; re-upholstery. VAT: Stan.

The Oriental Rug Shop
763 Abbeydale Rd. S7 2BG. (Kian A. Hezaveh). Est. 1880. Open 10-5. *STOCK: Handmade rugs and carpets especially large carpets.* LOC: A621. TEL: 0114 2552240; fax - 0114 2509088; website - www.rugs.btinternet.co.uk.

Paraphernalia
66/68 Abbeydale Rd. S7 1FD. (W.K. Keller). Est. 1972. Open 9.30-5. *STOCK: General antiques,*

stripped pine, lighting, brass and iron beds. LOC: Main road. PARK: Easy. TEL: 0114 2550203.

Renishaw Antiques
32 Main Rd., Renishaw. S21 3UT. (B. Findley). Open Mon.-Sat. 9-3. *STOCK: Furniture, architectural items, pine doors and leaded glass.* LOC: 1 mile off M1, junction 30. TEL: 01246 435521. SER: Door stripping.

N.P. and A. Salt Antiques   LAPADA
Abbeydale House, Barmouth Rd. S7 2DH. Open 10-5, Sun. 11-4. SIZE: Large. *STOCK: Victorian furniture, shipping goods, smalls and toys.* TEL: 0114 2582672/2552711. SER: Valuations; packing and shipping; courier.

Sheffield Antiques Emporium
15 Clyde Rd., Heeley. S8 0YD. Est. 1994. Open 10-5, Sun. 10.30-4.30. SIZE: 70+ dealers. *STOCK: Furniture, collectables, linens, glass, militaria, china, books, Art Deco, £1-£5,000.* LOC: 1st right off Broadfield Rd., opposite Broadfield public house on Abbeydale Rd. PARK: Easy. TEL: 0114 258 4863; fax - 0114 255 5609; website - www.sheffieldantiques emporium.com.

Tilley's Vintage Magazine Shop
281 Shoreham St. (A.G.J. and A.A.J.C. Tilley). Est. 1978. Open Tues.-Sat. 9.30-4.30, other times by appointment. SIZE: Large. *STOCK: Magazines, comics, newspapers, books, postcards, programmes, posters, cigarette cards, prints, ephemera.* LOC: Opposite Sheffield United F.C. PARK: Easy. TEL: 0114 2752442; fax - same; e-mail - tilleys281@aol.com; website - www.tilleysmagazines.com. SER: Mail order; valuations.

Paul Ward Antiques
Owl House, 8 Burnell Rd., Owlerton. S6 2AX. Resident. Est. 1976. Open by appointment. SIZE: Large. *STOCK: Matched sets of Victorian dining and kitchen chairs, country chairs, general antiques.* LOC: 2 miles north of city on A61. TEL: 0114 2335980. VAT: Stan/Spec.

WENTWORTH, Nr. Rotherham

Wentworth Arts, Crafts and Antiques Ltd
The Old Builders Yard, Cortworth Lane. S62 7SB. Est. 1999. Open 10-5 including Sun. SIZE: Large - 50 dealers. *STOCK: Georgian to Edwardian furniture, to £1,200; Royal Doulton and collectables.* PARK: Easy. TEL: 01226 744333; website - www.wentwortharts craftsandantiques.co.uk.

Parr figure of Water from a set of The Elements, c.1860, £200.

From an article entitled "Water Figures - A rich vein for collectors of Victorian Staffordshire pottery" by Arnold Shelton which appeared in the September 2002 issue of *Antique Collecting*. For more details and to subscribe see page 21.

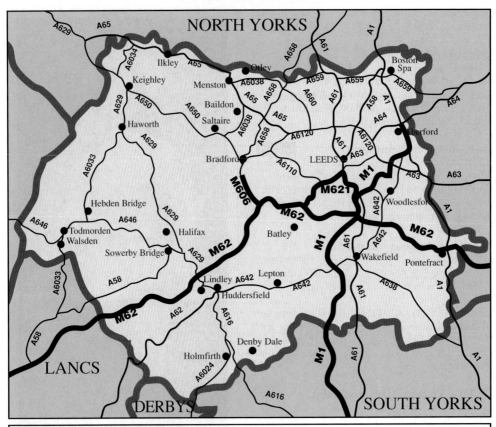

Dealers and Shops in West Yorkshire						
Aberford	1	Halifax	4	Keighley	1	Saltaire	1
Baildon	2	Haworth	1	Leeds	8	Sowerby Bridge	2
Batley	1	Hebden Bridge	1	Lepton	1	Todmorden	2
Boston Spa	1	Holmfirth	4	Lindley	1	Wakefield	1
Bradford	3	Huddersfield	4	Menston	2	Walsden	1
Denby Dale	1	Ilkley	2	Otley	2	Woodlesford	1
				Pontefract	2		

ABERFORD

Aberford Antiques Ltd t/a Aberford Country Furniture

Hicklam House. LS25 3DP. (J.W.H. Long and C.A. Robinson). Est. 1973. Open 9-5.30, Sundays 10-5.30. CL: Mon. SIZE: Large. *STOCK: French oak furniture; pine and mahogany, £10-£4,000; Victoriana and collectables, £5-£1,000.* LOC: Large detached property at south end of village. PARK: Easy. TEL: 0113 2813209; fax - 0113 2813121; e-mail - jwhlong@aol.com; website - www.aberfordpine.co.uk. VAT: Stan/Spec.

BAILDON, Nr. Shipley

The Baildon Furniture Co.

Spring Mills, Otley Rd. BD17 6AD. (Richard Parker). Est. 1972. Open 9.30-5, Sat. 10.30-5, Sun. by appointment. SIZE: Large. *STOCK: Furniture, architectural fitments, pottery and metalware, 17th-20th C, £5-£5,000.* PARK: Easy. TEL: 01274 414345; fax - same; e-mail - baildon furniture@aol.com. SER: Valuations; restorations (cabinet work, repolishing, upholstery, pottery). VAT: Stan/Spec.

Browgate Antiques

13 Browgate. BD17 6BP. (Dianne and David Shaw). Est. 1992. Open 10.30-5 including Sun. CL: Thurs. SIZE: Medium. *STOCK: Georgian, Victorian and Edwardian furniture, £500-£5,000.* PARK: Easy. TEL: 01274 597494; mobile - 07950 638166.

BATLEY

Tansu Japanese Antiques

Redbrick Mill, 218 Bradford Rd, Batley Carr.

WF17 6JF. (Stephen P. and C.J. Battye). Est. 1993. Open 9.30-5.30, Sun. 11-5. SIZE: Medium. *STOCK: Japanese furniture, chests including staircase and shop display, wheeled trunks, calligraphy boxes, granite lanterns, 1850-1900, £350-£20,000; kimonos, 1930-1960, £20-£200.* LOC: Close to M1 and M62. PARK: Own large. TEL: 01924 460044/459441; fax - 01924 462844. SER: Valuations; restorations (Japanese antique furniture). VAT: Spec/Margin.

BOSTON SPA, By Wetherby

London House Oriental Rugs and Carpets
London House, High St. LS23 6AD. (M.J.S. Roe). Open 10-5.30 including Sun. CL: Mon. SIZE: Large. *STOCK: Caucasian, Turkish, Afghan and Persian rugs, runners and carpets, £50-£10,000; kelims and textiles.* LOC: Off A1, south of Wetherby. PARK: Easy. TEL: 01937 845123; home - same. SER: Restorations (Oriental carpets and rugs); buys at auction (Oriental carpets and rugs). VAT: Stan.

BRADFORD

The Corner Shop
89 Oak Lane. BD9 4QU. (Miss Badland). Est. 1961. Open Tues. and Thurs. 2-5.30, Sat. 11-5.30. *STOCK: Pottery, small furniture, clocks and general items.*

Cottingley Antiques
286 Keighley Rd., Frizinghall. BD9. (Peter and Barbara Nobbs). Est. 1981. Open 9-5. SIZE: Medium. *STOCK: Victorian stripped and restored pine, £100-£500.* LOC: Right hand side of A650 from Keighley. PARK: Easy. TEL: 01274 545829; home - 01274 569091. SER: Restorations (furniture).

Heaton Antiques
1 Hammond Place, Emm Lane, Heaton. BD9 4AN. (T. Steward). Est. 1991. Open 10-5. CL: Mon. SIZE: Medium. *STOCK: Furniture, silver plate and bric-a-brac, pre 1930, £10-£1,000.* LOC: Near A650. PARK: Easy. TEL: 01274 480630. SER: Valuations. FAIRS: Harrogate.

DENBY DALE, Nr. Huddersfield

Worlds Apart
Unit 6A Springfield Mill, Norman Rd. HD8 8TH. (Sharon Dawson). Est. 1995. Open Tues.-Sat. 10-5, Sun. 12-4.30. SIZE: Medium. *STOCK: General antiques, including furniture, and collectables - Denby Dale pie memorabilia, bakelite dial telephones.* PARK: Easy. TEL: 01484 866713; home - 01226 380093; mobile - 07801 349960. SER: Restorations and conversions (bakelite dial telephones). *Trade Only.*

HALIFAX

Collectors Old Toy Shop and Antiques
89 Northgate. HX1 1XF. (S. Haley). Est. 1983. Open Tues., Wed., Fri. and Sat. 10.30-4.30. SIZE: 2 floors. *STOCK: Collectors toys, clocks and antiques.* PARK: Nearby. TEL: 01422 360434/822148; e-mail - collectorsoldtoy@aol.com; website - www. collectorsoldtoyshop.com.

Halifax Antiques Centre
Queens Rd. HX1 4LR. (M. and A. Carroll). Est. 1981. Open Tues.-Sat. 10-5. SIZE: Large - 30 dealers. *STOCK: Art Deco, jewellery, porcelain, linen, costume, pine, oak, mahogany, French and English furniture, kitchenalia, decorative collectables.* LOC: A58 to King Cross, turn at Trafalgar Inn into Queens Rd. corner, 3rd set of lights. PARK: Own. TEL: 01422 366657.

Muir Hewitt Art Deco Originals
Halifax Antiques Centre, Queens Rd. Mills. HX1 4LR. Est. 1982. Open Tues.-Sat. and Bank Holidays 10.30-5. CL: Mon. *STOCK: 20th C ceramics including Clarice Cliff, Susie Cooper, Charlotte Rhead, Shelley; furniture, metalware, lighting and mirrors.* LOC: 1 mile west of town centre off A58 (A646) Aachen Way/Burnley Rochdale road. Turn right at Trafalgar Inn traffic lights. Centre at 3rd set of traffic lights at junction of Queens Rd. and Gibbet St. PARK: Easy. TEL: 01422 347377; fax - same; website - www.muirhewitt.com. SER: Valuations. FAIRS: Ann Zierold Art Deco; Leeds Royal Armouries; Chester. VAT: Spec.

Andy Thornton Architectural Antiques Ltd
Victoria Mills, Stainland Rd., Greetland. HX4 8AD. SALVO. Est. 1976. Open 8.30-5.30, Sat. 9-5. SIZE: Large. *STOCK: Architectural antiques - doors, stained glass, fireplaces, panelling, garden statuary, furniture, light fittings, decor items, church interiors including pews.* LOC: Off junction 24, M62. PARK: Easy. TEL: 01422 377314; fax - 01422 310372; e-mail - antiques@ataa.co.uk; website - www.andy thornton.com. SER: Delivery; worldwide shipping. VAT: Stan.

HAWORTH, Nr. Keighley

Bingley Antiques
Springfield Farm Estate, Flappit. BD21 5PT. (J.B. and J. Poole). Est. 1965. Open Thurs.-Sat. 8.30-5, other days by appointment. SIZE: Large. *STOCK: Furniture, 18th-19th C; shipping goods, porcelain, architectural antiques.* LOC: Near Haworth. PARK: Easy. TEL: 01535 646666 (Tues.-Sat); e-mail - john@bingleyantiques.com; website - www.bingleyantiques.com. VAT: Stan/Spec.

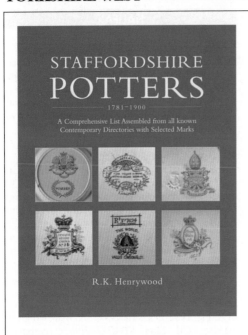

Staffordshire Potters
1781-1900

R.K. Henrywood

- *Contains a comprehensive list of the many manufacturers who worked in the Staffordshire Potteries between 1781 and 1900*

- *A new standard reference work for all interested in British ceramics*

- *Contains new information unavailable in existing literature*

- *Includes a useful selection of marks employed by many of the lesser potters*

This book presents a comprehensive list of manufacturers working in the Staffordshire Potteries in the period between 1781 and 1900. This area produced some ninety per cent of the pots made in England and is of prime importance in the study of British ceramics. The list has been assembled by extracting the data contained in directories published in the period, covering more than 10,000 entries from some sixty-one volumes. The book itself consists of introductory chapters covering historical aspects of the survey, a fascinating evaluation of the area under review and the directory of authors and publishers, followed by two major chapters — the assembled alphabetical list of over 3,000 potters and listings of all the original directory entries in date order. This is the most comprehensive list of Staffordshire potters ever published and includes much information unavailable in existing literature. The work covers all potters, regardless of their products, working between 1781, the date of the earliest surviving directory, and the beginning of the twentieth century, by far the most popular period for collectors. The book will easily become a standard reference work for all who are interested in British pottery and porcelain, collected throughout the world.

Dick Henrywood was an aeronautical engineer with a long list of technical papers to his credit and he worked for many years as a business manager. He moved away from engineering and now works as a freelance author and lecturer on antiques and related subjects. He was a founder member of the Friends of Blue and first Keeper of the Records. His other books include the ACC *Dictionary of Blue and White Pottery 1780-1880,* and cover subjects as diverse as jugs, bookmarkers and cat names.

11 x 8½in./279 x 216mm.
416pp., 420 b.&w.
1 85149 370 0
£45.00

Available from all good booksellers and direct from the publisher:
ANTIQUE COLLECTORS' CLUB
Sandy Lane, Old Martlesham, Woodbridge, Suffolk, IP12 4SD.
Tel: 01394 389950   Fax: 01394 389999
Email: sales@antique-acc.com
Website: www.antique-acc.com

HEBDEN BRIDGE, Nr. Halifax

Cornucopia Antiques
9 West End. HX7 8JP. (C. Nassor). Open Thurs., Fri. and Sun. 1-5, Sat. 11-5. *STOCK: Furniture, Art Deco, lighting, mirrors, stoves and bric-a-brac.* LOC: Town centre behind Pennine Information Centre. PARK: Easy. TEL: 01422 844497.

HOLMFIRTH

Bruton Gallery
PO Box 145HD9 1YU. (Helen Robinson). Est. 1969. Open by appointment. SIZE: Medium. *STOCK: French sculpture, 19th-20th C, from £1,000+; contemporary British art, to £10,000.* PARK: Limited. TEL: Mobile - 0870 747 1800; e-mail - art@BrutonGallery.co.uk; website - www. BrutonGallery.co.uk. SER: Valuations; buys at auction. FAIRS: Glasgow; Oxford; London. VAT: Stan/Spec.

Chapel House Fireplaces
Netherfield House, St. Georges Rd., Scholes. HD9 1UH. (J. and M. Forster). Est. 1979. Open strictly by appointment Tues.-Sat. 9-5. SIZE: Large. *STOCK: Georgian, Victorian and Edwardian grates and mantels; French chimneypieces.* PARK: Own. TEL: 01484 682275; e-mail - info@chapelhouse fireplaces.co.uk; website - www.chapelhouse fireplaces.co.uk. SER: Restorations.

The Toll House Bookshop
32/34 Huddersfield Rd. HD9 2JS. (Elaine V. Beardsell). ABA, PBFA. Est. 1978. Open 10-5. *STOCK: Books including antiquarian.* PARK: Nearby. TEL: 01484 686541; e-mail - tollhouse.bookshop@virgin.net; website - www.toll-house.co.uk. SER: Valuations. FAIRS: Major ABA and PBFA.

Upperbridge Antiques
9 Huddersfield Rd. HD9 2JR. (I. and B. Ridings). Open Wed., Thurs. and Sat. 1-5, Sun. 2-5. SIZE: Small. *STOCK: Pottery, metalware, lighting, linen, interesting items, Victorian to 1950's, £5-£200.* Not Stocked: Clocks and jewellery. LOC: A635. PARK: Nearby. TEL: 01484 687200.

HUDDERSFIELD

D.W. Dyson (Antique Weapons)
Wood Lea, Shepley. HD8 8ES. Est. 1974. Open by appointment. *STOCK: Antique weapons including cased duelling pistols, armour, miniature arms, cigar and smoking related accessories, rare and unusual items.* LOC: Off A629. PARK: Easy. TEL: 01484 607331; home - same; fax - 01484 604114; website - www.dwdhallmark.com. SER: Valuations; buys at auction (antique weapons); special presentation items made to order in precious metals; restorations; interior design; finder (film props). FAIRS: Dorchester Hotel, London; Dortmund, Stuttgart and other major foreign. VAT: Spec.

Huddersfield Picture Framing Co
Cloth Hall Chambers, Cloth Hall St. HD1 2EG. (Miss Pamela Ward). Est. 1962. Open 9-5, Wed. 9-1, Sat. 9-4. SIZE: Large. *STOCK: Watercolours, picture mouldings, swept frames, ovals and circles.* LOC: Between Market St. and New St. PARK: Meters or nearby. TEL: 01484 546075; home - 01484 687598. SER: Valuations; restorations (especially oil paintings). VAT: Stan.

Geoff Neary (incorporating Fillans Antiques Ltd)
2 Market Walk. HD1 2QA. NAG, FGA. Est. 1852. Open 9.30-5.15. SIZE: Small. *STOCK: English silver, 1700-1980; Sheffield plate, 1760-1840, jewellery, 1800-1980, £50-£20,000.* LOC: Town centre. PARK: Multi-storey. TEL: 01484 531609; fax - 01484 432688; website - www. geoffneary-jewellers.co.uk. SER: Valuations; restorations. VAT: Stan/Spec.

Objects of Vertu
26 Lidget St., Lindley. HD3 3JP. (Christopher J.L. Dawes). Est. 1995. Open 10-5. CL: Mon. and Wed. SIZE: Small. *STOCK: Silver, glass and porcelain, 19th-20th C, £20-£400.* PARK: Nearby. TEL: 01484 649515. SER: Valuations; buys at auction. FAIRS: Newark; Elliott Antiques & Collectors.

ILKLEY

Coopers of Ilkley   **LAPADA**
46-50 Leeds Rd. LS29 8EQ. (Charles and Jane Cooper). Est. 1910. Open 9-1 and 2-5.30. SIZE: Large. *STOCK: English and Continental furniture, pre-1900, £100-£10,000; porcelain and metalware.* LOC: A65. PARK: Own. TEL: 01943 608020; fax - 01943 604321; e-mail - enquiries@ cooperantiquesilkley.co.uk; website - www. cooperantiquesilkley.co.uk. SER: Valuations; restorations (mainly furniture). VAT: Stan/Spec.

Jack Shaw and Co
The Old Grammar School, Skipton Rd. LS29 9EJ. Est. 1945. Open Thurs., Fri. and Sat. 9.30-12.45 and 2-5.30. *STOCK: Silver especially cutlery and 18th C domestic.* TEL: 01943 609467. VAT: Spec.

KEIGHLEY

Clock House Antiques
2 Janet St. BD22 9ET. (P.A. Langham). Open

Tues., Wed. and Thurs. 1-4, Sat. 11-4, Sun. 2-4. SIZE: Medium. *STOCK: Clocks, porcelain and small furniture.* PARK: Easy. TEL: 01535 648777. SER: Valuations; repairs (clocks).

LEEDS

Aladdin's Cave
19 Queens Arcade. LS1 6LF. (A. and R. Spencer). Est. 1954. SIZE: Small. *STOCK: Jewellery, £15-£5,000; collectors' items.* LOC: Town centre. PARK: 100 yards. TEL: 0113 245703. SER: Valuations; repairs. VAT: Stan.

Aquarius Antiques
Abbey Mills, Abbey Rd. LS5 3HP. (P.I. McGlade). Open 9-5. SIZE: Medium. *STOCK: Furniture, 18th C to Edwardian, £100-£1,000.* LOC: A65, 4 miles from city centre. PARK: Easy. TEL: 0113 278 9216. SER: Valuations; restorations.

Geary Antiques
114 Richardshaw Lane, Stanningley, Pudsey. LS28 6BN. (J.A. Geary). Est. 1933. Open 10-5.30, Sun. 12-4. SIZE: Large + warehouse. *STOCK: Furniture, Georgian, Victorian and Edwardian; copper and brass.* LOC: 500 yards from West Leeds Ring Rd. PARK: Easy. TEL: 0113 2564122; e-mail - jag@t-nlbi.demon.co.uk. SER: Restorations (furniture); interior design. VAT: Stan/Spec.

Headrow Antiques Centre
Level 3 Headrow Shopping Centre, The Headrow. (Sally Hurrell). Est. 1991. Open 10-5, Sun.11-4 (Dec). SIZE: 25 dealers. *STOCK: Ceramics, jewellery and furniture, £5-£2,000.* LOC: City centre. PARK: NCP Albion St. TEL: 0113 2455344; home - 0113 2749494; website - www.headrowantiques.co.uk.

J. Howorth Antiques/Swiss Cottage Furniture
85 Westfield Crescent, Burley. LS3 1DJ. Est. 1986. Open 10-5.30, Sun. 1-5.30. CL: Tues. SIZE: Warehouse. *STOCK: Collectables, furniture, architectural items, £5-£3,000.* LOC: Town hall to Burley Rd., road opposite YTV. PARK: Easy. TEL: 0113 2306268/2429994. SER: Prop. hire for film and TV. FAIRS: Newark. VAT: Stan/Spec.

Oakwood Gallery
613 Roundhay Rd., Oakwood. Open 9-6. *STOCK: Fine paintings and prints.* PARK: Easy. TEL: 0113 2401348. SER: Framing; restorations; conservation.

The Piano Shop
39 Holbeck Lane. LS11 9UL. (B. Seals). Open 9-5. SIZE: 2 floors. *STOCK: Pianos, especially decorated cased grand.* LOC: 5 mins. from City centre. TEL: 0113 2443685; e-mail - thepianoshop @freenet.co.uk; website - www.thepianoshop.co.uk. SER: Restorations; French polishing; hire.

Year Dot
16 Market St. Arcade. LS1 6DH. (A. Glithro). Est. 1977. Open 9.30-5. *STOCK: Jewellery, watches, silver, pottery, porcelain, glass, clocks, prints, paintings, bric-a-brac.* LOC: Briggate. TEL: 0113 2460860.

LEPTON, Nr. Huddersfield

K.L.M. & Co. Antiques
The Antique Shop, Wakefield Rd. HD8 0EL. (K.L. & J. Millington). Est. 1980. Open 10.30-5, other times by appointment. SIZE: 8 showrooms and warehouse. *STOCK: Furniture including stripped pine, satin walnut, to 1940's; pianos, all £25-£1,500.* LOC: A642 Wakefield road from Huddersfield, shop opposite church. PARK: Easy and at rear. TEL: 01484 607763; home - 01484 607548. VAT: Stan.

LINDLEY, Nr. Huddersfield

Objects of Vertu
26 Lidget St. HD3 3JP. (Christopher J.L. Dawes). Est. 1993. Open Tues., Thurs., Fri. and Sat. 10-5. SIZE: Small. *STOCK: Regency and Georgian items, £80-£700; small silver, 1870-1930, £30-£500.* LOC: Main street. PARK: Nearby. TEL: 01484 649515. SER: Valuations. FAIRS: Newark; Mytholmroyd.

MENSTON

Antiques
101 Bradford Rd. LS29. (W. and J. Hanlon). Est. 1974. Open Thurs.-Sat. 2.30-5. *STOCK: Handworked linen, textiles, pottery, porcelain, Art Nouveau, Art Deco, silver, plate, jewellery, small furniture, collectors items.* LOC: A65 near Harry Ramsden. PARK: Forecourt. TEL: 01943 877634; home - 01943 463693. FAIRS: Newark.

Park Antiques
2 North View, Main St. LS29 6JU. Resident. Est. 1975. Open Thurs.-Sat. 12-5.30. SIZE: Medium. *STOCK: Furniture, Georgian to Edwardian, £500-£5,000; decorative items, £100-£1,000, soft furnishings, £500-£2,000.* Not Stocked: Pine, silver. LOC: Opposite the park. PARK: Easy. TEL: 01943 872392. VAT: Stan/Spec.

OTLEY

Mayfair Antiques
26 Cross Green. LS21 1HD. (Ivor Hughes). Est. 1998. Open 10-6. CL: Wed. SIZE: Medium.

STOCK: French faience, garden antiques, metalware, 19th C; French decorative art, 1850-1930. LOC: A658, on left leaving Otley towards Harrogate. PARK: Easy. TEL: 01943 463380; mobile - 07802 740012; e-mail - ivor@frantique. fsnet.co.uk; website - www.frantique.co.uk. SER: Valuations; translation. FAIRS: Harrogate.

Otley Antique Centre

6 Bondgate. LS21 3AB. (A. Monkman). Est. 1991. Open 10-5. CL: Wed. SIZE: Small. *STOCK: 20th C collectables; jewellery, paintings, 19th-20th C: all £50-£100.* LOC: Top of High St., opposite parish church on Leeds road. PARK: Next to church. TEL: 01943 850342.

PONTEFRACT

Cottage Antiques

Heaton House, 24 Wakefield Rd., Ackworth. WF7 7AB. (Sheila Whittaker). Est. 1987. Open by appointment. *STOCK: 18th-19th C pine and country furniture; bedroom and kitchen furniture, ceramics, linen and kitchenalia.* PARK: Easy. TEL: 01977 611146; mobile - 07944 853624. SER: Restorations (furniture). FAIRS: Newark.

D. Turner Antiques

The Old Coach House, Bondgate. (Dennise Turner). Est. 1988. Open 11-5. CL: Thurs. SIZE: Medium. *STOCK: Furniture, £30-£300; pottery, £20-£100, both late 19th to early 20th C; collectables, £5-£25.* LOC: Just off A1 towards town. PARK: Easy. TEL: 01977 798818; home - 01226 751802. SER: Valuations; buys at auction (furniture). FAIRS: Newark, Harrogate; Ardingly.

SALTAIRE, Nr Shipley

The Victoria Centre

3-4 Victoria Rd. BD18 3LA. (M. and M. Gray and Andrew Draper). Est. 1995. Open 10.30-5. SIZE: Large - 40+ dealers. *STOCK: Wide range of general antiques including fine furniture, paintings, silver, clocks, porcelain, pine and collectables, £5-£10,000.* PARK: Nearby. TEL: 01274 530611; fax - 01274 533722; e-mail - info@victoriacentre.co.uk. SER: Valuations; restorations (furniture and pictures). VAT: Stan/Spec.

SOWERBY BRIDGE, Nr. Halifax

Memory Lane

69 Wakefield Rd. HX6 2UX. (L. Robinson). Est. 1978. Open 10.30-5. SIZE: Warehouse + showroom. *STOCK: Pine, oak and teddy bears.* PARK: Easy. TEL: 01422 833223.

Talking Point Antiques

66 West St. HX6 3AP. (Paul Austwick). Est. 1986. Usually open Thurs., Fri., Sat. 10.30-5.30, prior telephone call advisable. *STOCK: Restored gramophones and phonographs, 78rpm records, gramophone accessories and related items.* PARK: Nearby. TEL: 01422 834126; e-mail - tpagrams@aol.com; website - www.talking pointgramophones.co.uk. SER: Restorations (gramophones). FAIRS: NEC. Leeds.

TODMORDEN

Echoes

650a Halifax Rd., Eastwood. OL14 6DW. (P. Oldman). Est. 1980. CL: Mon. and Tues. SIZE: Medium. *STOCK: Costume, textiles, linen and lace, £5-£500; jewellery, £5-£150; all 19th-20th C.* LOC: A646. PARK: Easy. TEL: 01706 817505; home - same. SER: Valuations; restorations (costume); buys at auction (as stock).

Todmorden Antiques Centre

Sutcliffe House, Halifax Rd. OL14 5DG. (Mr and Mrs Hoogeveen). Open 10-5, Sat. 10-4, Sun. 12-4. SIZE: 30 dealers. *STOCK: General antiques, furniture and jewellery.* TEL: 01706 818040.

WAKEFIELD

Robin Taylor Fine Arts

36 Carter St. WF1 1XJ. Est. 1981. Open 9.30-5.30. *STOCK: Oils and watercolours.* TEL: 01924 381809; website - www.picturerestoration.co.uk.

WALSDEN, Nr. Todmorden

Cottage Antiques (1984) Ltd

788 Rochdale Rd. OL14 7UA. (G. Slater). Resident. Est. 1978. Open Tues.-Sun. SIZE: Medium. *STOCK: Pine, oak and mahogany country furniture, decorative painted furniture, kitchanalia; collectables.* LOC: A6033 Todmorden to Littleborough road. PARK: Easy. TEL: 01706 813612. SER: Restorations; stripping (pine); import/export of European pine and collectables.

WOODLESFORD, Nr. Leeds

Trafalgar Antiques Centre

Trafalgar Works, Astley Lane, Bowers Row. LS26 8AN. Open 9-5.30, Sat. 10-5, Sun. 11-5.30. SIZE: Large. *STOCK: Mahogany, walnut and oak, 18th to early 20th C.* LOC: Off M62, junction 30 towards Garforth, into Swillington, 2 miles down Astley Lane. PARK: Own. TEL: 0113 287 5955; fax - 0113 287 5966. SER: Valuations; restorations. VAT: Stan/Spec

CHANNEL ISLANDS

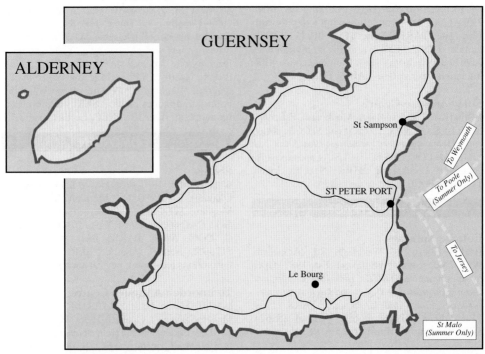

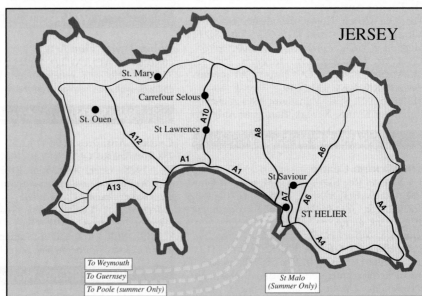

Dealers and Shops on the Channel Islands

ALDERNEY	2	St Sampson	2	St Lawrence	1
GUERNSEY		JERSEY		St. Mary	1
Le Bourg Forest	1	Carrefour Selous	1	St. Ouen	1
St Peter Port	7	St Helier	10	St Saviour	1

Alderney

Beverley J. Pyke - Fine British Watercolours
22 Victoria St. GY9 3TA. Est. 1988. Open by appointment. *STOCK: 20th C watercolours, £150-£2,000.* TEL: 01481 824092.

Victoria Antiques
St. Catherine's, Victoria St. GY9 3TA. (P.A. Nightingale). Open 10-12.30 or by appointment. *STOCK: Period and Victorian furniture, glass, silver, china, jewellery, small objets d'art.* TEL: 01481 823260. SER: Valuations.

Guernsey

LE BOURG FOREST

Mark Blower (Antiques) Ltd
The Rectory. Est. 1978. Open by appointment. SIZE: Small. *STOCK: Furniture, 18th C, £1,000-£20,000; garden ornaments, pictures, 18th-19th C, £500-£5,000.* PARK: Easy. TEL: 01481 239098. SER: Valuations; restorations (furniture and pictures); fine art packing; shipping; buys at auction.

ST PETER PORT

Stephen Andrews Gallery
5 College Terrace, Grange. GY1 2PX. (J. Geddes and S. Wilkowski). Est. 1984. Open 9.30-5. SIZE: Medium. *STOCK: Furniture, pottery and porcelain, paintings, 19th-20th C.* LOC: Main road. PARK: Adjacent. TEL: 01481 710380. SER: Buys at auction. FAIRS: Local.

Channel Islands Galleries Ltd
Trinity Square Centre, Trinity Sq. GY1 1LX. (G.P. and Mrs C. Gavey). Est. 1970. Open 10-5. SIZE: Medium. *STOCK: Antique maps, sea charts, prints, oil paintings and watercolours; books, illustrated, historical, social, geographical and natural history; banknotes and coins; all Channel Islands.* LOC: Near town centre. PARK: Easy. TEL: 01481 723247; home - 01481 247337; fax - 01481 714669; e-mail - geoff.gavey@cigalleries.f9.co.uk; website - www.cigalleries.f9.co.uk. SER: Framing.

The Collectors Centre
1 Sausmarez St. GY1 2PT. (Andrew Rundle). Est. 1984. Open 11-6. SIZE: Small. *STOCK: Prints, engravings, maps, coins, banknotes, stamps, postcards, books and ephemera.* PARK: Opposite. TEL: 01481 725209. SER: Valuations.

567

W. De la Rue Antiques
29 Mill St. GY1 1HG. Est. 1972. Open 10-12.30 and 2-4. CL: Thurs. pm. SIZE: Small. *STOCK: General antiques and collectors' items.* PARK: Nearby. TEL: 01481 723177.

N. St. J. Paint & Sons Ltd
26-29 The Pollet. GY1 1WQ. (Michael St John Paint). NAG. Est. 1947. Open 9-5. SIZE: Large. *STOCK: Jewellery, silver and objets d'art, 18th-20th C, £50-£75,000.* LOC: Town centre. TEL: 01481 721096; fax - 01481 710241; e-mail - paint @guernsey.net. SER: Valuations; restorations (silver and jewellery).

The Pine Collection
La Route de la Garenne, Pitronnerie Road Industrial Estate. GY1 2RL. (P. Head). Est. 1986. Open 9.30-5.30. *STOCK: Pine.* TEL: 01481 726891.

St. James's Gallery Ltd
18-20 Smith St. GY1 2JQ. (Mrs C.O. Whittam). Est. 1955. Open 10-1 and 2-5, Sat. 10-1. SIZE: Large. *STOCK: Furniture, 19th C, £300-£30,000; paintings, 19th-20th C, £100-£20,000; silver, 19th-20th C, £10-£5,000.* LOC: Town centre, just off High St. PARK: Nearby. TEL: 01481 720070; fax - 01481 721132; home - 01481 723999.

ST. SAMPSON

The Curiosity Shop
Commercial Rd. GY2 4QP. Est. 1978. Open Sat. pm. *STOCK: Old and antiquarian books, prints, postcards, coins, ephemera, paintings, small furniture, china, glass, silver, brass, £1-£5,000.* TEL: 01481 245324. FAIRS: Organiser.

Ray & Scott Ltd
The Bridge. GY2 4QN. (M. J. Search). NAG. Est. 1962. Open 9-5.15, Sat. 9-5. SIZE: Medium. *STOCK: Jewellery and watches, 19th C, £500-£1,000+.* PARK: Easy. TEL: 01481 244610; fax - same. SER: Valuations; restorations (jewellery and engraving).

Jersey

CARREFOUR SELOUS, ST. LAWRENCE

David Hick Interiors
Alexandra House. JE3 1GL. Est. 1977. Open Wed., Fri. and Sat. 9.30-5. CL: Aug. SIZE: Large and warehouse. *STOCK: Furniture and objets d'art.* PARK: Own. TEL: 01534 865965; fax - 01534 865448; e-mail - hickantiques@localdial. com. SER: Shipping (UK and overseas).

ST. HELIER

John Blench & Son
50 Don St. JE2 4TR. (W. and J. Blench). Est. 1972. Open 9.30-5, Thurs. and Sat. 9.30-12.30. SIZE: Medium. *STOCK: Fine books, bindings, local maps, prints and paintings.* LOC: Town centre. PARK: Nearby. TEL: 01534 725281; fax - 01534 758789; e-mail - segart@itl.net; website - www.selectiveeye.com. SER: Valuations; restorations.

John Cooper Antiques
16 The Market. JE2. *STOCK: General antiques.* TEL: 01534 723600.

Falle Fine Art Limited `LAPADA`
94 Halkett Place. JE2 4WH. (John Falle). Est. 1993. Open Tues.-Fri. 11-5, Sat. 9.30-1, Mon. by appointment. SIZE: Large. *STOCK: 20th C paintings, watercolours and bronzes.* LOC: Opposite Public Library. PARK: Easy. TEL: 01534 887877; fax - 01534 723459; e-mail -gallery@ fallefineart.com; website - www.fallefineart.com. SER: Valuations; restorations; exhibitions.

David Hick Antiques
45 Halkett Place. JE2 4WQ. Open 10-5. *STOCK: Furniture and smalls.* TEL: 01534 721162; fax - same; e-mail - hickantiques@localdial.com.

Peter Le Vesconte's Collectables
62 Stopford Rd. JE2 4LZ. Est. 1979. Open 10-3. CL: Thurs. SIZE: Medium. *STOCK: Toys, 1920-1999, £5-£500; militaria, 1900-1945, £1-£500; small items, 1900-1970, £5-£300.* LOC: Road opposite Hotel de France. PARK: Easy. TEL: 01534 732481; fax - same. SER: Valuations; buys at auction (toys and militaria).

A. & R. Ritchie
7 Duhamel Place. JE2. Est. 1973. Open 9.30-4.30. SIZE: Medium. *STOCK: Silver, militaria, jewellery, small items.* LOC: Behind central library. PARK: Opposite. TEL: 01534 873805.

Roberts Antiques
14 York St. JE2 3RQ. (Robert Michieli). Est. 1975. Open 9.30-4.45. SIZE: Medium. *STOCK: English silver, ceramics, clocks, glass, jewellery, 19th C, £50-£10,000.* LOC: Opposite town hall. PARK: Easy. TEL: 01534 509071; home - 01534 865005; mobile - 07798 876553; e-mail - count. roberto@jerseymail.co.uk. SER: Valuations; buys at auction (as stock).

The Selective Eye Gallery
50 Don St. JE2 4TR. (John and Warwick Blench).

Est. 1958. Open 9-5. CL: Thurs. and Sat. pm. SIZE: Medium. *STOCK: Oil paintings, 19th-20th C; maps, prints and antiquarian books, 16th-20th C.* Not Stocked: General antiques. LOC: Town centre. PARK: Multi-storey 100yds. TEL: 01534 725281; fax - 01534 758789; e-mail - segart@itl. net; website - www.selectiveeye.com. SER: Valuations; restorations (pictures). FAIRS: Jersey.

Thesaurus (Jersey) Ltd
3 James St. JE2 4TT. (I. Creaton). Est. 1973. Open 9-5.30. SIZE: Small. *STOCK: Antiquarian and out of print books, £1-£2,000; maps and prints.* LOC: Town centre. PARK: 100yds. TEL: 01534 37045. SER: Buys at auction. VAT: Spec.

Thomson's
60 Kensington Place and 44 Don St. JE2 3PA. Est. 1967. Open 10-6. SIZE: Large. *STOCK: General antiques and collectors's items, mainly furniture.* LOC: 60 Kensington Place at the side of Grand Hotel; 44 Don St. opposite Bonhams. PARK: Easy. TEL: 01534 723673/618673; mobile - 07797 766806. SER: Valuations.

ST. LAWRENCE

I.G.A. Old Masters Ltd
5 Kimberley Grove, Rue de Haut. (I.G. and Mrs C.B.V.Appleby). Est. 1953. Open by appointment. *STOCK: Old Master and 19th C paintings.* LOC: Near glass church. PARK: Easy. TEL: 01534 724226; home - same.

ST MARY

Country House and Cottage Antiques
La Foret, Rue es Boeufs. JE3 3EQ. (Mrs Sarah Johnson). Resident. Est. 1985. Open Tues.-Sat. 10-5, Wed. 10-1 or by appointment. SIZE: Large. *STOCK: Furniture - Jacobean, Georgian, Victorian, Art Nouveau, Art Deco; china, glass, pictures and decorative items.* PARK: Easy. TEL: 01534 862547. SER: Valuations; restorations; interior design.

ST OUEN

Stephen Cohu Antiques
La Ville de L'Eglise. JE3 2LR. Est. 1990. Open Sat. 10-5, other times by appointment. SIZE: Medium + warehouse. *STOCK: Furniture and clocks, 18th-20th C, £50-£10,000; porcelain and pottery, 17th-20th C, £10-£2,000; glass, 18th-20th C, £5-£1,000; paintings and prints, £5-£2,000; silver including Channel Islands.* LOC: Opposite church. PARK: Own. TEL: 01534 485177; fax - same; mobile - 07797 723895; website - www.stephencohuantiques.co.uk. SER: Valuations; restorations (furniture and china); buys at auction. FAIRS: NEC; Newark.

ST. SAVIOUR

Grange Gallery - Fine Arts Ltd
10 Victoria Rd. JE2 7QG. (G.J. Morris). Est. 1973. Open 9-5.30. SIZE: Medium. *STOCK: 19th-20th C oil paintings and watercolours, local items, £10-£10,000.* LOC: 1 mile east of St Helier. PARK: Forecourt. TEL: 01534 720077; e-mail - morris@jerseymail.co.uk. SER: Valuations; restorations (paintings); framing.

Thomas Bush Hardy (1842-1897), 'Southampton Water'. Signed and dated 1891, watercolour with scratching out, 6in. x 17½in. A good but late example. Note the careful detail of the figures on the shore and the cluster of boats in the far distance. A weaker artist would have lost control of this detail.

From an article entitled "English Watercolours - The Longer View" by Richard Kay which appeared in the June 2003 issue of *Antique Collecting*. For more details and to subscribe see page 21.

NORTHERN IRELAND

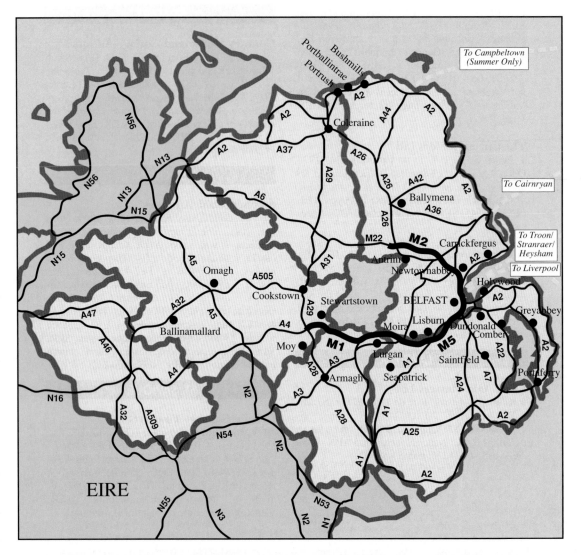

NORTHERN IRELAND		Co Down	
		Comber	1
		Dundonald	1
Belfast	7	Greyabbey	2
		Holywood	2
Co Antrim		Portaferry	1
Antrim	1	Saintfield	7
Ballymena	1	Seapatrick	1
Bushmills	1		
Carrickfergus	1	**Co Fermanagh**	
Lisburn	1	Ballinamallard	1
Newtownabbey	1		
Portballintrae	1	**Co Londonderry**	
Portrush	2	Londonderry	2
		Coleraine	2
Co Armagh		**Co Tyrone**	
Armagh	1	Cookstown	2
Lurgan	1	Moy	2
Moira	1	Omagh	1
		Stewartstown	1

Co. Antrim

ANTRIM

The Country Antiques LAPADA
219B Lisnevenagh Rd. BT41 2JT. (David Wolfenden). Est. 1982. Open 10-6. SIZE: Large. *STOCK: Furniture, £200-£5,000; jewellery and porcelain, £100-£3,000; all 19th C.* LOC: Main Antrim-Ballymena line. PARK: Easy. TEL: 028 9442 9498; e-mail - antiquewolfirl@aol.com; website - www.country-antiques-wolfenden.co. uk. SER: Valuations; restorations. FAIRS: Dublin. VAT: Stan/Spec.

BALLYMENA

Once upon a Time Antiques
The Old Mill, 2 Parkfield Rd., Ahoghill. BT42 2QS. (Ronan McLaughlin). Est. 1971. Open 10-5.30. SIZE: Medium. *STOCK: Furniture, porcelain and jewellery, 18th-20th C; Art Nouveau, Art Deco.* LOC: Edge of village. PARK: Easy. TEL: 028 2587 1244; fax - same; mobile - 07703 360447. SER: Valuations; restorations (jewellery, furniture, brass and copper, pictures and frames). FAIRS: Galgorm Manor, Ballymena; Kings Hall, Belfast.

BELFAST

Archives Antiques
88 Donegall Pass. BT7 1BX. (L. Johnston). Est. 1992. Open 10.30-5.30 or by appointment. SIZE: Medium. *STOCK: Irish silver, light fittings, porcelain, glass, coins and medals, collectables, bottles, advertising signs, pharmacy.* PARK: Easy. TEL: 028 9023 2383; mobile - 07889 104719. SER: Valuations; restorations (copper and brass polishing and repairs, re-wiring). FAIRS: Kings Hall, Belfast.

The Bell Gallery
13 Adelaide Park. BT9 6FX. (J.N. Bell). Est. 1964. Open Mon.-Thurs. 10-6 or by appointment. SIZE: Medium. *STOCK: British and Irish art, 19th-20th C.* LOC: Off Malone Rd. PARK: Easy. TEL: 028 9066 2998; e-mail - bellgallery@ btinternet.com; website - www.bellgallery.com. SER: Valuations; restorations (paintings); buys at auction. VAT: Stan/Spec.

T.H. Kearney & Sons
Treasure House, 123 University St. BT7 1HP. Resident. *STOCK: Small antiques.* TEL: 028 9023 1055. SER: Restorations and upholstery. VAT: Stan.

Kennedy Wolfenden
218 Lisburn Rd. BT9 6GD. (Miss Eleanor Wolfenden). Est. 1977. Open 9-5.30. SIZE: Medium. *STOCK: Furniture, porcelain, paintings, antique and modern jewellery.* PARK: Nearby. TEL: 028 9068 2903/7083 2295; fax - 028 9068 2903; mobile - 07831 453038; home - 01648 50228; e-mail - eleanorwolfenden@hotmail.com; website - www.antiquesni.co.uk and www.kwauctionsni. co.uk. SER: Valuations; restorations (silver, furniture including upholstery).

Oakland Antiques
135 Donegall Pass. BT7 1DS. (Alberta and Donald McCluskey). Est. 1977. *STOCK: Furniture, Georgian to Edwardian, £100-£25,000; silver, porcelain, glass, bronze and pictures, 18th-20th C, £20-£5,000.* LOC: Near city centre. PARK: Easy. TEL: 028 9023 0176; fax - 028 9024 8144; home - 028 9047 1146; mobile - 07831 176438; e-mail - sales@ oaklandni.com; website - www.oaklandni.com. SER: Valuations.

Past & Present
58-60 Donegall Pass. BT7 1BU. (Trevor McNally). Est. 1987. Open Tues.-Sat. 10.30-5. SIZE: Small. *STOCK: Art & Crafts, Art Nouveau, Victorian and Edwardian furniture; collectables, oil paintings and prints.* PARK: Easy. TEL: 028 9033 3137. SER: Framing.

Terrace Antiques
441A Lisburn Rd. BT9 7EY. (Anne and Peter Houston). Est. 1985. Open Tues.-Fri. 11.30-5, Sat. 10.30-5. SIZE: Small. *STOCK: Jewellery, Victorian and secondhand; linen, cutlery, porcelain and small furniture.* PARK: Easy. TEL: 028 9066 3943; home - 028 9070 2740; mobile - 07740 597689; e-mail - peter.houston@btclick. com. SER: Valuations; restorations (jewellery).

BUSHMILLS

Dunluce Antiques
33 Ballytober Rd. BT57 8UU. (Mrs C. Ross). Est. 1978. Open 2-6 or by appointment. CL: Fri. SIZE: Small. *STOCK: Furniture, £100-£5,000; porcelain and glass, £10-£2,000; silver, £10-£2,000; all Georgian to 1930's; paintings, mainly Irish, £100-£25,000.* LOC: 1.5 miles off Antrim coast road, at Dunluce Castle. PARK: Easy. TEL: 028 2073 1140. SER: Restorations (porcelain).

CARRICKFERGUS

Robert Christie Antiques
The Courtyard, 38 Scotch Quarter. BT38 7DP.

IADA. Est. 1976. Open 11-5. SIZE: Medium. *STOCK: Furniture, 1750-1900, £200-£3,000; clocks, 1750-1900, £500-£2,000; decorative objects, 1800-1900, £50-£500.* PARK: Easy. TEL: 028 9336 1333/9334 1149; mobile - 07802 968846. SER: Valuations. FAIRS: Kings Hall, Belfast; all RDS fairs.

LISBURN

Parvis Sigaroudinia
Mountainview House, 40 Sandy Lane, Ballyskeagh. BT27 5TL. IADA. Est. 1974. Open any time by appointment and 11-8 during quarterly exhibitions. *STOCK: Oriental and European carpets and tapestries; cushions, lamps, furniture, architectural items, William Yeoward crystal, bronze sculpture by David Williams-Ellis and Anthony Scott, Irish art, hand-crafted furniture by Richard Reade.* LOC: Take Malone Road from Belfast, then Upper Malone Road towards Lisburn, cross Ballyskeagh bridge over M1, 1st left into Sandy Lane. PARK: Easy. TEL: 028 9062 1824; home - same; fax - 028 9062 1334; mobile - 07801 347358; e-mail - parvissig@aol.com; website - www.parvis.co.uk. SER: Valuations; buys at auction; exhibitions held in Belfast. FAIRS: IADA in RDS Dublin and King's Hall, Belfast. VAT: Stan.

NEWTOWNABBEY

MacHenry Antiques
Caragh Lodge, Glen Rd., Jordanstown. BT37 0RY. (R. and A. MacHenry). IADA. Est. 1964. Open Fri. and Sat. 12-6 or by appointment. SIZE: Medium. *STOCK: Georgian and Victorian furniture and objects.* LOC: 6 miles from Belfast on M2/M5 to Whiteabbey village, left at traffic lights at Woody's, then left into Old Manse Rd. and continue into Glen Rd. PARK: Easy. TEL: 028 9086 2036; fax - 028 9085 3281; mobile - 07831 135226; e-mail - rupert.machenry@ ntlworld.com. SER: Valuations. FAIRS: Dublin, Belfast and Irish. VAT: Stan/Spec.

PORTBALLINTRAE, Nr. Bushmills

Brian R. Bolt Antiques
88 Ballaghmore Rd. BT57 8RL. (Brian and Helen Bolt). Est. 1977. Open 11-5.30 and by appointment. CL: Wed. am and Fri. am. SIZE: Small. *STOCK: Silver - small and unusual items, objects of vertu, snuff boxes, vesta cases, table, Scottish and Irish provincial; treen; English and Continental glass, antique and 20th C; art and studio glass and ceramics; Arts and Crafts, Art Nouveau and Art Deco jewellery and metalwork; vintage fountain pens.* LOC: 1 mile from Bushmills. PARK: Nearby. TEL: 028 2073 1129; fax - same; e-mail - brianbolt@antiques88. freeserve.co.uk. SER: Search; illustrated catalogues available; worldwide postal service; valuations. FAIRS: Local.

PORTRUSH

Alexander Antiques
108 Dunluce Rd. BT56 8NB. (Mrs M. and D. Alexander). Est. 1974. Open 10-6. CL: Sun. except by appointment. SIZE: Large. *STOCK: Furniture, silver, porcelain, fine art, 18th-20th C; oils and watercolours, 19th-20th C.* LOC: 1 mile from Portrush on A2 to Bushmills. PARK: Easy. TEL: 028 7082 2783. SER: Valuations; buys at auction. VAT: Stan/Spec.

Kennedy Wolfenden
86 Main St. BT56 8BN. (Miss Eleanor Wolfenden). Est. 1977. Open 9-5.30, until 7.30 July and Aug. SIZE: Medium. *STOCK: Furniture, porcelain, paintings, antique and modern jewellery.* TEL: 028 7082 5587; mobile - 07831 453038; home - 01648 50228; e-mail - eleanorwolfenden@hotmail.com; website - www. antiquesni.co.uk and www.kwauctions.co.uk. SER: Valuations; restorations (silver and furniture including upholstery).

Co. Armagh

ARMAGH

The Hole-in-the-Wall
Market St. BT61 7BW. (I. Emerson). Est. 1953. *STOCK: General antiques.* LOC: City centre. VAT: Stan/Spec.

LURGAN

Charles Gardiner Antiques
48 High St. BT66 8AU. Est. 1968. Open 9-1 and 2-6. CL: Wed. *STOCK: Clocks, furniture and general antiques.* PARK: Own. TEL: 028 3832 3934.

MOIRA

Fourwinds Antiques
Moira House, 66A Main St. BT67 0LQ. (John and Tina Cairns). Est. 1997. Open 10-5. *STOCK: Quality longcase and bracket clocks; Georgian to Edwardian furniture, porcelain and paintings.* LOC: Village centre. PARK: Beside premises. TEL: 028 9261 2226; fax - same; home - 028 3833 6352; mobile - 07713 081748; e-mail -

fourwindsantiques@freeserve.co.uk. SER: Valuations. FAIRS: Bohill House Hotel, Coleraine; Kings Hall, Belfast.

Co. Down

COMBER

Bobby Douglas Antiques
9 Killinchy St. BT23 5SD. (B. and N.R.G. Douglas). Open by appointment. SIZE: Medium and trade barn. *STOCK: Irish furniture, 18th-19th C, £1,000-£25,000; unusual collectors' items, 19th C, under £1,000.* PARK: Easy. TEL: 028 9752 8351. SER: Valuations. VAT: Stan/Spec. *Trade only.*

DUNDONALD, Nr. Belfast

Stacks Bookshop
67 Comber Rd. BT16 2AA. (Jim Tollerton). Est. 1992. Open 10-6. SIZE: Medium. *STOCK: Books - paperback fiction; military, religious, ancient and modern Irish, Arts & Crafts, travel, educational text.* LOC: Near Stormont. PARK: Easy. TEL: 028 9048 6880. SER: Valuations.

GREYABBEY, Nr. Newtownards

Phyllis Arnold Gallery Antiques
Hoops Courtyard. BT22 2NE. (Phyllis and Mike Arnold). Est. 1968. Open Wed., Fri. and Sat. 11-5. *STOCK: General antiques, jewellery, small furniture, Irish paintings and watercolours, portrait miniatures, maps and engravings of Ireland.* LOC: On shore of Strangford Lough. PARK: Easy. TEL: 028 4278 8199; home - 028 9185 3322; fax - same; website - www.antiquesni.com. SER: Restorations (maps, prints, watercolours, portrait miniatures); conservation framing. FAIRS: Ramada International.

HOLYWOOD

Herbert Gould and Co.
21-23 Church Rd. BT18 9BU. (Robert Brown). Est. 1897. Open 9.15-5.30. SIZE: Medium. *STOCK: Pine, 19th C, £75-£200; collectables, architectural antiques, 19th-20th C, £10-£100.* LOC: 20 yards from maypole in town centre. PARK: Opposite. TEL: 028 9042 7916. SER: Valuations; stripping (pine); buys at auction (as stock). VAT: Stan.

Jacquart Antiques
10-12 Hibernia St. BT18 9JE. (Daniel Uprichard). Open 10-5.30, Sun. and other times by appointment. SIZE: Medium. *STOCK: Town and country French antiques including fruitwood, walnut, oak and rosewood dining tables, chairs, beds, sideboards and occasional furniture; mirrors, chandeliers, kitchenalia and champagne memorabilia, mainly 1820-1939.* LOC: Just off High St. PARK: Nearby. TEL: 02890 426642; mobile - 07831 548803; e-mail - jacquart@ nireland.com. SER: Advice; interior designers and architects supplier; minor repairs. FAIRS: Belfast - Ramada and King's Hall.

PORTAFERRY

Time & Tide Antiques
36 Shore Rd. BT22 1JZ. (D. Dunlop). Open Wed., Fri., Sat. and Sun. 12-5.30 or by appointment. SIZE: Medium. *STOCK: Clocks, barometers, marine instruments, pictures, nautical memorabilia and small furniture, £50-£10,000.* LOC: A20 from Newtownards through Greyabbey. PARK: On Promenade. TEL: 028 4272 8935; home - same. SER: Valuations; restorations and repairs.

SAINTFIELD

Agar Antiques
92 Main St. BT24 7AD. (Rosie Agar). Est. 1990. Open 11-5. SIZE: Medium. *STOCK: Furniture, mainly Victorian, some Georgian and Edwardian, £30-£1,000; light fittings, Victorian and Edwardian, £15-£650; general small items including oil lamps, £1-£500; jewellery, Victorian and Edwardian, £10-£350.* PARK: Nearby. TEL: 028 975 11214. SER: Valuations.

The Anvil Gallery
55 Main St. BT24. (Sheila Duff). Est. 1996. Open 11-5.30. CL: Mon. and Tues. SIZE: Small. *STOCK: Works of art including paintings and prints, ceramics, wallhangings, sculpture, furniture and jewellery, to £2,000.* PARK: Easy. TEL: 028 9751 1991; fax - same; home - 028 4488 1627; e-mail - sheilamduff@hotmail.com; website - www.anvilgallery.com. SER: Framing.

Ashley Pine
88 Main St. BT24 7AB. (Mrs Truda K. Martin). Est. 1995. Open Mon. 1-5, Tues.-Fri. 10.30-5 and Sat. 10-5.30. SIZE: Small. *STOCK: General antiques and pine.* PARK: Easy. TEL: 028 9751 1855. SER: Restorations (furniture).

Attic Antiques
88 Main St. (Caesar and Reuben Doyle). Est. 1992. Open 10-5, Sat. 10-5.30. SIZE: Large. *STOCK: Victorian and Edwardian furniture, £50-*

£2,000; Victorian jewellery, £5-£1,000; bric-a-brac, to £100. (+ Irish, European and reclaimed pine, £30-£1,000 at Attic Pine). PARK: Easy. TEL: 028 9751 1057. SER: Valuations.

Peter Francis Antiques
92 Main St. BT24 7AD. Est. 1998. Open 11-5. SIZE: Medium. *STOCK: English, Irish and Oriental ceramics, 18th-20th C; English and Irish glass, mainly 18th-19th, some 20th C; smalls including ethnographic, Indian, European, bronzes, metalwork, treen and prints; all £5-£500.* PARK: Nearby. TEL: 028 9751 1214; e-mail - irishantiq@aol. com. SER: Valuations.

Saintfield Antiques & Fine Books
68 Main St. BT24 7AB. (Joseph Leckey). Est. 1978. Open Thurs., Fri. and Sat. 11.30-5. SIZE: Small. *STOCK: Silver, 18th-20th, £25-£750; porcelain, 18th-19th C, £50-£500; fine and antiquarian books, 19th-20th C, £10-£500.* PARK: Easy. TEL: Home - 028 9752 8428; fax - same; e-mail - home@antiquesireland.com; website - www.antiquesireland.com. FAIRS: All L&M Ltd.

Town & Country Antiques
92 Main St. BT24 7AB. (Patricia Keller). Est. 1997. Open Wed.-Sat. 10.30-5. SIZE: Medium. *STOCK: Prints, botanical, ornithological and sporting, £100-£400; 18th-19th C French tapestries, £600-£1,500; French chandeliers £300-£600; Venetian, French and Victorian mirrors, £400-£700; Georgian, Victorian and Edwardian small mahogany furniture, £500-£1,000; table lamps, rugs and equestrian items, desks.* PARK: Easy. TEL: 028 4461 4721; home - same; fax - 028 4461 9716; mobile - 07710 840090; e-mail - l.w.k@btinternet.com. SER: Restorations (furniture, prints and tapestries). VAT: Stan.

SEAPATRICK, Nr. Banbridge

Millcourt Antiques
99 Lurgan Rd. BT32 4NE. (Gillian Close). Est. 1982. Open 11-5.30. CL: Thurs. SIZE: Small. *STOCK: Furniture, 18th-19th C, £30-£4,000; work and writing boxes, clocks; china, glass and collectables, to Art Deco, to £1,000; linen, quilts and textiles; jewellery, Victorian and 20th C, £20-£500.* PARK: Easy. TEL: 028 4066 2909; e-mail - gillian@drumbanagher.freeserve.co.uk. SER: Valuations.

Co. Fermanagh

BALLINAMALLARD

Ballindullagh Barn Antique Pine
Ballindullagh. BT94 2NY. (Roy and Diana Armstrong). Est. 1990. Open 10-5.30, evenings by appointment.SIZE: Large. *STOCK: Eastern European pine including dressers, settles and benches, chests, blanket boxes, wardrobes, cupboards and beds, 1700-1920, £75-£450.* PARK: Easy. TEL: 028 6862 1548; fax - 028 6862 1802; e-mail - enquiries@ballindullagh barn.com; website - www.ballindullaghbarn. com. SER: Valuations; restorations; stripping.

Co. Londonderry

COLERAINE

The Forge Antiques
24 Long Commons. BT52 1LH. (M.W. and R.G.C. Walker). Est. 1977. Open 10-5.30. CL: Thurs. SIZE: Medium. *STOCK: General antiques, silver, clocks, jewellery, porcelain, paintings.* PARK: Easy. TEL: 028 7035 1339. VAT: Stan.

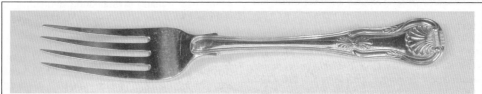

This King's pattern table fork was made in London in 1817 by Sarah Purver (who is presumed to be the widow of the spoon-maker Thomas Purver). It is in excellent condition and it is worth noting the length and evenness of the tines, the crispness of the raised decoration and the square (unworn) edges of the sides of the tines and handle. (Private Collection)

From an article entitled "Buying a set of Old Silver Spoons and Forks" by Jane Ewart which appeared in the May 2002 issue of ***Antique Collecting***. For more details and to subscribe see page 21.

Homes, Pubs and Clubs
1-5 Portrush Rd. BT52 1RL. (McNulty Wholesalers). Resident. Est. 1983. Open 9-6, Sun. 2.30-6. SIZE: Large. *STOCK: Pine and mahogany, small interesting items.* LOC: Main Portrush road, near traffic lights. PARK: At rear. TEL: 028 7035 5733. SER: Valuations; restorations. FAIRS: Newark. VAT: Stan.

LONDONDERRY

Foyle Antiques/Whitehouse Furniture
16 Whitehouse Rd. BT48 0NE. (John Helferty). Est. 1982. Open 9.30-5.30, Sun. 3-6. SIZE: Large. *STOCK: Victorian and Edwardian furniture, £200-£3,000; lamps, pictures, ornaments, prints, clocks and decorative items, £30-£300; reproduction furniture, four-poster beds, bedroom and dining suites, £1,000-£5,000.* LOC: Buncrana Rd., just out of Londonderry. PARK: Own. TEL: 028 7126 7626; fax - same; e-mail - John@foyleantiques.com; website - www. foyleantiques.com. SER: Valuations; restorations (furniture including upholstery).

Foyle Books
12 Magazine St. BT48 6HH. (A. Byrne and K. Thatcher). Est. 1982. Open 11-5. SIZE: Medium. *STOCK: Antiquarian books on Ireland, Derry, Donegal, theology, French and general.* LOC: Town centre. PARK: Quayside. TEL: 028 7137 2530. SER: Valuations.

Co. Tyrone

COOKSTOWN

Cookstown Antiques
16 Oldtown St. BT80 8EF. (G. Jebb). Est. 1976. Open Thurs. and Fri. 2-5.30, Sat. 10.30-5.30. SIZE: Small. *STOCK: Jewellery, silver, £10-£2,000; coins, £25-£200; pictures, ceramics and militaria, £5-£1,000; general antiques, all 19th-20th C.* LOC: Going north, through both sets of traffic lights, on left at rear of estate agency. PARK: Easy. TEL: 028 8676 5279; fax - 028 8676 2946; home - 028 8676 2926. SER: Valuations; buys at auction.

The Saddle Room Antiques
4 Coagh St. BT80 8NG. (C.J. Leitch). Est. 1968. Open 10-5.30. CL: Mon. and Wed. SIZE: Medium. *STOCK: China, silver, furniture, glass, jewellery.* TEL: 028 8676 4045.

MOY, Nr. Dungannon

Moy Antique Pine
15 Charlemont St. BT71 7SG. (Barry J. MacNeice). Est. 1972. Open 10-6. SIZE: Large. *STOCK: Reclaimed pine hand crafted furniture including free standing kitchens; Eastern European, English and Irish original pine furniture.* LOC: Main street. PARK: Nearby. TEL: 028 8778 9909; fax - same; home - 028 8778 4895; mobile - 07909 538784; e-mail - info@moyantiques.com; website - www.moy antiques.com. SER: Valuations; restorations. FAIRS: Ideal Home, Belfast; Dublin.

Moy Antiques
12 The Square. BT71 7SG. (Laurence MacNeice). Open 9.30-5.30. SIZE: Large. *STOCK: Georgian to pre-1940's furniture, paintings, clocks, mirrors, objets d'art and fireplaces; cast-iron, marble and bronze garden statuary.* LOC: Village centre. PARK: Easy. TEL: 028 8778 4755; home - same; fax - 028 8778 4895; mobile - 07778 373509; e-mail - macneice @moyantiques.fsnet.co.uk; website - www.moy antiques.com. SER: Valuations; restorations. FAIRS: IDA, Dublin.

OMAGH

Kelly Antiques
Mullaghmore House, Old Mountfield Rd. BT79 7EX. (Louis Kelly). Est. 1932. Open 9-7, Sat. 10-5.30. SIZE: Large. *STOCK: Fireplaces, from early Adam inlaid to Edwardian slate, European chimney pieces, £80-£125,000; hardwood furniture, Georgian to early Victorian, £150-£40,000; early architectural salvage, £10-£10,000.* LOC: One mile from town centre. PARK: Easy. TEL: 028 8224 2314; home - same; fax - 028 8225 0262; e-mail - sales@kellyantiques.com; website - www.kellyantiques.com. SER: Valuations; restorations (Elizabethan to Edwardian furniture; fireplaces); short and full time courses for conservation, heritage and restoration.

STEWARTSTOWN

P. J. Smith (Antiques)
1 North St. BT71 5JE. Est. 1977. Open 10.30-1 and 2-6, Thurs. until 9, Sat. 10-6. SIZE: Large. *STOCK: Fireplaces, from early Georgian - marble, £1,500-£60,000; metal, £250-£10,000; wooden, £950-£20,000; slate, £1,150-£5,000; antique leaded and stained glass, brass and brass and iron beds.* LOC: Town centre. PARK: Town sqaure. TEL: 028 8773 8071; fax - 028 8773 8059. SER: Valuations; restorations (fireplaces). FAIRS: Ideal Home, Belfast.

SCOTLAND

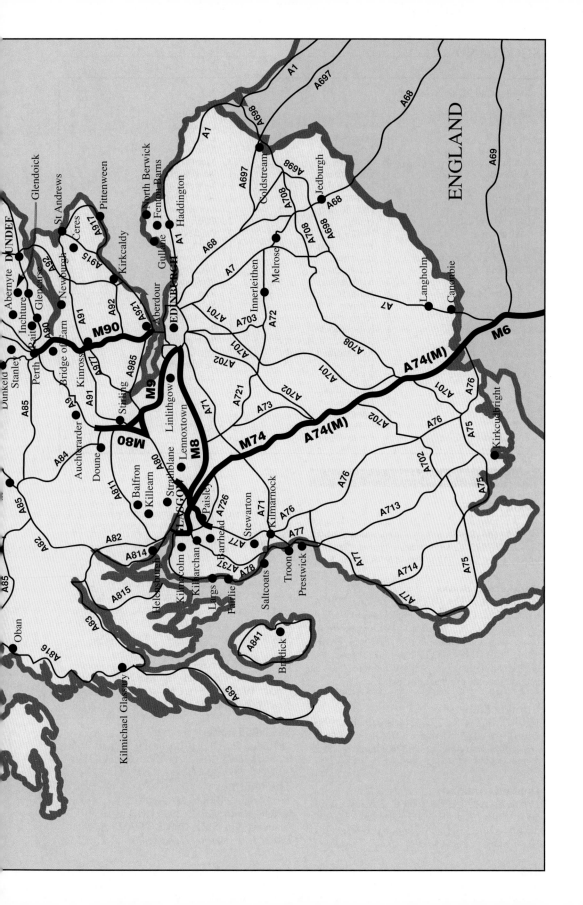

Dealers and Shops in Scotland

Aberdeen	11	Forfar	1	Linlithgow	3
Aberdour	1	Forres	1	Lockerbie	1
Aberfeldy	1	Fortrose	1	Longhaven	1
Abernyte	1	Friockheim	1	Melrose	1
Auchterarder	4	Glasgow	18	Montrose	2
Auldearn	1	Glencarse	1	Newburgh	1
Balfron	1	Glendoick	2	Newport-on-Tay	1
Ballater	2	Gullane	1	Newtonmore	1
Beauly	1	Haddington	2	North Berwick	3
Blair Atholl	1	Huntly	2	Oban	1
Blairgowrie	2	Inchture	2	Paisley	2
Bridge of Earn	1	Innerleithen	1	Perth	7
Brodick and Whiting Bay	1	Inverness	1	Pittenweem	2
Canonbie	1	Jedburgh	1	Portsoy	1
Ceres	2	Kilbarchan	2	Prestwick	1
Clola by Mintlaw	1	Killearn	1	Rait	1
Coldstream	3	Killin	2	Saltcoats	1
Cove	1	Kilmacolm	1	St. Andrews	2
Cromarty	1	Kilmarnock	1	Stanley	1
Dornoch	2	Kilmichael Glassary	1	Stewarton	1
Doune	1	Kincardine O'Neil	1	Stirling	1
Dundee	4	Kingston-on-Spey	1	Strathblane	1
Dunecht	1	Kirkcaldy	1	Troon	2
Dunkeld	1	Kirkcudbright	2	Ullapool	1
Edinburgh	57	Kirkmahoe	1	Upper Largo	1
Fairlie	1	Langholm	1	Whithorn	1
Falkirk	1	Largs	1	Wigtown	1
Fochabers	3	Lennoxtown	1		

ABERDEEN

Atholl Antiques
322 Great Western Rd. AB10 6PL. Est. 1971. Open 10.30-1 and 2.30-6 or by appointment. SIZE: Small. *STOCK: Scottish paintings and furniture.* PARK: Easy. TEL: 01224 593547. VAT: Stan/Spec.

Bon-Accord Books
69-75 Spital. AB24 3HX. (Andy Milne). PBFA. Est. 1998. Open 11-5, Sat.11-4.30. SIZE: Medium. *STOCK: Scottish, sporting, childrens, travel and antiquarian books, £5-£800.* PARK: Easy. TEL: 01224 643209; e-mail - bonaccord. books@btinternet.com. SER: Valuations; buys at auction (books, prints and maps).

Burning Embers
165-167 King St. AB2 3AE. (J. Bruce). Est. 1988. Open 10-5. SIZE: Medium. *STOCK: Fireplaces, bric-a-brac and pine.* LOC: Off Union St. TEL: 01224 624664. SER: Installations.

Denburn Antiques
25 Spa St. AB25 1PU. (John C. Lawrence). Est. 2000. Open Tues.-Fri. 12-5.30, Sat. 10-5.30. SIZE: Small. *STOCK: Furniture, Georgian to Edwardian, £200-£3,000; glass, ceramics,* *mirrors, watercolours, oils and etchings, Victorian to early 20th C, £50-£1,000.* LOC: Town centre. PARK: Easy and nearby. TEL: 01224 624101; mobile - 07866 037217; e-mail - johnc.lawrence@virgin.net. SER: Valuations; restorations (furniture).

Gallery
239 George St. AB25 1ED. (M. Gray). Est. 1981. Open 9-5.30. SIZE: Large. *STOCK: Jewellery, post 1850; curios and Victoriana, paintings and prints, post 1800.* TEL: 01224 632522. SER: Valuations; repairs (jewellery and clocks).

McCalls (Aberdeen)
90 King St. AB1 2JH. (B. McCall). Est. 1948. Open 10-5.30. *STOCK: Jewellery.* PARK: Nearby. TEL: 01224 641916.

McCalls Limited
11 Bridge St. AB11 6JL. Open 9.30-5.30, Thurs. 9.30-8. *STOCK: Jewellery.* TEL: 01224 405303.

The Odd Lot
18 Adelphi, Union St. AB11 5BL. (George Knight-Mudie). Est. 1995. Open 10.30-5.30 including Sun. SIZE: Small. *STOCK: Furniture, £30-£1,000; jewellery and china, £5-£750; all*

SCOTLAND
DISTRICTS

19th -20th C. LOC: 2 mins. from Tourist Information Office. PARK: Easy. TEL: 01224 592551; fax - 01224 575813; home - 07833 773772; e-mail - info@theoddlot.com; website - www.theoddlot.com. SER: Valuations; restorations (furniture and china).

The Rendezvous Gallery
100 Forest Ave. AB15 4TL. Est. 1973. Open 10-1 and 2.30-6. CL: Fri. SIZE: Medium. *STOCK: Art Nouveau, Art Deco, glass, jewellery, bronzes, furniture, £100-£5,000; paintings, watercolours, Scottish School, £200-£6,000.* LOC: Just off Great Western Rd. to Braemar. PARK: Easy. TEL: 01224 323247; fax - 01224 326029; e-mail - info@rendezvous-gallery.co.uk; website - www.rendezvous-gallery.co.uk. VAT: Stan/ Spec.

Thistle Antiques　LAPADA
28 Esslemont Ave. AB25 1SN. (P. and Mrs M. Bursill). Est. 1967. Open 10-5, Sat. 10-1. CL: Wed. SIZE: Medium. *STOCK: General antiques, Georgian and Victorian furniture, period lighting.* LOC: City centre. PARK: Easy. TEL: 01224 634692. VAT: Spec.

Colin Wood (Antiques) Ltd
25 Rose St. AB10 1TX. Est. 1968. Open 9.30-5, Wed. and Thurs. 10-5. SIZE: Medium. *STOCK: Furniture, 17th-19th C; works of art, Scottish paintings, prints and silver; specialist in maps of Scotland, 16th-19th C.* PARK: Multi-storey in Chapel St. TEL: 01224 644786 (answerphone); fax - same. VAT: Stan/Spec.

ABERDOUR

Antiques and Gifts
26 High St. KY3 0SW. Est. 1976. CL: Mon., Tues. am. and Wed. pm. SIZE: Small. *STOCK: China, pottery, glass and collectables.* LOC: A921. PARK: Nearby. TEL: 01383 860523. SER: Restorations (china).

ABERFELDY

Sonia Cooper
19 Bridgend. PH15 2DF. Est. 1983. Open Thurs.-Sat. 11-4, Mon. in summer. SIZE: Medium. *STOCK: China, glass, wood and metal, from 18th C, £1-£100.* LOC: 10 miles from A9. PARK: Easy. TEL: 01887 820266. SER: Buys at auction.

ABERNYTE

Scottish Antique & Arts Centre
PH14 9SJ. (Templemans). Open 10-5 including Sun. SIZE: Large - 100 dealers. *STOCK: Furniture, £50-£5,000; accessories, £5-£2,000; collectibles, £5-£50; all 18th-19th C.* LOC: 1.5 miles from A90 Perth-Dundee link road. PARK: Own. TEL: 01828 686401; fax - 01828 686199. SER: Valuations; restorations. VAT: Stan/Spec/ Global.

AUCHTERARDER

Ian Burton Antique Clocks
at The Antique Galleries, 125 High St. PH3 1AA. Open 9-5, Sat. 10-5. *STOCK: Clocks.* TEL: 01334 471426; mobile - 07785 114800; e-mail - ian@ianburton.com; website - www.ianburton.com.

Nigel Stacy-Marks Ltd　LAPADA
92 High St. PH3 1BJ. (Nigel and Ginny Marks). Open 10-5. SIZE: Medium. *STOCK: Oils and watercolours, 19th-20th C, £250-£30,000; British etchings, late 19th C to mid 20th C, £100-£5,000.* LOC: Opposite library, next to Tourist Information Centre. PARK: Easy. TEL: 01764 663525; fax - same; e-mail - paintings@stacy-marks.co.uk; website - www.stacy-marks.co.uk. SER: Valuations; restorations; framing; regular exhibitions (catalogues on request). FAIRS: Antiques For Everyone, SECC, Glasgow. VAT: Stan/Spec.

Times Past Antiques
Broadfold Farm. PH3 1DR. (J.M. Brown). Est. 1970. Open 8-4.30, weekends and holidays 10-3. SIZE: Large. *STOCK: Stripped pine, 19th-20th C, from £50; shipping goods, £5-£500.* LOC: From town centre take Abbey Rd. to flyover A9 at T junction. Turn left, 1st farm on left. PARK: Easy. TEL: 01764 663166; fax - same. SER: Restorations (pine); courier; container-packing.

John Whitelaw and Sons Antiques LAPADA
125 High St. PH3 1AA. Open 9-5, Sat. 9-1 and 2-5. *STOCK: General antiques; furniture, 17th-19th C.* PARK: Easy. TEL: 01764 662482; fax - 01764 663577; e-mail - jwsantique@aol.com; website - www.whitelawantiques.com. VAT: Stan/Spec.

AULDEARN, Nr. Nairn

Auldearn Antiques
Dalmore Manse, Lethen Rd. IV12 5HZ. Est. 1980. Open 9.30-5.30 including Sun. SIZE: Medium. *STOCK: Victorian linen and lace, kitchenalia, china, furniture, architectural items.* LOC: 1 mile from village. TEL: 01667 453087; home - same.

BALFRON

Amphora Galleries
16-18 Buchanan St. G63 0TT. (L. Ruglen). Resident. Est. 1961. Open 10-5.30 and by appointment. SIZE: Large. *STOCK: General antiques, furniture, decorative items.* LOC: A81. PARK: Easy. TEL: 01360 440329. SER: Polishing; repairs.

BALLATER

The McEwan Gallery LAPADA
Bridge of Gairn. AB35 5UB. (D., P. and R. McEwan). Est. 1968. Open 2-5.30, Sun. 2-5, prior telephone call advisable during winter. SIZE: Medium. *STOCK: 18th-20th C British and European paintings, specialising in Scottish; rare and elusive polar, Scottish, golf, sporting and natural history books.* LOC: First house on the east side of A939 after its junction with A93 outside Ballater. PARK: Easy. TEL: 01339 755429; fax - 01339 755995. SER: Valuations; restorations; framing; buys at auction (paintings, watercolours, books); golf catalogues. VAT: Spec.

Treasures of Ballater
1 Victoria Rd. AB35 5QQ. (Mrs. Nichola L. Henderson). Est. 1982. Open 10.30-5.30 (including Sun. April-Oct). SIZE: Small. *STOCK: Victorian furniture, porcelain and pottery, Scottish silver and jewellery, antique, fine and estate jewellery, paintings and engravings, £10-£3,000.* LOC: Village centre. PARK: Easy. TEL: 01339 755122; home - 01339 755676; e-mail - nikki.rowan@lineone.net; website - www.treasuresofBallater.com. SER: Valuations; restorations (jewellery); upholstery; shipping. FAIRS: Treetops Hotel, Aberdeen (monthly).

BEAULY

Iain Marr Antiques
3 Mid St. IV4 7DP. (I. and A. Marr). HADA. Est. 1975. Open 10.30-1 and 2-5.30. CL: Thurs. *STOCK: Silver, jewellery, clocks, porcelain, scientific instruments, arms, oils, watercolours, small furniture.* LOC: Off the square, on left going north (next to Coffee Shop). PARK: Easy. TEL: 01463 782372; e-mail - info@iain-marr-antiques.com; website - www.iain-marr-antiques.com. VAT: Stan/Spec/Global.

BLAIR ATHOLL, Nr. Pitlochry

Blair Antiques
By Bruar Falls. PH18 5TW. (Duncan Huie). Est. 1976. Open 9-5. SIZE: Medium. *STOCK: Period furniture, Scottish oil paintings, silver - some provincial, curios, clocks, pottery and porcelain.* PARK: Easy. TEL: 01796 483264. SER: Valuations; buys at auction. VAT: Stan/Spec.

BLAIRGOWRIE

Blairgowrie Books
3 Meadow Place, Wellmeadow. PH10 6NQ. (Marlene Hughes). Est. 1982. Open 10.30-1 and 2-5, Sat. 10.30-5, Sun. by appointment. CL: Tues. SIZE: Medium. *STOCK: Books - mainly on Scottish fishing, shooting, hunting and climbing, £2.50-£150; children's and general.* LOC: Next to River Ericht, town centre. PARK: Easy. TEL: 01250 875855. SER: Valuations.

Roy Sim Antiques
The Granary Warehouse, Lower Mill St. PH10 6AQ. (Roy and Ann Sim). Est. 1977. Open 9-5.30, Sun. 12-5. SIZE: Large. *STOCK: Furniture, clocks, silver, EPNS, collectables, decorative and furnishing items.* LOC: Town centre. PARK: Own. TEL: 01250 873860. SER: Shipping. VAT: Spec.

BRIDGE OF EARN

Imrie Antiques LAPADA
Back St. PH2 9AE. (Mr and Mrs I. Imrie). Est. 1969. Open 10-1 and 2-5.30. SIZE: Large. *STOCK: Victorian and 18th C shipping goods.* PARK: Easy. TEL: 01738 812784. VAT: Stan.

BRODICK AND WHITING BAY

Kames Antiques & Jewellery
Shore Rd. KA27 8AJ. (C.J. and J.M. Fieldhouse).
Open 10-5. *STOCK: Furniture, porcelain,
paintings, jewellery, collectables, objets d'art,
silver and artists' materials.* TEL: 01770 302213.

CANONBIE, Nr. Carlisle

The Clock Showrooms
DG14 0SY. (John R. Mann). MCWG. Est. 1987.
Open by appointment. SIZE: Large. *STOCK:
Clocks - over 80 restored longcase, 17th-19th C,
£2,500-£90,000; bracket, 17th-19th C, £3,500-
£35,000; wall, 19th C, £500-£6,000; small
antiques and collectables.* LOC: Leave M6,
junction 44, A7 north through Longtown, follow
sign to village, premises next to Cross Keys
Hotel. PARK: Easy. TEL: 01387 371337/71827;
fax - 01387 371337; mobile - 07850 606147; e-
mail - jmannclock@aol.com; website - www.john
mannantiqueclocks.co.uk. SER: Valuations;
restorations (clock movements, cases and dials);
buys at auction (clocks). VAT: Stan.

CERES

Ceres Antiques
1 High St. KY15. (Mrs E. Norrie). SIZE:
Medium. *STOCK: General antiques, china and
linen.* PARK: Easy. TEL: 01334 828384.

Steeple Antiques
38 Main St. KY15 5NH. (Mrs Elizabeth Hart).
Est. 1980. Open 2-5 including Sun., mornings by
appointment. CL: Wed. pm. SIZE: Medium.
*STOCK: Porcelain including some Wemyss,
1800-1950, £5-£500; cutlery, silver and plate, £5-
£200+; Victorian linen, some furniture, £50-
£400.* LOC: 3 miles from Cupar. PARK: Easy.
TEL: Home - 01334 828553. SER: Valuations;
buys at auction (silver, china and furniture).

CLOLA BY MINTLAW, Nr. Peterhead

Clola Antiques Centre
Shannas School House. AB42 5AE. (Joan and
DavidBlackburn). Est. 1985. Open 10-5, Sun. 11-
4.30 or by appointment. SIZE: Large - 10 dealers.
*STOCK: Victorian and Edwardian furniture,
antique and modern jewellery, collectables, china
and militaria.* LOC: 3 miles south of Mintlaw and
25 miles north of Aberdeen on A952. PARK:
Own. TEL: 01771 624584; fax - 01771 624751;
e-mail - clolaantique@aol.com; website - www.
clolaantiquecentre.co.uk. VAT: Margin.

COLDSTREAM

Coldstream Antiques
44 High St. TD12 4AS. (Mr and Mrs J. Trinder).
Resident. Open daily. SIZE: Large. *STOCK:
Furniture, 17th-20th C; general antiques, clocks,
silver and shipping goods, 17th-19th C.* LOC:
A697. TEL: 01890 882552. VAT: Stan/Spec.

Fraser Antiques
65 High St. TD12 4DL. Est. 1968. Open Tues.-Fri.
10-5, Sat. 9.30-5, other times by appointment.
SIZE: Medium. *STOCK: Porcelain, glass, pictures,
silver, small furniture, general antiques.* PARK:
Easy. TEL: 01890 882450; fax - 01890 882451.
SER: Valuations; restorations. VAT: Spec.

Hand in Hand
Hirsel Law Schoolhouse. (Mrs Ruth Hand). Est.
1969. Open by appointment. *STOCK: Paisley
shawls, period costume, fine linens, quilts,
curtains and interesting textiles.* PARK: Own.
TEL: 01890 883496; e-mail - ruth.hand@virgin.
net; website - www.handinhand.uk.com. SER:
Restorations; valuations. FAIRS: Textile
(London, Manchester).

COVE

Cove Curios
Shore Rd. G84 0LR. (R. and K.J. Young). Open
weekends and daily May-Sept., other times by
appointment. *STOCK: General antiques.* PARK:
Easy. TEL: 01436 842222

CROMARTY

Cromarty Antiques
24 Church St. IV11 8XA. (Jean and Jenny
Henderson). Est. 2000. Open Tues.-Sat. 10-5 in
summer, other days and winter by appointment.
SIZE: Large. *STOCK: Georgian, Victorian and
Edwardian fine furniture, especially dining room
tables; porcelain, glass, metalware, silver
including Scottish provincial.* LOC: On the Black
Isle (just north of Inverness), follow signs for
Cromarty from A9. PARK: Easy. TEL: 01381
600404; fax - 01381 610408; home - 01381
610269. FAIRS: Robert Soper - Hopetown
House; Scone Palace; Galloway - Perth;
Drumossie - Inverness. VAT: Spec.

DORNOCH

Castle Close Antiques
Castle Close. IV25 3SN. (Mrs J. Maclean). Est.
1982. Open 10-1 and 2-5. CL: Thurs. pm. SIZE:
Medium. *STOCK: General antiques including,*

furniture, stripped pine, porcelain, jewellery and silver, paintings. PARK: Easy. TEL: 01862 810405; home - 01862 81057; e-mail - enquiries @castle-close-antiques.com. VAT: Spec.

Little Treasures
Shore Rd. IV25 3LS. (Allison Taylor). Est. 1993. Open 10-5, Sun. 12-4 (summer only). SIZE: Small. STOCK: Jewellery, ceramics and glass, 19th-20th C, £5-£1,000. LOC: Just off cathedral square, road opposite tourist Information. PARK: Easy. TEL: 01862 811175; e-mail - alliandtrev@ aol.com. SER: Valuations.

DOUNE

Scottish Antique & Arts Centre
FK16 6HE. (Robert Templeman). Est. 1999. Open 10-5 including Sun. SIZE: Large. STOCK: General antiques, collectables, Georgian and Victorian furniture, jewellery, glass, paintings, books. LOC: A84 Stirling to Callander road, 1 mile north of Doune. PARK: Own. TEL: 01786 841203; fax - 01786 842561; e-mail - vic templeman@aol.com; website - www.scottish-antiques.com. VAT: Stan./Spec.

DUNDEE

Angus Antiques
4 St. Andrews St. DD1 2EX. (Stanley Paget and John Czerek). Est. 1964. Open 10-4. CL: Sat. STOCK: Militaria, badges, medals, swords, jewellery, silver, gold, collectors items, Art Nouveau, Art Deco, advertising and decorative items, tins, toys, teddy bears. LOC: City centre. PARK: Nearby. TEL: 01382 322128.

Neil Livingstone
LAPADA
3 Old Hawkhill. DD2 1LS. Open any time by appointment. SIZE: Small. STOCK: Jewellery, Continental furniture and decorative items, 18th-20th C. TEL: 01382 907788/221751; fax - 01382 566332; mobile - 07775 877715; e-mail - npl88@onetel.net. SER: Shipping worldwide.

Westport Gallery
48 Westport. DD1 5ER. Est. 1976. Open 9-5. SIZE: Medium. STOCK: Antique jewellery. LOC: City centre end of Perth Rd, turn into Tay St. and bear left, shop on the left. PARK: Easy. TEL: 01382 221751; fax - 01382 229707. SER: Valuations; repairs. VAT: Stan/Spec.

Yesterday, To-day, Tomorrow
38 Constitution St. DD3 6ND. (A.J.M. Pinto). Est. 1998. Open 10-6, Tues. 10-1. SIZE: Small. STOCK: Furniture, including French, 1870-1885,

£200-£1,200; Victorian coins, to £700. LOC: Hilltown. PARK: Easy. TEL: 01382 206661; fax - same; home - 01382 453171; mobile - 07747 146949. FAIRS: Local. Trade Only.

DUNECHT

The Magic Lantern
Nether Corskie. AB32 7EL. (Mr and Mrs P. Whyte). Est. 1978. SIZE: Medium. STOCK: Georgian and Victorian furniture, £500-£2,000; silver and plate Victorian cutlery, £50-£100; china, porcelain, Scottish pottery, candlesticks, £25-£200. LOC: A944, turn towards Kintore. PARK: Easy. TEL: 01330 860678; home - same. SER: Restorations (china).

DUNKELD

Dunkeld Antiques
LAPADA
Tay Terrace. PH8 0AQ. (D. Dytch). Est. 1986. Open 10-5.30, Sun. 12-5.30. SIZE: Large. STOCK: 18th-19th C items especially dining furniture, clocks, shooting memorabilia and out of print books. LOC: Converted church, overlooking River Tay. PARK: Easy. TEL: 01350 728832; fax - 01350 727008; e-mail - sales@ dunkeldantiques.com. SER: Valuations. FAIRS: Battersea. VAT: Spec.

EDINBURGH

Antiques
48 Thistle St. EH2 1EN. (E. Humphrey). Est. 1946. Open mornings or by appointment. STOCK: Paintings, etchings, china and glass. TEL: 0131 226 3625.

Armchair Books
72 West Port. EH1 2LE. (David Govan). Est. 1993. Open 11-5.30 and most Sun. SIZE: Small. STOCK: Books, secondhand and Victorian, £2-£50. LOC: West from Grassmarket. PARK: Nearby. TEL: 0131 229 5927; e-mail - armchairbooks@hotmail.com. SER: Valuations; restorations (books).

Bebes et Jouets
c/o Lochend Post Office. 165 Restalrig Rd. EH7 6HW. Est. 1988. Open by appointment. SIZE: Small. STOCK: Fine French and German dolls, vintage teddy bears, dolls' houses and miniature doll-related items, dolls' clothing and accessories. LOC: 1/2 mile from Princes St. PARK: Easy. TEL: 0131 332 5650; e-mail - bebesetjouets@u.genie.co.uk; website - www. you.genie.co.uk/bebesetjouets. SER: Photographs and videos of stock available.

Berland's of Edinburgh
143 Gilmore Place. EH3 9PW. (R. Melvin). Open 9-5. *STOCK: Restored antique light fittings.* TEL: 0131 228 6760.

Joseph Bonnar, Jewellers
72 Thistle St. EH2 1EN. Open 10.30-5 or by appointment. SIZE: Medium. *STOCK: Antique and period jewellery.* LOC: Parallel with Princes St. TEL: 0131 226 2811; fax - 0131 225 9438. VAT: Stan/Spec.

Bourne Fine Art Ltd
6 Dundas St. EH3 6HZ. (P. Bourne). Est. 1978. Open 10-6, Sat. 11-2. SIZE: Medium. *STOCK: British paintings, 1700-1950.* PARK: Easy. TEL: 0131 557 4050. SER: Valuations; restorations; buys at auction; framing. VAT: Stan/Spec.

Bow-well Antiques
103-105 West Bow. EH1 2JP. (Murdoch J. McLeod). Est. 1984. Open 10-5 or by appointment. SIZE: Medium. *STOCK: Scottish items - jewellery, dress items, weapons, ceramics and glass, silver, £50-£10,000; clocks and barometers, £200-£8,000; prints, some paintings, £50-£3,000; furniture, £100-£10,000; all mainly 18th-19th C. Scientific and medical items, 19th C, £10-£2,000.* LOC: Grassmarket area of old town. PARK: Grassmarket. TEL: 0131 225 3335; fax - 0131 226 1259; mobile - 07710 600431; e-mail - murdoch.mcleod@virgin.net. SER: Valuations.

Broughton Books
2A Broughton Place. EH1 3RX. (P. Galinsky). Est. 1964. Open Tues.-Fri. 12-6, Sat. 10.30-5.30. SIZE: Medium. *STOCK: Books, secondhand and antiquarian, £2.50-£250.* LOC: Off Broughton St, close to Waverley station and top of Leith Walk. TEL: 0131 557 8010; home - 0131 478 0614.

Caboodle
127 Gilmore Place. EH3 9PP. (Gordon Inglis). Est. 1990. Open 12-5. SIZE: *STOCK: General antiques including pictures, small collectables, vintage clothing, glass, china and ephemera.* TEL: 0131 221 1192; mobile - 07966 505219; e-mail - gordon@inglisantiques.com; website - www.inglisantiques.com.

Calton Gallery — BADA
10 Royal Terr. EH7 5AB. (A.G. Whitfield). Est. 1979. Open 10-6, Sat. by appointment. SIZE: Large. *STOCK: Paintings, especially Scottish marine and watercolours, £100-£100,000; prints, £10-£1,000; sculpture, to £20,000; all 19th to early 20th C. PARK: Easy. TEL: 0131 556 1010; home - same; fax - 0131 558 1150;
e-mail - mail@caltongallery.co.uk; website - www.caltongallery.co.uk. SER: Valuations; restorations (oils, watercolours, prints); buys at auction (paintings). VAT: Stan/Spec.

The Carson Clark Gallery - Scotland's Map Heritage Centre
181-183 Canongate, The Royal Mile. EH8 8BN. (A. Carson Clark). FRGS. FBCartS. Est. 1969. Open 10.30-5.30. *STOCK: Maps, sea charts and prints.* TEL: 0131 556 4710; fax - same; e-mail - scotmap@aol.com. SER: Collections valued and purchased.

The Collectors Shop
49 Cockburn St. EH1 1BS. (D. Cavanagh). Est. 1960. Open 11-5. *STOCK: Coins, medals, militaria, cigarette and postcards, small collectors' items, jewellery, silver and plate.* Not Stocked: Postage stamps. TEL: 0131 226 3391. SER: Buys at auction.

Craiglea Clocks
88 Comiston Rd. EH10 5QJ. (R.J. Rafter). Est. 1977. Open 10-5. SIZE: Small. *STOCK: Antique clocks and barometers.* LOC: On Biggar road from Morningside. PARK: Adjacent streets. TEL: 0131 452 8568; website - www.craigleaclocks.com. SER: Restorations (clocks and barometers).

Da Capo Antiques
68 Henderson Row. EH3 5BJ. (Nick Carter). Est. 1975. Open Wed.-Sun. 10.30-5.30. SIZE: Medium. *STOCK: Furniture including brass bedsteads; lighting, 18th to early 20th C, £500-£1,000.* LOC: Off Dundas St. PARK: Easy. TEL: 0131 557 1918; home - 0131 557 3621. SER: Valuations; restorations (furniture including upholstery). VAT: Spec.

Alan Day Antiques — LAPADA
25A Moray Place. EH3 6DA. Open by appointment. *STOCK: Furniture and paintings, 18th-19th C; general antiques.* TEL: 0131 225 2590.

A.F. Drysdale Ltd
35 and 20 North West Circus Place. EH3 6TW. Est. 1974. Open 9.30-1 and 2-6. *STOCK: Quality Continental reproduction lamps, decorative furniture; antique prints.* TEL: 0131 225 4686. VAT: Stan.

George Duff Antiques
254 Leith Walk. EH6 5EL. Open by appointment. *STOCK: Shipping goods, pre-1940.* TEL: 0131 554 8164; home - 0131 337 1422. VAT: Stan. *Export Only.*

Duncan & Reid

5 Tanfield, Inverleith. EH3 5DA. (Margaret Duncan, Susan Reid and Pippa Scott). Est. 1992. Open Tues.-Sat. 12-5.30. SIZE: Small. *STOCK: 18th-19th C English, Chinese and Continental ceramics, glass and decorative objects; books including sets, modern and antiquarian.* LOC: Near Royal Botanic Gardens. PARK: Easy. TEL: 0131 556 4591.

EASY - Edinburgh Architectural Salvage Yard

31 West Bowling Green St. Off Coburg St., Leith. EH6 5NX. Est. 1985. Open 9-5, Sat. 12-5. SIZE: Large. *STOCK: Fireplaces, stained glass, roll-top baths, carriage gates, panelled doors, cast iron radiators.* TEL: 0131 554 7077; fax - 0131 554 3070; e-mail - enquiries@easy-arch-salv.co.uk; website - www.easy-arch-salv.co.uk.

Edinburgh Coin Shop

11 West Crosscauseway. EH8 9JW. (T.D. Brown). Open 10-5. *STOCK: Coins, medals, badges, militaria, postcards, cigarette cards, stamps, jewellery, clocks and watches, general antiques; bullion dealers.* TEL: 0131 668 2928/667 9095; fax - 0131 668 2926. VAT: Stan.

Donald Ellis incorporating Bruntsfield Clocks

7 Bruntsfield Place. EH10 4HN. (D.G. and C.M. Ellis). Est. 1970. Open 9.30-5.30. CL: Wed. pm. SIZE: Medium. *STOCK: Clocks and general antiques.* LOC: Opposite Links Garage at Bruntsfield Links. PARK: Nearby. TEL: 0131 229 4720. SER: Repairs (clocks). FAIRS: Buxton (May).

Georgian Antiques   LAPADA

10 Pattison St., Leith Links. EH6 7HF. Est. 1976. Open 8.30-5.30, Sat. 10-2. SIZE: 2 large warehouses. *STOCK: Furniture, Georgian, Victorian, inlaid, Edwardian; shipping goods, smalls, £10-£10,000.* LOC: Off Leith Links. PARK: Easy. TEL: 0131 553 7286 (24 hrs.); fax - 0131 553 6299; e-mail - info@georgianantiques. net; website - www.georgianantiques.net. SER: Valuations; restorations; buys at auction; packing and shipping; courier. VAT: Stan/Spec.

Gladrags

17 Henderson Row. EH3 5DH. (Kate Cameron). Est. 1977. Open Tues.-Sat. 10.30-6. *STOCK: Period clothes, linen, lace, beadwork, silk and paisley shawls, costume jewellery, silks and satins, cashmeres and accessories.* TEL: 0131 557 1916.

Goodwin's Antiques Ltd

15-16 Queensferry St. and 106A-108 Rose St. EH2 4QW. Est. 1952. Open 9-5.30, Sat. 9-5. SIZE: Medium. *STOCK: Antique and modern silver and jewellery.* LOC: Off Princes St., west end. TEL: 0131 225 4717; fax - 0131 220 1412; Rose St. - 0131 220 1230. VAT: Stan/Spec.

Harlequin Antiques

30 Bruntsfield Place. EH10 4HJ. (C. S. Harkness). Est. 1995. Open 10-5 and Sun. (Dec. only) 12-4. SIZE: Small. *STOCK: Clocks and watches, silver, ceramics, small furniture, £25-£3,000.* LOC: 2 miles south of Princes St. (west end). PARK: Easy. TEL: 0131 228 9446. SER: Valuations; restorations (clocks); buys at auction (clocks).

Hawkins & Hawkins   BADA

9 Athol Crescent. EH3 8HA. (Emma H. Hawkins). Resident. Est. 1994. Open by appointment. SIZE: Medium. *STOCK: Taxidermy, 1890-1920, £100-£10,000; English furniture, 1800-1910, £500-£100,000.* LOC: Off Princes St. PARK: Easy. TEL: 0131 229 2828; fax - 0131 229 2128; mobile - 07831 093198; e-mail - emma@emmahawkins.co.uk; website - www.emmahawkins.demon.co.uk. FAIRS: Olympia (June). VAT: Spec/Stan.

Holyrood Architectural Salvage

Holyrood Business Park, 146 Duddingston Rd. West. EH16 4AP. (Ken Fowler). Est. 1993. Open 9-5. SIZE: Large. *STOCK: Original and reproduction fireplaces, rolltop baths, doors, radiators, pews.* LOC: 5 minutes drive from Holyrood Palace, 2 mins. from Duddingston village - telephone for directions. PARK: Easy and free. TEL: 0131 661 9305; fax - 0131 656 9404; website - www.holyroodarchitectural salvage.com. SER: Fireplace fitting. VAT: Stan/Global.

Allan K. L. Jackson

67 Causewayside. EH9 1QF. Est. 1974. Open 10-6. SIZE: Medium. *STOCK: General small antiques, from Victorian, £5-100.* PARK: Easy. TEL: 0131 668 4532; mobile - 07989 236443. SER: Valuations.

Kaimes Smithy Antiques

79 Howdenhall Rd. EH16 6PW. (J. Lynch). Est. 1972. Open 1.30-5. CL: Mon. and Thurs. SIZE: Medium. *STOCK: Furniture, clocks, porcelain, glass, paintings, curios, 18th-20th C, £10-£3,000.* LOC: From City bypass take A701 (at Straiton junction) into city centre, located at 1st set of traffic lights. PARK: Easy. TEL: 0131 441 2076/664 0124. SER: Valuations; restorations.

London Road Antiques
15 Earlston Place, London Rd. EH7 5SU. (Randall Forrest and Tim Hardie). Est. 1990. Open 10-5, Sun. 1-5, or by appointment. SIZE: Large + trade store. *STOCK: Georgian, Victorian and stripped pine furniture.* TEL: 0131 652 2790; e-mail - LRA@19thC.com; website - www. 19thC.com. VAT: Spec.

J. Martinez Antiques
17 Brandon Terrace. EH3 5DZ. Est. 1975. Open 11-5. SIZE: Small. *STOCK: Clocks, jewellery and general antiques, mainly Victorian, £50-£1,000.* LOC: Off Dundas St. PARK: Easy. TEL: 0131 558 8720; fax - same. SER: Valuations; restorations (porcelain, clocks and watches); buys at auction. FAIRS: Midland Clock & Watch, NEC; Antique Clock & Watch, Haydock Park; Ingliston, Edinburgh; Freemasons Hall, Edinburgh.

McNaughtan's Bookshop
3a and 4a Haddington Place. EH7 4AE. Est. 1957. Open 9.30-5.30. CL: Mon. *STOCK: Antiquarian books.* PARK: Limited. TEL: 0131 556 5897; fax - 0131 556 8220; e-mail - mcn books@btconnect.com. FAIRS: ABA Olympia; Chelsea.

Meadows Antiques Ltd
111 St. Leonard's St. EH8 9RB. Open Mon.-Fri. 12-6, prior telephone call advisable. *STOCK: Period furniture, mainly Georgian.* PARK: Easy. TEL: 0131 667 0092; fax - 0131 667 4333. SER: Restorations; upholstery.

The Meadows Lamp Gallery
48 Warrender Park Rd. EH9 1HH. (Scott Robertson). Est. 1992. Open Tues., Thurs. and Sat. 10-6. SIZE: Small. *STOCK: Old glass lampshades, table lamps, brass light fittings and accessories.* LOC: 10 minutes walk from city centre. PARK: Easy. TEL: 0131 221 1212; mobile - 07836 223311; e-mail - sarok@aol.com. SER: Restorations (cleaning, polishing, lacquering, silver plating).

T. and J. W. Neilson Ltd
76 Coburg St., Leith. EH6 6HJ. (J. and A. Neilson). NFA. Est. 1932. Open 9.30-5, Sat. 9.30-4. SIZE: Large. *STOCK: Fireplaces, 18th-20th C, £100-£20,000; interiors, stoves, fenders, fire irons; marble (including French), wood and stone chimney pieces.* LOC: Continuation of Ferry Rd. PARK: Own. TEL: 0131 554 4704; fax - 0131 555 2071; website - www.chimneypiece.co.uk. SER: Installations (fireplaces). VAT: Stan.

Now and Then (Toy Centre)
7 and 9 West Crosscauseway. EH8 9JW. Usually open from 2.30 pm, prior telephone call advisable. *STOCK: Telephones, tin and diecast toys, clockwork and electric model trains, collectable mechanical ephemera, automobilia, juvenalia, clocks, gold and silver watches, small furniture, old advertisements, bric-a-brac.* LOC: City centre off A68. PARK: Nearby. TEL: 0131 668 2927; evenings - 0131 226 2867; mobile - 07976 360283; e-mail - gtab@oldtoysand antiques.co.uk; website - www.oldtoysand antiques.co.uk. SER: Valuations; buys at auction.

The Old Town Bookshop
8 Victoria St. EH1 2HG. (Ronald Wilson). Est. 1982. Open 10.30-5.45. SIZE: Medium. *STOCK: Books, 16th-20th C; prints, from 1450's to 19th C.* LOC: Centre of old town. PARK: Nearby. TEL: 0131 225 9237; fax - 0131 229 1503; website - www.oldtownbookshop.com. SER: Valuations. FAIRS: Book - London, York, Oxford, Cambridge, Edinburgh and Glasgow.

Open Eye Gallery Ltd
75/79 Cumberland St. EH3 6RD. (T. and P. Wilson). Est. 1976. Open 10-6, Sat. 10-4. SIZE: Medium. *STOCK: Early 20th C etchings, contemporary paintings, ceramics and jewellery.* LOC: From Princes St. go east, left into Frederick St. right at bottom of hill. PARK: Easy. TEL: 0131 557 1020; e-mail - open.eye@virgin.net; website - www.openeyegallery.co.uk. SER: Valuations; restorations (paintings and ceramics); buys at auction. VAT: Mainly Spec.

H. Parry
Castle Antiques, 330 Lawnmarket. EH1 2PN. *STOCK: Silver, porcelain, English and Continental furniture, clocks.* TEL: 0131 225 7615.

R.L. Rose Oriental Carpets Ltd
8 Howe St. EH3 6TD. GMC. Est. 1919. Open 9.30-5.30. *STOCK: Antique, decorative, modern and fine old Oriental rugs and carpets.* PARK: Nearby. TEL: 0131 225 8785; fax - 0131 226 7827. SER: Valuations; repairs; cleaning.

Royal Mile Curios
363 High St. EH1 1PW. (L. Bosi and R. Eprile). Open 10.30-5. *STOCK: Jewellery and silver.* TEL: 0131 226 4050.

Royal Mile Gallery
272 Canongate, Royal Mile. EH8 8AA. (J. A. Smith). Est. 1970. Open 11.30-5. SIZE: Medium. *STOCK: Maps, engravings, etchings and lithographs.* LOC: Between castle and Holyrood

Palace. PARK: New Street. TEL: 0131 558 1702; home - 0131 668 4007; e-mail - james@royalmile gallery.co.uk. SER: Valuations; restorations; framing; buys at auction.

Samarkand Galleries
LAPADA

16 Howe St. EH3 6TD. (Brian MacDonald). CINOA. FRGS. Est. 1979. Open 10-5.30, Sun. by appointment. SIZE: Medium. *STOCK: Tribal and village rugs and artefacts, 19th C, £100-£10,000; fine decorative carpets, 19th-20th C, £1,000-£10,000+; kelims, 19th-20th C, £200-£2,000; also unique contemporary rugs and carpets.* LOC: Corner of Jamaica St. PARK: Heriot Row. TEL: 0131 225 2010; e-mail - howe@ samarkand.co.uk; website - www.samarkand.co. uk. SER: Exhibitions. FAIRS: Hali, Olympia. VAT: Stan/Spec.

James Scott
43 Dundas St. EH3 6JN. Est. 1964. Open 11-1 and 2-5.30. CL: Thurs. pm. *STOCK: Curiosities, unusual items, silver, jewellery, small furniture.* TEL: 0131 556 8260; mobile - 07714 004370. VAT: Stan.

The Scottish Gallery
16 Dundas St. EH3 6HZ. (Aitken Dott Ltd). Est. 1842. Open 10-6, Sat. 10-4. *STOCK: 20th C and contemporary Scottish paintings and contemporary crafts.* LOC: New Town. TEL: 0131 558 1200; e-mail - mail@scottish-gallery. co.uk; website - www.scottish-gallery.co.uk. VAT: Stan/Spec.

Second Edition
9 Howard St. EH3 5JP. (Mr and Mrs W.A. Smith). Est. 1978. Open 12-5.30, Sat. 9.30-5.30. SIZE: Medium. *STOCK: Antiquarian and secondhand books, £10-£750; late 19th to early 20th C maps and prints, £7-£75.* LOC: 200 yards south of Royal Botanical Gardens. PARK: Nearby. TEL: 0131 556 9403; home - 0131 552 1850; website - www.secondeditionbookshop.com. SER: Valuations; book-binding.

Still Life
54 Candlemaker Row. EH1 2QE. (Ewan Lamont). Est. 1984. Open 12-5. SIZE: Small. *STOCK: Small antiques and collectables.* LOC: City centre. PARK: Crichton St. TEL: 0131 225 8524; e-mail - ewanlamont@mac.com; website - www.homepage.mac.com; www.homepage.mac. com/ewanlamont/PhotoAlbum14.SER: Valuations; restorations.

The Talish Gallery
168 Canongate. EH8 8DF. (John R. Martin). Est.

1970. Open 11-3. SIZE: Medium. *STOCK: Silver, plate, collectors' items, rugs, pictures, small furniture, £10-£10,000.* LOC: Bottom of Royal Mile, opposite clock. PARK: Easy. TEL: 0131 557 8435. SER: Valuations. VAT: Spec.

The Thrie Estaits
49 Dundas St. EH3 6RS. (Peter D.R. Powell). Est. 1970. Open Tues.-Sat. 11-5. *STOCK: Pottery, porcelain, glass, contemporary and period paintings and prints, unusual and decorative items, some early oak and country furniture.* TEL: 0131 556 7084; e-mail - TheThrieEstaits @aol.com.

Trinity Curios
4-6 Stanley Rd.,Trinity. (Alan Ferguson). Resident. Est. 1987. Open 10-5, Wed. and Sat. 12-6, Sun. 2-5. CL: Mon. SIZE: Medium. *STOCK: Furniture, ceramics and silver, 19th C, £50-£1,000.* LOC: From Ferry Rd. turn north on to Newhaven Rd., shop 300 yards on left. PARK: Easy. TEL: 0131 552 8481. SER: Restorations (furniture including upholstery). VAT: Stan.

Unicorn Antiques
65 Dundas St. EH3 6RS. (N. Duncan). Est. 1967. Usually open 10.30-7. SIZE: Medium. *STOCK: Architectural and domestic brassware, lights, mirrors, glass, china, cutlery and bric-a-brac.* Not Stocked: Weapons, coins, jewellery. LOC: From Princes St. turn into Hanover St. - Dundas St. is a continuation. PARK: Meters. TEL: 0131 556 7176; home - 0131 332 9135.

John Whyte
116b Rose St. EH2 3JF. Est. 1928. Open 9.30-5.15, Sat. 9.30-5. *STOCK: Jewellery, watches, clocks and silver.* TEL: 0131 225 2140. VAT: Stan.

Whytock and Reid
Sunbury House, Belford Mews. EH4 3DN. (D.C. Reid). Est. 1807. Open 9-5.30, Sat. 10-2. SIZE: Large. *STOCK: Furniture, English and Continental, 18th-19th C, £50-£20,000; Eastern rugs, carpets, £50-£10,000.* LOC: 1/2 mile from West End, off Belford Rd. PARK: Own. TEL: 0131 226 4911; fax - 0131 226 4595; website - www.whytockandreid.com. SER: Restorations (furniture, rugs); buys at auction; interiors. VAT: Stan/Spec.

Wild Rose Antiques
15 Henderson Row. EH3 5DH. (K. and E. Cameron). Est. 1975. Open Tues.-Sat. 10.30-6. *STOCK: General antiques - silver, jewellery, glass, pottery, porcelain, small furniture, objects, Paisley shawls, brassware.* TEL: 0131 557 1916.

Richard Wood Antiques

66 Westport. EH1 2LD. Est. 1972. Open 10-5. SIZE: Small. *STOCK: Small collectable silver and Oriental objects, art glass, Art Deco, Art Nouveau, Arts and Crafts, pottery and porcelain, Scottish items, bayonets, daggers, pistols; ivory, pewter, Scottish jewellery.* LOC: Central. PARK: Grassmarket (meters). TEL: 0131 229 6344. FAIRS: Ingliston.

Anthony Woodd Gallery

4 Dundas St. EH3 6HZ. Est. 1981. Open 10-6, Sat. 11-4. *STOCK: Scottish landscape, sporting and military pictures; furniture and decorative items.* TEL: 0131 558 9544/5; fax - 0131 558 9525; e-mail - sales@anthonywoodd.com; website - www.anthonywoodd.com. SER: Valuations; restorations; buys at auction; framing. VAT: Spec.

Young Antiques

185 Bruntsfield Place. EH10 4DG. (T.C. Young). Est. 1979. Open 10.30-1.30 and from 2.30. CL: Wed. pm. SIZE: Medium. *STOCK: Victorian and Edwardian furniture, £50-£1,000; ceramics, £20-£2,000; Persian rugs, oils and watercolours, £50-£1,500.* PARK: Easy. TEL: 0131 229 1361. SER: Valuations.

FAIRLIE

Fairlie Antique Shop

86 Main Rd. KA29 0AD. (E.A. Alvarino). Est. 1976. Open Thurs.-Sat. 12-5. SIZE: Small. *STOCK: Ornaments, £10-£1,000; small furniture, clocks and silver, £50-£2,000; jewellery, all Georgian to Edwardian.* LOC: A78. PARK: 25yds. TEL: 01475 568613; e-mail - sales@alvarinoantiques.com. SER: Valuations. FAIRS: NEC; SECC; Scone Palace; Hopetown House.

FALKIRK

Steeple Antiques

54 Cow Wynd. FK1 1PU. (Bill Hastings). Est. 1992. Open 10-5. SIZE: Small. *STOCK: Pottery and porcelain including Scottish, Beswick and Shelley; watches and clocks, furniture, silver, collectables, tools.* LOC: Near town centre. PARK: Easy - behind shop. TEL: 01324 617400; home - 01324 624221; fax - same; mobile - 07734 571697; e-mail - william.hastings@btinternet.com. SER: Valuations. FAIRS: Ingliston; Caygill; Newcastle, Kendal, Carlisle, Penrith.

Antiques (Fochabers)

22 The Square. IV32. (J. and M.L. Holstead). Est. 1983. Open 10.15-5. SIZE: Medium. *STOCK: General collectables, Oriental, clocks including longcase, from 18th C oak to 1930's.* PARK: Easy. TEL: 01343 820838; home - 01343 820572.

Pringle Antiques

High St. IV32 7EP. (G. A. Christie). Est. 1983. Open 10.30-4.30 April-Sept. SIZE: Medium. *STOCK: Furniture, Victorian, £20-£5,000; general antiques, pictures, brass, pottery, silver and jewellery.* Not Stocked: Books and clothing. LOC: A96, premises are a converted church. PARK: Easy. TEL: 01343 821204; home - 01343 820599.

Marianne Simpson

61/63 High St. IV32 7DU. (M.R. Simpson). Est. 1990. Open Easter-Oct: Mon.-Sat. 10-1 and 2-4; Oct.-Easter: Tues., Thurs., Sat. 10-1 and 2-4, or by appointment. SIZE: Small. *STOCK: Books and ephemera, 19th-20th C, £1-£100.* LOC: A96. PARK: Easy. TEL: 01343 821192; home - same.

FORFAR

Gow Antiques

Pitscandly Farm. DD8 3NZ. (Jeremy Gow). BAFRA. Est. 1986. Open by appointment. SIZE: Medium. *STOCK: 17th-19th C furniture, £50-£20,000.* LOC: 3 miles off A90, take B9134 out of Forfar, through Lunenhead, first right at sign Myreside, premises next left, in farmyard. PARK: Easy. TEL: 01307 465342; mobile - 07711 416786; e-mail - jeremy@gowantiques.co.uk; website - www.gowantiques.co.uk. SER: Restorations; valuations. FAIRS: Antiques For Everyone, Glasgow (Aug.).

FORRES

Michael Low Antiques

45 High St. IV36 2PB. Est. 1967. Open 10-1 and 2-5. *STOCK: Small antiques.* TEL: 01309 673696.

FORTROSE

Cathedral Antiques

45 High St. IV10 8SU. (Patricia MacColl). Est. 1996. Open Fri. and Sat. March to Dec. (extra days in summer months). CL: Jan. and Feb. except by appointment. SIZE: Small. *STOCK: Fine furniture, 1780-1920, £100-£5,000; silver and plate, 1780-1940, £5-£1,000; porcelain and Scottish pottery, glass, 1820-1940, £5-£500.* PARK: Easy. TEL: 01381 620161; home - same;

mobile - 07778 817074; e-mail - cathant@ hotmail.com. SER: Valuations. FAIRS: Pollock House, Glasgow; Hopetoun House, Edinburgh, Blair Castle, Perthshire; Highland, Nairn.

FRIOCKHEIM, Nr. Arbroath

M.J. and D. Barclay
29 Gardyne St. DD11 4SQ. Est. 1965. Open 2-5.30. CL: Thurs. *STOCK: General antiques including furniture, jewellery, silver, porcelain and clocks.* Not Stocked: Stamps, books, coins. PARK: Easy. TEL: 01241 828265. FAIRS: Aberdeen. VAT: Stan.

GLASGOW

All Our Yesterdays
6 Park Rd., Kelvinbridge. G4 9JG. (Susie Robinson). Est. 1989. Open 11.30-5.30. SIZE: Small. *STOCK: Kitchenalia, mainly 1850-1949, £5-£500; smalls, especially decorative arts, advertising related items, books, etchings and postcards, mechanical items, crystals and minerals, smokers sundries and oddities, to £500.* LOC: Near junction with Gt. Western Rd. and university. PARK: Easy. TEL: 0141 334 7788; answerphone/fax - 0141 339 8994; e-mail - antiques@allouryesterdays.fsnet.co.uk. SER: Valuations; buys at auction; search and hire.

The Antiques Warehouse
Unit 3b, Yorkhill Quay Estate. G3 8QE. (P. Mangan). Open 9-5, Sat. 10-5, Sun. 12-5. SIZE: 19 dealers. *STOCK: Antique pine, Oriental rugs and carpets, general antiques, furnishings, smalls and fine arts.* TEL: 0141 334 4924. SER: Import and export worldwide.

The Roger Billcliffe Fine Art
134 Blythswood St. G2 4EL. Est. 1992. Open 9.30-5.30, Sat. 10-1. SIZE: Large. *STOCK: British paintings, watercolours, drawings, sculpture, especially Scottish, from 1850; jewellery, metalwork, glass and woodwork.* TEL: 0141 332 4027; fax - 0141 332 6573; e-mail - roger@rbfa.demon.co.uk; website - www.bill cliffegallery.com. VAT: Spec.

Brown's Clocks
13 Radnor St., Kelvingrove. G3 7UA. (J. Wilson and J. Cairns). Est. 1933. Open 9.30-5, Sat. 10.30-12.30. *STOCK: Fine clocks and barometers.* TEL: 0141 334 6308. SER: Restorations.

Butler's Furniture Galleries
39 Camelon St., Carntyne Industrial Estate. G32 6JS. (Laurence Butler). Est. 1951. Open 10-5 or by appointment. CL: Sat. SIZE: Large. *STOCK: Georgian, Victorian and Edwardian furniture, £200-£5,000.* LOC: From M8 to Edinburgh, off at Stepps Cutoff, right at traffic lights down to bottom of road. Left on to dual carriageway, right at first traffic lights and straight down to sign for industrial estate, turn right. PARK: Easy. TEL: 0141 778 5720; home - 0141 639 3396; mobile - 07950 312355. SER: Valuations; restorations; repolishing. VAT: Spec.

Circa Vintage
37 Ruthven Lane and 6 Kersland St. G12 9BG. (Sheila Murdoch). Est. 1977. Open 11.30-5.30. SIZE: Small. *STOCK: Vintage costume, bags, jewellery, quilts and textiles.* LOC: West end. PARK: Nearby. TEL: 0141 581 3307; e-mail - sheilaanne.m@ntlworld.com. SER: Valuations. FAIRS: London Vintage Textile, Hammersmith.

A.D. Hamilton and Co
7 St. Vincent Place. G1 2DW. (Jeffrey Lee Fineman). Est. 1890. Open 9-5.15. SIZE: Small. *STOCK: Jewellery and silver, 19th to early 20th C, £100-£3,000; British coins, medals and banknotes, £10-£1,000.* LOC: City centre, next to George square. PARK: Meters. TEL: 0141 221 5423; fax - 0141 248 6019. SER: Valuations. VAT: Stan/Spec.

Kittoch Antiques
336 Crow Rd., Broomhill. G11 7HT. (Laura McAlohan and Una Lambie). Est. 1987. Open Tues.-Sat. 12-5. SIZE: Small. *STOCK: China, silver and plate, glass, metal, textiles, small furniture, collectables, decorative items, from Victorian, £5-£1,000.* LOC: Main road. PARK: Easy. TEL: 0141 339 7318; home - 0141 644 3902/1315. SER: Valuations. FAIRS: SEEC, Scotland (Aug); NEC.

Ewan Mundy Fine Art Ltd
Lower Ground Floor, 211 West George St. G2 2LW. Est. 1981. Open daily. SIZE: Medium. *STOCK: Fine Scottish, English and French oils and watercolours, 19th-20th C, from £250; Scottish and English etchings and lithographs, 19th-20th C, from £100; Scottish contemporary paintings, from £50.* LOC: City centre. PARK: Nearby. TEL: 0141 248 9755. SER: Valuations; restorations arranged; buys at auction (pictures). FAIRS: New York. VAT: Stan/Spec.

Pastimes Vintage Toys
126 Maryhill Rd. G20 7QS. (Gordon and Anne Brown). Est. 1980. Open 10-5. SIZE: Medium. *STOCK: Vintage toys, die-cast, railways and*

dolls' houses, from 1910, £1-£300. LOC: From the west off junction 17, M8; from the east junction 16, M8. PARK: Easy. TEL: 0141 331 1008. SER: Valuations. VAT: Stan.

The Renaissance Furniture Store
103 Niddrie Rd., Queens Park. G42 8PR. (Bruce Finnie). Open 10.30-5, Sat. and Sun. 12.30-5. CL: Mon. *STOCK: General antiques; Arts and Crafts and Art Nouveau furniture; fire inserts and surrounds.* PARK: Easy. TEL: 0141 423 0022. SER: Buys at auction.

R.L. Rose Oriental Carpets Ltd
Unit 3b, Yorkhill Quay. G3 8QE. Open 9-5, Sat. 10-5, Sun. 12-5. *STOCK: Oriental and decorative carpets.* TEL: 0141 339 7290; fax - 0141 334 1499. SER: Repairs; cleaning.

Jeremy Sniders Antiques
158 Bath St. G2 4TB. Est. 1983. Open 9-5, Sat. 10-5. SIZE: Medium. *STOCK: British decorative arts including furniture, 1850-1960, £30-£1,000; Scandinavian decorative arts including furniture, silver and jewellery, 1900 to date, £30-£5,000; silver, mainly 19th-20th C, £30-£3,000.* LOC: Next door to Christies. PARK: Nearby - Sauchiehall St. Centre. TEL: 0141 332 0043; fax - 0141 332 5505; e-mail - snidersantiques@aol.com; websites - www.jeremysnidersantiques.com and www.jeremysnidersantiques.co.uk. SER: Will source Scandinavian articles - eg. Georg Jensen, Royal Copenhagen, etc; repairs (Georg Jensen silverware). VAT: Spec.

Strachan Antiques
40 Darnley St., Pollokshields. G41 2SE. (Alex and Lorna Strachan). Est. 1990. Open 10-5, Sun. 12-5. SIZE: Warehouse. *STOCK: Furniture especially Arts and Crafts, Art Nouveau and Glasgow Style, £50-£5,000; some decorative items.* LOC: 2 mins. from M8, junction 20 westbound, junction 21 eastbound. PARK: Own. TEL: 0141 429 4411; e-mail - alex@strachan-antiques.freeserve.uk; website - www.strachanantiques.co.uk. FAIRS: SECC Glasgow. VAT: Stan/Spec.

Victoria Antiques Ltd
350 Pollokshaws Rd., G41 1QS. Est. 1963. Open 9.30-5, Sat. 10.30-4, Sun. 12.30-4. SIZE: Large. *STOCK: General antiques, Victoriana, shipping goods.* LOC: South side of city. TEL: 0141 423 7216; fax - 0141 423 6497. SER: Valuations; buys at auction. VAT: Stan/Spec.

The Victorian Village Antiques
93 West Regent St. G2 2BA. Open 10-5. SIZE: 3 floors. LOC: Near Hope St. PARK: At rear and meters. TEL: 0141 332 0808/9808. VAT: Stan/Spec. Below are listed the dealers at these premises.

Golden Oldies
Jewellery. SER: Repairs; commissions.

Cathy McLay - Saratoga Trunk
Textiles, lace, jewellery. TEL: 0141 331 2707.

Stuart Myler
Silverware.

Putting-on-the-Ritz
Art Deco, china, jewellery, 1920's curios. TEL: 0141 332 9808.

Rosamond Rutherford
Victorian jewellery, Scottish agate, silver, Sheffield plate. TEL: 0141 332 9808.

Voltaire & Rousseau
12-14 Otago Lane. G12 8PB. (Joseph McGonigle). Est. 1972. Open 10-6. SIZE: Medium. *STOCK: Books - classic, literature, foreign, literature, Scottish, some rare and first editions; student textbooks.* PARK: Gibson St. TEL: 0141 339 1811. SER: Valuations (books).

Tim Wright Antiques   `LAPADA`
147 Bath St. G2 4SQ. (T. and J. Wright). Est. 1971. Open 9.45-5, Sat. 10.30-4 or by appointment. SIZE: 6 showrooms. *STOCK: Furniture, European and Oriental ceramics and glass, decorative items, silver and plate, brass and copper, mirrors and prints, textiles, samplers, all £50-£6,000.* LOC: On opposite corner to Christie's. PARK: Multi-storey opposite and meters. TEL: 0141 221 0364; fax - same; e-mail - tim@timwright-antiques.com; website - www.timwright-antiques.com. VAT: Mainly Spec.

GLENCARSE, Nr. Perth

Michael Young Antiques at Glencarse
PH2 7LX. Est. 1887. Open 10-6 and by appointment SIZE: Large. *STOCK: 17th-19th C furniture, paintings and silver.* LOC: A90 3 miles east of Perth. PARK: Easy. TEL: 01738 860001; fax - same; e-mail - volenti@btopenworld.com. SER: Restorations.

GLENDOICK

Becca Gauldie Antiques
The Old School. PH2 7HR. Est. 1992. Open 10-5. SIZE: Medium. *STOCK: Scottish country items, 1750-1900, snuff boxes, treen, Mauchlineware (including tartan, fern transfer and photographic), pottery, sewing tools, prints and pictures, small furniture, glass oddities and*

curios, from £50. LOC: Next to garden centre. PARK: Own. TEL: 01738 860870; mobile - 07770 741636; e-mail - becca@gauldie. freeserve.co.uk. FAIRS: NEC (April, June & Nov.); SECC, Glasgow (June); various London.

Scribe Books & Ephemera
The Old School. PH2 7NR. (Enid Gauldie). Est. 1996. Open 10-5. SIZE: Medium. *STOCK: Antiquarian, out of print and secondhand books including Scottish and local history, children's, Scottish music and gardening, from £10.* LOC: Next to garden centre. PARK: Own. TEL: 01738 860870; e-mail - scribe@gauldie.freeserve.co.uk.

GULLANE

Gullane Antiques
5 Rosebery Place. EH31 2AN. (E.A. Lindsey). Est. 1981. Open 10.30-1 and 2.30-5. CL: Wed. and Thurs. SIZE: Medium. *STOCK: China and glass, 1850-1930, £5-£150; prints and watercolours, early 20th C, £25-£100; metalwork, 1900's, £5-£150.* LOC: 6 miles north of Haddington, off A1. PARK: Easy. TEL: 01620 842994.

HADDINGTON

Leslie and Leslie
EH41 3JJ. (R. Skea). Open 9-1 and 2-5. CL: Sat. *STOCK: General antiques.* PARK: Nearby. TEL: 01620 822241; fax - same. VAT: Stan.

Yester-Days
79 High St. EH41 8ET. (Betty Logan). Est. 1992. *STOCK: General antiques and collectables.* TEL: 01620 824543.

HUNTLY

Bygones
1 Bogie St. AB54 8DX. (Sue and Bruce Watts).

Est. 1996. Open Wed. and Sat. 10-2, other days by appointment. SIZE: Medium. *STOCK: Clocks and pocket watches, £50-£3,000; furniture, barometers, Victoriana, curios and collectables, 19th-20th C, £10-£3,000.* LOC: Off Duke St. towards rail station. PARK: Nearby. TEL: 01466 794412. FAIRS: Swinderby; Newark.

Huntly Antiques
43 Duke St. AB54 8DT. (Mrs J. Barker). Open Mon. and Sat. 10-1 and 2-5, Thurs. 10-1, other times by appointment. SIZE: Small. *STOCK: Jewellery, china, glass and furniture, 19th-20th C, £5-£250.* LOC: Off Aberdeen/Inverness road. PARK: Easy. TEL: 01466 793307.

INCHTURE

Inchmartine Fine Art
Inchmartine House. PH14 9QQ. (P. M. Stephens). Est. 1998. Open 9-5.30. SIZE: Medium. *STOCK: Mainly Scottish oils and watercolours, £150-£2,500.* LOC: Take A90 Perth/Dundee road, entrance on left at Lodge. PARK: Easy. TEL: 01828 686412; home - same; fax - 01828 686748; mobile - 07702 190128; e-mail - fineart@inchmartine.freeserve.co.uk. SER: Cleaning; restorations; framing. FAIRS: Buxton; SECC (Glasgow); Chester. VAT: Spec.

C.S. Moreton (Antiques)
Inchmartine House. PH14 9QQ. (P. M. and Mrs M. Stephens). Est. 1922. Open 9-5.30. SIZE: Large. *STOCK: Furniture, £100-£10,000; carpets and rugs, £50-£3,000; ceramics, metalware; all 16th C to 1860; old cabinet makers' tools.* LOC: Take A90 Perth/Dundee road, entrance on left at Lodge. PARK: Easy. TEL: 01828 686412; home - same; fax - 01828 686748; mobile - 07702 190128; e-mail - moreton@inchmartine. freeserve.co.uk. SER: Valuations; cabinet making and repairs. FAIRS: Buxton; SECC (Glasgow); Chester. VAT: Mainly Spec.

Keepsakes
96 High St. EH44 6HF. (Margaret Maxwell). CL: Tues., Wed. and lunchtimes. SIZE: Small. *STOCK: Ceramics and glass, £50-£200; dolls, teddies and toys, £100-£500; books, post and cigarette cards, £5-£25; jewellery, £5-£100; all 20th C.* LOC: A72. PARK: Easy. TEL: 01896 831369; home - 01896 830701. FAIRS: Ingliston; some Border.

Gallery Persia
Upper Myrtlefield, Nairnside. IV2 5BX. (G. MacDonald). *STOCK: Persian, Turkoman, Afghanistan, Caucasus, Anatolian rugs and carpets, late 19th C to 1940, £500-£2,000+; quality contemporary pieces, £100+.* LOC: From A9 1st left after flyover, 1st left at roundabout, then 2.25 miles on B9006, then 1st right, 1st left. PARK: Easy. TEL: 01463 798500; home - 01463 792198; fax - same; e-mail - mac@gallerypersia. co.uk; website - www.gallerypersia.co.uk. SER: Valuations; restorations; cleaning; repairs. FAIRS: Game, Scone Palace, Perth (July).

Mainhill Gallery
Ancrum. TD8 6XA. (Diana Bruce). Est. 1981. Open by appointment. SIZE: Medium. *STOCK: Oil paintings, watercolours, etchings, some sculpture and ceramics, 19th C to contemporary, £35-£7,000.* LOC: Just off A68, 3 miles north of Jedburgh, centre of Ancrum. PARK: Easy. TEL: 01835 830545; fax - 01835 830518. SER: Exhibitions; valuations. FAIRS: Glasgow; London; Edinburgh. VAT: Spec.

R. and M. Turner (Antiques Ltd) `LAPADA`
34-36 High St. TD8 6AG. (R.J. Turner). Est. 1965. Open 9.30-5.30, Sat. 10-5. SIZE: 6 large showrooms and warehouse. *STOCK: Furniture, clocks, porcelain, paintings, silver, jewellery, 17th-20th C and fine reproductions.* LOC: On A68 to Edinburgh. PARK: Own. TEL: 01835 863445; fax - 01835 863349. SER: Valuations; packing and shipping. VAT: Stan/Spec.

Gardner's The Antique Shop `LAPADA`
Wardend House, Kibbleston Rd. PA10 2PN. (G.D., R.K.F. and D.D. Gardner). Est. 1950. Open to Trade 7 days, retail 9-6, Sat. 10-5. SIZE: 11 showrooms. *STOCK: Smalls, furniture,*

general antiques. LOC: 12 miles from Glasgow, at far end of Tandlehill Rd. 10 mins. from Glasgow Airport. PARK: Easy. TEL: 01505 702292; e-mail - gardantiques@cqm.co.uk; website - www.gardnersantiques.co.uk. SER: Valuations. VAT: Spec.

McQuade Antiques
7 Shuttle St. PA10 2JN. (W. G. & W. J. McQuade). Est. 1975. Open 10-5.30, Sun. 2-5.30. CL: Sat. SIZE: Large. *STOCK: Furniture, porcelain, clocks, brass and silver, 19th-20th C.* LOC: Next to Weavers Cottage. PARK: Easy. TEL: 01505 704249; e-mail - walterjmcquade antiques@supanet.com. SER: Valuations. FAIRS: Newark. VAT: Spec.

Country Antiques
G63 9AJ. (Lady J. Edmonstone). Est. 1975. Open Mon.-Sat. *STOCK: Small antiques and decorative items.* Not Stocked: Reproduction. LOC: A81. In main street. PARK: Easy. TEL: Home - 01360 770215. SER: Interior decoration.

Maureen H. Gauld
Craiglea, Main St. FK21 8UN. Est. 1975. Open March-Oct. 10-5, Nov.-Feb. Thurs., Fri., Sat. SIZE: Medium. *STOCK: General antiques, furniture, silver, paintings and etchings, £5-£3,500.* PARK: Easy. TEL: 01567 820475; home - 01567 820605; e-mail - killingallery@fsbdial. co.uk; website - www.killingallery.co.uk.

Killin Gallery
Craiglea, Main St. FK21 8UN. (J.A. Gauld). Est. 1992. Open 10-5, Sun. by appointment. SIZE: Medium. *STOCK: Etchings and drypoints, £100-£1,000; paintings, £300-£3,000; furniture, £100-£2,000; all 1860-1960.* PARK: Easy. TEL: 01567 820605; fax - same; e-mail - killingallery@ btopenworld.com; website - www.killingallery. co.uk. SER: Valuations.

Kilmacolm Antiques Ltd
Stewart Place. PA13 4AF. (H. Maclean). Est. 1973. Open 10-1 and 2.30-5.30. CL: Sun. except by appointment. SIZE: Medium. *STOCK: Furniture, 18th-19th C, £100-£8,000; objets d'art, 19th C; jewellery, £5-£5,000; paintings, £100-£5,000.* LOC: First shop on right when travelling from Bridge of Weir. PARK: Easy. TEL: 01505 873149. SER: Restorations

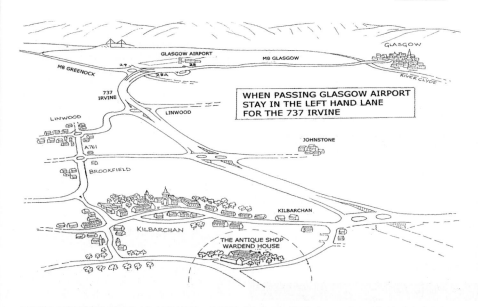

(furniture, silver, jewellery, porcelain). FAIRS: Hopetown, Pollock House, Edinburgh, Inverness. VAT: Stan/Spec.

KILMARNOCK

QS Antiques and Cabinetmakers
Moorfield Industrial Estate. KA2 0DP. (J.R. Cunningham and D.A. Johnson). Est. 1980. Open 9-5.30, Sat. 9-5. SIZE: Large. *STOCK: Furniture including stripped pine, 18th-19th C; shipping goods, architectural and collectors' items.* PARK: Easy. TEL: 01563 571071. SER: Restorations (upholstery, stripping); custom-built kitchens and furniture. VAT: Stan.

KILMICHAEL GLASSARY, By Lochgilphead

Rhudle Mill
PA31 8QE. (D. Murray). Est. 1979. Open daily, weekends by appointment. SIZE: Medium. *STOCK: Furniture, 18th C to Art Deco, £30-£3,000; small items and bric-a-brac, £5-£500.* LOC: Signposted 3 miles south of Kilmartin on A816 Oban to Lochgilphead road. PARK: Easy. TEL: 01546 605284; home - same; fax - 01546 606173. SER: Restorations (furniture); French polishing; buys at auction.

KINCARDINE O'NEIL, Nr. Aboyne

Dunmore Antiques
27 North Deeside Rd. AB34 5AA. (Pauline Baird). Est. 1988. Open Thurs., Fri. and Sat. 10-5, other times by appointment. SIZE: Small. *STOCK: China, 1800-1960, £10-£1,000; glass, silver, 20th C, £10-£500.* PARK: Easy. TEL: 01339 884449; home - 01339 882640; fax - same; e-mail - dunmore-antiques@talk21.com. SER: Valuations. FAIRS: Treetops, Newark. VAT: Global.

KINGSTON-ON-SPEY

Collectables
Lein Rd. IV32 7NW. (J. Penman and B. Taylor). Est. 1987. Open daily including most weekends by appointment. SIZE: Small. *STOCK: Militaria, jewellery, lap desks, china, collectables, small silver, £5-£1,000.* LOC: On B9105. PARK: Easy. TEL: 01343 870462. SER: Valuations. FAIRS: Inverness; Aberdeen.

KIRKCALDY

A. K. Campbell & Sons
277 High St. KY1 1LA. Est. 1977. SIZE: Small. *STOCK: Coins, medals, old banknotes, militaria, china and porcelain, pictures, small furniture,*

die-cast models, postcards. PARK: Easy. TEL: 01592 597022. SER: Valuations.

Second Notions Antiques
4B Normand Rd., Dysart. KY1 2XJ. (James Sinclair). Est. 1995. Open 12-5, Sat. 10-5. SIZE: Medium. *STOCK: General antiques especially furniture and longcase clocks, £2-£3000; shipping furniture.* LOC: A92. PARK: Easy. TEL: 01592 650505; fax - same; home - 01592 573341; e-mail - james@sinclair1155.freeserve.co.uk; website - www.secondnotionsantiques.co.uk. SER: Valuations. FAIRS: Swinderby; Newark.

KIRKCUDBRIGHT

The Antique Shop
67 St Mary St. DG6 4DU. (Paul and Marisa Mairs). Est. 1993. Open 10-5. *STOCK: General antiques, collectors' items, linen and lace, kichenalia, furniture,bric-a-brac, 18th-20th C, to £1,500.* LOC: Near entrance of town, at junction to Gatehouse of Fleet. PARK: Easy. TEL: 01557 332400; e-mail - mjmantiques@hotmail.com.

Osborne Antiques   `LAPADA`
41 Castle St. and 63 High St. DG6 4JD. (David and Robert A. Mitchell). Est. 1949. Open 9-12.30 and 1.30-5, or by appointment. SIZE: Large. *STOCK: Georgian and Victorian furniture, smalls.* PARK: Easy. TEL: 01557 330441; e-mail - mitch0106@hotmail.com. SER: Free UK delivery. VAT: Stan/Spec.

KIRKMAHOE, Nr. Dumfries

Quarrelwood Art & Antiques Ltd
Quarrelwood. DG1 1TE. (Oscar and Miranda van Nieuwenhuizen). Est. 1999. Open Wed.-Sat. 10-5, Sun. 1-5. SIZE: Small. *STOCK: Georgian and Victorian furniture, £200-£10,000; period jewellery, £40-£20,000; silver, £50-£5,000; Georgian and Victorian glass, ceramics and objets d'art.* LOC: 5 miles north of Dumfries. PARK: Easy. TEL: 01387 740654; fax - 01387 740000; e-mail - miranda@quarrelwoodantiques.com; website - www.quarrelwoodantiques.com. SER: Valuations.

LANGHOLM

The Antique Shop
High St. DG13 0DH. (R. and V. Baird). Est. 1970. Open 10.30-5. CL: Wed. pm. SIZE: Small. *STOCK: China, glass, pictures, 18th-20th C; jewellery, rugs, 19th-20th C; trade warehouse - furniture, shipping goods and antiquarian books.* LOC: 20 miles north of Carlisle on A7. PARK: 100yds. TEL: 01387 380238. SER: Restorations (furniture).

LARGS

Narducci Antiques
11 Waterside St. KA30 9LN. (G. Narducci). Open Tues., Thurs. and Sat. 2.30-5.30 or by appointment - trade any time. SIZE: Warehouse. *STOCK: General antiques and shipping goods.* TEL: 01475 672612; 01294 461687; fax - 01294 470002; mobile - 07771 577777; website - www.narducci-antiques.co.uk. SER: Packing and shipping; road haulage (Europe). *Mainly Trade and Export.*

LENNOXTOWN

Campsie Antiques
2 Service St. G65. (R. Allen). Open 10-5.30, Sun.12-4. SIZE: Small. *STOCK: Collectables.* LOC: A891. PARK: Easy. TEL: 01360 311100.

LINLITHGOW

County Antiques
30 High St. EH49 7AE. (Mrs. M. Flynn). Est. 1977. Open 10-5. SIZE: Medium. *STOCK: Jewellery and small antiques.* LOC: East end High St. PARK: Nearby. TEL: 01506 671201. SER: Valuations; jewellery repairs.

Mir Russki
Est. 1994. *STOCK: Russian silver, 18th C to 1917.* TEL: 01506 843973; website - www.russiansilver.co.uk. SER: Mail order. FAIRS: NEC and other major.

Town & Country Antiques
20 High St. EH49 7AE. (Mrs. M. Flynn). Est. 1977. Open 10-5. *STOCK: Furniture and general antiques.* PARK: Nearby. TEL: 01506 671201.

LOCKERBIE

Cobwebs of Lockerbie Ltd
30 Townhead St. DG11 2AE. (Irene M. Beck). Est. 1992. Open 9-5. SIZE: Medium. *STOCK: Victorian furniture and china, collectables, to £650.* LOC: Outskirts of town. PARK: Easy. TEL: 01576 202554; fax - 01576 203737; home - 01387 811284; e-mail - sales@cobwebs-antiques.co.uk; website - www.cobwebs-antiques.co.uk.

LONGHAVEN, Nr Peterhead

Grannie Used To Have One
Sanderling. AB42 0NX. (Mrs Jacqui Harvey). Est. 1991. Open Thurs. and Fri. 1-5, Sat. and Sun. 11-5, Mon and Tues and other times by appointment. SIZE: Large. *STOCK: Pottery including Scottish, 18th-19th C, £5-£2,000; porcelain, glass, wooden items, curios, furniture, 18th-20th C.* LOC: A90 6 miles south of Peterhead. PARK: Own. TEL: 01779 813223; fax/home - same; e-mail - jacqui@grannieusedto.co.uk; website - www.grannieusedto.co uk SER: Valuations; buys at auction. FAIRS: Hilton Treetops, Aberdeen.

MELROSE

Michael Vee Design - Birch House Antiques
High St. TD6 9PB. (Michael Vee and Enid Cranston). Est. 1990. Open 9.30-12.30 and 1.30-5, Sat. 9.30-4, Sun. by appointment. SIZE: Medium. *STOCK: Mirrors and lighting, French, English, decorative and some garden furniture, 1850-1920, £20-£5,000.* LOC: 1.5 miles off A68. PARK: Easy. TEL: 01896 822116; home - 01896 822835. SER: Restorations; interior design.

MONTROSE

Harper-James LAPADA
25-27 Baltic St. DD10 8EX. (D.R. James). Resident. Est. 1990. Open 9-5, Sat. 10-4, other times by appointment. SIZE: Large. *STOCK: Furniture, clocks, silver and jewellery, 1690-1910, £50-£15,000; ceramics and pottery, 1800-1945, £10-£650+; general antiques and curios, £2-£750.* LOC: From south turn right at Peel statue, then first left. PARK: Easy. TEL: 01674 671307; home - same; e-mail - antiques@telco4u.net; website - www.harperjamesantiques.com. SER: Valuations; restorations (furniture and upholstery); French polishing; export. FAIRS: Major U.K. VAT: Stan/Spec.

Sticks & Stones
36-40 Baltic St. DD10 8EX. (Loris McEwan). Est. 1999. Open 10-5. SIZE: Medium. *STOCK: Oak country furniture, Art Nouveau, Arts & Crafts, Victorian and Edwardian; some mahogany and pine; architectural items - baths, fire surrounds and inserts.* LOC: Rear of town centre. PARK: Easy. TEL: 01674 676764; home - 01241 430475. FAIRS: Treetops; Ardoe House, Aberdeen.

NEWBURGH

Newburgh Antiques
222 High St. KY14 6DZ. (Dorothy Fraser). Est. 1991. Open 10.30-12 and 1.30-5. CL: Mon. SIZE: Small. *STOCK: Wemyss ware, 1882-1930, £100-£2,000; Scottish watercolours and oil*

An oak draw-leaf table, late 16th/early 17th century. (Huntington Antiques Ltd)

From an article entitled "An Extended Family" by Peter Philp which appeared in the February 2003 issue of **Antique Collecting**. For more details and to subscribe see page 21.

paintings, 1800-1950's, £100-£1,500; furniture, 1750-1900, £200-£2,000. LOC: A913. PARK: Easy. TEL: 01337 841026; home - 01337 827158; e-mail - antiques@wemyss-ware.com; website - www.wemyss-ware.com. SER: Valuations.

NEWPORT-ON-TAY

Mair Wilkes Books
3 St. Mary's Lane. DD6 8AH. (James Mair and Alan Wilkes). PBFA. Est. 1969. Open Tues.-Fri. 10-12.30 and 2-4.30, Sat. 10-5. SIZE: Small. *STOCK: Books, all subjects, from 16th C to date, £1-£1,000.* PARK: Nearby. TEL: 01382 542260; fax - same; e-mail - mairwilkes.books@zoom. co.uk. SER: Valuations.

NEWTONMORE

The Antique Shop
Main St. PH20 1DD. (J. Harrison). Est. 1990. Open 9.30-5.30. SIZE: Medium. *STOCK: Furniture, £20-£1,000; glass, china, silver, plate, copper, brass, secondhand books, vintage fishing tackle.* LOC: On A86 opposite Mains Hotel. PARK: Easy. TEL: 01540 673272. VAT: Global.

NORTH BERWICK

Kirk Ports Gallery
49A Kirk Ports. EH39 4HL. (Alan Lindsey). Est. 1995. Open 10-5. CL: Thurs. SIZE: Medium. *STOCK: Oil paintings, £100-£1,000; watercolours, £50-£600; etchings and prints, £30-£100; all 19th C to 1940.* LOC: Behind main street. PARK: Own. TEL: 01620 894114. SER: Valuations.

Lindsey Antiques
49a Kirk Ports. EH39 4HL. (Stephen Lindsey). Est. 1995. Open 10-1 and 2-5. CL: Thurs. SIZE: Medium. *STOCK: Ceramics and glass, 1800-1935, £20-£500; furniture, 1750-1910, £150-£2,000.* LOC: Behind main street. PARK: Own. TEL: 01620 894114. SER: Valuations.

Penny Farthing
23 Quality St. EH39 4HR. (S. Tait). Est. 1981. Open daily. SIZE: Medium. *STOCK: Secondhand books, collectables, 20th C, £5-£500.* LOC: On corner with High St. PARK: Easy. TEL: 01620 890114; fax - same; mobile - 07817 721928; e-mail - pennyfarthing@amserve. net. SER: Valuations; buys at auction. FAIRS: Scot, Meadowbank, Edinburgh.

OBAN

Oban Antiques
35 Stevenson St. PA34 5NA. (Peter and Pam Baker). Est. 1970. Open 10-5, some seasonal variation. SIZE: Medium. *STOCK: Furniture and general antiques, mainly 19th to early 20th C; books, prints, jewellery, silver, ceramics and collectables, £5-£1,500.* LOC: Off George (main) St. PARK: Easy. TEL: 01631 566203; e-mail - partners@obantiques.com; website - www.obantiques.com.

PAISLEY

Corrigan Antiques
Woodlands, High Calside. PA2 6BY. Open by appointment. SIZE: Small. *STOCK: Furniture and accessories.* LOC: 5 mins. from Glasgow Airport. TEL: 01418 896653; fax - 0141 848 9700; mobile - 07802 631110.

Paisley Fine Books
17 Corsebar Crescent. PA2 9QA. (Mr and Mrs B. Merrifield). Est. 1985. Open by appointment. SIZE: Small. *STOCK: Books on architecture, art, antiques and collecting.* TEL: 0141 581 0095; fax - 0141 884 2661; e-mail - bernieafc@aol.com. SER: Free book search; catalogues issued.

PERTH

Ainslie's Antique Warehouse
Unit 3, Gray St. PH2 0JH. (T.S. and A. Ainslie). Open 9-5, by appointment at weekends. SIZE: Large. *STOCK: General antiques.* TEL: 01738 636825.

Design Interiors and Perth Antiques
46-50 South St. PH2 8PD. (Margaret J.S. and Robert J. Blane). Est. 1990. Open 10.30-6. SIZE: Medium. *STOCK: Victorian and Edwardian furniture, £40-£1,000; paintings and etchings, paperweights, silver, porcelain and pottery, mainly 18th-20th C, £20-£600.* PARK: Easy. TEL: 01738 635360; e-mail - robert-blane@btinternet.com. SER: Valuations; restorations (clocks and china).

A.S. Deuchar and Son
10-12 South St. PH2 8PG. (A.S. and A.W.N. Deuchar). Est. 1911. Open 10-1 and 2-5. CL: Sat. SIZE: Large. *STOCK: Victorian shipping goods, furniture, 19th C paintings, china, brass, silver and plate.* LOC: Glasgow to Aberdeen Rd., near Queen's Bridge. PARK: Easy. TEL: 01738 626297; home - 01738 551452. VAT: Stan/Spec.

Hardie Antiques
25 St. John St. PH1 5SH. (T.G. Hardie). PADA. Est. 1980. Open 9.30-5, Sat. 10-4.30. SIZE: Medium. *STOCK: Jewellery and silver, 18th-20th C, £5-£5,000.* PARK: Nearby. TEL: 01738 633127; fax - same; home - 01738 551764; e-mail - info@timothyhardie.co.uk. SER: Valuations. VAT: Stan/Spec.

Henderson
5 North Methven St. PH1 5PN. (S.G. Henderson). Est. 1938. Open 9.15-5.15. SIZE: Small. *STOCK: Silver, jewellery, medals, £5-£2,000.* LOC: A9. PARK: Easy. TEL: 01738 624836; e-mail - wtg.henderson@virgin.net. SER: Valuations. VAT: Stan/Margin.

Nigel Stacy-Marks Ltd `LAPADA`
23 George St. PH1 5JY. (Nigel and Ginny Stacy-Marks). Open 9.30-5.30. SIZE: Medium. *STOCK: Oils and watercolours, 19th-20th C, £250-£30,000; British etchings, late 19th C to mid 20th C, £100-£5,000.* LOC: Town centre, just south of museum. PARK: Nearby. TEL: 01738 626300; fax - 01738 620460; e-mail - paintings@stacy-marks.co.uk; website - www.stacy-marks.co.uk. SER: Valuations; restorations; framing; regular exhibitions (catalogues on request). FAIRS: Antiques For Everyone, SECC, Glasgow. VAT: Stan/Spec.

Yesterdays Today
267 High St. PH1 5QN. (Bill and Nora MacGregor). Est. 1996. Open 9-5. SIZE: Small. *STOCK: General collectables especially china, £25-£1,000.* LOC: Follow signs for Tourist Information Centre. PARK: Nearby. TEL: 01738 443534. SER: Valuations; buys at auction. VAT: Global.

PITTENWEEM

The Antiques Shop
27 High St. KY10 2RQ. (R. J. Clark). Est. 1985. Open 10,30-5, Sun. 11-4. SIZE: Medium. *STOCK: Scottish pottery including Wemyss, furniture, 19th C, £100-£1,000; collectibles.* PARK: Easy. TEL: 01333 312870; home - 01333 720331; website - www.arbourantiques.co.uk. SER: Valuations.

The Little Gallery
20 High St. KY10 2LA. (Dr. Ursula Ditchburn-Bosch). Est. 1988. Open 10-5, Sun. 2-5. CL: Mon. and Tues. SIZE: Small. *STOCK: China, 18th C to 1950's, £5-£100; small furniture, mainly Victorian, £30-£500; rustica, £5-£150; contemporary paintings, £40-£1,000.* LOC: From Market Sq.

towards church, on right. PARK: Easy. TEL: 01333 311227; home - same. SER: Valuations.

PORTSOY

Other Times Antiques
13-15 Seafield St. AB45 2QT. (D. McLean and T. Matheson). Est. 1986. Open 10-5 including Sun. CL: Wed. *STOCK: General antiques, 1700-1950.* LOC: A98. PARK: At rear. TEL: 01261 842866. VAT: Stan/Spec.

PRESTWICK

Crossroads Antiques
7 The Cross. KA9 1AJ. (Timothy Okeeffe). Est. 1989. Open 9-5. SIZE: Medium. *STOCK: Furniture, 18th-20th C, £5-£1,000+; china and silver, 19th-20th C, £5-£500+.* PARK: Nearby. TEL: 01292 474004. SER: Valuations; buys at auction.

RAIT

Rait Village Antiques Centre
PH2 7RT. Est. 1985. Open 10-5, Sun. 12.30-4.30. SIZE: 7 showrooms. *STOCK: General antiques, furniture.* LOC: Midway between Perth and Dundee, 1 mile north of A90. PARK: Easy. Below are listed the dealers at this centre. TEL: 01821 670379.

Court One
General antiques.

Court Two
General antiques.

Fair Finds
(Lynda Templeman). *Large stock of antique and early 20th C country house furnishings, pictures, rugs, silver and clocks, £50-£10,000.* TEL: 01821 670379.

Gordon Loraine Antiques
(Liane and Gordon Loraine). *Georgian, Victorian and Edwardian furniture, decorative items and collectables.* TEL: 01821 670760.

Valentine Moon
General antiques. TEL: 01821 670505. SER: Art exhibitions.

Whimsical Wemyss
(Lynda Templeman and Chris Comben). *Wemyssware, £50-£3,000.* TEL: 01821 67039.

SALTCOATS

Narducci Antiques
Factory Place. KA21 5LA. (G. Narducci). Est.

1972. Open by appointment. *STOCK: Furniture, general antiques and shipping goods.* PARK: Easy. TEL: 01294 461687 and 01475 672612; fax - 01294 470002; mobile - 07771 577777. SER: Packing, export, shipping and European haulage. *Mainly Trade and Export.*

ST. ANDREWS

The David Brown (St. Andrews) Gallery
9 Albany Place. KY16 9HH. (Mr and Mrs D.R. Brown). Est. 1973. CL: 1-2 daily. SIZE: Medium. *STOCK: Golf memorabilia, 19th C, £100-£20,000; silver, jewellery especially Scottish, 18th-20th C, £100-£10,000; general antiques, from 18th C, £50-£5,000.* LOC: Main street. PARK: Easy. TEL: 01334 477840; fax - 01334 476915. SER: Valuations; restorations (jewellery, silver); buys at auction (golf memorabilia). VAT: Stan.

St. Andrews Fine Art
84 Market St. KY16 9PA. (J. Carruthers). Open 10-5. *STOCK: Scottish oils, watercolours and drawings, 19th-20th C.* PARK: Easy. TEL: 01334 474080.

STANLEY

Coach House Antiques Ltd
Charleston. PH1 4PN. (John Walker). Est. 1971. Open by appointment. SIZE: Medium. *STOCK: Period furniture, decorative items, 18th-19th C; garden furniture.* LOC: 9 miles north of Perth off A9. Take B9099 to Luncarty and Stanley, continue 2 miles through village, sign at end of road Charleston. PARK: Easy. TEL: 01738 828627; home - same; mobile - 07710 122244. SER: Valuations; restorations; buys at auction (furniture). VAT: Spec.

STEWARTON

Woolfsons of James Street Ltd t/a Past & Present
3 Lainshaw St. KA3 5BY. Est. 1983. Open 9.30-5.30, Sun. 12-5.30. SIZE: Medium. *STOCK: Furniture, £100-£500; porcelain, £25-£500; bric-a-brac, £5-£50; all from 1800.* LOC: Stewarton Cross. PARK: Easy. TEL: 01560 484113; fax - same. SER: Valuations; restorations (French polishing, upholstery, wood). VAT: Stan/Spec.

STIRLING

Abbey Antiques
35 Friars St. FK8 1HA. (S. Campbell). Resident. Est. 1980. Open 9-5. SIZE: Small. *STOCK:*

Jewellery, £10-£5,000; silver and plate, £5-£1,000; furniture including pine, £20-£1,000; paintings, £50-£2,500; bric-a-brac, £1-£100; coins and medals, £1-£1,000; all 18th-20th C; china, porcelain, collectables. LOC: Off Murray Place, part of main thoroughfare. PARK: Nearby. TEL: 01786 447840. SER: Valuations.

STRATHBLANE

Whatnots
16 Milngavie Rd. G63 9EH. (F. Bruce). Est. 1965. *STOCK: Furniture, paintings, jewellery, silver and plate, clocks, small items, shipping goods, horse drawn and old vehicles.* LOC: A81, 10 miles NW of Glasgow. PARK: Easy. TEL: 01360 770310. VAT: Stan/Spec.

TROON

Old Troon Sporting Antiques
49 Ayr St. KA10 6EB. (R.S. Pringle). Est. 1984. CL: Wed. pm. and Sat. SIZE: Medium. *STOCK: Golf items, 19th C, to £500+.* LOC: 5 mins. from A77. PARK: Easy. TEL: 01292 311822; home - 01292 313744; fax - 01292 313111. SER: Valuations; buys at auction (golf items). VAT: Stan.

Tantalus Antiques
79 Templehill. KA10 6BQ. (Iain D. Sutherland). BWCMG. Open 10-5, Sun. by appointment. SIZE: Medium. *STOCK: Furniture, clocks and watches, pictures and paintings, silverware, jewellery, ceramics.* LOC: Town centre, main road to the harbour. PARK: Easy. TEL: 01292 315999; fax - 01292 316611; e-mail - idsantique @aol.com; website - www.scottishantiques.com. SER: Valuations; restorations.

ULLAPOOL

Wishing Well Antiques
Shore St. IU26 2RL. (Simon and Eileen Calder). Est. 1988. Open 10-6, including Sun. in summer. SIZE: Medium. *STOCK: China, glass, silver, pottery, furniture, country artefacts, curiosities; books, prints and paintings.* LOC: Village centre. PARK: Easy. TEL: 01854 613265; mobile - 07905 073273. SER: Valuations; restorations; wood stripping.

UPPER LARGO

Waverley Antiques
13 Main St. KY8 6EL. (D.V. and C.A. St. Clair). Est. 1958. Open 10.30-5.30, Sun. by appointment. SIZE: Medium. *STOCK: Pictures,* *furniture, china, pottery, glass and works of art.* LOC: Coast road from Leven to St. Andrews. PARK: Easy. TEL: 01333 360437; home - same. SER: Valuations.

WHITHORN

Priory Antiques
29 George St. DG8 8NS. (Mary Arnott). Est. 1988. Open most days 11-4, prior telephone call advisable. CL: Thurs. SIZE: Small. *STOCK: Silver, ceramics and furniture, pre 1940, £5-£500.* LOC: Town centre. PARK: Easy. TEL: 01988 500517; home - same. SER: Valuations.

WIGTOWN, Nr. Newton Stewart

Ming Books
Beechwood House, Acre Place. DG8 9DU. (Marion and Robin Richmond). Est. 1982. Open 10-6. SIZE: Small. *STOCK: Books.* PARK: Easy. TEL: 01988 402653; home - same; e-mail - postmaster@mingbooks.com; website - www. mingbooks.com. SER: Valuations. FAIRS: Belfast Book; Las Vegas.

A vase from David Hammond's Bodiam service for Thomas Webb & Sons, 1966, geometrically cut with vertical and horizontal prisms. (20th Century Glass/web-mouse.com)

From an article entitled "Post-War British Cut Glass" by Andy McConnell which appeared in the March 2003 issue of ***Antique Collecting***. For more details and to subscribe see page 21.

WALES

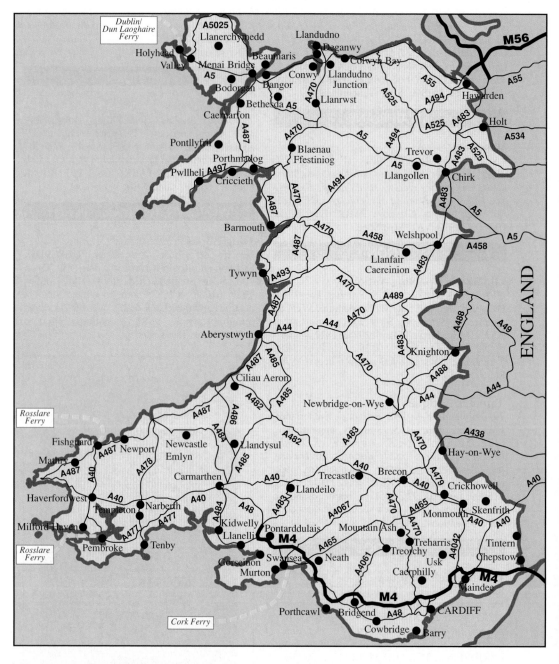

ABERYSTWYTH

The Furniture Cave
33 Cambrian St. SY23 1NZ. (P. David). Est. 1975. Open 9-5, Sat. 10-5. *STOCK: Pine, 1700-1930, from £100; general antiques, Victorian and Edwardian, £30-£3,000; small items, 19th C, £10-£500; maps.* LOC: First right off Terrace Rd., at rail station end. PARK: Nearby. TEL: 01970 611234; e-mail - info@the-furniture-cave.co.uk; website - www.the-furniture-cave.co.uk. SER: Restorations. VAT: Spec.

BANGOR

David Windsor Gallery
173 High St. LL57 1NU. FATG. Est. 1970. Open 10-5. CL: Wed. *STOCK: Oils and watercolours, 18th-20th C; maps, engravings, lithographs.* TEL: 01248 364639. SER: Restorations; framing; mounting. VAT: Stan/Spec.

BARMOUTH

Chapel Antiques Centre
High St. LL42 1DS. (Danny Jones). Est. 1985. Open 10.30-5. CL: Wed. SIZE: Medium. *STOCK: General antiques including furniture and glass, 18th-20th C, £5-£2,000.* PARK: Nearby. TEL: 01341 281377; fax - same; website - www.chapelantiqueswales.co.uk.

Fronhouse Antiques
Jubilee Rd. LL42 1EE. (Tony and Barbara Howard). Est. 1967. Open seven days 10-5. CL: Wed. and Sun. Dec to Mar. SIZE: Small. *STOCK: Nautical items, 19th C £5-£250; oil lamps, bric-a-brac and small furniture, £5-£200.* LOC: On corner of Church St. PARK: Easy. TEL: 01341 280649; home/fax - same. SER: Valuations; restorations (nautical items). FAIRS: Swinderby, Newark.

BARRY

Flame 'n' Grate
99-100 High St. CF6 8DS. (A. Galsworthy). Open 9-5.30. *STOCK: Antique and reproduction fireplaces and surrounds.* TEL: 01446 744788.

BEAUMARIS (Anglesey)

Museum of Childhood Memories
1 Castle St. LL58 8AP. (R. and J. Brown). Est. 1973. Open 10.30-5. CL: Jan. and Feb. *STOCK: Children's toys and memorabilia collectables.* LOC: Opposite castle. PARK: Nearby. TEL: 01248 712498; e-mail - bryn.brown@amserve.net; website - www.aboutbritain.com/museumof childhoodmemories.htm.

BETHESDA

A.E. Morris (Books)
40 High St. LL57 3AN. Est. 1980. Open 10-5. SIZE: Medium. *STOCK: Antiquarian and secondhand books.* PARK: Easy. TEL: 01248 602533.

BLAENAU FFESTINIOG

The Antique Shop
Bryn Marian. LL41 3HD. (Mrs R. Roberts). Est. 1971. *STOCK: Victoriana, furniture, brass and copper, oil lamps, clocks and watches.* TEL: 01766 830629/830041.

BODORGAN (Anglesey)

Michael Webb Fine Art　　　LAPADA
Cefn-Llwyn. LL62 5DN. Est. 1972. Open by appointment. *STOCK: Victorian and 20th C oil paintings and watercolours.* TEL: 01407 840336. SER: Valuations; restorations; framing. FAIRS: NEC; Chester; Carmarthen; Newbury Racecourse; Anglesey. VAT: Spec.

BRECON

Books, Maps and Prints
7 The Struet. LD3 7LL. (A. and W. Wakley). ABA. Est. 1961. Open 9-5, Wed. 9-1. SIZE: Medium. *STOCK: Books, maps and prints, from 17th C, £10-£1,000.* LOC: A438, opposite Kwik Save. PARK: Opposite. TEL: 01874 622714. SER: Framing. VAT: Stan.

Hazel of Brecon
6 The Bulwark. LD3 7LB. (H. Hillman). Est. 1969. Open 10-5.30. CL: Wed. SIZE: Medium. *STOCK: Jewellery, 19th-20th C, £20-£10,000.* LOC: Main square, town centre. PARK: Easy. TEL: 01874 625274 (24 hr. answering service). SER: Valuations; repairs.

Silvertime
6 The Bulwark. LD3 7LB. (L. Hillman). Open 10-5.30. CL: Wed. SIZE: Small. *STOCK: Silver and gold watches; antique and collectors' clocks; 19th-20th C silver and plate.* LOC: Town centre, on main square. PARK: Easy. TEL: 01874 625274 (24 hr. answering service). SER: Valuations; repairs.

BRIDGEND

J. & A. Antiques
1 Prince Rd., Kenfig Hill. CF33 6ED. (Jennifer Lawson). Est. 1990. Open 10-12.30 and 2-4.30,

Wed. and Sat. 10-12.30. SIZE: Small. *STOCK: Furniture, china and clocks, 19th to early 20th C, £10-£600.* LOC: From A48 Pyle take B4281. PARK: Easy. TEL: 01656 746681; home - 01656 744709.

Nolton Antiques
66 Nolton St. CF31 3BP. (Gittings and Beynon). Est. 1997. Open 9.30-5. CL: Wed. SIZE: Large. *STOCK: General antiques including Clarice Cliff, majolica and Victorian furniture.* LOC: Turn off M4 at junction 35. PARK: Nearby. TEL: 01656 667774; website - www.welsh-antiques. com. SER: Valuations; buys at auction (named china).

CAERNARFON

Days Gone By Antiques
6 Palace St. LL55 1RR. (Geraint and Sue Prytherch). Est. 1992. Open 10-5.30 including Sun. *STOCK: Furniture, jewellery, china especially Royal Doulton, glass, collectables, silver, Staffordshire, new Brambly Hedge and Beswick.* LOC: Within walled town. PARK: Easy. TEL: 01286 678010; fax - 01286 678554; home - 01286 672526; e-mail - sue@daysgone byantiques.co.uk. SER: Valuations.

CAERPHILLY

Yesterday's Future - G.J. Gittins and Son
10 Clive St. CF8 1GE. Open 9-4, Sat. 10-5. CL: Wed. *STOCK: General antiques, jewellery and shipping goods.* TEL: 02920 868835; e-mail - gittinsantiques@supornet.com.

CARDIFF

Cardiff Antiques Centre
10/12 Royal Arcade. CF1 2AE. Open 10-5.30. SIZE: 3 floors. *STOCK: Antiques, collectables and classic clothing.* LOC: Town centre. TEL: 02920 398891.

Cardiff Reclamation
Site 7 Tremorfa Industrial Estate, Rover Way. CF24 5SD. (Jeff and John Evans). Est. 1990. Open 9-5, Sat. 9-1, Sun. 10-1. SIZE: Large. *STOCK: Architectural antiques, fireplaces, doors, wood flooring, stained glass, bathrooms, church fittings, flagstones, chimney pots, £10-£3,000.* PARK: Easy. TEL: 02920 458995; fax - same; mobile - 07855 038629. SER: Restorations.

Jacobs Antique Centre
West Canal Wharf. CF10 5DB. Open Thurs.-Sat.

9.30-5. SIZE: Large - 50 dealers. *STOCK: General antiques and collectables.* LOC: 2 mins. from main rail and bus stations. PARK: 100yds. TEL: 02920 390939. SER: Valuations; restorations.

Kings Fireplaces, Antiques and Interiors
The Old Church, Adamsdown Sq., Adamsdown. CF2 1EZ. (B. Quinn). Est. 1984. Open 10-5. SIZE: Medium. *STOCK: Period fireplaces, mirrors and lighting.* TEL: 02920 492439. SER: Restorations (furniture and fireplaces); fireplace installations and spares. VAT: Stan.

Llanishen Antiques
26 Crwys Rd., Cathays. CF2 4NL. (Mrs J. Boalch). Open 10.30-4.30. CL: Wed. except by appointment. *STOCK: Furniture, silver, china, glass, bric-a-brac.* TEL: 02920 397244.

Roberts Emporium
58-60 Salisbury Rd. CF24 4AD. Est. 1980. Open 11-5. SIZE: Large. *STOCK: General antiques, Victorian, £5-£1,000; collectables, 50s, 60s, 70s.* LOC: In road near Museum of Wales. PARK: Easy. TEL: 02920 235630; fax - 02920 395935; e-mail - robertsflea@yahoo.co.uk; website - www.robertsfleamarket.com. SER: Valuations; restorations (ceramics and furniture); buys at auction; prop. hire. FAIRS: Newark.

San Domenico Stringed Instruments
175 Kings Rd., Pontcanna. CF1 9DF. (H.W. Morgan). Est. 1978. Open 10-4, Sat. 10-1. SIZE: Small. *STOCK: Fine violins, violas, cellos and bows, mainly 18th-19th C, £300-£20,000.* LOC: Off Cathedral Rd. or Cowbridge Rd. PARK: Easy. TEL: 02920 235881; fax - 02920 344510; home - 02920 777156; e-mail - HWM@san-domenico.co.uk; website - www.san-domenico. co.uk. SER: Valuations; restorations; buys at auction. FAIRS: Musicora, Paris. VAT: Stan/Spec.

CARMARTHEN

Audrey Bull
2 Jacksons Lane. SA31 1QD. Open 10-5. *STOCK: Period and Welsh country furniture, general antiques especially jewellery and silver.* TEL: 01267 222655; home - 01834 813425. VAT: Spec.

Cwmgwili Mill
Bronwydd Arms. SA33 6HX. (M.J. Sandell). Est. 1950. Open 9-1 and 2-6, Sat. 9-1 and 2-6, Sun. by appointment. SIZE: Large. *STOCK: Furniture, oak, mahogany, pine, 18th-20th C.* PARK: Easy.

TEL: 01267 231500; home - 01267 237215.

Merlins Antiques
Market Hall. SA31 1QY. (Mrs J.R. Perry). Est. 1984. Open 9-4.30. *STOCK: Small items - porcelain, pottery, glass, silver and plate, postcards.* TEL: 01267 233814; mobile - 07967 131109.

The Mount Antiques Centre
1 and 2 The Mount, Castle Hill. SA31. (R. Lickley). Est. 1987. Open 10-5.30, Sun. 11-3. SIZE: Large. *STOCK: Fine furniture including country, 18th-19th C, £500-£1,000+; china and collectables, 19th-20th C, £50-£500; architectural salvage, musical instruments, 19th C, £50-£1,500.* LOC: A40 near county hall. PARK: Easy. TEL: 01267 220005. SER: Valuations; restorations (furniture and china). FAIRS: Towy - Cowbridge, Bristol; Cardiff.

CHEPSTOW

Foxgloves
20 St. Mary St. NP16 5EW. (Lesley Brain). Est. 1994. Open 10ish-5. CL: Wed. SIZE: Medium. *STOCK: Period and antique furniture; pictures, china and objet d'art.* LOC: Central. PARK: Nearby. TEL: 01291 622386. SER: Restorations.

Glance Back Bookshop
17 Upper Church St. NP6 5EX. Est. 1980. Open 10ish-5.30, including Bank Holidays, Easter-October. SIZE: 8 rooms. *STOCK: Books including antiquarian; stamps, coins, tokens, medals, postcards pre-1930, banknotes, military cap badges, antiquarian maps and prints.* LOC: Town centre. PARK: Easy. TEL: 01291 626562; e-mail - Greg@GlanceBack.demon.co.uk. SER: Restorations (works of art on paper, canvas or board); framing and colouring.

Glance Gallery
17a Upper Church St. NP6 5EX. Est. 1980. Open 10ish-5.30. SIZE: Large. *STOCK: Antiquarian prints and maps.* LOC: Town centre. PARK: Easy. TEL: 01291 626562; e-mail - Greg@ GlanceBack.demon.co.uk. SER: Valuations; restorations (canvas, board or paper); framing; hand-colouring.

Intaglio
(John Harrison). Est. 1995. Open by appointment. SIZE: Small. *STOCK: Sculpture, marble, 19th to early 20th C, £500-£20,000.* PARK: Easy. TEL: 01291 621476 or 01873 810036; fax - 01291 621476; e-mail - intaglio@tiscali.co.uk; authorised seller on - Sothebys.com. SER:

Valuations; restorations; cleaning; conservation; buys at auction (bronze and marble sculpture). FAIRS: NEC; Bailey.

Plough House Interiors
Upper Church St. NP6 5HU. (Mr and Mrs P. Jones). Est. 1972. Open 10-5, Sat. 10-4.30, Sun. by appointment. CL: Wed. SIZE: Large. *STOCK: Victorian and Edwardian furniture and shipping goods.* LOC: 2 miles from Severn Bridge and M4. PARK: Easy. TEL: 01291 625200; home - same. SER: Valuations; restorations; buys at auction. VAT: Stan/Spec.

CHIRK

Seventh Heaven
Chirk Mill. LL14 5BU. Est. 1971. Open every day. SIZE: Large. *STOCK: Brass, iron and wooden beds including half-tester, four-poster and canopied, mainly 19th C.* LOC: B5070, below village, off A5 bypass. PARK: Easy. TEL: 01691 777622/773563; fax - 01691 777313; e-mail - requests@seventh-heaven.co.uk; website - www.seventh-heaven.co.uk. VAT: Stan.

CILIAU AERON

K.W. Finlay Antiques
The Forge, Neuaddlwyd. SA48 8DQ. Est. 1969. Usually open but prior telephone call advisable. SIZE: Medium. *STOCK: Furniture, 18th-20th C, £50-£3,000.* LOC: A482, 2.5 miles from Aberaeron. PARK: Easy. TEL: 01545 570536; home - same. VAT: Stan/Spec.

COLWYN BAY

North Wales Antiques - Colwyn Bay
58 Abergele Rd. LL29 7PP. (F. Robinson). Est. 1958. Open 9-5. SIZE: Large warehouse. *STOCK: Shipping items, Victorian, early oak, mahogany and pine.* LOC: On A55. PARK: Easy. TEL: 01492 530521; evenings - 01352 720253. VAT: Stan.

CONWY

Paul Gibbs Antiques and Decorative Arts
25 Castle St. LL32 8AY. Open 10-5. *STOCK: Antiques and Decorative Arts, 1880-1940s; art pottery, especially major factories.* TEL: 01492 593429; fax - same.

Teapot World - Museum and Shop
25 Castle St. LL32 8AY. Open every day Easter to end Oct. *STOCK: Traditional and novelty teapots and tea-related items. Also permanent*

display of 1,000+ antique, rare and novelty teapots, from 1730. TEL: 01492 596533; 01492 593429; fax - same; website - www.teapotworld. co.uk.

COWBRIDGE

Cowbridge Antique Centre
75 Eastgate. CF7 7AA. (T.C. Monaghan). Est. 1974. Open 10-5. SIZE: Medium. *STOCK: Furniture, 18th-19th C, £50-£1,000+; ceramics, 18th-20th C, £10-£750; collectables, 19th-20th C, £10-£500.* LOC: Town centre. PARK: Easy. TEL: 01446 775841; home - same; e-mail - terryval@cowbridgeantiques.freeserve.co.uk. SER: Valuations; restorations; upholstery. FAIRS: NEC, Birmingham.

Eastgate Antiques
6 High St. CF7 7AG. (Liz Herbert). Est. 1984. Open 10-1 and 2-5.30. CL: Mon. SIZE: Medium. *STOCK: Furniture, silver, jewellery, 18th C to Edwardian.* LOC: Off A48. PARK: Nearby. TEL: 01446 775; home - 01446 773505. SER: Buys at auction (furniture). VAT: Stan/Spec.

Havard and Havard   `LAPADA`
59 Eastgate. CF71 7EL. (Philip and Christine Havard). Est. 1992. Open 10.30-1 and 2-5. CL: Mon. and Wed. SIZE: Small. *STOCK: Oak, mahogany and walnut furniture especially provincial, £100-£10,000; metalware and samplers, £25-£1,000; all 18th-19th C.* LOC: Main street, 500 yards after lights on right. PARK: Easy. TEL: 01446 775021; e-mail - cphavard@aol.com. SER: Valuations. VAT: Stan/Spec.

Renaissance Antiques
The Antiques Centre, Ebenezer Chapel, 48A Eastgate. CF7 7AB. (R.W. and J.A. Barnicott). Est. 1984. Open 10-5. SIZE: Small. *STOCK: Small furniture, Georgian, Victorian and Edwardian, £100-£3,000; brass, copper, plate, decorative ceramics, Staffordshire figures, objets d'art, 18th to 20th C, £5-£500.* Not Stocked: Coins, militaria, reproductions. LOC: Main street. TEL: 01446 771190.

CRICCIETH

Capel Mawr Collectors Centre
21 High St. LL52 0BS. (Alan and Dee Turner). Resident. Est. 1998. Open in summer 10-5; winter - Tues., Fri. and Sat. only. SIZE: Large. *STOCK: Books, from 18th C, £1-£500; postcards, 1894-1960, £1-£50; Sylvac, £5-£100.* LOC: A497. PARK: Nearby. TEL: 01766 523600;

home - 01766 523435; e-mail - books@ capelmawr.idps.co.uk. SER: Valuations. VAT: Stan.

Criccieth Gallery
London House, High St. LL52 0RN. (Mrs. Anita Evens). Est. 1972. Open 9-5.30. CL: Wed pm. Nov-Feb. SIZE: Small. *STOCK: General antiques, Staffordshire figures, china and porcelain, paintings and prints, clocks and watches (mainly pocket), small furniture, mainly 19th C, £5-£250+.* PARK: Easy. TEL: 01766 522836. SER: Valuations; restorations (china, watch and clock repairs). FAIRS: Newark; Mona, Anglesey.

CRICKHOWELL

Gallop and Rivers Architectural Antiques
Ty'r Ash, Brecon Rd. NP8 1SF. (G. P. Gallop and R. A.Rivers). Open 9.30-5. *STOCK: Architectural items, pine and country furniture.* TEL: 01873 811084. VAT: Stan.

DEGANWY

Acorn Antiques
Castle Buildings. LL31 9EJ. (K.S. Bowers-Jones). Open 10-5. *STOCK: Ceramics, glass, furniture, pictures, brass and copper, 19th C.* PARK: Opposite. TEL: 01492 584083.

Castle Antiques
71 Station Rd. LL31 9DF. (J. and D. Nickson Ltd). Est. 1977. Open 10-5. SIZE: Medium. *STOCK: Mainly 19th C furniture, jewellery, copper and brass, watercolours and silver.* LOC: Opposite Castle Hotel. PARK: Nearby. TEL: 01492 583021; fax - 01492 596664; home - 01492 582586; mobile - 07831 245391. SER: Valuations.

FISHGUARD

Manor House Antiques
Main St. SA65 9HG. (R.E. Davies). Est. 1987. Open in summer 10-5, prior telephone call advisable Nov.-March. *STOCK: General antiques especially porcelain and pottery.* PARK: Limited and nearby. TEL: 01348 873260.

GORSEINON, Nr. Swansea

Gold and Silver Shop
1 Cross St. SA1 1BA. (D. Paine). Open 9-2. *STOCK: Gold and silver, general antiques.* TEL: 01792 891874.

HAVERFORDWEST

Dyfed Antiques and Architectural Salvage
The Wesleyan Chapel, Perrots Rd. SA61 2JD. (Giles Chapman and Pam Kiernan). SALVO. Est. 1968. Open 10-5. SIZE: Large. *STOCK: Fireplaces including restored Georgian and Victorian tiled, £200-£2,000; reclaimed doors, £25-£500; flooring including slate slabs and quarry tiles; pine farmhouse furniture, general antiques.* PARK: Opposite. TEL: 01437 760496; fax - same; mobile - 07775 915237; home - 01994 419260; website - www.dyfedantiques.com. SER: Furniture stripping; hand-made bespoke furniture.

Kent House Antiques
Kent House, Market St. SA61 1NF. (G. Fanstone and P. Thorpe). Est. 1987. Open 10-5. CL: Mon. SIZE: Medium. *STOCK: Victoriana, decorative items, hand-made rugs, £5-£500+.* LOC: Town centre. PARK: Easy. TEL: 01437 768175; home - same. SER: Valuations; restorations (furniture, some china).

Gerald Oliver Antiques
14 Albany Terrace, St. Thomas Green. SA61 1RH. Est. 1957. Open 10-4.30. *STOCK: Furniture, pre-1910, £20-£6,000; ceramics, treen, metalwork, silver, from £20; unusual, decorative and local interest items.* LOC: Via Freemans Way by-pass and up Merlins Hill. PARK: Easy. TEL: 01437 762794. SER: Valuations. VAT: Spec.

HAWARDEN

On the Air Ltd
The Vintage Technology Centre, The Highway. CH5 3DN. (Steve Harris). Est. 1990. Open 10-5, Sun. 11-4.30. CL: Mon. Christmas to Easter. SIZE: Small. *STOCK: Vintage wireless, gramophones and telephones, £50-£500.* LOC: Near St. David's Park, Ewloe, opposite Crown & Liver public house. PARK: Rear of premises. TEL: 01244 530300; fax - same; website - www.vintageradio.co.uk. SER: Valuations; restorations (vintage wireless and gramophones). FAIRS: National Vintage Communications, NEC; Wembley.

HAY-ON-WYE

Richard Booth's Bookshop Ltd
44 Lion St. and Hay Castle. HR3 5AA. (Richard and Hope Booth). WBA. Est. 1974. Open 7 days 9-5.30, later at weekends and during summer. SIZE: Very large. *STOCK: Books, magazines, photographs, records, postcards, leather bindings.* LOC: Town centre. TEL: 01497 820322; fax - 01497 821150; Hay Castle - 01497 820503; e-mail - enquiries@richardbooth bookseller.com; website - www.booktown.org (Hay-on-Wye Bookbuyers Ltd).

Hay Antique Market
6 Market St. HR3 5AF. Est. 1990. Open 10-5, Sun. 11-5. SIZE: 17 units. *STOCK: Antiques and collectables.* LOC: By the Butter Market. PARK: Easy. TEL: 01497 820175.

Hebbards of Hay
7 Market St. HR3 5AF. (P.E. Hebbard). Est. 1958. Open 10-5. SIZE: Small. *STOCK: Pottery and porcelain.* LOC: A438, opposite the Post Office. PARK: Own. TEL: 01497 820413.

Lion Fine Arts
19 Lion St. HR3 5AD. (Charles Spencer). Est. 1986. Open Mon., Thurs. and Sat. 10-5, prior telephone call advisable other days. SIZE: Small. *STOCK: Pottery, porcelain and glass, 18th to mid 19th C, £25-£250; furniture, prints and objets d'art, £30-£900; some second-hand and antiquarian books.* LOC: Turn right from Oxford Rd. car park, then second turning left. PARK: Limited. TEL: 01497 821726; home - same.

Rose's Books
14 Broad St. HR3 5DB. (Maria Goddard). Resident. Est. 1982. Open 7 days. SIZE: Medium. *STOCK: Children's books, 1900-1960, £5-£25.* TEL: 01497 820013; fax - 01497 820031; e-mail - enquiry@rosesbooks.com; website - www. roses.books.com. VAT: Stan.

Mark Westwood Antiquarian Books
High Town. HR3 5AE. ABA. PBFA. Est. 1976. Open 10.30-5.30, including Sun. *STOCK: Antiquarian and secondhand books on most subjects, £2-£1,000.* TEL: 01497 820068; fax - 01497 821641; e-mail - books@markwestwood. demon.co.uk. SER: Valuations; buys at auction (antiquarian books). VAT: Stan.

HOLT, Nr. Wrexham

Furn Davies Partnership
Rock Cottage, Bridge St. LL13 9JG. Open Thurs., Fri. and Sat. 10-5, other times by appointment. *STOCK: Furniture, 18th-19th C; decorative items.* TEL: 01829 270210. SER: Valuations; restorations.

HOLYHEAD (ANGLESEY)

Gwynfair Antiques
74 Market St. LL65 1UW. (Mrs A.D. McCann). Est. 1984. Open Mon., Wed., Fri. and Sat. 10.30-4.30.

SIZE: Small. *STOCK: China, ornaments, £5-£250, furniture, £20-£1,000; all 1860-1950's.* PARK: Loading outside shop, parking 100 yds. TEL: 01407 763740; home - same. SER: Valuations.

KIDWELLY

Antiques in Wales
31 Bridge St. SA17 4UU. (R. and L. Bebb). Est. 1971. Open by appointment. SIZE: Medium. *STOCK: Georgian and Victorian furniture.* LOC: Leave bypass (A484), into centre of village, castle side of bridge. PARK: Opposite shop. TEL: 01554 890534; e-mail - info@antiquesinwales. fsnet.co.uk; website - www.antiquesinwales.com. VAT: Stan/Spec.

Country Antiques (Wales) Ltd   `BADA`
Castle Mill. SA17 4UU. (Richard Bebb). **Est. 1971. Open Fri. and Sat. 10-5, other times by appointment. SIZE: Large. STOCK: Welsh oak furniture and folk art; Welsh dressers, cupboards, clocks, pottery and treen. LOC: Leave bypass (A484), into centre of village, turn opposite war memorial, turn right by Boot and Shoe public house. PARK: Own. TEL: 01554 890534; e-mail - info@welshantiques.com; website - www.welsh antiques.com. SER: Valuations; lectures; research. VAT: Stan/Spec.**

KNIGHTON

Offa's Dyke Antique Centre
4 High St. LD7 1AT. (Mrs H. Hood and I. Watkins). Est. 1985. Open 10-1 and 2-5. SIZE: Medium - 16 dealers. *STOCK: Pottery, glass, bijouterie, 18th-19th C furniture, £5-£1,000.* LOC: Near town clock. PARK: Easy. TEL: 01547 528635; evenings - 01547 528940/560272.

Islwyn Watkins
4 High St. LD7 1AT. Est. 1978. Open 10-1 and 2-5. SIZE: Small. *STOCK: Pottery including studio, 18th-20th C, £25-£1,000; country and domestic bygones, treen, 18th-20th C, £5-£200; small country furniture, 18th-19th C, £20-£600.* Not Stocked: Jewellery, silver, militaria. LOC: By town clock. PARK: Easy. TEL: 01547 520145; home - 01547 528940. SER: Valuations.

LLANDEILO

Jim and Pat Ash
The Warehouse, 5 Station Rd. SA19 6NG. Est. 1977. Open 9.30-5. SIZE: Large. *STOCK: Victorian and antique furniture, Welsh country, oak, mahogany, walnut.* LOC: 50yds. off A40. PARK: Easy. TEL: 01558 823726/822130; fax - same. SER: Valuations. VAT: Stan/Margin/ Export.

ISLWYN WATKINS ANTIQUES

Detail of Sprigs on a Derbyshire/Yorkshire saltglazed jug dated 1861. Jug 16" high.

EIGHTEENTH AND NINETEENTH CENTURY POTTERY, COUNTRY ANTIQUES AND BYGONES.

Opening times of shop: Mon-Sat. 10.00-1.00, 2.00-5.00 or by appointment.

4 High Street, Knighton, Powys, LD7 1AT
Tel: (01547) 520145 Evenings: (01547) 528940

The Works Antiques Centre
Station Rd. SA19 6NH. (Steve Watts and Jon Storey). Est. 2000. Open Tues.-Sat. 10-6, Sun. 10-5. SIZE: Large. *STOCK: Period furniture including country oak and Welsh country; china, treen, books, jewellery, architectural salvage, clocks, brass and copper, dolls and toys, musical instruments, lighting, textiles and clothing.* LOC: On outskirts of village, near A40 roundabout. PARK: Easy. TEL: 01558 823964; e-mail - theworks@storeyj.clara.co.uk; website - www. works-antiques.co.uk. SER: Restorations (furniture repair and renovation, picture framing and upholstery).

LLANDUDNO

The Antique Shop
24 Vaughan St. LL30 1AH. (C.G. Lee). Est. 1938. Open 9-5.30. SIZE: Medium. *STOCK: Jewellery, silver, porcelain, glass, ivories, metalware, from 1700; period furniture, shipping goods.* LOC: Near promenade. PARK: Easy. TEL: 01492 875575.

LLANDUDNO JUNCTION

Collinge Antiques
Old Fyffes Warehouse, Conwy Rd. LL31 9LU. (Nicky Collinge). Est. 1978. Open seven days. SIZE: Large. *STOCK: General antiques including Welsh dressers, dining, drawing and bedroom furniture, clocks, porcelain and pottery, silver, copper and brass, paintings, prints, glass and collectables, mainly Victorian and Edwardian.* LOC: Just off A55, Deganwy exit (A546). PARK: Easy. TEL: 01492 580022; fax - same; e-mail - salescollinge-antiques.co.uk; website - www.collinge-antiques.co.uk. SER: Valuations; restorations including French polishing; buys at auction. VAT: Stan/Spec.

The Country Seat
35 Conwy Rd. LL31 9LU. (Steve and Helen Roberts). Est. 1994. Open 10-5, Sun. 12.30-4.30. SIZE: Small. *STOCK: Old and interesting items including paintings, pottery and porcelain, jewellery, furniture, linen, ephemera and bric-a-brac; decorative arts, 19th-20th C.* LOC: Just off A55. PARK: Easy. TEL: 01492 573256; e-mail - hkjroberts@hotmail.com; website - www. thecountryseat.co.uk. FAIRS: Newark; Birmingham Rag; Chester Northgate; Wrexham.

LLANDYSUL

Michael Lloyd Antiques
The Alma, Wind St. SA44 4BD. Est. 1987. Open Tues., Thurs. and Sat. 10-5.30 or by appointment. SIZE: Small. *STOCK: Country furniture, decorative items.* LOC: Village centre. TEL: 01559 363880. VAT: Stan/Spec.

LLANELLI

John Carpenter
SA14 7HA. Resident. Est. 1973. Open by appointment. SIZE: Large. *STOCK: Musical instruments, furniture, general antiques and shipping goods.* LOC: 5 mins. from Cross Hands. TEL: 01269 831094; e-mail - sales@ cjcantiques.co.uk. SER: Repairs (musical instruments); container packing.

LLANERCHYMEDD (Anglesey)

Two Dragons Oriental Antiques
8 High St. LL71 8EA. (Tony Andrew). Est. 1976. Open by appointment. SIZE: Large + warehouse. *STOCK: Chinese country furniture, signed prints by C.F. Tunnicliffe.* PARK: Easy. TEL: 01248 470204/470100; fax - 01248 470040. FAIRS: Newark.

LLANFAIR CAEREINION, Nr. Welshpool

Heritage Restorations
Maes y Glydfa. SY21 0HD. (Jo and Fran Gluck). Est. 1970. Open 9-5. SIZE: Large. *STOCK: Pine and country furniture, £50-£5,000; some oak and architectural items; all 18th-19th C.* LOC: A458 from Welshpool. Past village, after 2 miles take first left after river bridge and caravan park, then follow signs. PARK: Easy. TEL: 01938 810384; home - same; fax - 01938 810900; website - www.heritagerestorations.co.uk. SER: Restorations (furniture); stripping (pine). VAT: Stan/Spec.

LLANGOLLEN

J. and R. Langford
12 Bridge St. LL20 8PF. (P. and M. Silverston). Est. 1960. CL: Thurs. pm. and 1-2 daily. SIZE: Medium. *STOCK: Furniture, £100-£7,000; pottery and porcelain, £50-£2,000; silver, general antiques, clocks, paintings, £20-£4,000; all 18th-20th C.* LOC: Turn right at Royal Hotel, shop on right. PARK: Easy. TEL: 01978 860182; home - 01978 860493. SER: Valuations.

Passers Buy (Marie Evans)
Oak St/Chapel St. LL20 8NR. (Mrs M. Evans). Est. 1970. Open 11-5 always on Tues., Fri. and Sat., often on Mon., Wed. and Thurs., prior telephone call advisable, Sun. by appointment. SIZE: Medium. *STOCK: Furniture, Staffordshire figures, Gaudy Welsh, fairings, general antiques, copper and brass and fenders.* LOC: Just off A5. Junction of Chapel St. and Oak St. PARK: Easy. TEL: 01978 860861/757385. FAIRS: Anglesey (June and Oct.)

LLANRWST

Carrington House
26 Ancaster Sq. LL26 0LD. (Richard Newstead). Est. 1975. Open 10.30-1.30 and 2.30-5, Mon. pm. and Sun. by appointment. SIZE: Medium. *STOCK: 19th C pine, £200-£1,000; oak and mahogany, 19th-20th C, £150-£2,000.* LOC: From A55 take A470 towards Betws-y-Coed. PARK: Easy. TEL: 01492 642500; fax - same; home - 01492 641279; website - www.carringtonhouse.co.uk. SER: Valuations. VAT: Spec.

Prospect Books
18 Denbigh St. LL26 0LL. (M.R. and M.R. Dingle). WBA. Est. 1980. CL: Mon. SIZE: Small. *STOCK: Books.* LOC: A55. PARK: Easy. TEL: 01492 640111; fax - same; mobile - 07801 844430.

Snowdonia Antiques
LL26 0EP. (J. Collins). Est. 1961. Open 9-5.30, Sun. by appointment. SIZE: Medium. *STOCK: Period furniture especially longcase clocks.* LOC: Turn off A5 just before Betws-y-Coed on to A496 for 4 miles. PARK: Easy. TEL: 01492 640789. SER: Restorations (furniture); repairs (grandfather clocks).

MAINDEE, Nr. Newport

Callie's Curiosity Shop
2 Speke St. NP19 8EX. (Kerry and Richard Strangward). Est. 1987. Open Mon.-Thurs. 10-4, Sat. 10-2. SIZE: Small. *STOCK: Ceramics and glass, Victorian to 1960's, to £1,500; furniture, Georgian to 1930's, £50-£3,000; books, linen, jewellery, postcards, militaria, boxes, toys.* LOC: Opposite Lloyds TSB. PARK: Nearby. TEL: 01633 222005; mobile - 07801 149805; e-mail - callies-2@ntlworld.com. SER: Valuations. FAIRS: Local.

MATHRY

Cartrefle Antiques
SA62 5AD. (M. Hughes and Y. Chesters). Open in summer 10-5.30; in winter Wed.-Sat. 10.30-4. *STOCK: General antiques especially jewellery.* PARK: Easy. TEL: 01348 831591/837868.

MENAI BRIDGE, (Anglesey)

Better Days
The Basement, 31 High St. LL59 5EF. (A. and Mrs E. Rutter). Est. 1988. Open 10.30-4.30, Wed. 11-1, Sat. 10.30-5. CL: Mon. SIZE: Small. *STOCK: Decorative smalls, early 19th to mid 20th C, £5-£200; furniture, late 19th to mid 20th C, £50-£1,000; metal and miscellaneous, mid 19th C to early 20th C, £10-£150.* PARK: Rear of premises. TEL: 01248 716657; e-mail - elaine@andytoo.freeserve.co.uk. SER: Buys at auction. FAIRS: Mona Showground, Anglesey.

Peter Wain
44 High St. LL59. (Peter and Susan Wain). Est. 1980. Open by appointment. SIZE: Small. *STOCK: Chinese ceramics and works of art, over 1000 years, £100-£10,000.* PARK: Opposite. TEL: 01407 710077; fax - 01407 710294; mobile - 07860 302945; e-mail - peterwain@supanet.com. SER: Valuations.

MILFORD HAVEN

Milford Haven Antiques
Robert St. SA73 2JQ. Est. 1968. Open 10-5. *STOCK: General antiques.* TEL: 01646 692152.

MONMOUTH

Frost Antiques & Pine
8 Priory St. NP25 3BR. (Nicholas Frost). Resident. Est. 1960. Open 9-5, Sun. and other times by appointment. SIZE: Small. *STOCK: Pine furniture and Staffordshire pottery, 19th C, £100-£1,500.* LOC: When entering town from east - first shop on left. PARK: Easy. TEL: 01600 716687; website - www.frostantiques.com. SER: Valuations; restorations (furniture); buys at auction (Victorian furniture and ceramics).

The House 1860-1925
6-8 St. James St. NP25 3DL. (Nick Wheatley). Open Tues.-Sat. 10-6. SIZE: Medium. *STOCK: Arts & Crafts furniture, Gothic Revival, Aesthetic movement, Art Nouveau, Art Deco, post-war.* PARK: Nearby. TEL: 01600 772721; e-mail - nick@thehouse1860-1925.com; website - www. thehouse1860-1925.com. SER: Valuations.

MOUNTAIN ASH

Trading Post
3-4 Oxford Buildings, Oxford St. CF45 3HE. (D. Francis and Julie Thomas). Open 10-5. CL: Thurs. SIZE: Large. *STOCK: Edwardian and Victorian pine, satinwood and mahogany furniture; Continental items, china, glass, pictures and textiles, especially Welsh wool blankets and quilts.* LOC: Take A4059 off A470. PARK: Opposite. TEL: 01443 478855; mobile - 07813 674253.

MURTON, Nr. Swansea

West Wales Antiques   LAPADA
18 Manselfield Rd. SA3 3AR. (W.H. Davies). Est. 1956. Open 10-1 and 2-5. CL: Mon. *STOCK: Porcelain, 18th C, £20-£800; Welsh porcelain, 1800-1820; 18th-19th C furniture, silver, pottery, glass, jewellery and collectors' items.* LOC: M4-A4067-B4436, entrance to Gower Peninsula. TEL: 01792 234318. VAT: Stan/Spec.

NARBERTH

Malt House Antiques
Back Lane. SA67 7AR. (P. Griffiths). Est. 1995. Open 10-5.30, Sun. 11-4. SIZE: Large. *STOCK: Country furniture, 18th-20th C, £5-£5,000.* LOC: Village centre. PARK: Easy. TEL: 01834 860303.

NEATH

Neath Antiques
6 Alfred St. SA11 1EF. (Sue Thomas). Est. 1986. Open 10-5, Sat. 10-1. CL: Thurs. SIZE: Medium. *STOCK: Clocks including longcase - 8 day and 30 hour, twin weight Vienna and regulators, £500-£1,800; Victorian, Edwardian and satinwood furniture.* LOC: Town centre. PARK: Easy. TEL: 01639 645740; e-mail - enquiries@ neathantiques.co.uk; website - www.neath antiques.co.uk. SER: Valuations.

NEWBRIDGE-ON-WYE, Nr. Llandrindod Wells

Allam Antiques
Old Village Hall. LD1 6HL. (Paul Allam). Est. 1985. Open Sat. 10-5. SIZE: Medium. *STOCK: Furniture, 1700-1930, £50-£3,000.* LOC: A470. PARK: Easy. TEL: 01597 860654; home - 01597 860455. SER: Valuations; paint stripping.

NEWCASTLE EMLYN

The Old Saddlers Antiques
Bridge St. SA38 9DU. (P.C. and E. Coomber). Est. 1982. Open 10-5. CL: Wed. SIZE: Large. *STOCK: Country furniture, ceramics, pictures and prints, textiles, country bygones, kitchenalia, collectables and decorative items.* LOC: Lower end of High St., last shop before bridge. PARK: Own. TEL: 01239 711615. FAIRS: Towy, Carmarthen.

NEWPORT, (Pembs.)

The Carningli Centre
East St. SA42 05Y. (Ann Gent and Graham Coles). Est. 1994. Open 10-5.30, Sun. by appointment. SIZE: Medium. *STOCK: Furniture, 17th-19th C, £50-£5,000; railwayana, nautical items, country collectables including oil lamps and tools, £1-£500; secondhand books, fine art gallery.* LOC: A487, town centre. PARK: Free in Long St. TEL: 01239 820724; website - www.carningli.co.uk. SER: Valuations; restorations (furniture); polishing; turning; buys at auction (railwayana). VAT: Spec.

PEMBROKE

Pembroke Antiques Centre
Wesley Chapel, Main St. SA71 4DE. (Michael Blake). Est. 1986. Open 10-5. SIZE: Large. *STOCK: Pine, oak, mahogany and shipping furniture; china, rugs, paintings, Art Deco enamel signs, kitchenalia, pottery, toys, curios and collectables.* PARK: Free. TEL: 01646 687017. SER: Valuations; restorations; delivery.

PONTARDDULAIS, Nr. Swansea

The Emporium
112 St Teilo St. SA4 1SS. (Laura Jeremy). Est. 1992. Open 10.30-6. SIZE: Medium. *STOCK: Furniture, 1900-1950, £5-£500; Victorian metalware, collectables and bric-a-brac.* LOC: Off M4, junction 48. PARK: Easy. TEL: 01792 885185; e-mail - laura@the-emporium. freeserve.co.uk. SER: Restorations. FAIRS: Local.

PONTLLYFRII, Nr. Caernarfon

Sea View Antiques
LL54 5EF. (David A. Ramsell). Resident. Est. 1995. Open daily. SIZE: Small. *STOCK: General antiques and collectables, 18th-20th C, £5-£1,500.* LOC: Main Caernarfon to Pwllheli road. PARK: Easy. TEL: 01286 660436.

PORTHCAWL

Harlequin Antiques
Dock St. CF36 3BL. (Ann and John Ball). Est. 1974. Open 10-4. *STOCK: General antiques, textiles, early 19th to 20th C books.* TEL: 01656 785910; mobile - 07980 837844.

Nostalgia Antiques & Collectables
5 South Rd. CF36 3DH. (Paul Rossini). Est. 1981. Open Tues., Thurs., Fri. and Sat. 10-5. SIZE: Medium. *STOCK: General antiques including Victorian and Edwardian furniture; china, porcelain, mirrors, lamps, curios and collectables.* PARK: Easy. TEL: 01656 782933; fax - 01656 783422; mobile - 07967 006820. SER: Restorations (furniture).

PORTHMADOG

Huw Williams Antiques
Madoc St. LL49 9LR. Est. 1993. Open 10-5, Mon. 12-5. CL: Wed. SIZE: Small. *STOCK: Weapons, 18th-19th C, £50-£3,000; country furniture, 18th-19th C, £100-£1,000; general antiques, 19th-20th C, to £300.* LOC: Opposite entrance to main car park. PARK: Opposite. TEL: 01766 514741; mobile - 07785 747561; website - www.antiquegunswales.co.uk. FAIRS: Stockport Arms; International Arms, Motorcycle Museum, Birmingham; Gwyn Davies, Mona, Anglesey; Big Brum (Rag Market).

PWLLHELI

Rodney Adams Antiques
Hall Place, Old Town Hall, Penlan St. and 62 High St. LL53 5DH. (R. and C. Adams). Resident. Est. 1965. Open 9-5. CL: Sun. except by appointment. *STOCK: Longcase clocks, country oak and period furniture.* PARK: At rear. TEL: 01758 613173; evenings - 01758 614337. SER: Delivery. VAT: Stan/Spec.

SKENFRITH, Nr. Abergavenny

Singleton Antiques
Birch Hill Farm. NP7 8UH. (J.W. & A.A. Chapman). Est. 1994. Open any time by appointment. SIZE: Medium. *STOCK: Oak, 17th-19th C, £200-£5,000; country furniture, 18th-19th C, £100-£2,000; decorative items and pictures, 18th-20th C, £10-£2,000.* LOC: Telephone for directions. PARK: Easy. TEL: 01600 750671; e-mail - singletonantiques@ 4mail-biz. SER: Valuations. VAT: Stan/Spec.

SWANSEA

Aladdin's Cave
56 Uplands Crescent. SA2 0NP. (Pat Callen and D. Walker). Est. 1967. Open Mon.-Fri. 9.30-4.30. SIZE: Medium. *STOCK: Doulton, Wade, Sylvac, Clarice Cliff, majolica, Limoges, cranberry glass, silver, copper and brass jugs, fenders.* PARK: Opposite. TEL: 01792 459576; home - 01792 589305; e-mail - aladdinscave.swansea@ ntlworld.com; website - www.aladdinscave swansea.co.uk. SER: Valuations. FAIRS: Bob Evans, Hereford; Robert Preston, Cowbridge & Chepstow.

Keith Chugg Antiques
Gwydr Lane, Uplands. Open 9-5.30, Sat. 9-1. *STOCK: Pianos and general antiques including furniture.* TEL: 01792 472477.

Clydach Antiques
83 High St., Clydach. SA6 5LJ. (R.T. Pulman). Open 10-5, Sat. 10-1. *STOCK: General antiques.* TEL: 01792 843209.

Dylan's Bookstore
Salubrious Passage. SA1 3RT. (J.M. Towns). ABA. PBFA. Est. 1971. Open 10-5, prior telephone call advisable. *STOCK: Antiquarian books on Welsh history and topography, Anglo/Welsh literature and general books.* PARK: Adjacent. TEL: 01792 655255; fax - same; mobile - 07850 759199; e-mail - jefftowns@dylans.com; website - www.dylans. com. FAIRS: London; Boston; Los Angeles; San Francisco.

Magpie Antiques

57 St. Helens Rd. SA1 4BH. (H. Hallesy). Est. 1984. Open 10-5. CL: Thurs. *STOCK: Ceramics including Swansea and other Welsh potteries; oak, pine and mahogany furniture; small antiques.* PARK: Opposite. TEL: 01792 648722; e-mail - helen@magpie-antiques.co.uk. SER: Valuations; restorations (furniture).

Swansea Antiques Centre

1 King Edward Rd. SA1 4LH. (Roderick Sparks and Bill Wright). Est. 1982. Open 10-6, Sun. by appointment. SIZE: Large. *STOCK: Georgian, Victorian, Edwardian, pine and country furniture, £10-£3,000; local pottery and porcelain, glass, clocks, collectables, architectural salvage - fireplaces, surrounds, gates, stained glass; brass beds, lighting.* LOC: Outskirts of Swansea, near Brangwyn Hall. PARK: Easy. TEL: 01792 475194; mobile - 07870 324204. FAIRS: Newark, Swinderby and Kempton Park.

TEMPLETON, Nr. Narberth

Barn Court Antiques, Crafts & Tearoom

Barn Court. SA67 8SL. (D., A. and M. Evans). Est. 1989. Open 10-5. SIZE: Medium. *STOCK: Mahogany, walnut, rosewood and oak furniture, Georgian to late Victorian, £10-£3,000; china and glass, mainly Victorian, £10-£500; decorative items.* LOC: Off A40 on A478 Narberth to Tenby road. PARK: Easy. TEL: 01834 861224; e-mail - info@barncourtantiques.com; website - www. barncourtantiques.com. VAT: Margin.

TENBY

Audrey Bull

15 Upper Frog St. SA70 7DJ. (Jonathan and Jane Bull). Est. 1945. Open 9.30-5. *STOCK: Period and Welsh country furniture, paintings, general antiques especially jewellery and silver; secondhand and designer jewellery.* TEL: 01834 843114; workshop - 01834 871873; home - 01834 813425. VAT: Spec.

Potboard Antiques

Astridge Farm. SA70 8RE. (Nigel and Gill Batten). Est. 1987. Open by appointment. *STOCK: 18th-19th C pine and country furniture.* LOC: Three miles from Tenby. TEL: 01834 842699; fax - 01834 842788; website - www. potboard.co.uk. SER: Restorations (furniture); stripping; buys at auction (pine).

Worcester, c.1772. Part tea and coffee service of reeded form. Crescent marks. (Bonhams, London)

From an article entitled "The Origins of Saucer Dishes" by Richard van Aswegen which appeared in the October 2002 issue of ***Antique Collecting***. For more details and to subscribe see page 21.

TINTERN

Tintern Antiques
The Old Bakehouse. NP6 6SE. (Dawn Floyd).
Open 9.30-5.30. *STOCK: Antique jewellery and
general antiques.* TEL: 01291 689705.

TRECASTLE, Nr. Brecon

Trecastle Antiques Centre
The Old School. LD3 8YA. (A. Perry). Est. 1980.
Open 10-5 including Sun. SIZE: Large. *STOCK:
General antiques, £5-£1,500.* LOC: A40. PARK:
Easy. TEL: 01874 638007. SER: Valuations;
restorations. FAIRS: Newark, Shepton Mallet.

TREHARRIS

Treharris Antiques & Collectables
18 Perrott St. CF46 5ER. (Mrs Janet Barker). Est.
1974. Open 9.30-5. SIZE: Medium. *STOCK:
Local mining memorablia - lamp checks and
miners' lamps, twist boxes; tokens, English coins,
banknotes, medals, military and civil badges,
local maps and history books and artifacts,
general collectors' items.* LOC: Opposite police
station. PARK: Easy. TEL: 01443 413081; home
- same. SER: Valuation and indentification (coins
and antiquities).

TREORCHY

Steven Evans Antiques
Melvin Wine Cellars, Regent St. CF42 6EP. Est.
1981. Open 9-5, Sat 10-5. SIZE: Warehouse.
*STOCK: Victorian mahogany, Edwardian to
1920's oak, shipping goods.* LOC: Junction 34,
M4, then A4119. PARK: Own. TEL: 01443
776410/431756; fax - 01443 776982; mobile -
07785 308567. SER: North American and
Japanese market specialists; container packing
and shipping. VAT: Stan/Spec.

TREVOR, Nr. Llangollen

Romantiques
Bryn Seion Chapel, Station Rd. LL20 7TP. (Miss
S.E. Atkin). Est. 1994. Open 10-5 including Sun.,
or by appointment. SIZE: Large. *STOCK:
Furniture, £50-£4,000; collectables, £1-£1,000;
clocks and barometers, £50-£3,000.* LOC: Off A5
and A539 Llangollen roads. PARK: Easy. TEL:
01978 822879; mobile - 07778 279614; website -
www.romantiques.co.uk. SER: Valuations;
restorations (furniture, upholstery and clocks);
courier. VAT: Stan/Spec.

TYWYN

Welsh Art
(Miles Wynn Cato). Open by appointment (also
in London). *STOCK: Welsh paintings, 1550-
1950; Welsh portraits of all periods and
historical Welsh material.* TEL: 020 7259 0306
and 01654 711715; e-mail - wynncato@welshart.
co.uk.

USK

Mynde Art and Antiques
67 Bridge St. NP15 1BQ. (T.M. and P.A.
Greenhaf). Est. 2001. Open 10-5, Wed. 10-1.
SIZE: Small. *STOCK: Victorian tables, clocks
and boxes, £100-£12,500; French provincial
dressers, tables and chairs, £200-£2,000.* PARK:
Nearby. TEL: 01291 672318; fax - 01291
672796; e-mail - mynde@hotmail.com.

VALLEY, Nr. Holyhead (Anglesey)

Ann Evans `LAPADA`
Carna Shop, Station Rd. LL65 3HB. Est. 1990.
Open Thurs.-Sat. 10-4.30, other days by
appointment. SIZE: Medium. *STOCK: Welsh oak
dressers and pottery; 18th-19th C cranberry
glass, Staffordshire figures, silver and jewellery.*
LOC: Just off junction 3, A55, 100 yards from
traffic lights, turn left towards Trearddur Bay.
PARK: Easy. TEL: 01407 741733; mobile -
07753 650376. SER: Valuations. VAT: Spec.

WELSHPOOL

F.E. Anderson and Son `LAPADA`
5 High St. SY21 7JF. (I. Anderson). Est. 1842.
Open 9-5. SIZE: 3 large showrooms. *STOCK:
Furniture, 17th-19th C; mirrors, paintings and
decorative items.* TEL: 01938 553340; home -
01938 590509; mobile - 07773 795931; e-mail -
feandersonandson@yahoo.co.uk. FAIRS: Olympia;
LAPADA. VAT: Margin.

Rowles Fine Art `LAPADA`
The Old Brewery, Brook St. SY21 7LF. (Mark
and Glenn Rowles). CINOA. Est. 1978. Open
9.30-5.30, Sat. 9.30-3, other times by
appointment. SIZE: Large. *STOCK: Victorian
paintings and watercolours, some contemporary;
small furniture.* PARK: Own. TEL: 01938
558811; fax - 01938 558822; mobiles - 07836
348688; 07802 303506; e-mail - enquiries@
rowlesfineart.co.uk; website - www.rowlesfine
art.co.uk. SER: Valuations; restorations
(paintings). FAIRS: NEC; LAPADA; Olympia
(June); Chester; Harrogate.

Tiffany Silver Flatware

1845-1905:
When Dining was an Art

William Hood, Roslyn Berlin & Edward Wawrynek

- *The first time most of Tiffany's multitude of flatware piece types have been enumerated and illustrated*

- *The first in-depth discussion of markings on Tiffany flatware, including limitations of 'date letters' and patent dates*

- *Provides unique self-assessment feature: pretest/post-test on Tiffany silver flatware*

The antique silver flatware of Tiffany & Co., New York City, is highly sought after, but the collector is frustrated by the lack of available information on and pictures of patterns and pieces (Tiffany's early catalogues "Blue Books" did not always list what pieces were made in each pattern and never had illustrations). This definitive book relates the history of the silver flatware made by others and retailed by Tiffany 1845-c.1876 as well as that designed and made in-house 1869-1905. The story is woven into the broader fabric of the history of flatware in general and that of dining and food. The development and proliferation of many different flatware pieces in America are analyzed and compared with the same in England, France and Germany.

Based on research in the Tiffany Archives and elsewhere, this volume discusses and illustrates twenty-three Tiffany-made full-line patterns (plus variations), numerous not-full-line patterns and ten custom patterns. Detailed descriptions and superb photographs document the extraordinary creativity and craftsmanship that distinguished much of Tiffany & Co.'s prolific Victorian flatware production, including more than 125 piece types – many unique to Tiffany – used for eating and serving fifty food items or categories.

Containing a wealth of well-referenced information set in efficiently organised and easily readable text, strengthened further by a detailed index, this book will be of interest to scholars as well as collectors.

'…the whole subject of the Tiffany tablewares and their designs and manufacture is examined throroughly and after reading this splendid book you are very likely to know all that there is about the subject to date' **Birmingham Post**

11 x 8½in./279 x 216mm.
350pp.
250 col., 150 b.&w.
1 85149 325 5
£45.00

Available from all good booksellers and direct from the publisher:

ANTIQUE COLLECTORS' CLUB
Sandy Lane, Old Martlesham, Woodbridge, Suffolk, IP12 4SD.
Tel: 01394 389950   Fax: 01394 389999
Email: sales@antique-acc.com
Website: www.antique-acc.com

Index of
Packers and Shippers:
Exporters of Antiques (Containers)

ANGLO PACIFIC INTERNATIONAL
SPECIALIST PACKERS AND WORLDWIDE SHIPPERS OF
BESPOKE FURNITURE, ANTIQUES AND FINE ART

FOR ADVICE ON SHIPPING OR FOR AN IMMEDIATE SHIPPING
QUOTATION PLEASE CONTACT OUR EXPERIENCED SALES TEAM

Anglo Pacific Int.
Units 1 & 2 Bush Industrial Estate
Standard Road
London NW10 6DF
Tel: +44 (0) 208 838 8008
Fax: +44 (0) 208 453 0225
Email: antiques@anglopacific.co.uk

LONDON

Anglo Pacific International plc LAPADA
Standard Rd. NW10 6DF. Tel: 020 8838 8008;
fax - 020 8453 0225; e-mail - antiques@
anglopacific.co.uk. *Specialist antique and fine art
packers and shippers serving worldwide
destinations by land, sea or air. Free estimates
and advice. Courier services available.*

AR. GS International Transport Ltd
North London Freight Centre, York Way, Kings
Cross. N1 0BB. Tel: 020 7833 3955; fax - 020
7837 8672; e-mail - sales@args.co.uk; website -
www.args.co.uk. *Fine art and antiques removals*
*by road transport, Europe, especially Italy, door-
to-door service. Documentation.*

Art Logistics Ltd
Unit 1, Victoria Industrial Estate, Victoria Rd. W3
6UU. Tel: 020 8993 8811; fax - 020 8993 8833;
e-mail - mail@artlogistics.co.uk. *Fine art
packing, freight forwarding.*

B B F Fine Art Services Ltd
Copenhagen House, Copenhagen Place. E14
7DE. Tel: 020 7515 7005; fax - 020 7515 6001; e-
mail - mailbox@bbfwwide.demon.co.uk; website
- www.bbfwwide.demon.co.uk. *Fine art packers,
worldwide shippers by sea, air and road.*

AR · GS International Transport Ltd.

SHIPPERS & PACKERS OF ANTIQUES, FINE ART & REMOVALS TO **ITALY**

Tel: 020 7833 3955 or 07836 612376
Fax: 020 7837 8672
Email: sales@args.co.uk   www.args.co.uk

North London Freight Centre,
York Way, Kings Cross, London N1 OBB

Robert Boys Shipping LAPADA
Unit D Tunnel Avenue Trading Estate, Tunnel Avenue, Greenwich. SE10 0QH. Tel: 020 8858 3355; fax - 020 8858 3344; e-mail - boysship@ talk21.com. *Worldwide shipping. Air and sea cargo. Specialists in fine art and furniture to Japan with part load containers to Japan on a weekly basis. Japanese speaking staff.*

Constantine Ltd LAPADA
Constantine House, 134 Queens Rd. SE15 2HR. Tel: 020 7732 8123; fax - 020 7732 2631. *Specialists in the international movement of antiques and fine art for over a hundred and fifty years - services incorporate all requirements from case making to documentation and insurance. Freight groupage specialists.*

Davies Turner Worldwide Movers Ltd
London Headquarters : 49 Wates Way, Mitcham. CR4 4HR. Tel: 020 7622 4393; fax - 020 7720 3897; e-mail - antiques@daviesturner.co.uk. *Fine art and antiques packers and shippers. Courier and finder service. Full container L.C.L. and groupage service worldwide.*

International Fine Art Packers & Shippers

Founded in London in 1933, Gander & White has established a reputation as one of the world's leading packers and shippers of antiques and works of art. A family owned business with staff of over 100, we pride ourselves on our skills at combining the traditional standards of service with the modern skills and expertise needed to meet the requirements of museums, dealers and individuals for the packing, shipping and storage of antiques and fine art.

London   – 21 Lillie Road, London SW6 1UE
Tel: (020) 7381 0571 Fax: (020) 7381 5428

Sussex   – Newpound, Wisborough Green, Nr. Billingshurst
West Sussex, RH14 0AZ
Tel: (01403) 700044 Fax: (01403) 700814

Paris   – 2 Boulevard de la Liberation
93200 Saint Denis, Paris
Tel: 01 55 87 67 10 Fax: 01 48 09 15 48

New York   – 21-44 44th Road, Long Island City, New York 11101
Tel: (718) 784 8444 Fax: (718) 784 9337

Palm Beach – Units 30-31, 1300 North Florida Mango Road,
West Palm Beach, Florida 33409
Tel: (561) 687 5665 Fax: (561) 687 5383

Focus Packing Services Ltd
37-39 Peckham Rd. SE5 8UH. Tel: 020 7703 4715; fax - same; e-mail - focuspacking@aol.com.

Gander and White Shipping Ltd `LAPADA`
Head Office, 21 Lillie Rd. SW6 1UE. Tel: 020 7381 0571; fax - 020 7381 5428. *Specialist packers and shippers of antiques and works of art.*

Hedleys Humpers Ltd `LAPADA`
3 St Leonards Rd., North Acton. NW10 6SX. IATA. BAR (overseas group). RMA. Tel: 020 8965 8733; fax - 020 8965 0249; e-mail - gasb@hedleyshumpers.com; website - www.hedleyshumpers.com. *Weekly door to door services to Europe, plus part load shipments by air and sea worldwide. Offices in London, Paris, Nice, Avignon and New York.*

Interdean.Interconex
Central Way, Park Royal. NW10 7XW. Tel: 020 8961 4141; telex - 922119; fax - 020 8965 4484. *Antiques and fine art packed, shipped and airfreighted worldwide. Storage and international removals. Full container L.C.L. and groupage service worldwide.*

Kuwahara Ltd `LAPADA`
6 McNicol Drive, NW10 7AW. Tel: 020 8963 5995; fax - 020 8963 0100; e-mail - info@kuwahara.co.uk; website - www.kuwahara.co.uk. *Specialist packers and shippers of antiques and works of art. Regular groupage service to Japan.*

Locksons Services Ltd
See entry under Essex.

Momart Ltd
199-205 Richmond Rd. E8 3NJ. ARTIM. Tel: 020 8986 3624; fax - 020 8533 0122; e-mail - enquiries@momart.co.uk; website - www.momart.co.uk. *Fine art handling including transportation, case making and packing: import/export services, exhibition installation and storage.*

Stephen Morris Shipping plc `LAPADA`
Unit 4, Brent Trading Estate, 390 North Circular Rd. NW10 0JF. Tel: 020 8830 1919; fax - 020 8830 1999; e-mail - enquiries@stemo.co.uk; website - www.stemo.co.uk. *Specialist packers and shippers of antiques and fine art worldwide. Weekly European service.*

Nelson Shipping
Unit C3, Six Bridges Trading Estate, Marlborough Grove. SE1 5JT. Tel: 020 7394 7770; fax - 020 7394 7707. *Expert export and packing service.*

The Packing Shop
`LAPADA`
6-12 Ponton Rd. SW8 5BA. Tel: 020 7498 3255; fax - 020 7498 9017. *Fine art and antiques export packed. World-wide shipping, scheduled European vehicles, New York weekly consols. International exhibitions. High security bonded storage. New York office and warehouse.*

Pitt and Scott Ltd
60 Coronation Rd. NW10 7PX. Tel: 020 7278 5585; fax - 020 7278 5592; e-mail - enquiries@pittandscott.co.uk. *Packers and shippers of antiques and fine art. Shipping, forwarding and airfreight agents. Comprehensive service provided for visiting antique dealers. Insurance arranged.*

Robinsons International
`LAPADA`
The Gateway, Staples Corner. NW2 7AJ. Tel: 020 8208 8484; fax - 020 8208 8488; website - www.robinsons-intl.com. *Specialist packers and shippers of antiques and fine art worldwide. Established over 100 years.*

T. Rogers and Co. Ltd
PO Box No. 8, 1A Broughton St. SW8 3QL. Tel: 020 7622 9151; fax - 020 7627 3318; e-mail - trogersco@ukonline.co.uk. *Specialists in storage, packing, removal, shipping and forwarding antiques and works of art. Insurance.*

BUCKINGHAMSHIRE

Clark's of Amersham
Higham Mead, Chesham. HP5 2AH. Tel: 01494 774186; fax - 01494 774196; website - www.bluelorry.com. *Removals and storage, domestic and commercial; export packing and shipping - worldwide door to door.*

CHESHIRE

The Rocking Chair Antiques
Unit 3, St. Peters Way, Warrington. WA27 7BL. Tel: 01925 652409; fax - same; mobile - 07774 492891. *Exporters and packers.*

DEVON

Barnstaple Removal
14/15 Meadow Way, Treebeech Rural Enterprise Park, Gunn, Barnstaple. EX32 7NZ. Tel: 01271 831164; fax - 01271 831165; e-mail -

barnstaple.removals@sosi.net; website - www. barnstaple.removals.co.uk. *Container packing and shipping worldwide.*

Bishop's Blatchpack
Kestrel Way, Sowton Industrial Estate, Exeter. EX2 7PA. Tel: 01392 202040; fax - 01392 201251. *International fine art packers and shippers.*

DORSET

Alan Franklin Transport   LAPADA
26 Blackmoor Rd., Ebblake Industrial Estate, Verwood. BH31 6BB. Tel: 01202 826539; fax - 01202 827337; e-mail - enquiries@afteurope. co.uk. *Worldwide container packing and shipping. Weekly door-to-door European service. Paris office - 2 Rue Etienne Dolet, 93400 St. Ouen, Paris. Tel: 00 33140 115000; fax - 00 33140 114821. South of France office - Quartier La Tour de Sabran, 84440 Robion (Vaucluse). Tel: 00 33490 764900; fax - 00 33490 764902. Belgian office - De Klerckstraat 41, B8300, Knokke. Tel: 00 3250 623579; fax - same.*

ESSEX

Geo. Copsey and Co. Ltd
178 Crow Lane, Romford. RM7 0ES. Tel: 01708 740714 or 020 8592 1003. *Worldwide packers and shippers.*

Crown Relocations
Security House, Abbey Wharf Industrial Estate, Kingsbridge Rd., Barking. IG11 0BD. Tel: 020 8591 3388; fax - 020 8594 4571. *Packers and shippers - 12 offices throughout U.K.*

Lockson Services Ltd   LAPADA
Unit 1, Heath Park Industrial Estate, Freshwater Rd., Chadwell Heath. RM8 1RX. BIFA. Tel: 020 8597 2889; fax - 020 8597 5265; mobile (weekends) - 07831 621428; New York office - 201 392 9800; fax - 201 392 8830; e-mail - shipping@lockson.co.uk; website - www. lockson.co.uk. *Specialist packers and shippers of fine art and antiques by air, sea and road to the USA, Japan, Far East, Canada and other worldwide destinations. A complete personalised service. At all Olympia, Newark and Ardingly fairs.*

L.J. Roberton   LAPADA
Mallard House, 402 Roding Lane South, Woodford Green. IG8 8EY. Tel: 020 8551 9188; fax - 020 8551 9199; e-mail - international@ harrowgreen.com

GLOUCESTERSHIRE

The Shipping Company Ltd
Bourton Industrial Park, Bourton-on-the-Water. GL54 2HQ. Tel: 01451 822451; fax - 01451 810985; website - www.theshippingcompanyltd. com. *Export packers and shippers specialising in the antique, fine art and interior design markets worldwide. Single, consolidated and full container shipments by air and sea. All risks insurance offered.*

Chinese lacquer screen (late 17th century). This was one of the few large items of Oriental lacquerware which translated directly into English houses. Alternatively, the screens could be used as wall panelling, or broken up and used for making small furniture. (Mallett & Son (Antiques) Ltd)

From an article entitled "The Trade in Oriental Lacquerware" by Adam Bowett which appeared in the April 2002 issue of *Antique Collecting*. For more details and to subscribe see page 21.

SOME ARE MORE EQUAL THAN OTHERS

ALAN FRANKLIN TRANSPORT
Specialist Carriers to the Continent

England
26 Black Moor Road, Verwood, Dorset BH31 6BB
Tel: +44 1202 826539 Fax: +44 1202 827337

France
2 Rue Etienne Dolet, 93400 St. Ouen, Paris
Tel: +33 1 40 11 50 00 Fax: +33 1 40 11 48 21

France
Quartier La Tour de Sabran, 84440 Robion (Vaucluse)
Tel: +33 4 90 76 49 00 fax: +33 4 90 76 49 02

Belgium
De Klerckstraat 41, B8300 Knokke
Tel: +32 50 623 579 Fax: +32 50 623 579

Our door to door weekly service throughout
Europe is well known and very reliable.
Visit our Paris warehouse and offices located
within the famous Paris flea market area.
Container and Air Freight Services Worldwide.

LOCKSON

Leading specialists
in packing and
shipping of fine art
and antiques,
worldwide.

UK
T: 0208 597 2889
F: 0208 597 5265
E: shipping@lockson.co.uk

USA
T: 201 392 9800
F: 201 392 8830
E: locksoninc@aol.com

www.lockson.co.uk

*a moving
experience...*

The Removal Company - Loveday & Loveday
2 Wilkinson Rd., Cirencester. GL7 1YT. Tel: 01285 651505. *Shipping and packing.*

Robinsons International   LAPADA
Aldermoor Way, Longwell Green, Bristol. BS30 7DA. Tel: 0117 980 5858; fax - 0117 980 5830; website - www.robinsons-intl.com. *Specialist packers and shippers of antiques and fine art worldwide. Established over 100 years.*

A.J. Williams (Shipping)   LAPADA
607 Central Park, Petherton Rd., Hengrove, Bristol. BS14 9BZ. Tel: 01275 892166; fax - 01275 891333; e-mail - aj.williams@btclick. com; website - www.ajwilliamsshipping.co.uk. *Packing and shipping of antiques and fine art. Courier service.*

HAMPSHIRE

Robinsons International   LAPADA
16 Millbank St., Southampton. SO14 5QQ. Tel: 023 8022 0069; fax - 023 8033 1274; e-mail - southampton@robinsons-intl.com; website - www.robinsons-intl.com. *Specialist packers and shippers of antiques and fine art worldwide. Established over 100 years.*

Robinsons International   LAPADA
Telford Rd., Basingstoke. RG21 6YU. Tel: 01256 465533; fax - 01256 324959; website - www.robinsons-intl.com. *Specialist packers and shippers of antiques and fine art worldwide. Established over 100 years.*

KENT

Sutton Valence Antiques
Unit 4, Haslemere Estate, Sutton Rd., Maidstone. ME15 9NL. Tel: 01622 675332; fax - 01622 692593; e-mail - svantiques@aol.com; website - www.svantiques.co.uk. *Antique and shipping furniture. Container packing and shipping. Facilities for 20ft. and 40ft. containers, all documentation. Worldwide service.*

LANCASHIRE

Robinsons International   LAPADA
32 Stanley Rd., Manchester. M45 8QX. Tel: 0161 766 8414; fax - 0161 767 9057; website - www.robinsons-intl.com. *Specialist packers and shippers of antiques and fine art worldwide. Established over 100 years.*

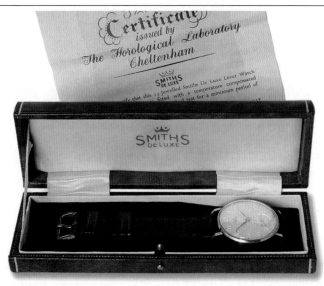

9ct gold cased De Luxe watch complete in its original silk-lined leather box and certificate issued by the Horological Laboratory at Cheltenham. The certificate states that De Luxe watches received final testing in all six positions (imagine the six faces of a cube) over a period of twelve days and were guaranteed for twelve months.

From an article entitled "English Wristwatches" by David Penney which appeared in the April 2003 issue of *Antique Collecting*. For more details and to subscribe see page 21.

MIDDLESEX

Air-Sea Packing Group Ltd `LAPADA`
Air-Sea House, Third Cross Rd., Twickenham. TW2 5EB. Tel: 020 8893 3303; fax - 020 8893 3068; e-mail - sales@airseapacking.com; website - www.airseapacking.com. *Specialist packers and shippers.*

McN International
Unit 10 Shield Drive, West Cross Centre, Brentford. TW8 8EX. Tel: 020 8580 1001; fax - 020 8580 1002. *Fine interiors project management, antique and fine art shippers, incorporating Vitesse in conjunction with Federal Express.*

Nippon Express (UK) Ltd
Ocean Freight Division, Unit 7, Parkway Trading Estate, Cranford Lane, Heston, Hounslow. TW5 9NE. Tel: Commercial (Export) - 020 8737 4240; fax - 020 8737 4249; (Import) - 020 8737 4260; fax - 020 8737 4269; Removal (Cargo) - 020 8737 4200; fax - 020 8737 4209. *Mainly Japanese imports/exports, both commercial and removals. Also import/export all other Far East countries.*

Sovereign International Freight Ltd
Sovereign House, 8-10 St. Dunstans Rd., Feltham. TW13 4JU. Tel: 020 8751 3131; fax - 020 8751 4517; e-mail - info@sovereign london.co.uk. *Heathrow Airport based shippers and packers registered to ISO 9002 quality. Holders of the Queen's Award for Export and National Training Award. Specialist in antiques and the fine art trades.*

Vulcan International Services Ltd `LAPADA`
Unit 1A, Avia Park, Westgate 1, Staines Rd., Bedfont. TW14 8RS. Tel: 01784 244152; 01784 248183; e-mail - bjb@vulcan-group.co.uk; website - www.vulcan-group.co.uk. *Fine art packers and shippers worldwide.*

PDQ-Art Move `LAPADA`
Unit 4, Court 1, Challenge Rd., Ashford, TW15 1AX. Tel: 01784 243695; fax - 01784 242237; e-mail - art@pdq.uk.com. *Fine art air freight packers and shippers.*

OXFORDSHIRE

Cotswold Carriers
Unit 2 The Walk, Hook Norton Rd., Chipping Norton. OX7 5TG. Tel: 01608 730500; fax -

**Commercial Packing
and Shipping Services**

WORLD WIDE SHIPPING SERVICE

FOR A PROMPT QUOTE CALL ROBINSONS INTERNATIONAL

Telephone: (44) 117 980 5858

Fax: (44) 117 980 5830

We'll take it there, *with care...*

e-mail: antiques@robinsons-intl.com   www.robinsons-intl.com/antiques

01608 730600. *Removals, storage, shipping, door-to-door Continental deliveries.*

Robinsons International
Nuffield Way, Abingdon. OX14 1TN. Tel: 01235 552255; fax - 01235 553573; website - www. robinsons-intl.com. *Specialist packers and shippers of antiques and fine art worldwide. Established over 100 years.*

Hugh Thomas Antiques Ltd
Park House, Bladon, Woodstock. OX20 1RW. Tel: 01993 812817; fax - 01993 812912; e-mail - hughthomas@htshipping.com; website - www. htshipping.com. *Antique furniture exporter and shipper. Finder service. Single items or many shipped to all USA cities. Large free pick up area. Large dealer co-operative in USA. Full and half container rates also available.*

SOMERSET

Mark Chudley Ltd
The Old Station, Gt. Western Rd., Chard. TA20 1EQ. Tel; 01460 62800; website - www. markchudley.com. *International shipping.*

Louis Degregorio
Vicarage Chambers,Victoria St., Burnham-on-Sea. TA8 1AW. Tel: 01278 788590/788603. *Packing, transport, shipping goods.*

STAFFORDSHIRE

Acorn G.D.S Ltd
183 Queen's Rd., Penkhull, Stoke-on-Trent. ST4 7LF. Tel: 01782 817700. *Open Mon.-Fri. 8.30-5. Container packing and export documentation. Freight forwarding.*

Crown Relocations
Crown House, Unit 1 Ninian Way, Tame Valley

Industrial Estate, Wilnecote, Tamworth. B77 5ES. Tel: 01827 264100; fax - 01827 264101; mobile - 07740 747664; e-mail - birmingham@ crownrelo.com; website - www.crownrelo.com. *UK, Europe and worldwide removal and relocation services.*

SURREY

W. Ede & Co
The Edes Business Park, Restmor Way, Wallington. SM2 5AA. Tel: 020 8773 9933; fax - 020 8773 9011. *Worldwide packing and shipping, complete documentation and removals service, container packing.*

Traders Delivery Service
105 King's Rd., Long Ditton, Surbiton, KT6 5JE. Tel; 020 8398 3681. *Removals and carriers; courier, part loads.*

SUSSEX EAST

Global Services
West St., Lewes. BN7 2NJ. Tel: 01273 475903. *Packers and shippers of antiques, arms, armour and fine works of art.*

SUSSEX WEST

Gander and White Shipping Ltd   LAPADA
Newpound, Wisborough Green, Billingshurst. RH14 0AZ. Tel: 01403 700044; fax - 01403 700814; e-mail - ukinfo@ganderandwhite.com. *Specialist packers and shippers of fine art and antiques.*

Martells International
Queen's Rd., East Grinstead. RH19 1BA. Tel: 01342 321303; fax - 01342 317522. *National and international removers, export packers and shippers.*

TYNE AND WEAR

Owen Humble (Packing and Shipping) Ltd
Clayton House, Walbottle Rd., Lemington, Newcastle-upon-Tyne. NE15 9RU. Tel: 0191 267 7220. *Worldwide service.*

WEST MIDLANDS

The British Shop - Shipping U.S.A
Old Sandwell House, Sandwell St., Walsall. WS1 3DR. Tel: 01922 721088; fax - 01922 723123; (USA - 336 434 4645; fax - 336 434 7765) *Weekly container from Birmingham to High Point, North Carolina, USA. Pick-up and pack, no minimums.*

Clentons Removals Ltd
94 Caldmore Rd., Walsall. WS1 3PD. Tel; 01922 624431; fax - 01922 613053; e-mail - clentons@yahoo.co.uk; website - www.clentonsremovals.com. *Collections arranged in UK and Europe for clients' goods. Storage available. Packing and wrapping of all goods for container shipments. All paperwork done for containers. Packing of containers and shipment of containers.*

Robinsons International   LAPADA
22A Bartleet Rd., Washford, Redditch. B98 0DG. Tel: 01527 830860; fax - 01527 500777; website - www.robinsons-intl.com. *Specialist packers and shippers of antiques and fine art worldwide. Established over 100 years.*

WILTSHIRE

Martin Bros Ltd
The Old Sawmills, The Street, Kilmington, Nr. Warminster. BA12 6RG. Tel: 01985 844144; fax - 01985 844113; website - www.martinbros ltd.com. *Specialist carriers of fine art and furniture throughout mainland UK.*

WORCESTERSHIRE

Simon Hall Ltd
Willersey Industrial Estate, Willersey, Nr. Broadway. WR12 7RR. Tel: 01386 858555; fax - 01386 858501; e-mail - enquiries@ simonhalllimited.com. *Specialist packers and shippers for fine art and antiques world wide. UK collections and deliveries. Humidity controlled containerised and conventional storage.*

SCOTLAND

Crown Relocations
Containerbase, Gartsherrie Rd., Coatbridge, Lanarkshire. ML5 2DT. Tel: 01236 449666; fax - 01236 449888. *Packers and shippers.*

AUCTIONEERS

Bloomsbury Book Auctions

3 and 4 Hardwick St., EC1R 4RY. Tel: 020 7833 2636/7; fax - 020 7833 3954; e-mail - info@ bloomsbury-book-auct.com; website - www. bloomsbury-book-auct.com. *Twenty-four sales a year of books on all subjects and of all values, manuscripts, autograph letters, prints, maps, drawings, photographs, posters and ephemera. Valuations. Collection service.*

Bonhams

101 New Bond St., W1S 1SR. Tel: 020 7629 6602; fax - 020 7629 8876; website - www.phillips-auctions.com. *Regular sales of fine furniture, paintings, ceramics, jewellery, silver, clocks, watches, Oriental works of art, textiles, books, musical instruments, works of art, stamps, medals and decorative arts.*

Bonhams & Brooks, Knightsbridge

Montpelier St., Knightsbridge, SW7 1HH. Tel: 020 7393 3900; fax - 020 7393 3905. *Regular auctions of vintage motor cars, automobilia, sporting items, watercolours, Old Masters, European and modern pictures, portrait miniatures, prints, carved frames, furniture, clocks and watches, Lalique, commercial scent bottles, Oriental and contemporary ceramics, objects of art, tribal art and antiquities, silver, jewellery, objects of vertu, books and manuscripts, antique and modern guns, musical instruments, Oriental carpets and rugs. Annual theme sales to coincide with Cowes Week, The Boat Show and The Westminster Dog Show, NY - pictures, sculptures and related works of art. Viewing Mon.-Fri. 9-4.30, Sun. 11-3.*

Christie's

8 King St., St.James's, SW1Y 6QT. Tel: 020 7839 9060; fax - 020 7839 1611. *Porcelain, pottery, objets d'art and miniatures, pictures including Old Masters, English, Victorian, Continental, Impressionist, contemporary, prints, drawings, watercolours, Art Deco, Art Nouveau; Japanese and Chinese, Islamic and Persian works of art; glass, silver, jewellery, books, modern guns, furniture, carpets, tapestries, clocks and watches, garden statuary, photographs, Russian works of art, sculpture, wine, house sales (contents only).*

Christie's South Kensington Ltd

85 Old Brompton Rd., SW7 3LD. Tel: 020 7581 7611; fax - 020 7321 3311. *Sales of jewellery, silver, pictures, watercolours, drawings and prints; furniture and carpets, ceramics and works of art, printed books; costume, textiles and embroidery; toys and games, dolls, wines, Art Nouveau, Art Deco, cameras. Periodic sales of automata, mechanical music and vintage machines, motoring and aeronautical items including car mascots; Staffordshire portrait figures, miniatures.*

Criterion Auctioneers

53 Essex Rd., Islington. N1 2BN. Tel: 020 7359 5707; fax - 020 7354 9843; e-mail - info@ criterion-auctioneers.co.uk; website - www. criterion-auctioneers.co.uk. *Sales every Mon. at 4 pm of general antiques, reproduction and contemporary furniture, glass, china, rugs and smalls. Viewing Fri. 4-8, Sat. and Sun. 10-6, Mon. prior to sale.*

Stanley Gibbons Auctions

399 Strand, WC2R 0LX. Tel: 020 7836 8444; fax - 020 7836 7342; e-mail - auctions@stanley gibbons.co.uk; website - www.stanleygibbons. com. Est. 1901. *Regular auctions throughout the year.*

Harmers of London Stamp Auctioneers Ltd

11 Power Rd., Chiswick, W4 5PY. Tel: 020 8747 6100; fax - 020 8996 0649; e-mail - auctions@ harmers.demon.co.uk; website - www.harmers. com. Est. 1918. *Monthly auctions of Great Britain, British Commonwealth, foreign countries, airmail stamps, also postal history and literature, stamp boxes, postal scales and related ephemera. Fully illustrated catalogues. Valuations for sale, probate or insurance.*

Hornsey Auctions Ltd

54-56 High St., Hornsey. N8 7NX. Tel: 020 8340 5334; fax - same. *Sales weekly on Wed. at 6.30. Viewing Tues. 5-7.30 and Wed. from 10 am. Open Thurs., Fri. 9.30-5.30 and Sat. 10-4 to take in for next auction.*

Lloyds International Auction Galleries Ltd

9 Lydden Rd., Wandsworth. SW18. Tel: 020 8788 7777; fax - 020 8874 5390; website - www. lloyds-auction.co.uk. *Fortnightly Sat. sales of antique and modern furniture, china, glassware, pictures and collectables. Website catalogue.*

Lots Road Auctions

71-73 Lots Rd., Chelsea, SW10 0RN. Tel: 020 7376 6800; fax - 020 7376 6899; website - www.lotsroad.com. Est. 1978. *Auctions every Sunday at 2 pm (modern and reproduction) and 4.30 pm (antique), approx. 600 lots of antique, traditional and decorative furniture, Oriental carpets, paintings, prints, ceramics, clocks, glass,* silver, objets d'art and soft furnishings. On view Thurs. 2-7, Fri. and Sat. 10-4, Sun. from 10 am. Goods accepted Mon.-Fri. Payment by direct credit 10 days after the sale. Catalogue details and auction results by fax, telephone, live auction line or on website. Valuers, consultants and carriers. VAT registered.

Rippon Boswell and Co
The Arcade, South Kensington Station. SW7 2NA. Tel: 020 7589 4242. International specialist auctioneers of old and antique Oriental carpets. Periodical auctions in London. Also in Germany, Switzerland, USA and Far East.

Rosebery's
74-76 Knights Hill, West Norwood. SE27 0JD. Tel: 020 8761 2522; fax - 020 8761 2524. Quarterly selected and monthly antique and collectors auctions on Tues. and Wed. Fortnightly Mon. general auctions. Specialist auctions of toys and collectors' items, decorative arts, modern design, musical instruments, books and textiles held periodically.

Sotheby's
34-35 New Bond St., W1A 2AA. Tel: 020 7293 5000. Open for free valuations Mon.-Fri. 9-5. Daily sales of paintings, drawings, watercolours, prints, books and manuscripts, European sculpture and works of art, antiquities, silver, ceramics, glass, jewellery, Oriental works of art, furniture, musical instruments, clocks and watches, vintage cars, wine, postage stamps, coins, medals, toys and dolls and other collectors' items.

Southgate Auction Rooms
55 High St., Southgate. N14 6LD. Tel: 020 8886 7888; website - www.southgateauctionrooms.com. Est. 1977. Weekly Mon. sales at 5 pm of jewellery, silver, china, porcelain, paintings, furniture. Viewing Sat. 9-12 noon and from 9 am on day of sale.

BEDFORDSHIRE

W. & H. Peacock
The Auction Centre, 26 Newnham St., Bedford. MK40 3JR. Tel: 01234 266366; website - www.peacockauctions.co.uk. Est. 1901. Antiques sales first Fri. monthly. Viewing Fri. prior 9 am-8 pm. General sales every Sat. at 9.30 am.

Douglas Ross (Auctioneers)
The Old Town Hall, Woburn. MK17 9PZ. Tel: 01525 290502. Sales every four weeks on Thurs.

BERKSHIRE

Dreweatt Neate
Donnington Priory, Donnington, Nr. Newbury. RG14 2JE. Tel: 01635 553553; fax - 01635 553599; e-mail - fineart@dreweatt-neate.co.uk; website - www.auctions.dreweatt-neate.co.uk. Est. 1759. Sales on the premises mainly on a weekly basis. General furnishings - fortnightly on Tues. Antique furniture - six annually. Paintings, books, prints, silver and jewellery, ceramics - three of each annually. Buyers' premium 17.625% including VAT.

Martin and Pole
The Auction House, Milton Rd., Wokingham. RG40 1DB. Tel: 0118 979 0460; fax - 0118 977 6166. Sale of antiques and collectables held usually on 3rd Wed. every month at above address.

Thimbleby & Shorland
Market House, PO Box 175, 31 Great Knollys St., Reading. RG1 7HU. Tel: 01189 508611; fax - 01189 505896; mobile - 07778 766172; e-mail - sarah.needham@thimbleby-shorland.co.uk; website - www.tsauction.co.uk. Est. 1901. Collective sales of antique and modern furniture held monthly at Reading Auction Market. Also sales and valuations of horse-drawn carriages and driving equipment with four sales annually in Reading.

BUCKINGHAMSHIRE

Amersham Auction Rooms
125 Station Rd., Amersham. HP7 0AH. Tel: 01494 729292; fax - 01494 722337; e-mail - info@amershamauctionrooms.co.uk; website - www.amershamauctionrooms.co.uk. Est. 1877. Weekly general and monthly selected antique sales held on Thurs. at 10.30 am.

CAMBRIDGESHIRE

Bonhams
The Golden Rose, 17 Emmanuel Rd., Cambridge. CB1 1JW. Tel: 01223 366523; fax - 01223 300208; website - www.bonhams.com. Regular sales of good furniture, pictures, silver, ceramics and Victoriana. Enquiries to Clodagh Sapsford.

Cheffins
Clifton House, 1 and 2 Clifton Rd., Cambridge. CB1 7EA. Tel: 01223 213343 (10 lines); website - www.cheffins.co.uk. Regular fine art and general auction sales including pictures, furniture, works of art, silver and jewellery, ceramics and collectors' items.

Grounds and Co
2 Nene Quay, Wisbech. PE13 1AQ. Tel: 01945 585041/2. *Three specialist sales annually, each approximately 600 lots.*

Hyperion Auctions Ltd
Station Rd., St. Ives. PE27 5BH. Tel: 01480 464140; fax - 01480 497552; e-mail - enquiries@hyperionauctions.co.uk; website - www.hyperionauctions.co.uk. Est. 1995. *Regular sales of antiques and collectables.*

W. & H. Peacock
The Auction Centre, 75 New St., St Neots. PE19 1AJ. Tel: 01480 474550. *General sales every Thurs. at 11 am.*

Rowley Fine Art Auctioneers & Valuers
8 Downham Rd., Ely. CB6 1AH. Tel: 01353 653020; fax - 01353 653022; website - www.rowleyfineart.com. *Monthly general sales held on the 2nd Sat. Regular sales of fine art and antiques at Tattersalls Sale Ring, Newmarket. Valuations.*

Willingham Auctions
25 High St., Willingham. CB4 5ES. Tel: 01954 261252/201396; website - www.willingham auctions.com. *Sales of antique and fine furniture, silver, ceramics and clocks.*

CHESHIRE

Andrew, Hilditch and Son Ltd
Hanover House, 1A The Square, Sandbach. CW11 0AP. Tel: 01270 767246/762048. Est. 1866. *Quarterly sales of fine pictures and period furnishings. General and Edwardian furniture sales held weekly.*

Bonhams
New House, 150 Christleton Rd., Chester. CH3 5TD. Tel: 01244 313936; fax - 01244 340028; website - www.bonhams.com. Est. 1793. *14 salerooms countrywide including Chester, New Bond Street, Knightsbridge and Chelsea.*

Cheyne's
38 Hale Rd., Altrincham. WA14 2EX. Tel: 0161 941 4879. *Bi-monthly sales held at St Peter's Assembly Rooms, Cecil Road, Hale. Viewing day prior 2-4.30 and 6-8 and sale morning 9-10.30.*

Halls Fine Art
Booth Mansion, 30 Watergate St., Chester. CH1 2LA. Tel: 01244 312300; fax - 01244 312112. *Quarterly antique sales Fri. and fortnightly Victoriana and collectors sales on Wed.*

Frank R. Marshall and Co
Marshall House, Church Hill, Knutsford. WA16 6DH. Tel: 01565 653284; fax - 01565 652341; e-mail - antiques@frankmarshall.co.uk. Est. 1948. *Regular sales of antique furniture, objets d'art, silver, pewter, glass, porcelain, pictures, brass and copper. Fortnightly household collective sales including bric-a-brac. Specialised sales at The Knutsford Auction Salerooms.*

Peter Wilson Fine Art Auctioneers
Victoria Gallery, Market St., Nantwich. CW5 5DG. Tel: 01270 623878; fax - 01270 610508; e-mail - auctions@peterwilson.co.uk; website - www.peterwilson.co.uk. Est. 1955. *Five catalogued (illustrated in colour) two-day sales each year. Uncatalogued auctions every Thurs., shipping goods and household effects (500+ lots).*

Wright Manley Auctioneers
Beeston Castle Salerooms, Tarporley. CW6 9NZ. Tel: 01829 262150; fax - 01829 261829. *Fortnightly Victoriana and household sales and quarterly catalogued fine art and furniture sales.*

CORNWALL

Bonhams Cornwall
Cornubia Hall, Par. PL24 2AQ. Tel: 01726 814047. *Monthly sales of antiques, Victorian and later furnishings, silver, jewellery, pictures and collectors' items.*

Jefferys
The Auction Rooms, 5 Fore St., Lostwithiel. PL22 0BP. Tel: 01208 872245; fax - 01208 873260; e-mail - jefferys.lostwithiel@btinternet. com. *Fortnightly sales of antique furniture, ceramics, glass, jewellery, silver and plate, pictures, prints and collectors' items, on Wed. at 10 am.*

Lambrays
Polmorla Walk Galleries, The Platt, Wadebridge. PL27 7AE. Tel: 0120 881 3593. *Fortnightly sales of antiques and pine. Quarterly auctions of antiques and objets d'art. Illustrated catalogues.*

W. H. Lane & Son
Jubilee House, Queen St., Penzance. TR18 4DF. Tel: 01736 361447; fax - 01736 350097; e-mail - info@whlane.co.uk. *Six picture sales annually (specialists in the Newlyn and St. Ives Schools). Valuations for insurance, probate and family division.*

David Lay FRICS
The Penzance Auction House, Alverton,

Penzance. TR18 4RE. Tel: 01736 361414; fax - 01736 360035; e-mail - david.lays@ btopenworld.com. *Regular sales of fine art, antiques, collectors' items, books and studio pottery. Three-weekly general household sales.*

Martyn Rowe Auctioneers and Valuers
Triplets Business Park, Poldice Valley, Nr Chacewater, Truro. TR16 5PZ. Tel: 01209 822266; fax - 01209 821782. *Weekly on Thurs. at 10 am - Victorian, Edwardian and general sales. Viewing morning of sale and Wed. prior 2-6. Antique and picture sales every 6-8 weeks. Collectors and sporting sales - every 6-8 weeks. Quarterly sales of vintage and classic motorcycles, cars and automobilia. House, commercial, industrial and receivership sales on site or at auction centre.*

H. & H. King
Cumbria Auction Rooms, 12 Lowther St., Carlisle. CA3 8DA. Tel: 01228 525259. *Weekly sales of antique, Victorian and later furnishings, collectors' items and household effects. Quarterley catalogue sales of fine art, furniture and general antiques.*

Mitchell's Auction Co
The Furniture Hall, 47 Station Rd., Cockermouth. CA13 9PZ. Tel: 01900 827800; fax - 01900 828073; e-mail - mfineart@aol.com. Est. 1873. *Weekly (Thurs.) sales of antique, reproduction and modern furniture and effects, approximately 800 lots, starting at 9.30 am. Viewing Wed. 2-7 and throughout sale. Six fine art sales per annum, viewing prior Tues. 11-5 and Wed. 10-7 and prior to sale.*

Penrith Farmers' and Kidds plc
Skirsgill Saleroom, Skirsgill, Penrith. CA11 0DN. Tel: 01768 890781; fax - 01768 895058; e-mail - penrith.farmers@virgin.net. *Weekly sales of household furniture and effects on three Wed. each month, commencing 9.30 am., view Tues. prior 3-6. Monthly sales of antiques and Victoriana on Wed., usually each month, except when quarterly sales of antiques and collectors' items are held at end of Mar., June, Sept. and Dec. - 10.30 am. start. Viewing 2 days prior - Mon. 10-5, Tues. 10-7.*

James Thompson
64 Main St., Kirkby Lonsdale. LA6 2AJ. Tel: 015242 71555; fax - 015242 72939; e-mail-sales@jthompson-auctioneers.co.uk; website - www.jthompson-auctioneers.co.uk. Est. 1945.

Monthly two-day sales of silver, ceramics, general antiques. Picture sales six times a year.

Thomson, Roddick and Medcalf
Coleridge House, Shaddongate, Carlisle. CA2 5TU. Tel: 01228 528939; fax - 01228 592128. Est. 1880. *Monthly catalogue sales of antiques and collectors' items and regular specialist sales particularly antiquarian books. Monthly general furniture sales at Wigton.*

Noel Wheatcroft & Son
Matlock Auction Gallery, The Old Picture Palace, Dale Rd., Matlock. DE4 3LU. Tel: 01629 57460; fax - 01629 57956; website - www.wheatcroft-noel.co.uk. Est. 1923. *Monthly sales of antiques and general items.*

Bearne's
St Edmund's Court, Okehampton St., Exeter. EX4 1DU. Tel: 01392 207000. Est. 1945. *Regular sales of antique furniture, works of art, silver, jewellery, collectors' items, books, clocks and watches, paintings, ceramics and glass, carpets and rugs.*

Bonhams
Dowell St., Honiton. EX14 1LX. Tel: 01404 41872; fax - 01404 43137. Est. 1793. *Regular monthly auctions of furniture, works of art, ceramics, silver and jewellery, collectors' items and fishing memorabilia.*

Bonhams
38/39 Southernhay East, Exeter. EX1 1PE. Tel: 01392 455955; fax - 01392 455962. *Seasonal sales of antiques and fine art held at Powderham Castle, near Exeter, to include silver, plated articles, European ceramics and glass, objects and works of art, clocks, antique furniture and West Country pictures.*

Robin A. Fenner
The Stannary Gallery, Drake Rd., Tavistock. PL19 0AX. Tel: 01822 617799; fax - 01822 617595; e-mail - sales@rafenner.com; website - www.rafenner.com. Est. 1968. *Eight fine art and antique sales a year. Part of The Fine Art Auction Group.*

S.J. Hales Antique & Fine Art Auctioneers & Valuers
Tracey House Salerooms, Newton Rd., Bovey Tracey, Newton Abbot. TQ13 9AZ. Tel: 01626

836684; fax - 01626 836318; e-mail - info@sjhales.com; website - www.sjhales.com. *Sales held at The Edgemoor Hotel, Haytor, Bovey Tracey monthly on Wed. at 10 am. Viewing Mon. 9-5, Tues. 9-7, Wed. 8-10 prior. Valuations.*

Hampton & Littlewood Auctioneers
The Auction Rooms, Alphinbrook Rd., Alphington, Exeter, EX2 8TH. Tel: 01392 413100; fax - 01392 413110; e-mail - enquries@hamptonandlittlewood. co.uk. *Monthly antiques and collectables auctions; quarterly fine sales of selected antiques. All sales held on Wed. Viewing - monthly sales - Sat. morning prior 9-12, Mon. and Tues. prior 9-5.30; quarterly - Sat. prior 9-1, Sun. prior 2-4, Mon. prior 9-7, Tues. prior 9-5.30.*

Honiton Galleries,
205 High St., Honiton. EX14 1LQ. Tel: 01404 42404; fax - 01404 46510; e-mail - sales@ honitongalleries.com; website - www.honiton galleries.com. Est. 1948. *Eight fine art and antique sales a year, including specialist picture and railwayanna. Monthly sales of Victorian and later furniture and effects. Part of The Fine Art Auction Group.*

Kingsbridge Auction Sales
113 Fore St., Kingsbridge. TQ7 1BG. Tel: 01364 631439. *Regular sales of antique and general household furniture and effects.*

Lyme-Bay Auction Galleries
28 Harbour Rd., Seaton. EX12 2NA. Tel: 01297 22453; fax - 01297 23386; e-mail - info@ lymebayauction.co.uk; website - www.lyme bayauction.co.uk. *General household and antique auctions held every four to six weeks.*

Potbury and Sons
The Auction Rooms, Temple St., Sidmouth. EX10 8LN. Tel: 01395 515555/517300; fax - 01395 512608. *Fortnightly sales of fine art every two months.*

Rendells
Stone Park, Ashburton. TQ13 7RH. Tel: 01364 653017: fax - 01364 654251. *Sales every four weeks (Thurs. and Fri.) of antique and reproduction furniture, ceramics, silver, jewellery, pictures, clocks and barometers, copper and brass, miscellanea, toys and collectables. No buyers premium.*

Ward and Chowen
Tavistock Auction Rooms, Market Rd., Tavistock. PL19 0BW. Tel: 01822 612603; fax - 01822 617311.

Whitton and Laing
32 Okehampton St., Exeter. EX4 1DY. Tel: 01392 252621; fax - 01392 496607. Est. 1884. *Monthly auctions of antiques, silver and jewellery. Book and stamp auctions two or three times a year. Picture sales bi-monthly. General auctions weekly.*

DORSET

Cottees
The Market, East St., Wareham. BH20 4NR. Tel: 01929 552826; fax - 01929 554916; e-mail - auctions@cottees.fsnet.co.uk; website - www. auctionsatcottees.co.uk. Est. 1903. *Sales of furniture, silver and jewellery, pottery and porcelain etc. fortnightly on Tues. Viewing previous day 2-5 and 6-8.*

Hy. Duke and Son
Dorchester Fine Art Salerooms, Weymouth Avenue, Dorchester. DT1 1QS. Tel: 01305 265080; fax - 01305 260101; e-mail - enquiries@dukes-auctions.com. Est. 1823. *Regular six weekly sales including specialist sections of silver and jewellery, Oriental and English porcelain, English and Continental furniture, pictures, books and Oriental rugs. Complete valuation and advisory service including insurance, probate and forward tax planning.*

Hy. Duke and Son
The Weymouth Salerooms, Nicholas St., Weymouth. Tel: 01305 761499; fax - 01305 260101. *Regular bi-weekly sales of Victoriana and later furniture and effects.*

House and Son
Lansdowne House, Christchurch Rd., Bournemouth. BH1 3JW. Tel: 01202 298044. *Fortnightly sales of selected furniture, pictures, books, silver, porcelain and glass. Catalogues £2.50 including postage.*

Wm. Morey and Sons
Salerooms, St. Michaels Lane, Bridport. DT6 3RB. Tel: 01308 422078; website - www. saleroomservices.co.uk. Est. 1870. *Household and general items 1st. and 3rd. Sat. in the month. Antiques and collectables every four weeks on Thurs. Website catalogue*

Onslow Auctions Ltd
The Coach House, Manor Rd., Stourpaine. DT11 8TQ. Tel: 01258 488838; mobile - 07831 473400; e-mail - bogue.onslows@btinternet.com. Est. 1984. *Sales 3-4 times a year including posters,*

railwayana, aero and motor, printed ephemera, Titanic and maritime, Louis Vuitton luggage. Viewing as published prior to sale.

Riddetts of Bournemouth
177 Holdenhurst Rd., Bournemouth. BH8 8DQ. Tel: 01202 555686; fax - 01202 311004; e-mail - auctions@riddetts.co.uk; website - www. auctionhammer.co.uk. Est. 1879. *Fortnightly sales of fine antiques, jewellery, silver, plate, pictures. Free illustrated sale programme. Catalogue subscription £55 p.a.*

DURHAM

Denis Edkins
Auckland Auction Rooms, 58 Kingsway, Bishop Auckland. DL14 7JF. Tel: 01388 603095. Est. 1907. *General and antique sales from time to time.*

Barry Potter Auctions
Fleck Way, Thornaby, Stockton- on-Tees. TS17 9JZ. Tel: 01642 767116; fax - 01642 769478; e-mail - vicky@vectis.co.uk. Est. 1988. *Sales of trains held six times a year at the Benn Hall, Rugby. Viewing Fri. evening 5.30-7.30 and Sat. morning 8.30-10.30.*

Vectis Auctions Ltd
Fleck Way, Thornaby, Stockton-on-Tees. TS17 9JZ. Tel: 01642 750616; fax - 01642 769478; e-mail - vicky@vectis.co.uk. Est. 1988. *Specialist sales held once a month on Wed. at the Community Centre, Buckingham, mainly diecast, dolls, teddies, tinplate and lead. Two-day sales held on Wed. and Thurs.*

Thomas Watson and Son
Northumberland St., Darlington. DL3 7HJ. Tel: 01325 462559. *Regular sales of antiques and good quality house contents.*

ESSEX

Ambrose
Ambrose House, Old Station Rd., Loughton. IG10 4PE. Tel: 020 8502 3951; fax - 020 8532 0833; e-mail - info@ambroseauction.co.uk; website - www.ambroseauction.co.uk. *Monthly antique sales.*

Reeman Dansie Howe & Son
Head Gate Auction Rooms, 12 Head Gate, Colchester. CO3 3BT. Tel: 01206 574271. *Sales held every Wed. Viewing Tues. 9-7 prior. Bi-monthly fine art sales.*

Simon H. Rowland
Chelmsford Auction Rooms, 42 Mildmay Rd., Chelmsford. CM2 0DZ. Tel: 01245 354251. *Regular sales by order of the Sheriff of Essex and private vendors.*

Saffron Walden Auctions
1 Market St., Saffron Walden. CB10 1JB. Tel: 01799 513281. *Sales of antique and fine furniture, antique effects and objets d'art held every six weeks.*

John Stacey & Sons (Leigh-on-Sea) Ltd
Leigh Auction Rooms, 86-90 Pall Mall, Leigh-on-Sea. SS9 1RG. Tel: 01702 477051. *Monthly sales of period and other furniture, works of art and collectors' items. Catalogue subscription £40.*

Stanfords
Colchester Cattle Market, Wyncolls Rd., Colchester. CO4 9HU. Tel: 01206 842156. *Weekly Sat. sales at 10.30 along with the country market and intermittent fine art and antiques sales. Viewing Fri. prior 2-6 and morning of sale from 8.30.*

G.E. Sworder and Sons
14 Cambridge Rd., Stansted Mountfitchet. CM24 8BZ. Tel: 01279 817778; fax - 01279 817779; e-mail - auctions@sworder.co.uk; website - www.sworder.co.uk. Est. 1782. *Eight auctions of antique furniture, ceramics, silver, pictures, clocks, decorative items. Viewing Fri. 10-5, Sat. and Sun. 10-1, Mon. 10-5, Tues. 9 am onwards prior to sale. Weekly Thurs. 11 am auction of Victorian, Edwardian and later furniture and collectables. Viewing morning of sale and Wed. 2-5. Fully illustrated catalogue available.*

Trembath Welch (incorporating J.M. Welch & Son)
Old Town Hall, Great Dunmow. CM6 1AU. Tel: 01371 873014; fax - 01371 878239; e-mail - trembathwelch@ic24.net. Est. 1886. *At the Salerooms, Chequers Lane - selected antique furniture and effects sales quarterly. Sales of collectables, household furniture and antiques every two weeks. Catalogue subscription service available.*

GLOUCESTERSHIRE

BK The Property Assets Consultancy
Bisley House, Green Farm Business Park, Bristol Rd., Gloucester. GL2 4LY. Tel: 01452 880000; fax - 01452 880088; e-mail - artantiques@ bkonline.co.uk; website - www.bkonline.co.uk. Est. 1862. *Free auction valuations; confidential valuation services. Auctions held regularly.*

Bristol Auction Rooms Ltd

St. John's Place, Apsley Rd., Clifton, Bristol. BS8 2ST. Tel: 0117 973 7201; fax - 0117 973 5671; website - www.bristolauctionrooms.com. *Monthly auctions of antique furniture, clocks, rugs, textiles, paintings and prints, glass, pottery, porcelain, books and ephemera, silver, objects of vertu, toys and collectables. View Sat. prior 9.30-1; day prior from 9.30-7, and on sale day from 9. Fortnightly auctions of Victorian and modern household furniture and effects. View day prior to sale from 12-6 and on sale day from 9. Specialist auctions and house sales held throughout the year. Catalogue subscription service. Buyers' premium.*

Corinium Galleries

25 Gloucester St., Cirencester. GL7 2DJ. Tel: 01285 659057. Est. 1976. *Mon. sales of postcards and printed ephemera every five weeks.*

The Cotswold Auction Co

Chapel Walk Saleroom, Chapel Walk, Cheltenham. GL50 3DS. Tel: 01242 256363; fax - 01242 571734; e-mail - info@cotswoldauction.co.uk. *Three sales monthly - specialist and general.*

The Cotswold Auction Company

City Chambers, 4/6 Clarence St., Gloucester. GL1 1DX. Tel: 01452 521177. *Sales of Georgian, Victorian, Edwardian and later furniture, ceramics, glass, metalwork, silver, plate, jewellery, miscellanea, collectors' items, books, pictures and outside effects every 4-6 weeks.*

Fraser Glennie and Partners

53 Castle St. Cirencester. GL7 1QD. Tel: 01285 659677; fax - 01285 642256. Est. 1984. *Monthly sales of antiques, other furniture, collectors' items and musical instruments at the Bingham Hall, Cirencester.*

Mallams Fine Art Auctioneers and Valuers

26 Grosvenor St., Cheltenham. GL52 2SG. Tel: 01242 235712; fax - 01242 241943; e-mail - cheltenham@mallams.co.uk; website - www. mallams.co.uk/fineart. Est. 1788. *Regular sales of furniture, ceramics, paintings, textiles, rugs and works of art, sporting, toy and collectors' items.*

Moore, Allen & Innocent

The Salerooms, Norcote, Cirencester. GL7 5RH. Tel: 01285 646050; fax - 01285 652862; e-mail - fineart@mooreallen.co.uk; website - www. mooreallen.co.uk. Est. 1852. *Fortnightly sales of over 1,000 lots of antique and other furniture and effects. Quarterly sales of selected antiques. Bi-annual specialist picture and sporting sales. Fri. at 9.30 am. Viewing day prior 10.30-8. 10% buyers premium.*

Wotton Auction Rooms Ltd

(formerly Sandoe Luce Panes) Tabernacle Rd., Wotton-under-Edge. GL12 7EB. Tel: 01453 844733; fax - 01453 845448; website - www.wottonauctionrooms.co.uk. *Monthly two-day sales of antiques and collectables, 1,500+ lots. Calendar cards on request. Valuations.*

HAMPSHIRE

Bonhams Auctioneers

54 Southampton Rd., Ringwood. BH24 1JD. Tel: 01425 473333.

Jacobs and Hunt Fine Art Auctioneers

26 Lavant St., Petersfield. GU32 3EF. Tel: 01730 233933; fax - 01730 262323; e-mail - auctions@ jacobsandhunt.co.uk; website - www.jacobsand hunt.co.uk. Est. 1895. *Monthly general antique sales held on Fri.*

George Kidner Auctioneers

The Old School, The Square, Pennington, Lymington. SO41 8GN. Tel: 01590 670070; fax - 01590 675167; e-mail - info@georgekidner. co.uk; website - www.georgekidner.co.uk; Emsworth Rd. - 01590 679487. *Monthly specialist sales - furniture, works of art, silver and jewellery, collectors' items, oils, prints and watercolours, European ceramics, Oriental works of art, books and marine items, collectable toys, model railways and railwayana. Viewing - Mon. 9.30-4.30, Tues. 9.30-7. Also saleroom at Emsworth Rd., Lymington - Victorian, Edwardian and later furniture and effects. Viewing previous day 9.30-7.*

May and Son

The Old Stables, 9A Winchester Rd., Andover. SP10 2EG. Tel: 01264 323417; fax - 01264 338841; e-mail - office@mayandson.com; website - www.mayandson.com. Est. 1940. *Monthly sales on 3rd Wed. of antique furniture and collectables at Penton Mewsey Village Hall (Lots from private sources only). Viewing previous day 8.30-6, and morning of sale from 8 am. Buyers premium 10% + tax.*

D.M. Nesbit and Co

7 Clarendon Rd., Southsea, Portsmouth. PO5 2ED. Tel: 023 9286 4321; fax - 023 9229 5522; e-mail - auctions@nesbits.co.uk. *Monthly sales of antique furniture, silver, porcelain and pictures.*

HEREFORDSHIRE

Brightwells

The Fine Art Saleroom, Ryelands Rd.,

Leominster. HR6 8NZ. Tel: 01568 611122; fax - 01568 610519. Est. 1846. *Monthly two-day sales of antiques and collectors' items (approx. 1,200 lots per sale). Two or three sales per month of antique and household effects. Specialist sales of ceramics and glass, toys, dolls and bears.*

HERTFORDSHIRE

G. E. Sworder & Sons
Office - 42 St Andrews St., Hertford, SG14 1JA. Tel: 01992 583508; fax - same.

Tring Market Auctions
Brook St., Tring. HP23 5EF. Tel: 01442 826446. *Fortnightly Sat. sales of antiques and collectables held at The Market Premises, Brook St., Tring. Fine art sales held on last Fri. of alternate months.*

ISLE OF WIGHT

Shanklin Auction Rooms
79 Regent St., Shanklin. PO37 7AP. Tel: 01983 863441. *Monthly auctions of antiques and fine art.*

Ways
The Auction House, Garfield Rd., Ryde. PO33 2PT. Tel: 01983 562255; e-mail - ways@waysauctionrooms.fsbusiness.co.uk; website - www.waysauctionrooms.fsbusiness.co.uk. *Five-weekly sales of antique and modern furniture, silver, copper and brass, oils, watercolours and prints, jewellery, china, clocks. No buyers premium.*

KENT

Bonhams
13 Lime Tree Walk, Sevenoaks. TN13 1YH. Tel: 01732 740310; fax - 01732 741842. *Monthly sales of antique furniture and objects of art.*

Bracketts
Fine Art Auctioneers, Auction Hall, The Pantiles, Tunbridge Wells. TN2 5QL. Tel: 01892 544500; fax - 01892 515191; e-mail - sales@bfaa.co.uk; website - www.bfaa.co.uk. Est. 1886. *Eight fine art and antique sales a year, including specialist sales of Tunbridge Ware. Fortnightly Mon. sales of Victorian and later furniture and effects through Salehurst Auctioneers in Ninfield. Part of The Fine Art Auction Group.*

The Canterbury Auction Galleries
40 Station Rd. West, Canterbury. CT2 8AN. Tel: 01227 763337; fax - 01227 456770; e-mail - auctions@thecanterburyauctiongalleries.com; website - www.thecanterburyauctiongalleries.com. Est. 1911. *Fine art and antique sales held bi-monthly on Tues. commencing at 10.30 am viewing Mon. prior 10-7. Monthly auctions of Victorian and later furniture, usually 1st. Sat. each month, at 10 am. Viewing Fri. prior 3-8. Free valuation service held most Fri. from 10-1. Professional valuations for insurance, probate, family division or sale by auction.*

Gorringes inc. Julian Dawson
15 The Pantiles, Tunbridge Wells, TN2 5TD. Tel: 01892 619670; fax - 01892 619671; e-mail - tunbridge.wells@gorringes.co.uk and books@gorringes.co.uk. *Office and bookshop. Valuations undertaken for sale, probate and insurance by appointment at the office, at your home or your bank. Items can be entered for auction in our Lewes or Bexhill salerooms. Bookshop - wide range of reference books on antiques, fine art and collectables.*

Halifax Property Services
15 Cattle Market, Sandwich. CT13 9AW. Tel: 01304 614369; fax - 01304 612023. *Antique and other furniture and effects on Wed., 16 sales per year held at The Drill Hall, The Quay, Sandwich.*

Hobbs Parker
Romney House, Ashford Market, Orbital Park, Ashford. TN24 0HB. Tel: 01233 502222; fax - 01233 502211; e-mail - info@hobbsparker.co.uk; website - www.hobbsparker.co.uk. Est. 1850. *Monthly sales of antiques and household furniture.*

Hogben Fine Art Auctioneers & Valuers
Unit C Highfield Industrial Estate, Off Warren Rd., Folkestone. CT19 6DD. Tel: 01303 240808/246810; fax - 01303 246256. *Fine art saleroom - monthly sales.*

Ibbett, Mosely
125 High St., Sevenoaks. TN13 1UT. Tel: 01732 456731; fax - 01732 740910. Est. 1900. *Antiques and objets d'art.*

Lambert & Foster Auction Sale Room
102 High St., Tenterden. TN30 6HU. Tel: 01580 762083. *Four offices in Kent. Monthly general sales of antique and other furniture and effects.*

LANCASHIRE

Acorn Philatelic Auctions
PO Box 152, Salford, Manchester. M17 1BP. Tel: 0161 877 8818; e-mail - george@traffordbooks.

fsnet.co.uk. Est. 1980. *Tues. sales, approximately every five weeks, held at Unit 6, Block C, Astra Business Centre, Guiness Rd., Trafford Park, Manchester. 10 per year all specialising in paper collectables - postage stamps and history, manuscripts, autographs, picture and cigarette cards, books, prints, drawings and watercolours. Sales commence at 2 pm. Viewing Mon. prior 10.30-6.30, and sale morning 9-1.15.*

Capes Dunn & Co Fine Art Auctioneers & Valuers
The Auction Galleries, 38 Charles St., Manchester. M1 7DB. Tel: 0161 273 1911; fax - 0161 273 3474; e-mail - enquiries@capesdunn. com; website - www.capesdunn.com. Est. 1826. *Catalogues of specialist sales available on request. Regional office in Lytham.*

Kingsway Auction Rooms Ltd
The Galleries, Kingsway, Ansdell, Lytham St. Annes. FY8 1AB. Tel: 01253 735442. *Sales of antique, reproduction and modern furnishings and appointments fortnightly or every three weeks on Tues. Approximately 400-600 lots commencing 9.30 am. Viewing Fri. 2-4, Sat. 10-12, Mon. 9-4. Buyers' premium 15%.*

Warren & Wignall Ltd
The Mill, Earnshaw Bridge, Leyland. PR5 3PH. Tel: 01772 451430; fax - 01772 454516. *Sales of general antiques every three weeks on Wed. at 10 am. Viewing Tues. 9-7.*

LEICESTERSHIRE

Freckeltons
1 Leicester Rd., Loughborough. LE11 2AE. Tel: 01509 214564; fax - 01509 236114. Est. 1919. *Monthly sales of general antiques.*

Gilding's Auctioneers and Valuers
Roman Way, Market Harborough. LE16 7PQ. Tel: 01858 410414; fax - 01858 432956; e-mail - sales@gildings.co.uk; website - www.gildings. co.uk. *Regular antique and Victoriana sales and free, over-the-counter valuations.*

Heathcote Ball & Co
Castle Auction Rooms, 78 St. Nicholas Circle, Leicester. LE1 5NW. Tel: 0116 2536789; fax - 0116 2538517; e-mail - heathcote-ball@ clara.co.uk. Est. 1977. *Auctions every 4-6 weeks.*

LINCOLNSHIRE

Eleys Auctioneers
26 Wide Bargate, Boston. PE21 6RX. Tel: 01205 361687; fax - 01205 351091; e-mail - sales@ eleysestateagents.co.uk; website - www.eleys estateagents.co.uk. Est. 1882. *Regular antique and collectors sales.*

Thomas Mawer & Son Ltd
Dunston House, Portland St., Lincoln. LN5 7NN. Tel: 01522 524984; fax - 01522 535600; e-mail - auctions@thos-mawer.co.uk; website - www. thos-mawer.co.uk. Est. 1864. *Sales on first Sat. every month at 10 am. Viewing Fri. prior 12-4 and sale morning from 8.30. Catalogue sales quarterly.*

Richardsons
Bourne Auction Rooms, Spalding Rd., Bourne. PE10 9LE. Tel: 01778 422686; fax - 01778 425726; e-mail - enquiries@richardsonsauctions. co.uk. *Antiques sales every month. Antique and modern sales every other Sat. Various specific sales periodically, eg silver, clocks, bygones, transport.*

Marilyn Swain
The Old Barracks, Sandon Rd., Grantham. NG31 9AS. Tel: 01476 568861; fax - 01476 576100. *Bi-monthly antique, fine art and collectable sales. Fortnightly sales of Victorian and later furniture, general effects and collectables. Valuations.*

UK Auction Rooms Ltd
t/a DDM Auction Rooms, Old Court Rd., Brigg. DN20 8JJ. Tel: 01652 650172; fax - 01652 650085. *Fine art and antique auctions every seven weeks. Victorian and household auctions fortnightly on Sat. Valuations for insurance, probate and sale. Free valuation "clinic" every Thurs. 9.30-12.*

MERSEYSIDE

Cato Crane & Co
6 Stanhope St., Liverpool. L8 5RF. Tel: 0151 709 5559; fax - 0151 707 2454; e-mail - johncrane@ cato-crane.co.uk. *Collectors, antiques, fine art and maritime sales fortnightly on Thurs. Viewing Wed. prior 10-3.*

Kingsley Auctions Ltd.
3/4 The Quadrant, Hoylake. L47 2EE. Tel: 0151 632 5821; fax - 0151 632 5823. *Sales every Tues. at 10 am., of antiques, fine art, general chattels. Viewing Sat. 9-12.30, Mon. 9-5 and Tues. 9-10.*

Outhwaite and Litherland
Kingsway Galleries, Fontenoy St., Liverpool. L3 2BE. Tel: 0151 236 6561; fax - 0151 236 1070; e-mail - auction@lots.uk.com; website - www.lots.

uk.com. *Victorian, Edwardian and later furnishings - weekly Tues. Collectors cavalcade sale of general antiques and collectibles - monthly Tues. Fine art and antiques - quarterly Wed. Clocks, watches, scientific instruments - bi-annually Wed. Specialist sales of books, wines, stamps etc. periodically. Members of SOFAA. Branch offices at Southport and Hoylake, Wirral.*

MIDDLESEX

Bainbridge's
The Auction Room, Ickenham Rd., Ruislip. HA4 7DL. Tel: 01895 621991; fax - 01895 623622. *Monthly sales on Thurs. at 11 am. Viewing on sale day from 9.30 and day before 1-7.*

NORFOLK

James Beck Auctions
The Cornhall, Cattle Market St., Fakenham. NR21 9AW. Tel: 01328 851557. *Weekly sales of antique furniture and collectables every Thurs. at 11 am.*

Clowes Nash Auctions
Norwich Livestock & Commercial Centre, Hall Rd., Norwich. NR4 6EQ. Tel: 01603 504488. *Antiques and general furniture weekly sales.*

Ewings
Market Place, Reepham, Norwich. NR10 4JJ. Tel: 01603 870473. *Periodic sales of antiques and modern furniture and effects.*

Thos. Wm. Gaze and Son
Diss Auction Rooms, Roydon Rd., Diss. IP22 4LN. Tel: 01379 650306; fax - 01379 644313; website - www.twgaze.com. Est. 1857. *Weekly Fri. auctions (over 2,000 lots) including antiques and collectables, Victorian pine and country furniture. Regular specialist sales including special antiques, decorative arts, modern design, toys and nostalgia, rural bygones, architectural salvage and statuary etc. Online catalogues.*

Horners Auctioneers
North Walsham Salerooms, Midland Rd., North Walsham. NR28 9JR. Tel: 01493 750225; fax - 01493 750506; e-mail - auction@horners.co.uk; website - www.horners.co.uk. *Special bi-monthly (Sat.) auctions of antiques and collectables held at Acle. Viewing Fri. prior 10-8. Weekly general sales (Thurs. - Acle; Fri. - North Walsham). Details and catalogue on website.*

Keys - Aylsham Salerooms
Auctioneers & Valuers, 8 Market Place, Aylsham.

NR11 6EH. Tel: 01263 733195; fax - 01263 732140; e-mail - mail@aylshamsalerooms.co.uk; website - www.aylshamsalerooms.co.uk. Est. 1953. *Three-weekly sales of period, antique and Victorian furniture, silver, porcelain etc. Bi-monthly picture sales - oils, watercolours and prints etc. Six book sales annually and regular collectors sales. Weekly sales of modern and secondhand furniture.*

NORTHAMPTONSHIRE

Goldsmith Howard
15 Market Place, Oundle. PE8 4BA. Tel: 01832 272349. *Sales approximately bi-monthly.*

Wilfords Ltd
76 Midland Rd., Wellingborough. NN8 1NB. Tel: 01933 222760/222762. *Weekly antique and general sales on Thurs. from 9.30 am (1400 lots).*

NORTHUMBERLAND

Jack Dudgeon
76 Ravensdowne, Berwick-upon-Tweed. TD15 1DQ. Tel: 01289 332700; fax - 01289 332701; e-mail - jack@jackdudgeon.co.uk. *Antiques and fine art, collectables every two months on Mon. Viewing Wed., Thurs., Fri. and Sat. prior.*

NOTTINGHAMSHIRE

Arthur Johnson and Sons (Auctioneers)
The Nottingham Auction Centre, Meadow Lane, Nottingham. NG2 3GY. Tel: 0115 986 9128; fax - 0115 986 2139. *Approximately 1,000 lots weekly on Sat. at 10 am. of antique and shipping furniture, silver, gold, porcelain, metalware and collectables.*

Mellors & Kirk Fine Art Auctioneers
Gregory St., Nottingham. NG7 2NL. Tel: 0115 979 0000; e-mail - enquiries@mellors-kirk.com; website - www.mellors-kirk.com. Est. 1993. *Two-day fine art sales every six weeks of antique furniture, clocks, pictures, ceramics, Oriental works of art, books and ephemera, collectors' toys and dolls, coins and medals and other specialist items. Weekly general sales of 500-800 lots on Tues. 10.30 am. Viewing Sat. 9-12 and Mon. 9-5.*

Neales
192-194 Mansfield Rd., Nottingham. NG1 3HU. Tel: 0115 962 4141; fax - 0115 985 6890; e-mail - fineart@neales.co.uk; website - www.neales.co.uk. *Bi-monthly specialist sales of paintings, drawings, prints and books; silver, jewellery,*

bijouterie and watches; European and Oriental ceramics and works of art, glass; furniture and decoration; clocks, barometers and mechanical music; metalwork, fabrics, needlework, carpets and rugs; collectors' toys and dolls; stamps, coins and medals, post and cigarette cards; autographs and collectors' items. Weekly collective sales (Mon.) of general antique and later furnishings, shipping goods and reproduction furnishings. Period and later ceramics, glass and decorative effects. Contents sales on the premises of town and country properties.

Northgate Auction Rooms Ltd

17 Northgate, Newark. NG24 1EX. Tel: 01636 605905; fax - 01636 640051; e-mail - auctions@ northgateauctionroomsnewark.co.uk; website - www.northgateauctionroomsnewark.co.uk. *Monthly sales of antique and Victorian furniture, oil paintings, silver etc. Weekly sales of early 20th C and general household furniture.*

OXFORDSHIRE

Bonhams Auctioneers

39 Park End St., Oxford. OX1 1JD. Tel: 01865 723524; fax - 01865 791064; website - www.phillips-auctions.com. *Fortnightly sales of*

Victoriana and general effects. Specialist sales of fine furniture, rugs, works of art, silver, jewellery, ceramics, collectors' items and paintings throughout the year.

Holloways

49 Parsons St., Banbury. OX16 5PF. Tel: 01295 817777; fax - 01295 817701; e-mail - enquiries@ hollowaysauctioneers.co.uk; website - www. hollowaysauctioneers.co.uk. *General or specialist sales on own premises every other week.*

Mallams

Fine Art Auctioneers, Bocardo House, 24 St. Michael's St., Oxford. OX1 2EB. SOFAA. Tel: 01865 241358; fax - 01865 725483; e-mail - oxford@mallams.co.uk; website - www.mallams. co.uk/fineart. Est. 1788. *Frequent sales of furniture, silver, paintings and works of art. House sales arranged on the premises.*

Mallams incorporating Messengers

Pevensey House, 27 Sheep St., Bicester. OX26 7JF. SOFAA. Tel: 01869 252901; fax - 01869 320283; e-mail - bicester@mallams.co.uk; website - www.mallams.co.uk/fineart. *Regular sales of antiques and later furniture, clocks, ceramics and glass, paintings, books and miscellany. Special annual garden sale.*

Simmons and Sons

32 Bell St., Henley-on-Thames. RG9 2BH. Tel: 01491 571111; fax - 01491 579833; website - www.simmonsandsons.com. Est. 1802. *Eight antique and eight general sales per year held at The Saleroom Watcombe Manor, Ingham Lane, Watlington, Oxon. Sales start 10.30 am. Viewing Sat. previous 9.30-12.30, Mon. prior 2-7, Tues. prior 10-6 and morning of sale.*

SHROPSHIRE

Halls Fine Art

Welsh Bridge Salerooms, Shrewsbury. SY3 8LA. Tel: 01743 231212; fax - 01743 271014. *Weekly Fri. household and Victoriana sales. Monthly catalogued antique sales.*

Perry and Phillips

Auction Rooms, Old Mill Antique Centre, Mill St., Bridgnorth. WV15 5AG. Tel: 01746 762248. Est. 1853. *Monthly Tues. antiques and collectables sales.*

Potteries Specialist Auctions

48 High St., Whitchurch. SY13 1BB. Tel: 01948 662050; e-mail - enquiries@potteriesauctions. com. *Specialist auctions every month, usually*

Wed. at 11 am. Viewing Tues. prior 10-4. Free valuations Thurs. 10-4.

Walker Barnett and Hill
Cosford Auction Rooms, Long Lane, Cosford. TF11 8PJ. Tel: 01902 375555; fax - 01902 375556. *Monthly sales of Victoriana, reproduction, shipping, modern furniture and effects on Tues. 10.30. Fine art and antiques sales every 6-8 weeks.*

SOMERSET

Adam Auctions
28 Adam St., Bath. TA8 1PQ. Tel: 01278 783193/793709. Est. 1973. *Monthly sales of general antiques usually held on Wed. Telephone for details.*

Aldridges of Bath
Newark House, 26-45 Cheltenham St., Bath. BA2 3EX. Tel: 01225 462830; fax - 01225 311319. *Fortnightly Tues. sales, broken down into specialist categories:- antique furniture to include clocks and Oriental carpets; silver and porcelain, glass and metalware; paintings and prints; collector's sales; Victorian and general furniture. Viewing Sat. 9-12 and Mon. 9-6. Catalogues available upon annual subscription.*

Bonhams
1 Old King St., Bath. BA1 2JT. Tel: 01225 788988; fax - 01225 446675. *Regular sales of antique furniture and Victoriana as well as silver, pictures, books and fine wine, ceramics, glass and 20th C art and design.*

Clevedon Salerooms
The Auction Centre, Kenn Rd., Kenn, Clevedon. BS21 6TT. Tel: 01934 830111; fax - 01934 832538; e-mail - info@clevedon-salerooms.com; website - www.clevedon-salerooms.com. *Quarterly auctions of antique furniture, fine art and collectors' items. Fortnightly sales of Victorian, Edwardian and general furniture and effects. Occasional specialist sales and sales held on vendors' property. Valuations.*

Cooper & Tanner Chartered Surveyors
The Agricultural Centre, Standerwick, Frome. BA11 2QB. Tel: 01373 831010. Est. 1890. *Weekly sales of antiques and general household chattels on Wed. at 10.30 am. Viewing morning of sale. Haulage service.*

Gardiner Houlgate
9 Leafield Way, Corsham, Bath. SN13 9SW. Tel: 01225 812912; fax - 01225 811777; e-mail - auctions@gardiner-houlgate.co.uk. *Regular sales of antique furniture and works of art. Frequent sales of Victorian and later furnishings. Fortnightly jewellery sales, quarterly musical instrument sales, specialist clocks and watches sales. Valuations.*

Greenslade Taylor Hunt Fine Art
Magdalene House, Church Square, Taunton. TA1 1SB. Tel: 01823 332525; fax - 01823 353120. *Monthly, last Thurs., sales of antique furniture, ceramics, glass, metalwork, paintings and prints. Specialist sales of silver and jewellery; collectors' items, printed books, clocks and watches, sporting. Fortnightly Wed. sales of antique and shipping furniture, china, glass and effects.*

Lawrence Fine Art Auctioneers Ltd
South St., Crewkerne. TA18 8AB. Tel: 01460 73041; fax - 01460 270799; e-mail - enquiries@ lawrences.co.uk; website - www.lawrences.co.uk. *Specialist auctioneers and valuers. Regular sales of antiques and fine art. General sales every Wed.*

The London Cigarette Card Co. Ltd
Sutton Rd., Somerton. TA11 6QP. Tel: 01458 273452; fax - 01458 273515; e-mail - cards@ londoncigcard.co.uk; website - www. londoncigcard.co.uk. Est. 1927. *Suppliers of thousands of different series of cigarette and trade cards and special albums. Publishers of catalogues, reference books and monthly magazine. Regular auctions in London and Somerset. S.A.E. for details. Showroom in West St. open Mon-Sat. or mail order.*

Tamlyn and Son
56 High St., Bridgwater. TA6 3BN. Tel: 01278 458241; fax - 01278 458242; saleroom - 01278 445251.

Wellington Salerooms
Mantle St., Wellington. TA21 8AR. Tel: 01823 664815. Est. 1971. *Six-weekly sales of general antiques. Three-weekly sales of Victorian, Edwardian and shipping goods.*

STAFFORDSHIRE

Bagshaws Wintertons Fine Arts
The Estate Saleroom, 17 High St., Uttoxeter. ST14 7HP. Tel: 01889 562811; fax - 01889 563795. Est. 1864. *Bi-monthly sales of Victorian and general household furniture and effects.*

John German
1 Lichfield St., Burton-on-Trent. DE14 3QZ. Tel:

01283 512244; fax - 01283 517896. *Occasional sales of major house contents. Specialist fine art valuation department.*

Potteries Specialist Auctions

271 Waterloo Rd., Cobridge, Stoke-on-Trent. ST6 3HR. Tel: 01782 286622; fax - 01782 213777; e-mail - enquiries@potteriesauctions. com. *Specialist auctions every month, usually Wed. at 11 am. Viewing Tues. prior 10-4.*

Louis Taylor Fine Art Auctioneers

Britannia House, 10 Town Rd., Hanley, Stoke-on-Trent. ST1 2QG. Tel: 01782 214111; fax - 01782 215283. Est. 1877. *Quarterly fine art sales including furniture, pictures, pottery, porcelain, silver and works of art. Specialist Royal Doulton and Beswick auctions. General Victoriana auctions held every two weeks.*

Wintertons Fine Arts

Lichfield Auction Centre, Fradley Park, Fradley, Lichfield. WS13 8NF. Tel: 01543 263256; fax - 01543 415348; e-mail - enquiries@wintertons. co.uk; website - www.wintertons.co.uk. Est. 1864. *Bi-monthly sales of antiques and fine art and sales of Victorian and general furniture every two weeks.*

SUFFOLK

Abbotts Auction Rooms

Campsea Ashe, Woodbridge. IP13 0PS. Tel: 01728 746323; fax - 01728 748173. *Extensive calendar of fine art and antique auctions held on Wed. Sales calendar and catalogues available. Weekly sales of Victoriana & household furniture held on Mon. Viewing Sat. 9-11.*

Boardman - Fine Art Auctioneers

PO Box 99, Haverhill. CB9 7YS. Tel: 01440 730414. *Large sales held twice a year specialising in selected fine furniture (particularly oak), clocks, paintings and early metalware.*

Bonhams Auctioneers

32 Boss Hall Rd., Ipswich. IP1 5DJ. Tel: 01473 740494. *Five two-day specialist sales annually at Bury St. Edmunds. Eight mixed sales in Ipswich.*

Diamond Mills and Co. Fine Art Auctioneers

117 Hamilton Rd., Felixstowe. IP11 7BL. Tel: 01394 282281 (3 lines). Ipswich office - 01473 218600. *Periodic fine art sales. Monthly general sales. Auctions at The Orwell Hall, Orwell Rd., Felixstowe.*

Durrant's

The Auction Rooms, Gresham Rd., Beccles. NR34 9QN. Tel: 01502 713490; e-mail - info@durrantsauctionrooms.com. *Antique and general furniture auctions every Fri.*

Dyson & Son

The Auction Room, Church St., Clare. CO10 8PD. Tel: 01787 277993; e-mail - info@dyson-auctioneers.co.uk; website - www.dyson-auctioneers.co.uk. Est. 1978. *Sales of antiques and chattels every three weeks on Sat. at 11 am. Viewing Fri. 9-9, Sat. from 9 am.*

Lacy Scott and Knight Fine Art & Furniture

10 Risbygate St., Bury St. Edmunds. IP33 3AA. Tel: 01284 748600; fax - 01284 748620. Est. 1868. *Quarterly sales of fine art including antique and decorative furniture, silver, pictures, ceramics etc. on behalf of executors and private vendors. Regular (every three weeks) sales of Victoriana and general household contents. Also quarterly sales of live steam models, scale models, diecast and tinplate toys.*

Neal Sons and Fletcher

26 Church St., Woodbridge. IP12 1DP. Tel: 01394 382263; fax - 01394 383030; e-mail - allatnsf@aol.com; website - www.nsf.co.uk. *Two special mixed antiques sales annually. Individual specialised sales and complete house contents sales as required. Household furniture sales monthly on Wed.*

Olivers

The Saleroom, Burkitts Lane, Sudbury. CO10 1HB. Tel: 01787 880305; fax - 01787 883107; e-mail - oliversauctions@btconnect.com. *Fortnightly sales of Victorian and later furniture and household effects. Regular sales of antiques and works of art. Enquiries to James Fletcher FRICS.*

SURREY

Clarke Gammon Fine Art Auctioneers

The Guildford Auction Rooms, Bedford Rd., Guildford. GU1 4SJ. Tel: 01483 880915; fax - 01483 880918; website - www.invaluable.com/clarkegammon. Est. 1919.

Croydon Auction Rooms (Rosan and Co.) (incorporating E.Reeves Auctions)

145/151 London Rd., Croydon. CR0 2RG. Tel: 020 8688 1123. *Fortnightly Sat. collective sales at 10 am. Viewing Fri. prior.*

Ewbank Auctioneers
Burnt Common Auction Rooms, London Rd., Send, Woking. GU23 7LN. Tel: 01483 223101; fax - 01483 222171. *Monthly general and fine art sales on Thurs. Viewing Wed. 10-8 and Tues. 2-5.*

Hamptons International
Baverstock House, 93 High St., Godalming. GU7 1AL. Tel: 01483 423567; fax - 01483 426392; e-mail - fineartauctions@hamptons-int.com; website - www.hampton.co.uk/fineart. *Regular (Wed. and Thurs.) fine art sales at 93 High Street, specialising in selected fine furniture, rugs, paintings and watercolours, porcelain, glass, jewellery, silver, objets d'art and books. Two sales each month of general and Victorian furniture, shipping goods and household effects, held on first and third Sat. House sales conducted on the premises when instructed. Valuations for probate, insurance and sale purposes.*

Lawrences' - Auctioneers Limited
Norfolk House, 80 High St., Bletchingley. RH1 4PA. Tel: 01883 743323; fax - 01883 744578. *Six-weekly antique and reproduction furniture and effects.*

Parkins
18 Malden Rd., Cheam. SM3 8SD. Tel: 020 8644 6633/4. *Sales of general household furniture and effects 2nd and 4th Mon. at 10 am. Viewing Fri. 2-4 and Sat. 10-4. Special antique sale on 1st Mon. at 10 am. Small antiques and collectables one Fri. evening each month at 7 pm - please telephone for details.*

Richmond and Surrey Auctions
The Old Railway Parcels Depot, Kew Rd., Richmond. TW9 2NA. Tel: 020 8948 6677; fax - 020 8948 2021. Est. 1992. *Auctioneers, valuers and consultants. Sales every Thurs.at 6 pm.*

P.F. Windibank Fine Art Auctioneers & Valuers
The Dorking Halls, Reigate Rd., Dorking. RH4 1SG. Tel: 01306 884556/876280; fax - 01306 884669; e-mail - sjw@windibank.co.uk; website - www.windibank.co.uk. Est. 1945. *Antique auctions held every 4-5 weeks on Sat. at 10.30 am. Viewing Thurs. evening prior 5-9, Fri. prior 9-5 and morning of sale 8.15-10.15. Catalogues available 1 week before. 10% buyers premium.*

SUSSEX EAST

Burstow and Hewett
Abbey Auction Galleries and Granary Sale Rooms, Battle. TN33 0AT. Tel: 01424 772374. *Monthly sales of antique furniture, silver, jewellery, porcelain, brass, rugs etc. at the Abbey Auction Galleries. Also monthly evening sales of fine oil paintings, watercolours, prints, and engravings. At the Granary Sale Rooms - monthly sales of furniture, china, silver, brass, etc.*

Eastbourne Auction Rooms
Auction House, Finmere Rd., Eastbourne. BN22 8QL. Tel: 01323 431444; fax - 01323 417638; e-mail - enquiries@eastbourneauction.com; website - www.eastbourneauction.com. *Sales held weekly, usually Fri. and Sat. at 10 am.*

Gorringes inc. Julian Dawson
Terminus Rd., Bexhill-on-Sea. TN39 3LR. Tel: 01424 212994; fax - 01424 224035; website - www.gorringes.co.uk. *Fine art and antique sales held every six weeks.*

Gorringes inc. Julian Dawson
15 North St., Lewes. BN7 2PD. Tel: 01273 472503; fax - 01273 479559; website - www.gorringes.co.uk. *Fine art and antique sales held every six weeks.*

Gorringes inc. Julian Dawson
Garden St., Lewes. BN7 1XE. Tel: 01273 478221; fax - 01273 487369; website - www.gorringes.co.uk. *General sales held weekly on Mon. at 10.30 am.*

Edgar Horn's Fine Art Auctioneers
46-50 South St., Eastbourne. BN21 4XB. Tel: 01323 410419; fax - 01323 416450; e-mail - sales@edgarhorns.com; website - www.edgarhorns.com. *Eight fine art and antique sales a year. Fortnightly Mon. sales of Victorian and later furniture and effects through Salehurst Auctioneers in Ninfield. Part of The Fine Art Auction Group.*

Raymond P. Inman
The Auction Galleries, 35 and 40 Temple St., Brighton. BN1 3BH. Tel: 01273 774777; fax - 01273 735660. Est. 1929. *Monthly sales of antiques, furniture, china, glass, pictures, silver, jewellery, collectables, etc.*

Salehurst Auctioneers,
Bexhill Rd., Ninfield, Battle. TN33 9EE. Tel: 01424 893293; fax - 01424 893393; e-mail - sales@salehurstauctions.com; website - www.salehurstauctions.com. Est. 2002. *Fortnightly Mon. sales of Victorian and later furniture and effects. Part of The Fine Art Auction Group.*

Scarborough Perry Fine Arts

Hove St., Hove. BN3 2GL. Tel: 01273 735266; fax - 01273 723813. Est. 1896. *Monthly sales of fine art including antique furniture, pictures, silver, Oriental carpets and rugs and ornamental items. Specialised sales of primitive art, coins, books and jewellery.*

Wallis and Wallis

West Street Auction Galleries, Lewes. BN7 2NJ. Tel: 01273 480208; fax - 01273 476562; e-mail - auctions@wallisandwallis.co.uk; website - www. wallisandwallis.co.uk. Est. 1928. *Nine annual sales of arms and armour, militaria, coins and medals. Specimen catalogue £3.50. Current catalogues £8.50. Die-cast and tin plate toys and models - catalogue £6.50. Commission bids (without charge) accepted. Valuations.*

SUSSEX WEST

Henry Adams Fine Art Auctioneers

Baffins Hall, Baffins Lane, Chichester. PO19 1UA. Tel: 01243 532223; fax - 01243 532299; e-mail - enquiries@henryadamsfineart.co.uk. website - www.henryadamsfineart.co.uk. *Monthly catalogue specialist sales, usually on Wed. Viewing Sat. morning, Mon. and Tues. prior. Valuations for sales, insurance and probate.*

John Bellman Ltd

New Pound, Wisborough Green, Billingshurst. RH14 0AZ. Tel: 01403 700858; fax - 01403 700059. *Two-day sale once a month - Thurs. am - ceramics and Oriental, Thurs. pm - silver, jewellery, clocks; Fri. am - collectors' items, works of art, paintings, Fri. pm - furniture. Viewing Sat. 9-12, Mon. 9-4, Tues. 9-7, Wed. 9-1. Book sales quarterly.*

Denham's

The Auction Galleries, Warnham, Horsham. RH12 3RZ. Tel: 01403 255699; fax - 01403 253837; e-mail - denhams@lineone.net. Est. 1884. *Antique sales held monthly - good furniture of all periods, silver, jewellery, European and Oriental ceramics and collectors' items, paintings, drawings, prints, bronzes, metalware and Oriental carpets and rugs. Also monthly sales of general antiques, modern and shipping furniture. Periodic sales of books, stamps, coins and medals, arms and armour and specialist collections as advertised.*

R.H. Ellis and Sons

44/46 High St., Worthing. BN11 1LL. Tel: 01903 238999. *Monthly specialist auctions of antique, Victorian and Edwardian furniture and porcelain.*

Quarterly auctions of silver, watercolours, paintings, Oriental carpets and rugs.

King & Chasemore

Midhurst Auction Rooms, West St., Midhurst. GU29 9NQ. Tel: 01730 812456; fax - 01730 814514. Est. 1840. *General sales of antique and modern furniture and effects every six weeks.*

Sotheby's Sussex

Summers Place, Billingshurst. RH14 9AD. Tel: 01403 833500; fax - 01403 833699. *Regular sales of paintings, furniture, clocks, ceramics, glass, silver, jewellery, vertu, sporting guns, militaria, Oriental items and garden statuary.*

Stride and Son

Southdown House, St. John's St., Chichester. PO19 1XQ. Tel: 01243 780207; fax - 01243 786713. Est. 1890. *Sales last Fri. monthly - antiques and general; periodic book and document sales.*

Worthing Auction Galleries

Fleet House, Teville Gate, Worthing. BN11 1UA. Tel: 01903 205565. *Monthly sales of antique, 20th C and reproduction furniture, ceramics, glass, silver, silver plate, jewellery, pictures and collectables. View Sat. prior 9-12, Fri. and Mon. prior 9-1 and 2-4. Sale Tues. and Wed. both days commencing at 10 am.*

TYNE AND WEAR

Anderson and Garland

Fine Art Salerooms, Marlborough House, Marlborough Crescent, Newcastle-upon-Tyne. NE1 4EE. Tel: 0191 232 6278; fax - 0191 261 8665; e-mail - agarland@compuserve.com; website - www.auction-net.co.uk. *Regular sales of paintings, prints, antique furniture, silver and collectors' items.*

Anderson and Garland

Kepier Chare, Crawcrook, Ryton. NE40 4TS. Tel: 0191 413 8348. *Fortnightly sales of Victorian and later furnishings.*

Boldon Auction Galleries

24a Front St., East Boldon. NE36 0SJ. Tel: 0191 537 2630; e-mail - boldon@onyxnet.co.uk; website - www.boldonauctions.co.uk. Est. 1981. *Quarterly antique auctions.*

Thomas N. Miller Auctioneers

Algernon Rd., Byker, Newcastle-upon-Tyne. NE6 2UN. Tel: 0191 265 8080; fax - 0191 265 5050; e-mail - millerlot1@aol.com; website -

www.millersauctioneers.co.uk. Est. 1902. *China and glass auctions every Tues. at 10 am. Antique auctions every Wed. at 10 am.*

WARWICKSHIRE

Bigwood Auctioneers Ltd
The Old School, Tiddington, Stratford-upon-Avon. CV37 7AW. SOFAA. Tel: 01789 269415; fax - 01789 294168; e-mail - enquiries@Bigwood auctioneers.co.uk; website - www.Bigwood auctioneers.co.uk. *Bi-monthly Victoriana sales. Monthly sales of fine furniture and works of art. Quarterly sales of wines, sporting goods and other specialist sales. Catalogues and calendars on request. Valuations for all purposes. Sales every Friday at Stratford-upon-Avon.*

Henley-in-Arden Auction Sales Ltd
The Estate Office, Warwick Rd., Henley-in-Arden. B95 5BH. Tel: 01564 792154. *Sales of antique and modern furniture and effects, second and fourth Sat. each month.*

Locke & England
18 Guy St., Leamington Spa. CV32 4RT. Tel: 01926 889100; e-mail - valuers@leaction.co.uk; websites - www.leauction.co.uk and www. invaluable.com. Est. 1834. *Antique sales monthly.*

Warwick and Warwick Ltd
Chalon House, Scar Bank, Millers Rd., Warwick. CV34 5DB. Tel: 01926 499031; fax - 01926 491906. Est. 1958. *Philatelic auctioneers and private treaty specialists. Stamp auctions held monthly. Postcards, cigarette cards, autographs, ephemera, medals, militaria, coins, banknotes, sports memorabilia, and other collectables sold by auction periodically.*

WEST MIDLANDS

Biddle & Webb
Ladywood Middleway, Birmingham. B16 0PP. Tel: 0121 455 8042; e-mail - fineart@ biddleandwebb.com. *Fine art sales first Fri. monthly; antique sales on second Fri. monthly; silver, jewellery, medals, coins and watches on fourth Fri. monthly; toys, dolls, model railways and juvenalia sales on Fri. alternate months, all sales at 11 am. Two collectors sales a month on Sat. mornings, of Victoriana and later furnishings. Periodic decorative art and 20th C ceramic sales a year.*

Bonhams
The Old House, Station Rd., Knowle, Solihull. B93 0HT. Tel: 01564 776151; fax - 01564 778069; website - www.bonhams.com. *Specialised weekly sales of furniture, paintings, works of art, clocks, carpets, silver and jewellery, ceramics, 19th-20th C decorative arts, collectors' items, cameras, mechanical music, textiles and books. Valuation day every Fri. 10-4. Subscription available. Free sales programmes on request.*

Fellows and Sons
Augusta House, 19 Augusta St., Hockley, Birmingham. B18 6JA. Tel: 0121 212 2131; fax - 0121 212 1249; e-mail - info@fellows.co.uk; website - www.fellows.co.uk. Est. 1876. *Auctioneers and valuers of jewels, silver, fine art.*

Old Hill Antiques & Auction Rooms
220 Halesowen Rd., Old Hill, Cradley Heath. B64 6HN. Tel: 01384 411121. Est. 1990. *Auctioneers and valuers.*

Weller and Dufty Ltd
141 Bromsgrove St., Birmingham. B5 6RQ. Tel: 0121 692 1414; fax - 0121 622 5605. *Ten sales annually, approximately every five weeks, of antique and modern firearms, edged weapons, militaria etc. Periodic sales of specialist items - military vehicles and associated military equipment. Six fine art and antiques sales per year Postal bids accepted. Illustrated catalogue available.*

WILTSHIRE

Woolley and Wallis
Salisbury Salerooms Ltd 51-61 Castle St., Salisbury. SP1 3SU. Tel: 01722 424500; fax - 01722 424508; e-mail - enquiries@woolleyand wallis.co.uk; website - www.woolleyandwallis. co.uk. *Specialist sales of antique furniture, ceramics, pictures, silver and jewellery, rugs, textiles and books. Fortnightly general sales. Written valuations for probate and insurance.*

WORCESTERSHIRE

Andrew Grant Fine Art
St Mark's House, St Mark's Court, Cherry Orchard, Worcester. WR5 3DL. Tel: 01905 357547; fax - 01905 763942; e-mail - fineart@andrew-grant.co.uk. *Victoriana and collectables sales held monthly; fine art sales quarterly. Viewing day before sale.*

Griffiths & Charles
57 Foregate St., Worcester. WR1 1DZ. Tel: 01905 720160; e-mail - info@griffiths-charles.co.uk. Est. 1870. *General auctioneers.*

AUCTIONEERS

Philip Laney - FRICS - Fine Art
Malvern Auction Centre, Portland Rd., off Victoria Rd., Malvern. WR14 2TA. Tel: 01684 893933. *Monthly sales of antiques and collectors' items.*

Phipps and Pritchard
31 Worcester St., Kidderminster. DY10 1EQ. Tel: 01562 822244; fax - 01562 825401; website - www.phippsandpritchard.co.uk. Est. 1848. *Regular eight-weekly sales of antique furniture, clocks and watches, watercolours and oil paintings, copper, brass, glass, china and porcelain, stamps and coins, silver. Private house sales also conducted.*

Philip Serrell - Auctioneers & Valuers
The Malvern Sale Room, Barnards Green Rd., Malvern. Tel: 01684 892314. *Bi-monthly catalogued antique and fine art auctions. Fortnightly general sales. Specialist on the premises sales. Free sales estimates.*

YORKSHIRE EAST

Gilbert Baitson
The Edwardian Auction Galleries, Wiltshire Rd, Hull. HU4 6PG. Tel: 01482 500500; after hours - 01482 645241; fax - 01482 500501; e-mail - info@gilbert-baitson.co.uk; website - www.gilbert-baitson.co.uk. Est. 1935. *Sales of antique and modern furnishings every sixth Wed. at 10.30 am. Viewing day prior until 7 pm.*

Dee Atkinson & Harrison - Agricultural and Fine Arts
The Exchange Saleroom, Driffield. YO25 6LD. Tel: 01377 253151; fax - 01377 241041; e-mail - exchange@dee-atkinson-harrison; website - www.dee-atkinson-harrison.co.uk. *Regular bi-monthly sales of antiques, Victorian, Edwardian and quality furnishings, paintings, silver, jewellery etc. Viewing two days prior. Fortnightly household sales. Biannual collectors' toys and sporting sales.*

Haller Evans - Auctioneers and Valuers
1 Parliament St., Hull. HU1 2AR. Tel: 01482 323033; fax - 01482 211954. Est. 1889. *Regular auctions of antiques and modern furniture and effects.*

Spencers Auctioneers and Estate Agents
The Imperial and Repository Salerooms, 18 Quay Rd., Bridlington. YO15 2AP. Tel: 01262 676724. Est. 1892. *General auctions every Thurs. Regular sales of antiques and fine art.*

YORKSHIRE NORTH

Bairstow Eves Fine Art
West End Rooms, The Paddock, Whitby. YO21 3AX. Tel: 01947 820033/820011. *Monthly antiques sales. 10% buyers premium including VAT.*

Boulton and Cooper Ltd
St. Michaels House, Market Place, Malton. YO17 0LR. Tel: 01653 696151. *Members of SOFAA. Alternating monthly antique sales at Malton and York. Fortnightly general sales at Pickering.*

Hutchinson-Scott
The Grange, Marton-le-Moor, Ripon. HG4 5AT. Tel: 01423 324264. *Periodic general sales plus two or three catalogue sales annually. Specialist in fine antiques and works of art.*

Morphets of Harrogate
6 Albert St., Harrogate. HG1 1JL. Tel: 01423 530030; fax - 01423 500717; website - www.morphets.co.uk. Est. 1895. *Sales of antiques and works of art, interspersed with regular sales of general furniture and effects. Catalogue subscription scheme.*

Scarthingwell Auction Centre
Scarthingwell, Tadcaster. LS24 9PG. Tel: 01937 557955; fax - same; e-mail - scarthingwell@lineone.net; website - www.scarthingwell auctions.co.uk. *Evening antique and general sales held twice-monthly on Mon. and Tues. evenings, approx 1,000 lots. Viewing on prior Sun. 12-5 and sale days Mon. from 2 pm and Tues. from 4 pm.*

Stephensons
10 Colliergate, York. YO1 8BP. Tel: 01904 625533. Est. 1871. *Six sales annually of antique and Victorian furniture, silver and paintings.*

Summersgill Auctioneers
8 Front St., Acomb, York. YO24 3BZ. Tel: 01904 791131. Est. 1967. *Auctions of antiques and collectors' items.*

Tennants
The Auction Centre, Leyburn. DL8 5SG. Tel: 01969 623780; fax - 01969 624281. (Office - 34 Montpellier Parade, Harrogate. Tel : 01423 531661; fax - 01423 530990); e-mail - enquiry@tennants-ltd.co.uk; website - www.tennants.co.uk. *Minimum of three 1000 lot non-catalogue sales each month of antiques and later house contents, mainly on Sat. at 9.30 am. Viewing Fri. 9-7. Three fine art sales each year. Catalogue*

subscription service. Specialist sales of collectors' items, books, etc.

YORKSHIRE SOUTH

A.E. Dowse and Son

Cornwall Galleries, Scotland St., Sheffield. S3 7DE. Tel: 0114 2725858; fax - 0114 2490550; e-mail - aedowse@talk21.com. Est. 1915. *Monthly Sat. sales of antiques. Quarterly fine art and antique sales. Quarterly sales of diecast, tin plate and collectors' toys. Monthly sales of modern furniture and shipping goods.*

Wilkinson & Beighton Auctioneers Ltd

Woodhouse Green, Thurcroft, Rotherham. S66 9AQ. Tel: 01709 700005; fax - 01709 700244; website - www.wilkinsons-auctioneers.co.uk. Est. 1997. *General sales every two weeks on Sun. from 11 am. Viewing Fri. 11-4 and sale day from 9 am. Quarterly sales of furniture and fine art.*

Wilkinson's Auctioneers Ltd

28 Netherhall Rd. Doncaster. DN1 2PW. Tel: 01302 814884; fax - 01302 814883; website - www.wilkinsons-auctioneers.co.uk. Est. 1997. *Catalogue sales every two months, alternating between fine furniture, paintings, bronzes and effects and period oak, country furniture and carvings.*

YORKSHIRE WEST

Bonhams Auctioneers

Hepper House, 17a East Parade, Leeds. LS1 2BH. Tel: 0113 2448011; fax - 0113 2429875. *Quarterly fine sales of pictures, silver and jewellery, ceramics and furniture. Monthly general sales. Sales calendars sent on request.*

De Rome

12 New John St., Westgate, Bradford. BD1 2QY. Tel: 01274 734116/9. *Regular sales.*

Andrew Hartley Fine Arts

Victoria Hall Salerooms, Little Lane, Ilkley. LS29 8EA. Tel: 01943 816363; fax- 01943 817610; e-mail - info@andrewhartleyfinearts.co.uk; website - www.andrewhartleyfinearts.co.uk. Est. 1906. *Fifty sales annually including six good antique and fine art and other specialist sales.*

John H. Raby & Son

Salem Auction Rooms, 21 St. Mary's Rd., Bradford. BD8 7QL. Tel: 01274 491121. *Sales of antique furniture and pictures every 4-6 weeks, shipping goods and collectables every week.*

CHANNEL ISLANDS

Bonhams & Langlois Auctioneers

Westaway Chambers, Don St., St. Helier, Jersey. JE2 4TR. Tel: 01534 722441; fax - 01534 759354. *Regular antique and specialised auctions, general sales on Wed.*

SCOTLAND

Auction Rooms

Castle Laurie, Bankside, Falkirk. FK2 7XF. Tel: 01324 623000; fax - 01324 630343; e-mail - robert@auctionroomsfalkirk.co.uk; website - www.auctionroomsfalkirk.co.uk. *Weekly, Wed., sales at 6 pm. Mixed sale of antique, general household and new furniture. Specialised sales are held, details available on website. Viewing Tues. 8-8, Wed. 8-6.*

Bonhams Scotland

65 George St., Edinburgh, Midlothian. EH2 2JL. Tel: 0131 225 2266. *Regular specialist sales of oils and watercolours, furniture, clocks, rugs and works of art, silver and jewellery, Oriental and European ceramics and books. Decorative arts, post war, garden and dolls and textiles sales are also held. Monthly general sales. Annual Scottish Sale, held during the Edinburgh Festival, includes important Scottish furniture, paintings, silver, books and sporting memorabilia.*

Frasers (Auctioneers)

8a Harbour Rd., Inverness, Inverness-shire. IV1 1SY. Tel: 01463 232395; fax - 01463 233634. *Weekly sales on Wed. at 6 pm.*

Leslie and Leslie

Haddington, East Lothian. EH41 3JJ. Tel: 01620 822241; fax - same. *Antique auctions every three months.*

Lindsay Burns & Co

6 King St., Perth. PH2 8JA. Tel: 01738 633888; fax - 01738 441322; e-mail - lindsayburns@btconnect.com. *General sales bi-weekly on Thurs. at 10.30 am., viewing day prior 9-5. Quarterly fine art sales (illustrated colour catalogues available on website) held on Tues. Viewing previous Sat. 9-1 and Mon. 9-6.*

Loves Auction Rooms

52-54 Canal St., Perth. PH2 8LF. Tel: 01738 633337; fax - 01738 629830. Est. 1869. *Regular sales of antique and decorative furniture, jewellery, silver and plate, ceramics, works of art, metalware, glass, pictures, clocks, mirrors, pianos, Eastern carpets and rugs, garden furniture, architectural items. Weekly Fri. sales of Victoriana and household effects at 10.30 am. Specialist sales of books and collectors' items. Valuations.*

Macdougalls Auctioneers & Valuers

Lower Breakish, Breakish, Isle of Skye. IV42 8QA. Tel: 01471 822777; fax - same. *Sales held every eight weeks of antiques and general furniture. Sales held Sat. at 2 pm in Broadford Hall (10 mins. from the Skye bridge).*

McTear's

Skypark, 8 Elliot Place, Glasgow. G3 8EP. Tel: 0141 221 4456; fax - 0141 204 5035;l e-mail - enquiries@mctears.co.uk; website - www. mctears.co.uk. *Weekly Fri. sales at 10.30 am. of antique, reproduction and shipping furniture, jewellery, silver, porcelain and paintings. Viewing Thurs. prior 10-7. Monthly auctions of fine art and antiques.*

John Milne

9 North Silver St., Aberdeen. AB1 1RJ. Tel: 01224 639336. *Weekly general sales, regular catalogue sales of antiques, silver, paintings, books, jewellery and collectors' items.*

Paterson's

8 Orchard St., Paisley. PA1 1UZ. Tel: 0141 889 2435. Est. 1848. *Fortnightly Tues. sales.*

L.S. Smellie and Sons Ltd

The Furniture Market, Lower Auchingramont Rd., Hamilton. ML10 6BE. Tel: 01698 282007. *Fine antiques auctions on third Thurs. in Feb., May, Aug. and Nov. Weekly sales every Mon. at 9.30 am. (600 lots) household furniture, porcelain and jewellery.*

Taylor's Auction Rooms

11 Panmure Row, Montrose. DD10 8HH. Tel: 01674 672775; fax - 01674 672479; e-mail - jonathan@taylors-auctions.demon.co.uk; website - www.scotlandstreasures.co.uk. *Antiques sales held every second Sat.*

Thomson, Roddick & Medcalf

20 Murray St., Annan. DG12 6EG. Tel: 01387 279879. *Fortnightly sales of household furnishing and effects.*

Thomson, Roddick & Medcalf Ltd

60 Whitesands, Dumfries. DG1 2RS. Tel: 01387 279879; fax - 01387 266236; e-mail - office.trm @virgin.net. Est. 1880. *Quarterly catalogued antique and collectors sales including art pottery, silver and jewellery. Fortnightly general sales. Bi-annual fishing tackle and sporting sales.*

Thomson Roddick & Medcalf Ltd

44/3 Hardengreen Business Park, Eskbank, Edinburgh. EH22 3NX. Tel: 0131 454 9090; fax - 0131 454 9191. *Weekly auctions of antiques and general furnishings, regular specialist sales, particularly Scottish provincial silver, quarterly catalogued fine art and antique sales; also quarterly sales in Dumfries and bi-monthly general sales in Annan.*

Dodds Property World

Victoria Auction Galleries, Mold. CH7 1EB. Tel: 01352 755705; fax - 01352 752542; e-mail - auctions@door-key.com; website - www.door-key.com. Est. 1952. *Weekly Wed. auctions of general furniture and shipping goods at 10.30 am. Bi-monthly auctions of antique furniture, silver, porcelain and pictures etc. at 10.30 am on Sat. Catalogues available.*

Peter Francis

Curiosity Salerooms, 19 King St., Carmarthen. SA31 1BH. Tel: 01267 233456/7; fax - 01267 233458; website - www.peterfrancis.co.uk. *Catalogued antiques and fine art sales every six weeks. Regular general sales.*

Newland Rennie Wilkins

87 Monnow St., Monmouth. NP5 3EW. Tel: 01600 712916. *Periodic sales of antique furniture and effects, usually on Thurs.*

Harry Ray & Co

Lloyds Bank Chambers, Broad St., Welshpool. SY21 7RR. Tel: 01938 552555; e-mail - info@harryray.com; website - www.harryray. com. Est. 1946. *Monthly country sales.*

Fairs Calendar

In an attempt to make the Fairs listings for England more logical, we have rearranged the regional boundaries. At the beginning of each section there is a list of the counties included.
Because this list is compiled in advance, alterations or cancellations to the Fairs listed can occur. We strongly advise anyone wishing to attend a Fair, especially if they have to travel any distance, to telephone the organiser to confirm the details given.

LONDON including Greater London

Arms Fairs Ltd
01432 355416.
The 71st London Antique Arms Fair Autumn 2003, The Royal National Hotel, Woburn Place, Russell Square, WC1 - **Sept 27-28**

Bead Society of Great Britain
01775 762996:
14th Annual Beadwork & Bead Fair, Byron Hall, Harrow Leisure Centre, Harrow (NW London) - **Oct 5**

Centre Exhibitions
0121 767 2596:
The Autumn LAPADA Antiques & Fine Art Fair, The Commonwealth Institute Galleries, Kensington High Street, W8 - **Oct 8-12**

Clarion Events Ltd,
Róisín Fogarty 020 7370 8211:
The Winter Olympia Fine Art & Antiques Fair, The National Hall, Olympia Exhibition Centre, Hammersmith Road, W14 - **Nov 10-16**
The Spring Olympia Fine Art & Antiques Fair, (same venue) - **Mar 2-7 2004**
The Summer Olympia Fine Art & Antiques Fair, (same venue) - **June 3-13 2004**

DMG Fairs
01636 702326:
Brunel Antiques & Collectors Fair, Brunel University, Uxbridge, Middlesex - **Dec 27**

Gay Hutson
020 8742 1611:
The 20/21 British Art Fair, Commonwealth Institute Galleries, Kensington High Street, W8 - **Sept 17-21**

Granny's Goodies
020 8693 5432:
The London International Antique & Artist Dolls, Toys, Miniatures & Teddy Bear Fair, Kensington Town Hall, Exhibition & Conference Centre, Hornton Street, W8 - **Sep 7; Nov 16**

Harvey (Management Services) Ltd
020 7624 5173:
The Autumn Decorative Antiques & Textiles Fair, The Marquee, Battersea Park (through Chelsea Gate), SW11 - **Sept 23-28**

Mainwarings Antique Fairs
01273 735086:

Chelsea Antiques Fair, Chelsea Town Hall, King's Road, SW3 - **Sep 7; Nov 2, 16; Dec 7**

Marcel Fairs
020 8950 1844:
Antiques Fair, St Paul's Church Hall, The Ridgeway, NW7 - **Aug 2; Sept 6; Oct 4; Nov 1; Dec 6**

Penman Antique Fairs
0870 3502442:
Chelsea Antiques Fair, Chelsea Old Town Hall, Kings Road, SW3 - **Sept 17-22**
Antiques & Fine Art Fair, Kensington Town Hall, W8 - **Jan 15-18, 2004**

Pig & Whistle Promotions
020 8883 7061:
Alexandra Palace Antique & Collectors' Fair, The Great Hall, Alexandra Palace, Wood Green, N22 - **Sept 21; Nov 16**

Simmons Gallery
020 7831 2080:
The London Coin Fair, Holiday Inn (formerly The Posthouse), Coram Street, Bloomsbury, WC1 - **Nov 8**

Talbot Promotions
020 8969 7011:
The 34th International Antique Scientific & Medical Instrument Fair, The Radisson SAS Portman Hotel, Portman Square, W1 - **Oct 26**

Towy Antiques Fairs
01267 236569 or 01792 402525:
The Little Chelsea Antiques Fair, Chelsea Town Hall, Kings Road, SW3 - **Oct 6-7**

West Promotions
020 8641 3224:
The London Paper Money Fair, The Bonnington Hotel, 92 Southampton Row, WC1 - **Sept 7; Nov 16**

SOUTH EAST AND EAST ANGLIA

Including Beds, Cambs, Essex, Herts, Kent, Norfolk, Suffolk, Surrey, Sussex.

Antique & Collectors' World
01737 812 989:
Antique & Collectors' Fair, Goodwood Racecourse, Goodwood, Near Chichester, West Sussex - **Aug 25; Nov 2, 30**
Antique & Collectors' Fair, Lingfield Racecourse, Lingfield, Surrey (M25 junction 6, 5 miles South on A22) - **Nov 9; Dec 14**

FRIENDLY SMALL FAIRS OF DISTINCTION

ART & ANTIQUES STYLISHLY DISPLAYED,
EXPERTLY AUTHENTICATED &
OFFERED BY DEALERS OF INTEGRITY.

2003

September 5 - 7
PETERSFIELD ANTIQUES FAIR
Festival Hall, Heath Rd, Hants. (off A3)
43 stands of friendly dealers.

September 17 - 22
CHELSEA ANTIQUES FAIR
Chelsea Old Town Hall, Kings Rd, SW3
40 stands, bright & varied top quality.

October 23 - 26
CHESTER ANTIQUES & FINE ART SHOW
Chester Racecourse, Cheshire.
60 stands on 3 floors. Wide variety.

2004

January 15 - 18
WEST LONDON
ANTIQUES & FINE ART FAIR
Kensington Town Hall, W8.   60 stands

Feb 6 - 8 PETERSFIELD (as Sept)

Feb 12-15 CHESTER (as Oct)

For dates beyond February 2004
please phone or visit the Website
after August 2003.
Some new Venues may be included!

www.penman-fairs.co.uk

T: 0870 350 2442, F: 0870 350 2443
info@penman-fairs.co.uk

Best of Fairs
01787 280306:
Antiques & Collectors' Fair, The Old School,
Long Melford, Suffolk - **Aug 23-25; Sept 27-28; Oct 25-26; Nov 29-30; Dec 13-14, 27-28**
Antiques & Collectors' Fair, The Village Hall,
Copdock, Near Ipswich, Suffolk - **Aug 3; Sept 7; Oct 5; Nov 2; Dec 7**

Camfair Antiques Fairs
01945 870160/07860 517048:
Antiques Fair, The Castle Hall, Hertford, Herts -
Aug 30; Sept 27; Oct 25; Nov 15; Dec 20

Mr & Mrs Dennis & Jacqui Charlton
01379 677313:
Antique & Collectors' Fair, Central Hall,
Wymondham, Norfolk - **Aug 1; Sept 5; Oct 3; Nov 7; Dec 5**
Antique & Collectors' Fair, Corn Hall, Diss,
Norfolk - **Aug 15; Sept 26; Oct 24; Nov 14; Dec 5**

Cross Country Fairs Ltd
0147483 4120:
Antiques & Collectors' Fair, The Copthorne
Effingham Park Hotel, West Park Road,
Copthorne (near East Grinstead), West Sussex -
Aug 3; Sept 7; Oct 5; Nov 2; Dec 7

DMG Antiques Fairs
01636 702326:
Antiques & Collectors' Fair, Rowley Mile
Racecourse, Newmarket, Suffolk - **Aug 10; Nov 23**
International Antiques & Collectors' Fair, Kent
County Showground, Detling, Maidstone, Kent -
Sept 6-7; Nov 8-9
International Antiques & Collectors' Fair, The
South of England Showground, Ardingly, West
Sussex - **Sept 9-10, 28; Nov 4-5**

DPL Fairs
020 8205 1518:
Toy & Train Fair, Elm Court Youth &
Community Centre, Mutton Lane, Potters Bar,
Herts (M25 J24) - **Sept 14; Nov 2**
Toy & Train Fair, John Bunyan Upper School,
Mile Road (A5134, 8 miles west of Sandy
Roundabout), Beds - **Sept 28; Dec 7**
Camera Fair, St Peter's Catholic School,
Horseshoe Lane East, Merrow, Guildford,
Surrey (2 miles east of city centre, A25 towards
Dorking Close J10 M25 & A3) - **Oct 12**
Camera Fair, Allum Hall, Allum Lane
(A5135/B5378) (opposite Elstree &
Borehamwood Station) - **Nov 9**

E W Services Antiques Fairs
01933 225674:
The Whipsnade Antique Fair, Cloisters Function
Suite, Whipsnade Animal Park, Whipsnade,
Dunstable, Beds - **Oct 25-26**

Galloway Antiques Fairs
01423 522122:
Antiques Fair, Firle Place, Near Lewes, East Sussex - **Sept 12-14**
Antiques Fair, Seaford College, Near Petworth, West Sussex - **Oct 31- Nov 2**

Gemsco
01525 402596:
The 56th Luton Antiques Fair, Putteridge Bury House (on the A505 Luton to Hitchin Road, Beds - M1 junction 10) - **Oct 11-12**
The 6th Mid Beds Antiques Fair, Silsoe Conference Centre, Silsoe, Beds (just off the A6, midway between Luton & Bedford - M1 Junction 12) - **Nov 22-23**

Hallmark Antiques Fairs Ltd
01702 710383:
Antiques Fair, Cressing Temple Barns (between Witham & Braintree on the B1018), Essex - **Sept 6-7**
Antiques Fair, Southend Tennis & Leisure Centre, Eastern Avenue, Southend on Sea, Essex - **Sept 21**
Antiques Fair, Courage Hall, Brentwood School, Middleton Hall Lane, Brentwood, Essex - **Oct 5**
Antiques Fair, Southend Cliffs Pavilion, Station Road, Westcliff on Sea, Essex - **Oct 19**
Antiques Fair, The Palms Hotel, Southend Arterial Road (A127), Romford, Essex - **Nov 9**

Hands Militaria Fairs
01892 730233:
Militaria & Collectors' Fair, The Maltings, Farnham, Surrey - **Aug 24; Oct 26; Dec 7**
Militaria & Collectors' Fair: 2003 A Military Odyssey - a large multi-period outdoor event at the Kent County Showground, Detling, Near Maidstone, Kent - **Sept 13-14**
Militaria & Collectors' Fair, Wolsey Hall, Cheshunt, Herts - **Oct 12**
Militaria & Collectors' Fair, The Grange, Midhurst, West Sussex - **Nov 16**

Harlequin Fairs
01462 671688:
Antiques Fair, Elstree Moat House Hotel (on A1 adjacent to Borehamwood exit, 2 miles south of M25), Herts - **Sept 28**
Saffron Walden Antiques & Fine Art Fair, Saffron Walden County High School, Audley End Road, Saffron Walden, Essex - **Oct 18-19**

Janba Fairs
01945 870160/07860 517048:
Antiques Fair, Burgess Hall, St Ivo Recreation Centre, St Ives, Cambs - **Aug 24-25; Oct 12; Nov 22-23**
Antiques Fair, Knights Hill Hotel, South Wootton, King's Lynn, Norfolk - **Aug 31; Sept 28; Oct 26; Nov 30; Dec 21**

Lomax Antiques Fairs
01603 737631:
The 12th East Anglian Antique Dealers' Fair, Langley Park School, Loddon, Norfolk - **Oct 24-26**

Magnum Antiques Fairs
01491 681009:
Antiques Fair, The Grange Centre, Bepton Road, Midhurst, West Sussex - **Aug 3; Oct 5; Dec 7**

Marie Brown
01273 885184:
Ditchling Antique & Collectors' Fair (previously organised by Graham Deakin), Ditchling Village Hall, Lewes Road, West Sussex - **Oct 12; Dec 14**

Pantheon Fairs Ltd.
01738 446534:
Antiques Fair, Michelham Priory, Hailsham, East Sussex - **Sept 19-21**
Antiques Fair, Goodwood House, Chichester, West Sussex - **Nov 14-16**

Ridgeway Fairs
01702 710383:
Antiques Fair, The Belvedere, Billericay, Essex (just off A127) - **Aug 9-10**
Antiques Fair, Southend Bandstand, Clifftown Parade, Southend on Sea, Essex - **Aug 17**
Antiques Fair, Freight House, Rochford, Essex - **Aug 25**
Antiques Fair, University of Essex, Sports Centre, Colchester, Essex - **Sept 13-14**
Antiques Fair, Thurrock Civic Hall, Blackshott's Lane, Grays, Essex - **Oct 26**
Antiques Fair, Marconi Sports & Social Club, Beehive Lane, Great Baddow, Chelmsford, Essex - **Nov 2**
Antiques Fair, Mill Hall, Bellingham Lane, Rayleigh, Essex - **Nov 16**
Antiques Fair, Castle View School, Canvey Island, Essex - **Nov 23**
Antiques Fair, Keys Hall, Eagle Way, Great Warley, Near Brentwood, Essex - **Nov 30**
Antiques Fair, Sports & Leisure Centre, Main Road, Danbury, Essex - **Dec 7**
Antiques Fair, Community Centre, Elm Road, Leigh on Sea, Essex - **Dec 14**

Robert Bailey Fairs
01277 214677:
The 21st Hertfordshire Antiques & Fine Art Fair, Hatfield House, Hatfield, Herts - **Oct 31 - Nov 2**
The 4th Tattersalls Antiques & Fine Art Fair, Park Paddock, The Avenue, Newmarket, Suffolk - **Nov 7-9**
The Petworth Antiques & Fine Art Fair, Seaford College, Petworth, W Sussex - **Dec 12-14**

Take Five Fairs
020 8894 0218:
Antiques & Collectables Fair, Woking Leisure Centre, Kingfield Road, Woking, Surrey - **Aug 10; Sept 14; Oct 12; Dec 14, 28**
Art Nouveau/Deco Fair, Woking Leisure Centre, Kingfield Road, Woking, Surrey - **Aug 25; Oct 26**
Grand Glass Fair, Woking Leisure Centre, Kingfield Road, Woking, Surrey - **Oct 5**
Antiques & Collectables Fair, Canons Leisure Centre, Madeira Road, Mitcham, Surrey - **Nov 9**

Trident Exhibitions Limited
01822 614671:
The 36th Surrey Antiques Fair, Guildford Civic, Guildford, Surrey - **Oct 2-5**

Wade Collectors' Club
01782 255255:
Wade Collectors' Fair, Dunstable Leisure Centre, Dunstable, Bedfordshire - **Sept 28**

Wakefield Antiques Fairs
01303 258635:
Antiques Fair, Farringtons & Stratford House, Perry Street, Chislehurst, Kent - **Aug 30-31; Dec 13-14**
Antiques fair, Ramada Hotel (formerly Great Danes Hotel), Hollingbourne, Near Maidstone, Kent - **Sept 14; Oct 12; Nov 9; Dec 7**
Two Day Quality Dateline Antiques Fairs, Higham Park, Bridge, Near Canterbury, Kent - **Sept 20-21; Nov 29-30**
Two Day Quality Dateline Antiques Fairs, Sutton Valence School, Sutton Valence, Kent - **Oct 25-26**

Wonder Whistle Enterprises
020 7249 4050:
Antique Fair, The Exhibition Centre, Sandown Park Racecourse, Esher, Surrey - **Oct 7; Nov 18**

SOUTH WEST

Including Berks, Bucks, Cornwall, Devon, Dorset, Glos, Hants, Isle of Wight, Oxon, Somerset, Wilts.

Cooper Antiques Fair
01278 784912; mobile - 07768 953629:
The South Cotswolds Antiques Fair, Westonbirt School, Near Tetbury, Glos - **Aug 29-31**
Wiltshire County Antiques Fair, Marlborough College, Wilts - **Oct 31-Nov 2**
The South Cotswolds Xmas Antiques Fair, Westonbirt School, Near Tetbury, Glos - **Dec 20-21**

Crispin Fairs
0118 983 3020:
Antiques & Collectables Fair, St Crispin's Sports Centre, London Road (A329), Wokingham, Berks - **Aug 3; Sept 7; Oct 5; Nov 2; Dec 7**
Antiques & Collectors' Fair, Victoria Hall, Hartley Wintney, Hants (situated on the main A30 between Camberley & Basingstoke) - **Aug 19; Sept 14, 16; Oct 12, 21; Nov 9, 18; Dec 14, 16**

DMG Antiques Fairs
01636 702326:
Antiques & Collectors' Fair, The Royal Bath & West Showground, Shepton Mallet, Somerset - **Sept 19-21; Nov 14-16**

DPL Fairs
020 8205 1518:
Toy & Train Fair, Beaconsfield School, Wattleton Road, Beaconsfield, Bucks - **Sept 20; Nov 15**
Camera Fair, Beaconsfield School, Wattleton Road, Beaconsfield, Bucks - **Sept 21; Nov 30**
Camera Fair, Trinity School, Love Lane, Newbury, Berks - **Oct 19**

Devon County Antiques Fairs
01363 82571:
Yeovil Antique & Collectors' Fair, Westland Sports & Social Club, Westbourne Close, Yeovil, Somerset - **Aug 10; Oct 5; Dec 14**
Matford Antiques & Collectables Fair, Exeter Livestock Centre, Matford Park Road, Marsh Barton, Exeter, Devon - **Aug 23; Oct 11; Nov 22**
Westpoint Antiques & Collectables Fair, Westpoint Exhibition Centre, Clyst St Mary, Exeter, Devon - **Sept 6-7; Nov 1-2**
Salisbury Antiques & Collectables Fair, Salisbury Leisure Centre, The Butts, Hulse Road, Salisbury, Wilts - **Sept 27; Dec 6**

E W Services Antiques Fairs
01933 225674:
Antiques & Collectors' Fair, Buckingham Community Centre, Cornwalls Meadows Shopping Precinct, Bucks - **Aug 2; Sept 6; Nov 1**
Milton Keynes Antiques Fair, Middleton Hall, Central Milton Keynes Regional Shopping Centre, Milton Keynes, Bucks - **Oct 2-5**

Fat Cat Fairs
01865 301 705:
Antiques Fair, The New Memorial Hall, Lechlade-on-Thames, Glos - **Aug 3; Sept 7; Oct 5; Nov 2; Dec 7**
Antiques Fair, Burford School (A40), Burford, Oxon - **Sept 28; Oct 26; Nov 23**

Galloway Antiques Fairs
01423 522122:
Antiques Fair, Rookesbury Park, Wickham, Hants - **Aug 22-25**
Stansted House, Rowlands Castle, Hants - **Nov 21-23**

Gemsco
01525 402596:
3rd South Bucks Antiques Fair, Missenden Abbey, Great Missenden, Bucks (short distance from M1, M25 & M40) - **Aug 30-31**

FAIRS

Grandma's Attic Antiques Fairs
01590 677687:
Antiques & Collectors' Fair, The Masonic Hall
(bottom of High Street), Lymington, Hants -
Aug 23; Oct 4, 25; Nov 1
Antiques & Collectors' Fair, Brockenhurst Village
Hall, Highwood Road (off Sway Road), New
Forest, Brockenhurst, Hants - **Aug 24; Nov 16**
Antiques & Collectors' Fair, The Allendale
Centre, Hanham Road, Wimborne, Dorset - **Aug
25; Oct 26; Dec 28**
Antiques & Collectors' Fair, Pavilion Ballroom
(Westover Road), Bournemouth, Dorset - **Sept
6-7; Nov 22-23**
Antiques & Collectors' Fair, Kingston Maurward
House, Dorchester, Dorset - **Sept 27-28; Nov 29-30**
Antiques & Collectors' Fair, Lyndhurst Park
Hotel, High Street, Lyndhurst, Hants - **Oct 5**
Antiques & Collectors' Fair, The Littledown
Centre, Castle Lane, north east of Bournemouth
(A3060), Dorset - **Oct 12**
Antiques & Collectors' Fair, Botleigh Grange
Hotel, Botley, Hedge End, Near Southampton,
Hants (Junction 7, M27) - **Oct 19**
Antiques & Collectors' Fair, Winchester
Guildhall, The Broadway, Winchester (off the
M3), Hants - **Nov 2**

Hands Militaria Fairs
01892 730233:
Militaria & Collectors' Fair, The Didcot Civic,
Didcot, Oxon - **Oct 5**

Harlequin Fairs
01462 671688:
Antiques Fair, Centre for Epilepsy, Chalfont
Lane, Chalfont St Peter, Bucks - **Sept 7; Oct 5;
Nov 2; Dec 7**

Legacy Fairs
01844 281311:
Antiques & Collectors' Fair, Masonic Hall, Old
Beaconsfield, Bucks - **Sept 11; Oct 9; Nov 13;
Dec 4**

Magnum Antiques Fairs
01491 681009:
Antiques Fair, River Park Leisure Centre,
Gordon Road, Winchester, Hants - **Aug 25**

Midas Fairs
01494 674170:
Antique Fair, The Bellhouse Hotel, Oxford Road
(A40), Beaconsfield, Bucks (from Junction 2,
M40, follow A40 sign to Gerrards Cross) - **Aug
10; Sept 14; Oct 12; Nov 9; Dec 14**

Penman Antique Fairs
0870 3502442:
Petersfield Antiques Fair, The Festival Hall,
Heath Road, Petersfield, Hants - **Sept 5-7**

Renaissance Fairs
01929 400343:
Antique & Collectors' Fair, Corfe Castle Village
Hall, Corfe Castle, Dorset - **Aug 3; Sept 7; Oct
5; Nov 2; Dec 7**
Antiques & Collectors' Fair, Osmington Village
Hall, Osmington, Dorset - **Sept 21; Oct 19; Nov
16; Dec 21**

Silhouette Fairs
01635 44338:
Antique & Collectors' Fair, The Abbey Hall
(Guildhall), Abingdon, Oxon - **Aug 17; Sept 21;
Oct 19; Nov 16; Dec 14**
Antique & Collectors' Fair, The Mall, Kennet
Centre, Newbury - **Sept 14; Oct 12; Nov 2**

Talisman Fairs
01225 872522:
Antique & Collectors' Fair, St Margaret's Hall,
Bradford on Avon, Wilts - **Aug 16; Sept 20; Oct
18; Nov 15; Dec 13**
Bristol Antique & Collectors' Fair, Brunel Great
Train Shed, Temple Meads Station, Bristol -
Sept 14; Oct 12; Nov 9; Dec 14

WEST MIDLANDS

**Including Birmingham, Coventry, Herefordshire,
Shropshire, Staffs, Warwickshire, Worcs.**

Bowman Antiques Fairs
07071 284 333:
Giant 3 Day Quality Antiques Fair, The Bingley
Hall, County Showground, Weston Road, Staffs
(A518, 5 mins J14, M6) - **Oct 3-5; Dec 12-14**

Centre Exhibitions
0121 767 2760:
Antiques for Everyone, Hall 5, NEC,
Birmingham, West Midlands - **Aug 7-10; Nov
27-30**
The LAPADA Antiques & Fine Art Fair, NEC,
Hall 12, Birmingham, West Midlands - **Jan 14-
18, 2004**

DMG Antiques Fairs
01636 702326:
Antiques & Collectors' Fair, The Three Counties
Showground, Malvern, Worcs - **Aug 3; Sept 7;
Oct 12; Nov 2; Dec 7**

Hands Militaria Fairs
01892 730233:
Militaria & Collectors' Fair, Hands on History,
Whittington Barrack, Lichfield, Staffs - **Aug 2-3**

Midland & Northern Fairs
01827 69666:
Antique & Collectors' Fairs, The Royal
Agricultural Showground, Stoneleigh, Warks -
Sept 24; Nov 26

Profile Promotions
0121 449 4246:
Antiques & Collectors' Fair, King Edward VI
Camp Hill Schools, Vicarage Road, Kings Heath,
Birmingham, W. Midlands - **Sept 28; Nov 23**
Antiques & Collectors' Fair, The At7 Centre,
Bell Green Road (1½ miles from junction 3 M6),
Coventry, W. Midlands - **Oct 5**
Antiques & Collectors' Fair, The Royal Spa
Centre, Newbold Terrace, Leamingtom Spa,
Warks - **Oct 11**
Antiques & Collectors' Fair, Abbey Hotel, Golf &
Country Club, Hither Green Lane, Dagnell End
Road, Redditch (5 minutes from junction 2 M42,
along A441), Alvechurch, W. Midlands - **Dec 7**

Waverley Fairs
0121 550 4123:
Antique & Collectors' Fair, New Market Hall,
Bromsgrove, Worcs - **Every Wednesday**
Sunday Antique & Collectors' Fair, Kinver
Community Centre, Kinver, Staffs (off A449, 5
miles north of Kidderminster) - **Aug 3; Sept 7;
Oct 5; Nov 2; Dec 7**
Sunday Book Fair, Kinver Community Centre,
Kinver, Staffs (off A449, 5 miles north of
Kidderminster) - **Aug 17; Sept 21; Oct 19; Nov
16; Dec 21**
Sunday Antique & Collectors' Fair, New Market
Hall, Bromsgrove, Worcs - **Aug 24; Sept 28;
Oct 26; Nov 22; Dec 28**
Worcestershire Monthly Sunday Book Fair,
Powick village hall (from Worcs (Powick) take
A449) - **Sept 14; Oct 12; Nov 9; Dec 14**

EAST MIDLANDS

**Including Derbys, Leics, Lincs, Northants, Notts,
Rutland, Sheffield.**

Arthur Swallow Fairs
01298 27493/73188:
International Antiques & Collectors' Fair, RAF
Swinderby (between Newark & Lincoln on the
A46) - **Aug 15-17; Oct 17-19; Nov 28-30**

DMG Antiques Fairs
01636 702326:
International Antiques & Collectors' Fair, The
Newark & Notts Showground, Newark, Notts -
Aug 18-19; Oct 20-21; Dec 1-2

Robert Bailey Fairs
01277 214677:
The 11th Buxton Autumn Fine Art & Antiques Fair,
Pavilion Gardens, Buxton, Derbys - **Oct 17-19**

Top Hat Exhibitions
0115 941 9143/925 8769:
The National Art Deco Fair, Town Hall,
Loughborough, Leics - **Sept 21; Nov 2**

Unicorn Fairs Ltd
0161 773 7001:
Antiques & Collectors' Fair, The Pavilion
Gardens, Buxton, Derbys - **Aug 23-25; Oct 4-5;
Nov 1-2, 29-30; Dec 27-28**

NORTH

**Including Cheshire, Co Durham, Cumbria,
Humberside, Lancs, Manchester,
Northumberland, Tyne and Wear, Yorks.**

Abbey Antiques Fairs
01482 445785:
Antiques Fair, Willerby Manor, Hull, East Yorks
- **Sept 28; Oct 26; Nov 30; Dec 28**

Cartmel Antiques Fairs
01253 396209:
Antiques Fair, The Village Hall, Cartmel,
Cumbria - **Aug 1-3, 28-31; Sept 19-21; Oct 17-
19; Nov 14-16**

Centaur Exhibitions
020 7970 6543:
Northern Period Living & Traditional Homes,
Harrogate International Centre, Harrogate, North
Yorks - **Nov 1-2**

Colin Caygill Events
0191 261 9632:
Antique & Collectors' Fair, The County Hall,
Durham - **Aug 17**
Antique & Collectors' Fair, The Wentworth Leisure
Centre, Hexham, Northumberland - **Aug 19**
Antique & Collectors' Fair, The International
Stadium, Gateshead, Tyne & Wear - **Aug 25**

Cooper Antiques Fairs
01249 661111:
The Cheshire County Antiques Fair, Arley Hall,
Near Knutsford, Cheshire - **Oct 10-12**

Galloway Antiques Fairs
01423 522122:
Antiques Fair, Naworth Castle, Brampton,
Cumbria - **Aug 29-31**
Antiques Fair, The Old Swan Hotel, Harrogate,
North Yorks - **Sep 19-21**
Antiques Fair, Stonyhurst College, Near
Clitheroe, Lancs - **Oct 24-26**
The Duncombe Park Antiques Fair, Helmsley,
North Yorks - **Nov 7-9**
Antiques Fair, Brandling House, High Gosforth
Park, Newcastle upon Tyne - **Dec 5-7**

Neville Baker
01565 722 144:
Antique & Collectors' Fair, Plumley Village
Hall, Plumley Moor Road, Plumley (M6
junction 19 near Knutsford off A556) - **Aug 31;
Sep 28; Oct 26; Nov 30**

Penman Antique Fairs
0870 3502442:
Chester Antiques & Fine Art Show, The County Grandstand, Chester Racecourse, Chester, Cheshire - **Oct 23-26**

Robert Bailey Fairs Ltd
01277 214677:
The 34th Cheshire Autumn Antiques & Fine Art Fair, Tatton Park, Knutsford, Cheshire - **Sept 4-7**
The 53rd Northern Antiques Fair, Pavilions of Harrogate, Great Yorkshire Showground, Wetherby Road, Harrogate, N. Yorks - **Sept 17-21**
The 4th Wirral Antiques & Fine Art Fair, Hulme Hall, Port Sunlight, Wirral - **Nov 14-16**
The 25th Lancashire Christmas Antiques & Fine Art Fair, The Swallow Trafalgar Hotel (immediately off J31, M6, on A59 towards Clitheroe), Preston New Road, Samlesbury, Preston, Lancs - **Nov 21-23**

Unicorn Fairs Ltd
0161 773 7001:
Antiques & Collectors' Fair, The Exhibition Halls, Park Hall, Charnock Richard, Lancs - **every Sunday**

IRELAND

L & M Fairs Ltd
028 9752 8428:
Antique Fair, Methodist Church Hall, 262 Lisburn Road, Belfast - **Aug 2; Sep 6; Oct 1; Nov 2; Dec 6, 20; Jan 3, 2004**
Antique Fair, Saintfield Second Presbyterian - **Oct 25**
Antique Fair, Moira Presbyterian Church Hall - **Nov 22**
Antique Fair, Crozier Hall, Armagh - **Nov 29**
Antique Fair, Community Centre, Ballynahinch - **Dec 13**
Antique Fair, Greenisland Presbyterian Church Hall - **Jan 10, 2004**

SCOTLAND

Galloway Antiques Fairs
01423 522122:
Antiques Fair, Scone Palace, Perth - **Nov 14-16**

Pantheon Fairs Ltd
01738 446534.
Edinburgh Festival Fair, The Edinburgh Academy - **Aug 15-17**
Antiques Fair, Hopetoun House, South Queensferry, Edinburgh - **Oct 10-12**
Antiques Fair, Oxenfoord Castle, Pathhead, Near Edinburgh (off A68 Near Pathhead, 10 miles south of Edinburgh) - **Dec 5-7**

WALES

Allen Lewis Fairs
01202 604306:
The Antique Dealers' Fair of Wales, The Orangery, Margam Country Park, Port Talbot, West Glam., (RAC signposted from Junction 38, M4) - **Sept 5-7**
The Portmeirion Antiques Fair, Portmeirion village, Gwynedd, (RAC signposted A487) - **Nov 7-9**

Towy Antiques Fairs
01267 236569:
Antiques & Collectors' Fair, Ysgol Penweddig, Llanbadarn, Aberystwyth - **Aug 16-17; Oct 25-26**
Antique & Collectors' Fair, Sophia Gardens, Cardiff - **Aug 30-31**
Antiques & Collectors' Fair, The United Counties Showground, Carmarthen - **Sept 13-14; Dec 13-14**

Services

This section has been included to enable us to list those businesses which do not sell antiques but are in associated trades, mainly restorations. The following categories are included.

Art, Books, Carpets & Rugs, Ceramics, Clocks & Barometers, Consultancy, Courier, Enamel, Engraving, Fireplaces, Framing, Furniture, Glass, Insurance & Finance, Ivory, Jewellery & Silver, Locks & Keys, Metalwork, Musical Instruments, Photography, Reproduction Stonework, Suppliers, Textiles, Tortoiseshell, Toys.

We would point out that the majority of dealers also restore and can give advice in this field.

Below are listed the trade associations mentioned within this section.

BAFRA	-	British Antique Furniture Restorers' Assn
FATG	-	Fine Art Trade Guild
GADAR	-	Guild of Antique Dealers & Restorers
GMC	-	Guild of Master Craftsmen
MBHI	-	Member of British Horological Institute
UKIC	-	UK Institute for Conservation
CGCG	-	Ceramic & Glass Conservation Group
BTCM	-	British Traditional Cabinet Makers
BFMA	-	British Furniture Manufacturers' Assn
BCFA	-	British Contract Furniture Assn
ASFI	-	Assn of Suppliers to Furniture Industry
GAI	-	Guild of Architectural Ironmongers
MBWCG	-	Member British Watch & Clockmakers Guild

ART

The Antique Restoration Studio
See entry under Furniture.

Armor Paper Conservation Ltd
Glebe Cottage, 2 The Green, Garsington, Oxon. OX44 9DF. Tel: 01865 361741; fax - 01865 361815. TVADA. *Conservation and restoration of drawings, prints, watercolour paintings, documents and archive material.*

Paul Congdon-Clelford
The Conservation Studio, 59 Peverells Wood Ave., Chandler's Ford, Hants. SO53 2FX. Est. 1894. Tel: 02380 268167; fax - same; e-mail - winstudio@aol.com; website - www. conservationstudio.org. IPC. ABPR. FATG. GADAR. Open by appointment. *Conservators of oil paintings and western art on paper; home and business consultations. Collection and delivery. All areas. Conservators to museums, institutions, dealers and private owners.*

Kirkgate Fine Art & Conservation
The Studio, 3 Gillings Yard, Thirsk, Yorks North. YO7 1SY. (Richard Bennett). Est. 1979. Tel: 01845 524085; home - same; e-mail - reb@ kirkgateconservation.co.uk; website - www. kirkgateconservation.co.uk. UKIC. BAPCR. Open by appointment. *Oil paintings cleaned and lined on the premises; gilt/gesso frames restored and repaired; framing.* LOC: 100 yards from Market Place, off Kirkgate.

Manor House Fine Arts
73 Pontcanna St. Cardiff. CF11 9HS. (S.K. Denley-Hill). Est. 1976. Tel: 02920 227787; fax - 02920 641132; e-mail - valuers@ manorhousefinearts.co.uk; website - www. manorhousefinearts.co.uk. NAVA. Open 10-5.30. *Auctioneers, valuers, restorers, fine arts, antiques and chattels.*

Stephen Messer Picture Restoration
Tarifa, Millstream Moorings, Mill Lane, Clewer, Windsor, Berks. SL4 5JH. Tel: 01753 622335. Associate member ABPR. *Restorations - paintings, mainly oils including re-lining, frames including gilding.*

Claudio Moscatelli Oil Painting Restoration

46 Cambridge St., London SW1V 4QH. (P. Moscatelli). Tel: 020 7828 1304; e-mail - claudio4@btinternet.com. BPR. Open 10-6. *Oil paintings cleaned, relined, retouched and varnished.*

The Picture Restoration Studios

The Old Coach House, 16A Tarrant St., Arundel, West Sussex. BN18 9DJ. (Garve Hessenberg). Tel: 01903 885775; fax - 01903 889649; mobile - 07971 184477; e-mail - picturerestoration@ hotmail.com; website - www.picturerestoration. net. UKIC. Open by appointment only. *Cleaning and restoration of oil paintings, watercolours, prints and old gilded frames. Antique, traditional and contemporary framing. Also in Oxford - 01865 200289; Guildford - 01483 479666; Haslemere 01428 641010; Chichester - 01243 778785.*

Plowden & Smith Ltd

190 St Ann's Hill, London SW18 2RT. Tel: 020 8874 4005; fax - 020 8874 7248; e-mail - Info@plowden-smith.co.uk; website - www. plowden-smith.co.uk. *Conservation and restoration of fine art and antiques. Specialist departments for furniture, ceramics, paintings, metal, stone, decorative arts, mounting/display.* VAT: Stan.

Colin A. Scott

1st Floor Studio, Anthony Hurst Antiques, 13 Church St., Woodbridge, Suffolk. IP12 1DS. Tel: 01394 388528; home - 01473 622127. Open 9-5.30, Sat. 9-1. *Picture restoration and framing.*

Thicke Gallery

SA2 8BG. (T.G. Thicke). Est. 1981. Tel: 01792 207515. Open by appointment. *Advice on purchase/sale of paintings; valuations; restorations (oils, watercolours, samplers).*

BOOKS

Brignell Bookbinders

25 Gwydir St., Cambridge, Cambs. CB1 2LG. Est. 1982. Tel: 01223 321280; fax - same. SOBB. GMC. Open 8.30-4.45, Fri. 7.30-4. CL: Sat. *Book restoration, conservation including paper, leather photo cases, journal and theses bindings, boxes and limited editions.* VAT: Stan.

The Manor Bindery Ltd

Calshot Rd., Fawley, Southampton, Hants. SO4 1BB. Tel: 023 8089 4488; fax - 023 8089 9418. *Manufacturers of false books, either to use as a display or for cabinet makers to apply to doors and cupboards. Also decorative objects and accessories, various decorative replica book boxes. Leather library shelf edging.*

CARPETS AND RUGS

Barin Carpets Restoration

57a New Kings Rd., London SW6 4SE. Est. 1976. Tel: 020 7731 0546; fax - 020 7384 1620. GMC. Conservation Register Museums and Galleries Commission. UKIC. *Oriental carpets, rugs, European tapestries, Aubussons expertly cleaned, restored and lined. Expert advice, free estimates.*

The Restoration Studio

Unit 11 Kolbe House, 63 Jeddo Rd., London W12 9EE. (Ela Sosmowska). Est. 1987. Tel: 020 8740 4977; website - www.restorationstudio.co.uk. Member Rug Restorers Assn. Open 8-5. CL: Sat. *Restoration, cleaning, lining and mounting of tapestries, Aubusson carpets, kilims and all kinds of needlework.*

CERAMICS

The Antique Restoration Studio

See entry under Furniture.

China Repair by Roger Carter

P O Box 647, Lincoln, Lincs. LN4 2XG. (Roger and Angela Carter). Tel: 01522 792888; fax - 01522 792777; mobile - 07799 896350; e-mail - rogercarter@enterprise.net; website - www. ceramicrepair.com. GMC; Assn. of Restorers. Open Mon.-Fri. 9-5. *Repairs, restoration and conservation od all china and related items including ivory and papier maché. Attendance at Swinderby, Newark and Lincoln antiques fairs for delivery and collection.* VAT: Stan.

China Repairers

The Old Coach House, King's Mews, off King Street, London N2 8DY. (V. Baron). Est. 1952. Tel: 020 8444 3030; website - www. chinarepairers.co.uk. Open 10-4. CL: Fri. and Sat. *Specialised restoration of all pottery and porcelain; restoration courses.*

The China Repairers

1 Street Farm Workshops, Doughton, Tetbury, Glos. GL8 8TH. (Mrs Amanda Chalmers). Est. 1990. Tel: 01666 503551. TADA. Open 9-4.30. CL: Sat. *Specialised restoration of porcelain and pottery, mirror frame gilding.* LOC: Entrance to Highgrove House.

Porcelain Repairs Ltd

240 Stockport Rd., Cheadle Heath, Stockport, Cheshire. SK3 0LX. Est. 1970. Tel: 0161 428 9599; fax - 0161 286 6702. CGCG. UKIC. *Highest standard restorations of European and Oriental ceramics, especially under glaze blue and white, museum repairs, carat gilding and modelling. Cracks and crazing removed without any overpainting or glazing.*

CLOCKS AND BAROMETERS

Apollo Southerns

Penygraig Industrial Estate, Tonypandy, Mid. Glam., South Wales. CS40 1JA. Tel: 01443 420420. BJA. MBWCG. Jewellery Industry Distributors Assn. *Watch and clock replacement and restoration materials; specialised tools for the horological trade.* VAT: Stan. *Trade Only.*

The Clock Gallery

Clarke's Rd., North Killingholme, Lincs. DN40 3JQ. Tel: 01469 540901; fax - 01469 541512. Guild of Lincolnshire Craftsmen. *Clock movements and dials, brass work. Agent for several German clock movement makers.* VAT: Stan.

Clive and Lesley Cobb

3 Pembroke Crescent, Hove, East Sussex. BN3 5DH. Est. 1972. Tel: 01273 772649; e-mail - londinifecit@aol.com. Listed by the Conservation Unit of the Museum and Galleries Commission. *Quality, sympathetic restoration of lacquer clock cases and furniture, and painted clock dials.*

Edmund Czajkowski and Son

See entry under Furniture.

Richard Higgins (Conservation)

See entry under Furniture.

E. Hollander (David Pay)

1 Bennetts Castle,89 The Street, Capel, Dorking, Surrey. RH5 5JX. Tel: 01306 713377; fax - 01306 712013. Open Mon.-Fri. 8-4.30, or by appointment. *Restoration of all forms of clocks, mechanisms, cases, dials and barometers.*

A.C. Layne

48 Cecil St., Carlisle, Cumbria. CA1 1NT. Tel: 01228 545019. Open 8-11.30 and 1-4. *Repairs to antique clocks.*

Robert B. Loomes

3 St Leonard's Street, Stamford, Lincs. PE9 1HD. Est. 1966. Tel: 01780 481319; website - www.

dialrestorer.co.uk. MBWCG. MBHI. Open 9-5. *Restoration of longcase, lantern and bracket clocks, also painted dials.*VAT: Stan.

William Mansell

24 Connaught St., Marble Arch, London W2 2AF. (Bill and Karen Salisbury). Est. 1864. Tel: 020 7723 4154; fax - 020 7724 2273; e-mail - williammansell@email.com; website - www. williammansell.co.uk. MBHI. NAG. BWCG. Open 9-6, Sat. 10-1. *Repair/restoration/sales of all types of clocks, watches and barometers etc., also antique jewellery and silverware. Online catalogue of antique, vintage and modern watches, clocks, jewellery and silverware.*

Meadows and Passmore Ltd

1 Ellen Street, Portslade, Brighton, East Sussex. BN41 1EU. Tel: 01273 421321; fax - 01273 421322. *Clock and barometer parts, tools and materials.*

Menim Restorations

Bow St., Langport, Somerset. Est. 1830. Tel: 01458 252157. GMC. *Specialists in English clocks, full cabinet making and horological service; French polishing.*

Repton Clocks

Acton Cottage,48 High St., Repton, Derbys. DE65 6GF. (P.Shrouder). Tel: 01283 703657; fax - 01283 702367; e-mail - paul@pshrouder. freeserve.co.uk. MBWCMG. MBHI. Open by appointment 9-6. CL: Sat. *Antique and modern watch and clock restoration; musical box repairs; gear cutting; clocks made to order.*

Kevin Sheehan

15 Market Place, Tetbury, Glos. GL8 8DD. Est. 1978. Tel: 01666 503099. Open 9-4.30, Sat. 10-12. *Specialist repairer of English and French 18th-19th C clocks. Written estimates given, all work guaranteed. Awarded Royal Warrant.*

CONSULTANCY

Athena Antiques of Fleet

59 Elvetham Rd., Fleet, Hants. GU13 8HH. (Richard Briant). Est. 1975. Tel: 01252 615526; home - same; mobile - 07881 541748. Available seven days by appointment. *Consultancy; valuations (jewellery, silver, clocks and furniture); restorations (clocks and furniture); buys at auction on commission; militaria.* LOC: Near Fleet railway station.

John Fell-Clark
LAPADA

Wall Farm, Harkstead Rd., Holbrook, Ipswich,

Suffolk. IP9 2RQ. Est. 1971. Tel: 01473 327707. Open by appointment. *Valuations; restorations; consultancy and interior design; buys at auction (17th-20th C furniture and textiles).* VAT: Spec.

Geoffrey Godden
3 The Square, Findon, West Sussex. BN14 0TE. Tel: 01903 873456. *Consultant and lecturer in ceramics.*

Gerald Sattin   BADA
P O Box 20627, London NW6 7GA. (G. and M.S. Sattin). Est. 1967. Tel: 020 8451 3295; fax - same; e-mail - gsattin@compuserve.com. **Open by appointment.** *Consultants and commission agents for the purchase of English and Continental porcelain, 1720-1900; English glass, 1700-1900; English collectible silver, 1680-1920.* VAT: Stan/Spec.

COURIER

Antique Tours & Conrad Chauffeur Hire
11 Farleigh Rise, Monkton Farleigh, Nr. Bradford-on-Avon, Wilts. BA15 2QP. (John Veal). Est. 1988. Tel: 01225 858527 (answerphone); fax - same; mobile - 07860 489831; e-mail - conradveal@hotmail.com. *Chauffeur service for up to four persons; tours of antique shops, fairs, dealers and warehouses in and around the West Country, (other areas as requested); packing and shipping arranged; air and sea port transfers.*

The English Room
London SW11 4PY. (Mrs Val Cridland). Est. 1985. Tel: 020 7720 6655; mobile - 07770 275414; fax - 020 7978 2397. Open by appointment. *Search and courier (trade and private), London and country - shipment of goods purchased arranged.* VAT: Stan/Spec.

ENGRAVING

Eastbourne Engraving
12 North Street, Eastbourne, East Sussex. BN21 3HG. (D. Ricketts). Est. 1882. Tel: 01323 723592. Open Tues.-Fri. 9.15-4.45. *Engraving trophies, polishing, silver plating, repairs, hardwood plinths, etc.*

FIREPLACES

Antiques and Restoration
Old Town Hall, 965 Stockport Rd, Levenshulme, Manchester, Lancs. (A. Warburton). Tel: 0161 256 4644; mobile - 07976 985982. Open 10-5,

Sun. 11-4. *Antiques, fireplaces and restoration, also carpentry and re-claimed pine furniture.*

FRAMING

Sebastian D'Orsai Ltd
39 Theobalds Rd., Holborn, London WC1X 8NW. (A. Brooks). Est. 1967. Tel: 020 7405 6663; fax - 020 7831 3300. Open Mon.-Fri. 9.30-4.30. *Framing, traditional to museum standard including hand-coloured finishing to suit individual pictures.* VAT: Stan.

Natural Wood Framing
Eight Bells Gallery, 14 Church St., Tetbury, Glos. GL8. Tel: 01666 505070. FATG. *Bespoke framing specialising in antiques, textiles and restorations. Contemporary and sporting art stocked.*

FURNITURE

Abbey Antiques & Furnishings Ltd
Plot 1 Maldon Rd., Danes Road Industrial Estate, Off Crow Lane, Romford, Essex. RM7 0JB. Est. 1992. Tel: 01708 741135; fax - 01708 746419; home - 01708 343103. Open 8-5, Fri. 8-1, Sat. and Sun. by appointment. *Copies of Victorian and Edwardian four door breakfront bookcases, bureau bookcases, partners and pedestal desks, walnut or mahogany, old or new timber, £1,500-£2,500. Furniture repairs - glazing, leathering, gilding, turnings, inlays, veneering.* LOC: Near Oldchurch Hospital. VAT: Stan.

Timothy Akers - Antique Furniture Restorations
The Forge, 39 Chancery Lane, Beckenham, Kent. BR3 2NR. Est. 1978. Tel: 020 8650 9179; website - www.akersofantiques.com. BAFRA. *Restorer of and dealer in of 17th-19th C English furniture; dealer of objets d'art.*

Alan's Antique Restorations
PO Box 355. Woking, Surrey. GU22 9QE. (A.V. Wellstead). Tel: 01483 724666; fax - 01483 750366.

Anthony Allen Antique Restorers
Old Wharf Workshop, Redmoor Lane, New Mills, High Peak, Derbys. SK22 3JL. Tel: 01663 745274. BAFRA. UKIC. Listed on Register of Conservation Unit Museums and Galleries Commission. *Early oak and walnut furniture; conservation; clocks, cases, and movements; artifacts and metalwork.*

The Antique Restoration Centre
14 Suffolk Rd., Cheltenham, Glos. GL50 2AQ.

(M.H. Smith-Wood). Est. 1974. Tel: 01242 262549. Open Mon-Fri 9.30-5. *All types of restoration - all restorers BADA qualified.*

The Antique Restoration Studio
The Stable Block, Milwich Rd. Stafford, Staffs. ST18 0EG. (P. Albright). Est. 1980. Tel: 01889 505544; fax - 01889 505543; e-mail - ars@uk-hq.demon.co.uk; website - www.uk-hq.demon.co.uk. Open 9-5. *Repairs and restoration (furniture, rush and cane, French polishing, leatherwork and upholstery, ceramics, glassware, paintings, clocks and watches, rare books, documents and photographs). Five year guarantee on all work. Collection and delivery service.* LOC: 4 miles NE of Stafford.

Antiques and Restoration
See entry under Fireplaces.

Antom Ltd t/a Antiques of Tomorrow
The Glue Pot, 6 Kyles, Stockinish, Isle of Harris, Scotland. HS3 3EN. (Dr. Carole Green and Simon Burke). Tel: 01859 530300; mobile - 07769 721428. Open by appointment. *Wholesale and mail order of reproduction chairs, stools and armchairs - unpolished or polished frames or fully upholstered.* VAT: Stan.

Michael Barrington
The Old Rectory, Warmwell, Dorchester, Dorset. DT2 8HQ. Est. 1983. Tel: 01305 852104; fax - 854822. ACR. BAFRA. UKIC. *Conservator and restorer of 17th-20th C furniture, clocks, barometers, gilding, upholstery, metalwork, music boxes and barrel pianos, automatons and rocking horses, historic lighting eg. Colza Oil and Argand.*

Batheaston
20 Leafield Way, Corsham, Wilts. SN13 9SW. Tel: 01225 811295; fax - 01225 810501. BFMA. BCFA. *Oak reproduction furniture made from solid kiln dried timbers, antique hand finish. Extensive range of Windsor, ladderback and country Hepplewhite chairs; refectory, gateleg and other extendable tables, Welsh dressers, sideboards and other cabinet models. Trade Only.*

David Battle
Brightley Pound, Umberleigh, Devon. EX37 9AL. Est. 1984. Tel: 01769 540483. BAFRA. Open by appointment. *Cabinet making, restoration and conservation work; polishing, clock cases, veneer and marquetry work, woodturning. Specialists in 17th-19th C English and Continental furniture. Collections and deliveries.*

Keith Bawden - Restorer of Antiques
Mews Workshops, Montpellier Retreat, Cheltenham, Glos. GL50 2XG. Tel: 01242 230320. BAFRA. *All period furniture, plus restoration of items made from wood, metals, porcelain, pottery, fabrics, leather, ivory, papier-mâché, etc.*

Clive Beardall
104b High St., Maldon, Essex. CM9 5ET. Est. 1982. Tel: 01621 857890; fax - 01621 850753; website - www.clivebeardall.co.uk. BAFRA. Conservation Register. *Comprehensive restoration and conservation services to all types of period furniture.*

Belvedere Reproductions
11 Dove St., Ipswich, Suffolk. IP4 1NG. (S.M. Curtis). Est. 1984. Tel: 01473 214573; fax - 01473 253229; mobile - 07860 782888. Open 8-5. *Suppliers of traditionally constructed and hand polished oak and fruitwood country furniture.* VAT: Stan.

Berry & Crowther
The Workshops, Nine Whitestones, Stocksmoor, Huddersfield, West Yorks. HD4 6XQ. (Peter N. Berry and David Crowther). Est. 1979. Tel:

01484 609800; fax - same; e-mail - peternberry@aol.com. Open 9-6.30. *Fine antique restorers and conservators; restoration with traditional methods to highest standards on fine furniture and clocks. Insurance work approved.*

Rupert Bevan
40 Fulham High St., London SW6 3LQ. Tel: 020 7731 1919; fax - same. *Gilding, carving and painting.* VAT: Stan.

Peter Binnington
Barn Studio, Botany Farm, East Lulworth, Wareham, Dorset. BH20 5QH. Est. 1979. Tel: 01929 400224; fax - 01929 400744; e-mail - p. binnington@virgin.net; website - www. freespace.virgin.net/p.binnington. BAFRA. SoG. Open 9-5.30. CL: Sat. *Restoration of verre églomisé, giltwork, decorated surfaces, period furniture.*

Martin Body - Giltwood Restoration
7 Addington Sq., London SE5 7JZ. Est. 1988. Tel: 020 7703 4351; fax - 020 7703 1047; e-mail - giltwooduk@aol.com. Open 9-5. *Specialist conservation of fine gilded furniture and frames.* LOC: Camberwell.

Richard Bolton
The Old Brewery, Mangerton Mill, Mangerton, Bridport, Dorset. DT6 3SG. Est. 1982. Tel: 01308 485000. BAFRA. Open 9-5. CL: Sat. *All aspects of furniture restoration using traditional cabinet making and polishing techniques.*

A.E. Booth & Son
Crows Nest, Edgeley Rd., Barton, Torquay, Devon. TQ2 8ND. Tel: 01803 312091. *Restorations, polishing, upholstery. Barometers, longcase, mahogany and walnut.*

Stuart Bradbury - M & S Bradbury
The Barn, Hanham Lane, Paulton, Somerset. BS39 7PF. Est. 1988. Tel: 01761 418910; e-mail - enquiries@mandsbradbury.co.uk; website - www.mandsbradbury.co.uk. BAFRA. Open 8-5. *All aspects of antique furniture restoration.*

Lawrence Brass
154 Sutherland Avenue, Maida Vale, London W9. Tel: 0122 585 2222. UKIC. Approved by the Museums and Galleries Commission. *Conservation and restoration of fine antiques, metal work, gilding and upholstery.*

A. J. Brett & Co Ltd
168c Marlborough Rd., London N19 4NP. Est. 1965. Tel: 020 7272 8462; fax - 020 7272 5102; e-mail - ajbretts@aol.com; website - www. ajbrett.co.uk. GMC. Open 7-3.30. *Restorers of antique furniture and upholstery; French polishing and gilding; free estimates.*

Bruton Classic Furniture Company Ltd
Unit 1 Station Road Industrial Estate, Bruton, Somerset. BA10 0EH. Tel: 01749 813266; fax - same; mobile - 07973 342047. *Quality antique replica furniture - mahogany, teak and pine.*

Peter Campion Restorations
The Old Dairy, Rushley Lane, Winchcombe, Glos. GL54 5JE. Est. 1959. Tel: 01242 604403; fax - same; website - www.petercampion.co.uk. BAFRA. Open 9-5.30 or by appointment. *Furniture restoration, conservation, polishing, insurance work, furniture designed and made to order.* LOC: Opposite the exit of Sudeley Castle car park.

Cane & Able Antiques - Cane & Rush Furniture Restoration
The Limes, 22 The Street, Beck Row, Bury St. Edmunds, Suffolk. IP28 8AD. Est. 1991. Tel: 01638 515529; fax - 01638 583905; e-mail - bobcaneandable@yahoo.co.uk. *Specialists in antique and designer cane, upholstery and rush seating, furniture restoration and copying.*

John B. Carr - Charles Perry Restorations Ltd
Praewood Farm, Hemel Hempstead Rd., St. Albans, Herts. AL3 6AA. Tel: 01727 853487; fax - 01727 846668; e-mail - cperry@praewood. freeserve.co.uk. BAFRA.

Carvers & Gilders Ltd
9 Charterhouse Works, Eltringham St., London SW18 1TD. Est. 1979. Tel: 020 8870 7047; fax - 020 8874 0470; e-mail - acc@carversand gilders.com; website - www.carversandgilders. com. UKIC. Master Carver's Assn. Furniture History Society. GMC. *Restoration and conservation of fine decorative woodcarving and giltwood. Specialists in fine water gilding. Designers and makers of carved and giltwood furniture, mirror frames and other decorative pieces in both period and contemporary styles.* VAT: Stan.

Peter G. Casebow
Pilgrims, Mill Lane, Worthing, West Sussex. BN13 3DE. Tel: 01903 264045. BAFRA. *Period furniture, turning, marquetry, metalwork, fretwork, polishing.*

Castle House Antique Restoration Limited
1 Bennetts Field Estate, Wincanton, Somerset.

BA9 9DT. (Michael Durkee). Tel: 01963 33884; fax - 01963 31278. BAFRA. Conservation register. Open 8.30-5.30. CL: Sat. *Restoration, conservation and finishing of all styles of period furniture. Boulle and inlay work.*

Graham Childs - Alpha (Antique) Restorations

High St., Compton, Newbury, Berks. RG20 6NL. Est. 1972. Tel: 01635 578245; mobile - 07860 575203. BAFRA. *Fine oak, walnut and mahogany. Traditional hand finishes. Veneering and inlaying. Clock cases.*

Clare Hall Company

The Barns, Clare Hall, Cavendish Rd., Clare, Nr. Sudbury, Suffolk. CO10 8PJ. (Michael Moore). Est. 1970. Tel: 01787 278445; fax - 01787 278803; 01787 277510 (ansaphone). Open 8-4.30. *Replicas of 18th and 19th C floor standing and table globes. Full cabinet making especially four poster beds; restoration of all antiques and upholstery.* VAT: Stan/Spec.

Classic Reproductions

Swan Corner, Pewsey, Wilts. SN9 5HL. Tel: 01672 563333; fax - 01672 562391. *Suppliers of replica antiques from Java and manufacturers of custom designed pine furniture including tables, beds, chests, bookcases and desks.*

Benedict Clegg

Rear of 20 Camden Rd., Tunbridge Wells, Kent. TN1 2PT. Tel: 01892 548095. BAFRA.

Lucinda Compton of Compton & Schuster Ltd

The Old Laundry, Newby Hall, Ripon, North Yorks. HG4 5AE. Est. 1986. Tel: 01423 324290; website - www.comptonandschuster.com. BAFRA. Conservation register. UKIC. Open 9-5. CL: Sat. *Furniture - painted, gilded, lacquer, papier mâché, tôle.*

Compton & Schuster Ltd

Studio A133 Riverside Business Centre, Haldane Place, London SW18 4UQ. (Lucinda Compton and Dominic Schuster). Est. 1990. Tel: 020 8874 0762; fax - 020 8870 8060; website - www.comptonandschuster.com. BAFRA. *Conservation and restoration - lacquer, gilding, painted furniture, paper-mâché, tôle, architectural gilding.*

William Cook

167 Battersea High St., London SW11 3JS. Tel: 020 7736 5329 or 01672 513017. BAFRA. *18th C and English period furniture.*

William Cook

High Trees House, Savernake Forest, Marlborough, Wilts. SN8 4NE. Tel: 01672 513017. BAFRA.

Crawley Studios

39 Woodvale, London SE23 3DS. Est. 1985. Tel: 020 8516 0002; fax - same. BAFRA. *Painted furniture, papier-mâché, tôle ware, lacquer and gilding.*

J.W. Crisp Antiques

1-9 Tennyson Rd., Wimbledon, London SW19 8SH. (Michael Murren). Est. 1926. Tel: 020 8543 1118; fax - same. Open by appointment. *Restoration of antique furniture and French polishing.*

Michael Czajkowski - Edmund Czajkowski and Son

96 Tor-o-Moor Rd., Woodhall Spa, Lincs. LN10 6SB. Tel: 01526 352895; fax - same; e-mail - sales@czajkowskiandson.co.uk. BAFRA. *Furniture, clocks (including church) and barometers restored. Veneering, marquetry, English lacquer and boulle work, carving and gilding.*

D.H.R. Limited

8/10 Lea Lane, Thame Rd., Long Crendon, Aylesbury, Bucks. HP18 9RN. Tel: 01844 202213; fax - 01844 202214. BAFRA. *Boulle, cabinetwork, carving, gilding, lacquer, leather, marble, marquetry, ormolu, upholstery.*

Michael Dolling

Church Farm Barns, Glandford, Holt, Norfolk. NR25 7JR. Also at White Hart St., East Harling, Norfolk. NR16 2NE. Est. 1984. Tel: 01263 741115. BAFRA. Open 9-5. *Furniture repairs; veneering; marquetry; French polishing.*

Brian Duffy and Katie Keat - Hope & Piaget

12 and 13 Burmarsh Workshops, Marsden St., London NW5 3JA. Tel: 020 7267 6040; fax - same; e-mail - mail@hope-piaget.co.uk; website - www.hope-piaget.co.uk. BAFRA. UKIC. *Conservation and restoration of fine furniture.*

EFMA

4 Northgate Close, Rottingdean, Brighton, East Sussex. BN2 7DZ. (Anthony and Patrick Hoole). Est. 1973. Tel: 01273 589744; fax - 01273 589745; e-mail - info@efma.co.uk; website - www.efma.co.uk. Fed. of Sussex Industries. IDDA. Inst. of Export. Inst. of Linguists. *Hand-finished reproductions in walnut, elm, myrtle, yew, mahogany, satinwood. Custom-work and*

EFMA

**4 Northgate Close Rottingdean
Brighton BN2 7DZ England
Tel: 01273-589744
Fax: 01273-589745
www.efma.co.uk**

**Tony &
Patrick Hoole**

**Workshops for
hand-finished
reproductions.
Walnut, elm, yew,
mahogany,
satinwood -**

**Separate range
solid oak, cherry
country pieces.
Members IDDA,
Inst. of Export.
Colour catalogue
available.**

bespoke polishing - 18th C, Biedermeier, Victorian, mahogany dining tables. Country furniture - distressed oak and cherry refectory, gateleg and coffee tables, Windsor chairs. Tables reproduced from old timber. VAT: Stan.

D.S. Embling - The Cabinet Repair Shop
Woodlands Farm, Blacknest, Alton, Hants. GU34 4QB. Est. 1977. Tel: 01252 794260; fax - 01252 793084; website - www.dsembling.co.uk. C&G London Inst. GMC. League of Professional Craftsmen. Open 8-5. CL: Sat. *Antique and modern furniture restoration and repair including marquetry and veneering, French polishing, modern finishes. Parts made, wood turning, collection and delivery; insurance claim repairs.*

Everitt and Rogers
Dawsnest Workshop, Grove Rd., Tiptree, Essex. CO5 0JE. Est. 1969. Tel: 01621 816508; fax - 01621 814685. GADAR. *Expert antique furniture restoration.*

Duncan Everitt - D.M.E. Restorations Ltd
11 Church St., Ampthill, Beds. MK45 2PL. Est. 1986. Tel: 01525 405819; fax - 01525 756177; e-mail - info@dmerestorations.com; website - www.dmerestorations.com. BAFRA. *Restoration of English and European furniture.*

John Farbrother Furniture Restoration
Ivy House, Main St., Shipton-by-Beningbrough, York, North Yorks. YO30 1AB. Est. 1987. Tel: 01904 470187; website - www.johnfarbrother.co.uk. GADAR. *All repairs undertaken, refinishing process from complete strip to reviving existing finish. French polishing, oil, wax and lacquers. Pressurised fluid application woodworm treatment.*

Fauld Town and Country Furniture
Whitestone Park, Whitestone, Hereford, Herefs. HR1 3SE. Est. 1972. Tel: 01432 851992; fax - 01432 851994; e-mail - enquiries@fauld.com; website - www.fauld.com. Open 8-5, appointment advisable. *Windsor chairs, extensive range of farmhouse tables, dressers and racks and many other case pieces. Bespoke work a speciality to traditional styles and methods.* VAT: Stan.

Fenlan
17B Stilebrook Rd., Yardley Road Industrial Estate, Olney, Bucks. Est. 1982. Tel: 01234 711799; fax - same. *Furniture restoration. Restoration products and fittings supplied; cabinet making and non-caustic stripping.* VAT: Stan/Spec.

Andrew Foott
4 Claremont Rd., Cheadle Hulme, Cheshire. SK8 6EG. Tel: 0161 485 3559. *Sympathetic restoration and conservation of antique furniture and mercurial barometers; free advice and estimates; quality items occasionally for sale.*

Forge Studio Workshops
Stour St., Manningtree, Essex. CO11 1BE. Tel: 01206 396222. BAFRA. *Carving, general restoration, copying and bespoke cabinet making.*

Glen Fraser-Sinclair - G. and R. Fraser-Sinclair
Hays Bridge Farm, Brickhouse Lane, South Godstone, Surrey. RH9 8JW. Tel: 01342 844112. BAFRA. *18th C furniture.*

Alistair J. Frayling-Cork
2 Mill Lane, Wallingford, Oxon. OX10 0DH. Est. 1979. Tel: 01491 826221. BAFRA. *Antique and period furniture, clock cases, ebonising, wood turning, stringed instruments and brass fittings repaired.*

Georgian Cabinets Manufacturers Ltd
Unit 4 Fountayne House, 2-8 Fountayne Rd., London N15 4QL. Est. 1964. Tel: 020 8885 1293; fax - 020 8365 1114. *Manufacturers, restorers*

and polishers. Large stock of inlaid furniture. Container services worldwide. LOC: Near Seven Sisters underground, Tottenham. PARK: Own. VAT: Stan.

Sebastian Giles Furniture
11 Junction Mews, London W2 1PN. Tel: 020 7258 3721. BAFRA.

Melven Glander
Suffolk. Est. 1988. Tel: 01284 828429. *Restoration and repair service to furniture, woodwork, clocks and period fixtures and fittings; free estimates and advice. Collection and delivery. Upholstery arranged.*

Gow Antiques & Restoration
Pitscandly Farm, Forfar, by Lunanhead, Angus, Scotland. DD8 3NZ. (Jeremy Gow). Tel: 01307 465342; mobile - 07711 416786; e-mail - Jeremy@gowantiques.co.uk; website - www.gowantiques.co.uk. BAFRA. Accredited by GMC. Historic Scotland and the Museums and Galleries Commission. Appointment advisable. *17th-19th C English and Continental furniture. Specialist in marquetry, tortoiseshell and fine furniture.*

Jeffrey Hall - Malvern Studios
56 Cowleigh Rd., Malvern, Worcs. WR14 1QD. Est. 1961. Tel: 01684 574913; fax - 01684 569475. BAFRA. Open 9-5.15, Fri. and Sat. 9-4.45. CL: Wed. *Antique furniture restoration.*

Jeremy Hall - Peter Hall & Son
Danes Rd., Staveley, Kendal, Cumbria. LA8 9PL. Tel: 01539 821633; fax - 01539 821905.

John Hartley
Johnson's Barn, Waterworks Rd., Sheet, Petersfield, Hants. GU32 2BY. Est. 1977. Tel: 01730 233792; fax - 01730 233922. BAFRA. UKIC. Open 8-5.30. CL: Sat. *Comprehensive restoration and conservation service, including carving, gilding, painted furniture, lacquer, marquetry, boulle and architectural woodwork. Adviser to The National Trust.*

Philip Hawkins
Glebe Workshop, Semley, Shaftesbury, Dorset. SP7 9AP. Tel: 01747 830830; e-mail - hawkinssemley@hotmail.com. BAFRA. *16th to early 18th C oak furniture restoration.*

Roland Haycraft
The Lamb Arcade, Wallingford, Oxon. Tel: 01491 839622. *All aspects of antique restorations; one-off reproductions and copying service. Fine furniture designed and made to traditional standards.*

Hedgecoe and Freeland   `LAPADA`
21 Burrow Hill Green, Chobham, Surrey. GU24 8QS. Tel: 01276 858206; fax - 01276 857352. BAFRA. *General restorations, cabinet work, polishing, upholstery, chair making.*

Heritage Antiques
Unit 2 Trench Farm, Tilley Green, Wem, Shrops. SY4 5PJ. (M.R. Nelms). Est. 1989. Tel: 01939 235463; fax - 01939 235416; e-mail - heritageantiques@btconnect.com; website - www.heritageantiques.co.uk. GADAR. Open 9-5, Sat. by appointment. *Furniture, including antique and fitted, full restoration service, antique boxes and clock cases a speciality.*

Alan Hessel
The Old Town Workshop, St. George's Close, Moreton-in-Marsh, Glos. GL56 0LP. Est. 1976. Tel: 01608 650026; fax - same; e-mail - alan.hessel@virgin.net. BAFRA. Open Mon.-Fri. 9-5 or by appointment. *Comprehensive restoration service. English and Continental fine period furniture.*

Richard Higgins (Conservation)
The Old School, Longnor, Nr. Shrewsbury, Shrops. SY5 7PP. Est. 1988. Tel: 01743 718162; fax - 01743 718022; e-mail - richardhigginsco @aol.com. BAFRA. LBHI. Conservation Register Museums and Galleries Commission. UKIC. Open by appointment. *Comprehensive restoration of all fine furniture and clocks, including movements and dials; specialist work to boulle, marquetry, carving, turning, cabinet and veneer work, lacquer, ormolu, metalwork, casting, glazing, polishing, upholstery, cane and rush seating. Stocks of old timber, veneers, tortoiseshell etc. held to ensure sympathetic restoration.*

Stuart Hobbs Antique Furniture Restoration
Meath Paddock, Meath Green Lane, Horley, Surrey. RH6 8HZ. Tel: 01293 782349. GMC. BAFRA. *Full restoration service for period furniture.*

John Hubbard Antique Restorations   `LAPADA`
Castle Ash, Birmingham Rd., Blakedown, Worcs. DY10 3SE. Est. 1968. Tel: 01562 701020; e-mail - jhantiques@aol.com; website - www. antiquesbulletin.com/JohnHubbardAntiques. CINOA. GMC. Open by appointment.

Restorations of furniture including French polishing, desk leathers and upholstery. LOC: A456. VAT: Stan.

Christian Macduff Hunt - Hunt and Lomas
Village Farm Workshops, Preston Village, Cirencester, Glos. GL7 5PR. Est. 1988. Tel: 01285 640111. BAFRA. Open 8-5. *17th-19th C oak, mahogany, walnut, satinwood, carving.*

Donald Hunter
The Old School Room, Shipton Oliffe, Cheltenham, Glos. GL54 4JB. Tel: 01242 820755. *Restoration of fine antiques, cabinet making, water gilding, lacquer work, decorative finishes.*

D. Hurst Restoration
4 Gleneldon Mews, London SW16 2AZ. (Deborah Hurst). Est. 1996. Tel: 020 8696 0315; e-mail - deborah.h@ukgateway.net. Open 9-6. *French polishing, gilding, wood carving, restoration.*

George Justice
12A Market St., Lewes, East Sussex. BN7 2HE. (J.C., C.C. and S.M. Tompsett). Tel: 01273 474174; website - www.lewesartisans.com. GMC. Open 8-1 and 2-5. CL: Sat. *Furniture restorations, cabinet making, upholstery, French polishing; caning, rushing and leathering can be arranged.*

Rodney F. Kemble
16 Crag Vale Terrace, Glusburn, Nr. Keighley, West Yorks. BD20 8QU. Est. 1987. Tel: 01535 636954. BAFRA. Open 9-5.30. *Cabinet restorations, clock cases, traditional hand finishes and upholstery.* LOC: A6068.

Raymond Konyn Antique Restorations
The Old Wheelwright's, Brasted Forge, Brasted, Kent. TN16 1JL. Est. 1979. Tel: 01959 563863; fax - 01959 561262; e-mail - antique@antique-restorations.org.uk; website - www.antique-restorations.org.uk. BAFRA. Open by appointment. *Furniture, traditional upholstery, longcase and bracket clock cases, polishing, brass casting; consultancy.* VAT: Spec.

Roderick Larwood
The Oaks, Station Rd., Larling, Norfolk. NR16 2QS. Est. 1983. Tel: 01953 717937; fax - same; e-mail - rodlar@tinyworld.co.uk. BAFRA. Open 8-5.30. CL: Sat. *Brass inlay, 18th to early 19th C furniture; French polishing; traditional finishes.*

E.C. Legg and Son
3 College Farm Buildings, Tetbury Rd., Cirencester, Glos. GL7 6PY. Est. 1902. Tel: 01285 650695. Open 9-5. CL: Sat. *Restoration of furniture including rushing, caning and re-leathering desk tops.*

David C. E. Lewry
Wychelms, 66 Gorran Avenue, Rowner, Gosport, Hants. PO13 0NF. Est. 1979. Tel: 01329 286901; fax - 01329 289964; mobile - 07785 766844. BAFRA. *17th to early 19th C furniture.*

John Lloyd
Bankside Farm, Ditchling Common, West Sussex. RH15 0SJ. Tel: 01444 480388; fax - same; mobile - 07941 124772; e-mail - lloydjohn@aol.com; website - www.johnlloydfurniture.co.uk. BAFRA. *Sympathetic restoration and conservation of English and Continental furniture; traditional hand finishing, veneering, marquetry and inlay work, carving and turning, gilding, upholstery, rush/cane work, leather lining and tooling, lock repairs and keys. Antique furniture copied or designed and made to order. Regular delivery/collection service to London. Short courses in furniture restoration and gilding.*

Lomas Pigeon & Co. Ltd
37 Beehive Lane, Great Baddow, Chelmsford, Essex. CM2 9TQ. Est. 1938. Tel: 01245 353708; fax - 01245 355211; e-mail - wpigeon@compuserve.com; website - www.lomas-pigeon.co.uk. BAFRA. AMU. Open 10-4, Sat. 9-12. CL: Wed. *Antique restoration, French polishing, traditional and modern upholstery. Retailers and makers of fine furniture and rocking horses. Curtains and soft furnishings made to order. Leather table top linings.*

Timothy Long Restoration
St. John's Church, London Rd., Dunton Green, Sevenoaks, Kent. TN13 2 TE. Est. 1987. Tel: 01732 743368; fax - 01732 742206; e-mail - info@timlong.co.uk. BAFRA. Open 8-5. CL: Sat. *Cabinet restoration, French polishing, upholstery.*

Bruce Luckhurst
The Little Surrenden Workshops, Ashford Rd., Bethersden, Kent. TN26 3BG. Est. 1976. Tel: 01233 820589; e-mail - training@woodwise.newnet.co.uk; website - www.bruceluckhurst.co.uk. BAFRA. *Conservation and restoration training plus comprehensive restoration service.*

Oliver Manning Press
Shalmsford St., Chartham, Canterbury, Kent.

CT4 7BX. Tel: 01227 731765; mobile - 07808 001844; e-mail - omanningpress@yahoo.co.uk. AF RF; Dip European Centre of Conservation, Venice; Dip Conservation Antique Furniture. Open by appointment only. *Antique furniture restoration - insurance and museum work. Cabinet making; wax finishing; French polishing. Small stock quality items and 'breakers'.*

Timothy Naylor
24 Bridge Rd., Chertsey, Surrey. KT16 8JN. Est. 1990. Tel: 01932 567129; fax - 01932 564948. BAFRA. *Antique furniture restoration.*

Nicholas J. Newman
22 Eastcroft Rd., West Ewell, Surrey. KT19 9TX. Est. 1983. Tel: 020 8224 3347. Open by appointment. *Comprehensive restorations including exterior woodwork and locks.*

Ben Norris & Co
Knowl Hill Farm, Knowl Hill, Kingsclere, Newbury, Berks. RG20 4NY. Tel: 01635 297950; fax - 01635 299851. BAFRA. *All aspects of furniture restoration including carving, gilding, copy chair making and architectural woodwork. Excellent storage facilities.* VAT: Stan.

Nigel Northeast Cabinet Makers
Furniture Workshops, Back Drove, West Winterslow, Salisbury, Wilts. SP5 1RY. Est. 1982. Tel: 01980 862051; fax - 01980 863986; website - www.nigelnortheast.co.uk. GADAR. *Antique restoration and French polishing. New furniture made to order, chairs made to complete sets. Cane and rush seating; fire and flood damage service.* VAT: Stan.

Simon Paterson Fine Furniture Restoration
Whitelands, West Dean, Chichester. West Sussex. PO18 0RL. Tel: 01243 811900; e-mail - hotglue@lineone.net. BAFRA.

Clive Payne
`LAPADA`
Unit 4 Mount Farm,Churchill, Chipping Norton, Oxon. OX7 6NP. Est. 1987. Tel: 01608 658856; fax - same; mobile - 07801 088363; e-mail - clive.payne@virgin.net; website - www.clive.payne.com. BAFRA. Open 8-5.30. *Restorations.*

Noel Pepperall
Dairy Lane Cottage, Walberton, Arundel, West Sussex. BN18 0PT. Tel: 01243 551282; e-mail - pepperall@amserve.net; website - www. pepperall.co.uk. BAFRA. *Antique furniture restoration.*

Eva-Louise Pepperall
Dairy Lane Cottage, Walberton, Arundel, West Sussex. BN18 0PT. Tel: 01243 551282; e-mail - pepperall@amserve.net; website - www. pepperall.co.uk. BAFRA. *Gilding and japanning.*

T. L. Phelps - Fine Furniture Restoration
8 Mornington Terrace, Harrogate, North Yorks. HG1 5DH. Est. 1984. Tel: 01423 524604. BAFRA. UKIC. Conservation Register. Open Mon.-Fri. 8.30-1 and 2-6, prior telephone call advisable. *Specialist restoration (especially water damaged surfaces), and conservation services; all cabinet work, including dining tables, breakfront bookcases; all veneer work; architectural woodwork; traditional hand polishing, colouring and waxed finishes. Condition and treatment reports, reports for insurance loss adjustors;* LOC: Map available on request, easy parking outside property. VAT: Stan.

Pinewood Furniture Studio Ltd
1 Eagle Trading Estate, Stourbridge Rd., Halesowen, West Midlands. B63 3UA. Tel: 0121 550 8228; fax - 0121 585 5611. *Manufacturers of pine furniture. Special orders undertaken.* VAT: Stan.

Plain Farm Workshop
The Old Dairy, Plain Farm, East Tisted, Alton, Hants. GU34 3RT. (Simon Worte). Est. 1990. Tel: 01420 588362. Open 10-5.30. *18th to 19th C English furniture restoration.*

Plowden & Smith Ltd
See entry under Art.

Albert Plumb Furniture Co
Briarfield, Itchenor Green, Chichester, West Sussex. PO20 7DA. (Albert and Sherryl Plumb). Est. 1977. Tel: 01243 513700/1; fax - same. BAFRA. Open 8.30-6. *Oak, walnut, mahogany and country furniture, upholstery and cabinet making.*

A.J. Ponsford Antiques at Decora
Northbrook Rd., off Eastern Ave., Barnwood, Glos. GL4 3DP. (A.J. and R.L. Ponsford). Est. 1962. Tel: 01452 307700. Open 8-5. CL: Sat. *Valuations; restorations (furniture); rushing; caning; upholstery; picture framing; manufacturers of period book simulations and decorative accessories.* LOC: Off junction 11A, M5. VAT: Stan.

Neil Postons Restorations
29 South St., Leominster, Herefs. HR6 8JQ. Est. 1988. Tel: 01568 616677; fax - same; mobile -

07710 297602. UKIC. Registered with the Museums and Galleries Commission. Open 8.45-5.30, Sat. and other times by appointment. *Antique and fine furniture restorations including re-construction, veneering, carving, turning, French and wax polishing, re-upholstery, rush and cane seating.*

Ludovic Potts Restorations

Unit 1/1A, Haddenham Business Park, Station Rd., Haddenham, Ely, Cambs. CB6 3XD. Tel: 01353 741537; fax - 01353 741822; e-mail - mail@restorers.co.uk. BAFRA.

The Real Wood Furniture Company

London House, 16 Oxford St, Woodstock, Oxon. OX20 1TS. (Chris Baylis). Tel: 01993 813887; fax - 01993 812379; e-mail - info@ realwoodfurniture.co.uk; website - www.real woodfurniture.co.uk. Open Tues.-Sat. 10.30-5.30, Sun. 11-5. *Large stock of superb hand crafted country furniture in traditional antique styles - solid oak, ash and cherry. Tables, dressers etc made to order. Large range of rush seated, Windsor and kitchen style chairs.* VAT: Stan.

Rectory Bungalow Workshop

Station Rd., Elton, Bingham, Notts. NG13 9LF. (E.M. Mackie) Est. 1981. Tel: 01949 850878. Open by appointment. *Restorations - cane and rush seating, painted furniture.*

Riches

Wixamtree, 69 Wood Lane, Cottonend, Beds. MK45 3AP. (R.J. Jennings). Est. 1980. Tel: 01234 742121; e-mail - riches.upholstery@ntlworld. com. *Re-upholstery, repairs and re-caning.*

Raymond Robertson - Tolpuddle Antique Restorers

The Stables, Southover House, Tolpuddle, Dorchester, Dorset. DT2 7HF. Tel: 01305 848739. West Dean/BADA Award Winner. *Furniture, clock and barometer cases, marquetry, veneering and boulle work, lacquer, lacquer, japanning and gilding, insurance work undertaken.*

Romark Ltd

Unit 3 Shaftesbury Industrial Centre, Ickneild Way, Letchworth, Herts. SG6 1HE. (Mark Tracy and Robert Helder). Tel: 01462 684855; fax - 01462 684833; e-mail - romarkltd@aol.com. Open 7.30-4. *Antique furniture restoration, bespoke cabinet making and specialist woodworking. On site restoration to panelling and listed buildings.*

R.S. Rust (Replicas)

83 Main Rd., Kesgrave, Ipswich, Suffolk. IP5 1AF. Est. 1977. Tel: 01473 623092; e-mail - bobandedwina@onetel.net.uk. Open Tues. and Thurs. 9-5, or by appointment. *Replica hardwood furniture. Trade only.*

David A. Sayer - Courtlands Restorations

Courtlands, Park Rd., Banstead, Surrey. SM7 3EF. Est. 1985. Tel: 01737 352429; fax - 01737 373255; e-mail - dsayer@courtlands98.freeserve. co.uk; website - www.antiquerestoration surrey.com. BAFRA. Open 8-5, Sat. and Sun. by appointment. *Comprehensive restoration service including repairs, polishing, carving, turning, veneering, gilding. Metal parts - replacement or repair.*

Michael Schryver Antiques Ltd

The Granary, 10 North Street, Dorking, Surrey. RH4 1DN. Est. 1970. Tel: 01306 881110. Open 8.30-5.30, Sat. 8-12. *Cabinet work, polishing, upholstery, metal work.* VAT: Stan/Spec.

Phillip Slater

93 Hewell Rd., Barnt Green, Worcs. B45 8NL. Tel: 0121 445 4942. BAFRA.

Alun Courtney Smith

45 Windmill Rd., Brentford, Middx. TW8 0QQ. Tel: 020 8568 5249; fax - same. BAFRA.

Eric Smith - Antique Furniture Restorations

The Church, Park Rd., Darwen, Lancs. BB3 2LD. Tel: 01254 776222; e-mail - workshop@ ericsmithrestorations.co.uk; website - www. ericsmithrestorations.co.uk. BAFRA. UKIC. Conservation Register Museums & Galleries Commission. Open 9-6. *Restoration of longcase clocks and furniture. Comprehensive conservation and restoration of fine furniture.*

Alan & Kathy Stacey Tea Caddies & Fine Boxes LAPADA

Yeovil, Somerset. Tel: 01963 441333; home - same; fax - 01963 441330; mobile - 07810 058078; website - www.antiqueboxes.uk.com. BAFRA. Open every day by appointment. *Conservation, specialising in tea caddies, fine boxes, objects, tortoiseshell, ivory, MOP, Shagreen, horn, bone, exotic timber items. Worldwide collection and delivery, sales, maintenance of existing collections. Consultancy, valuations, search.* LOC: 2 miles from A303. Own parking. Collection service from station. VAT: Stan.

Julian Stanley Woodcarving - Furniture
Unit 5 Bourton Link, Bourton Industrial Park, Bourton-on-the-Water, Glos. GL54 2HQ. Est. 1983. Tel: 01451 822577; fax - same; e-mail - julian@julianstanley-woodcarvingfurniture.co.uk; website - www.julianstanley-wood carvingfurniture.co.uk. MCA. *Carved furniture - the classical work of the 18th C is re-created alongside contemporary designs, figure work and architectural pieces. Showroom on site includes contemporary paintings and sculpture.* VAT: Stan/Spec.

Robert Tandy Restoration
Lake House Barn, Lake Farm, Colehouse Lane, Kenn, Clevedon. Somerset. BS21 6TQ. Est. 1987. Tel: 01275 875014. BAFRA. *Furniture restoration especially 17th-19th C longcase clock cases; French polishing and traditional oil and wax finishing.* VAT: Stan.

Thakeham Furniture
Marehill Rd., Pulborough, West Sussex. RH20 2DY. (Timothy Chavasse). Est. 1984. Tel: 01798 872006; mobile - 07803 086828. Open 9-5. CL: Sat. *Cabinet work, veneer repairs, wax and French polishing, turning, marquetry, carving, etc.* LOC: 1 mile east of Pulborough next to White Horse Inn.

Titian Studio
32 Warple Way, Acton, London W3 0DJ (Rodrigo and Rosaria Titian). Est. 1963. Tel: 020 8222 6600; fax - 020 8749 2220; e-mail - enquiries@titianstudios.co.uk; website - www.titianstudios.co.uk. BAFRA. Open 8.30-5.30. *Carving, gilding, lacquer, painted furniture, French polishing, japanning.*

Treen Antiques
Treen House, 72 Park Rd., Prestwich, Manchester, Lancs. M25 0FA. (Simon J Feingold). Est. 1988. Tel: 0161 720 7244; fax - same; mobile - 07973 471185; e-mail - simonfeingold@hotmail.com; website - www.treenantiques.com. GADAR. RFS. FHS. UKIC. Open by appointment. *Conservation and restoration of all antique furniture (including vernacular) and woodwork, with emphasis on preserving original finish. Research undertaken, housekeeping advice, environmental monitoring and all aspects of conservation. Furniture assessment and advice on purchase and sales. Courses in restoration work held on request. Listed in Bonham's Directory.*

Neil Trinder Furniture Restoration
Burrowlee House, Broughton Road, Hillsborough, Sheffield, South Yorks. S6 2AS. Tel: 0114 2852428. *Boulle, gilding, marquetry, carving, upholstery, fine furniture.*

William Trist
135 St Leonard's St., Edinburgh, Scotland. EH8 9RB. Est. 1978. Tel: 0131 667 7775; fax - 0131 667 4333. BAFRA. Open Mon.-Fri. 8-6. *Furniture restoration and conservation; cabinet making, desk leathers, architectural mouldings, French polishing, cane and rush seating, traditional upholstery; chair making; stock of 18th-19th C furniture held; collection and delivery.* LOC: Southside with easy parking.

Tony Vernon
15 Follett Rd., Topsham, Devon. EX3 0JP. Est. 1975. Tel: 01392 874635; e-mail - tonyvernon@antiquewood.co.uk; website - www.antiquewood.co.uk. BAFRA. *Furniture, cabinet making, upholstery, gilding, veneering, inlay and French polishing.*

Fabio Villani
Clover, Alves, Forres, Scotland. IV36 2RA. Tel: 01343 850007; mobile - 07990 694972; e-mail - fabio@fabiovillani.co.uk; website - www.fabiovillani.co.uk. BAFRA. *Consultation and tuition for conservation of gilded frames and sculptures, objets d'art, furniture and wooden fittings. Traditional finishes and patina imitation. Lectures.*

E.F. Wall
32 Church St. Woodbridge, Suffolk. IP12 1DH. (Libby Wall). Tel: 01394 610511; fax - same; mobile - 07885 374917; e-mail - e.f.wall@btinternet.co.uk; website - www.efwall.co.uk. Open 10-5.30. CL: Wed. *Makers of fine furniture.* VAT: Stan/Spec.

Barry J. Wateridge
Padouk, Portsmouth Rd., Bramshott Chase, Hindhead, Surrey. GU26 6DB. Tel: 01428 607235. *French polishing and antique furniture restorations.*

Weaver Neave and Daughter
17 Lifford St. Putney, London SW15 1NY. Est. 1977. Tel: 020 8785 2464. *Re-caning and re-rushing of antique furniture in traditional manner with traditional materials.*

Gerald Weir Antiques
Unit 1, Riverside Industrial Park, Wherstead Rd., Ipswich, Suffolk. 1PZ 8JX. Tel: 01473 692300; fax - 01473 692333; e-mail - geraldweirantiques@btinternet.com. Open by appointment.

Suppliers of reproduction oak and cherry country furniture, mainly for European and American markets. Trade Only.

Laurence Whitfield
The Old School, Winstone, Cirencester, Glos. GL7 7LP. Est. 1979. Tel: 01285 821342; e-mail - whit@onetel.net.uk. BAFRA. Open 8.30-6. *Conservation and restoration of fine English and Continental furniture.*

Wick Antiques
LAPADA

Fairlea House, 110-112 Marsh Lane, Lymington. Hants. SO41 8EE. Tel: 01590 677558; fax - same. *Furniture polishing, repairs, upholstery and re-gilding.*

Bryan Wigington - Antique Furniture Restoration
The Courtyard, 4 Hightown, Hay-on-Wye, Herefs. HR3 5AE. Est. 1961. Tel: 01497 820545 (24 hr.) Open any time by appointment. *Furniture conservation and restoration.* LOC: Behind Post Office.

Jonathan Wilbye
Blue Bell Farm, North Stainmore, Kirkby Stephen, Cumbria. CA17 4DY. Est. 1983. Tel: 01768 341715. Open by appointment. *Full*

restoration service including all carving, inlay, turning and polishing. Longcase clock cases a speciality. Free delivery in Cumbria, Yorkshire and Lancashire.

Peter Williams Antique Furniture Restoration
Silkmill House, 4 Charlton Rd., Tetbury, Glos. GL8. Tel: 01666 502311. *Early oak, period mahogany, walnut and country furniture. Woodturning, French polishing and wax finish, gold tooled leather. Insurance claims. Antiques bought and sold. Established over 25 years.*

GLASS

F.W. Aldridge Ltd
Unit 3 St John's Industrial Estate, Dunmow Rd., Takeley, Essex. CM22 6SP. (J.L. Garwood). Tel: 01279 874000/874001; fax - 01279 874002; e-mail - angela@fwaldridge.abel.co.uk; website - www.fwaldridgeglass.com. Open 9-5. *Antique glass restoration including removing chips; suppliers of Bristol blue glass liners and stoppers; makers of stems for glasses and claret jugs.*

The Antique Restoration Studio
See entry under Furniture.

(Top row) Fops, oak leaves and crown, George and the Dragon. (Bottom Row) Gilt oak leaves, Britannia with two small oak leaves above, tinned back oak leaves over pearl.

From an article entitled "Commemorative Buttons" by Gillian Meredith which appeared in the June 2002 issue of *Antique Collecting*. For more details and to subscribe see page 21.

INSURANCE AND FINANCE

Antique & Fine Art Finance Ltd
1 Farmhouse Court, Bowerhill Park, Melksham, Wilts. SN12 6FG. Tel: 01225 707480; mobile - 07970 651253. *Provision of finance facilities to the clients of antique and fine art dealers.*

Penelope Brittain.
The Old Stores, High St., Elmdon, Saffron Walden, Essex. CB11 4NL. Tel: 01763 837224; fax - 01763 838092; mobile - 07850 932894; e-mail - artservice@clara.net. *Professional valuations for insurance and probate, family division. Buying specific items or total refurbishments including architectural - fireplaces, doors. Advice on building up or scaling down collections and placing items for sale.*

London Market Insurance Brokers Ltd
Fifth Floor, London Underwriting Centre, 3 Minster Court, Mincing Lane. London EC3R 7DD. Tel: 020 7515 8600; fax - 020 7515 4866; e-mail - info@lmib.co.uk. *Specialists in all types of fine art, exhibition and memorabilia insurance.*

Shearwater Insurance Services Ltd incorporating Allen Flindall & Assoc. Ltd
Shearwater House, 8 Regent Gate, High St., Waltham Cross, Herts. EN8 7AE. Tel: 08700 718666; fax - 08700 750043; e-mail - enquiries @shearwater-insurance.co.uk. *Specialist insurance scheme for antique and fine art dealers, collectors, household and all risks insurance.*

Anthony Wakefield & Company Ltd
Suite C, South House, 21-37 South St., Dorking, Surrey. RH4 2JZ. Est. 1983. Tel: 01306 740555; fax - 01306 740770; e-mail - info@ anthonywakefield.com; website - www. anthonywakefield.com. Members IIB. *Fine art and household insurance brokers; special terms for collectors; exclusive antique and fine art dealers policy with Axa Insurance UK plc; exclusive Connoisseur household policy with dealers/fairs extension.*

Windsor Insurance Brokers
America House, 2 America Square, London EC3 2LU. Tel: 020 7133 1200; fax - 020 7133 1500. Lloyds Insurance Brokers. *Specialist Lloyd's brokers in antique and fine art dealers, fine art galleries, contemporary art galleries, restorers and conservators, antique centres, auctioneers and valuers "Heirloom" designed for dealers' own collections and household and all risks insurance brokers. Official brokers to LAPADA, BAFRA, The Fine Art Trade Guild, IDDA.*

IVORY

Coromandel
Leominster. Herefs. HR6 0HS. *See entry under Leominster, Herefs. in dealer listing.*

E. and C. Royall Antiques
See entry under Metalwork.

Alan & Kathy Stacey Tea Caddies & Fine Boxes
See entry under Furniture.

JEWELLERY AND SILVER

Eastbourne Engraving
See entry under Engraving.

Goldcare
5 Bedford St., Middlesborough, TS1 2LL. Tel: 01642 231343; website - www.goldcarerepairs. co.uk. *Jewellery repair, engraving, re-stringing, stone cutting. Restoration of silver and cutlery; brass, copper, pinchbeck restoration.* VAT: Stan.

LOCKS & KEYS

Bramah Security Centres Ltd
31 Oldbury Place, London W1U 5PT. Est. 1784. Tel: 020 7935 7147; fax - 020 7935 2779; e-mail - locksmiths@bramah.co.uk; website - www. bramah.co.uk. M.L.A. Open 8.30-5.30, Sat. 9-1. *Keys cut to old locks; old locks opened; repair of old locks; new locks made to an old design; original Bramah locks dated. Quotation provided. Overseas work undertaken.* LOC: Near Baker Street tube station. VAT: Stan.

METALWORK

Rupert Harris Conservation
Studio 5c, 1 Fawe St., London E14 6PD. Est. 1982. Tel: 020 7987 6231/7515 2020; fax - 020 7987 7994; e-mail - enquiries@rupertharris.com; website - www.rupertharris.com. UKIC. IIC. NACE. SPAB. ICOM. Open by appointment. *Conservation of fine metalwork and sculpture including bronze, lead, zinc and electrotype; chandeliers, lanterns, gold and silver, fine ironwork, arms and armour, ecclesiastical metalwork, casting, replication and gilding; consultancy and maintenance. Appointed metalwork advisors to the National Trust for England and Wales.*

Optimum Brasses

7 Castle St., Bampton, Devon. EX16 9NS. (Robert and Rachel Byles). Est. 1981. Tel: 01398 331515; fax - 01398 331164; e-mail - brass@obida.com; website - www.obida.com. Open 9-1 and 2-4, Sat. and other times by appointment. *Over 5,000 replica brass handles etc. for antique furniture. Copying service.* LOC: On Wiveliscombe road. VAT: Stan.

Plowden & Smith Ltd

See entry under Art.

E. and C. Royall Antiques

10 Waterfall Way, Medbourne, Leics. LE16 8EE. Est. 1981. Tel: 01858 565744. Open 9-5. *Restorations - English and Oriental furniture, bronzes, ivories, brass including inlay work, metalware, woodcarving, French polishing.* VAT: Stan.

H.E. Savill Period Furniture Fittings

9-12 St Martin's Place, Scarborough, North Yorks. YO11 2QH. Tel: 01723 373032; fax - 01723 376984. Open 9-5.30. *Period brass cabinet fittings.* VAT: Stan. *Trade Only.*

Shawlan Antiques Metal Restorers

LAPADA

Croydon/South London area. (Shawn Parmakis). Est. 1976. Tel: 020 8684 5082; fax - same. Open 9-9. *High quality restoration of metalware, using traditional methods and materials. Over 25 years experience.*

MUSICAL INSTRUMENTS

J V Pianos & Cambridge Pianola

85 High St.,Landbeach, Cambridge, Cambs. CB4 8DR. (Tom Poole) Est. 1972. Tel: 01223 861348/861408; fax - 01223 441276; e-mail - ftpoole@talk21.com; website - www.cambridge pianolacompany.co.uk. Open Mon.-Fri., prior telephone call advisable, or by appointment. *Restoration and sales of period pianos, pianolas and player pianos; music rolls, repair materials, books and accessories.*

PHOTOGRAPHY

Gerry Clist Photography

Unit 235 Webheath Workshops, Netherwood St. London NW6 2JX. Est. 1991. Tel: 020 7691 3200; mobile - 07798 838839; e-mail - gerry@gerryclist.biz; website - www. gerryclist.biz. Open 10-6. *Specialising in sculptures, antiques and works of art photography - studio and location.*

REPRODUCTION STONEWORK

Hampshire Gardencraft

Rake Industries, Rake, Nr. Petersfield, Hants. GU31 5DR. Est. 1984. Tel: 01730 895182; fax - 01730 893216; e-mail - sales@hampshire-gardencraft.com; website - www.hampshire-gardencraft.com *Manufacturers of antiqued garden ornaments, troughs and pots in reconstituted stone in an old Cotswold stone finish. Many designs, catalogue available.*

Lucas Garden Statuary

Firsland Park Estate, Henfield Road, Albourne, West Sussex. BN6 9JJ. Tel: 01273 494931; fax - 01273 495125; e-mail - trade@lucasstone.co.uk; website - www.lucasstone.co.uk. *Manufacturers of Lucas Stone since 1970, huge range of aged reconstituted stone statuary. Available in two unique finishes, original classical and contempory designs. Large full colour catalogue available.*

SUPPLIERS

C. and A.J. Barmby
140 Lavender Hill, Tonbridge, Kent. TA9 2NJ. (Chris and Angela Barmby). Est. 1980. Tel: 01732 771590; fax - same; e-mail - Bookpilot@ aol.com. Open by appointment. *Suppliers of display stands in wire; reference books and catalogues on antiques and antiquarian books. Mail order service.* VAT: Stan.

Dauphin Museum Services Ltd
PO Box 602, Oxford, Oxon. OX44 9LU. (John Harrison-Banfield). Est. 1985. Tel: 01865 343542; fax - 01865 343307. Open 9-5, Sat. by appointment. Please telephone for directions. *Design and manufacture of stands, mounts, cabinets and environmental cases. Mounting service. Acrylic display stands - other materials utilised include glass, wood, metal, stone, marble, brass and bronze. Free mail order catalogue available.*

Just Bros. and Co
Roeder House, Vale Rd., London N4 1QA. Tel: 020 8880 2505; fax - 020 8802 0062; e-mail - just@freenet.co.uk. Member British Jewellery and Giftware Federation Ltd. Open 9-5, Fri. 9-12.30. *One of the largest suppliers of quality jewellery and presentation cases in Europe. Catalogue on request.*

Marshall Brass
Keeling Hall Rd., Foulsham, Norfolk. NR20 5PR. Tel: 01362 684105; fax - 01362 684280; e-mail - admin@marshall-brass.com; website - www. marshall-brass.com. GMC. *Suppliers of quality period furniture fittings in brass and iron.*

Martin and Co. Ltd
119 Camden St., Birmingham, West Midlands. B1 3DJ. Tel: 0121 233 2111; fax - 0121 236 0488; website - www.martin.co.uk-onlinecatalogue. ASFI. GAI. Open 9-5.30. CL: Sat. *Cabinet hardware supplied - handles, locks, hinges, castors etc.* LOC: Jewellery Quarter. *Trade Only.*

Alan Morris Wholesale
Stonecourt, Townsend, Nympsfield, Glos. GL10 3UF. Tel: 01453 861069. *Display stands - coated wire, plastic, acrylic and wood for plates, cups, saucers, bowls etc; wire and disc; jewellery boxes, polishing and cleaning cloths, peelable white labels and strung tickets. Mail order available.* VAT: Stan.

Relics of Witney Ltd
35 Bridge St., Witney, Oxon. OX28 1DA. Est. 1987. Tel: 01993 704611; website - www.tryrelics.co.uk. Open 9-5. *Suppliers of furniture restoration materials, brass castors, handles, locks, waxes and polish, upholstery and caning requisites, Farrow & Ball and reproduction paints, stencils etc. Mail order also. Online catalogue.* LOC: Main road.

J. Shiner and Sons Ltd
8 Windmill St., London W1T 2JE. Tel: 020 7636 0740; fax - 020 7580 0740. *Suppliers of brass handles, castors, locks, brass grills and leathers.*

Suffolk Brass
2 & 3 Victoria Way, Exmouth, Devon. EX8 1EW. (Mark Peters). Est. 1987. Tel: 01395 272846; fax - 01395 276688. Open 8.30-5. CL: Sat. *Period replica cabinet fittings. Catalogue £5.* VAT: Stan. *Trade Only.*

The Victorian Ring Box Company
Unit 1, Fleetside, Gatehouse of Fleet, Kirkcudbrightshire, Scotland. DG7 2JY. (The Franca Bruno Company). Est. 1990. Tel: 01557 814466/814054; fax - same; e-mail - franca mbruno@hotmail.com. Open by appointment. *Manufacturers and distributors of high quality antique style presentation boxes; also available with sterling silver tops and in tartan.*

TEXTILES

The Textile Conservancy Company Ltd
Unit 3A Pickhill Business Centre, Smallhythe Road, Tenterden, Kent. TN30 7LZ. Est. 1997. Tel: 01580 761600; fax - same; e-mail - alex@textile-conservation.co.uk; website - www. textile-conservation.co.uk. UKIC. *Cleaning and repair of historic textiles, tapestries and rugs. Professional advice on correct storage and display.*

The Textile Restoration Studio
2 Talbot Rd., Bowdon, Altrincham, Cheshire. WA14 3JD. (Jacqueline and Michael Hyman). Est. 1982. Tel: 0161 928 0020; fax - same; websites - www.textilerestoration.co.uk and www.conservationconsortium.com. Conservation Register. UK Institute for Conservation. *Cleaning and repair of all antique textiles including tapestries, samplers, canvas work, beadwork, lace, costume, ecclesiastical vestments and furnishings, dolls and fans. Mail order catalogue of specialist textile conservation materials (free with large stamped addressed envelope).*

Alan & Kathy Stacey Tea Caddies & Fine Boxes
See entry under Furniture.

Robert Mullis Rocking Restoration Services Ltd
55 Berkeley Rd., Wroughton, Swindon, Wilts. SN4 9BN. Tel: 01793 813583; fax - 01793 813577; e-mail - robert@rockinghorses. freeserve.co.uk; website - www.rocking horsemaker.com. BTG. Strictly by appointment. *Full or partial restorations of antique horses, some wooden toy restoration. Traditional methods and materials used. Collection and delivery. New rocking horses made in five sizes, commissions undertaken.*

Tobilane Designs
The Toyworks, Holly House, Askham, Penrith, Cumbria. CA10 2PG. (Paul and Elaine Commander). Est. 1985. Tel: 01931 712077; e-mail - info@thetoyworks.co.uk; website - www.thetoyworks.co.uk. Open Wed - Sat. 10-5, Sun. 11-4. *Traditional toymakers and restorers of old toys including rocking horses and teddies. Identification and valuation service.* LOC: Opposite Queen's Head public house, village centre, 5 miles south of Penrith. VAT: Stan.

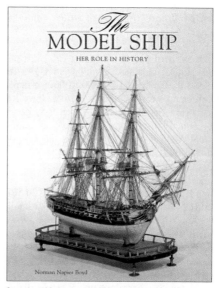

ALPHABETICAL LIST OF TOWNS AND VILLAGES AND COUNTIES UNDER WHICH THEY ARE LISTED.

A

Abbots Leigh, Somerset.
Aberdeen, Scotland.
Aberdour, Scotland.
Aberfeldy, Scotland.
Aberford, Yorks. West.
Abernyte, Scotland.
Aberystwyth, Wales.
Abinger Hammer, Surrey.
Abridge, Essex.
Accrington, Lancs.
Acrise, Kent.
Alcester, Warks.
Aldeburgh, Suffolk.
Alderley Edge, Cheshire.
Aldermaston, Berks.
Alderney, Alderney, Channel Islands.
Alford, Lincs.
Alfreton, Derbys.
Alfriston, Sussex East.
Allington, Lincs.
Allonby, Cumbria.
Alnwick, Northumbs.
Alresford, Hants.
Alrewas, Staffs.
Alsager, Cheshire.
Alston, Cumbria.
Alton, Hants.
Altrincham, Cheshire.
Amersham, Bucks.
Ampthill, Beds.
Andover, Hants.
Angmering, Sussex West.
Ansley, Warks.
Antrim, Co. Antrim, Northern Ireland.
Appledore, Kent.
Ardingly, Sussex West.
Armagh, Co. Armagh, Northern Ireland.
Arthingworth, Northants.
Arundel, Sussex West.
Ascot, Berks.
Ascott-under-Wychwood, Oxon.
Ash, Kent.
Ash Vale, Surrey.
Ashbourne, Derbys.
Ashburton, Devon.
Ashby-de-la-Zouch, Leics.

Ashford, Kent.
Ashtead, Surrey.
Ashurst, Kent.
Aston Clinton, Bucks.
Aston Tirrold, Oxon.
Atcham, Shrops.
Attleborough, Norfolk.
Atworth, Wilts.
Auchterarder, Scotland.
Auldearn, Scotland.
Axminster, Devon.
Aylesby, Lincs.
Aylsham, Norfolk.

B

Bagshot, Surrey.
Baildon, Yorks. West.
Bakewell, Derbys.
Balcombe, Sussex West.
Baldock, Herts.
Balfron, Scotland.
Ballater, Scotland.
Ballinamallard, Co. Fermanagh, Northern Ireland.
Ballymena, Co. Antrim, Northern Ireland.
Balsham, Cambs.
Bampton, Devon.
Bangor, Wales.
Barham, Kent.
Barkham, Berks.
Barley Mow, Northants.
Barlow, Derbys.
Barmouth, Wales.
Barnard Castle, Durham.
Barnet, Herts.
Barnstaple, Devon.
Barnt Green, Worcs.
Barrington, Somerset.
Barry, Wales.
Barton, Cambs.
Barton, Cheshire.
Basingstoke, Hants.
Bath, Somerset.
Batheaston, Somerset.
Batley, Yorks. West.
Battlesbridge, Essex.
Baythorne End, Essex.
Beaconsfield, Bucks.
Beauly, Scotland.
Beaumaris (Anglesey), Wales.

Beccles, Suffolk.
Beckenham, Kent.
Bedale, Yorks. North.
Bedford, Beds.
Bedingfield, Suffolk.
Beech, Hants.
Beer, Devon.
Beeston, Notts.
Beetham, Cumbria.
Belfast, Co. Antrim, Northern Ireland.
Belper, Derbys.
Bembridge, Isle of Wight.
Bentley, Suffolk.
Bere Regis, Dorset.
Berkeley, Glos.
Berkhamsted, Herts.
Berwick-upon-Tweed, Northumbs.
Bessacarr, Yorks. South.
Betchworth, Surrey.
Bethesda, Wales.
Beverley, Yorks. East.
Bewdley, Worcs.
Bexley, Kent.
Bibury, Glos.
Bicester, Oxon.
Bideford, Devon.
Biggleswade, Beds.
Billingham, Durham.
Billingshurst, Sussex West.
Bilsington, Kent.
Binfield, Berks.
Birchington, Kent.
Birdbrook, Essex.
Birkenhead, Merseyside.
Birmingham, West Mids.
Bishop's Castle, Shrops.
Bishop's Stortford, Herts.
Bishops Cleeve, Glos.
Blackburn, Lancs.
Blackmore, Essex.
Blackpool, Lancs.
Bladon, Oxon.
Blaenau Ffestiniog, Wales.
Blair Atholl, Scotland.
Blairgowrie, Scotland.
Blakeney, Glos.
Blandford Forum, Dorset.

Bletchingley, Surrey.
Blewbury, Oxon.
Bloxham, Oxon.
Blythburgh, Suffolk.
Bodicote, Oxon.
Bodmin, Cornwall.
Bodorgan (Anglesey), Wales.
Bolton, Lancs.
Bolton Abbey, Yorks. North.
Bolton-by-Bowland, Lancs.
Borehamwood, Herts.
Boroughbridge, Yorks. North.
Boscastle, Cornwall.
Boston, Lincs.
Boston Spa, Yorks. West.
Botley, Hants.
Bottisham, Cambs.
Boughton, Kent.
Bourne, Lincs.
Bourne End, Bucks.
Bournemouth, Dorset.
Bowdon, Cheshire.
Bower Ashton, Somerset.
Bowness on Windermere, Cumbria.
Brackley, Northants.
Bradford, Yorks. West.
Bradford-on-Avon, Wilts.
Bradwell, Derbys.
Brambridge, Hants.
Bramley, Surrey.
Brampton, Cambs.
Brampton, Cumbria.
Brancaster Staithe, Norfolk.
Brandsby, Yorks. North.
Branksome, Dorset.
Brasted, Kent.
Braunton, Devon.
Brecon, Wales.
Brentwood, Essex.
Brereton, Staffs.
Brewood, Staffs.
Bridge of Earn, Scotland.
Bridgend, Wales.
Bridgnorth, Shrops.
Bridlington, Yorks. East.

Bridport, Dorset.
Brierfield, Lancs.
Brightlingsea, Essex.
Brighton, Sussex East.
Brinklow, Warks.
Brinkworth, Wilts.
Bristol, Glos.
Brixham, Devon.
Broadstairs, Kent.
Broadway, Worcs.
Brockenhurst, Hants.
Brodick and Whiting Bay, Scotland.
Bromley, Kent.
Brook, Hants.
Broseley, Shrops.
Broughton Astley, Leics.
Bruton, Somerset.
Buckingham, Bucks.
Budby, Notts.
Budleigh Salterton, Devon.
Bungay, Suffolk.
Burford, Oxon.
Burgess Hill, Sussex West.
Burghfield Common, Berks.
Burlton, Shrops.
Burneston, Yorks. North.
Burnham Market, Norfolk.
Burnham-on-Sea, Somerset.
Burnley, Lancs.
Burscough, Lancs.
Burton Salmon, Yorks. North.
Burton-upon-Trent, Staffs.
Burwash, Sussex East.
Burwell, Cambs.
Bury, Lancs.
Bury St. Edmunds, Suffolk.
Bushey, Herts.
Bushmills, Co. Antrim, Northern Ireland.
Buxton, Derbys.

C

Cadnam, Hants.
Caernarfon, Wales.
Caerphilly, Wales.
Caistor, Lincs.
Callington, Cornwall.
Calne, Wilts.
Camborne, Cornwall.
Cambridge, Cambs.

Cambridge, Glos.
Camelford, Cornwall.
Canonbie, Scotland.
Canterbury, Kent.
Cardiff, Wales.
Carhampton, Somerset.
Carlisle, Cumbria.
Carlton-on-Trent, Notts.
Carmarthen, Wales.
Carrefour Selous, St. Lawrence, Jersey, Channel Islands.
Carrickfergus, Co. Antrim, Northern Ireland.
Carshalton, Surrey.
Cartmel, Cumbria.
Castle Ashby, Northants.
Castle Cary, Somerset.
Castle Donington, Leics.
Castletown, Isle of Man.
Cavendish, Suffolk.
Caversham, Berks.
Cawood, Yorks. North.
Ceres, Scotland.
Cerne Abbas, Dorset.
Chacewater, Cornwall.
Chagford, Devon.
Chale, Isle of Wight.
Chalfont St. Giles, Bucks.
Chalford, Glos.
Chalgrove, Oxon.
Chard, Somerset.
Cheadle Hulme, Cheshire.
Cheam, Surrey.
Cheltenham, Glos.
Chepstow, Wales.
Cherhill, Wilts.
Chertsey, Surrey.
Chesham, Bucks.
Chester, Cheshire.
Chesterfield, Derbys.
Chichester, Sussex West.
Chilcompton, Somerset.
Chilton, Oxon.
Chippenham, Wilts.
Chipping Campden, Glos.
Chipping Norton, Oxon.
Chipping Sodbury, Glos.
Chirk, Wales.

Chislehurst, Kent.
Chittering, Cambs.
Chobham, Surrey.
Chorley, Lancs.
Christchurch, Dorset.
Christian Malford, Wilts.
Church Stretton, Shrops.
Churt, Surrey.
Ciliau Aeron, Wales.
Cirencester, Glos.
Clare, Suffolk.
Cleethorpes, Lincs.
Cleobury Mortimer, Shrops.
Clevedon, Somerset.
Clitheroe, Lancs.
Clola by Mintlaw, Scotland.
Clutton, Somerset.
Clyst Honiton, Devon.
Coalville, Leics.
Cobham, Surrey.
Cockermouth, Cumbria.
Cocking, Sussex West.
Codford, Wilts.
Coggeshall, Essex.
Colchester, Essex.
Coldstream, Scotland.
Coleraine, Co. Londonderry, Northern Ireland.
Coleshill, Warks.
Coltishall, Norfolk.
Colwyn Bay, Wales.
Colyton, Devon.
Combe Martin, Devon.
Comber, Co. Down, Northern Ireland.
Comberton, Cambs.
Compton Dando, Somerset
Congleton, Cheshire.
Conisholme, Lincs.
Connor Downs, Cornwall.
Consett, Durham.
Conwy, Wales.
Cookham Rise, Berks.
Cookstown, Co. Tyrone, Northern Ireland.
Corbridge, Northumbs.
Corringham, Essex.
Corsham, Wilts.
Cottered, Herts.
Coulsdon, Surrey.
Cove, Scotland.
Coventry, West Mids.
Cowbridge, Wales.

Cowes, Isle of Wight.
Coxley, Somerset.
Cranborne, Dorset.
Cranbrook, Kent.
Craven Arms, Shrops.
Crawley, Hants.
Crayford, Kent.
Crediton, Devon.
Cremyll, Cornwall.
Crewe, Cheshire.
Crewkerne, Somerset.
Criccieth, Wales.
Crickhowell, Wales.
Cricklade, Wilts.
Cromarty, Scotland.
Cromer, Norfolk.
Crosby Ravensworth, Cumbria.
Cross Hills, Yorks. North.
Cross in Hand, Sussex East.
Croydon, Surrey.
Crudwell, Wilts.
Cuckfield, Sussex West.
Cullompton, Devon.

D

Danbury, Essex.
Darlington, Durham.
Darlton, Notts.
Dartmouth, Devon.
Darwen, Lancs.
Datchet, Berks.
Deal, Kent.
Debden, Essex.
Debenham, Suffolk.
Deddington, Oxon.
Deganwy, Wales.
Denby Dale, Yorks. West.
Depden, Suffolk.
Derby, Derbys.
Devizes, Wilts.
Disley, Cheshire.
Diss, Norfolk.
Ditchling, Sussex East.
Ditton Priors, Shrops.
Dobwalls, Cornwall.
Doncaster, Yorks. South.
Dorchester, Dorset.
Dorchester-on-Thames, Oxon.
Dorking, Surrey.
Dornoch, Scotland.
Dorridge, West Mids.
Douglas, Isle of Man.
Doune, Scotland.
Doveridge, Derbys.
Downham Market,

Norfolk.
Downton, Wilts.
Driffield, Yorks. East.
Drinkstone, Suffolk.
Droitwich, Worcs.
Duffield, Derbys.
Dulverton, Somerset.
Dundee, Scotland.
Dundonald, Co.
   Down, Northern
   Ireland.
Dunecht, Scotland.
Dunham-on-Trent,
   Notts.
Dunkeld, Scotland.
Dunsfold, Surrey.
Dunster, Somerset.
Durham, Durham.
Durrington, Wilts.
Duxford, Cambs.

E

Earl Shilton, Leics.
Earsham, Norfolk.
Easingwold, Yorks.
   North.
East Budleigh, Devon.
East Dereham,
   Norfolk.
East Grinstead, Sussex
   West.
East Hagbourne,
   Oxon.
East Molesey, Surrey.
East Peckham, Kent.
East Pennard,
   Somerset.
Eastbourne, Sussex
   East.
Ebrington, Glos.
Edenbridge, Kent.
Edgware, Middx.
Edinburgh, Scotland.
Elham, Kent.
Elstead, Surrey.
Ely, Cambs.
Empingham, Rutland.
Emsworth, Hants.
Enderby, Leics.
Enfield, Middx.
Epsom, Surrey.
Ermington, Devon.
Eversley, Hants.
Evesham, Worcs.
Ewell, Surrey.
Exeter, Devon.
Exmouth, Devon.
Exning, Suffolk.
Eye, Suffolk.

F

Fairford, Glos.

Fairlie, Scotland.
Fakenham, Norfolk.
Faldingworth, Lincs.
Falkirk, Scotland.
Falmouth, Cornwall.
Fareham, Hants.
Faringdon, Oxon.
Farnborough, Hants.
Farnham, Surrey.
Farningham, Kent.
Faversham, Kent.
Felixstowe, Suffolk.
Feniscowles, Lancs.
Filey, Yorks. North.
Finchingfield, Essex.
Finedon, Northants.
Finningham, Suffolk.
Fishguard, Wales.
Fishlake, Yorks. South.
Fladbury, Worcs.
Flamborough, Yorks.
   East.
Flaxton, Yorks. North.
Flimwell, Sussex East.
Flore, Northants.
Fochabers, Scotland.
Folkestone, Kent.
Fontmell Magna,
   Dorset.
Fordham, Cambs.
Fordingbridge, Hants.
Forest Row, Sussex
   East.
Forfar, Scotland.
Forres, Scotland.
Fortrose, Scotland.
Four Elms, Kent.
Four Oaks, West Mids.
Framlingham, Suffolk.
Frampton, Dorset.
Freshford, Somerset.
Freshwater, Isle of
   Wight.
Frinton-on-Sea, Essex.
Friockheim, Scotland.
Frome, Somerset.
Froxfield, Wilts.

G

Gainsborough, Lincs.
Gants Hill, Essex.
Gargrave, Yorks.
   North.
Gateshead, Tyne and
   Wear.
Gilberdyke, Yorks.
   East.
Gillingham, Dorset.
Glasgow, Scotland.
Glencarse, Scotland.
Glendoick, Scotland.
Glossop, Derbys.

Gloucester, Glos.
Godalming, Surrey.
Godney, Somerset.
Gomshall, Surrey.
Gorseinon, Wales.
Gosforth, Cumbria.
Gosforth, Tyne and
   Wear.
Gosport, Hants.
Goudhurst, Kent.
Grampound, Cornwall.
Grantham, Lincs.
Grasmere, Cumbria.
Grays, Essex.
Great Baddow, Essex.
Great Bookham,
   Surrey.
Great Glen, Leics.
Great Harwood,
   Lancs.
Great Malvern, Worcs.
Great Missenden,
   Bucks.
Great Salkeld,
   Cumbria.
Great Shefford, Berks.
Great Shelford,
   Cambs.
Great Torrington,
   Devon.
Great Waltham, Essex.
Great Yarmouth,
   Norfolk.
Green Hammerton,
   Yorks. North.
Greyabbey, Co. Down,
   Northern Ireland.
Greystoke, Cumbria.
Grimsby, Lincs.
Grimston, Leics.
Guildford, Surrey.
Gullane, Scotland.

H

Hacheston, Suffolk.
Haddenham, Bucks.
Haddington, Scotland.
Hadlow Down, Sussex
   East.
Hainault, Essex.
Hale, Cheshire.
Halesowen, West
   Mids.
Halesworth, Suffolk.
Halfway, Berks.
Halifax, Yorks. West.
Hallow, Worcs.
Halstead, Essex.
Hampton, Middx.
Hamstreet, Kent.
Harpenden, Herts.
Harpole, Northants.

Harrogate, Yorks.
   North.
Hartlepool, Durham.
Hartley Wintney,
   Hants.
Harwich, Essex.
Haslemere, Surrey.
Haslingden, Lancs.
Hastings, Sussex East.
Hatherleigh, Devon.
Hatton, Warks.
Haverfordwest, Wales.
Hawarden, Wales.
Hawes, Yorks. North.
Haworth, Yorks. West.
Hay-on-Wye, Wales.
Hayfield, Derbys.
Hayle, Cornwall.
Hayling Island, Hants.
Haywards Heath,
   Sussex West.
Heacham, Norfolk.
Headington, Oxon.
Headley, Hants.
Heanor, Derbys.
Heathfield, Sussex
   East.
Hebden Bridge, Yorks.
   West.
Helmsley, Yorks.
   North.
Helsby, Cheshire.
Hemel Hempstead,
   Herts.
Hemswell Cliff, Lincs.
Henfield, Sussex West.
Henley-in-Arden,
   Warks.
Henley-on-Thames,
   Oxon.
Hereford, Herefs.
Hertford, Herts.
Heswall, Merseyside.
High Wycombe,
   Bucks.
Highbridge, Somerset.
Hinckley, Leics.
Hindhead, Surrey.
Hingham, Norfolk.
Hitchin, Herts.
Hoby, Leics.
Hodnet, Shrops.
Holbeach, Lincs.
Holland-on-Sea,
   Essex.
Holmfirth, Yorks.
   West.
Holt, Norfolk.
Holt, Wales.
Holyhead (Anglesey),
   Wales.
Holywood, Co. Down,

Northern Ireland.
Honiton, Devon.
Hook, Hants.
Hook, Surrey.
Horley, Surrey.
Horncastle, Lincs.
Horton, Berks.
Houghton, Sussex
  West.
Hoveton, Norfolk.
Hoylake, Merseyside.
Hucknall, Notts.
Huddersfield, Yorks.
  West.
Hull, Yorks. East.
Hungerford, Berks.
Hunstanton, Norfolk.
Huntercombe, Oxon.
Huntingdon, Cambs.
Huntly, Scotland.
Hursley, Hants.
Hurst, Berks.
Hurst Green, Sussex
  East.
Hurstpierpoint, Sussex
  West.
Hythe, Kent.

I
Ibstock, Leics.
Ilchester, Somerset.
Ilfracombe, Devon.
Ilkley, Yorks. West.
Ilminster, Somerset.
Inchture, Scotland.
Ingatestone, Essex.
Innerleithen, Scotland.
Inverness, Scotland.
Ipswich, Suffolk.
Ironbridge, Shrops.
Islip, Northants.
Iver, Bucks.
Ixworth, Suffolk.

J
Jedburgh, Scotland.
Jesmond, Tyne and
  Wear.

K
Keighley, Yorks. West.
Kelling, Norfolk.
Kelvedon, Essex.
Kendal, Cumbria.
Keswick, Cumbria.
Kettering, Northants.
Kew, Surrey.
Kew Green, Surrey.
Kidderminster, Worcs.
Kidwelly, Wales.
Kilbarchan, Scotland.
Killamarsh, Derbys.

Killearn, Scotland.
Killin, Scotland.
Kilmacolm, Scotland.
Kilmarnock, Scotland.
Kilmichael Glassary,
  Scotland.
Kincardine O'Neil,
  Scotland.
King's Lynn, Norfolk.
Kingsbridge, Devon.
Kingsclere, Hants.
Kingsthorpe,
  Northants.
Kingston-on-Spey,
  Scotland.
Kingston-upon-
  Thames, Surrey.
Kingswear, Devon.
Kington, Herefs.
Kirk Deighton, Yorks.
  North.
Kirkby Lonsdale,
  Cumbria.
Kirkby Stephen,
  Cumbria.
Kirkcaldy, Scotland.
Kirkcudbright,
  Scotland.
Kirkmahoe, Scotland.
Kirton, Lincs.
Kirton in Lindsey,
  Lincs.
Knaresborough, Yorks.
  North.
Knebworth, Herts.
Knighton, Wales.
Knipton, Leics.
Knutsford, Cheshire.

L
Lake, Isle of Wight.
Laleham, Surrey.
Lamberhurst, Kent.
Lancaster, Lancs.
Landbeach, Cambs.
Langford, Notts.
Langford, Somerset.
Langholm, Scotland.
Langley Burrell, Wilts.
Largs, Scotland.
Launceston, Cornwall.
Lavenham, Suffolk.
Le Bourg Forest,
  Guernsey, Channel
  Islands.
Leagrave, Beds.
Leamington Spa,
  Warks.
Leatherhead, Surrey.
Leavenheath, Suffolk.
Lechlade, Glos.
Leckhampstead,

Berks.
Ledbury, Herefs.
Leeds, Yorks. West.
Leek, Staffs.
Leicester, Leics.
Leigh, Lancs.
Leigh, Staffs.
Leigh-on-Sea, Essex.
Leighton Buzzard,
  Beds.
Leiston, Suffolk.
Lennoxtown, Scotland.
Leominster, Herefs.
Lepton, Yorks. West.
Lewes, Sussex East.
Leyburn, Yorks. North.
Lichfield, Staffs.
Limpsfield, Surrey.
Lincoln, Lincs.
Lindfield, Sussex
  West.
Lindley, Yorks. West.
Linlithgow, Scotland.
Lisburn, Co. Antrim,
  Northern Ireland.
Liss, Hants.
Little Dalby, Leics.
Little Horsted, Sussex
  East.
Little Malvern, Worcs.
Littlebourne, Kent.
Littlehampton, Sussex
  West.
Littleton, Cheshire.
Littleton, Somerset.
Litton Cheney, Dorset.
Liverpool, Merseyside.
Llandeilo, Wales.
Llandudno, Wales.
Llandudno Junction,
  Wales.
Llandysul, Wales.
Llanelli, Wales.
Llanerchymedd
  (Anglesey), Wales.
Llanfair Caereinion,
  Wales.
Llangollen, Wales.
Llanrwst, Wales.
Lockerbie, Scotland.
Londonderry, Co.
  Londonderry,
  Northern Ireland.
Long Eaton, Derbys.
Long Marston, Warks.
Long Marton,
  Cumbria.
Long Melford,
  Suffolk.
Long Sutton, Lincs.
Longhaven, Scotland.
Looe, Cornwall.

Lostwithiel, Cornwall.
Loughborough, Leics.
Louth, Lincs.
Low Newton,
  Cumbria.
Lower Stondon, Beds.
Lubenham, Leics.
Ludlow, Shrops.
Lurgan, Co. Armagh,
  Northern Ireland.
Luton, Beds.
Lydford, Devon.
Lye, West Mids.
Lymington, Hants.
Lymm, Cheshire.
Lyndhurst, Hants.
Lyneham, Wilts.
Lynton, Devon.
Lytchett Minster,
  Dorset.
Lythe, Yorks. North.

M
Macclesfield,
  Cheshire.
Maidencombe, Devon.
Maidenhead, Berks.
Maidstone, Kent.
Maindee, Wales.
Maldon, Essex.
Malmesbury, Wilts.
Malton, Yorks. North.
Malvern Link, Worcs.
Manchester, Lancs.
Manfield, Yorks.
  North.
Manningford Bruce,
  Wilts.
Manningtree, Essex.
Mansfield, Notts.
Manton, Rutland.
Marazion, Cornwall.
Margate, Kent.
Market Bosworth,
  Leics.
Market Deeping,
  Lincs.
Market Drayton,
  Shrops.
Market Harborough,
  Leics.
Market Weighton,
  Yorks. East.
Markington, Yorks.
  North.
Marlborough, Wilts.
Marlesford, Suffolk.
Marlow, Bucks.
Marple Bridge,
  Cheshire.
Martlesham, Suffolk.
Martock, Somerset.

Masham, Yorks. North.
Matching Green, Essex.
Mathry, Wales.
Matlock, Derbys.
Melbury Osmond, Dorset.
Melksham, Wilts.
Melrose, Scotland.
Melton Mowbray, Leics.
Menai Bridge, Wales.
Mendlesham Green, Suffolk.
Menston, Yorks. West.
Mere, Wilts.
Merstham, Surrey.
Merton, Devon.
Middle Aston, Oxon.
Middleham, Yorks. North.
Middleton Village, Lancs.
Middleton-in-Teesdale, Durham.
Midgham, Berks.
Midhurst, Sussex West.
Midsomer Norton, Somerset.
Mildenhall, Suffolk.
Milford, Surrey.
Milford Haven, Wales.
Milton Keynes, Bucks.
Milton Lilbourne, Wilts.
Minchinhampton, Glos.
Mobberley, Cheshire.
Modbury, Devon.
Moira, Co. Armagh, Northern Ireland.
Monkton, Devon.
Monmouth, Wales.
Montrose, Scotland.
Morchard Bishop, Devon.
Morden, Surrey.
Morecambe, Lancs.
Moreton-in-Marsh, Glos.
Mountain Ash, Wales.
Moy, Co. Tyrone, Northern Ireland.
Much Wenlock, Shrops.
Murton, Wales.

N

Nantwich, Cheshire.
Narberth, Wales.

Nayland, Suffolk.
Neath, Wales.
Needham, Norfolk.
Needham Market, Suffolk.
Nelson, Lancs.
Nether Stowey, Somerset.
Nettlebed, Oxon.
New Bolingbroke, Lincs.
Newark, Notts.
Newbridge-on-Wye, Wales.
Newburgh, Scotland.
Newby Bridge, Cumbria.
Newcastle Emlyn, Wales.
Newcastle-under-Lyme, Staffs.
Newcastle-upon-Tyne, Tyne and Wear.
Newent, Glos.
Newhaven, Sussex East.
Newington, Kent.
Newmarket, Suffolk.
Newport, Essex.
Newport, Isle of Wight.
Newport, Wales.
Newport-on-Tay, Scotland.
Newton Abbot, Devon.
Newton St. Cyres, Devon.
Newton Tony, Wilts.
Newtonmore, Scotland.
Newtownabbey, Co. Antrim, Northern Ireland.
North Aston, Oxon.
North Berwick, Scotland.
North Cave, Yorks. East.
North Newton, Somerset.
North Petherton, Somerset.
North Shields, Tyne and Wear.
North Walsham, Norfolk.
North Wraxall, Wilts.
Northallerton, Yorks. North.
Northampton, Northants.
Northchapel, Sussex

West.
Northfleet, Kent.
Northleach, Glos.
Northwich, Cheshire.
Norton, Durham.
Norton, Yorks. North.
Nottingham, Notts.
Nutley, Sussex East.

O

Oakham, Rutland.
Oban, Scotland.
Ockbrook, Derbys.
Odiham, Hants.
Old Bedhampton, Hants.
Oldbury, West Mids.
Oldham, Lancs.
Ollerton, Notts.
Olney, Bucks.
Omagh, Co. Tyrone, Northern Ireland.
Orford, Suffolk.
Ormskirk, Lancs.
Osgathorpe, Leics.
Oswestry, Shrops.
Otford, Kent.
Otley, Yorks. West.
Outwell, Cambs.
Oxford, Oxon.
Oxted, Surrey.

P

Paignton, Devon.
Painswick, Glos.
Paisley, Scotland.
Pamphill, Dorset.
Pangbourne, Berks.
Parkstone, Dorset.
Pateley Bridge, Yorks. North.
Patrington, Yorks. East.
Peasenhall, Suffolk.
Pembroke, Wales.
Penistone, Yorks. South.
Penkridge, Staffs.
Penn, Bucks.
Penrith, Cumbria.
Penryn, Cornwall.
Penzance, Cornwall.
Pershore, Worcs.
Perth, Scotland.
Peterborough, Cambs.
Petersfield, Hants.
Petts Wood, Kent.
Petworth, Sussex West.
Pevensey Bay, Sussex East.
Pewsey, Wilts.

Pickering, Yorks. North.
Pittenweem, Scotland.
Plumley, Cheshire.
Plymouth, Devon.
Polegate, Sussex East.
Polperro, Cornwall.
Pontarddulais, Wales.
Pontefract, Yorks. West.
Pontllyfrii, Wales.
Poole, Dorset.
Porlock, Somerset.
Portaferry, Co. Down, Northern Ireland.
Portballintrae, Co. Antrim, Northern Ireland.
Porthcawl, Wales.
Porthmadog, Wales.
Portrush, Co. Antrim, Northern Ireland.
Portsmouth, Hants.
Portsoy, Scotland.
Potter Heigham, Norfolk.
Potterspury, Northants.
Potton, Beds.
Poulton-le-Fylde, Lancs.
Poundgate, Sussex East.
Poynton, Cheshire.
Preston, Lancs.
Prestwick, Scotland.
Princes Risborough, Bucks.
Puckeridge, Herts.
Puddletown, Dorset.
Pulborough, Sussex West.
Pwllheli, Wales.

Q

Queen Camel, Somerset.
Queniborough, Leics.
Quorn, Leics.

R

Rainford, Merseyside.
Rait, Scotland.
Ramsbury, Wilts.
Ramsey, Cambs.
Ramsgate, Kent.
Raughton Head, Cumbria.
Raveningham, Norfolk.
Ravenstonedale, Cumbria.
Rayleigh, Essex.

Reading, Berks.
Redbourn, Herts.
Redditch, Worcs.
Redhill, Surrey.
Redruth, Cornwall.
Reepham, Norfolk.
Reigate, Surrey.
Retford, Notts.
Richmond, Surrey.
Richmond, Yorks. North.
Rickmansworth, Herts.
Ringmer, Sussex East.
Ringstead, Norfolk.
Ringway, Cheshire.
Ringwood, Hants.
Ripley, Derbys.
Ripley, Surrey.
Ripon, Yorks. North.
Risby, Suffolk.
Robin Hood's Bay, Yorks. North.
Rochdale, Lancs.
Rochester, Kent.
Rolvenden, Kent.
Romiley, Cheshire.
Romsey, Hants.
Ross-on-Wye, Herefs.
Rothbury, Northumbs.
Rotherfield, Sussex East.
Rotherham, Yorks. South.
Rottingdean, Sussex East.
Rowlands Castle, Hants.
Roxwell, Essex.
Rugeley, Staffs.
Runfold, Surrey.
Rushden, Northants.
Ryde, Isle of Wight.
Rye, Sussex East.

S

Sabden, Lancs.
Saffron Walden, Essex.
Saintfield, Co. Down, Northern Ireland.
Salisbury, Wilts.
Saltaire, Yorks. West.
Saltcoats, Scotland.
Samlesbury, Lancs.
Sandbach, Cheshire.
Sanderstead, Surrey.
Sandgate, Kent.
Sandhurst, Berks.
Sandhurst, Kent.
Sandiacre, Notts.
Sandwich, Kent.
Sawbridgeworth,

Herts.
Saxmundham, Suffolk.
Scarborough, Yorks. North.
Scratby, Norfolk.
Screveton, Notts.
Scunthorpe, Lincs.
Seaford, Sussex East.
Seapatrick, Co. Down, Northern Ireland.
Seaton, Devon.
Sedbergh, Cumbria.
Seething, Norfolk.
Semley, Wilts.
Settle, Yorks. North.
Sevenoaks, Kent.
Shaftesbury, Dorset.
Shaldon, Devon.
Shanklin, Isle of Wight.
Shardlow, Derbys.
Sheffield, Yorks. South.
Shefford, Beds.
Shenfield, Essex.
Shenton, Leics.
Shepton Mallet, Somerset.
Sherborne, Dorset.
Shere, Surrey.
Sheringham, Norfolk.
Shifnal, Shrops.
Shipston-on-Stour, Warks.
Shoreham-by-Sea, Sussex West.
Shrewsbury, Shrops.
Sible Hedingham, Essex.
Sidcup, Kent.
Sidmouth, Devon.
Sileby, Leics.
Skenfrith, Wales.
Skipton, Yorks. North.
Slad, Glos.
Sleaford, Lincs.
Sleights, Yorks. North.
Snainton, Yorks. North.
Snape, Suffolk.
Solihull, West Mids.
Somersham, Cambs.
Somerton, Somerset.
Sonning-on-Thames, Berks.
South Brent, Devon.
South Harting, Sussex West.
South Molton, Devon.
South Petherton, Somerset.
South Shields, Tyne

and Wear.
Southampton, Hants.
Southborough, Kent.
Southend- on- Sea, Essex.
Southport, Merseyside.
Southwell, Notts.
Southwold, Suffolk.
Sowerby Bridge, Yorks. West.
Spalding, Lincs.
Spennithorne, Yorks. North.
St. Albans, Herts.
St. Andrews, Scotland.
St Helen Auckland, Durham.
St. Helier, Jersey, Channel Islands.
St. Ives, Cambs.
St. Lawrence, Jersey, Channel Islands.
St. Leonards-on-Sea, Sussex East.
St Mary, Jersey, Channel Islands.
St. Neots, Cambs.
St Ouen, Jersey, Channel Islands.
St. Peter Port, Guernsey, Channel Islands.
St Sampson, Guernsey, Channel Islands.
St. Saviour, Jersey, Channel Islands.
Stafford, Staffs.
Staines, Surrey.
Stalham, Norfolk.
Stamford, Lincs.
Standlake, Oxon.
Stanley, Scotland.
Stansted, Essex.
Stanton upon Hine Heath, Shrops.
Staplehurst, Kent.
Staunton Harold, Leics.
Staveley, Cumbria.
Stewarton, Scotland.
Stewartstown, Co. Tyrone, Northern Ireland.
Steyning, Sussex West.
Stickney, Lincs.
Stiffkey, Norfolk.
Stillington, Yorks. North.
Stirling, Scotland.
Stockbridge, Hants.
Stockbury, Kent.
Stockland, Devon.

Stockport, Cheshire.
Stockton-on-Tees, Durham.
Stoke Ferry, Norfolk.
Stoke-on-Trent, Staffs.
Stoke-sub-Hamdon, Somerset.
Storrington, Sussex West.
Stourbridge, West Mids.
Stow-on-the-Wold, Glos.
Stowmarket, Suffolk.
Stratford-upon-Avon, Warks.
Strathblane, Scotland.
Stratton, Cornwall.
Stretton-on-Fosse, Warks.
Sturminster Newton, Dorset.
Suckley, Worcs.
Sudbury, Suffolk.
Sunderland, Tyne and Wear.
Sundridge, Kent.
Surbiton, Surrey.
Sutton, Surrey.
Sutton Bonington, Notts.
Sutton Bridge, Lincs.
Sutton Coldfield, West Mids.
Sutton Valence, Kent.
Sutton-in-Ashfield, Notts.
Sutton-on-Sea, Lincs.
Swaffham, Norfolk.
Swafield, Norfolk.
Swanage, Dorset.
Swansea, Wales.
Swindon, Wilts.
Swinstead, Lincs.

T

Tacolneston, Norfolk.
Taddington, Glos.
Tadley, Hants.
Tarporley, Cheshire.
Tarvin, Cheshire.
Tarvin Sands, Cheshire.
Tattenhall, Cheshire.
Tattershall, Lincs.
Taunton, Somerset.
Tavistock, Devon.
Taynton, Oxon.
Tedburn St Mary, Devon.
Teddington, Middx.
Teignmouth, Devon.

Telford, Shrops.
Templeton, Wales.
Tenby, Wales.
Tenterden, Kent.
Tetbury, Glos.
Tetsworth, Oxon.
Tewkesbury, Glos.
Teynham, Kent.
Thame, Oxon.
Thames Ditton,
   Surrey.
Thaxted, Essex.
Thirsk, Yorks. North.
Thornbury, Glos.
Thornton-le-Dale,
   Yorks. North.
Tilston, Cheshire.
Tintern, Wales.
Titchfield, Hants.
Tockwith, Yorks.
   North.
Toddington, Beds.
Todenham, Glos.
Todmorden, Yorks.
   West.
Tonbridge, Kent.
Topsham, Devon.
Topsham, Devon.
Torquay, Devon.
Totnes, Devon.
Tottenhill, Norfolk.
Towcester, Northants.
Trawden, Lancs.
Trecastle, Wales.
Tregony, Cornwall.
Treharris, Wales.
Treorchy, Wales.
Tresillian, Cornwall.
Trevor, Wales.
Tring, Herts.
Troon, Scotland.
Truro, Cornwall.
Tunbridge Wells,
   Kent.
Tutbury, Staffs.
Tuxford, Notts.
Twickenham, Middx.
Twyford, Berks.
Twyford, Norfolk.
Tynemouth, Tyne and
   Wear.
Tywyn, Wales.

U

Uckfield, Sussex East.
Uffculme, Devon.
Ullapool, Scotland.
Ulverston, Cumbria.

Upper Largo,
   Scotland.
Uppingham, Rutland.
Upton-upon-Severn,
   Worcs.
Usk, Wales.
Uttoxeter, Staffs.
Uxbridge, Middx.

V

Valley, Wales.
Ventnor, Isle of Wight.

W

Wadebridge, Cornwall.
Wadhurst, Sussex
   East.
Wainfleet, Lincs.
Wakefield, Yorks.
   West.
Wallasey, Merseyside.
Wallingford, Oxon.
Walsall, West Mids.
Walsden, Yorks. West.
Walton-on-Thames,
   Surrey.
Walton-on-the-Hill
   and Tadworth,
   Surrey.
Wansford, Cambs.
Wantage, Oxon.
Wareham, Dorset.
Warfield, Berks.
Wargrave, Berks.
Warlingham, Surrey.
Warminster, Wilts.
Warrington, Cheshire.
Warwick, Warks.
Washington, Tyne and
   Wear.
Watchet, Somerset.
Waterlooville, Hants.
Watford, Herts.
Watlington, Oxon.
Wattisfield, Suffolk.
Waverton, Cheshire.
Weedon, Northants.
Weeford, Staffs.
Welling, Kent.
Wellingborough,
   Northants.
Wellington, Somerset.
Wells, Somerset.
Wells-next-the-Sea,
   Norfolk.
Welshpool, Wales.
Wendover, Bucks.
Wentworth, Yorks.

South.
West Auckland,
   Durham.
West Bridgford, Notts.
West Buckland,
   Somerset.
West Burton, Yorks.
   North.
West Byfleet, Surrey.
West Haddon,
   Northants.
West Kirby,
   Merseyside.
West Malling, Kent.
West Yatton, Wilts.
Westcliff-on-Sea,
   Essex.
Westerham, Kent.
Weston, Herts.
Weston-Super-Mare,
   Somerset.
Weybridge, Surrey.
Weymouth, Dorset.
Whaley Bridge,
   Derbys.
Whalley, Lancs.
Wheathampstead,
   Herts.
Whimple, Devon.
Whitby, Yorks. North.
Whitchurch, Bucks.
Whitchurch, Shrops.
White Colne, Essex.
White Roding, Essex.
Whitefield, Lancs.
Whitehaven, Cumbria.
Whithorn, Scotland.
Whitley Bay, Tyne and
   Wear.
Whitstable, Kent.
Whittington, Glos.
Whitwick, Leics.
Whixley, Yorks. North.
Wickham Bishops,
   Essex.
Wickham Market,
   Suffolk.
Wickwar, Glos.
Widnes, Cheshire.
Wigan, Lancs.
Wigtown, Scotland.
Willingham, Cambs.
Williton, Somerset.
Wilstead
   (Wilshamstead),
   Beds.
Wilstone, Herts.
Wilton, Wilts.

Wimborne Minster,
   Dorset.
Wincanton, Somerset.
Winchcombe, Glos.
Winchester, Hants.
Windermere, Cumbria.
Windsor and Eton,
   Berks.
Wing, Rutland.
Winslow, Bucks.
Wisbech, Cambs.
Witney, Oxon.
Wittersham, Kent.
Wiveliscombe,
   Somerset.
Woburn, Beds.
Woking, Surrey.
Wokingham, Berks.
Wolverhampton, West
   Mids.
Woodbridge,
   SuffolWoodbury,
   Devon.
Woodford Green,
   Essex.
Woodhall Spa, Lincs.
Woodlesford, Yorks.
   West.
Woodseaves, Staffs.
Woodstock, Oxon.
Woodville, Derbys.
Wooler, Northumbs.
Woolhampton, Berks.
Woolpit, Suffolk.
Worcester, Worcs.
Worsley, Lancs.
Wortham, Suffolk.
Worthing, Sussex
   West.
Wraysbury, Berks.
Wrentham, Suffolk.
Writtle, Essex.
Wroxham, Norfolk.
Wychbold, Worcs.
Wymeswold, Leics.
Wymondham, Leics.
Wymondham, Norfolk.

Y

Yarnton, Oxon.
Yazor, Herefs.
Yealmpton, Devon.
Yeovil, Somerset.
York, Yorks. North.
Yoxall, Staffs.
Yoxford, Suffolk.

Specialist Dealers' Index

Most antique dealers in Britain sell a wide range of goods from furniture, through porcelain and pottery, to pictures, prints and clocks. Much of the interest in visting antiques shops comes from this diversity. However, there are a number of dealers who specialise and the following is a list of these dealers. Most of them will stock a representative selection of the items found under their classification.

The name of the business, together with the area of London or the town and county under which the detailed entry can be found are given in the listing. Again we would like to repeat the advice given in the introduction that, if readers are looking for a particular item, they are advised to telephone first, before making a long journey.

CLASSIFICATIONS

Antiques Centres and Markets
Antiquarian Books
Antiquities
Architectural Items
Arms & Armour
Art Deco & Art Nouveau
Barometers - see also Clock Dealers
Beds
Brass (see Metalwork)
Bronzes
Carpets & Rugs
Cars & Carriages
Chinese Art - see Oriental
Church Furniture & Furnishings
Clocks & Watches
Coins & Medals
Dolls & Toys
Etchings & Engravings
Fire Related Items
Frames
Furniture-
  Continental (mainly French)
  Country
  Georgian
  Oak
  Pine
  Victorian
Garden Furniture, Ornaments & Statuary
Glass - see also Glass Domes &
  Paperweights
Glass Domes
Icons - see Russian Art
Islamic Art
Japanese Art - see Oriental
Jewellery - see Silver & Jewellery
Lighting

Maps & Prints
Metalware/work
Miniatures
Mirrors
Musical Boxes, Instruments & Literature
Nautical Instruments - see Scientific
Needlework - see Tapestries
Netsuke - see Oriental
Oil Paintings
Oriental Items
Paperweights
Photographs & Equipment
Porcelain & Pottery
Prints - see Maps
Rugs - see Carpets
Russian/Soviet Art
Scientific Instruments
Sculpture
Shipping Goods & Period Furniture for the
  Trade
Silver and Jewellery
Sporting Items & Associated Memorabilia
Sporting Paintings & Prints
Stamps
Tapestries, Textiles & Needlework
Taxidermy
Tools - including Needlework & Sewing
Toys - see Dolls
Trade Dealers - see Shipping Goods
Treen
Vintage Cars - see Carriages & Cars
Watercolours
Wholesale Dealers - see Shipping Goods
Wine Related Items

Antique Centres & Markets

Georgian Village Antiques Market, London E17.

The Angel Arcade, London N1.

Camden Passage Antiques Market and Pierrepont Arcade Antiques Centre, London N1.

The Fleamarket, London N1.

London Militaria Market, London N1.

The Mall Antiques Arcade, London N1.

Palmers Green Antiques Centre, London N13.

Hampstead Antique and Craft Emporium, London NW3.

Alfies Antique Market, London NW8.

Bermondsey Antiques Market, London SE1.

Greenwich Antiques Market, London SE10.

Sydenham Antiques Centre, London SE26.

Cobwebs, London SE9.

Northcote Road Antiques Market, London SW11.

Antiquarius, London SW3.

Bourbon-Hanby Antiques Centre, London SW3 .

Bond Street Antiques Centre, London W1.

Grays Antique Markets, London W1.

Admiral Vernon Antiques Market , London W11.

Arbras Gallery, London W11.

The Corner Portobello Antiques Supermarket, London W11.

Crown Arcade, London W11.

Kleanthous Antiques , London W11.

The Red Lion Antiques Arcade , London W11.

Roger's Antiques Gallery, London W11.

The Silver Fox Gallery (Portobello), London W11.

World Famous Portobello Market, London W11.

The Old Cinema Antique Department Store, London W4.

Kensington Church Street Antiques Centre, London W8.

Apple Market Stalls, London WC2.

Covent Garden Flea Market, London WC2.

The London Silver Vaults, London WC2.

Ampthill Antiques Emporium, Ampthill, Beds.

The Woburn Abbey Antiques Centre, Woburn, Beds.

Barkham Antique Centre, Barkham, Berks.

Great Grooms of Hungerford, Hungerford, Berks.

Hungerford Arcade, Hungerford, Berks.

Berkshire Antiques Centre, Midgham, Berks.

Moss End Antique Centre, Warfield, Berks.

Wokingham Antiques Centre, Wokingham, Berks.

Buck House Antique Centre, Beaconsfield, Bucks.

Buckingham Antiques Centre, Buckingham, Bucks.

Marlow Antique Centre, Marlow, Bucks.

The Antiques Centre at Olney, Olney, Bucks.

Well Cottage Antiques Centre, Princes Risborough, Bucks.

Antiques at .. Wendover Antiques Centre, Wendover, Bucks.

Winslow Antiques Centre, Winslow, Bucks.

Gwydir Street Antiques Centre, Cambridge, Cambs.

The Hive, Cambridge, Cambs.

Waterside Antiques Centre, Ely, Cambs.

Huntingdon Trading Post, Huntingdon, Cambs.

Fitzwilliam Antiques Centre, Peterborough, Cambs.

Knutsford Antiques Centre, Knutsford, Cheshire.

Northwich Antiques Centre, Northwich, Cheshire.

Tarporley Antique Centre, Tarporley, Cheshire.

Bodmin Antiques Centre, Bodmin, Cornwall.

Waterfront Antiques Market, Falmouth, Cornwall.

Chapel Street Antiques Arcade, Penzance, Cornwall.

The Coinage Hall Antiques Centre, Truro, Cornwall.

The Cumbrian Antiques Centre, Brampton, Cumbria.

Carlisle Antiques Centre, Carlisle, Cumbria.

Cockermouth Antiques Market, Cockermouth, Cumbria.

Alfreton Antiques Centre, Alfreton, Derbys.

Chappells Antiques Centre, Bakewell, Derbys.

Bradwell Antiques Centre, Bradwell, Derbys.

Heanor Antiques Centre, Heanor, Derbys.

Matlock Antiques and Collectables Centre, Matlock, Derbys.

Memory Lane Antiques Centre, Ripley, Derbys.

The Shambles, Ashburton, Devon.

North Devon Antiques Centre, Barnstaple, Devon.

Colyton Antiques Centre, Colyton, Devon.

The Antique Centre on the Quay, Exeter, Devon.

McBains Antiques, Exeter, Devon.

Phantique, Exeter, Devon.

The Quay Gallery Antiques Emporium, Exeter, Devon.

Honiton Antique Centre, Honiton, Devon.

St Leonards Antiques & Craft Centre, Newton Abbot, Devon.

Barbican Antiques Centre, Plymouth, Devon.

New Street Antique Centre, Plymouth, Devon.

Parade Antiques Market, Plymouth, Devon.

Sidmouth Antiques and Collectors Centre, Sidmouth, Devon.

The Furniture Antique Market, South Molton, Devon.

Topsham Quay Antiques Centre, Topsham, Devon.

Colliton Antique Centre, Dorchester, Dorset.

De Danann Antique Centre, Dorchester, Dorset.

Mr. Punch's Antique Market, Shaftesbury, Dorset.

Sherborne World of Antiques, Sherborne, Dorset.

SPECIALIST DEALERS

Battlesbridge Antique Centre, Battlesbridge, Essex.
Trinity Antiques Centre, Colchester, Essex.
Finchingfield Antiques Centre, Finchingfield, Essex.
Baddow Antique Centre, Great Baddow, Essex.
Gallerie Antiques, Hainault, Essex.
Townsford Mill Antiques Centre, Halstead, Essex.
Harwich Antiques Centre, Harwich, Essex.
Maldon Antiques and Collectors Market, Maldon, Essex.
Saffron Walden Antiques Centre, Saffron Walden, Essex.
Curio City, Southend- on- Sea, Essex.
Berkeley Antiques Market, Berkeley, Glos.
St. Nicholas Markets, Bristol, Glos.
Cheltenham Antique Market, Cheltenham, Glos.
Sixways Antique Centre, Cheltenham, Glos.
Cirencester Arcade, Cirencester, Glos.
Gloucester Antique Centre, Gloucester, Glos.
Jubilee Hall Antiques Centre, Lechlade, Glos.
Lechlade Arcade, Lechlade, Glos.
The Old Ironmongers Antiques Centre, Lechlade, Glos.
London House Antique Centre, Moreton-in-Marsh, Glos.
Windsor House Antiques Centre, Moreton-in-Marsh, Glos.
Durham House Antiques Centre, Stow-on-the-Wold, Glos.
Fox Cottage Antiques, Stow-on-the-Wold, Glos.
The Antiques Emporium, Tetbury, Glos.
Tewkesbury Antiques & Collectables Centre, Tewkesbury, Glos.
Appleton Eves Ltd, Alton, Hants.
Dolphin Quay Antique Centre, Emsworth, Hants.
Cedar Antiques Centre Ltd, Hartley Wintney, Hants.
Lymington Antiques Centre, Lymington, Hants.
Lyndhurst Antiques Centre, Lyndhurst, Hants.
The Folly Antiques Centre, Petersfield, Hants.
Samuels Spencers Antiques and Decorative Arts Emporium, Winchester, Hants.
Winchester Furniture, Winchester, Hants.
Hereford Antique Centre, Hereford, Herefs.
Chapel Walk Antique Centre, Leominster, Herefs.
Leominster Antiques Market, Leominster, Herefs.
Ross-on-Wye Antiques Gallery, Ross-on-Wye, Herefs.
Bushey Antiques Centre, Bushey, Herts.
Hertford Antiques, Hertford, Herts.
The Herts and Essex Antiques Centre, Sawbridgeworth, Herts.
By George! Antiques Centre, St. Albans, Herts.
Victoria Antiques, Ryde, Isle of Wight.

Beckenham Antiques & Collectors' Market, Beckenham, Kent.
Southdown House Antiques, Brasted, Kent.
Burgate Antique Centre, Canterbury, Kent.
Antiques at Cranbrook, Cranbrook, Kent.
Malthouse Arcade, Hythe, Kent.
Beehive, Petts Wood, Kent.
Barden House Antiques, Tonbridge, Kent.
Tunbridge Wells Antiques, Tunbridge Wells, Kent.
Castle Antiques Centre, Westerham, Kent.
Bolton Antique Centre, Bolton, Lancs.
Ironchurch Antiques Centre, Bolton, Lancs.
King's Mill Antique Centre, Burnley, Lancs.
Antiques and Crafts Centre, Chorley, Lancs.
Heskin Hall Antiques, Chorley, Lancs.
Belgrave Antique Centre, Darwen, Lancs.
Holden Wood Antiques Centre, Haslingden, Lancs.
The Assembly Rooms Market, Lancaster, Lancs.
G.B. Antiques Ltd, Lancaster, Lancs.
Lancaster Leisure Park Antiques Centre, Lancaster, Lancs.
Antiques Village, Manchester, Lancs.
The Antique Centre, Preston, Lancs.
Preston Antique Centre, Preston, Lancs.
Walter Aspinall Antiques, Sabden, Lancs.
Pendle Antiques Centre Ltd, Sabden, Lancs.
Leicester Antiques Warehouse, Leicester, Leics.
Oxford Street Antique Centre, Leicester, Leics.
Whitemoors Antiques and Fine Art, Shenton, Leics.
Portobello Row Antique & Collectors' Centre, Boston, Lincs.
Bourne Antiques & Arts, Bourne, Lincs.
Brownlow Antiques Centre, Faldingworth, Lincs.
Notions Antiques Centre, Grantham, Lincs.
Abbeygate Gallery & Antiques Centre, Grimsby, Lincs.
Astra House Antiques Centre, Hemswell Cliff, Lincs.
Hemswell Antique Centres, Hemswell Cliff, Lincs.
Great Expectations, Horncastle, Lincs.
The Trinity Centre, Horncastle, Lincs.
The Chapel Emporium Antique Centre, Long Sutton, Lincs.
Old Maltings Antique Centre, Louth, Lincs.
St. Martins Antiques Centre, Stamford, Lincs.
Phelps Antiques, Twickenham, Middx.
The Antiques & Collectors Centre (Diss), Diss, Norfolk.
Fakenham Antique Centre, Fakenham, Norfolk.
Le Strange Old Barns Antiques, Arts & Craft Centre, Hunstanton, Norfolk.
The Old Granary Antiques and Collectors Centre, King's Lynn, Norfolk.
Black Horse Antiques Centre, Norwich, Norfolk.

Cloisters Antique & Collectors Fair, Norwich, Norfolk.

Tombland Antiques Centre, Norwich, Norfolk.

Ringstead Village Antique Centre,, Ringstead, Norfolk.

Wells Antique Centre, Wells-next-the-Sea, Norfolk.

Antique and Collectors Fair, Wymondham, Norfolk.

Wymondham Antique and Collectors Centre, Wymondham, Norfolk.

Brackley Antique Cellar, Brackley, Northants.

E.K. Antiques, Finedon, Northants.

Finedon Antiques (Centre), Finedon, Northants.

The Village Antique Market, Weedon, Northants.

Antiques and Bric-a-Brac Market, Wellingborough, Northants.

Antiques Trade Space, Newark, Notts.

Castle Gate Antiques Centre, Newark, Notts.

Newark Antiques Centre, Newark, Notts.

Newark Antiques Warehouse, Newark, Notts.

Top Hat Antiques, Nottingham, Notts.

Antiques @ The George, Burford, Oxon.

Country Markets Antiques and Collectables, Chilton, Oxon.

Chipping Norton Antique Centre, Chipping Norton, Oxon.

Manchester House Antiques Centre, Chipping Norton, Oxon.

The Quiet Woman Antiques Centre, Chipping Norton, Oxon.

Station Mill Antiques Centre, Chipping Norton, Oxon.

Deddington Antiques Centre, Deddington, Oxon.

Friday Street Antique Centre (The Ferret), Henley-on-Thames, Oxon.

Antiques on High Ltd, Oxford, Oxon.

The Swan at Tetsworth, Tetsworth, Oxon.

The Lamb Arcade, Wallingford, Oxon.

The Arbery Centre, Wantage, Oxon.

Antiques at Heritage, Woodstock, Oxon.

Yarnton Antiques Centre, Yarnton, Oxon.

Rutland Antiques Centre, Uppingham, Rutland.

Old Mill Antique Centre, Bridgnorth, Shrops.

Stretton Antiques Market, Church Stretton, Shrops.

Princess Antique Centre, Shrewsbury, Shrops.

Shrewsbury Antique Centre, Shrewsbury, Shrops.

Shrewsbury Antique Market, Shrewsbury, Shrops.

Assembly Antiques Centre, Bath, Somerset.

Bartlett Street Antiques Centre, Bath, Somerset.

Bath Saturday Antiques Market, Bath, Somerset.

Old Bank Antiques Centre, Bath, Somerset.

Paragon Antiques and Collectors Market, Bath, Somerset.

Chard Antique Centre, Chard, Somerset.

Crewkerne Antique Centre, Crewkerne, Somerset.

County Antiques, Ilminster, Somerset.

Somerton Antiques Centre, Somerton, Somerset.

Cider Press Antiques Centre, Taunton, Somerset.

Taunton Antiques Market - Silver Street, Taunton, Somerset.

Green Dragon Antiques Centre, Wincanton, Somerset.

Rugeley Antique Centre, Brereton, Staffs.

The Leek Antiques Centre (Barclay House), Leek, Staffs.

Antique Forum, Newcastle-under-Lyme, Staffs.

Windmill Antiques, Stafford, Staffs.

Old Chapel Antique & Collectables Centre, Tutbury, Staffs.

Tutbury Mill Antiques Centre, Tutbury, Staffs.

Clare Antique Warehouse, Clare, Suffolk.

Long Melford Antiques Centre, Long Melford, Suffolk.

The Old Town Hall Antique Centre, Needham Market, Suffolk.

The Risby Barn, Risby, Suffolk.

Snape Antiques and Collectors Centre, Snape, Suffolk.

Memories, Bramley, Surrey.

Mimbridge Antiques Centre, Chobham, Surrey.

Dorking House Antiques, Dorking, Surrey.

Great Grooms of Dorking, Dorking, Surrey

Pilgrims Antique Centre, Dorking, Surrey.

Victoria and Edward Antiques Centre, Dorking, Surrey.

Journeyman Antiques Centre, East Molesey, Surrey.

Nostradamus II, East Molesey, Surrey.

Bourne Mill Antiques, Farnham, Surrey.

Maltings Monthly Market, Farnham, Surrey.

Haslemere Antique Market, Haslemere, Surrey.

Wood's Wharf Antiques Bazaar, Haslemere, Surrey.

Kingston Antique Market, Kingston-upon-Thames, Surrey.

Town & Country Decorative, Richmond, Surrey.

Talbot Walk Antique Centre, Ripley, Surrey.

Shere Antiques Centre, Shere, Surrey.

Brighton Flea Market, Brighton, Sussex East.

Brighton Lanes Antique Centre, Brighton, Sussex East.

Chateaubriand Antiques Centre, Burwash, Sussex East.

Eastbourne Antiques Market, Eastbourne, Sussex East.

Enterprise Collectors Market, Eastbourne, Sussex East.

The Old Town Antiques Centre, Eastbourne, Sussex East.

Pharoahs Antiques, Eastbourne, Sussex East.

George Street Antiques Centre, Hastings, Sussex East.

Church-Hill Antiques Centre, Lewes, Sussex East.

SPECIALIST DEALERS

Cliffe Antiques Centre, Lewes, Sussex East.

The Emporium Antique Centre, Lewes, Sussex East.

Lewes Antique Centre, Lewes, Sussex East.

Lewes Flea Market, Lewes, Sussex East.

Newhaven Flea Market, Newhaven, Sussex East.

The Courtyard Antiques Market, Seaford, Sussex East.

Seaford's "Barn Collectors' Market" and Studio Bookshop, Seaford, Sussex East.

The Hastings Antique Centre, St. Leonards-on-Sea, Sussex East.

Rocking Horse Antique Market, Ardingly, Sussex West.

Nineveh House, Arundel, Sussex West.

The Old Cornstore Antiques, Arundel, Sussex West.

Almshouses Arcade, Chichester, Sussex West.

Chichester Antiques Centre, Chichester, Sussex West.

Roundabout Antiques Centre, Haywards Heath, Sussex West.

Spongs Antiques Centre, Lindfield, Sussex West.

Petworth Antique Centre, Petworth, Sussex West.

Newcastle Antique Centre, Newcastle-upon-Tyne, Tyne and Wear.

Malthouse Antiques Centre, Alcester, Warks.

The Stables Antique Centre, Hatton, Warks.

Barn Antiques Centre, Long Marston, Warks.

Stratford Antique Centre, Stratford-upon-Avon, Warks.

The Stratford Antiques and Interiors Centre Ltd, Stratford-upon-Avon, Warks.

Vintage Antiques Centre, Warwick, Warks.

The Warwick Antique Centre, Warwick, Warks.

The Birmingham Antique Centre, Birmingham, West Mids.

Warley Antique Centre, Birmingham, West Mids.

Antiques Adventure, Coventry, West Mids.

Regency Antique Trading Ltd., Stourbridge, West Mids.

Wolverhampton Antiques and Collectors Market, Wolverhampton, West Mids.

The Marlborough Parade Antique Centre, Marlborough, Wilts.

King Street Curios, Melksham, Wilts.

Antique and Collectors Market, Salisbury, Wilts.

The Avonbridge Antiques and Collectors Market, Salisbury, Wilts.

Dairy House Antiques, Semley, Wilts.

Penny Farthing Antiques Arcade, Swindon, Wilts.

Warminster Antiques Centre, Warminster, Wilts.

Bewdley Antiques, Bewdley, Worcs.

The Hayloft Antique Centre, Fladbury, Worcs.

Antiques and Curios, Worcester, Worcs.

Worcester Antiques Centre, Worcester, Worcs.

St Crispin Antique Centre, Beverley, Yorks. East.

Vicar Lane Antique Centre, Beverley, Yorks. East.

The Georgian Rooms, Bridlington, Yorks. East.

Grannie's Treasures, Hull, Yorks. East.

Hull Antique Centre, Hull, Yorks. East.

Mount Pleasant Antiques Centre, Market Weighton, Yorks. East.

The Ginnel Antiques Centre, Harrogate, Yorks. North.

Montpellier Mews Antique Market, Harrogate, Yorks. North.

Castle Antiques Centre, Middleham, Yorks. North.

Pickering Antique Centre, Pickering, Yorks. North.

Skipton Antiques Centre, Skipton, Yorks. North.

Antiques Centre York, York, Yorks. North.

Cavendish Antiques & Collectors Centre, York, Yorks. North.

The Red House Antiques Centre, York, Yorks. North.

York Antiques Centre, York, Yorks. North.

Foster's Antique Centre, Rotherham, Yorks. South.

Barmouth Court Antiques Centre, Sheffield, Yorks. South.

Chapel Antiques Centre, Sheffield, Yorks. South.

Court House Antique Centre, Sheffield, Yorks. South.

Langtons Antiques & Collectables, Sheffield, Yorks. South.

Nichols Antique Centre, Sheffield, Yorks. South.

Sheffield Antiques Emporium, Sheffield, Yorks. South.

Wentworth Arts, Crafts and Antiques Ltd, Wentworth, Yorks. South.

Halifax Antiques Centre, Halifax, Yorks. West.

Headrow Antiques Centre, Leeds, Yorks. West.

Otley Antique Centre, Otley, Yorks. West.

The Victoria Centre, Saltaire, Yorks. West.

Todmorden Antiques Centre, Todmorden, Yorks. West.

Trafalgar Antiques Centre, Woodlesford, Yorks. West.

Scottish Antique & Arts Centre, Abernyte, Scotland.

Clola Antiques Centre, Clola by Mintlaw, Scotland.

The Antiques Warehouse, Glasgow, Scotland.

The Victorian Village Antiques, Glasgow, Scotland.

Rait Village Antiques Centre, Rait, Scotland.

Cardiff Antiques Centre, Cardiff, Wales.

Jacobs Antique Centre, Cardiff, Wales.

Cowbridge Antique Centre, Cowbridge, Wales.

Hay Antique Market, Hay-on-Wye, Wales.

Offa's Dyke Antique Centre, Knighton, Wales.

The Works Antiques Centre, Llandeilo, Wales.
Pembroke Antiques Centre, Pembroke, Wales.
Swansea Antiques Centre, Swansea, Wales.
Trecastle Antiques Centre, Trecastle, Wales.

Antiquarian Books
Ash Rare Books, London EC3.
Judith Lassalle, London N1.
Zeno Booksellers, London N12.
Barrie Marks Ltd, London N2.
Nicholas Goodyer, London N5.
Fisher and Sperr, London N6.
P.G. de Lotz, London NW3.
Keith Fawkes, London NW3.
Hosains Books and Antiques, London NW6.
Marcet Books, London SE10.
Rogers Turner Books, London SE10.
Classic Bindings, London SW1.
Thomas Heneage Art Books, London SW1.
The O'Shea Gallery, London SW1.
Sims, Reed Ltd, London SW1.
Hünersdorff Rare Books, London SW10.
John Thornton, London SW10.
Paul Foster's Bookshop, London SW14.
Hanshan Tang Books, London SW15.
Earlsfield Bookshop, London SW18.
Peter Harrington Antiquarian Bookseller,
   London SW3.
Russell Rare Books, London SW3.
Robin Greer, London SW6.
The Gloucester Road Bookshop, London SW7.
Paul Orssich, London SW8.
Altea Maps & Books, London W1.
G. Heywood Hill Ltd, London W1.
Holland & Holland, London W1.
Maggs Bros Ltd, London W1.
Marlborough Rare Books Ltd, London W1.
Paralos Ltd, London W1.
Pickering and Chatto, London W1.
Jonathan Potter Ltd, London W1.
Bernard Quaritch Ltd (Booksellers), London
   W1.
Robert G. Sawers, London W1.
Bernard J. Shapero Rare Books, London W1.
Henry Sotheran Ltd, London W1.
Crawley and Asquith Ltd, London W10.
Demetzy Books, London W11.
D. Parikian, London W14.
Adrian Harrington, London W8.
Atlantis Bookshop, London WC1.
Book Art & Architecture Bookshop & Volume
   Gallery, London WC1.
Cinema Bookshop, London WC1.
Fine Books Oriental, London WC1.
Michael Finney Antique Prints and Books,
   London WC1.
Robert Frew Ltd, London WC1.
The Museum Bookshop, London WC1.
Skoob Russell Square, London WC1.

Blackwell's, London WC2.
David Drummond at Pleasures of Past Times,
   London WC2.
P. J. Hilton (Books), London WC2.
Marchpane, London WC2.
Henry Pordes Books Ltd, London WC2.
Reg and Philip Remington, London WC2.
Bertram Rota Ltd, London WC2.
Stage Door Prints, London WC2.
Storey's Ltd, London WC2.
Tindley and Chapman, London WC2.
Watkins Books Ltd, London WC2.
Nigel Williams Rare Books, London WC2.
Books for Collectors Ltd., Toddington, Beds.
Eton Antique Bookshop, Windsor and Eton,
   Berks.
Penn Barn, Penn, Bucks.
The Bookshop, Cambridge, Cambs.
G. David, Cambridge, Cambs.
Galloway and Porter Ltd, Cambridge, Cambs.
Sarah Key, Cambridge, Cambs.
Stothert Old Books, Chester, Cheshire.
Lion Gallery and Bookshop, Knutsford,
   Cheshire.
Mereside Books, Macclesfield, Cheshire.
Iain Campbell, Widnes, Cheshire.
New Street Bookshop, Penzance, Cornwall.
Penzance Rare Books, Penzance, Cornwall.
Bonython Bookshop, Truro, Cornwall.
Norman Kerr - Gatehouse Bookshop, Cartmel,
   Cumbria.
Peter Bain Smith (Bookseller), Cartmel,
   Cumbria.
Archie Miles Bookshop, Gosforth, Cumbria.
Lakes Crafts & Antiques Gallery, Grasmere,
   Cumbria.
G.K. Hadfield, Great Salkeld, Cumbria.
The Book House, Ravenstonedale, Cumbria.
R. F. G. Hollett and Son, Sedbergh, Cumbria.
Michael Moon - Antiquarian Booksellers,
   Whitehaven, Cumbria.
Derventio Books, Derby, Derbys.
Dartmoor Bookshop, Ashburton, Devon.
Chantry Bookshop and Gallery, Dartmouth,
   Devon.
Exeter Rare Books, Exeter, Devon.
High Street Books, Honiton, Devon.
Honiton Old Bookshop, Honiton, Devon.
Graham York Rare Books, Honiton, Devon.
The Pocket Bookshop, Paignton, Devon.
P.M. Pollak, South Brent, Devon.
R. M. Young Bookseller, South Molton, Devon.
The Schuster Gallery, Torquay, Devon.
Collards Books, Totnes, Devon.
The Exchange, Totnes, Devon.
Pedlars Pack Books, Totnes, Devon.
Ancient and Modern Bookshop (including
   Garret's Antiques), Blandford Forum, Dorset.
Bridport Old Books, Bridport, Dorset.

Words Etcetera, Dorchester, Dorset.
Christopher Williams Antiquarian Bookseller, Parkstone, Dorset.
Antique Map and Bookshop, Puddletown, Dorset.
Chapter House Books, Sherborne, Dorset.
Keeble Antiques, Sherborne, Dorset.
Reference Works Ltd., Swanage, Dorset.
Books Afloat, Weymouth, Dorset.
Books & Bygones, Weymouth, Dorset.
Minster Books, Wimborne Minster, Dorset.
J. Shotton Antiquarian Books, Prints and Coins, Durham, Durham.
Castle Bookshop, Colchester, Essex.
Bookworm, Holland-on-Sea, Essex.
Pastimes, Bristol, Glos.
David Bannister FRGS, Cheltenham, Glos.
Michael Rayner, Cheltenham, Glos.
Ian Hodgkins and Co. Ltd, Slad, Glos.
Tetbury Old Books, Tetbury, Glos.
Laurence Oxley, Alresford, Hants.
Bookends, Emsworth, Hants.
Kingsclere Old Bookshop (Wyseby House Books), Kingsclere, Hants.
The Petersfield Bookshop, Petersfield, Hants.
Academy Books, Portsmouth, Hants.
SPCK Bookshops, Winchester, Hants.
Castle Hill Books, Kington, Herefs.
Keith Smith Books, Ledbury, Herefs.
Ross Old Book and Print Shop, Ross-on-Wye, Herefs.
Gillmark Gallery, Hertford, Herts.
Eric T. Moore, Hitchin, Herts.
Clive A. Burden Ltd, Rickmansworth, Herts.
Ventnor Rare Books, Ventnor, Isle of Wight.
The Canterbury Bookshop, Canterbury, Kent.
Chaucer Bookshop, Canterbury, Kent.
J. Clarke-Hall Ltd, Deal, Kent.
Baggins Book Bazaar - The Largest Secondhand Bookshop in England, Rochester, Kent.
Sandwich Fine Books, Sandwich, Kent.
Hall's Bookshop, Tunbridge Wells, Kent.
Taylor-Smith Books, Westerham, Kent.
Siri Ellis Books, Bolton, Lancs.
Gibb's Bookshop Ltd, Manchester, Lancs.
Eric J. Morten, Manchester, Lancs.
Halewood and Sons, Preston, Lancs.
Preston Book Co, Preston, Lancs.
The Book Shop, Castle Donington, Leics.
Anthony W. Laywood, Knipton, Leics.
Clarendon Books, Leicester, Leics.
Elaine Lonsdale Bookseller and Bookbinder, Hemswell Cliff, Lincs.
P.J. Cassidy (Books), Holbeach, Lincs.
Golden Goose Books, Lincoln, Lincs.
Harlequin Gallery and Golden Goose Globe Restorers, Lincoln, Lincs.
Staniland (Booksellers), Stamford, Lincs.
C.K. Broadhurst and Co Ltd, Southport, Merseyside.

Ian Sheridan's Bookshop, Hampton, Middx.
Chris Hollingshead, Teddington, Middx.
Anthony C. Hall, Twickenham, Middx.
John Ives Bookseller, Twickenham, Middx.
Rita Shenton, Twickenham, Middx.
Books Etc., Cromer, Norfolk.
David Ferrow, Great Yarmouth, Norfolk.
Simon Finch Norfolk, Holt, Norfolk.
The Old Reading Room Gallery and Tea Room, Kelling, Norfolk.
The Angel Bookshop, North Walsham, Norfolk.
Peter J. Hadley Bookseller, Norwich, Norfolk.
The Tombland Bookshop, Norwich, Norfolk.
R.L. Cook, Sheringham, Norfolk.
Turret House, Wymondham, Norfolk.
The Old Hall Bookshop, Brackley, Northants.
Occultique, Northampton, Northants.
Park Gallery & Bookshop, Wellingborough, Northants.
Barter Books, Alnwick, Northumbs.
Priest Popple Books, Hexham, Northumbs.
E.M. Lawson and Co, East Hagbourne, Oxon.
Jonkers Rare Books, Henley-on-Thames, Oxon.
Richard J. Kingston, Henley-on-Thames, Oxon.
Richard Way Bookseller, Henley-on-Thames, Oxon.
Blackwell's Rare Books, Oxford, Oxon.
Jericho Books, Oxford, Oxon.
Waterfield's, Oxford, Oxon.
Toby English, Wallingford, Oxon.
Tooley Adams & Co, Wallingford, Oxon.
Goldmark Books, Uppingham, Rutland.
M. and M. Baldwin, Cleobury Mortimer, Shrops.
Candle Lane Books, Shrewsbury, Shrops.
George Bayntun, Bath, Somerset.
Camden Books, Bath, Somerset.
George Gregory, Bath, Somerset.
Patterson Liddle, Bath, Somerset.
Gresham Books, Crewkerne, Somerset.
Rothwell and Dunworth, Dulverton, Somerset.
Janet Clarke, Freshford, Somerset.
Steven Ferdinando, Queen Camel, Somerset.
Sterling Books, Weston-Super-Mare, Somerset.
M.A.J. Morris, Burton-upon-Trent, Staffs.
Mike Abrahams Books, Lichfield, Staffs.
Besleys Books, Beccles, Suffolk.
Trinders' Fine Tools, Clare, Suffolk.
Abington Books, Finningham, Suffolk.
Claude Cox at College Gateway Bookshop, Ipswich, Suffolk.
R.G. Archer (Books), Lavenham, Suffolk.
R.E. and G.B. Way, Newmarket, Suffolk.
Honeypot Antiques, Elstead, Surrey.
Vandeleur Antiquarian Books, Epsom, Surrey.
J.W. McKenzie, Ewell, Surrey.
Lloyds of Kew, Kew, Surrey.
A. Burton-Garbett, Morden, Surrey.
Secondhand Bookshop, Oxted, Surrey.
Wagstaffs, Oxted, Surrey.

Reigate Galleries, Reigate, Surrey.

Raymond Slack FRSA & Shirley Warren, Sanderstead, Surrey.

Colin Page Antiquarian Books, Brighton, Sussex East.

Camilla's Bookshop, Eastbourne, Sussex East.

Roderick Dew, Eastbourne, Sussex East.

A. & T. Gibbard, Eastbourne, Sussex East.

Howes Bookshop, Hastings, Sussex East.

Bow Windows Book Shop, Lewes, Sussex East.

A. & Y. Cumming, Lewes, Sussex East.

The Fifteenth Century Bookshop, Lewes, Sussex East.

Chapter & Verse Booksellers, Rye, Sussex East.

The Book Jungle, St. Leonards-on-Sea, Sussex East.

Baskerville Books, Wadhurst, Sussex East.

Canon Gate Bookshop, Chichester, Sussex West.

Muttonchop Manuscripts, Petworth, Sussex West.

R.D. Steedman, Newcastle-upon-Tyne, Tyne and Wear.

Keel Row Books, North Shields, Tyne and Wear.

Olivers Bookshop, Whitley Bay, Tyne and Wear.

The Stratford Bookshop, Stratford-upon-Avon, Warks.

Robert Vaughan, Stratford-upon-Avon, Warks.

Duncan M. Allsop, Warwick, Warks.

David Temperley Fine and Antiquarian Books, Birmingham, West Mids.

Clive Farahar and Sophie Dupré - Rare Books, Autographs and Manuscripts, Calne, Wilts.

Hilmarton Manor Press, Calne, Wilts.

The Military Parade Bookshop, Marlborough, Wilts.

Heraldry Today, Ramsbury, Wilts.

The Barn Book Supply, Salisbury, Wilts.

Victoria Bookshop, Swindon, Wilts.

Bookworms of Evesham, Evesham, Worcs.

Malvern Bookshop, Great Malvern, Worcs.

Antique Map and Print Gallery, Hallow, Worcs.

Grove Rare Books, Bolton Abbey, Yorks. North.

Potterton Books, Thirsk, Yorks. North.

Cobweb Books, Thornton-le-Dale, Yorks. North.

Barbican Bookshop, York, Yorks. North.

Jack Duncan Books, York, Yorks. North.

Minster Gate Bookshop, York, Yorks. North.

Janette Ray Rare and Out of Print Books, York, Yorks. North.

Ken Spelman, York, Yorks. North.

Alan Hill Books, Sheffield, Yorks. South.

The Toll House Bookshop, Holmfirth, Yorks. West.

C.I Galleries Ltd, St. Peter Port, Guernsey, C.I.

John Blench & Son, St. Helier, Jersey, C.I.

The Selective Eye Gallery, St. Helier, Jersey, C.I.

Thesaurus (Jersey) Ltd, St. Helier, Jersey, C.I.

Stacks Bookshop, Dundonald, Co. Down, N. Ireland.

Saintfield Antiques & Fine Books, Saintfield, Co. Down, N. Ireland.

Foyle Books, Londonderry, Co. Londonderry, N. Ireland.

Bon-Accord Books, Aberdeen, Scotland.

The McEwan Gallery, Ballater, Scotland.

Blairgowrie Books, Blairgowrie, Scotland.

Armchair Books, Edinburgh, Scotland.

Broughton Books, Edinburgh, Scotland.

McNaughtan's Bookshop, Edinburgh, Scotland.

The Old Town Bookshop, Edinburgh, Scotland.

Second Edition, Edinburgh, Scotland.

Marianne Simpson, Fochabers, Scotland.

Mair Wilkes Books, Newport-on-Tay, Scotland.

Penny Farthing, North Berwick, Scotland.

Paisley Fine Books, Paisley, Scotland.

Ming Books, Wigtown, Scotland.

A.E. Morris (Books), Bethesda, Wales.

Books, Maps and Prints, Brecon, Wales.

Glance Back Bookshop, Chepstow, Wales.

Capel Mawr Collectors Centre, Criccieth, Wales.

Richard Booth's Bookshop Ltd, Hay-on-Wye, Wales.

Rose's Books, Hay-on-Wye, Wales.

Mark Westwood Antiquarian Books, Hay-on-Wye, Wales.

Prospect Books, Llanrwst, Wales.

Dylan's Bookstore, Swansea, Wales.

Antiquities

C.J. Martin (Coins) Ltd, London N14.

Robin Symes Ltd, London SW1.

Aaron Gallery, London W1.

Charles Ede Ltd, London W1.

Hadji Baba Ancient Art, London W1.

Mansour Gallery, London W1.

Seaby Antiquities, London W1.

Rupert Wace Ancient Art Ltd, London W1.

Town Hall Antiques, Woburn, Beds.

Valued History, Ely, Cambs.

Potter's Antiques and Coins, Bristol, Glos.

Ancient & Oriental Ltd, Grimston, Leics.

Architectural Items

LASSCO, London EC2.

Westland London, London EC2.

Willesden Green Architectural Salvage, London NW10.

Townsends, London NW8.

Lamont Antiques Ltd, London SE10.

The Old Station, London SE13.

Camberwell Architectural Salvage & Antiques, London SE5.

Humphrey-Carrasco, London SW1.

Thornhill Galleries Ltd. in association with A. & R. Dockerill Ltd, London SW15.

Fairfax Antiques and Fireplaces, London SW6.

Rodney Franklin Antiques, London SW9.

Architectural Antiques, London W6.

SPECIALIST DEALERS

Architectural Antiques, Bedford, Beds.
Tomkinson Stained Glas, Leagrave, Beds.
Rules Antiques, Windsor and Eton, Berks.
Dismantle and Deal Direct - Architectural
    Salvage Brokers, Aston Clinton, Bucks.
Solopark Plc, Cambridge, Cambs.
Nostalgia Architectural Antiques, Stockport,
    Cheshire.
Cheshire Brick and Slate Co, Tarvin Sands,
    Cheshire.
The Great Northern Architectural Antique
    Company Ltd, Tattenhall, Cheshire.
Architectural Antiques, Kendal, Cumbria.
W.R.S. Architectural Antiques, Low Newton,
    Cumbria.
Cumbria Architectural Salvage, Raughton Head,
    Cumbria.
Havenplan's Architectural Emporium,
    Killamarsh, Derbys.
Ashburton Marbles, Ashburton, Devon.
Fagins Antiques, Exeter, Devon.
Dorset Reclamation, Bere Regis, Dorset.
Talisman, Gillingham, Dorset.
Antique Fireplace Centre, Hartlepool, Durham.
Robert Mills Architectural Antiques Ltd, Bristol,
    Glos.
Cox's Architectural Reclamation Yard, Moreton-
    in-Marsh, Glos.
Architectural Heritage, Taddington, Glos.
Burgess Farm Antiques, Winchester, Hants.
The Pine Cellars, Winchester, Hants.
Baileys Home & Garden, Ross-on-Wye, Herefs.
Curios of Chale, Chale, Isle of Wight.
The Architectural Emporium, Tunbridge Wells,
    Kent.
Old Smithy, Feniscowles, Lancs.
Antique Fireplace Warehouse, Manchester,
    Lancs.
In-Situ Manchester, Manchester, Lancs.
In-Situ Manchester South Architectural
    Antiques, Manchester, Lancs.
Old Bakery Antiques, Wymondham, Leics.
Lindsey Court Architectural Antiques,
    Horncastle, Lincs.
D & T Architectural Salvage, Birkenhead,
    Merseyside.
Peco, Hampton, Middx.
Mongers, Hingham, Norfolk.
Stiffkey Antiques, Stiffkey, Norfolk.
Rococo Antiques, Architectural Goods and
    Furnishings, Weedon, Northants.
Woodside Reclamation (Architectural Antiques),
    Berwick-upon-Tweed, Northumbs.
Hallidays (Fine Antiques) Ltd, Dorchester-on-
    Thames, Oxon.
Aston Pine Antiques, Faringdon, Oxon.
Oxford Architectural Antiques, Faringdon,
    Oxon.
The Country Seat, Huntercombe, Oxon.

Willow Antiques and the Nettlebed Antique
    Merchants, Nettlebed, Oxon.
North Shropshire Reclamation, Burlton, Shrops.
Antique Centre, Cleobury Mortimer, Shrops.
Priors Reclamation, Ditton Priors, Shrops.
David Bridgwater, Bath, Somerset.
Source, Bath, Somerset.
Walcot Reclamation, Bath, Somerset.
Chris's Crackers, Carhampton, Somerset.
Wells Reclamation Company, Coxley, Somerset.
Frome Reclamation, Frome, Somerset.
Castle Reclamation, Martock, Somerset.
Asianart.co.uk.Ltd., North Newton, Somerset.
Blackbrook Antiques Village, Weeford, Staffs.
E.T. Webster, Blythburgh, Suffolk.
Antique Buildings Ltd, Dunsfold, Surrey.
Drummonds Architectural Antiques, Hindhead,
    Surrey.
The Packhouse, Runfold, Surrey.
Antique Church Furnishings, Walton-on-
    Thames, Surrey.
Brighton Architectural Salvage, Brighton,
    Sussex East.
Shiners, Snobs Knobs, Jesmond, Tyne and Wear.
Turnburrys, Jesmond, Tyne and Wear.
Tynemouth Architectural Salvage, Tynemouth,
    Tyne and Wear.
The Victorian Ironmonger, Brinklow, Warks.
Thomas Crapper & Co, Stratford-upon-Avon,
    Warks.
Harriet Fairfax Fireplaces and General Antiques,
    Langley Burrell, Wilts.
Kevin Marshall's Antiques Warehouse, Hull,
    Yorks. East.
Old Flames, Easingwold, Yorks. North.
The White House Antiques & Architectural
    Reclamation, Easingwold, Yorks. North.
Daleside Antiques, Markington, Yorks. North.
Renishaw Antiques, Sheffield, Yorks. South.
The Baildon Furniture Co., Baildon, Yorks.
    West.
Andy Thornton Architectural Antiques Ltd,
    Halifax, Yorks. West.
EASY - Edinburgh Architectural Salvage Yard,
    Edinburgh, Scotland.
Holyrood Architectural Salvage, Edinburgh,
    Scotland.
Cardiff Reclamation, Cardiff, Wales.
Gallop and Rivers Architectural Antiques,
    Crickhowell, Wales.
Dyfed Antiques and Architectural Salvage,
    Haverfordwest, Wales.

Arms & Armour
London Militaria Market, London N1.
Finchley Fine Art Galleries, London N12.
Laurence Corner, London NW1.
The Armoury of St. James's Military
    Antiquarians, London SW1.

Peter Dale Ltd, London SW1.
Blunderbuss Antiques, London W1.
Holland & Holland, London W1.
Michael German Antiques Ltd, London W8.
Robert Hales Antiques, London W8.
Trafalgar Square Collectors Centre, London WC2.
MJM Antiques, Hungerford, Berks.
Anthony D. Goodlad, Chesterfield, Derbys.
Rex Antiques, Chagford, Devon.
Boscombe Militaria, Bournemouth, Dorset.
Sterling Coins and Medals, Bournemouth, Dorset.
Chris Grimes Militaria, Bristol, Glos.
Pastimes, Bristol, Glos.
Q & C Militaria, Cheltenham, Glos.
Military Curios, HQ84, Gloucester, Glos.
Hampton Gallery, Tetbury, Glos.
J F F Fire Brigade & Military Collectables, Old Bedhampton, Hants.
H.S. Greenfield and Son, Gunmakers (Est. 1805), Canterbury, Kent.
Sporting Antiques, Tunbridge Wells, Kent.
Jean's Military Memories, Great Harwood, Lancs.
Anything Old & Military Collectables, Lancaster, Lancs.
Garth Vincent Antique Arms and Armour, Allington, Lincs.
The Old Brigade, Kingsthorpe, Northants.
R. G. Antiques, Dunham-on-Trent, Notts.
Michael D. Long, Nottingham, Notts.
Quillon Antiques of Tetsworth, Tetsworth, Oxon.
English Heritage, Bridgnorth, Shrops.
One Bell, Lavenham, Suffolk.
West Street Antiques, Dorking, Surrey.
Casque and Gauntlet Militaria, Farnham, Surrey.
The Lanes Armoury, Brighton, Sussex East.
St. Pancras Antiques, Chichester, Sussex West.
Arbour Antiques Ltd, Stratford-upon-Avon, Warks.
Edred A.F. Gwilliam, Cricklade, Wilts.
Cannon Militaria, Durrington, Wilts.
Magpie Jewellers and Antiques and Magpie Arms & Armour, Evesham, Worcs.
Cawood Antiques, Cawood, Yorks. North.
Cairncross and Sons, Filey, Yorks. North.
Hanover Antiques & Collectables, Scarborough, Yorks. North.
Adamson Armoury, Skipton, Yorks. North.
D.W. Dyson (Antique Weapons), Huddersfield, Yorks. West.
A. & R. Ritchie, St. Helier, Jersey, C.I.
Angus Antiques, Dundee, Scotland.
Bow-well Antiques, Edinburgh, Scotland.
Huw Williams Antiques, Porthmadog, Wales.

Art Deco & Art Nouveau
After Noah, London N1.

The Antique Trader, London N1.
Style Gallery, London N1.
Tadema Gallery, London N1.
Mike Weedon, London N1.
Crafts Nouveau, London N10
Art Furniture, London NW1.
Beverley, London NW8.
Bizarre, London NW8.
The Studio, London NW8.
Behind the Boxes - Art Deco, London SE26.
Ciancimino Ltd, London SW1.
Gallery '25, London SW1.
Keshishian, London SW1.
Twentieth Century, London SW12.
The Arts & Crafts Furniture Co Ltd, London SW14.
After Noah, London SW3.
Butler and Wilson, London SW3.
David Gill, London SW3.
Gordon Watson Ltd, London SW3.
Victor Arwas Gallery - Editions Graphiques Gallery Ltd, London W1.
Liberty, London W1.
Mayfair Gallery Ltd, London W1.
B. and T. Antiques, London W11.
The Facade, London W11.
Hickmet Fine Arts, London W11.
Themes and Variations, London W11.
Haslam and Whiteway, London W8.
John Jesse, London W8.
New Century, London W8.
Pruskin Gallery, London W8.
Bizarre Decorative Arts North West, Altrincham, Cheshire.
Aldersey Hall Ltd, Chester, Cheshire.
Maggie Mays, Buxton, Derbys.
Altamiradeco, Bournemouth, Dorset.
Lionel Geneen Ltd, Bournemouth, Dorset.
Omega, Newport, Essex.
Ruskin Decorative Arts, Stow-on-the-Wold, Glos.
Alexanders, Titchfield, Hants.
Brian West Antiques, Sandgate, Kent.
Peter Hoare Antiques, Southborough, Kent.
The Design Gallery 1850-1950, Westerham, Kent.
A.S. Antique Galleries, Manchester, Lancs.
Circa 1900, Liverpool, Merseyside.
Osiris Antiques, Southport, Merseyside.
Arbiter, Wallasey, Merseyside.
Aspidistra Antiques, Finedon, Northants.
Willow Antiques and the Nettlebed Antique Merchants, Nettlebed, Oxon.
Decorative Antiques, Bishop's Castle, Shrops.
Expressions, Shrewsbury, Shrops.
A J Antiques, Bath, Somerset.
Puritan Values at the Dome, Southwold, Suffolk.
Decodream, Coulsdon, Surrey.
The Gooday Gallery, Richmond, Surrey.

Cockrell Antiques, Surbiton, Surrey.
Aspidistra Antiques, Woking, Surrey.
Art Deco Etc, Brighton, Sussex East.
Jezebel, Brighton, Sussex East.
Oasis Antiques, Brighton, Sussex East.
Wardrobe, Brighton, Sussex East.
Peter Hancock Antiques, Chichester, Sussex West.
Cradlewell Antiques, Jesmond, Tyne and Wear.
Tango Art Deco & Antiques, Warwick, Warks.
Lamb Antique Fine Arts & Crafts Originals,
    Wolverhampton, West Mids.
Muir Hewitt Art Deco Originals, Halifax, Yorks. West.
The Rendezvous Gallery, Aberdeen, Scotland.
The Renaissance Furniture Store, Glasgow,
    Scotland.
Jeremy Sniders Antiques, Glasgow, Scotland.
Strachan Antiques, Glasgow, Scotland.
Rhudle Mill, Kilmichael Glassary, Scotland.
Paul Gibbs Antiques and Decorative Arts,
    Conwy, Wales.
The House 1860-1925, Monmouth, Wales.

Barometers- see also Clock Dealers
Frosts of Clerkenwell Ltd, London EC1.
The Antique Barometer Co., The Mall Antiques
    Arcade, London N1.
Strike One, London N5.
R.E. Rose FBHI, London SE9.
John Carlton-Smith, London SW1.
Trevor Philip and Sons Ltd, London SW1.

The Clock Clinic Ltd, London SW15.
Ronald Phillips Ltd, London W1.
Stair and Company Ltd, London W1.
Old Father Time Clock Centre, London W11.
Raffety & Walwyn, London W8.
The Clock Workshop, Caversham, Berks.
Alan Walker, Halfway, Berks.
The Old Malthouse, Hungerford, Berks.
Carlton Clocks, Amersham, Bucks.
M.V. Tooley, CMBHI, Chesham, Bucks.
John Beazor and Sons Ltd, Cambridge, Cambs.
Antique Barometers, Ramsey, Cambs.
T. W. Pawson - Clocks, Somersham, Cambs.
Derek and Tina Rayment Antiques, Barton,
    Cheshire.
Andrew Foott Antiques, Cheadle Hulme,
    Cheshire.
Mike Read Antique Sciences, St. Ives, Cornwall.
Musgrave Bickford Antiques, Crediton, Devon.
Honiton Clock Clinic, Honiton, Devon.
Barometer World Ltd, Merton, Devon.
Leigh Extence, Antique Clocks, Shaldon,
    Devon.
M.C. Taylor, Bournemouth, Dorset.
Timecraft Clocks, Sherborne, Dorset.
Tom Tribe and Son, Sturminster Newton,
    Dorset.
Mark Marchant (Antiques), Coggeshall, Essex.
Chris L. Papworth Antique Clocks and Watches,
    Kelvedon, Essex.

Littlebury Antiques - Littlebury Restorations
Ltd, Saffron Walden, Essex.
It's About Time, Westcliff-on-Sea, Essex.
Montpellier Clocks, Cheltenham, Glos.
Antony Preston Antiques Ltd, Stow-on-the-
Wold, Glos.
Styles of Stow, Stow-on-the-Wold, Glos.
Vanbrugh House Antiques, Stow-on-the-Wold,
Glos.
Evans and Evans, Alresford, Hants.
The Clock Workshop (Winchester), Winchester,
Hants.
G.E. Marsh Antique Clocks Ltd, Winchester,
Hants.
Barometer Shop, Leominster, Herefs.
Robert Horton Antiques, Hertford, Herts.
John Chawner, Birchington, Kent.
PatricCapon, Bromley, Kent.
Michael Sim, Chislehurst, Kent.
City Antiques Ltd, Rochester, Kent.
Neill Robinson Blaxill, Sevenoaks, Kent.
Tankerton Antiques, Whitstable, Kent.
Drop Dial Antiques, Bolton, Lancs.
Harrop Fold Clocks (F. Robinson), Bolton-by-
Bowland, Lancs.
N. Bryan-Peach Antiques, Wymeswold, Leics.
Robin Fowler (Period Clocks), Aylesby, Lincs.
David J. Hansord & Son, Lincoln, Lincs.
Timepiece Repairs, Lincoln, Lincs.
Rita Shenton, Twickenham, Middx.
Keith Lawson Antique Clocks, Scratby, Norfolk.
Peter Wiggins, Chipping Norton, Oxon.
Rosemary and Time, Thame, Oxon.
R.G. Cave and Sons Ltd, Ludlow, Shrops.
Adrian Donnelly Antique Clocks, Shrewsbury,
Shrops.
Dodington Antiques, Whitchurch, Shrops.
Kembery Antique Clocks Ltd, Bath, Somerset.
Bernard G. House, Wells, Somerset.
James A. Jordan, Lichfield, Staffs.
Patrick Marney, Long Melford, Suffolk.
Suthburgh Antiques, Long Melford, Suffolk.
Trident Antiques, Long Melford, Suffolk.
Horological Workshops, Guildford, Surrey.
Surrey Clock Centre, Haslemere, Surrey.
B. M. and E. Newlove, Surbiton, Surrey.
Baskerville Antiques, Petworth, Sussex West.
Time in Hand, Shipston-on-Stour, Warks.
Summersons, Warwick, Warks.
R. Collyer, Birmingham, West Mids.
P.A. Oxley Antique Clocks and Barometers,
Cherhill, Wilts.
Time Restored & Co, Pewsey, Wilts.
Inglenook Antiques, Ramsbury, Wilts.
Hansen Chard Antiques, Pershore, Worcs.
Time and Motion, Beverley, Yorks. East.
Lewis E. Hickson FBHI, Gilberdyke, Yorks. East.
Craiglea Clocks, Edinburgh, Scotland.
Brown's Clocks, Glasgow, Scotland.

Beds
La Maison, London E1.
Tobias and The Angel, London SW13.
And So To Bed Limited, London SW6.
Simon Horn Furniture Ltd, London SW6.
The French House (Antiques) Ltd, London
SW8.
Hirst Antiques, London W11.
French Countrystyle, Hale, Cheshire.
Victoria Imports, Stockport, Cheshire.
The Country Bedroom, Keswick, Cumbria.
Staveley Antiques, Staveley, Cumbria.
The Antiques Warehouse, Buxton, Derbys.
R.C. Associates, Cullompton, Devon.
The Grove Antiques Centre, Honiton, Devon.
Pugh's Farm Antiques, Monkton, Devon.
Annterior Antiques, Plymouth, Devon.
Antique Bed Shop, Halstead, Essex.
Deja Vu Antiques, Leigh-on-Sea, Essex.
Antique Bed Company, Emsworth, Hants.
Victorian Dreams, Headley, Hants.
Serendipity, Ledbury, Herefs.
Harriet Ann Sleigh Beds, Rolvenden, Kent.
Peggottys, Teynham, Kent.
House Things Antiques, Hinckley, Leics.
A Barn Full of Brass Beds, Conisholme, Lincs.
Graham Pickett Antiques, Stamford, Lincs.
Antiques & Gifts, Downham Market, Norfolk.
Manor Farm Antiques, Standlake, Oxon.
Swans, Oakham, Rutland.
Malthouse Antiques, Bridgnorth, Shrops.
Antique Centre, Cleobury Mortimer, Shrops.
Bedsteads, Bath, Somerset.
Antique Four-Poster Beds, Bower Ashton,
Somerset.
Wessex Antique Bedsteads, Stoke-sub-Hamdon,
Somerset.
Yew Tree Antiques Warehouse, Wiveliscombe,
Somerset.
Bed Bazaar, Framlingham, Suffolk.
Goodbreys, Framlingham, Suffolk.
Sleeping Beauty Antique Beds, Brighton, Sussex
East.
The Victorian Brass Bedstead Company,
Cocking, Sussex West.
Timeless Beds, Malvern Link, Worcs.
S.W. Antiques, Pershore, Worcs.
Penny Farthing Antiques, North Cave, Yorks.
East.
Northern Antiques Company, Norton, Yorks.
North.
The French House (Antiques) Ltd., York, Yorks.
North.
Paraphernalia, Sheffield, Yorks. South.
P. J. Smith (Antiques), Stewartstown, Co.
Tyrone, N. Ireland.
Seventh Heaven, Chirk, Wales.

Brass - see Metalware

SPECIALIST DEALERS

Bronzes

Furniture Vault, London N1.
Kevin Page Oriental Art, London N1.
Style Gallery, London N1.
Finchley Fine Art Galleries, London N12.
No. 28 Antiques, London NW8.
Tara Antiques, London NW8.
Robert Bowman, London SW1.
Victor Franses Gallery, London SW1.
M. and D. Lewis, London SW1.
Peter Nahum at The Leicester Galleries, London SW1.
Christine Bridge, London SW13.
Anthony James and Son Ltd, London SW3.
Victor Arwas Gallery - Editions Graphiques Gallery Ltd, London W1.
Barry Davies Oriental Art, London W1.
Eskenazi Ltd, London W1.
The Sladmore Gallery of Sculpture, London W1.
Elizabeth Bradwin, London W11.
Gavin Douglas Fine Antiques Ltd, London W11.
M. and D. Lewis, London W11.
David Brower Antiques, London W8.
H. and W. Deutsch Antiques, London W8.
John Jesse, London W8.
Pruskin Gallery, London W8.
Mary Wise & Grosvenor Antiques, London W8.
West End Galleries, Buxton, Derbys.
The John Davies Gallery, Stow-on-the-Wold, Glos.
Michael Sim, Chislehurst, Kent.
Apollo Antique Galleries, Westerham, Kent.
London House Antiques, Westerham, Kent.
Edward Cross - Fine Paintings, Weybridge, Surrey.

Carpets & Rugs

Alexander Juran and Co, London N4.
Kennedy Carpets, London N4.
Joseph Lavian, London N4.
David J. Wilkins, London NW1.
Sabera Trading Co, London NW2.
Soviet Carpet & Art Galleries, London NW2.
Lida Lavender, London NW5.
Orientalist, London NW5.
Coats Oriental Carpets, London SE5.
Belgrave Carpet Gallery Ltd, London SW1.
Victor Franses Gallery, London SW1.
S. Franses Ltd, London SW1.
Keshishian, London SW1.
Gideon Hatch Rugs, London SW11.
Shaikh and Son (Oriental Rugs) Ltd, London SW19.
Gallery Yacou, London SW3.
Orientalist, London SW3.
Perez, London SW3.
Robert Stephenson, London SW3.
Perez Antique Carpets Gallery, London SW6.
Anglo Persian Carpet Co, London SW7.

Atlantic Bay Carpets Gallery, London SW7.
David Aaron Ancient Arts & Rare Carpets, London W1.
Sibyl Colefax & John Fowler, London W1.
John Eskenazi Ltd, London W1.
Essie Carpets, London W1.
C. John (Rare Rugs) Ltd, London W1.
Mayfair Carpet Gallery Ltd, London W1.
Rabi Gallery Ltd, London W1.
Gordon Reece Gallery, London W1.
Vigo Carpet Gallery, London W1.
A. Zadah, London W1.
Graham and Green, London W11.
Rezai Persian Carpets, London W11.
David Black Carpets, London W2.
Oriental Rug Gallery Ltd, Windsor and Eton, Berks.
Peter Norman Antiques and Restorations, Burwell, Cambs.
J.L. Arditti, Christchurch, Dorset.
Christchurch Carpets, Christchurch, Dorset.
Hamptons, Christchurch, Dorset.
Eric Pride Oriental Rugs, Cheltenham, Glos.
Anthony Hazledine, Fairford, Glos.
Samarkand Galleries, Stow-on-the-Wold, Glos.
The Odiham Gallery, Odiham, Hants.
The Bakhtiyar Gallery, Stockbridge, Hants.
Oriental Rug Gallery Ltd, St. Albans, Herts.
Desmond and Amanda North, East Peckham, Kent.
Samovar Antiques, Hythe, Kent.
Woven Magic, Sevenoaks, Kent.
Pantiles Oriental Carpets, Tunbridge Wells, Kent.
The Rug Gallery, Leicester, Leics.
Country and Eastern Ltd., Norwich, Norfolk.
M.D. Cannell Antiques, Raveningham, Norfolk.
Richard Purdon Antique Carpets, Burford, Oxon.
Thames Oriental Rug Co, Henley-on-Thames, Oxon.
Christopher Legge Oriental Carpets, Oxford, Oxon.
Oriental Rug Gallery Ltd, Oxford, Oxon.
Tattersall's, Uppingham, Rutland.
Haliden Oriental Rug Shop, Bath, Somerset.
Michael and Amanda Lewis Oriental Carpets and Rugs, Wellington, Somerset.
The Persian Carpet Studio, Long Melford, Suffolk.
Karel Weijand Fine Oriental Carpets, Farnham, Surrey.
Oriental Rug Gallery, Guildford, Surrey.
Clive Rogers Oriental Rugs, Staines, Surrey.
Lindfield Galleries - David Adam, Lindfield, Sussex West.
Persian Carpet Gallery of Petworth, Petworth, Sussex West.
A.W. Hone and Son Oriental Carpets, Birmingham, West Mids.
D & J Lines Antiques, Wychbold, Worcs.

London House Oriental Rugs and Carpets, Harrogate, Yorks. North.
Omar (Harrogate) Ltd, Knaresborough, Yorks. North.
The Oriental Rug Shop, Sheffield, Yorks. South.
London House Oriental Rugs and Carpets, Boston Spa, Yorks. West.
Parvis Sigaroudinia, Lisburn, Co. Antrim, N. Ireland.
R.L. Rose Oriental Carpets Ltd, Edinburgh, Scotland.
Samarkand Galleries, Edinburgh, Scotland.
Whytock and Reid, Edinburgh, Scotland.
Young Antiques, Edinburgh, Scotland.
R.L. Rose Oriental Carpets Ltd, Glasgow, Scotland.
C.S. Moreton (Antiques), Inchture, Scotland.
Gallery Persia, Inverness, Scotland.

Cars & Carriages
Finesse Fine Art, Dorchester, Dorset.
Fieldings Antiques, Haslingden, Lancs.
The Complete Automobilist, Bourne, Lincs.
C.A.R.S. (Classic Automobilia & Regalia Specialists), Brighton, Sussex East.
Whatnots, Strathblane, Scotland.

Chinese Art - see Oriental

Church Furniture & Furnishings
Whiteway and Waldron Ltd, London SW6.
Havenplan's Architectural Emporium, Killamarsh, Derbys.
Robert Mills Architectural Antiques Ltd, Bristol, Glos.
Pew Corner, Guildford, Surrey.
Antique Church Furnishings, Walton-on-Thames, Surrey.
Cardiff Reclamation, Cardiff, Wales.

Clocks & Watches
City Clocks, London EC1.
Frosts of Clerkenwell Ltd, London EC1.
Sugar Antiques, London N1.
Strike One, London N5.
North London Clock Shop Ltd, London SE25.
R.E. Rose FBHI, London SE9.
Camerer Cuss and Co, London SW1.
John Carlton-Smith, London SW1.
Charles Frodsham & Co Ltd, London SW1.
Harrods Ltd, London SW1.
Somlo Antiques, London SW1.
The Clock Clinic Ltd, London SW15.
W. F. Turk Antique Clocks, London SW20.
Norman Adams Ltd, London SW3.
Big Ben Antique Clocks, London SW6.
Gutlin Clocks and Antiques, London SW6.
A. & H. Page (Est. 1840), London SW7.
Carrington and Co. Ltd, London W1.

Mallett and Son (Antiques) Ltd, London W1.
Mallett at Bourdon House Ltd, London W1.
Pendulum of Mayfair Ltd, London W1.
Ronald Phillips Ltd, London W1.
Michael Rose - Source of the Unusual, London W1.
The Royal Arcade Watch Shop, London W1.
Central Gallery (Portobello), London W11.
Chelsea Clocks & Antiques, London W11.
Gavin Douglas Fine Antiques Ltd, London W11.
Kleanthous Antiques, London W11.
Mayflower Antiques, London W11.
Old Father Time Clock Centre, London W11.
The Silver Fox Gallery (Portobello), London W11.
David Brower Antiques, London W8.
Raffety & Walwyn, London W8.
Roderick Antique Clocks, London W8.
The London Silver Vaults, London WC2.
House of Clocks, Ampthill, Beds.
The Clock Workshop, Caversham, Berks.
The Old Malthouse, Hungerford, Berks.
Times Past Antiques, Windsor and Eton, Berks.
Wyrardisbury Antiques, Wraysbury, Berks.
Carlton Clocks, Amersham, Bucks.
M.V. Tooley, CMBHI, Chesham, Bucks.
Peter Wright Antiques, Great Missenden, Bucks.
Robin Unsworth Antiques, Olney, Bucks.
Peter Norman Antiques and Restorations, Burwell, Cambs.

SPECIALIST DEALERS

John Beazor and Sons Ltd, Cambridge, Cambs.

T. W. Pawson - Clocks, Somersham, Cambs.

Antiques & Curios (Steve Carpenter), Wisbech, Cambs.

Adams Antiques, Chester, Cheshire.

Chapel Antiques, Nantwich, Cheshire.

Coppelia Antiques, Plumley, Cheshire.

Little Jem's, Penzance, Cornwall.

Saint Nicholas Galleries Ltd. (Antiques and Jewellery), Carlisle, Cumbria.

G.K. Hadfield, Great Salkeld, Cumbria.

David Hill, Kirkby Stephen, Cumbria.

Derbyshire Clocks, Glossop, Derbys.

Around the Clock, Brixham, Devon.

Musgrave Bickford Antiques, Crediton, Devon.

Gold and Silver Exchange, Exeter, Devon.

John Nathan Antiques, Exeter, Devon.

Honiton Clock Clinic, Honiton, Devon.

Leigh Extence, Antique Clocks, Shaldon, Devon.

M.C. Taylor, Bournemouth, Dorset.

Derek J. Burgess - Horologist, Parkstone, Dorset.

Keeble Antiques, Sherborne, Dorset.

Timecraft Clocks, Sherborne, Dorset.

Tom Tribe and Son, Sturminster Newton, Dorset.

Eden House Antiques, West Auckland, Durham.

Mark Marchant (Antiques), Coggeshall, Essex.

Antique Clock Repair Shoppe, Gants Hill, Essex.

Chris L. Papworth Antique Clocks and Watches, Kelvedon, Essex.

It's About Time, Westcliff-on-Sea, Essex.

Antique Corner with A & C Antique Clocks, Bristol, Glos.

Montpellier Clocks, Cheltenham, Glos.

School House Antiques, Chipping Campden, Glos.

Arthur S. Lewis, Gloucester, Glos.

Jeffrey Formby Antiques, Moreton-in-Marsh, Glos.

Jillings Antiques - Distinctive Antique Clocks, Newent, Glos.

Keith Harding's World of Mechanical Music, Northleach, Glos.

Styles of Stow, Stow-on-the-Wold, Glos.

Vanbrugh House Antiques, Stow-on-the-Wold, Glos.

Evans and Evans, Alresford, Hants.

Clockwise, Emsworth, Hants.

A.W. Porter and Son, Hartley Wintney, Hants.

Barry Papworth, Lymington, Hants.

Gaylords, Titchfield, Hants.

The Clock Workshop (Winchester), Winchester, Hants.

G.E. Marsh Antique Clocks Ltd, Winchester, Hants.

Robin Lloyd Antiques, Ross-on-Wye, Herefs.

Howards, Baldock, Herts.

David Penney, Bishop's Stortford, Herts.

Robert Horton Antiques, Hertford, Herts.

The Clock Shop - Philip Setterfield of St. Albans, St. Albans, Herts.

Country Clocks, Tring, Herts.

Weston Antiques, Weston, Herts.

John Corrin Antiques, Douglas, Isle of Man.

Ye Olde Village Clock Shop, Freshwater, Isle of Wight.

John Chawner, Birchington, Kent.

Old Manor House Antiques, Brasted, Kent.

PatricCapon, Bromley, Kent.

Michael Sim, Chislehurst, Kent.

Gem Antiques, Maidstone, Kent.

City Antiques Ltd, Rochester, Kent.

Michael Fitch Antiques, Sandgate, Kent.

Neill Robinson Blaxill, Sevenoaks, Kent.

Gem Antiques, Sevenoaks, Kent.

Gaby's Clocks and Things, Tenterden, Kent.

Derek Roberts Fine Antique Clocks & Barometers, Tonbridge, Kent.

B.V.M. Somerset, Tonbridge, Kent.

Aaron Antiques, Tunbridge Wells, Kent.

Pantiles Spa Antiques, Tunbridge Wells, Kent.

Payne & Son (Silversmiths) Ltd, Tunbridge Wells, Kent.

The Vintage Watch Co., Tunbridge Wells, Kent.

The Old Clock Shop, West Malling, Kent.

Regal Antiques, Westerham, Kent.

Tankerton Antiques, Whitstable, Kent.

Drop Dial Antiques, Bolton, Lancs.

Harrop Fold Clocks (F. Robinson), Bolton-by-Bowland, Lancs.

Brittons - Watches and Antiques, Clitheroe, Lancs.

Fieldings Antiques, Haslingden, Lancs.

P.W. Norgrove - Antique Clocks, Haslingden, Lancs.

Charles Howell Jeweller, Oldham, Lancs.

H.C. Simpson and Sons Jewellers (Oldham) Ltd, Oldham, Lancs.

Hackler's Jewellers, Preston, Lancs.

Edmund Davies & Son Antiques, Whalley, Lancs.

Northern Clocks, Worsley, Lancs.

Lowe of Loughborough, Loughborough, Leics.

Oaktree Antiques, Lubenham, Leics.

Charles Antiques, Whitwick, Leics.

N. Bryan-Peach Antiques, Wymeswold, Leics.

Trade Antiques, Alford, Lincs.

Robin Fowler (Period Clocks), Aylesby, Lincs.

Grantham Clocks, Grantham, Lincs.

Marcus Wilkinson, Grantham, Lincs.

Second Time Around, Hemswell Cliff, Lincs.

David J. Hansord & Son, Lincoln, Lincs.

Timepiece Repairs, Lincoln, Lincs.

Marcus Wilkinson, Sleaford, Lincs.

Penman Clockcare (UK) Ltd, Spalding, Lincs.

Kevin Whay's Clocks & Antiques, Hoylake, Merseyside.

Howard Antiques & Fine Art, Southport, Merseyside.

Weldons Jewellery and Antiques, Southport, Merseyside.

Rita Shenton, Twickenham, Middx.

Village Clocks, Coltishall, Norfolk.

R.C. Woodhouse (Antiquarian Horologist), Hunstanton, Norfolk.

Tim Clayton Jewellery & Antiques, King's Lynn, Norfolk.

Jennifer and Raymond Norman Antiques, Needham, Norfolk.

Keith Lawson Antique Clocks, Scratby, Norfolk.

Parriss, Sheringham, Norfolk.

Norton Antiques, Twyford, Norfolk.

M.C. Chapman, Finedon, Northants.

Michael Jones Jeweller, Northampton, Northants.

Gordon Caris, Alnwick, Northumbs.

Gordon Caris, Hexham, Northumbs.

Goodacre Engraving, Sutton Bonington, Notts.

Horseshoe Antiques and Gallery, Burford, Oxon.

Hubert's Antiques, Burford, Oxon.

Jonathan Howard, Chipping Norton, Oxon.

Craig Barfoot, East Hagbourne, Oxon.

Rosemary and Time, Thame, Oxon.

Witney Antiques, Witney, Oxon.

C. Reynolds Antiques, Oakham, Rutland.

Mytton Antiques, Atcham, Shrops.

R.G. Cave and Sons Ltd, Ludlow, Shrops.

Mitre House Antiques, Ludlow, Shrops.

Corner Farm Antiques, Shifnal, Shrops.

Adrian Donnelly Antique Clocks, Shrewsbury, Shrops.

Dodington Antiques, Whitchurch, Shrops.

Kembery Antique Clocks Ltd, Bath, Somerset.

Quiet Street Antiques, Bath, Somerset.

Bernard G. House, Wells, Somerset.

The Essence of Time, Lichfield, Staffs.

James A. Jordan, Lichfield, Staffs.

Winder's Fine Art and Antiques, Newcastle-under-Lyme, Staffs.

R.A. James - The Clock Shop, Tutbury, Staffs.

Clock House, Leavenheath, Suffolk.

Suthburgh Antiques, Long Melford, Suffolk.

Village Clocks, Long Melford, Suffolk.

Edward Manson (Clocks), Woodbridge, Suffolk.

Antique Clocks by Patrick Thomas, Dorking, Surrey.

The Howard Gallery, Dorking, Surrey.

The Coach House Antiques, Gomshall, Surrey.

Roger A. Davis Antiquarian Horologist, Great Bookham, Surrey.

Horological Workshops, Guildford, Surrey.

Surrey Clock Centre, Haslemere, Surrey.

Hill Rise Antiques, Richmond, Surrey.

B. M. and E. Newlove, Surbiton, Surrey.

S. Warrender and Co, Sutton, Surrey.

The Clock Shop Weybridge, Weybridge, Surrey.

Yellow Lantern Antiques Ltd, Brighton, Sussex East.

W. Bruford, Eastbourne, Sussex East.

John Cowderoy Antiques, Eastbourne, Sussex East.

Coach House Antiques, Hastings, Sussex East.

Lewes Clock Shop, Lewes, Sussex East.

The Old Mint House, Pevensey, Sussex East.

Arundel Clocks, Arundel, Sussex West.

The Clock Shop, Hurstpierpoint, Sussex West.

Churchill Clocks, Midhurst, Sussex West.

Baskerville Antiques, Petworth, Sussex West.

Thakeham Furniture, Pulborough, Sussex West.

Peter Smith Antiques, Sunderland, Tyne and Wear.

Time in Hand, Shipston-on-Stour, Warks.

Summersons, Warwick, Warks.

R. Collyer, Birmingham, West Mids.

F. Meeks & Co, Birmingham, West Mids.

M. Allen Watch and Clockmaker, Four Oaks, West Mids.

Avon Antiques, Bradford-on-Avon, Wilts.

Moxhams Antiques, Bradford-on-Avon, Wilts.

Trevor Waddington Antique Clocks, Bradford-on-Avon, Wilts.

P.A. Oxley Antique Clocks and Barometers, Cherhill, Wilts.

Time Restored & Co, Pewsey, Wilts.

Inglenook Antiques, Ramsbury, Wilts.

Salisbury Antiques Warehouse Ltd, Salisbury, Wilts.

Chris Wadge Clocks, Salisbury, Wilts.

Allan Smith Antique Clocks, Swindon, Wilts.

Hansen Chard Antiques, Pershore, Worcs.

The Barber's Clock, Worcester, Worcs.

Time and Motion, Beverley, Yorks. East.

Lewis E. Hickson FBHI, Gilberdyke, Yorks. East.

Milestone Antiques, Easingwold, Yorks. North.

Chris Wilde Antiques, Harrogate, Yorks. North.

Middleham Antiques, Middleham, Yorks. North.

Brian Loomes, Pateley Bridge, Yorks. North.

Tomlinsons, Tockwith, Yorks. North.

Harpers Jewellers, York, Yorks. North.

Keith Stones Grandfather Clocks, Bessacarr, Yorks. South.

Fishlake Antiques, Fishlake, Yorks. South.

F S Antiques, Sheffield, Yorks. South.

Clock House Antiques, Keighley, Yorks. West.

Robert Christie Antiques, Carrickfergus, Co. Antrim, N. Ireland.

Fourwinds Antiques, Moira, Co. Armagh, N. Ireland.

Time & Tide Antiques, Portaferry, Co. Down, N. Ireland.

Stephen Cohu Antiques, St Ouen, Jersey, C.I.

Ian Burton Antique Clocks, Auchterarder, Scotland.

SPECIALIST DEALERS

The Clock Showrooms, Canonbie, Scotland.
Bow-well Antiques, Edinburgh, Scotland.
Craiglea Clocks, Edinburgh, Scotland.
Donald Ellis incorporating Bruntsfield Clocks,
    Edinburgh, Scotland.
Harlequin Antiques, Edinburgh, Scotland.
John Whyte, Edinburgh, Scotland.
Brown's Clocks, Glasgow, Scotland.
Bygones, Huntly, Scotland.
Silvertime, Brecon, Wales.
Snowdonia Antiques, Llanrwst, Wales.
Neath Antiques, Neath, Wales.
Rodney Adams Antiques, Pwllheli, Wales.

Coins & Medals
George Rankin Coin Co. Ltd, London E2.
C.J. Martin (Coins) Ltd, London N14.
Christopher Eimer, London NW11.
Vale Stamps and Antiques, London SE3.
The Armoury of St. James's Military
    Antiquarians, London SW1.
Knightsbridge Coins, London SW1.
Beaver Coin Room, London SW5.
Michael Coins, London W8.
Simmons Gallery, London WC1.
Spink and Son Ltd, London WC1.
A.H. Baldwin and Sons Ltd, London WC2.
M. Bord (Gold Coin Exchange), London WC2.
Philip Cohen Numismatics, London WC2.
Trafalgar Square Collectors Centre, London
    WC2.
Valued History, Ely, Cambs.
B.R.M. Coins, Knutsford, Cheshire.
Souvenir Antiques, Carlisle, Cumbria.
Penrith Coin and Stamp Centre, Penrith,
    Cumbria.
Sterling Coins and Medals, Bournemouth,
    Dorset.
Dorset Coin Company, Parkstone, Dorset.
The Treasure Chest, Weymouth, Dorset.
Robin Finnegan (Jeweller), Darlington, Durham.
J. Shotton Antiquarian Books, Prints and Coins,
    Durham, Durham.
Potter's Antiques and Coins, Bristol, Glos.
Military Curios, HQ84, Gloucester, Glos.
Peter Morris, Bromley, Kent.
World Coins, Canterbury, Kent.
The Coin and Jewellery Shop, Accrington,
    Lancs.
Chard Coins, Blackpool, Lancs.
Gold and Silver Exchange, Great Yarmouth,
    Norfolk.
Clive Dennett Coins, Norwich, Norfolk.
Collectors World, Nottingham, Notts.
D.D. and A. Ingle, Nottingham, Notts.
NSE Medal Dept., Nottingham, Notts.
Barbara Radman, Witney, Oxon.
Bath Stamp and Coin Shop, Bath, Somerset.
Neate Militaria & Antiques, Sudbury, Suffolk.

St. Pancras Antiques, Chichester, Sussex West.
Intercoin, Newcastle-upon-Tyne, Tyne and Wear.
Format of Birmingham Ltd, Birmingham, West
    Mids.
Castle Galleries, Salisbury, Wilts.
Whitmore, Great Malvern, Worcs.
B.B.M. Coins, Kidderminster, Worcs.
C.J. and A.J. Dixon Ltd., Bridlington, Yorks. East.
Cookstown Antiques, Cookstown, Co. Tyrone,
    N.Ireland.
The Collectors Shop, Edinburgh, Scotland.
Edinburgh Coin Shop, Edinburgh, Scotland.
A.D. Hamilton and Co., Glasgow, Scotland.
Abbey Antiques, Stirling, Scotland.
Glance Back Bookshop, Chepstow, Wales.

Dolls & Toys
Donay Games & Pastimes, London N1.
Judith Lassalle, London N1.
Yesterday Child, London N1.
Dolly Land, London N21.
Bearly Trading of London, London SE20.
Engine 'n' Tender, London SE25.
Mimi Fifi, London W11.
Victoriana Dolls, London W11.
London Antique Gallery, London W8.
Rosina's, Falmouth, Cornwall.
Abbey House, Derby, Derbys.
Honiton Antique Toys, Honiton, Devon.
The Vintage Toy and Train Shop, Sidmouth,
    Devon.
Boscombe Models and Collectors Shop,
    Bournemouth, Dorset.
Rectory Rocking Horses, Pamphill, Dorset.
Tilly's Antiques, Leigh-on-Sea, Essex.
The Doll's House, Northleach, Glos.
Park House Antiques, Stow-on-the-Wold, Glos.
Peter Pan's of Gosport, Gosport, Hants.
The Attic, Baldock, Herts.
London House Antiques, Westerham, Kent.
C. and K.E. Dring, Lincoln, Lincs.
Norwich Collectors Toyshop, Norwich, Norfolk.
Granny's Attic, Nottingham, Notts.
Trench Puzzles, Stowmarket, Suffolk.
C.A.R.S. (Classic Automobilia & Regalia
    Specialists), Brighton, Sussex East.
Paul Goble Jewellers, Brighton, Sussex East.
Sue Pearson, Brighton, Sussex East.
Coach House Antiques, Hastings, Sussex East.
Recollect Dolls Hospital, Burgess Hill, Sussex
    West.
Antiquated, Petworth, Sussex West.
Cross's Curios, Birmingham, West Mids.
Dolly Mixtures, Birmingham, West Mids.
Broadway Dolls and Bears, Broadway, Worcs.
Grannie's Parlour, Hull, Yorks. East.
Classic Rocking Horses, Thirsk, Yorks. North.
Collectors Old Toy Shop and Antiques, Halifax,
    Yorks. West.

Memory Lane, Sowerby Bridge, Yorks. West.

Angus Antiques, Dundee, Scotland.

Bebes et Jouets, Edinburgh, Scotland.

Now and Then (Toy Centre), Edinburgh, Scotland.

Pastimes Vintage Toys, Glasgow, Scotland.

Museum of Childhood Memories, Beaumaris (Anglesey), Wales.

Etchings & Engravings

Gladwell and Company, London EC4.

Moreton Street Gallery, London SW1.

Old Maps and Prints, London SW1.

The Map House, London SW3.

Old Church Galleries, London SW3.

King's Court Galleries, London SW6.

The Wyllie Gallery, London SW7.

Agnew's, London W1.

Victor Arwas Gallery - Editions Graphiques Gallery Ltd, London W1.

Royal Exchange Art Gallery at Cork St., London W1.

William Weston Gallery, London W1.

Justin F. Skrebowski Prints, London W11.

Foye Gallery, Luton, Beds.

Antique Map and Bookshop, Puddletown, Dorset.

Oldfield Gallery, Portsmouth, Hants.

The Shanklin Gallery, Shanklin, Isle of Wight.

G. and D.I. Marrin and Sons, Folkestone, Kent.

London House Antiques, Westerham, Kent.

Graftons of Market Harborough, Market Harborough, Leics.

P.J. Cassidy (Books), Holbeach, Lincs.

TRADA, Chipping Norton, Oxon.

The Barry Keene Gallery, Henley-on-Thames, Oxon.

Elizabeth Harvey-Lee, North Aston, Oxon.

George Gregory, Bath, Somerset.

England's Gallery, Leek, Staffs.

King's Court Galleries, Dorking, Surrey.

Hampton Court Palace Antiques, East Molesey, Surrey.

Limpsfield Watercolours, Limpsfield, Surrey.

Reigate Galleries, Reigate, Surrey.

Palmer Galleries, Richmond, Surrey.

The Witch Ball, Brighton, Sussex East.

Faringdon Gallery, Arundel, Sussex West.

Ronald Carr, Salisbury, Wilts.

Heirloom & Howard Limited, West Yatton, Wilts.

The Drawing Room - Interiors & Antiques, Pershore, Worcs.

Nigel Stacy-Marks Ltd, Auchterarder, Scotland.

Open Eye Gallery Ltd, Edinburgh, Scotland.

Royal Mile Gallery, Edinburgh, Scotland.

Ewan Mundy Fine Art Ltd, Glasgow, Scotland.

Mainhill Gallery, Jedburgh, Scotland.

Killin Gallery, Killin, Scotland.

Nigel Stacy-Marks Ltd, Perth, Scotland.

David Windsor Gallery, Bangor, Wales.

Fire Related Items

Westland London, London EC2.

House of Steel Antiques, London N1.

Chesney's Antique Fireplace Warehouse, London N19.

Amazing Grates - Fireplaces Ltd, London N2.

Acquisitions (Fireplaces) Ltd, London NW5.

Townsends, London NW8.

Ward Antiques, London SE7.

The Fireplace, London SE9.

Nigel A. Bartlett, London SW1.

Nicholas Gifford-Mead, London SW1.

H.W. Poulter and Son, London SW10.

Thornhill Galleries Ltd. in association with A. & R. Dockerill Ltd, London SW15.

Mr Wandle's Workshop Ltd , London SW18.

O.F. Wilson Ltd, London SW3.

Fairfax Antiques and Fireplaces, London SW6.

Fulham Marble, London SW6.

Old World Trading Co, London SW6.

The Chiswick Fireplace Co., London W4.

Architectural Antiques, London W6.

Architectural Antiques, Bedford, Beds.

The Fire Place (Hungerford) Ltd, Hungerford, Berks.

Dismantle and Deal Direct - Architectural Salvage Brokers, Aston Clinton, Bucks.

Grosvenor House Interiors, Beaconsfield, Bucks.

Nostalgia Architectural Antiques, Stockport, Cheshire.

Antique Fireplaces, Tarvin, Cheshire.

Architectural Antiques, Kendal, Cumbria.

W.R.S. Architectural Antiques, Low Newton, Cumbria.

Cumbria Architectural Salvage, Raughton Head, Cumbria.

Staveley Antiques, Staveley, Cumbria.

Finishing Touches, Derby, Derbys.

Havenplan's Architectural Emporium, Killamarsh, Derbys.

Wooden Box Antiques, Woodville, Derbys.

Ashburton Marbles, Ashburton, Devon.

Toby's Architectural Antiques, Torquay, Devon.

Robson's Antiques, Barnard Castle, Durham.

Antique Fireplace Centre, Hartlepool, Durham.

Flame and Grate, Bristol, Glos.

Period Fireplaces, Bristol, Glos.

Cox's Architectural Reclamation Yard, Moreton-in-Marsh, Glos.

The Baldfaced Stag, Ashurst, Kent.

Bygones Reclamation, Canterbury, Kent.

Victorian Fireplace, Canterbury, Kent.

Elham Antiques, Elham, Kent.

Ward Antiques, Sidcup, Kent.

The Architectural Emporium, Tunbridge Wells, Kent.

Past & Present, Clitheroe, Lancs.
Old Smithy, Feniscowles, Lancs.
Antique Fireplace Warehouse, Manchester, Lancs.
In-Situ Manchester, Manchester, Lancs.
In-Situ Manchester South Architectural Antiques, Manchester, Lancs.
Colin Blakey Fireplaces, Nelson, Lancs.
House Things Antiques, Hinckley, Leics.
Britain's Heritage, Leicester, Leics.
D & T Architectural Salvage, Birkenhead, Merseyside.
Antique Fireplaces, Liverpool, Merseyside.
Peco, Hampton, Middx.
Marble Hill Gallery, Twickenham, Middx.
Mongers, Hingham, Norfolk.
Woodside Reclamation (Architectural Antiques), Berwick-upon-Tweed, Northumbs.
Hallidays (Fine Antiques) Ltd, Dorchester-on-Thames, Oxon.
Aston Pine Antiques, Faringdon, Oxon.
Oxford Architectural Antiques, Faringdon, Oxon.
Walcot Reclamation, Bath, Somerset.
Blackbrook Antiques Village, Weeford, Staffs.
Brighton Architectural Salvage, Brighton, Sussex East.
Recollections, Brighton, Sussex East.
Shiners, Snobs Knobs, Jesmond, Tyne and Wear.
Turnburrys, Jesmond, Tyne and Wear.
Tynemouth Architectural Salvage, Tynemouth, Tyne and Wear.
Grate Expectations (Fireplaces), Washington, Tyne and Wear.
The Victorian Ironmonger, Brinklow, Warks.
Tudor House Antiques, Halesowen, West Mids.
Harriet Fairfax Fireplaces and General Antiques, Langley Burrell, Wilts.
The Antique Centre, Kidderminster, Worcs.
Old Flames, Easingwold, Yorks. North.
Robert Aagaard & Co, Knaresborough, Yorks. North.
Andy Thornton Architectural Antiques Ltd, Halifax, Yorks. West.
Chapel House Fireplaces, Holmfirth, Yorks. West.
Kelly Antiques, Omagh, Co. Tyrone, N. Ireland.
P. J. Smith (Antiques), Stewartstown, Co. Tyrone, N. Ireland.
Burning Embers, Aberdeen, Scotland.
EASY - Edinburgh Architectural Salvage Yard, Edinburgh, Scotland.
Holyrood Architectural Salvage, Edinburgh, Scotland.
T. and J. W. Neilson Ltd, Edinburgh, Scotland.
The Renaissance Furniture Store, Glasgow, Scotland.
Flame 'n' Grate, Barry, Wales.
Cardiff Reclamation, Cardiff, Wales.

Kings Fireplaces, Antiques and Interiors, Cardiff, Wales.

Frames
Paul Mason Gallery, London SW1.
Nigel Milne Ltd, London SW1.
Arnold Wiggins and Sons Ltd, London SW1.
Paul Mitchell Ltd, London W1.
Rollo Whately Ltd, London W1.
Daggett Gallery, London W11.
Lacy Gallery, London W11.
Justin F. Skrebowski Prints, London W11.
The Fairhurst Gallery, Norwich, Norfolk.
Looking Glass of Bath, Bath, Somerset.
W. Greenwood (Fine Art), Burneston, Yorks. North.
Coulter Galleries, York, Yorks. North.
Huddersfield Picture Framing Co, Huddersfield, Yorks. West.

Furniture - Continental (mainly French)
Charlton House Antiques, London N1.
Michel André Morin, London N1.
Relic Antiques at Camden Passage, London N1.
C. Tapsell, London N1.
Frames Direct, London N12.
Relic Antiques Trade Warehouse, London NW1.
Davidson and Morgan, London NW8.
The Galleries, London SE1.
Melbourne Antiques & Interiors, London SE22.
Robert E. Hirschhorn, London SE5.
Didier Aaron (London) Ltd, London SW1.
ADEC, London SW1.
Appley Hoare Antiques, London SW1.
Blanchard Ltd, London SW1.
Andi Gisel, London SW1.
Ross Hamilton Ltd, London SW1.
Harris Lindsay, London SW1.
Hermitage Antiques plc, London SW1.
Carlton Hobbs, London SW1.
Christopher Howe, London SW1.
Jeremy Ltd, London SW1.
M. and D. Lewis, London SW1.
Odyssey Fine Arts Ltd, London SW1
Mark Ransom Ltd, London SW1.
Rogier et Rogier, London SW1.
Un Francais á Londres, London SW1.
Thomas Kerr Antiques Ltd, London SW10.
McVeigh & Charpentier, London SW10.
Orientation, London SW10.
David Alexander Antiques & Kate Thurlow, London SW11.
The Woodpigeon, London SW11.
No. 12, London SW3.
Prides of London, London SW3.
O.F. Wilson Ltd, London SW3.
275 Antiques, London SW6.
I. and J.L. Brown Ltd, London SW6.
Rupert Cavendish Antiques, London SW6.

Nicole Fabre, London SW6.
Birdie Fortescue Antiques, London SW6.
Judy Greenwood, London SW6.
Christopher Jones Antiques, London SW6.
Lewin, London SW6.
M. Pauw Antiques, London SW6.
The French House (Antiques) Ltd, London SW8.
Adrian Alan Ltd, London W1.
H. Blairman and Sons Ltd., London W1.
Howard Antiques, London W1.
Mallett at Bourdon House Ltd, London W1.
Partridge Fine Arts plc, London W1.
Pelham Galleries Ltd, London W1.
Jacob Stodel, London W1.
Toynbee-Clarke Interiors Ltd, London W1.
Barham Antiques, London W11.
Curá Antiques, London W11.
M. and D. Lewis, London W11.
Robin Martin Antiques, London W11.
Myriad Antiques, London W11.
Marshall Gallery, London W14.
David Brower Antiques, London W8.
Reindeer Antiques Ltd, London W8.
Sinai Antiques Ltd, London W8.
Pamela Teignmouth and Son, London W8.
David Litt Antiques, Ampthill, Beds.
Ulla Stafford Antiques, Binfield, Berks.
John A. Pearson Antiques, Horton, Berks.
Franklin Antiques, Hungerford, Berks.
Youll's Antiques, Hungerford, Berks.
La Maison, Bourne End, Bucks.
Jack Harness Antiques, Marlow, Bucks.
Archer's Antique and Country Furniture, Olney, Bucks.
Phoenix Antiques, Fordham, Cambs.
Ivor and Patricia Lewis Antique and Fine Art Dealers, Peterborough, Cambs.
Adams Antiques, Chester, Cheshire.
Harris & Holt, Chester, Cheshire.
French Countrystyle, Hale, Cheshire.
Antique Furniture Warehouse, Stockport, Cheshire.
Manchester Antique Company, Stockport, Cheshire.
Old Town Hall Antiques, Falmouth, Cornwall.
West End Galleries, Buxton, Derbys.
R.C. Associates, Cullompton, Devon.
Merchant House Antiques, Honiton, Devon.
Pilgrim Antiques, Honiton, Devon.
Pugh's Farm Antiques, Monkton, Devon.
Colystock Antiques, Stockland, Devon.
Lionel Geneen Ltd, Bournemouth, Dorset.
Georgina Ryder, Frampton, Dorset.
Talisman, Gillingham, Dorset.
Deja Vu Antiques, Leigh-on-Sea, Essex.
August Antiques and Interiors, Moreton-in-Marsh, Glos.
Gary Wright Antiques, Moreton-in-Marsh, Glos.

Ashton Gower Antiques, Stow-on-the-Wold, Glos.
Oonagh Black, Stow-on-the-Wold, Glos.
Annarella Clark Antiques, Stow-on-the-Wold, Glos.
Antony Preston Antiques Ltd, Stow-on-the-Wold, Glos.
The Decorator Source, Tetbury, Glos.
Sieff, Tetbury, Glos.
Geoffrey Stead, Todenham, Glos.
Whittington Barn Antiques, Whittington, Glos.
Cotswold Antiques. com, Winchcombe, Glos.
Artemesia, Alresford, Hants.
Cedar Antiques Limited, Hartley Wintney, Hants.
David Lazarus Antiques, Hartley Wintney, Hants.
Csaky's Antiques, Hook, Hants.
Wick Antiques, Lymington, Hants.
Gray's Antique Centre, Portsmouth, Hants.
Millers of Chelsea Antiques Ltd, Ringwood, Hants.
Antique Eyes, Stockbridge, Hants.
The Bakhtiyar Gallery, Stockbridge, Hants.
I. and J.L. Brown Ltd, Hereford, Herefs.
Great Brampton House Antiques Ltd, Hereford, Herefs.
Royal Standard Antiques, Cowes, Isle of Wight.
The Barn at Bislington, Bilsington, Kent.
Lennox Cato, Edenbridge, Kent.
Samovar Antiques, Hythe, Kent.
Antique Country Furniture and Interiors, Sandgate, Kent.
Henry Baines, Southborough, Kent.
Flower House Antiques, Tenterden, Kent.
Claremont Antiques, Tunbridge Wells, Kent.
Millennium Centre Antiques, Tunbridge Wells, Kent.
Up Country, Tunbridge Wells, Kent.
J. Green and Son, Queniborough, Leics.
Graham Pickett Antiques, Stamford, Lincs.
Birkdale Antiques, Southport, Merseyside.
Antique Interiors, Twickenham, Middx.
Ron Green, Towcester, Northants.
Helios & Co (Antiques), Weedon, Northants.
Jonathan Fyson Antiques, Burford, Oxon.
Gateway Antiques, Burford, Oxon.
Antique English Windsor Chairs, Chipping Norton, Oxon.
Summers Davis Antiques Ltd, Wallingford, Oxon.
Witney Antiques, Witney, Oxon.
Swans, Oakham, Rutland.
Malthouse Antiques, Bridgnorth, Shrops.
Garrard Antiques, Ludlow, Shrops.
Jadis Ltd, Bath, Somerset.
Hennessy, Crewkerne, Somerset.
Pennard House Antiques, East Pennard, Somerset.

SPECIALIST DEALERS

Country Brocante, Godney, Somerset.
Gilbert & Dale, Ilchester, Somerset.
Edward Marnier Antiques, Shepton Mallet,
  Somerset.
Rostrum Antiques, South Petherton, Somerset.
Yew Tree Antiques Warehouse, Wiveliscombe,
  Somerset.
Dix-Sept, Framlingham, Suffolk.
Heath-Bullocks, Godalming, Surrey.
Antique Mart, Richmond, Surrey.
Marryat, Richmond, Surrey.
Dermot and Jill Palmer Antiques, Brighton,
  Sussex East.
Graham Lower, Flimwell, Sussex East.
Graham Price Antiques Ltd, Polegate, Sussex
  East.
Julian Antiques, Hurstpierpoint, Sussex West.
Angel Antiques, Petworth, Sussex West.
Brownrigg, Petworth, Sussex West.
Oliver Charles Antiques, Petworth, Sussex West.
Ruddy Antiques, Petworth, Sussex West.
Little Theatre Antiques Centre, Jesmond, Tyne
  and Wear.
Apollo Antiques Ltd, Warwick, Warks.
L.P. Antiques (Mids) Ltd, Walsall, West Mids.
Avon Antiques, Bradford-on-Avon, Wilts.
Moxhams Antiques, Bradford-on-Avon, Wilts.
St Mary's Chapel Antiques, Devizes, Wilts.
Brocante Antiques Centre, Marlborough, Wilts.
European Accent, Warminster, Wilts.
Obelisk Antiques, Warminster, Wilts.
Coopers of Ilkley, Ilkley, Yorks. West.
Jacquart Antiques, Holywood, Co. Down, N.
  Ireland.
Whytock and Reid, Edinburgh, Scotland.
Jeremy Sniders Antiques, Glasgow, Scotland.
Michael Vee Design - Birch House Antiques,
  Melrose, Scotland.
Mynde Art and Antiques, Usk, Wales.

Furniture - County
At the Sign of the Chest of Drawers, London
  N6.
Relic Antiques Trade Warehouse, London NW1.
M. and D. Seligmann, London NW3.
Robert E. Hirschhorn, London SE5.
Rogier et Rogier, London SW1.
The Furniture Cave, London SW10.
Robert Young Antiques, London SW11.
Simon Coleman Antiques, London SW13.
I. and J.L. Brown Ltd, London SW6.
Alistair Sampson Antiques Ltd, London W1.
The Hampden Trading Company, Great
  Missenden, Bucks.
Jack Harness Antiques, Marlow, Bucks.
Simon and Penny Rumble Antiques, Chittering,
  Cambs.
A.P. and M.A. Haylett, Outwell, Cambs.
Boustead-Bland Antiques, Chester, Cheshire.

Farmhouse Antiques, Chester, Cheshire.
Adams Antiques, Nantwich, Cheshire.
Julie Strachey, Connor Downs, Cornwall.
Blackwater Pine Antiques, Truro, Cornwall.
Simon Starkie Antiques, Cartmel, Cumbria.
David Hill, Kirkby Stephen, Cumbria.
Utopia Antiques Ltd, Low Newton, Cumbria.
Sandgate Antiques, Penrith, Cumbria.
Winton Hall Antiques, Ravenstonedale,
  Cumbria.
Pine and Decorative Items, Ashbourne, Derbys.
Peter Bunting Antiques, Bakewell, Derbys.
Byethorpe Furniture, Barlow, Derbys.
Godolphin Antiques, Chagford, Devon.
Rex Antiques, Chagford, Devon.
Cobweb Antiques, Cullompton, Devon.
Miller Antiques, Cullompton, Devon.
The Grove Antiques Centre, Honiton, Devon.
Pugh's Farm Antiques, Monkton, Devon.
Timepiece, Teignmouth, Devon.
Fine Pine Antiques, Totnes, Devon.
Macintosh Antiques, Sherborne, Dorset.
English Rose Antiques, Coggeshall, Essex.
The Stores, Great Waltham, Essex.
Lennard Antiques, Sible Hedingham, Essex.
J. and R. Bateman Antiques, Chalford, Glos.
John P. Townsend, Cheltenham, Glos.
Mark Carter Antiques, Fairford, Glos.
Jon Fox Antiques, Moreton-in-Marsh, Glos.
Oonagh Black, Stow-on-the-Wold, Glos.
Annarella Clark Antiques, Stow-on-the-Wold,
  Glos.
Keith Hockin Antiques, Stow-on-the-Wold,
  Glos.
Huntington Antiques Ltd, Stow-on-the-Wold,
  Glos.
The Chest of Drawers, Tetbury, Glos.
Peter Norden Antiques, Tetbury, Glos.
Westwood House Antiques and Beehive
  Antiques, Tetbury, Glos.
Cedar Antiques Limited, Hartley Wintney,
  Hants.
Millers of Chelsea Antiques Ltd, Ringwood,
  Hants.
Burgess Farm Antiques, Winchester, Hants.
The Pine Cellars, Winchester, Hants.
I. and J.L. Brown Ltd, Hereford, Herefs.
Robin Lloyd Antiques, Ross-on-Wye, Herefs.
M. and J. Russell, Yazor, Herefs.
Tim Wharton Antiques, Redbourn, Herts.
Dinah Stoodley & Celia Jennings, Brasted, Kent.
Michael Pearson Antiques, Canterbury, Kent.
Douglas Bryan, Cranbrook, Kent.
Swan Antiques, Cranbrook, Kent.
Elham Antiques, Elham, Kent.
Mill House Antiques, Goudhurst, Kent.
Antique Country Furniture and Interiors,
  Sandgate, Kent.
Henry Baines, Southborough, Kent.

Claremont Antiques, Tunbridge Wells, Kent.
Ivy Hale, Tunbridge Wells, Kent.
Phoenix Antiques, Tunbridge Wells, Kent.
Up Country, Tunbridge Wells, Kent.
Edmund Davies & Son Antiques, Whalley, Lancs.
Oaktree Antiques, Lubenham, Leics.
Quorn Pine and Decoratives, Quorn, Leics.
Hunters Antiques & Interior Design, Stamford, Lincs.
Graham Pickett Antiques, Stamford, Lincs.
Sinclair's, Stamford, Lincs.
Holt Antique Centre, Holt, Norfolk.
Paul Hopwell Antiques, West Haddon, Northants.
Horseshoe Antiques and Gallery, Burford, Oxon.
Swan Gallery, Burford, Oxon.
Antique English Windsor Chairs, Chipping Norton, Oxon.
Key Antiques, Chipping Norton, Oxon.
Dorchester Antiques, Dorchester-on-Thames, Oxon.
Wychwood Antiques, Taynton, Oxon.
Witney Antiques, Witney, Oxon.
Antiques of Woodstock, Woodstock, Oxon.
Chris Baylis Country Chairs, Woodstock, Oxon.
Ark Antiques, Bishop's Castle, Shrops.
John Clegg, Ludlow, Shrops.
Garrard Antiques, Ludlow, Shrops.
G. & D. Ginger Antiques, Ludlow, Shrops.
Mackenzie & Smith Furniture Restoration, Ludlow, Shrops.
Marcus Moore Antiques, Stanton upon Hine Heath, Shrops.
Dodington Antiques, Whitchurch, Shrops.
Lansdown Antiques, Bath, Somerset.
Piccadilly Antiques, Batheaston, Somerset.
Chez Chalon, Chard, Somerset.
Hennessy, Crewkerne, Somerset.
Acorn Antiques, Dulverton, Somerset.
Anthony Sampson Antiques, Dulverton, Somerset.
Gilbert & Dale, Ilchester, Somerset.
Johnson's, Leek, Staffs.
The Suffolk Table Company, Debenham, Suffolk.
Dix-Sept, Framlingham, Suffolk.
The Theatre Antiques Centre, Framlingham, Suffolk.
Noel Mercer Antiques, Long Melford, Suffolk.
Antiques Warehouse (incorporating The Woodbridge Trading Co), Marlesford, Suffolk.
Michael Lewis, Saxmundham, Suffolk.
Suffolk House Antiques, Yoxford, Suffolk.
Stoneycroft Farm, Betchworth, Surrey.
Christopher's Antiques, Farnham, Surrey.
Elm House Antiques, Merstham, Surrey.
Anthony Welling Antiques, Ripley, Surrey.
E. and B. White, Brighton, Sussex East.

Hadlow Down Antiques, Hadlow Down, Sussex East.
Pastorale Antiques, Lewes, Sussex East.
Graham Price Antiques Ltd, Polegate, Sussex East.
Bob Hoare - Pine Antiques, Ringmer, Sussex East.
Ringles Cross Antiques, Uckfield, Sussex East.
Park View Antiques, Wadhurst, Sussex East.
Antiquities, Arundel, Sussex West.
Michael Wakelin and Helen Linfield, Billingshurst, Sussex West.
Alexander Antiques, Henfield, Sussex West.
Angel Antiques, Petworth, Sussex West.
John Bird, Petworth, Sussex west.
J.C. Tutt Antiques, Petworth, Sussex West.
King's Cottage Antiques, Leamington Spa, Warks.
L.P. Antiques (Mids) Ltd, Walsall, West Mids.
Matthew Eden, Corsham, Wilts.
Paul Martin Antiques, Marlborough, Wilts.
Annmarie Turner Antiques, Marlborough, Wilts.
Maxfield House Antiques, Warminster, Wilts.
D & J Lines Antiques, Wychbold, Worcs.
The Antique Pine & Country Furniture Shop, Driffield, Yorks. East.
Country Oak Antiques, Harrogate, Yorks. North.
Elaine Phillips Antiques Ltd, Harrogate, Yorks. North.
York Cottage Antiques, Helmsley, Yorks. North.
Early Oak, Knaresborough, Yorks. North.
Middleham Antiques, Middleham, Yorks. North.
Northern Antiques Company, Norton, Yorks. North.
John Gilbert Antiques, Robin Hood's Bay, Yorks. North.
E. Thistlethwaite, Settle, Yorks. North.
Coach House Antiques, Whitby, Yorks. North.
Ruth Ford Antiques, York, Yorks. North.
Fishlake Antiques, Fishlake, Yorks. South.
Cottage Antiques (1984) Ltd, Walsden, Yorks. West.
Audrey Bull, Carmarthen, Wales.
The Mount Antiques Centre, Carmarthen, Wales.
Havard and Havard, Cowbridge, Wales.
Gallop and Rivers Architectural Antiques, Crickhowell, Wales.
Country Antiques (Wales) Ltd, Kidwelly, Wales.
Islwyn Watkins, Knighton, Wales.
Jim and Pat Ash, Llandeilo, Wales.
Collinge Antiques, Llandudno Junction, Wales.
Michael Lloyd Antiques, Llandysul, Wales.
Heritage Restorations, Llanfair Caereinion, Wales.
Malt House Antiques, Narberth, Wales.
Rodney Adams Antiques, Pwllheli, Wales.
Singleton Antiques, Skenfrith, Wales.
Audrey Bull, Tenby, Wales.

SPECIALIST DEALERS

Furniture - Georgian

Peter Chapman Antiques and Restoration, London N1.
Furniture Vault, London N1.
Jonathan James, London N1.
Regent Antiques, London N1.
Restall Brown and Clennell Ltd, London N1.
C. Tapsell, London N1.
Vane House Antiques, London N1.
Finchley Fine Art Galleries, London N12.
Martin Henham (Antiques), London N2.
Betty Gould and Julian Gonnermann Antiques, London N6.
G. and F. Gillingham Ltd, London NW2.
Patricia Beckman Antiques, London NW3.
Davidson and Morgan, London NW8
Robert Gordon Antiques, London NW8.
Patricia Harvey Antiques and Decoration, London NW8.
Wellington Gallery, London NW8.
Young & Son, London NW8.
The Galleries, London SE1.
Tower Bridge Antiques, London SE1.
The Walpole Galleries, London SE18.
Robert E. Hirschhorn, London SE5.
Antique Warehouse, London SE8.
Anno Domini Antiques, London SW1.
John Bly, London SW1.
Ross Hamilton Ltd, London SW1.
Harrods Ltd, London SW1.
Hotspur Ltd, London SW1.
Christopher Howe, London SW1.
Humphrey-Carrasco, London SW1.
Jeremy Ltd, London SW1.
Westenholz Antiques Ltd, London SW1.
The Furniture Cave, London SW10.
Stephen Long, London SW10.
Pairs Antiques Ltd, London SW11.
The Dining Room Shop, London SW13.
H.C. Baxter and Sons, London SW16.
Norman Adams Ltd, London SW3.
Apter Fredericks Ltd, London SW3.
Richard Courtney Ltd, London SW3.
Robert Dickson and Lesley Rendall Antiques, London SW3.
Michael Foster, London SW3.
General Trading Co Ltd, London SW3.
Godson and Coles, London SW3.
Michael Hughes, London SW3
Anthony James and Son Ltd, London SW3.
Peter Jones at PJ2, London SW3.
John Keil Ltd, London SW3.
Peter Lipitch Ltd, London SW3.
Prides of London, London SW3.
Charles Saunders Antiques, London SW3.
Clifford Wright Antiques Ltd, London SW3.
313 Antiques, London SW6.
Alasdair Brown, London SW6.
John Clay, London SW6.

Fergus Cochrane and Leigh Warren Antiques, London SW6.
Floyd & James Antiques, London SW6.
HRW Antiques (London) Ltd, London SW6.
Christopher Jones Antiques, London SW6.
L. and E. Kreckovic, London SW6.
Michael Luther Antiques, London SW6.
Michael Marriott, London SW6.
David Martin-Taylor Antiques, London SW6.
Ossowski, London SW6.
Anthony Outred, London SW6.
M. Pauw Antiques, London SW6.
Rogers & Co, London SW6.
H. Blairman and Sons Ltd., London W1.
Antoine Cheneviere Fine Arts, London W1.
Sibyl Colefax & John Fowler, London W1.
Halcyon Days, London W1.
Mallett and Son (Antiques) Ltd, London W1.
Partridge Fine Arts plc, London W1.
Pendulum of Mayfair Ltd, London W1.
Ronald Phillips Ltd, London W1.
Scarisbrick and Bate Ltd, London W1.
Jeremy Seale Antiques/Interiors, London W1.
Stair and Company Ltd, London W1.
Toynbee-Clarke Interiors Ltd, London W1.
M. Turpin Ltd, London W1.
Windsor House Antiques Ltd, London W1.
B. and T. Antiques, London W11.
The Coach House, London W11.
Michael Davidson, London W11.
Judy Fox, London W11.
Robin Martin Antiques, London W11.
Trude Weaver, London W11.
Marshall Gallery, London W14.
J. Roger (Antiques) Ltd, London W14.
Aberdeen House Antiques, London W5.
Terrace Antiques, London W5.
Eddy Bardawil, London W8.
Butchoff Antiques, London W8.
C. Fredericks and Son, London W8.
Lewis and Lloyd, London W8.
Reindeer Antiques Ltd, London W8.
Brian Rolleston Antiques Ltd, London W8.
Patrick Sandberg Antiques, London W8.
Pamela Teignmouth and Son, London W8.
Neil Wibroe and Natasha MacIlwaine, London W8.
Fluss and Charlesworth Ltd, London W9.
Paris Antiques, Ampthill, Beds.
Pilgrim Antiques, Ampthill, Beds.
S. and S. Timms Antiques Ltd, Shefford, Beds.
Town Hall Antiques, Woburn, Beds.
Ulla Stafford Antiques, Binfield, Berks.
John A. Pearson Antiques, Horton, Berks.
Franklin Antiques, Hungerford, Berks.
Roger King Antiques, Hungerford, Berks.
The Old Malthouse, Hungerford, Berks.
Turpins Antiques, Hungerford, Berks.
Widmerpool House Antiques, Maidenhead, Berks.

Rupert Landen Antiques, Reading, Berks.
Cavendish Fine Arts, Sonning-on-Thames, Berks.
John Connell - Wargrave Antiques, Wargrave, Berks.
Eton Antiques Partnership, Windsor and Eton, Berks.
Marcelline Herald Antiques, Windsor and Eton, Berks.
Peter J. Martin, Windsor and Eton, Berks.
The Cupboard Antiques, Amersham, Bucks.
June Elsworth - Beaconsfield Ltd, Beaconsfield, Bucks.
Grosvenor House Interiors, Beaconsfield, Bucks.
Period Furniture Showrooms, Beaconsfield, Bucks.
The Sovereign Furniture Gallery, Chesham, Bucks.
The Hampden Trading Company, Great Missenden, Bucks.
Penn Village Antique Centre, Penn, Bucks.
David's, Brampton, Cambs.
Peter Norman Antiques and Restorations, Burwell, Cambs.
Jess Applin Antiques, Cambridge, Cambs.
John Beazor and Sons Ltd, Cambridge, Cambs.
Tavistock Antiques, St. Neots, Cambs.
Sara Frances Antiques, Alderley Edge, Cheshire.
Church Street Antiques, Altrincham, Cheshire.
Eureka Antiques, Bowdon, Cheshire.
Andrew Foott Antiques, Cheadle Hulme, Cheshire.
Adams Antiques, Chester, Cheshire.
Boustead-Bland Antiques, Chester, Cheshire.
Harris & Holt, Chester, Cheshire.
Melody's Antiques, Chester, Cheshire.
Moor Hall Antiques, Chester, Cheshire.
Glynn Interiors, Knutsford, Cheshire.
John Titchner and Sons, Littleton, Cheshire.
David Bedale, Mobberley, Cheshire.
Chapel Antiques, Nantwich, Cheshire.
Nantwich Antiques and The Passage to India, Nantwich, Cheshire.
Coppelia Antiques, Plumley, Cheshire.
Saxon Cross Antiques Emporium, Sandbach, Cheshire.
Manchester Antique Company, Stockport, Cheshire.
Antique Chairs and Museum, Launceston, Cornwall.
Todd's, Launceston, Cornwall.
John Bragg Antiques, Lostwithiel, Cornwall.
Antiques & Fine Art, Penzance, Cornwall.
Victoria Antiques, Wadebridge, Cornwall.
Anthemion - The Antique Shop, Cartmel, Cumbria.
Jennywell Hall Antiques, Crosby Ravensworth, Cumbria.
Haughey Antiques, Kirkby Stephen, Cumbria.
Townhead Antiques, Newby Bridge, Cumbria.

Winton Hall Antiques, Ravenstonedale, Cumbria.
Ashbourne Antiques Ltd, Ashbourne, Derbys.
Pamela Elsom - Antiques, Ashbourne, Derbys.
Martin and Dorothy Harper Antiques, Bakewell, Derbys.
MichaelPembery Antiques, Bakewell, Derbys.
Hackney House Antiques, Barlow, Derbys.
The Antiques Warehouse, Buxton, Derbys.
Ian Morris, Chesterfield, Derbys.
Brian Matsell, Derby, Derbys.
Wayside Antiques, Duffield, Derbys.
Shardlow Antiques Warehouse, Shardlow, Derbys.
Nimbus Antiques, Whaley Bridge, Derbys.
Wooden Box Antiques, Woodville, Derbys.
Antiques Ad Hoc, Ashburton, Devon.
J. Collins and Son, Bideford, Devon.
John Prestige Antiques, Brixham, Devon.
David J. Thorn, Budleigh Salterton, Devon.
Rex Antiques, Chagford, Devon.
Cullompton Old Tannery Antiques, Cullompton, Devon.
Mills Antiques, Cullompton, Devon.
McBains Antiques, Exeter, Devon.
Peter Wadham Antiques, Exeter, Devon.
Roderick Butler, Honiton, Devon.
Alison Gosling Antiques Studio, Honiton, Devon.
The Grove Antiques Centre, Honiton, Devon.
Hermitage Antiques, Honiton, Devon.
Lombard Antiques, Honiton, Devon.
Merchant House Antiques, Honiton, Devon.
Pilgrim Antiques, Honiton, Devon.
Upstairs, Downstairs, Honiton, Devon.
A. E. Wakeman & Sons Ltd, Tedburn St Mary, Devon.
Extence Antiques, Teignmouth, Devon.
Anthony James Antiques, Whimple, Devon.
Lionel Geneen Ltd, Bournemouth, Dorset.
Sainsburys of Bournemouth Ltd, Bournemouth, Dorset.
David Mack Antiques, Branksome, Dorset.
Benchmark Antiques, Bridport, Dorset.
Hamptons, Christchurch, Dorset.
Tower Antiques, Cranborne, Dorset.
Michael Legg Antiques, Dorchester, Dorset.
Legg of Dorchester, Dorchester, Dorset.
Laburnum Antiques, Poole, Dorset.
Stocks and Chairs, Poole, Dorset.
Shaston Antiques, Shaftesbury, Dorset.
Piers Pisani Antiques, Sherborne, Dorset.
Renaissance, Sherborne, Dorset.
James Hardy Antiques Ltd, Barnard Castle, Durham.
Joan and David White Antiques, Barnard Castle, Durham.
Margaret Bedi Antiques & Fine Art, Billingham, Durham.

SPECIALIST DEALERS

Alan Ramsey Antiques, Darlington, Durham.
Eden House Antiques, West Auckland, Durham.
Revival, Abridge, Essex.
Swan Antiques, Baythorne End, Essex.
Colton Antiques, Kelvedon, Essex.
Clive Beardall Antiques, Maldon, Essex.
West Essex Antiques (Stone Hall), Matching Green, Essex.
F.G. Bruschweiler (Antiques) Ltd, Rayleigh, Essex.
W.A. Pinn and Sons, Sible Hedingham, Essex.
Harris Antiques, Thaxted, Essex.
White Roding Antiques, White Roding, Essex.
Peter and Penny Proudfoot, Berkeley, Glos.
The Antiques Warehouse Ltd, Bristol, Glos.
Latchford Antiques, Cheltenham, Glos.
Triton Gallery, Cheltenham, Glos.
Forum Antiques, Cirencester, Glos.
Hares, Cirencester, Glos.
Rankine Taylor Antiques, Cirencester, Glos.
Patrick Waldron Antiques, Cirencester, Glos.
Bernard Weaver Antiques, Cirencester, Glos.
Blenheim Antiques, Fairford, Glos.
Mark Carter Antiques, Fairford, Glos.
August Antiques and Interiors, Moreton-in-Marsh, Glos.
Benton Fine Art, Moreton-in-Marsh, Glos.
Berry Antiques Ltd, Moreton-in-Marsh, Glos.
Dale House Antiques, Moreton-in-Marsh, Glos.
Seaford House Antiques, Moreton-in-Marsh, Glos.
Simply Antiques, Moreton-in-Marsh, Glos.
The Roger Widdas Gallery, Moreton-in-Marsh, Glos.
Gary Wright Antiques, Moreton-in-Marsh, Glos.
Robson Antiques, Northleach, Glos.
Ashton Gower Antiques, Stow-on-the-Wold, Glos.
Duncan J. Baggott, Stow-on-the-Wold, Glos.
Baggott Church Street Ltd, Stow-on-the-Wold, Glos.
Christopher Clarke Antiques Ltd, Stow-on-the-Wold, Glos.
Huntington Antiques Ltd, Stow-on-the-Wold, Glos.
T.M. King-Smith & Simon W. Nutter, Stow-on-the-Wold, Glos.
La Chaise Antique, Stow-on-the-Wold, Glos.
Roger Lamb Antiques & Works of Art, Stow-on-the-Wold, Glos.
Malt House Antiques, Stow-on-the-Wold, Glos.
Antony Preston Antiques Ltd, Stow-on-the-Wold, Glos.
Queens Parade Antiques Ltd, Stow-on-the-Wold, Glos.
Michael Rowland Antiques, Stow-on-the-Wold, Glos.
Stow Antiques, Stow-on-the-Wold, Glos.
Styles of Stow, Stow-on-the-Wold, Glos.

Tudor House, Stow-on-the-Wold, Glos.
Vanbrugh House Antiques, Stow-on-the-Wold, Glos.
Wyndhams, Stow-on-the-Wold, Glos.
Ball and Claw Antiques, Tetbury, Glos.
Breakspeare Antiques, Tetbury, Glos.
The Chest of Drawers, Tetbury, Glos.
JacquelineHall Antiques, Tetbury, Glos.
Bobbie Middleton, Tetbury, Glos.
Paul Nash Antiques, Tetbury, Glos.
Peter Norden Antiques, Tetbury, Glos.
Not Just Antiques, Tetbury, Glos.
Porch House Antiques, Tetbury, Glos.
Berkeley Antiques, Tewkesbury, Glos.
Gainsborough House Antiques, Tewkesbury, Glos.
Whittington Barn Antiques, Whittington, Glos.
Cotswold Antiques. com, Winchcombe, Glos.
In Period Antiques, Winchcombe, Glos.
Prichard Antiques, Winchcombe, Glos.
Mark Blower (Antiques) Ltd, Le Bourg Forest, Guernsey, C.I.
St. James's Gallery Ltd, St. Peter Port, Guernsey, C.I.
Tudor Antiques & Fine Art Ltd, Alresford, Hants.
The Furniture Trading Co, Botley, Hants.
Nicholas Abbott, Hartley Wintney, Hants.
Deva Antiques, Hartley Wintney, Hants.
David Lazarus Antiques, Hartley Wintney, Hants.
Csaky's Antiques, Hook, Hants.
Lita Kaye of Lyndhurst, Lyndhurst, Hants.
Millers of Chelsea Antiques Ltd, Ringwood, Hants.
Antique Eyes, Stockbridge, Hants.
The Bakhtiyar Gallery, Stockbridge, Hants.
Gasson Antiques and Interiors, Tadley, Hants.
Gaylords, Titchfield, Hants.
Burns and Graham, Winchester, Hants.
Great Brampton House Antiques Ltd, Hereford, Herefs.
John Nash Antiques and Interiors, Ledbury, Herefs.
Serendipity, Ledbury, Herefs.
Jeffery Hammond Antiques, Leominster, Herefs.
Linden House Antiques, Leominster, Herefs.
W. John Griffiths Antiques, Ross-on-Wye, Herefs.
Anthony Butt Antiques, Baldock, Herts.
Ralph and Bruce Moss, Baldock, Herts.
The Windhill Antiquary, Bishop's Stortford, Herts.
Tapestry Antiques, Hertford, Herts.
Michael Gander, Hitchin, Herts.
Phillips of Hitchin (Antiques) Ltd, Hitchin, Herts.
Tom Salusbury Antiques, Hitchin, Herts.
J.N. Antiques, Redbourn, Herts.

Tim Wharton Antiques, Redbourn, Herts.
Philip Dawes Antiques, Royston, Herts.
Charnwood Antiques and Arcane Antiques
    Centre, Sawbridgeworth, Herts.
John Bly, Tring, Herts.
New England House Antiques, Tring, Herts.
Weston Antiques, Weston, Herts.
Collins Antiques (F.G. and C. Collins Ltd.),
    Wheathampstead, Herts.
Michael Armson (Antiques) Ltd, Wilstone, Herts.
John Corrin Antiques, Douglas, Isle of Man.
Country House and Cottage Antiques, St Mary,
    Jersey, C.I.
Stephen Cohu Antiques, St Ouen, Jersey, C.I.
Stablegate Antiques, Barham, Kent.
David Barrington, Brasted, Kent.
Keymer Son & Co. Ltd, Brasted, Kent.
Roy Massingham Antiques, Brasted, Kent.
Old Bakery Antiques, Brasted, Kent.
Tilings Antiques, Brasted, Kent.
Conquest House Antiques, Canterbury, Kent.
Chislehurst Antiques, Chislehurst, Kent.
Michael Sim, Chislehurst, Kent.
Vestry Antiques, Cranbrook, Kent.
Lennox Cato, Edenbridge, Kent.
Alan Lord Antiques, Folkestone, Kent.
Mill House Antiques, Goudhurst, Kent.
Newington Antiques, Newington, Kent.
J.D. and R.M. Walters, Rolvenden, Kent.
Christopher Buck Antiques, Sandgate, Kent.
Finch Antiques, Sandgate, Kent.
Michael Fitch Antiques, Sandgate, Kent.
Freeman and Lloyd Antiques, Sandgate, Kent.
David M. Lancefield Antiques, Sandgate, Kent.
J. Luckhurst Antiques, Sandgate, Kent.
James Porter Antiques, Sandwich, Kent.
Gem Antiques, Sevenoaks, Kent.
Sargeant Antiques, Sevenoaks, Kent.
Steppes Hill Farm Antiques, Stockbury, Kent.
Sutton Valence Antiques, Sutton Valence, Kent.
Flower House Antiques, Tenterden, Kent.
Down Lane Hall Antiques, Tunbridge Wells,
    Kent.
Millennium Centre Antiques, Tunbridge Wells,
    Kent.
The Pantiles Antiques, Tunbridge Wells, Kent.
Pantiles Spa Antiques, Tunbridge Wells, Kent.
Phoenix Antiques, Tunbridge Wells, Kent.
John Thompson, Tunbridge Wells, Kent.
Up Country, Tunbridge Wells, Kent.
Apollo Antique Galleries, Westerham, Kent.
Peter Dyke, Westerham, Kent.
London House Antiques, Westerham, Kent.
Taylor-Smith Antiques, Westerham, Kent.
Westerham Antiques Warehouse, Westerham,
    Kent.
Westerham House Antiques, Westerham, Kent.
Laurens Antiques, Whitstable, Kent.
Tankerton Antiques, Whitstable, Kent.

Brun Lea Antiques (J. Waite Ltd), Burnley,
    Lancs.
K.C. Antiques, Darwen, Lancs.
P.J. Brown Antiques, Haslingden, Lancs.
Luigino Vescovi, Morecambe, Lancs.
Alan Grice Antiques, Ormskirk, Lancs.
Old Bakehouse Antiques and Gallery, Broughton
    Astley, Leics.
Ken Smith Antiques Ltd, Enderby, Leics.
Sitting Pretty, Great Glen, Leics.
Withers of Leicester, Hoby, Leics.
Corry's Antiques, Leicester, Leics.
Treedale Antiques, Little Dalby, Leics.
Lowe of Loughborough, Loughborough, Leics.
Oaktree Antiques, Lubenham, Leics.
Walter Moores and Son, Market Harborough,
    Leics.
J. Stamp and Sons, Market Harborough, Leics.
David E. Burrows, Osgathorpe, Leics.
J. Green and Son, Queniborough, Leics.
G. Baker Antiques, Horncastle, Lincs.
Alan Read - Period Furniture, Horncastle, Lincs.
Laurence Shaw Antiques, Horncastle, Lincs.
David J. Hansord & Son, Lincoln, Lincs.
Dawson of Stamford Ltd, Stamford, Lincs.
Hunters Antiques & Interior Design, Stamford,
    Lincs.
Graham Pickett Antiques, Stamford, Lincs.
St. George's Antiques, Stamford, Lincs.
Robin Shield Antiques, Swinstead, Lincs.
Underwoodhall Antiques, Woodhall Spa, Lincs.
V.O.C. Antiques, Woodhall Spa, Lincs.
Stefani Antiques, Liverpool, Merseyside.
Colin Stock, Rainford, Merseyside.
Tony and Anne Sutcliffe Antiques, Southport,
    Merseyside.
Helen Horswill Antiques and Decorative Arts,
    West Kirby, Merseyside.
Tobias Jellinek Antiques, Twickenham, Middx.
A.E. Bush and Partners, Attleborough, Norfolk.
M. and A. Cringle, Burnham Market, Norfolk.
Hamilton Antiques, Burnham Market, Norfolk.
Market House, Burnham Market, Norfolk.
Roger Bradbury Antiques, Coltishall, Norfolk.
Peter Robinson, Heacham, Norfolk.
James Brett, Norwich, Norfolk.
Nicholas Fowle Antiques, Norwich, Norfolk.
Echo Antiques, Reepham, Norfolk.
Country House Antiques, Seething, Norfolk.
Stalham Antique Gallery, Stalham, Norfolk.
Norton Antiques, Twyford, Norfolk.
T.C.S. Brooke, Wroxham, Norfolk.
Courtyard Antiques and Bazaar, Brackley,
    Northants.
Simon Banks Antiques, Finedon, Northants.
M.C. Chapman, Finedon, Northants.
Robert Cheney Antiques, Finedon, Northants.
Blockheads and Granary Antiques, Flore,
    Northants.

SPECIALIST DEALERS

Christopher Jones Antiques, Flore, Northants.
F. and C.H. Cave, Northampton, Northants.
Reindeer Antiques Ltd, Potterspury, Northants.
Barber Antiques, West Haddon, Northants.
Boadens Antiques, Hexham, Northumbs.
Hedley's of Hexham, Hexham, Northumbs.
James Miller Antiques, Wooler, Northumbs.
Dukeries Antiques Centre, Budby, Notts.
A.J. O'Sullivan Antiques, Darlton, Notts.
Antiques across the World, Nottingham, Notts.
Ranby Hall, Retford, Notts.
Strouds (of Southwell Antiques), Southwell, Notts.
William Antiques, Ascott-under-Wychwood, Oxon.
Burford Antique Centre, Burford, Oxon.
Gateway Antiques, Burford, Oxon.
Hubert's Antiques, Burford, Oxon.
David Pickup, Burford, Oxon.
Swan Gallery, Burford, Oxon.
Rupert Hitchcox Antiques, Chalgrove, Oxon.
Georgian House Antiques, Chipping Norton, Oxon.
Hallidays (Fine Antiques) Ltd, Dorchester-on-Thames, Oxon.
Richard J. Kingston, Henley-on-Thames, Oxon.
The Country Seat, Huntercombe, Oxon.
de Albuquerque Antiques, Wallingford, Oxon.
Chris and Lin O'Donnell Antiques, Wallingford, Oxon.
Mike Ottrey Antiques, Wallingford, Oxon.
Summers Davis Antiques Ltd, Wallingford, Oxon.
Cross Antiques, Watlington, Oxon.
Stephen Orton Antiques, Watlington, Oxon.
Colin Greenway Antiques, Witney, Oxon.
W.R. Harvey & Co (Antiques) Ltd, Witney, Oxon.
Joan Wilkins Antiques, Witney, Oxon.
Witney Antiques, Witney, Oxon.
Antiques of Woodstock, Woodstock, Oxon.
The Chair Set - Antiques, Woodstock, Oxon.
Robin Sanders and Sons, Woodstock, Oxon.
Churchgate Antiques, Empingham, Rutland.
Swans, Oakham, Rutland.
Treedale Antiques, Oakham, Rutland.
T.J. Roberts, Uppingham, Rutland.
Woodman's House Antiques, Uppingham, Rutland.
Robert Bingley Antiques, Wing, Rutland.
Mytton Antiques, Atcham, Shrops.
Bayliss Antiques, Ludlow, Shrops.
R.G. Cave and Sons Ltd, Ludlow, Shrops.
Valentyne Dawes Gallery, Ludlow, Shrops.
Raynalds Mansion, Much Wenlock, Shrops.
Corner Farm Antiques, Shifnal, Shrops.
Mansers Antiques, Shrewsbury, Shrops.
Marcus Moore Antiques, Stanton upon Hine Heath, Shrops.

Brian James Antiques, Telford, Shrops.
Dodington Antiques, Whitchurch, Shrops.
A J Antiques, Bath, Somerset.
Lawrence Brass, Bath, Somerset.
Geoffrey Breeze, Bath, Somerset.
Mary Cruz, Bath, Somerset.
Jadis Ltd, Bath, Somerset.
Quiet Street Antiques, Bath, Somerset.
Piccadilly Antiques, Batheaston, Somerset.
M.G.R. Exports, Bruton, Somerset.
Colin Dyte Antiques, Burnham-on-Sea, Somerset.
Chris's Crackers, Carhampton, Somerset.
Guy Dennler Antiques, Dulverton, Somerset.
Alderson, Compton Dando, Somerset.
Anthony Sampson Antiques, Dulverton, Somerset.
The Crooked Window, Dunster, Somerset.
Freshfords, Freshford, Somerset.
Abingdon House Antiques, Ilminster, Somerset.
Edward Marnier Antiques, Shepton Mallet, Somerset.
Rostrum Antiques, South Petherton, Somerset.
The Old Schoolroom Antiques, Wincanton, Somerset.
Wincanton Antiques, Wincanton, Somerset.
J.C. Giddings, Wiveliscombe, Somerset.
John Hamblin, Yeovil, Somerset.
Page Antiques, Leek, Staffs.
Winder's Fine Art and Antiques, Newcastle-under-Lyme, Staffs.
H.W. Heron and Son Ltd, Yoxall, Staffs.
Thompson's Gallery, Aldeburgh, Suffolk.
Saltgate Antiques, Beccles, Suffolk.
P. Dawson Furniture Restorers, Bentley, Suffolk.
Cavendish Rose Antiques, Cavendish, Suffolk.
Robin Butler, Clare, Suffolk.
F.D. Salter Antiques, Clare, Suffolk.
Debenham Antiques, Debenham, Suffolk.
Denzil Grant Antiques, Drinkstone, Suffolk.
English and Continental Antiques, Eye, Suffolk.
The Theatre Antiques Centre, Framlingham, Suffolk.
P & R Antiques Ltd, Halesworth, Suffolk.
Hubbard Antiques, Ipswich, Suffolk.
J. and J. Baker, Lavenham, Suffolk.
Warrens Antiques Warehouse, Leiston, Suffolk.
Sandy Cooke Antiques, Long Melford, Suffolk.
Curtis Antiques, Long Melford, Suffolk.
Alexander Lyall Antiques, Long Melford, Suffolk.
Seabrook Antiques, Long Melford, Suffolk.
Suthburgh Antiques, Long Melford, Suffolk.
Martlesham Antiques, Martlesham, Suffolk.
Frank Collins Antiques, Mendlesham Green, Suffolk.
Napier House Antiques, Sudbury, Suffolk.
Peppers Period Pieces, Wattisfield, Suffolk.
David Gibbins Antiques, Woodbridge, Suffolk.

Hamilton Antiques, Woodbridge, Suffolk.

Anthony Hurst Antiques, Woodbridge, Suffolk.

Sarah Meysey-Thompson Antiques, Woodbridge, Suffolk.

J.C. Heather, Woolpit, Suffolk.

Suffolk House Antiques, Yoxford, Suffolk.

John Anthony Antiques, Bletchingley, Surrey.

Arkell Antiques Ltd, Dorking, Surrey.

Austin Antiques, Dorking, Surrey.

G. D. Blay Antiques, Dorking, Surrey.

Ross Dodsworth Antiques Ltd, Dorking, Surrey.

Dolphin Square Antiques, Dorking, Surrey.

Dorking Desk Shop, Dorking, Surrey.

Hampshires of Dorking, Dorking, Surrey.

Harman's Antiques, Dorking, Surrey.

Holmwood Antiques, Dorking, Surrey.

The Howard Gallery, Dorking, Surrey.

Malthouse Antiques, Dorking, Surrey.

Mayfair Antiques, Dorking, Surrey.

Norfolk House Galleries, Dorking, Surrey.

Elaine Saunderson Antiques, Dorking, Surrey.

The Vinery, Dorking, Surrey.

West Street Antiques, Dorking, Surrey.

Honeypot Antiques, Elstead, Surrey.

Christopher's Antiques, Farnham, Surrey.

Heath-Bullocks, Godalming, Surrey.

The Coach House Antiques, Gomshall, Surrey.

M. J. Bowdery, Hindhead, Surrey.

A. E. Booth & Son, Hook, Surrey.

Glencorse Antiques, Kingston-upon-Thames, Surrey.

Elm House Antiques, Merstham, Surrey.

Michael Andrews Antiques, Milford, Surrey.

F.G. Lawrence and Sons, Redhill, Surrey.

The Gallery, Reigate, Surrey.

M. & M. White Antique & Reproduction Centre, Reigate, Surrey.

Hill Rise Antiques, Richmond, Surrey.

Marryat, Richmond, Surrey.

J. Hartley Antiques Ltd, Ripley, Surrey.

Sage Antiques and Interiors, Ripley, Surrey.

Cockrell Antiques, Surbiton, Surrey.

B. M. and E. Newlove, Surbiton, Surrey.

Clifford and Roger Dade, Thames Ditton, Surrey.

Ian Caldwell, Walton-on-the-Hill and Tadworth, Surrey.

Church House Antiques, Weybridge, Surrey.

Nostradamus Antiques, Weybridge, Surrey.

Alexandria Antiques, Brighton, Sussex East.

Dudley Hume, Brighton, Sussex East.

Patrick Moorhead Antiques, Brighton, Sussex East.

Michael Norman Antiques Ltd, Brighton, Sussex East.

The North Laine Antiques Market, incorporating Alan Fitchett Antiques, Brighton, Sussex East.

Ben Ponting Antiques, Brighton, Sussex East.

Yellow Lantern Antiques Ltd, Brighton, Sussex East.

Dycheling Antiques, Ditchling, Sussex East.

Hadlow Down Antiques, Hadlow Down, Sussex East.

The Old Mint House, Pevensey, Sussex East.

Bragge and Sons, Rye, Sussex East.

Cheyne House, Rye, Sussex East.

East Street Antiques, Rye, Sussex East.

Herbert Gordon Gasson, Rye, Sussex East.

The Old House, Seaford, Sussex East.

Aarquebus Antiques, St. Leonards-on-Sea, Sussex East.

Bygones, Angmering, Sussex West.

Michael Wakelin and Helen Linfield, Billingshurst, Sussex West.

Frensham House Antiques, Chichester, Sussex West.

Gems Antiques, Chichester, Sussex West.

David Foord-Brown Antiques, Cuckfield, Sussex West.

Richard Usher Antiques, Cuckfield, Sussex West.

Ashcombe Coach House, Henfield, Sussex West.

Stable Antiques, Lindfield, Sussex West.

Callingham Antiques, Northchapel, Sussex West.

Antiquated, Petworth, Sussex West.

Ronald G. Chambers Fine Antiques, Petworth, Sussex West.

J. Du Cros Antiques, Petworth, Sussex West.

Elliott's, Petworth, Sussex West.

Richard Gardner Antiques, Petworth, Sussex West.

Granville Antiques, Petworth, Sussex West.

William Hockley Antiques, Petworth, Sussex West.

Marston House, Petworth, Sussex West.

Oliver Charles Antiques, Petworth, Sussex West.

Red Lion Antiques, Petworth, Sussex West.

T.G. Wilkinson Antiques Ltd., Petworth, Sussex West.

Georgia Antiques, Pulborough, Sussex West.

Thakeham Furniture, Pulborough, Sussex West.

Wilsons Antiques, Worthing, Sussex West.

Ian Sharp Antiques Ltd., Tynemouth, Tyne and Wear.

Apollo Antiques Ltd, Warwick, Warks.

William J. Casey Antiques, Warwick, Warks.

Patrick and Gillian Morley Antiques, Warwick, Warks.

James Reeve, Warwick, Warks.

Don Spencer Antiques, Warwick, Warks.

Warwick Antiques Warehouse, Warwick, Warks.

Peter Clark Antiques, Birmingham, West Mids.

Moseley Emporium, Birmingham, West Mids.

Yoxall Antiques, Solihull, West Mids.

Thomas Coulborn and Sons, Sutton Coldfield, West Mids.

Avon Antiques, Bradford-on-Avon, Wilts.

Mac Humble Antiques, Bradford-on-Avon, Wilts.

SPECIALIST DEALERS

Moxhams Antiques, Bradford-on-Avon, Wilts.
Harley Antiques, Christian Malford, Wilts.
Blanchard, Froxfield, Wilts.
Andrew Britten Antiques, Malmesbury, Wilts.
Brocante Antiques Centre, Marlborough, Wilts.
William Cook (Marlborough), Marlborough, Wilts.
Katharine House Gallery, Marlborough, Wilts.
Robert Kime Antiques, Marlborough, Wilts.
Alan Jaffray, Melksham, Wilts.
Ray Best Antiques, Newton Tony, Wilts.
Boston Antiques, Salisbury, Wilts.
Robert Bradley Antiques, Salisbury, Wilts.
Edward Hurst Antiques, Salisbury, Wilts.
Myriad, Salisbury, Wilts.
Salisbury Antiques Warehouse Ltd, Salisbury, Wilts.
Mike Scott Repair & Restoration, Salisbury, Wilts.
Cassidy's Antiques, Warminster, Wilts.
Maxfield House Antiques, Warminster, Wilts.
Obelisk Antiques, Warminster, Wilts.
Bay Tree Antiques, Wilton, Wilts.
A.J. Romain and Sons, Wilton, Wilts.
Barnt Green Antiques, Barnt Green, Worcs.
Stephen Cook Antiques, Broadway, Worcs.
Fenwick and Fenwick Antiques, Broadway, Worcs.
H.W. Keil Ltd, Broadway, Worcs.
Robert Belcher Antiques, Droitwich, Worcs.
Miscellany Antiques, Great Malvern, Worcs.
The Drawing Room - Interiors & Antiques, Pershore, Worcs.
Lower House Fine Antiques, Redditch, Worcs.
Bygones by the Cathedral, Worcester, Worcs.
Bygones of Worcester, Worcester, Worcs.
M. Lees and Sons, Worcester, Worcs.
Priory Antiques, Bridlington, Yorks. East.
Houghton Hall Antiques, Market Weighton, Yorks. East.
Bennett's Antiques & Collectables, Bedale, Yorks. North.
St. James House Antiques, Boroughbridge, Yorks. North.
R.S. Wilson and Sons, Boroughbridge, Yorks. North.
Milestone Antiques, Easingwold, Yorks. North.
Elm Tree Antiques, Flaxton, Yorks. North.
Bernard Dickinson, Gargrave, Yorks. North.
R.N. Myers and Son, Gargrave, Yorks. North.
Nigel Adamson, Harrogate, Yorks. North.
Armstrong, Harrogate, Yorks. North.
Bryan Bowden, Harrogate, Yorks. North.
Derbyshire Antiques Ltd, Harrogate, Yorks. North.
Garth Antiques, Harrogate, Yorks. North.
David Love, Harrogate, Yorks. North.
Charles Lumb and Sons Ltd, Harrogate, Yorks. North.

Thorntons of Harrogate, Harrogate, Yorks. North.
Walker Galleries Ltd, Harrogate, Yorks. North.
Weatherell's of Harrogate Antiques and Fine Arts, Harrogate, Yorks. North.
Chris Wilde Antiques, Harrogate, Yorks. North.
Sturman's Antiques, Hawes, Yorks. North.
John Thompson Antiques, Knaresborough, Yorks. North.
Joan and David White, Manfield, Yorks. North.
Daleside Antiques, Markington, Yorks. North.
Aura Antiques, Masham, Yorks. North.
Milton Holgate, Ripon, Yorks. North.
Sigma Antiques and Fine Art, Ripon, Yorks. North.
Anderson Slater Antiques, Settle, Yorks. North.
Corn Mill Antiques, Skipton, Yorks. North.
Antony, David & Ann Shackleton, Snainton, Yorks. North.
N.J. and C.S. Dodsworth, Spennithorne, Yorks. North.
Tomlinsons, Tockwith, Yorks. North.
Garth Antiques, Whixley, Yorks. North.
Robert Morrison and Son, York, Yorks. North.
Dovetail Antiques, Sheffield, Yorks. South.
The Baildon Furniture Co., Baildon, Yorks. West.
Browgate Antiques, Baildon, Yorks. West.
Bingley Antiques, Haworth, Yorks. West.
Coopers of Ilkley, Ilkley, Yorks. West.
Geary Antiques, Leeds, Yorks. West.
Park Antiques, Menston, Yorks. West.
Victoria Antiques, Alderney, Alderney, C.I.
Oakland Antiques, Belfast, Co. Antrim, N. Ireland.
Dunluce Antiques, Bushmills, Co. Antrim, N. Ireland.
Robert Christie Antiques, Carrickfergus, Co. Antrim, N. Ireland.
MacHenry Antiques, Newtownabbey, Co. Antrim, N. Ireland.
Time & Tide Antiques, Portaferry, Co. Down, N. Ireland.
Millcourt Antiques, Seapatrick, Co. Down, N. Ireland.
Moy Antiques, Moy, Co. Tyrone, N. Ireland.
Kelly Antiques, Omagh, Co. Tyrone, N. Ireland.
Colin Wood (Antiques) Ltd, Aberdeen, Scotland.
Coldstream Antiques, Coldstream, Scotland.
The Magic Lantern, Dunecht, Scotland.
Georgian Antiques, Edinburgh, Scotland.
London Road Antiques, Edinburgh, Scotland.
Whytock and Reid, Edinburgh, Scotland.
Gow Antiques, Forfar, Scotland.
Cathedral Antiques, Fortrose, Scotland.
Butler's Furniture Galleries, Glasgow, Scotland.
Michael Young Antiques at Glencarse, Glencarse, Scotland.
C.S. Moreton (Antiques), Inchture, Scotland.

Kilmacolm Antiques Ltd, Kilmacolm, Scotland.
QS Antiques and Cabinetmakers, Kilmarnock, Scotland.
Rhudle Mill, Kilmichael Glassary, Scotland.
Osborne Antiques, Kirkcudbright, Scotland.
Quarrelwood Art & Antiques Ltd, Kirkmahoe, Scotland.
Michael Vee Design - Birch House Antiques, Melrose, Scotland.
Harper-James, Montrose, Scotland.
Newburgh Antiques, Newburgh, Scotland.
Crossroads Antiques, Prestwick, Scotland.
Coach House Antiques Ltd, Stanley, Scotland.
Cwmgwili Mill, Carmarthen, Wales.
The Mount Antiques Centre, Carmarthen, Wales.
K.W. Finlay Antiques, Ciliau Aeron, Wales.
Havard and Havard, Cowbridge, Wales.
Renaissance Antiques, Cowbridge, Wales.
Gerald Oliver Antiques, Haverfordwest, Wales.
Furn Davies Partnership, Holt, Wales.
Antiques in Wales, Kidwelly, Wales.
J. and R. Langford, Llangollen, Wales.
Snowdonia Antiques, Llanrwst, Wales.
Allam Antiques, Newbridge-on-Wye, Wales.
Rodney Adams Antiques, Pwllheli, Wales.
Barn Court Antiques, Crafts & Tearoom, Templeton, Wales.
F.E. Anderson and Son, Welshpool, Wales.

Furniture - Oak
Robert E. Hirschhorn, London SE5.
Christopher Howe, London SW1.
The Furniture Cave, London SW10.
Robert Young Antiques, London SW11.
Apter Fredericks Ltd, London SW3.
Alistair Sampson Antiques Ltd, London W1.
Beedham Antiques Ltd, Hungerford, Berks.
Simon and Penny Rumble Antiques, Chittering, Cambs.
Melody's Antiques, Chester, Cheshire.
Adams Antiques, Nantwich, Cheshire.
Marhamchurch Antiques, Stratton, Cornwall.
Simon Starkie Antiques, Cartmel, Cumbria.
Jennywell Hall Antiques, Crosby Ravensworth, Cumbria.
Kendal Studios Antiques, Kendal, Cumbria.
Sandgate Antiques, Penrith, Cumbria.
Winton Hall Antiques, Ravenstonedale, Cumbria.
J H S Antiques Ltd, Ashbourne, Derbys.
Peter Bunting Antiques, Bakewell, Derbys.
Richard Glass, Whaley Bridge, Derbys.
Robert Byles and Optimum Brasses, Bampton, Devon.
Rex Antiques, Chagford, Devon.
Cullompton Old Tannery Antiques, Cullompton, Devon.
Shaw Edwards, Hatherleigh, Devon.
Colystock Antiques, Stockland, Devon.

A. E. Wakeman & Sons Ltd, Tedburn St Mary, Devon.
Grant's Antiques, Barnard Castle, Durham.
Freemans Antiques, Roxwell, Essex.
Lennard Antiques, Sible Hedingham, Essex.
Peter and Penny Proudfoot, Berkeley, Glos.
J. and R. Bateman Antiques, Chalford, Glos.
William H. Stokes, Cirencester, Glos.
Mark Carter Antiques, Fairford, Glos.
Duncan J. Baggott, Stow-on-the-Wold, Glos.
Keith Hockin Antiques, Stow-on-the-Wold, Glos.
T.M. King-Smith & Simon W. Nutter, Stow-on-the-Wold, Glos.
Malt House Antiques, Stow-on-the-Wold, Glos.
Michael Rowland Antiques, Stow-on-the-Wold, Glos.
Arthur Seager Antiques, Stow-on-the-Wold, Glos.
Day Antiques, Tetbury, Glos.
Peter Norden Antiques, Tetbury, Glos.
Westwood House Antiques and Beehive Antiques, Tetbury, Glos.
In Period Antiques, Winchcombe, Glos.
Tudor Antiques & Fine Art Ltd, Alresford, Hants.
Quatrefoil, Fordingbridge, Hants.
Cedar Antiques Limited, Hartley Wintney, Hants.
Robin Lloyd Antiques, Ross-on-Wye, Herefs.
M. and J. Russell, Yazor, Herefs.
Tim Wharton Antiques, Redbourn, Herts.
Collins Antiques (F.G. and C. Collins Ltd), Wheathampstead, Herts.
R. Kirby Antiques, Acrise, Kent.
Dinah Stoodley & Celia Jennings, Brasted, Kent.
Michael Pearson Antiques, Canterbury, Kent.
Douglas Bryan, Cranbrook, Kent.
Vestry Antiques, Cranbrook, Kent.
Old English Oak, Sandgate, Kent.
Henry Baines, Southborough, Kent.
Ivy Hale, Tunbridge Wells, Kent.
Edmund Davies & Son Antiques, Whalley, Lancs.
Boulevard Antique and Shipping Centre, Leicester, Leics.
Treedale Antiques, Little Dalby, Leics.
Lowe of Loughborough, Loughborough, Leics.
Sinclair's, Stamford, Lincs.
Tobias Jellinek Antiques, Twickenham, Middx.
Pearse Lukies, Aylsham, Norfolk.
James Brett, Norwich, Norfolk.
Courtyard Antiques and Bazaar, Brackley, Northants.
Paul Hopwell Antiques, West Haddon, Northants.
Horseshoe Antiques and Gallery, Burford, Oxon.
Swan Gallery, Burford, Oxon.
Antique English Windsor Chairs, Chipping Norton, Oxon.

Key Antiques, Chipping Norton, Oxon.
Quillon Antiques of Tetsworth, Tetsworth, Oxon.
Witney Antiques, Witney, Oxon.
Antiques of Woodstock, Woodstock, Oxon.
Treedale Antiques, Oakham, Rutland.
G. & D. Ginger Antiques, Ludlow, Shrops.
Mackenzie & Smith Furniture Restoration, Ludlow, Shrops.
Marcus Moore Antiques, Stanton upon Hine Heath, Shrops.
Dodington Antiques, Whitchurch, Shrops.
Stuart Interiors Ltd, Barrington, Somerset.
Lawrence Brass, Bath, Somerset.
Anthony Sampson Antiques, Dulverton, Somerset.
The Crooked Window, Dunster, Somerset.
John Nicholls, Leigh, Staffs.
Winder's Fine Art and Antiques, Newcastle-under-Lyme, Staffs.
P. Dawson Furniture Restorers, Bentley, Suffolk.
Quercus, Debenham, Suffolk.
Denzil Grant Antiques, Drinkstone, Suffolk.
J. and J. Baker, Lavenham, Suffolk.
Curtis Antiques, Long Melford, Suffolk.
Noel Mercer Antiques, Long Melford, Suffolk.
Seabrook Antiques, Long Melford, Suffolk.
Suthburgh Antiques, Long Melford, Suffolk.
Trident Antiques, Long Melford, Suffolk.
Frank Collins Antiques, Mendlesham Green, Suffolk.
Peppers Period Pieces, Wattisfield, Suffolk.
Hamilton Antiques, Woodbridge, Suffolk.
Anthony Hurst Antiques, Woodbridge, Suffolk.
Suffolk House Antiques, Yoxford, Suffolk.
Stoneycroft Farm, Betchworth, Surrey.
Malthouse Antiques, Dorking, Surrey.
Sage Antiques and Interiors, Ripley, Surrey.
Anthony Welling Antiques, Ripley, Surrey.
B. M. and E. Newlove, Surbiton, Surrey.
Graham Lower, Flimwell, Sussex East.
Herbert Gordon Gasson, Rye, Sussex East.
Monarch Antiques, St. Leonards-on-Sea, Sussex East.
Ringles Cross Antiques, Uckfield, Sussex East.
Park View Antiques, Wadhurst, Sussex East.
Marston House, Petworth, Sussex West.
King's Cottage Antiques, Leamington Spa, Warks.
James Reeve, Warwick, Warks.
Mac Humble Antiques, Bradford-on-Avon, Wilts.
Louis Stanton, Mere, Wilts.
Boston Antiques, Salisbury, Wilts.
A.J. Romain and Sons, Wilton, Wilts.
Stephen Cook Antiques, Broadway, Worcs.
H.W. Keil Ltd, Broadway, Worcs.
Old Hall Antiques, Burton Salmon, Yorks. North.
R.N. Myers and Son, Gargrave, Yorks. North.

Country Oak Antiques, Harrogate, Yorks. North.
Derbyshire Antiques Ltd, Harrogate, Yorks. North.
Elaine Phillips Antiques Ltd, Harrogate, Yorks. North.
Thorntons of Harrogate, Harrogate, Yorks. North.
York Cottage Antiques, Helmsley, Yorks. North.
Early Oak, Knaresborough, Yorks. North.
Middleham Antiques, Middleham, Yorks. North.
John Gilbert Antiques, Robin Hood's Bay, Yorks. North.
Coach House Antiques, Whitby, Yorks. North.
Cwmgwili Mill, Carmarthen, Wales.
Country Antiques (Wales) Ltd, Kidwelly, Wales.
Allam Antiques, Newbridge-on-Wye, Wales.
Singleton Antiques, Skenfrith, Wales.

Furniture - Pine
Chest of Drawers, London N1.
Old School (Gardens & Interiors), London N19.
At the Sign of the Chest of Drawers, London N6.
Abbott Antiques and Country Pine, London SE26.
The Furniture Cave, London SW10.
The Pine Mine (Crewe-Read Antiques), London SW6.
The Pine Parlour, Ampthill, Beds.
Dee's Antique Pine, Windsor and Eton, Berks.
Bourne End Antiques Centre, Bourne End, Bucks.
T. Smith, Chalfont St. Giles, Bucks.
Jack Harness Antiques, Marlow, Bucks.
Archer's Antique and Country Furniture, Olney, Bucks.
Pine Antiques, Olney, Bucks.
Ward Thomas Antiques, Balsham, Cambs.
Cambridge Pine, Bottisham, Cambs.
Rookery Farm Antiques, Ely, Cambs.
Marie West Antiques, Ely, Cambs.
Abbey Antiques, Ramsey, Cambs.
Melody's Antiques, Chester, Cheshire.
Antique and Country Pine Ltd, Crewe, Cheshire.
Town House Antiques, Marple Bridge, Cheshire.
Chapel Antiques, Nantwich, Cheshire.
The White House, Waverton, Cheshire.
Pine and Period Furniture, Grampound, Cornwall.
Blackwater Pine Antiques, Truro, Cornwall.
Ben Eggleston Antiques Ltd, Long Marton, Cumbria.
Utopia Antiques Ltd, Low Newton, Cumbria.
Pine and Decorative Items, Ashbourne, Derbys.
Friargate Pine Company Ltd, Derby, Derbys.
Pine Antiques Workshop, Doveridge, Derbys.
Michael Allcroft Antiques, Hayfield, Derbys.
Wooden Box Antiques, Woodville, Derbys.
Pennsylvania Pine Co, Ashburton, Devon.

W.G. Potter and Son, Axminster, Devon.
Robert Byles and Optimum Brasses, Bampton, Devon.
Cobweb Antiques, Cullompton, Devon.
Cullompton Old Tannery Antiques, Cullompton, Devon.
C. Short Antiques, Great Torrington, Devon.
Annterior Antiques, Plymouth, Devon.
Colystock Antiques, Stockland, Devon.
King Street Curios, Tavistock, Devon.
Fine Pine Antiques, Totnes, Devon.
Chorley-Burdett Antiques, Bournemouth, Dorset.
English Rose Antiques, Coggeshall, Essex.
Partners in Pine, Coggeshall, Essex.
Phoenix Trading, Frinton-on-Sea, Essex.
The Stores, Great Waltham, Essex.
Fox and Pheasant Antique Pine, White Colne, Essex.
Oldwoods, Bristol, Glos.
Relics - Pine Furniture, Bristol, Glos.
John P. Townsend, Cheltenham, Glos.
Parlour Farm Antiques, Cirencester, Glos.
Berkeley Antiques, Tewkesbury, Glos.
Thornbury Antiques, Thornbury, Glos.
Campden Country Pine Antiques, Winchcombe, Glos.
The Furniture Trading Co, Botley, Hants.
Squirrels, Brockenhurst, Hants.
Buckingham's, Cadnam, Hants.
The Pine Barn, Crawley, Hants.
The Pine Emporium, Hursley, Hants.
Burgess Farm Antiques, Winchester, Hants.
The Pine Cellars, Winchester, Hants.
Waterfall Antiques, Ross-on-Wye, Herefs.
Country Life Interiors, Bushey, Herts.
The Pine Emporium, Hemel Hempstead, Herts.
Richard Back 2 Wood, Appledore, Kent.
Antique and Design, Canterbury, Kent.
Pinetum, Canterbury, Kent.
Vestry Antiques, Cranbrook, Kent.
Farningham Pine, Farningham, Kent.
Harriet Ann Sleigh Beds, Rolvenden, Kent.
Old English Pine, Sandgate, Kent.
Claremont Antiques, Tunbridge Wells, Kent.
Ann and Peter Christian, Blackpool, Lancs.
House Things Antiques, Hinckley, Leics.
Country Pine Antiques, Market Bosworth, Leics.
David E. Burrows, Osgathorpe, Leics.
Quorn Pine and Decoratives, Quorn, Leics.
R. A. James Antiques, Sileby, Leics.
Bell Antiques, Grimsby, Lincs.
Kate, Hemswell Cliff, Lincs.
Andrew Thomas, Stamford, Lincs.
Antiques & Gifts, Downham Market, Norfolk.
Earsham Hall Pine, Earsham, Norfolk.
Heathfield Antiques & Country Pine, Holt, Norfolk.
Holt Antique Centre, Holt, Norfolk.

Echo Antiques, Reepham, Norfolk.
Laila Gray Antiques, Kingsthorpe, Northants.
The Country Pine Shop, West Haddon, Northants.
Bailiffgate Antique Pine, Alnwick, Northumbs.
Jack Spratt Antiques, Newark, Notts.
Harlequin Antiques, Nottingham, Notts.
Aston Pine Antiques, Faringdon, Oxon.
Cotswold Pine & Associates, Middle Aston, Oxon.
Ark Antiques, Bishop's Castle, Shrops.
Garrard Antiques, Ludlow, Shrops.
Arty Faherty, Market Drayton, Shrops.
Lansdown Antiques, Bath, Somerset.
Antiques and Country Pine, Crewkerne, Somerset.
Hennessy, Crewkerne, Somerset.
Burton Antiques, Burton-on-Trent, Staffs.
Justin Pinewood Ltd, Burton-on-Trent, Staffs.
Antiques Within Ltd, Leek, Staffs.
Anvil Antiques Ltd, Leek, Staffs.
Gemini Trading, Leek, Staffs.
Roger Haynes - Antiques Finder, Leek, Staffs.
Coblands Farm Antiques, Depden, Suffolk.
The Theatre Antiques Centre, Framlingham, Suffolk.
Joyce Hardy Pine and Country Furniture, Hacheston, Suffolk.
Orwell Furniture For Life, Ipswich, Suffolk.
Vintage Pine, Long Melford, Suffolk.
Mildenhall Antique Furniture, Mildenhall, Suffolk.
Michael Lewis, Saxmundham, Suffolk.
House of Christian, Ash Vale, Surrey.
Cherub Antiques, Carshalton, Surrey.
M. & M. White Antique & Reproduction Centre, Reigate, Surrey.
The Packhouse, Runfold, Surrey.
Antique Church Furnishings, Walton-on-Thames, Surrey.
Hadlow Down Antiques, Hadlow Down, Sussex East.
Pastorale Antiques, Lewes, Sussex East.
Graham Price Antiques Ltd, Polegate, Sussex East.
Ann Lingard - Rope Walk Antiques, Rye, Sussex East.
Park View Antiques, Wadhurst, Sussex East.
Antiquities, Arundel, Sussex West.
Stable Antiques, Lindfield, Sussex West.
John Bird, Petworth, Sussex west.
Red Lion Antiques, Petworth, Sussex West.
Northumbria Pine, Whitley Bay, Tyne and Wear.
The Old Pine House, Leamington Spa, Warks.
Pine and Things, Shipston-on-Stour, Warks.
Christopher Peters Antiques, Warwick, Warks.
Tudor House Antiques, Halesowen, West Mids.
North Wilts Exporters, Brinkworth, Wilts.
Philip A. Ruttleigh Antiques incorporating

Crudwell Furniture, Crudwell, Wilts.
Pillars Antiques, Lyneham, Wilts.
Sambourne House Antiques Ltd, Swindon,
Wilts.
Gerard Guy Antiques, Bewdley, Worcs.
St. James Antiques, Little Malvern, Worcs.
The Antique Pine & Country Furniture Shop,
Driffield, Yorks. East.
Imperial Antiques, Hull, Yorks. East.
L.L. Ward and Son, Brandsby, Yorks. North.
Old Hall Antiques, Burton Salmon, Yorks.
North.
Milestone Antiques, Easingwold, Yorks. North.
The Main Pine Co, Green Hammerton, Yorks.
North.
Michael Green Pine & Country Antiques,
Harrogate, Yorks. North.
Havelocks, Harrogate, Yorks. North.
Shieling Antiques, Harrogate, Yorks. North.
Westway Pine, Helmsley, Yorks. North.
Daleside Antiques, Markington, Yorks. North.
Northern Antiques Company, Norton, Yorks.
North.
Manor Barn, Skipton, Yorks. North.
Eskdale Antiques, Sleights, Yorks. North.
Millgate Pine & Antiques, Thirsk, Yorks. North.
Ruth Ford Antiques, York, Yorks. North.
St. John Antiques, York, Yorks. North.
Fishlake Antiques, Fishlake, Yorks. South.
Penistone Pine and Antiques, Penistone, Yorks.
South.
Beech House, Sheffield, Yorks. South.
Dovetail Antiques, Sheffield, Yorks. South.
Aberford Antiques Ltd t/a Aberford Country
Furniture, Aberford, Yorks. West.
Cottingley Antiques, Bradford, Yorks. West.
K.L.M. & Co. Antiques, Lepton, Yorks. West.
Cottage Antiques, Pontefract, Yorks. West.
Memory Lane, Sowerby Bridge, Yorks. West.
Cottage Antiques (1984) Ltd, Walsden, Yorks.
West.
The Pine Collection, St. Peter Port, Guernsey,
C.I.
Herbert Gould and Co., Holywood, Co. Down,
N.Ireland.
Ashley Pine, Saintfield, Co. Down, N. Ireland.
Attic Antiques, Saintfield, Co. Down, N. Ireland.
Balindullagh Barn Antique Pine, Ballinamallard,
Co. Fermanagh, N. Ireland.
Homes, Pubs and Clubs, Coleraine, Co.
Londonderry, N. Ireland.
Moy Antique Pine, Moy, Co. Tyrone, N. Ireland.
Times Past Antiques, Auchterarder, Scotland.
London Road Antiques, Edinburgh, Scotland.
QS Antiques and Cabinetmakers, Kilmarnock,
Scotland.
Abbey Antiques, Stirling, Scotland.
The Furniture Cave, Aberystwyth, Wales.
Cwmgwili Mill, Carmarthen, Wales.

Jim and Pat Ash, Llandeilo, Wales.
Heritage Restorations, Llanfair Caereinion,
Wales.
Carrington House, Llanrwst, Wales.
Frost Antiques & Pine, Monmouth, Wales.
Trading Post, Mountain Ash, Wales.
Potboard Antiques, Tenby, Wales.

Furniture - Victorian
Old Cottage Antiques, London E11.
Peter Chapman Antiques and Restoration,
London N1.
Furniture Vault, London N1.
Jonathan James, London N1.
Chris Newland Antiques, London N1.
The Passage Antiques London N1
Regent Antiques, London N1.
Restall Brown and Clennell Ltd, London N1.
Marcus Ross Antiques, London N1.
C. Tapsell, London N1.
Finchley Fine Art Galleries, London N12.
Frames Direct, London N12.
Michael Slade Antiques, London N4
Betty Gould and Julian Gonnermann Antiques,
London N6.
Dome Antiques (Exports) Ltd, London N7.
Solomon, London N8.
G. and F. Gillingham Ltd, London NW2.
Patricia Beckman Antiques, London NW3.
Church Street Antiques, London NW8.
Robert Gordon Antiques, London NW8.
Just Desks, London NW8.
Wellington Gallery, London NW8.
Young & Son, London NW8.
The Galleries, London SE1.
Tower Bridge Antiques, London SE1.
The Waterloo Trading Co., London SE10.
Robert Whitfield Antiques, London SE10.
The Walpole Galleries, London SE18.
Abbott Antiques and Country Pine, London
SE26.
Oola Boola Antiques London, London SE26.
Ward Antiques, London SE7.
Antique Warehouse, London SE8.
Hilary Batstone Antiques inc. Rose Uniacke
Interiors, London SW1.
John Bly, London SW1.
Ross Hamilton Ltd, London SW1.
Harrods Ltd, London SW1.
Christopher Howe, London SW1.
Humphrey-Carrasco, London SW1.
M. and D. Lewis, London SW1.
Westenholz Antiques Ltd, London SW1.
Christopher Edwards, London SW11.
Garland Antiques, London SW11.
Overmantels, London SW11.
Pairs Antiques Ltd, London SW11.
A. and J. Fowle, London SW16.
Just a Second, London SW18.

General Trading Co Ltd, London SW3.
Michael Hughes, London SW3
Prides of London, London SW3.
275 Antiques, London SW6.
Alasdair Brown, London SW6.
John Clay, London SW6.
Fergus Cochrane and Leigh Warren Antiques, London SW6.
HRW Antiques (London) Ltd, London SW6.
L. and E. Kreckovic, London SW6.
Michael Luther Antiques, London SW6.
David Martin-Taylor Antiques, London SW6.
Rogers & Co, London SW6.
Adrian Alan Ltd, London W1.
Jeremy Seale Antiques/Interiors, London W1.
Windsor House Antiques Ltd, London W1.
Barham Antiques, London W11.
Judy Fox, London W11.
Graham and Green, London W11.
M. and D. Lewis, London W11.
Trude Weaver, London W11.
Marshall Gallery, London W14.
Craven Gallery, London W2.
Aberdeen House Antiques, London W5.
Terrace Antiques, London W5.
Butchoff Antiques, London W8.
Haslam and Whiteway, London W8.
Lewis and Lloyd, London W8.
Pamela Teignmouth and Son, London W8.
Paris Antiques, Ampthill, Beds.
Pilgrim Antiques, Ampthill, Beds.
W. J. West Antiques, Potton, Beds.
S. and S. Timms Antiques Ltd, Shefford, Beds.
Manor Antiques, Wilstead (Wilshamstead), Beds.
Town Hall Antiques, Woburn, Beds.
Franklin Antiques, Hungerford, Berks.
Roger King Antiques, Hungerford, Berks.
Hill Farm Antiques, Leckhampstead, Berks.
Widmerpool House Antiques, Maidenhead, Berks.
Rupert Landen Antiques, Reading, Berks.
John Connell - Wargrave Antiques, Wargrave, Berks.
Eton Antiques Partnership, Windsor and Eton, Berks.
Peter J. Martin, Windsor and Eton, Berks.
Studio 101, Windsor and Eton, Berks.
The Cupboard Antiques, Amersham, Bucks.
June Elsworth - Beaconsfield Ltd, Beaconsfield, Bucks.
Period Furniture Showrooms, Beaconsfield, Bucks.
The Sovereign Furniture Gallery, Chesham, Bucks.
Robin Unsworth Antiques, Olney, Bucks.
Penn Village Antique Centre, Penn, Bucks.
David's, Brampton, Cambs.
Jess Applin Antiques, Cambridge, Cambs.

Comberton Antiques, Comberton, Cambs.
Ivor and Patricia Lewis Antique and Fine Art Dealers, Peterborough, Cambs.
Antiques & Curios (Steve Carpenter), Wisbech, Cambs.
Sara Frances Antiques, Alderley Edge, Cheshire.
Church Street Antiques, Altrincham, Cheshire.
Andrew Foott Antiques, Cheadle Hulme, Cheshire.
Boustead-Bland Antiques, Chester, Cheshire.
Moor Hall Antiques, Chester, Cheshire.
The Old Warehouse Antiques, Chester, Cheshire.
W. Buckley Antiques Exports, Congleton, Cheshire.
Glynn Interiors, Knutsford, Cheshire.
John Titchner and Sons, Littleton, Cheshire.
Limited Editions, Mobberley, Cheshire.
Chapel Antiques, Nantwich, Cheshire.
Nantwich Antiques and The Passage to India, Nantwich, Cheshire.
Saxon Cross Antiques Emporium, Sandbach, Cheshire.
Country Living Antiques, Callington, Cornwall.
Old Town Hall Antiques, Falmouth, Cornwall.
Antique Chairs and Museum, Launceston, Cornwall.
John Bragg Antiques, Lostwithiel, Cornwall.
Ruby Antiques Ltd, Penryn, Cornwall.
Antiques & Fine Art, Penzance, Cornwall.
Victoria Antiques, Wadebridge, Cornwall.
Anthemion - The Antique Shop, Cartmel, Cumbria.
Haughey Antiques, Kirkby Stephen, Cumbria.
MichaelPembery Antiques, Bakewell, Derbys.
Hackney House Antiques, Barlow, Derbys.
The Antiques Warehouse, Buxton, Derbys.
Maggie Mays, Buxton, Derbys.
Ian Morris, Chesterfield, Derbys.
Wayside Antiques, Duffield, Derbys.
Nimbus Antiques, Whaley Bridge, Derbys.
Wooden Box Antiques, Woodville, Derbys.
Antiques Ad Hoc, Ashburton, Devon.
John Prestige Antiques, Brixham, Devon.
Mills Antiques, Cullompton, Devon.
Eclectique, Exeter, Devon.
McBains Antiques, Exeter, Devon.
Alison Gosling Antiques Studio, Honiton, Devon.
Hermitage Antiques, Honiton, Devon.
Lombard Antiques, Honiton, Devon.
Merchant House Antiques, Honiton, Devon.
Upstairs, Downstairs, Honiton, Devon.
Farthings, Lynton, Devon.
Pugh's Farm Antiques, Monkton, Devon.
The Antique Dining Room, Totnes, Devon.
Anthony James Antiques, Whimple, Devon.
Woodbury Antiques, Woodbury, Devon.
Chorley-Burdett Antiques, Bournemouth, Dorset.

SPECIALIST DEALERS

Victorian Chairman, Bournemouth, Dorset.
David Mack Antiques, Branksome, Dorset.
Benchmark Antiques, Bridport, Dorset.
Hamptons, Christchurch, Dorset.
Tower Antiques, Cranborne, Dorset.
Michael Legg Antiques, Dorchester, Dorset.
Hardy Country, Melbury Osmond, Dorset.
Laburnum Antiques, Poole, Dorset.
Stocks and Chairs, Poole, Dorset.
Shaston Antiques, Shaftesbury, Dorset.
Piers Pisani Antiques, Sherborne, Dorset.
Renaissance, Sherborne, Dorset.
James Hardy Antiques Ltd, Barnard Castle,
    Durham.
Joan and David White Antiques, Barnard Castle,
    Durham.
Margaret Bedi Antiques & Fine Art, Billingham,
    Durham.
Alan Ramsey Antiques, Darlington, Durham.
Paraphernalia, Norton, Durham.
Eden House Antiques, West Auckland, Durham.
Revival, Abridge, Essex.
Swan Antiques, Baythorne End, Essex.
Argentum Antiques, Coggeshall, Essex.
Colton Antiques, Kelvedon, Essex.
Deja Vu Antiques, Leigh-on-Sea, Essex.
Tilly's Antiques, Leigh-on-Sea, Essex.
Clive Beardall Antiques, Maldon, Essex.
West Essex Antiques (Stone Hall), Matching
    Green, Essex.
F.G. Bruschweiler (Antiques) Ltd, Rayleigh,
    Essex.
Bush Antiques, Saffron Walden, Essex.
Harris Antiques, Thaxted, Essex.
It's About Time, Westcliff-on-Sea, Essex.
White Roding Antiques, White Roding, Essex.
Peter and Penny Proudfoot, Berkeley, Glos.
The Antiques Warehouse Ltd, Bristol, Glos.
Bristol Guild of Applied Art Ltd, Bristol, Glos.
Oldwoods, Bristol, Glos.
Latchford Antiques, Cheltenham, Glos.
Cottage Farm Antiques, Chipping Campden,
    Glos.
Patrick Waldron Antiques, Cirencester, Glos.
Bernard Weaver Antiques, Cirencester, Glos.
Blenheim Antiques, Fairford, Glos.
Mark Carter Antiques, Fairford, Glos.
August Antiques and Interiors, Moreton-in-
    Marsh, Glos.
Benton Fine Art, Moreton-in-Marsh, Glos.
Berry Antiques Ltd, Moreton-in-Marsh, Glos.
Dale House Antiques, Moreton-in-Marsh, Glos.
Seaford House Antiques, Moreton-in-Marsh,
    Glos.
Simply Antiques, Moreton-in-Marsh, Glos.
Gary Wright Antiques, Moreton-in-Marsh, Glos.
Robson Antiques, Northleach, Glos.
Ashton Gower Antiques, Stow-on-the-Wold,
    Glos.

Christopher Clarke Antiques Ltd, Stow-on-the-
    Wold, Glos.
T.M. King-Smith & Simon W. Nutter, Stow-on-
    the-Wold, Glos.
La Chaise Antique, Stow-on-the-Wold, Glos.
Queens Parade Antiques Ltd, Stow-on-the-Wold,
    Glos.
Styles of Stow, Stow-on-the-Wold, Glos.
Tudor House, Stow-on-the-Wold, Glos.
Wyndhams, Stow-on-the-Wold, Glos.
Ball and Claw Antiques, Tetbury, Glos.
Balmuir House Antiques, Tetbury, Glos.
The Chest of Drawers, Tetbury, Glos.
Bobbie Middleton, Tetbury, Glos.
Porch House Antiques, Tetbury, Glos.
Berkeley Antiques, Tewkesbury, Glos.
Whittington Barn Antiques, Whittington, Glos.
Cotswold Antiques. com, Winchcombe, Glos.
Tudor Antiques & Fine Art Ltd, Alresford,
    Hants.
The Furniture Trading Co, Botley, Hants.
Eversley Antiques, Eversley, Hants.
Former Glory, Gosport, Hants.
Deva Antiques, Hartley Wintney, Hants.
Plestor Barn Antiques, Liss, Hants.
Wick Antiques, Lymington, Hants.
Gray's Antique Centre, Portsmouth, Hants.
Antique Eyes, Stockbridge, Hants.
Gasson Antiques and Interiors, Tadley, Hants.
Gaylords, Titchfield, Hants.
Warings of Hereford, Hereford, Herefs.
John Nash Antiques and Interiors, Ledbury,
    Herefs.
Serendipity, Ledbury, Herefs.
Jeffery Hammond Antiques, Leominster, Herefs.
Linden House Antiques, Leominster, Herefs.
W. John Griffiths Antiques, Ross-on-Wye,
    Herefs.
Anthony Butt Antiques, Baldock, Herts.
Wareside Antiques, Cottered, Herts.
Tapestry Antiques, Hertford, Herts.
Phillips of Hitchin (Antiques) Ltd, Hitchin,
    Herts.
Tom Salusbury Antiques, Hitchin, Herts.
J.N. Antiques, Redbourn, Herts.
Philip Dawes Antiques, Royston, Herts.
Charnwood Antiques and Arcane Antiques
    Centre, Sawbridgeworth, Herts.
New England House Antiques, Tring, Herts.
Collins Antiques (F.G. and C. Collins Ltd.),
    Wheathampstead, Herts.
The Old Bakery Antiques, Wheathampstead,
    Herts.
Michael Armson (Antiques) Ltd, Wilstone,
    Herts.
John Corrin Antiques, Douglas, Isle of Man.
Royal Standard Antiques, Cowes, Isle of Wight.
Stablegate Antiques, Barham, Kent.
Courtyard Antiques, Brasted, Kent.

Keymer Son & Co. Ltd, Brasted, Kent.
Roy Massingham Antiques, Brasted, Kent.
Old Bakery Antiques, Brasted, Kent.
Conquest House Antiques, Canterbury, Kent.
Chislehurst Antiques, Chislehurst, Kent.
Alan Lord Antiques, Folkestone, Kent.
Mill House Antiques, Goudhurst, Kent.
Samovar Antiques, Hythe, Kent.
Newington Antiques, Newington, Kent.
Northfleet Hill Antiques, Northfleet, Kent.
J.D. and R.M. Walters, Rolvenden, Kent.
Finch Antiques, Sandgate, Kent.
Michael Fitch Antiques, Sandgate, Kent.
David M. Lancefield Antiques, Sandgate, Kent.
J. Luckhurst Antiques, Sandgate, Kent.
BrianWest Antiques, Sandgate, Kent.
Forge Antiques and Restorations, Sandhurst,
    Kent.
Gem Antiques, Sevenoaks, Kent.
Sargeant Antiques, Sevenoaks, Kent.
Staplehurst Antiques, Staplehurst, Kent.
Steppes Hill Farm Antiques, Stockbury, Kent.
Down Lane Hall Antiques, Tunbridge Wells,
    Kent.
The Pantiles Antiques, Tunbridge Wells, Kent.
Pantiles Spa Antiques, Tunbridge Wells, Kent.
Phoenix Antiques, Tunbridge Wells, Kent.
Up Country, Tunbridge Wells, Kent.
Apollo Antique Galleries, Westerham, Kent.
Peter Dyke, Westerham, Kent.
Taylor-Smith Antiques, Westerham, Kent.
Westerham Antiques Warehouse, Westerham,
    Kent.
Westerham House Antiques, Westerham, Kent.
Laurens Antiques, Whitstable, Kent.
Tankerton Antiques, Whitstable, Kent.
Brun Lea Antiques (J. Waite Ltd), Burnley,
    Lancs.
Folly Antiques, Clitheroe, Lancs.
K.C. Antiques, Darwen, Lancs.
P.J. Brown Antiques, Haslingden, Lancs.
R.J. O'Brien and Son Antiques Ltd, Manchester,
    Lancs.
Luigino Vescovi, Morecambe, Lancs.
European Fine Arts and Antiques, Preston,
    Lancs.
The Glory Hole, Earl Shilton, Leics.
Ken Smith Antiques Ltd, Enderby, Leics.
Sitting Pretty, Great Glen, Leics.
House Things Antiques, Hinckley, Leics.
Withers of Leicester, Hoby, Leics.
Corry's Antiques, Leicester, Leics.
Oaktree Antiques, Lubenham, Leics.
J. Stamp and Sons, Market Harborough, Leics.
J. Green and Son, Queniborough, Leics.
Charles Antiques, Whitwick, Leics.
Grantham Furniture Emporium, Grantham,
    Lincs.
G. Baker Antiques, Horncastle, Lincs.

Seaview Antiques, Horncastle, Lincs.
Laurence Shaw Antiques, Horncastle, Lincs.
C. and K.E. Dring, Lincoln, Lincs.
Graham Pickett Antiques, Stamford, Lincs.
Sinclair's, Stamford, Lincs.
St. George's Antiques, Stamford, Lincs.
The Antique Shop, Sutton Bridge, Lincs.
Robin Shield Antiques, Swinstead, Lincs.
Underwoodhall Antiques, Woodhall Spa, Lincs.
V.O.C. Antiques, Woodhall Spa, Lincs.
Stefani Antiques, Liverpool, Merseyside.
Colin Stock, Rainford, Merseyside.
Howard Antiques & Fine Art, Southport,
    Merseyside.
Tony and Anne Sutcliffe Antiques, Southport,
    Merseyside.
Gallerie Veronique, Enfield, Middx.
Hunter's of Hampton, Hampton, Middx.
Antique Interiors, Twickenham, Middx.
A.E. Bush and Partners, Attleborough, Norfolk.
M. and A. Cringle, Burnham Market, Norfolk.
Antiques & Gifts, Downham Market, Norfolk.
Peter Robinson, Heacham, Norfolk.
Eric Bates and Sons Ltd., Hoveton, Norfolk.
Norfolk Galleries, King's Lynn, Norfolk.
Nicholas Fowle Antiques, Norwich, Norfolk.
Echo Antiques, Reepham, Norfolk.
Country House Antiques, Seething, Norfolk.
Stalham Antique Gallery, Stalham, Norfolk.
Jubilee Antiques, Tottenhill, Norfolk.
Brackley Antiques, Brackley, Northants.
Courtyard Antiques and Bazaar, Brackley,
    Northants.
Simon Banks Antiques, Finedon, Northants.
Robert Cheney Antiques, Finedon, Northants.
Blockheads and Granary Antiques, Flore,
    Northants.
Christopher Jones Antiques, Flore, Northants.
F. and C.H. Cave, Northampton, Northants.
Bryan Perkins Antiques, Wellingborough,
    Northants.
Barber Antiques, West Haddon, Northants.
Boadens Antiques, Hexham, Northumbs.
Hedley's of Hexham, Hexham, Northumbs.
James Miller Antiques, Wooler, Northumbs.
Dukeries Antiques Centre, Budby, Notts.
A.J. O'Sullivan Antiques, Darlton, Notts.
Fair Deal Antiques, Mansfield, Notts.
Antiques across the World, Nottingham, Notts.
Ranby Hall, Retford, Notts.
Strouds (of Southwell Antiques), Southwell,
    Notts.
William Antiques, Ascott-under-Wychwood,
    Oxon.
Burford Antique Centre, Burford, Oxon.
Gateway Antiques, Burford, Oxon.
Hubert's Antiques, Burford, Oxon.
David Pickup, Burford, Oxon.
Rupert Hitchcox Antiques, Chalgrove, Oxon.

SPECIALIST DEALERS

Georgian House Antiques, Chipping Norton, Oxon.
Hallidays (Fine Antiques) Ltd, Dorchester-on-Thames, Oxon.
Richard J. Kingston, Henley-on-Thames, Oxon.
The Country Seat, Huntercombe, Oxon.
de Albuquerque Antiques, Wallingford, Oxon.
Chris and Lin O'Donnell Antiques, Wallingford, Oxon.
Cross Antiques, Watlington, Oxon.
Stephen Orton Antiques, Watlington, Oxon.
Colin Greenway Antiques, Witney, Oxon.
W.R. Harvey & Co (Antiques) Ltd, Witney, Oxon.
Joan Wilkins Antiques, Witney, Oxon.
Bees Antiques, Woodstock, Oxon.
Robin Sanders and Sons, Woodstock, Oxon.
Swans, Oakham, Rutland.
T.J. Roberts, Uppingham, Rutland.
Woodman's House Antiques, Uppingham, Rutland.
Robert Bingley Antiques, Wing, Rutland.
Mytton Antiques, Atcham, Shrops.
Malthouse Antiques, Bridgnorth, Shrops.
Portcullis Furniture, Craven Arms, Shrops.
Hodnet Antiques, Hodnet, Shrops.
Bayliss Antiques, Ludlow, Shrops.
Valentyne Dawes Gallery, Ludlow, Shrops.
Corner Farm Antiques, Shifnal, Shrops.
Mansers Antiques, Shrewsbury, Shrops.
Quayside Antiques, Shrewsbury, Shrops.
Brian James Antiques, Telford, Shrops.
A J Antiques, Bath, Somerset.
The Antiques Warehouse, Bath, Somerset.
Lawrence Brass, Bath, Somerset.
Geoffrey Breeze, Bath, Somerset.
Mary Cruz, Bath, Somerset.
Tim Snell Antiques, Bath, Somerset.
Piccadilly Antiques, Batheaston, Somerset.
M.G.R. Exports, Bruton, Somerset.
Colin Dyte Antiques, Burnham-on-Sea, Somerset.
Chris's Crackers, Carhampton, Somerset.
Guy Dennler Antiques, Dulverton, Somerset.
Abingdon House Antiques, Ilminster, Somerset.
Edward Marnier Antiques, Shepton Mallet, Somerset.
Rostrum Antiques, South Petherton, Somerset.
Selwoods, Taunton, Somerset.
TheOld Schoolroom Antiques, Wincanton, Somerset.
Wincanton Antiques, Wincanton, Somerset.
Yew Tree Antiques Warehouse, Wiveliscombe, Somerset.
John Hamblin, Yeovil, Somerset.
Gilligans Antiques, Leek, Staffs.
Page Antiques, Leek, Staffs.
Brett Wilkins Ltd, Lichfield, Staffs.
Winder's Fine Art and Antiques, Newcastle-under-Lyme, Staffs.

White House Antiques, Uttoxeter, Staffs.
H.W. Heron and Son Ltd, Yoxall, Staffs.
Thompson's Gallery, Aldeburgh, Suffolk.
Saltgate Antiques, Beccles, Suffolk.
P. Dawson Furniture Restorers, Bentley, Suffolk.
Cavendish Rose Antiques, Cavendish, Suffolk.
Robin Butler, Clare, Suffolk.
Debenham Antiques, Debenham, Suffolk.
English and Continental Antiques, Eye, Suffolk.
P & R Antiques Ltd, Halesworth, Suffolk.
A. Abbott Antiques, Ipswich, Suffolk.
The Edwardian Shop, Ipswich, Suffolk.
Hubbard Antiques, Ipswich, Suffolk.
Warrens Antiques Warehouse, Leiston, Suffolk.
Alexander Lyall Antiques, Long Melford, Suffolk.
Napier House Antiques, Sudbury, Suffolk.
Peppers Period Pieces, Wattisfield, Suffolk.
Ashe Antiques Warehouse, Wickham Market, Suffolk.
Hamilton Antiques, Woodbridge, Suffolk.
Anthony Hurst Antiques, Woodbridge, Suffolk.
R.A and S.M. Lambert and Son, Woodbridge, Suffolk.
J.C. Heather, Woolpit, Suffolk.
House of Christian, Ash Vale, Surrey.
Country Antiques, Bagshot, Surrey.
Austin Antiques, Dorking, Surrey.
Ross Dodsworth Antiques Ltd, Dorking, Surrey.
Dolphin Square Antiques, Dorking, Surrey.
Dorking Desk Shop, Dorking, Surrey.
Harman's Antiques, Dorking, Surrey.
Holmwood Antiques, Dorking, Surrey.
Malthouse Antiques, Dorking, Surrey.
Mayfair Antiques, Dorking, Surrey.
Norfolk House Galleries, Dorking, Surrey.
The Vinery, Dorking, Surrey.
West Street Antiques, Dorking, Surrey.
Honeypot Antiques, Elstead, Surrey.
Christopher's Antiques, Farnham, Surrey.
The Coach House Antiques, Gomshall, Surrey.
M. J. Bowdery, Hindhead, Surrey.
A. E. Booth & Son, Hook, Surrey.
Glencorse Antiques, Kingston-upon-Thames, Surrey.
Elm House Antiques, Merstham, Surrey.
Michael Andrews Antiques, Milford, Surrey.
F.G. Lawrence and Sons, Redhill, Surrey.
The Gallery, Reigate, Surrey.
Antique Mart, Richmond, Surrey.
Hill Rise Antiques, Richmond, Surrey.
Marryat, Richmond, Surrey.
Sage Antiques and Interiors, Ripley, Surrey.
Cockrell Antiques, Surbiton, Surrey.
B. M. and E. Newlove, Surbiton, Surrey.
Brocante, Weybridge, Surrey.
Church House Antiques, Weybridge, Surrey.
Nostradamus Antiques, Weybridge, Surrey.
Alexandria Antiques, Brighton, Sussex East.

Ashton's Antiques, Brighton, Sussex East.
Dudley Hume, Brighton, Sussex East.
Patrick Moorhead Antiques, Brighton, Sussex East.
The North Laine Antiques Market, incorporating Alan Fitchett Antiques, Brighton, Sussex East.
Ben Ponting Antiques, Brighton, Sussex East.
Colonial Times, Cross in Hand, Sussex East.
Dycheling Antiques, Ditchling, Sussex East.
Timothy Partridge Antiques, Eastbourne, Sussex East.
Hadlow Down Antiques, Hadlow Down, Sussex East.
Coach House Antiques, Hastings, Sussex East.
Potter Antiques, Lewes, Sussex East.
The Old Mint House, Pevensey, Sussex East.
Graham Price Antiques Ltd, Polegate, Sussex East.
Cheyne House, Rye, Sussex East.
East Street Antiques, Rye, Sussex East.
The Old House, Seaford, Sussex East.
Aarquebus Antiques, St. Leonards-on-Sea, Sussex East.
Bygones, Angmering, Sussex West.
W.D. Priddy Antiques, Chichester, Sussex West.
Richard Usher Antiques, Cuckfield, Sussex West.
Stable Antiques, Lindfield, Sussex West.
Callingham Antiques, Northchapel, Sussex West.
Antiquated, Petworth, Sussex West.
J. Du Cros Antiques, Petworth, Sussex West.
Elliott's, Petworth, Sussex West.
Richard Gardner Antiques, Petworth, Sussex West.
Marston House, Petworth, Sussex West.
Red Lion Antiques, Petworth, Sussex West.
Ruddy Antiques, Petworth, Sussex West.
Georgia Antiques, Pulborough, Sussex West.
Wilsons Antiques, Worthing, Sussex West.
Little Theatre Antiques Centre, Jesmond, Tyne and Wear.
Ian Sharp Antiques Ltd., Tynemouth, Tyne and Wear.
Apollo Antiques Ltd, Warwick, Warks.
William J. Casey Antiques, Warwick, Warks.
John Goodwin and Sons, Warwick, Warks.
Patrick and Gillian Morley Antiques, Warwick, Warks.
James Reeve, Warwick, Warks.
Don Spencer Antiques, Warwick, Warks.
Warwick Antiques Warehouse, Warwick, Warks.
Peter Clark Antiques, Birmingham, West Mids.
Moseley Emporium, Birmingham, West Mids.
Martin Taylor Antiques, Wolverhampton, West Mids.
Mac Humble Antiques, Bradford-on-Avon, Wilts.
Cross Hayes Antiques, Chippenham, Wilts.
Blanchard, Froxfield, Wilts.

Andrew Britten Antiques, Malmesbury, Wilts.
Brocante Antiques Centre, Marlborough, Wilts.
WilliamCook (Marlborough), Marlborough, Wilts.
Katharine House Gallery, Marlborough, Wilts.
Alan Jaffray, Melksham, Wilts.
Myriad, Salisbury, Wilts.
Salisbury Antiques Warehouse Ltd, Salisbury, Wilts.
MikeScott Repair & Restoration, Salisbury, Wilts.
Cassidy's Antiques, Warminster, Wilts.
Isabella Antiques, Warminster, Wilts.
Maxfield House Antiques, Warminster, Wilts.
Obelisk Antiques, Warminster, Wilts.
K. and A. Welch, Warminster, Wilts.
Hingstons of Wilton, Wilton, Wilts.
Barnt Green Antiques, Barnt Green, Worcs.
Robert Belcher Antiques, Droitwich, Worcs.
Carlton Antiques, Great Malvern, Worcs.
Miscellany Antiques, Great Malvern, Worcs.
S.W. Antiques, Pershore, Worcs.
Lower House Fine Antiques, Redditch, Worcs.
M. Lees and Sons, Worcester, Worcs.
Priory Antiques, Bridlington, Yorks. East.
Houghton Hall Antiques, Market Weighton, Yorks. East.
Penny Farthing Antiques, North Cave, Yorks. East.
Bennett's Antiques & Collectables, Bedale, Yorks. North.
St. James House Antiques, Boroughbridge, Yorks. North.
R.S. Wilson and Sons, Boroughbridge, Yorks. North.
Milestone Antiques, Easingwold, Yorks. North.
Elm Tree Antiques, Flaxton, Yorks. North.
Garth Antiques, Harrogate, Yorks. North.
David Love, Harrogate, Yorks. North.
Chris Wilde Antiques, Harrogate, Yorks. North.
Sturman's Antiques, Hawes, Yorks. North.
John Thompson Antiques, Knaresborough, Yorks. North.
Lythe Cottage Antiques, Lythe, Yorks. North.
Joan and David White, Manfield, Yorks. North.
Milton Holgate, Ripon, Yorks. North.
Sigma Antiques and Fine Art, Ripon, Yorks. North.
John Gilbert Antiques, Robin Hood's Bay, Yorks. North.
Anderson Slater Antiques, Settle, Yorks. North.
Corn Mill Antiques, Skipton, Yorks. North.
Antony, David & Ann Shackleton, Snainton, Yorks. North.
Robert Morrison and Son, York, Yorks. North.
Acorn Antiques, Sheffield, Yorks. South.
Dovetail Antiques, Sheffield, Yorks. South.
N.P. and A. Salt Antiques, Sheffield, Yorks. South.

Paul Ward Antiques, Sheffield, Yorks. South.
Aberford Antiques Ltd t/a Aberford Country
  Furniture, Aberford, Yorks. West.
The Baildon Furniture Co., Baildon, Yorks.
  West.
Browgate Antiques, Baildon, Yorks. West.
Bingley Antiques, Haworth, Yorks. West.
Aquarius Antiques, Leeds, Yorks. West.
Geary Antiques, Leeds, Yorks. West.
Park Antiques, Menston, Yorks. West.
Victoria Antiques, Alderney, Alderney, C.I.
Country House and Cottage Antiques, St Mary,
  Jersey, C.I.
Stephen Cohu Antiques, St Ouen, Jersey, C.I.
The Country Antiques, Antrim, Co. Antrim, N.
  Ireland.
Oakland Antiques, Belfast, Co. Antrim, N.
  Ireland.
Dunluce Antiques, Bushmills, Co. Antrim, N.
  Ireland.
Robert Christie Antiques, Carrickfergus, Co.
  Antrim, N. Ireland.
MacHenry Antiques, Newtownabbey, Co.
  Antrim, N. Ireland.
Time & Tide Antiques, Portaferry, Co. Down, N.
  Ireland.
Agar Antiques, Saintfield, Co. Down, N. Ireland.
Attic Antiques, Saintfield, Co. Down, N. Ireland.
Millcourt Antiques, Seapatrick, Co. Down, N.
  Ireland.
Moy Antiques, Moy, Co. Tyrone, N. Ireland.
Kelly Antiques, Omagh, Co. Tyrone, N. Ireland.
Colin Wood (Antiques) Ltd, Aberdeen, Scotland.
Treasures of Ballater, Ballater, Scotland.
Coldstream Antiques, Coldstream, Scotland.
The Magic Lantern, Dunecht, Scotland.
Dunkeld Antiques, Dunkeld, Scotland.
Alan Day Antiques, Edinburgh, Scotland.
Georgian Antiques, Edinburgh, Scotland.
London Road Antiques, Edinburgh, Scotland.
Whytock and Reid, Edinburgh, Scotland.
Young Antiques, Edinburgh, Scotland.
Pringle Antiques, Fochabers, Scotland.
Gow Antiques, Forfar, Scotland.
Cathedral Antiques, Fortrose, Scotland.
Butler's Furniture Galleries, Glasgow, Scotland.
Strachan Antiques, Glasgow, Scotland.
Michael Young Antiques at Glencarse,
  Glencarse, Scotland.
Kilmacolm Antiques Ltd, Kilmacolm, Scotland.
QS Antiques and Cabinetmakers, Kilmarnock,
  Scotland.
Rhudle Mill, Kilmichael Glassary, Scotland.
Osborne Antiques, Kirkcudbright, Scotland.
Quarrelwood Art & Antiques Ltd, Kirkmahoe,
  Scotland.
Cobwebs of Lockerbie Ltd, Lockerbie, Scotland.
Michael Vee Design - Birch House Antiques,
  Melrose, Scotland.

Sticks & Stones, Montrose, Scotland.
Newburgh Antiques, Newburgh, Scotland.
Design Interiors and Perth Antiques, Perth,
  Scotland.
A.S. Deuchar and Son, Perth, Scotland.
The Antiques Shop, Pittenweem, Scotland.
Crossroads Antiques, Prestwick, Scotland.
Cwmgwili Mill, Carmarthen, Wales.
The Mount Antiques Centre, Carmarthen, Wales.
Plough House Interiors, Chepstow, Wales.
K.W. Finlay Antiques, Ciliau Aeron, Wales.
North Wales Antiques - Colwyn Bay, Colwyn
  Bay, Wales.
Havard and Havard, Cowbridge, Wales.
Renaissance Antiques, Cowbridge, Wales.
Furn Davies Partnership, Holt, Wales.
Antiques in Wales, Kidwelly, Wales.
Collinge Antiques, Llandudno Junction, Wales.
J. and R. Langford, Llangollen, Wales.
Carrington House, Llanrwst, Wales.
Trading Post, Mountain Ash, Wales.
Allam Antiques, Newbridge-on-Wye, Wales.
Barn Court Antiques, Crafts & Tearoom,
  Templeton, Wales.
Steven Evans Antiques, Treorchy, Wales.
Mynde Art and Antiques, Usk, Wales.

Garden Furniture, Ornaments & Statuary
LASSCO, London EC2.
Westland London, London EC2.
House of Steel Antiques, London N1.
Old School (Gardens & Interiors), London N19.
Relic Antiques Trade Warehouse, London NW1.
Appley Hoare Antiques, London SW1.
Chelminski, London SW6.
Charles Edwards, London SW6.
Mora & Upham Antiques, London SW6.
M. Pauw Antiques, London SW6.
Rodney Franklin Antiques, London SW9 .
Mallett at Bourdon House Ltd, London W1.
Myriad Antiques, London W11.
Marshall Phillips, London W4.
Below Stairs of Hungerford, Hungerford, Berks.
Garden Art, Hungerford, Berks.
The Antique Garden, Chester, Cheshire.
Cheshire Brick and Slate Co, Tarvin Sands,
  Cheshire.
The Great Northern Architectural Antique
  Company Ltd, Tattenhall, Cheshire.
Haughey Antiques, Kirkby Stephen, Cumbria.
Dorset Reclamation, Bere Regis, Dorset.
Talisman, Gillingham, Dorset.
I. Westrope, Birdbrook, Essex.
Jon Fox Antiques, Moreton-in-Marsh, Glos.
Robson Antiques, Northleach, Glos.
Duncan J. Baggott, Stow-on-the-Wold, Glos.
Architectural Heritage, Taddington, Glos.
Jardinique, Beech, Hants.
Baileys Home & Garden, Ross-on-Wye, Herefs.

Philip Dawes Antiques, Royston, Herts.
The Baldfaced Stag, Ashurst, Kent.
Bygones Reclamation, Canterbury, Kent.
Jimmy Warren Antiques, Littlebourne, Kent.
The Architectural Emporium, Tunbridge Wells, Kent.
Folly Antiques, Clitheroe, Lancs.
Lindsey Court Architectural Antiques, Horncastle, Lincs.
Mongers, Hingham, Norfolk.
Renney Antiques, Hexham, Northumbs.
Ranby Hall, Retford, Notts.
John Garner, Uppingham, Rutland.
Antique Centre, Cleobury Mortimer, Shrops.
David Bridgwater, Bath, Somerset.
Source, Bath, Somerset.
Walcot Reclamation, Bath, Somerset.
Austin Antiques, Dorking, Surrey.
Drummonds Architectural Antiques, Hindhead, Surrey.
Sweerts de Landas, Ripley, Surrey.
The Packhouse, Runfold, Surrey.
Brighton Architectural Salvage, Brighton, Sussex East.
Dermot and Jill Palmer Antiques, Brighton, Sussex East.
Spencer Swaffer, Arundel, Sussex West.
Antiquated, Petworth, Sussex West.
John Bird, Petworth, Sussex west.
Matthew Eden, Corsham, Wilts.
Holloways, Suckley, Worcs.
Juro Antiques, Worcester, Worcs.
The White House Antiques & Architectural Reclamation, Easingwold, Yorks. North.
Flaxton Antique Gardens, Flaxton, Yorks. North.
Moy Antiques, Moy, Co. Tyrone, N. Ireland.
Coach House Antiques Ltd, Stanley, Scotland.

Glass - see also Glass Domes & Paperweights
Carol Ketley Antiques, London N1.
Mike Weedon, London N1.
Wilkinson plc, London SE6.
Pullman Gallery, London SW1.
Christine Bridge, London SW13.
The Dining Room Shop, London SW13.
Mark J. West - Cobb Antiques Ltd, London SW19.
W.G.T. Burne (Antique Glass) Ltd, London SW20.
Thomas Goode and Co (London) Ltd, London W1.
Ronald Phillips Ltd, London W1.
Wilkinson plc, London W1.
Mercury Antiques, London W11.
Phillips, London W11.
Craven Gallery, London W2.
Denton Antiques, London W8.
Jeanette Hayhurst Fine Glass, London W8.
Peter Shepherd Antiques, Hurst, Berks.

Cavendish Fine Arts , Sonning-on-Thames, Berks.
Berkshire Antiques Co Ltd , Windsor and Eton, Berks.
Gabor Cossa Antiques, Cambridge, Cambs.
Saxon Cross Antiques Emporium, Sandbach, Cheshire.
Antiques, Marazion, Cornwall.
Just Glass, Alston, Cumbria.
Elizabeth and Son, Ulverston, Cumbria.
Martin and Dorothy Harper Antiques, Bakewell, Derbys.
Wessex Antiques, Sherborne, Dorset.
Robson's Antiques, Barnard Castle, Durham.
Potter's Antiques and Coins, Bristol, Glos.
Latchford Antiques, Cheltenham, Glos.
Rankine Taylor Antiques, Cirencester, Glos.
Grimes House Antiques & Fine Art , Moreton-in-Marsh, Glos.
Sargeant Antiques, Sevenoaks, Kent.
Jack Moore Antiques and Stained Glass, Trawden, Lancs.
Keystone Antiques, Coalville, Leics.
Liz Allport-Lomax, Norwich , Norfolk.
Dorothy's Antiques, Sheringham, Norfolk.
Tillmans Antiques, Potterspury, Northants.
Weedon Antiques, Weedon, Northants.
Laurie Leigh Antiques, Oxford, Oxon.
Joan Wilkins Antiques, Witney, Oxon.
Bees Antiques, Woodstock, Oxon.
Frank Dux Antiques, Bath, Somerset.
Somervale Antiques, Midsomer Norton, Somerset.
Curtis Antiques, Long Melford, Suffolk.
Marryat, Richmond, Surrey.
David R. Fileman, Steyning, Sussex West.
Asylum House Antiques, Bradford-on-Avon, Wilts.
Delomosne and Son Ltd, North Wraxall, Wilts.
Dragon Antiques, Harrogate, Yorks. North.
York Cottage Antiques, Helmsley, Yorks. North.
Dunluce Antiques, Bushmills, Co. Antrim, N. Ireland.
Brian R. Bolt Antiques, Portballintrae, Co. Antrim, N. Ireland.
Peter Francis Antiques, Saintfield, Co. Down, N. Ireland.

Glass Domes
Get Stuffed, London N1.
John Burton Natural Craft Taxidermy, Ebrington, Glos.
Heads 'n' Tails, Wiveliscombe, Somerset.

Icons - see Russian Art

Islamic Art
Hosains Books and Antiques, London NW6.
Atlantic Bay Carpets Gallery, London SW7.

David Aaron Ancient Arts & Rare Carpets, London W1.
Aaron Gallery, London W1.
Emanouel Corporation (UK) Ltd, London W1.
Hadji Baba Ancient Art, London W1.
Mansour Gallery, London W1.
Axia Art Consultants Ltd, London W11.
Sinai Antiques Ltd, London W8.
Clive Rogers Oriental Rugs, Staines, Surrey.

Japanese Art - see Oriental

Jewellery - see Silver

Lighting
Carlton Davidson Antiques, London N1.
Michel André Morin, London N1.
Turn On Lighting, London N1.
David Malik and Son Ltd, London NW10.
No. 28 Antiques, London NW8.
B.C. Metalcrafts, London NW9.
Wilkinson plc, London SE6.
Blanchard Ltd, London SW1.
Andi Gisel, London SW1.
Hermitage Antiques plc, London SW1.
Carlton Hobbs, London SW1.
Christopher Howe, London SW1.
Jeremy Ltd, London SW1.
Carlton Davidson Antiques, London SW10.
H.W. Poulter and Son, London SW10.
Joy McDonald Antiques, London SW13.
W.G.T. Burne (Antique Glass) Ltd, London SW20.
275 Antiques, London SW6.
The Antique Lamp Shop, London SW6.
Fergus Cochrane and Leigh Warren Antiques, London SW6.
Charles Edwards, London SW6.
Hector Finch Lighting, London SW6.
Fulham Marble, London SW6.
Michael Luther Antiques, London SW6.
Mora & Upham Antiques, London SW6.
Old World Trading Co, London SW6.
M. Pauw Antiques, London SW6.
The French House (Antiques) Ltd, London SW8.
Partridge Fine Arts plc, London W1.
W. Sitch and Co. Ltd., London W1.
Stair and Company Ltd, London W1.
M. Turpin Ltd, London W1.
Wilkinson plc, London W1.
Jones Antique Lighting, London W11.
Marshall Gallery, London W14.
Marshall Phillips, London W4.
Mrs. M.E. Crick Chandeliers, London W8.
Denton Antiques, London W8.
George and Peter Cohn, London WC1.
Manor Antiques, Wilstead (Wilshamstead), Beds.

Temple Lighting (Jeanne Temple Antiques), Milton Keynes, Bucks.
Starlight Period Lighting, Wansford, Cambs.
Peter Johnson, Penzance, Cornwall.
Staveley Antiques, Staveley, Cumbria.
Toby's Architectural Antiques, Torquay, Devon.
Triton Gallery, Cheltenham, Glos.
Antony Preston Antiques Ltd, Stow-on-the-Wold, Glos.
Queens Parade Antiques Ltd, Stow-on-the-Wold, Glos.
Government House, Winchcombe, Glos.
Fritz Fryer Antique Lighting, Ross-on-Wye, Herefs.
Magic Lanterns, St. Albans, Herts.
Chislehurst Antiques, Chislehurst, Kent.
Sargeant Antiques, Sevenoaks, Kent.
The Architectural Emporium, Tunbridge Wells, Kent.
Knicks Knacks Emporium, Sutton-on-Sea, Lincs.
Period Style Lighting, Enfield, Middx.
The Stiffkey Lamp Shop, Stiffkey, Norfolk.
Renney Antiques, Hexham, Northumbs.
Haygate Gallery, Telford, Shrops.
Antique Textiles & Lighting, Bath, Somerset.
Ian McCarthy, Clutton, Somerset.
Friend or Faux, Bungay, Suffolk .
Exning Antiques & Interiors, Exning, Suffolk.
Post House Antiques, Bletchingley, Surrey.
TheLamp Gallery, Ripley, Surrey.
Spencer Swaffer, Arundel, Sussex West.
Woodall and Emery Ltd, Balcombe, Sussex West.
David R. Fileman, Steyning, Sussex West.
L. O. G. G. Lights, Tynemouth, Tyne and Wear.
The Light Gallery, Leamington Spa, Warks.
Delomosne and Son Ltd, North Wraxall, Wilts.
Lion Antiques, Pershore, Worcs.
Old Flames, Easingwold, Yorks. North.
The French House (Antiques) Ltd., York, Yorks. North.
Kelly Lighting, Sheffield, Yorks. South.
Jacquart Antiques, Holywood, Co. Down, N. Ireland.
Agar Antiques, Saintfield, Co. Down, N. Ireland.
Berland's of Edinburgh, Edinburgh, Scotland.
The Meadows Lamp Gallery, Edinburgh, Scotland.
Michael Vee Design - Birch House Antiques, Melrose, Scotland.

Maps & Prints
Ash Rare Books, London EC3.
Judith Lassalle, London N1.
York Gallery Ltd, London N1.
The Totteridge Gallery, London N20.
Gallery Kaleidoscope incorporating Scope Antiques, London NW6.

The Warwick Leadlay Gallery, London SE10.
Adam Gallery Ltd, London SW1.
Julian Hartnoll, London SW1.
Paul Mason Gallery, London SW1.
The O'Shea Gallery, London SW1.
Old Maps and Prints, London SW1.
The Parker Gallery, London SW1.
Michael Parkin Fine Art Ltd, London SW1.
Gallery Lingard, London SW3.
Stephanie Hoppen Ltd, London SW3.
The Map House, London SW3.
Old Church Galleries, London SW3.
20th Century Gallery, London SW6.
King's Court Galleries, London SW6.
Michael Marriott, London SW6.
Trowbridge Gallery, London SW6.
York Gallery Ltd, London SW6.
Paul Orssich, London SW8.
Altea Maps & Books, London W1.
Andrew Edmunds, London W1.
H. Fritz-Denneville Fine Arts Ltd, London W1.
Map World, London W1.
Jonathan Potter Ltd, London W1.
Shapero Gallery, London W1.
Bernard J. Shapero Rare Books, London W1.
Stephen Somerville (W.A.) Ltd, London W1.
Henry Sotheran Ltd, London W1.
Crawley and Asquith Ltd, London W10.
Justin F. Skrebowski Prints, London W11.
Connaught Galleries, London W2.
Austin/Desmond Fine Art, London WC1.
Michael Finney Antique Prints and Books, London WC1.
Robert Frew Ltd, London WC1.
Grosvenor Prints, London WC2.
Lee Jackson, London WC2.
Stage Door Prints, London WC2.
Storey's Ltd, London WC2.
The Witch Ball, London WC2.
Graham Gallery, Burghfield Common, Berks.
The Studio Gallery, Datchet, Berks.
Omniphil Prints, Chesham, Bucks.
Penn Barn, Penn, Bucks.
The Lawson Gallery, Cambridge, Cambs.
J. Alan Hulme, Chester, Cheshire.
Moor Hall Antiques, Chester, Cheshire.
Lion Gallery and Bookshop, Knutsford, Cheshire.
Iain Campbell, Widnes, Cheshire.
John Maggs, Falmouth, Cornwall.
Souvenir Antiques, Carlisle, Cumbria.
Archie Miles Bookshop, Gosforth, Cumbria.
Kendal Studios Antiques, Kendal, Cumbria.
R. F. G. Hollett and Son, Sedbergh, Cumbria.
Medina Gallery, Barnstaple, Devon.
Chantry Bookshop and Gallery, Dartmouth, Devon.
Graham York Rare Books, Honiton, Devon.
The Schuster Gallery, Torquay, Devon.

Bridport Old Books, Bridport, Dorset.
Words Etcetera, Dorchester, Dorset.
F. Whillock, Litton Cheney, Dorset.
Antique Map and Bookshop, Puddletown, Dorset.
Keeble Antiques, Sherborne, Dorset.
The Swan Gallery, Sherborne, Dorset.
The Treasure Chest, Weymouth, Dorset.
J. Shotton Antiquarian Books, Prints and Coins, Durham, Durham.
Castle Bookshop, Colchester, Essex.
Newport Gallery, Newport, Essex.
Cleeve Picture Framing, Bishops Cleeve, Glos.
Alexander Gallery, Bristol, Glos.
David Bannister FRGS, Cheltenham, Glos.
Kenulf Fine Arts, Stow-on-the-Wold, Glos.
Talbot Court Galleries, Stow-on-the-Wold, Glos.
Vanbrugh House Antiques, Stow-on-the-Wold, Glos.
Tetbury Gallery, Tetbury, Glos.
Laurence Oxley, Alresford, Hants.
Kingsclere Old Bookshop (Wyseby House Books), Kingsclere, Hants.
The Petersfield Bookshop, Petersfield, Hants.
Oldfield Gallery, Portsmouth, Hants.
The Olympic Gallery, Southampton, Hants.
Bell Fine Art, Winchester, Hants.
Ross Old Book and Print Shop, Ross-on-Wye, Herefs.
Gillmark Gallery, Hertford, Herts.
Eric T. Moore, Hitchin, Herts.
Antique Print Shop, Redbourn, Herts.
Clive A. Burden Ltd, Rickmansworth, Herts.
James of St Albans, St. Albans, Herts.
The Shanklin Gallery, Shanklin, Isle of Wight.
Ventnor Rare Books, Ventnor, Isle of Wight.
The Canterbury Bookshop, Canterbury, Kent.
Chaucer Bookshop, Canterbury, Kent.
Cranbrook Gallery, Cranbrook, Kent.
G. and D.I. Marrin and Sons, Folkestone, Kent.
The China Locker, Lamberhurst, Kent.
Langley Galleries, Rochester, Kent.
London House Antiques, Westerham, Kent.
Halewood and Sons, Preston, Lancs.
P.J. Cassidy (Books), Holbeach, Lincs.
Golden Goose Books, Lincoln, Lincs.
Harlequin Gallery and Golden Goose Globe Restorers, Lincoln, Lincs.
Norman Blackburn, Stamford, Lincs.
The Boydell Galleries, Liverpool, Merseyside.
David Ferrow, Great Yarmouth, Norfolk.
Baron Art, Holt, Norfolk.
The Old Reading Room Gallery and Tea Room, Kelling, Norfolk.
Crome Gallery and Frame Shop, Norwich, Norfolk.
Right Angle, Brackley, Northants.
Park Gallery & Bookshop, Wellingborough, Northants.

TRADA, Chipping Norton, Oxon.

The Barry Keene Gallery, Henley-on-Thames, Oxon.

Elizabeth Harvey-Lee, North Aston, Oxon.

Sanders of Oxford Ltd, Oxford, Oxon.

Toby English, Wallingford, Oxon.

Tooley Adams & Co, Wallingford, Oxon.

Churchgate Antiques, Empingham, Rutland.

The Old House Gallery, Oakham, Rutland.

Marc Oxley Fine Art, Uppingham, Rutland.

Patterson Liddle, Bath, Somerset.

Sarah Russell Antiquarian Prints, Bath, Somerset.

Trimbridge Galleries, Bath, Somerset.

Michael Lewis Gallery - Antiquarian Maps & Prints, Bruton, Somerset.

Julian Armytage, Crewkerne, Somerset.

House of Antiquity, Nether Stowey, Somerset.

M.A.J. Morris, Burton-upon-Trent, Staffs.

Besleys Books, Beccles, Suffolk.

King's Court Galleries, Dorking, Surrey.

Vandeleur Antiquarian Books, Epsom, Surrey.

Reigate Galleries, Reigate, Surrey.

Palmer Galleries, Richmond, Surrey.

Leoframes, Brighton, Sussex East.

The Witch Ball, Brighton, Sussex East.

A. & T. Gibbard, Eastbourne, Sussex East.

Murray Brown, Pevensey Bay, Sussex East.

Baynton-Williams, Arundel, Sussex West.

The Antique Print Shop, East Grinstead, Sussex West.

Julia Holmes Antique Maps and Prints, South Harting, Sussex West.

Robert Vaughan, Stratford-upon-Avon, Warks.

Carleton Gallery, Birmingham, West Mids.

Andrew Dando, Bradford-on-Avon, Wilts.

Antique Map and Print Gallery, Hallow, Worcs.

Grove Rare Books, Bolton Abbey, Yorks. North.

McTague of Harrogate, Harrogate, Yorks. North.

Minster Gate Bookshop, York, Yorks. North.

Alan Hill Books, Sheffield, Yorks. South.

Oakwood Gallery, Leeds, Yorks. West.

C.I Galleries Ltd, St. Peter Port, Guernsey, C.I.

John Blench & Son, St. Helier, Jersey, C.I.

The Selective Eye Gallery, St. Helier, Jersey, C.I.

Thesaurus (Jersey) Ltd, St. Helier, Jersey, C.I.

Phyllis Arnold Gallery Antiques, Greyabbey, Co. Down, N. Ireland.

Colin Wood (Antiques) Ltd, Aberdeen, Scotland.

The McEwan Gallery, Ballater, Scotland.

Calton Gallery, Edinburgh, Scotland.

The Carson Clark Gallery - Scotland's Map Heritage Centre, Edinburgh, Scotland.

The Old Town Bookshop, Edinburgh, Scotland.

Royal Mile Gallery, Edinburgh, Scotland.

David Windsor Gallery, Bangor, Wales.

Books, Maps and Prints, Brecon, Wales.

Glance Back Bookshop, Chepstow, Wales.

Glance Gallery, Chepstow, Wales.

Metalware/work

House of Steel Antiques, London N1.

Robert Young Antiques, London SW11.

Christopher Bangs, London SW6.

Jack Casimir Ltd, London W11.

Johnny Von Pflugh Antiques, London W11.

Manor Antiques, Wilstead (Wilshamstead), Beds.

Christopher Sykes Antiques, Woburn, Beds.

The Fire Place (Hungerford) Ltd, Hungerford, Berks.

Turpins Antiques, Hungerford, Berks.

Berkshire Metal Finishers Ltd, Sandhurst, Berks.

Peter J. Martin, Windsor and Eton, Berks.

Sundial Antiques, Amersham, Bucks.

Phoenix Antiques, Fordham, Cambs.

A.P. and M.A. Haylett, Outwell, Cambs.

The Antique Shop, Chester, Cheshire.

Simon Starkie Antiques, Cartmel, Cumbria.

Pamela Elsom - Antiques, Ashbourne, Derbys.

J H S Antiques Ltd, Ashbourne, Derbys.

Martin and Dorothy Harper Antiques, Bakewell, Derbys.

Michael Pembery Antiques, Bakewell, Derbys.

Roderick Butler, Honiton, Devon.

Morchard Bishop Antiques, Morchard Bishop, Devon.

J.B. Antiques, Wimborne Minster, Dorset.

William H. Stokes, Cirencester, Glos.

Christopher Clarke Antiques Ltd, Stow-on-the-Wold, Glos.

Keith Hockin Antiques, Stow-on-the-Wold, Glos.

Huntington Antiques Ltd, Stow-on-the-Wold, Glos.

Tudor House, Stow-on-the-Wold, Glos.

Prichard Antiques, Winchcombe, Glos.

Cedar Antiques Limited, Hartley Wintney, Hants.

Michael Gander, Hitchin, Herts.

James Porter Antiques, Sandwich, Kent.

V.O.C. Antiques, Woodhall Spa, Lincs.

Peter Robinson, Heacham, Norfolk.

James Brett, Norwich, Norfolk.

M.D. Cannell Antiques, Raveningham, Norfolk.

Blockheads and Granary Antiques, Flore, Northants.

Jonathan Fyson Antiques, Burford, Oxon.

Horseshoe Antiques and Gallery, Burford, Oxon.

Mike Ottrey Antiques, Wallingford, Oxon.

Joan Wilkins Antiques, Witney, Oxon.

Brian and Caroline Craik Ltd, Bath, Somerset.

Source, Bath, Somerset.

Ian McCarthy, Clutton, Somerset.

Bernard G. House, Wells, Somerset.

Peppers Period Pieces, Wattisfield, Suffolk.

Anthony Welling Antiques, Ripley, Surrey.

Heritage Antiques, Brighton, Sussex East.

Park View Antiques, Wadhurst, Sussex East.

Michael Wakelin and Helen Linfield, Billingshurst, Sussex West.

J. Du Cros Antiques, Petworth, Sussex West.

Avon Antiques, Bradford-on-Avon, Wilts.

Harriet Fairfax Fireplaces and General Antiques, Langley Burrell, Wilts.

Rupert Gentle Antiques, Milton Lilbourne, Wilts.

H.W. Keil Ltd, Broadway, Worcs.

D & J Lines Antiques, Wychbold, Worcs.

Garth Antiques, Harrogate, Yorks. North.

Charles Lumb and Sons Ltd, Harrogate, Yorks. North.

Elaine Phillips Antiques Ltd, Harrogate, Yorks. North.

York Cottage Antiques, Helmsley, Yorks. North.

Aura Antiques, Masham, Yorks. North.

E. Thistlethwaite, Settle, Yorks. North.

Garth Antiques, Whixley, Yorks. North.

Geary Antiques, Leeds, Yorks. West.

Unicorn Antiques, Edinburgh, Scotland.

Tim Wright Antiques, Glasgow, Scotland.

Miniatures

D.S. Lavender (Antiques) Ltd, London W1.

S.J. Phillips Ltd, London W1.

H. and W. Deutsch Antiques, London W8.

Michael Sim, Chislehurst, Kent.

Regal Antiques, Westerham, Kent.

Arden Gallery, Henley-in-Arden, Warks.

Mirrors

Anno Domini Antiques, London SW1.

Hilary Batstone Antiques inc. Rose Uniacke Interiors, London SW1.

Chelsea Antique Mirrors, London SW1.

Ossowski, London SW1.

Overmantels, London SW11.

Joy McDonald Antiques, London SW13.

Norman Adams Ltd, London SW3.

Anthony James and Son Ltd, London SW3.

Peter Lipitch Ltd, London SW3.

Clifford Wright Antiques Ltd, London SW3.

275 Antiques, London SW6.

Judy Greenwood, London SW6.

House of Mirrors, London SW6.

Christopher Jones Antiques, London SW6.

Stair and Company Ltd, London W1.

M. Turpin Ltd, London W1.

Through the Looking Glass Ltd, London W8.

R. Wilding, Wisbech, Cambs.

Richmond Antiques, Bowdon, Cheshire.

Peter Wadham Antiques, Exeter, Devon.

Keeble Antiques, Sherborne, Dorset.

Simpsons - Mirrors & Carvings, Brentwood, Essex.

Triton Gallery, Cheltenham, Glos.

Ashton Gower Antiques, Stow-on-the-Wold, Glos.

Stow Antiques, Stow-on-the-Wold, Glos.

Balmuir House Antiques, Tetbury, Glos.

Jacqueline Hall Antiques, Tetbury, Glos.

Burns and Graham, Winchester, Hants.

The Windhill Antiquary, Bishop's Stortford, Herts.

Ranby Hall, Retford, Notts.

Looking Glass of Bath, Bath, Somerset.

Country Brocante, Godney, Somerset.

Molland Antique Mirrors, Leek, Staffs.

Maria Cass Interiors, Nayland, Suffolk.

Ross Dodsworth Antiques Ltd, Dorking, Surrey.

Malthouse Antiques, Dorking, Surrey.

International Interiors , Brighton, Sussex East.

Dermot and Jill Palmer Antiques, Brighton, Sussex East.

Julian Antiques, Hurstpierpoint, Sussex West.

Asylum House Antiques, Bradford-on-Avon, Wilts.

The Drawing Room - Interiors & Antiques, Pershore, Worcs.

Lion Antiques, Pershore, Worcs.

W. Greenwood (Fine Art), Burneston, Yorks. North.

The French House (Antiques) Ltd., York, Yorks. North.

Michael Vee Design - Birch House Antiques, Melrose, Scotland.

Musical Boxes, Instruments & Literature

Boxes and Musical Instruments, London E8.

Vincent Freeman, London N1.

Tony Bingham, London NW3.

Otto Haas (A. and M. Rosenthal), London NW3.

Talking Machine, London NW4.

Robert Morley and Co Ltd, London SE13.

J. & A. Beare Ltd, London W1.

Peter Biddulph, London W1.

Pelham Galleries Ltd, London W1.

Mayflower Antiques, London W11.

Travis and Emery, London WC2.

Times Past Antiques, Windsor and Eton, Berks.

J.V. Pianos and Cambridge Pianola Company, Landbeach, Cambs.

Mill Farm Antiques, Disley, Cheshire.

Miss Elany, Long Eaton, Derbys.

M.C. Taylor, Bournemouth, Dorset.

Mark Marchant (Antiques), Coggeshall, Essex.

Arthur S. Lewis, Gloucester, Glos.

Keith Harding's World of Mechanical Music, Northleach, Glos.

Vanbrugh House Antiques, Stow-on-the-Wold, Glos.

Evans and Evans, Alresford, Hants.

Thwaites Fine Stringed Instruments, Watford, Herts.

Old Smithy, Feniscowles, Lancs.

The Violin Shop, Hexham, Northumbs.

S. & E.M. Turner Violins, Beeston, Notts.

R.R. Limb Antiques, Newark, Notts.
Laurie Leigh Antiques, Oxford, Oxon.
John Cowderoy Antiques, Eastbourne, Sussex East.
Pianos Galore, Little Horsted, Sussex East.
Time Restored & Co, Pewsey, Wilts.
The Barber's Clock, Worcester, Worcs.
The Piano Shop, Leeds, Yorks. West.
K.L.M. & Co. Antiques, Lepton, Yorks. West.
Talking Point Antiques, Sowerby Bridge, Yorks. West.
San Domenico Stringed Instruments, Cardiff, Wales.
John Carpenter, Llanelli, Wales.
Keith Chugg Antiques, Swansea, Wales.

Nautical Instruments - see Scientific

Needlework - see Tapestries

Netsuke - see Oriental

Oil Paintings
Gladwell and Company, London EC4.
Peter Chapman Antiques and Restoration, London N1.
Swan Fine Art, London N1.
Finchley Fine Art Galleries, London N12.
Martin Henham (Antiques), London N2.
Lauri Stewart - Fine Art, London N2.
The Totteridge Gallery, London N20.
Chaucer Fine Arts Ltd, London N4.
Leask Ward, London NW3.
Duncan R. Miller Fine Arts, London NW3.
Newhart (Pictures) Ltd, London NW3.
Gallery Kaleidoscope incorporating Scope Antiques, London NW6.
Nicholas Drummond/Wrawby Moor Art Gallery Ltd, London NW8.
Robert Gordon Antiques, London NW8.
Patricia Harvey Antiques and Decoration, London NW8.
The Greenwich Gallery, London SE10.
Didier Aaron (London) Ltd, London SW1.
Ackermann & Johnson, London SW1.
Adam Gallery Ltd, London SW1.
Verner Åmell Ltd, London SW1.
Antiquus, London SW1.
Artemis Fine Arts Limited, London SW1.
Chris Beetles Ltd, London SW1.
John Bly, London SW1.
Brisigotti Antiques Ltd, London SW1.
Miles Wynn Cato, London SW1.
Cox and Company, London SW1.
Simon C. Dickinson Ltd, London SW1.
Douwes Fine Art Ltd, London SW1.
Eaton Gallery, London SW1.
Frost and Reed Ltd (Est. 1808), London SW1.
Martyn Gregory Gallery, London SW1.

Ross Hamilton Ltd, London SW1.
Harrods Ltd, London SW1.
Julian Hartnoll, London SW1.
Hazlitt, Gooden and Fox Ltd, London SW1.
Hermitage Antiques plc, London SW1.
Carlton Hobbs, London SW1.
Derek Johns Ltd, London SW1.
MacConnal-Mason Gallery, London SW1.
The Mall Galleries, London SW1.
Paul Mason Gallery, London SW1.
Mathaf Gallery Ltd, London SW1.
Matthiesen Fine Art Ltd., London SW1.
Messums, London SW1.
Moreton Street Gallery, London SW1.
Peter Nahum at The Leicester Galleries, London SW1.
Oakham Gallery, London SW1.
Paisnel Gallery, London SW1.
The Parker Gallery, London SW1.
Michael Parkin Fine Art Ltd, London SW1.
Portland Gallery, London SW1.
Steven Rich & Michael Rich, London SW1.
Julian Simon Fine Art Ltd, London SW1.
Bill Thomson - Albany Gallery, London SW1.
Trafalgar Galleries, London SW1.
Tryon Gallery (incorporating Malcolm Innes), London SW1.
Rafael Valls Ltd, London SW1.
Rafael Valls Ltd, London SW1.
Johnny Van Haeften Ltd, London SW1.
Waterman Fine Art Ltd, London SW1.
Whitford Fine Art, London SW1.
Wildenstein and Co Ltd, London SW1.
Jonathan Clark & Co, London SW10.
Collins and Hastie Ltd, London SW10.
Lane Fine Art Ltd, London SW10 .
Langton Street Gallery, London SW10.
Offer Waterman and Co. Fine Art, London SW10.
Park Walk Gallery, London SW10.
Pairs Antiques Ltd, London SW11.
Regent House Gallery, London SW11.
New Grafton Gallery, London SW13.
John Spink, London SW13.
Ted Few, London SW17.
The David Curzon Gallery, London SW19.
The Andipa Gallery, London SW3.
Campbell's of Walton Street, London SW3.
Gallery Lingard, London SW3.
Stephanie Hoppen Ltd, London SW3.
20th Century Gallery, London SW6.
Rupert Cavendish Antiques, London SW6.
Charles Edwards, London SW6.
The Taylor Gallery Ltd, London SW7.
The Wyllie Gallery, London SW7.
Agnew's, London W1.
Victor Arwas Gallery - Editions Graphiques Gallery Ltd, London W1.
Browse and Darby Ltd, London W1.

Burlington Paintings Ltd, London W1.
Andrew Clayton-Payne Ltd, London W1.
P. and D. Colnaghi & Co Ltd, London W1.
Connaught Brown plc, London W1.
Dover Street Gallery, London W1.
Elwes and Hanham Ltd, London W1.
The Fine Art Society plc, London W1.
H. Fritz-Denneville Fine Arts Ltd, London W1.
Deborah Gage (Works of Art) Ltd, London W1.
The Graham Gallery, London W1.
Richard Green, London W1.
Maas Gallery, London W1.
Mallett and Son (Antiques) Ltd, London W1.
Mallett Gallery, London W1.
Marlborough Fine Art (London) Ltd, London W1.
Messums (Contemporary), London W1.
John Mitchell and Son, London W1.
Partridge Fine Arts plc, London W1.
W.H. Patterson Fine Arts Ltd, London W1.
Pyms Gallery, London W1.
Royal Exchange Art Gallery at Cork St., London W1.
Stephen Somerville (W.A.) Ltd, London W1.
Stoppenbach & Delestre Ltd, London W1.
William Thuillier, London W1.
Walpole Gallery, London W1.
Waterhouse and Dodd, London W1.
The Weiss Gallery, London W1.
Wilkins and Wilkins, London W1.
Williams and Son, London W1.
Crawley and Asquith Ltd, London W10.
Caelt Gallery, London W11.
The Coach House, London W11.
Curá Antiques, London W11.
Charles Daggett Gallery, London W11.
Fleur de Lys Gallery, London W11.
Gavin Graham Gallery, London W11.
Lacy Gallery, London W11.
Milne and Moller, London W11.
Piano Nobile Fine Paintings, London W11 .
Justin F. Skrebowski Prints, London W11.
Stern Pissarro Gallery, London W11.
Johnny Von Pflugh Antiques, London W11.
Marshall Gallery, London W14.
Manya Igel Fine Arts Ltd, London W2.
Aberdeen House Antiques, London W5.
Ealing Gallery, London W5.
Richard Philp, London W6.
Baumkotter Gallery, London W8.
Butchoff Antiques, London W8.
The Lucy B. Campbell Gallery, London W8.
Pawsey and Payne, London W8.
Abbott and Holder, London WC1.
Austin/Desmond Fine Art, London WC1.
David Ball Antiques, Leighton Buzzard, Beds.
Foye Gallery, Luton, Beds.
Woburn Fine Arts, Woburn, Beds.
Omell Galleries, Ascot, Berks.

Graham Gallery, Burghfield Common, Berks.
The Studio Gallery, Datchet, Berks.
John A. Pearson Antiques, Horton, Berks.
June Elsworth - Beaconsfield Ltd, Beaconsfield, Bucks.
Grosvenor House Interiors, Beaconsfield, Bucks.
H.S. Wellby Ltd, Haddenham, Bucks.
Penn Barn, Penn, Bucks.
Cambridge Fine Art Ltd, Cambridge, Cambs.
Storm Fine Arts Ltd, Great Shelford, Cambs.
Baron Fine Art, Chester, Cheshire.
Harris & Holt, Chester, Cheshire.
Harper Fine Paintings, Poynton, Cheshire.
Copperhouse Gallery - W. Dyer & Sons, Hayle, Cornwall.
Tony Sanders Penzance Gallery and Antiques, Penzance, Cornwall.
St. Breock Gallery, Wadebridge, Cornwall.
Peter Haworth, Beetham, Cumbria.
R. F. G. Hollett and Son, Sedbergh, Cumbria.
Kenneth Upchurch, Ashbourne, Derbys.
Medina Gallery, Barnstaple, Devon.
J. Collins and Son, Bideford, Devon.
Godolphin Antiques, Chagford, Devon.
Mill Gallery, Ermington, Devon.
Honiton Fine Art, Honiton, Devon.
Skeaping Gallery, Lydford, Devon.
Farthings, Lynton, Devon.
Gordon Hepworth Fine Art, Newton St. Cyres, Devon.
Michael Wood Fine Art, Plymouth, Devon.
Hampshire Gallery, Bournemouth, Dorset.
The Swan Gallery, Sherborne, Dorset.
Margaret Bedi Antiques & Fine Art, Billingham, Durham.
T.B. and R. Jordan (Fine Paintings), Stockton-on-Tees, Durham.
Brandler Galleries, Brentwood, Essex.
Neil Graham Gallery, Brentwood, Essex.
S. Bond and Son, Colchester, Essex.
Newport Gallery, Newport, Essex.
Peter and Penny Proudfoot, Berkeley, Glos.
Cleeve Picture Framing, Bishops Cleeve, Glos.
The Priory Gallery, Bishops Cleeve, Glos.
Alexander Gallery, Bristol, Glos.
Manor House Gallery, Cheltenham, Glos.
Triton Gallery, Cheltenham, Glos.
Peter Ward Fine Paintings, Cheltenham, Glos.
School House Antiques, Chipping Campden, Glos.
Astley House - Fine Art, Moreton-in-Marsh, Glos.
Benton Fine Art, Moreton-in-Marsh, Glos.
Berry Antiques Ltd, Moreton-in-Marsh, Glos.
Grimes House Antiques & Fine Art, Moreton-in-Marsh, Glos.
Nina Zborowska, Painswick, Glos.
Baggott Church Street Ltd, Stow-on-the-Wold, Glos.

SPECIALIST DEALERS

Cotswold Galleries, Stow-on-the-Wold, Glos.
The John Davies Gallery, Stow-on-the-Wold, Glos.
The Fosse Gallery, Stow-on-the-Wold, Glos.
Kenulf Fine Arts, Stow-on-the-Wold, Glos.
Roger Lamb Antiques & Works of Art, Stow-on-the-Wold, Glos.
The Titian Gallery, Stow-on-the-Wold, Glos.
Balmuir House Antiques, Tetbury, Glos.
Tetbury Gallery, Tetbury, Glos.
Century Fine Arts, Lymington, Hants.
Robert Perera Fine Art, Lymington, Hants.
The Petersfield Bookshop, Petersfield, Hants.
The Wykeham Gallery, Stockbridge, Hants.
Bell Fine Art, Winchester, Hants.
Lacewing Fine Art Gallery, Winchester, Hants.
Webb Fine Arts, Winchester, Hants.
Linden House Antiques, Leominster, Herefs.
The Shanklin Gallery, Shanklin, Isle of Wight.
Cooper Fine Arts Ltd, Brasted, Kent.
Michael Sim, Chislehurst, Kent.
Francis Iles, Rochester, Kent.
Langley Galleries, Rochester, Kent.
Sundridge Gallery, Sundridge, Kent.
Pantiles Spa Antiques, Tunbridge Wells, Kent.
Redleaf Gallery, Tunbridge Wells, Kent.
Apollo Antique Galleries, Westerham, Kent.
Peter Dyke, Westerham, Kent.
London House Antiques, Westerham, Kent.
Fulda Gallery Ltd, Manchester, Lancs.
St. James Antiques, Manchester, Lancs.
European Fine Arts and Antiques, Preston, Lancs.
Henry Donn Gallery, Whitefield, Lancs.
Corry's Antiques, Leicester, Leics.
P. Stanworth (Fine Arts), Market Bosworth, Leics.
Graftons of Market Harborough, Market Harborough, Leics.
Robin Shield Antiques, Swinstead, Lincs.
Ailsa Gallery, Twickenham, Middx.
Baron Art, Holt, Norfolk.
The Old Reading Room Gallery and Tea Room, Kelling, Norfolk.
The Bank House Gallery, Norwich, Norfolk.
Crome Gallery and Frame Shop, Norwich, Norfolk.
The Fairhurst Gallery, Norwich, Norfolk.
Mandell's Gallery, Norwich, Norfolk.
The Westcliffe Gallery, Sheringham, Norfolk.
Staithe Lodge Gallery, Swafield, Norfolk.
Norton Antiques, Twyford, Norfolk.
Coughton Galleries Ltd, Arthingworth, Northants.
Right Angle, Brackley, Northants.
Castle Ashby Gallery, Castle Ashby, Northants.
Dragon Antiques, Kettering, Northants.
Clark Galleries, Towcester, Northants.
Ron Green, Towcester, Northants.

Bryan Perkins Antiques, Wellingborough, Northants.
Boadens Antiques, Hexham, Northumbs.
Anthony Mitchell Fine Paintings, Nottingham, Notts.
Ranby Hall, Retford, Notts.
H.C. Dickins, Bloxham, Oxon.
Horseshoe Antiques and Gallery, Burford, Oxon.
Hubert's Antiques, Burford, Oxon.
The Stone Gallery, Burford, Oxon.
Swan Gallery, Burford, Oxon.
Georgian House Antiques, Chipping Norton, Oxon.
Hallidays (Fine Antiques) Ltd, Dorchester-on-Thames, Oxon.
The Barry Keene Gallery, Henley-on-Thames, Oxon.
Churchgate Antiques, Empingham, Rutland.
The Old House Gallery, Oakham, Rutland.
John Garner, Uppingham, Rutland.
Marc Oxley Fine Art, Uppingham, Rutland.
John Boulton Fine Art, Broseley, Shrops.
Valentyne Dawes Gallery, Ludlow, Shrops.
Wenlock Fine Art, Much Wenlock, Shrops.
Adam Gallery Ltd, Bath, Somerset.
Mary Cruz, Bath, Somerset.
Anthony Hepworth Fine Art Dealers, Bath, Somerset.
Trimbridge Galleries, Bath, Somerset.
Freshfords, Freshford, Somerset.
Nick Cotton Fine Art, Watchet, Somerset.
Sadler Street Gallery, Wells, Somerset.
Everett Fine Art Ltd, West Buckland, Somerset.
England's Gallery, Leek, Staffs.
Thompson's Gallery, Aldeburgh, Suffolk.
J. and J. Baker, Lavenham, Suffolk.
Trident Antiques, Long Melford, Suffolk.
Peasenhall Art and Antiques Gallery, Peasenhall, Suffolk.
The Falcon Gallery, Wortham, Suffolk.
Suffolk House Antiques, Yoxford, Suffolk.
Cider House Galleries Ltd, Bletchingley, Surrey.
The Whitgift Galleries, Croydon, Surrey.
Antique Clocks by Patrick Thomas, Dorking, Surrey.
Hampton Court Palace Antiques, East Molesey, Surrey.
Glencorse Antiques, Kingston-upon-Thames, Surrey.
Bourne Gallery Ltd, Reigate, Surrey.
The Gallery, Reigate, Surrey.
Roland Goslett Gallery, Richmond, Surrey.
Marryat, Richmond, Surrey.
Sage Antiques and Interiors, Ripley, Surrey.
B. M. and E. Newlove, Surbiton, Surrey.
Edward Cross - Fine Paintings, Weybridge, Surrey.
Willow Gallery, Weybridge, Surrey.
Campbell Wilson, Brighton, Sussex East.

John Day of Eastbourne Fine Art, Eastbourne, Sussex East.

Stewart Gallery, Eastbourne, Sussex East.

Murray Brown, Pevensey Bay, Sussex East.

E. Stacy-Marks Limited, Polegate, Sussex East.

Nicholas Bowlby, Poundgate, Sussex East.

Chichester Gallery, Chichester, Sussex West.

The Canon Gallery, Petworth, Sussex West.

Oliver Charles Antiques, Petworth, Sussex West.

Georgia Antiques, Pulborough, Sussex West.

Wilsons Antiques, Worthing, Sussex West.

Anna Harrison Fine Antiques, Gosforth, Tyne and Wear.

MacDonald Fine Art, Gosforth, Tyne and Wear.

Arden Gallery, Henley-in-Arden, Warks.

Fine-Lines (Fine Art), Shipston-on-Stour, Warks.

Astley House - Fine Art, Stretton-on-Fosse, Warks.

Oldswinford Gallery, Stourbridge, West Mids.

Driffold Gallery, Sutton Coldfield, West Mids.

Salisbury Antiques Warehouse Ltd, Salisbury, Wilts.

Richard Hagen, Broadway, Worcs.

Haynes Fine Art of Broadway, Broadway, Worcs.

John Noott Galleries, Broadway, Worcs.

The Highway Gallery, Upton-upon-Severn, Worcs.

James H. Starkey Galleries, Beverley, Yorks. East.

W. Greenwood (Fine Art), Burneston, Yorks. North.

Garth Antiques, Harrogate, Yorks. North.

Sutcliffe Galleries, Harrogate, Yorks. North.

Walker Galleries Ltd, Harrogate, Yorks. North.

E. Stacy-Marks Limited, Helmsley, Yorks. North.

Rose Fine Art and Antiques, Stillington, Yorks. North.

Kirkgate Fine Art & Conservation, Thirsk, Yorks. North.

Garth Antiques, Whixley, Yorks. North.

Coulter Galleries, York, Yorks. North.

Oakwood Gallery, Leeds, Yorks. West.

Robin Taylor Fine Arts, Wakefield, Yorks. West.

Mark Blower (Antiques) Ltd, Le Bourg Forest, Guernsey, C.I.

C.I Galleries Ltd, St. Peter Port, Guernsey, C.I.

St. James's Gallery Ltd, St. Peter Port, Guernsey, C.I.

Falle Fine Art Limited, St Helier, Jersey, C.I.

The Selective Eye Gallery, St. Helier, Jersey, C.I.

I.G.A. Old Masters Ltd, St. Lawrence, Jersey, C.I.

Grange Gallery - Fine Arts Ltd, St. Saviour, Jersey, C.I.

The Bell Gallery, Belfast, Co. Antrim, N. Ireland.

Dunluce Antiques, Bushmills, Co. Antrim, N. Ireland.

Atholl Antiques, Aberdeen, Scotland.

The Rendezvous Gallery, Aberdeen, Scotland.

Colin Wood (Antiques) Ltd, Aberdeen, Scotland.

Nigel Stacy-Marks Ltd, Auchterarder, Scotland.

The McEwan Gallery, Ballater, Scotland.

Bourne Fine Art Ltd, Edinburgh, Scotland.

Calton Gallery, Edinburgh, Scotland.

Open Eye Gallery Ltd, Edinburgh, Scotland.

The Scottish Gallery, Edinburgh, Scotland.

Anthony Woodd Gallery, Edinburgh, Scotland.

Young Antiques, Edinburgh, Scotland.

The Roger Billcliffe Fine Art, Glasgow, Scotland.

Ewan Mundy Fine Art Ltd, Glasgow, Scotland.

Michael Young Antiques at Glencarse, Glencarse, Scotland.

Inchmartine Fine Art, Inchture, Scotland.

Mainhill Gallery, Jedburgh, Scotland.

Killin Gallery, Killin, Scotland.

Kilmacolm Antiques Ltd, Kilmacolm, Scotland.

Newburgh Antiques, Newburgh, Scotland.

Kirk Ports Gallery, North Berwick, Scotland.

Nigel Stacy-Marks Ltd, Perth, Scotland.

St. Andrews Fine Art, St. Andrews, Scotland.

Abbey Antiques, Stirling, Scotland.

David Windsor Gallery, Bangor, Wales.

Michael Webb Fine Art, Bodorgan (Anglesey), Wales.

Welsh Art, Tywyn, Wales.

Rowles Fine Art, Welshpool, Wales.

Oriental Items

Nanwani and Co, London EC3.

Japanese Gallery, London N1.

Kevin Page Oriental Art, London N1.

Marcus Ross Antiques, London N1.

Leask Ward, London NW3.

Malcolm Rushton - Early Oriental Art, London NW3.

B.C. Metalcrafts, London NW9.

Coats Oriental Carpets, London SE5.

Ciancimino Ltd, London SW1.

Brian Harkins Oriental Art, London SW1.

Jeremy Mason (Sainsbury & Mason), London SW1.

Orientation, London SW10.

Hungry Ghost, London SW3.

Sebastiano Barbagallo, London SW6.

Indigo, London SW6.

Daphne Rankin and Ian Conn, London SW6.

Soo San, London SW6.

Brandt Oriental Art, London W1.

Paul Champkins, London W1.

Barry Davies Oriental Art, London W1.

Eskenazi Ltd, London W1.

John Eskenazi Ltd, London W1.

Robert Hall, London W1.

SPECIALIST DEALERS

Gerard Hawthorn Ltd, London W1.
Roger Keverne, London W1.
Sydney L. Moss Ltd, London W1.
Nicholas S. Pitcher Oriental Art, London W1.
Robert G. Sawers, London W1.
A. & J. Speelman Ltd, London W1.
Toynbee-Clarke Interiors Ltd, London W1.
Jan van Beers Oriental Art, London W1.
Linda Wrigglesworth Ltd, London W1.
M.C.N. Antiques, London W11.
The Nanking Porcelain Co. Ltd, London W11.
Christina Truscott, London W11.
Oriental Furniture and Arts, London W4.
AntikWest AB, London W8.
Gregg Baker Asian Art, London W8.
Berwald Oriental Art, London W8.
David Brower Antiques, London W8.
Cohen & Cohen, London W8.
H. and W. Deutsch Antiques, London W8.
J.A.N. Fine Art, London W8.
Japanese Gallery, London W8.
Peter Kemp, London W8.
S. Marchant & Son, London W8.
R. and G. McPherson Antiques, London W8.
Santos, London W8.
Geoffrey Waters Ltd, London W8.
Jorge Welsh Oriental Porcelain & Works of Art,
    London W8.
Glade Antiques, High Wycombe, Bucks.
Gabor Cossa Antiques, Cambridge, Cambs.
Peter Johnson, Penzance, Cornwall.
Brian Matsell, Derby, Derbys.
David L.H. Southwick Rare Art, Kingswear,
    Devon.
The Dragon and the Phoenix, South Molton,
    Devon.
Mere Antiques, Topsham, Devon.
Lionel Geneen Ltd, Bournemouth, Dorset.
Bedford Antiques, Bridport, Dorset.
Oriental Gallery, Stow-on-the-Wold, Glos.
Artique, Tetbury, Glos.
Tudor Antiques & Fine Art Ltd, Alresford,
    Hants.
Oriental Rug Gallery Ltd, St. Albans, Herts.
Michael Sim, Chislehurst, Kent.
Mandarin Gallery - Oriental Art, Otford, Kent.
Flower House Antiques, Tenterden, Kent.
The Rug Gallery, Leicester, Leics.
M.D. Cannell Antiques, Raveningham, Norfolk.
Cathay Antiques, Nottingham, Notts.
Haliden Oriental Rug Shop, Bath, Somerset.
Han Classical Chinese Furniture, Bath,
    Somerset.
Indigo, Bath, Somerset.
Lopburi Art & Antiques, Bath, Somerset.
Antiquus, Castle Cary, Somerset.
The Crooked Window, Dunster, Somerset.
Robin Kennedy, Richmond, Surrey.
Clive Rogers Oriental Rugs, Staines, Surrey.

Patrick Moorhead Antiques, Brighton, Sussex
    East.
Brian Page Antiques, Brighton, Sussex East.
Gensing Antiques, St. Leonards-on-Sea, Sussex
    East.
John's Corner, Petworth, Sussex West.
Indigo, Manningford Bruce, Wilts.
Heirloom & Howard Limited, West Yatton,
    Wilts.
Paul M. Peters Antiques, Harrogate, Yorks.
    North.
Tansu Japanese Antiques, Batley, Yorks. West.
Two Dragons Oriental Antiques, Llanerchymedd
    (Anglesey), Wales.
Peter Wain, Menai Bridge, Wales.

Paperweights
Garrick D. Coleman, London W11.
Garrick D. Coleman, London W8.
Sweetbriar Gallery, Helsby, Cheshire.
Portique, Bournemouth, Dorset.
Todd and Austin Antiques of Winchester,
    Winchester, Hants.
The Stone Gallery, Burford, Oxon.
David R. Fileman, Steyning, Sussex West.

Photographs & Equipment
Vintage Cameras Ltd, London SE26.
Jessop Classic Photographica, London WC1.
Medina Gallery, Barnstaple, Devon.
Peter Pan's Bazaar, Gosport, Hants.
Through the Lens, Arundel, Sussex West.

Pottery & Porcelain
Diana Huntley, London N1.
Carol Ketley Antiques, London N1.
The Collector Limited, London N11.
Finchley Fine Art Galleries, London N12.
Martin Henham (Antiques), London N2.
Sabera Trading Co, London NW2.
Klaber and Klaber, London NW3.
Albert Amor Ltd, London SW1.
Ross Hamilton Ltd, London SW1.
M. and D. Lewis, London SW1.
Stephen Long, London SW10.
Robert Young Antiques, London SW11.
The Dining Room Shop, London SW13.
Rogers de Rin, London SW3.
Davies Antiques, London SW8.
Thomas Goode and Co (London) Ltd, London
    W1.
Harcourt Antiques, London W1.
Brian Haughton Antiques, London W1.
Alistair Sampson Antiques Ltd, London W1.
Judy Fox, London W11.
M. and D. Lewis, London W11.
Mercury Antiques, London W11.
Schredds of Portobello, London W11.
Staffordshire Pride, London W11.

Garry Atkins, London W8.
David Brower Antiques, London W8.
H. and W. Deutsch Antiques, London W8.
Hope and Glory, London W8.
Jonathan Horne, London W8.
Roderick Jellicoe, London W8.
Peter Kemp, London W8.
Libra Antiques, London W8.
London Antique Gallery, London W8.
E. and H. Manners, London W8.
Simon Spero, London W8.
Stockspring Antiques, London W8.
Mary Wise & Grosvenor Antiques, London W8.
Anchor Antiques Ltd, London WC2.
Graham Gallery, Burghfield Common, Berks.
The Studio Gallery, Datchet, Berks.
Omniphil Prints, Chesham, Bucks.
Penn Barn, Penn, Bucks.
The Lawson Gallery, Cambridge, Cambs.
J. Alan Hulme, Chester, Cheshire.
Moor Hall Antiques, Chester, Cheshire.
Lion Gallery and Bookshop, Knutsford,
   Cheshire.
Iain Campbell, Widnes, Cheshire.
John Maggs, Falmouth, Cornwall.
Souvenir Antiques, Carlisle, Cumbria.
Archie Miles Bookshop, Gosforth, Cumbria.
Kendal Studios Antiques, Kendal, Cumbria.
R. F. G. Hollett and Son, Sedbergh, Cumbria.
Medina Gallery, Barnstaple, Devon.
Chantry Bookshop and Gallery, Dartmouth,
   Devon.
Graham York Rare Books, Honiton, Devon.
The Schuster Gallery, Torquay, Devon.
Bridport Old Books, Bridport, Dorset.
Words Etcetera, Dorchester, Dorset.
F. Whillock, Litton Cheney, Dorset.
Antique Map and Bookshop, Puddletown,
   Dorset.
Keeble Antiques, Sherborne, Dorset.
The Swan Gallery, Sherborne, Dorset.
The Treasure Chest, Weymouth, Dorset.
J. Shotton Antiquarian Books, Prints and Coins,
   Durham, Durham.
Castle Bookshop, Colchester, Essex.
Newport Gallery, Newport, Essex.
Cleeve Picture Framing, Bishops Cleeve, Glos.
Alexander Gallery, Bristol, Glos.
David Bannister FRGS, Cheltenham, Glos.
Kenulf Fine Arts, Stow-on-the-Wold, Glos.
Talbot Court Galleries, Stow-on-the-Wold, Glos.
Vanbrugh House Antiques, Stow-on-the-Wold,
   Glos.
Tetbury Gallery, Tetbury, Glos.
Laurence Oxley, Alresford, Hants.
Kingsclere Old Bookshop (Wyseby House
   Books), Kingsclere, Hants.
The Petersfield Bookshop, Petersfield, Hants.
Oldfield Gallery, Portsmouth, Hants.

The Olympic Gallery, Southampton, Hants.
Bell Fine Art, Winchester, Hants.
Ross Old Book and Print Shop, Ross-on-Wye,
   Herefs.
Gillmark Gallery, Hertford, Herts.
Eric T. Moore, Hitchin, Herts.
Antique Print Shop, Redbourn, Herts.
Clive A. Burden Ltd, Rickmansworth, Herts.
James of St Albans, St. Albans, Herts.
The Shanklin Gallery, Shanklin, Isle of Wight.
Ventnor Rare Books, Ventnor, Isle of Wight.
The Canterbury Bookshop, Canterbury, Kent.
Chaucer Bookshop, Canterbury, Kent.
Cranbrook Gallery, Cranbrook, Kent.
G. and D.I. Marrin and Sons, Folkestone, Kent.
The China Locker, Lamberhurst, Kent.
Langley Galleries, Rochester, Kent.
London House Antiques, Westerham, Kent.
Halewood and Sons, Preston, Lancs.
P.J. Cassidy (Books), Holbeach, Lincs.
Golden Goose Books, Lincoln, Lincs.
Harlequin Gallery and Golden Goose Globe
   Restorers, Lincoln, Lincs.
Norman Blackburn, Stamford, Lincs.
The Boydell Galleries, Liverpool, Merseyside.
David Ferrow, Great Yarmouth, Norfolk.
Baron Art, Holt, Norfolk.
The Old Reading Room Gallery and Tea Room,
   Kelling, Norfolk.
Crome Gallery and Frame Shop, Norwich,
   Norfolk.
Right Angle, Brackley, Northants.
Park Gallery & Bookshop, Wellingborough,
   Northants.
TRADA, Chipping Norton, Oxon.
The Barry Keene Gallery, Henley-on-Thames,
   Oxon.
Elizabeth Harvey-Lee, North Aston, Oxon.
Sanders of Oxford Ltd, Oxford, Oxon.
Toby English, Wallingford, Oxon.
Tooley Adams & Co, Wallingford, Oxon.
Churchgate Antiques, Empingham, Rutland.
The Old House Gallery, Oakham, Rutland.
Marc Oxley Fine Art, Uppingham, Rutland.
Patterson Liddle, Bath, Somerset.
Sarah Russell Antiquarian Prints, Bath,
   Somerset.
Trimbridge Galleries, Bath, Somerset.
Michael Lewis Gallery - Antiquarian Maps &
   Prints, Bruton, Somerset.
Julian Armytage, Crewkerne, Somerset.
House of Antiquity, Nether Stowey, Somerset.
M.A.J. Morris, Burton-upon-Trent, Staffs.
Besleys Books, Beccles, Suffolk.
King's Court Galleries, Dorking, Surrey.
Vandeleur Antiquarian Books, Epsom, Surrey.
Reigate Galleries, Reigate, Surrey.
Palmer Galleries, Richmond, Surrey.
Leoframes, Brighton, Sussex East.

SPECIALIST DEALERS

The Witch Ball, Brighton, Sussex East.
A. & T. Gibbard, Eastbourne, Sussex East.
Murray Brown, Pevensey Bay, Sussex East.
Baynton-Williams, Arundel, Sussex West.
The Antique Print Shop, East Grinstead, Sussex West.
Julia Holmes Antique Maps and Prints, South Harting, Sussex West.
Robert Vaughan, Stratford-upon-Avon, Warks.
Carleton Gallery, Birmingham, West Mids.
Andrew Dando, Bradford-on-Avon, Wilts.
Antique Map and Print Gallery, Hallow, Worcs.
Grove Rare Books, Bolton Abbey, Yorks. North.
McTague of Harrogate, Harrogate, Yorks. North.
Minster Gate Bookshop, York, Yorks. North.
Alan Hill Books, Sheffield, Yorks. South.
Oakwood Gallery, Leeds, Yorks. West.
C.I Galleries Ltd, St. Peter Port, Guernsey, C.I.
John Blench & Son, St. Helier, Jersey, C.I.
The Selective Eye Gallery, St. Helier, Jersey, C.I.
Thesaurus (Jersey) Ltd, St. Helier, Jersey, C.I.
Phyllis Arnold Gallery Antiques, Greyabbey, Co. Down, N. Ireland.
Colin Wood (Antiques) Ltd, Aberdeen, Scotland.
The McEwan Gallery, Ballater, Scotland.
Calton Gallery, Edinburgh, Scotland.
The Carson Clark Gallery - Scotland's Map Heritage Centre, Edinburgh, Scotland.
The Old Town Bookshop, Edinburgh, Scotland.
Royal Mile Gallery, Edinburgh, Scotland.
David Windsor Gallery, Bangor, Wales.
Books, Maps and Prints, Brecon, Wales.
Glance Back Bookshop, Chepstow, Wales.
Glance Gallery, Chepstow, Wales.

Prints - see Maps

Rugs - see Carpets

Russian/Soviet Art
Soviet Carpet & Art Galleries, London NW2.
Hermitage Antiques plc, London SW1.
Iconastas, London SW1
Jeremy Ltd, London SW1.
Mark Ransom Ltd, London SW1.
The Andipa Gallery, London SW3.
Richardson and Kailas Icons, London SW6.
Antoine Cheneviere Fine Arts, London W1.
Wartski Ltd, London W1.
Temple Gallery, London W11.
The Mark Gallery, London W2.
Mir Russki, Linlithgow, Scotland.

Scientific Instruments
Finchley Fine Art Galleries, London N12.
Victor Burness Antiques and Scientific Instruments, London SE1.
Peter Laurie Antiques, London SE10.

Thomas Mercer (Chronometers) Ltd, London SW1.
Trevor Philip and Sons Ltd, London SW1.
Langford's Marine Antiques, London SW10.
Peter Delehar, London W11.
Mayflower Antiques, London W11.
Johnny Von Pflugh Antiques, London W11.
Gillian Gould at Ocean Leisure, London WC2.
Arthur Middleton, London WC2.
Christopher Sykes Antiques, Woburn, Beds.
Principia Fine Art, Hungerford, Berks.
Mike Read Antique Sciences, St. Ives, Cornwall.
Branksome Antiques, Branksome, Dorset.
Nautical Antique Centre, Weymouth, Dorset.
The Chart House, Shenfield, Essex.
Chris Grimes Militaria, Bristol, Glos.
Malt House Antiques, Stow-on-the-Wold, Glos.
Barometer Shop, Leominster, Herefs.
Michael Sim, Chislehurst, Kent.
Sporting Antiques, Tunbridge Wells, Kent.
Bernard G. House, Wells, Somerset.
Patrick Marney, Long Melford, Suffolk.
Roy Arnold, Needham Market, Suffolk.
Odin Antiques, Brighton, Sussex East.
Time & Tide Antiques, Portaferry, Co. Down, N. Ireland.

Sculpture
Mike Weedon, London N1.
Chaucer Fine Arts Ltd, London N4.
Duncan R. Miller Fine Arts, London NW3.
No. 28 Antiques, London NW8.
Tara Antiques, London NW8.
Robert E. Hirschhorn, London SE5.
Robert Bowman, London SW1.
Christopher Gibbs Ltd, London SW1.
Nicholas Gifford-Mead, London SW1.
Hazlitt, Gooden and Fox Ltd, London SW1.
Whitford Fine Art, London SW1.
Jonathan Clark & Co, London SW10.
Ted Few, London SW17.
Joanna Booth, London SW3.
Chelminski, London SW6.
Agnew's, London W1.
Adrian Alan Ltd, London W1.
Victor Arwas Gallery - Editions Graphiques Gallery Ltd, London W1.
Browse and Darby Ltd, London W1.
Eskenazi Ltd, London W1.
The Fine Art Society plc, London W1.
The Graham Gallery, London W1.
Daniel Katz Ltd, London W1.
Messums (Contemporary), London W1.
The Sladmore Gallery of Sculpture, London W1.
Stoppenbach & Delestre Ltd, London W1.
Curá Antiques, London W11.
Hickmet Fine Arts, London W11.
Hirst Antiques, London W11.
Milne and Moller, London W11.

Piano Nobile Fine Paintings, London W11.
Wolseley Fine Arts Ltd, London W11.
Richard Philp, London W6.
Quatrefoil, Fordingbridge, Hants.
Lacewing Fine Art Gallery, Winchester, Hants.
Cooper Fine Arts Ltd, Brasted, Kent.
Francis Iles, Rochester, Kent.
London House Antiques, Westerham, Kent.
Pearse Lukies, Aylsham, Norfolk.
James Brett, Norwich, Norfolk.
The Barry Keene Gallery, Henley-on-Thames, Oxon.
Calton Gallery, Edinburgh, Scotland.
Anthony Hepworth Fine Art Dealers, Bath, Somerset.
Everett Fine Art Ltd, West Buckland, Somerset.
Nicholas Bowlby, Poundgate, Sussex East.
Apollo Antiques Ltd, Warwick, Warks.
Patrick and Gillian Morley Antiques, Warwick, Warks.
Louis Stanton, Mere, Wilts.
Bruton Gallery, Holmfirth, Yorks. West.
The Roger Billcliffe Fine Art, Glasgow, Scotland.
Mainhill Gallery, Jedburgh, Scotland.
Intaglio, Chepstow, Wales.

Shipping Goods & Period Furniture to the Trade

Eccentricities, London N1.
Regent Antiques, London N1.
Madeline Crispin Antiques, London NW1.
Tower Bridge Antiques, London SE1.
The Waterloo Trading Co., London SE10.
Oola Boola Antiques London, London SE26.
Tavistock Antiques, St. Neots, Cambs.
R. Wilding, Wisbech, Cambs.
W. Buckley Antiques Exports, Congleton, Cheshire.
Michael Allcroft Antiques, Disley, Cheshire.
Ben Eggleston Antiques Ltd, Long Marton, Cumbria.
Shardlow Antiques Warehouse, Shardlow, Derbys.
John Prestige Antiques, Brixham, Devon.
Fagins Antiques, Exeter, Devon.
McBains Antiques, Exeter, Devon.
Sandy's Antiques, Bournemouth, Dorset.
Alan Ramsey Antiques, Darlington, Durham.
G.T. Ratcliff Ltd, Kelvedon, Essex.
Bristol Trade Antiques, Bristol, Glos.
Alan Lord Antiques, Folkestone, Kent.
Sutton Valence Antiques, Sutton Valence, Kent.
West Lancs. Antique Exports, Burscough, Lancs.
P.J. Brown Antiques, Haslingden, Lancs.
R.J. O'Brien and Son Antiques Ltd, Manchester, Lancs.
G G Antique Wholesalers Ltd, Middleton Village, Lancs.
Tyson's Antiques, Morecambe, Lancs.

John Robinson Antiques, Wigan, Lancs.
Boulevard Antique and Shipping Centre, Leicester, Leics.
Trade Antiques, Alford, Lincs.
Antique & Secondhand Traders, Bourne, Lincs.
Grantham Furniture Emporium, Grantham, Lincs.
C. and K.E. Dring, Lincoln, Lincs.
Old Barn Antiques Warehouse, Sutton Bridge, Lincs.
Swainbanks Ltd, Liverpool, Merseyside.
Molloy's Furnishers Ltd, Southport, Merseyside.
Tony and Anne Sutcliffe Antiques, Southport, Merseyside.
Pearse Lukies, Aylsham, Norfolk.
John Roe Antiques, Islip, Northants.
Bryan Perkins Antiques, Wellingborough, Northants.
T. Baker, Langford, Notts.
Fair Deal Antiques, Mansfield, Notts.
Red Lodge Antiques, Screveton, Notts.
Mitre House Antiques, Ludlow, Shrops.
M.G.R. Exports, Bruton, Somerset.
T.M. Dyte Antiques, Highbridge, Somerset.
Asianart.co.uk.Ltd., North Newton, Somerset.
J.C. Giddings, Wiveliscombe, Somerset.
Burton Antiques, Burton-on-Trent, Staffs.
Cordelia and Perdy's Den Of Antiquity, Lichfield, Staffs.
Brett Wilkins Ltd, Lichfield, Staffs.
Goodbreys, Framlingham, Suffolk.
A. Abbott Antiques, Ipswich, Suffolk.
The Edwardian Shop, Ipswich, Suffolk.
Laurence Tauber Antiques, Surbiton, Surrey.
The Old Mint House, Pevensey, Sussex East.
John H. Yorke Antiques, St. Leonards-on-Sea, Sussex East.
Peter Smith Antiques, Sunderland, Tyne and Wear.
Martin Taylor Antiques, Wolverhampton, West Mids.
North Wilts Exporters, Brinkworth, Wilts.
Cross Hayes Antiques, Chippenham, Wilts.
Pillars Antiques, Lyneham, Wilts.
K. and A. Welch, Warminster, Wilts.
Joan and David White, Manfield, Yorks. North.
Tomlinsons, Tockwith, Yorks. North.
Roger Appleyard Ltd, Rotherham, Yorks. South.
Philip Turnor Antiques, Rotherham, Yorks. South.
Dronfield Antiques, Sheffield, Yorks. South.
N.P. and A. Salt Antiques, Sheffield, Yorks. South.
Times Past Antiques, Auchterarder, Scotland.
Imrie Antiques, Bridge of Earn, Scotland.
Neil Livingstone, Dundee, Scotland.
George Duff Antiques, Edinburgh, Scotland.
Georgian Antiques, Edinburgh, Scotland.
Narducci Antiques, Largs, Scotland.

A.S. Deuchar and Son, Perth, Scotland.
Narducci Antiques, Saltcoats, Scotland.
Michael Lloyd Antiques, Llandysul, Wales.
Steven Evans Antiques, Treorchy, Wales.

Silver & Jewellery
George Rankin Coin Co. Ltd, London E2.
Finecraft Workshop Ltd, London EC1.
Jonathan Harris (Jewellery) Ltd, London EC1.
Hirsh Ltd, London EC1.
Joseph and Pearce Ltd, London EC1.
A.R. Ullmann Ltd, London EC1.
D. Horton, London EC2.
Nanwani and Co, London EC3.
Searle and Co Ltd, London EC3.
Eclectica, London N1.
John Laurie (Antiques) Ltd, London N1.
Piers Rankin, London N1.
Vale Stamps and Antiques, London SE3.
A.D.C. Heritage Ltd, London SW1.
N. Bloom & Son (1912) Ltd, London SW1.
J.H. Bourdon-Smith Ltd, London SW1.
Cornucopia, London SW1.
Kenneth Davis (Works of Art) Ltd, London
    SW1.
Alastair Dickenson Ltd, London SW1.
N. and I. Franklin, London SW1.
Harvey and Gore, London SW1.
Longmire Ltd (Three Royal Warrants), London
    SW1.
Nigel Milne Ltd, London SW1.
thesilverfund.com, London SW1.
Mary Cooke Antiques Ltd, London SW14.
James Hardy and Co, London SW3.
McKenna and Co, London SW3.
Christine Schell, London SW3.
Gordon Watson Ltd, London SW3.
M.P. Levene Ltd, London SW7.
A. & H. Page (Est. 1840), London SW7.
Fay Lucas Artmetal, London SW8.
Armour-Winston Ltd, London W1.
Victor Arwas Gallery - Editions Graphiques
    Gallery Ltd, London W1.
Paul Bennett, London W1.
Bentley & Skinner Ltd, London W1.
Daniel Bexfield Antiques, London W1.
Bond Street Silver Galleries, London W1.
John Bull (Antiques) Ltd JB Silverware, London
    W1.
Carrington and Co. Ltd, London W1.
Sandra Cronan Ltd, London W1.
A. B. Davis Ltd, London W1.
Simon Griffin Antiques Ltd, London W1.
Hancocks and Co, London W1.
Holmes Ltd, London W1.
Johnson Walker & Tolhurst Ltd, London W1.
D.S. Lavender (Antiques) Ltd, London W1.
Marks Antiques, London W1.
Moira, London W1.

Richard Ogden Ltd, London W1.
Partridge Fine Arts plc, London W1.
A. Pash & Sons, London W1
S.J. Phillips Ltd, London W1.
David Richards and Sons, London W1.
Michael Rose - Source of the Unusual, London
    W1.
Tessiers Ltd, London W1.
Wartski Ltd, London W1.
Central Gallery (Portobello), London W11.
The Coach House, London W11.
Kleanthous Antiques, London W11.
Portobello Antique Store, London W11.
Schredds of Portobello, London W11.
The Silver Fox Gallery (Portobello), London
    W11.
Colin Smith and Gerald Robinson Antiques,
    London W11.
Craven Gallery, London W2.
H. and W. Deutsch Antiques, London W8.
Green's Antique Galleries, London W8.
John Jesse, London W8.
Howard Jones - The Silver Shop, London W8.
Lev (Antiques) Ltd, London W8.
Nortonbury Antiques, London WC1.
Koopman Ltd & Rare Art (London) Ltd, London
    WC2.
The London Silver Vaults, London WC2.
The Silver Mouse Trap, London WC2.
Styles Silver, Hungerford, Berks.
Berkshire Antiques Co Ltd, Windsor and Eton, Berks.
Turks Head Antiques, Windsor and Eton, Berks.
Buckies, Cambridge, Cambs.
D.J. Massey and Son, Alderley Edge, Cheshire.
Cameo Antiques, Chester, Cheshire.
Kayes of Chester, Chester, Cheshire.
Lowe and Sons, Chester, Cheshire.
Watergate Antiques, Chester, Cheshire.
D.J. Massey and Son, Macclesfield, Cheshire.
Imperial Antiques, Stockport, Cheshire.
Little Jem's, Penzance, Cornwall.
Alan Bennett, Truro, Cornwall.
Saint Nicholas Galleries Ltd. (Antiques and
    Jewellery), Carlisle, Cumbria.
Elizabeth and Son, Ulverston, Cumbria.
Mark Parkhouse Antiques and Jewellery,
    Barnstaple, Devon.
Timothy Coward Fine Silver, Braunton, Devon.
David J. Thorn, Budleigh Salterton, Devon.
Gold and Silver Exchange, Exeter, Devon.
Mortimers, Exeter, Devon.
John Nathan Antiques, Exeter, Devon.
Boase Antiques, Exmouth, Devon.
Otter Antiques, Honiton, Devon.
Extence Antiques, Teignmouth, Devon.
G.B. Mussenden and Son Antiques, Jewellery
    and Silver, Bournemouth, Dorset.
Geo. A. Payne and Son Ltd, Bournemouth,
    Dorset.

R.E. Porter, Bournemouth, Dorset.
Portique, Bournemouth, Dorset.
Tregoning Antiques, Bournemouth, Dorset.
Batten's Jewellers, Bridport, Dorset.
Greystoke Antiques, Sherborne, Dorset.
Henry Willis (Antique Silver), Sherborne, Dorset.
Georgian Gems Antique Jewellers, Swanage, Dorset.
Heirlooms Antique Jewellers and Silversmiths, Wareham, Dorset.
James Hardy Antiques Ltd, Barnard Castle, Durham.
Robson's Antiques, Barnard Castle, Durham.
Robin Finnegan (Jeweller), Darlington, Durham.
Argentum Antiques, Coggeshall, Essex.
Elizabeth Cannon Antiques, Colchester, Essex.
Grahams of Colchester, Colchester, Essex.
E. J. Markham & Son Ltd, Colchester, Essex.
J. Streamer Antiques, Leigh-on-Sea, Essex.
Harris Antiques, Thaxted, Essex.
Whichcraft Jewellery, Writtle, Essex.
Peter and Penny Proudfoot, Berkeley, Glos.
Caledonian Antiques, Bristol, Glos.
Grey-Harris and Co, Bristol, Glos.
Kemps, Bristol, Glos.
Jan Morrison, Bristol, Glos.
Greens of Cheltenham Ltd, Cheltenham, Glos.
Martin and Co. Ltd, Cheltenham, Glos.
Scott-Cooper Ltd, Cheltenham, Glos.
Ross Hardie, Chipping Campden, Glos.
Sodbury Antiques, Chipping Sodbury, Glos.
Walter Bull and Son (Cirencester) Ltd, Cirencester, Glos.
Rankine Taylor Antiques, Cirencester, Glos.
Squirrel Collectors Centre, Basingstoke, Hants.
A.W. Porter and Son, Hartley Wintney, Hants.
Barry Papworth, Lymington, Hants.
Meg Campbell, Southampton, Hants.
Warings of Hereford, Hereford, Herefs.
Abbey Antiques - Fine Jewellery & Silver, Hemel Hempstead, Herts.
Forget-me-Knot Antiques, St. Albans, Herts.
J. and H. Bell Antiques, Castletown, Isle of Man.
R. J. Baker, Canterbury, Kent.
Owlets, Hythe, Kent.
Gem Antiques, Maidstone, Kent.
Kaizen International Ltd, Rochester, Kent.
Gem Antiques, Sevenoaks, Kent.
Steppes Hill Farm Antiques, Stockbury, Kent.
Chapel Place Antiques, Tunbridge Wells, Kent.
Glassdrumman Antiques, Tunbridge Wells, Kent.
Kent & Sussex Gold Refiners, Tunbridge Wells, Kent.
Pantiles Spa Antiques, Tunbridge Wells, Kent.
Payne & Son (Silversmiths) Ltd, Tunbridge Wells, Kent.
The Coin and Jewellery Shop, Accrington, Lancs.

Ancient and Modern, Blackburn, Lancs.
Mitchell's Antiques, Blackburn, Lancs.
Chard Coins, Blackpool, Lancs.
Brittons - Watches and Antiques, Clitheroe, Lancs.
Leigh Jewellery, Leigh, Lancs.
Cathedral Jewellers, Manchester, Lancs.
St. James Antiques, Manchester, Lancs.
Charles Howell Jeweller, Oldham, Lancs.
H.C. Simpson and Sons Jewellers (Oldham)Ltd, Oldham, Lancs.
Keystone Antiques, Coalville, Leics.
Corry's Antiques, Leicester, Leics.
Letty's Antiques, Leicester, Leics.
Stanley Hunt Jewellers, Gainsborough, Lincs.
Marcus Wilkinson, Grantham, Lincs.
Rowletts of Lincoln, Lincoln, Lincs.
James Usher and Son Ltd, Lincoln, Lincs.
Marcus Wilkinson, Sleaford, Lincs.
Dawson of Stamford Ltd, Stamford, Lincs.
C. Rosenberg, Heswall, Merseyside.
Kevin Whay's Clocks & Antiques, Hoylake, Merseyside.
Boodle and Dunthorne Ltd, Liverpool, Merseyside.
Edward's Jewellers, Liverpool, Merseyside.
Stefani Antiques, Liverpool, Merseyside.
Weldons Jewellery and Antiques, Southport, Merseyside.
Bond Street Antiques, Cromer, Norfolk.
Barry's Antiques, Great Yarmouth, Norfolk.
Folkes Antiques and Jewellers, Great Yarmouth, Norfolk.
Wheatleys, Great Yarmouth, Norfolk.
Tim Clayton Jewellery & Antiques, King's Lynn, Norfolk.
Albrow and Sons Family Jewellers, Norwich, Norfolk.
Clive Dennett Coins, Norwich, Norfolk.
Leona Levine Silver Specialist, Norwich, Norfolk.
Maddermarket Antiques, Norwich, Norfolk.
Oswald Sebley, Norwich, Norfolk.
Timgems, Norwich, Norfolk.
Tombland Jewellers & Silversmiths, Norwich, Norfolk.
Parriss, Sheringham, Norfolk.
Michael Jones Jeweller, Northampton, Northants.
Boadens Antiques, Hexham, Northumbs.
Melville Kemp Ltd, Nottingham, Notts.
Stanley Hunt Jewellers, Retford, Notts.
Reginald Davis Ltd, Oxford, Oxon.
Payne and Son (Goldsmiths) Ltd, Oxford, Oxon.
MGJ Jewellers Ltd., Wallingford, Oxon.
Churchgate Antiques, Empingham, Rutland.
English Heritage, Bridgnorth, Shrops.
The Little Gem, Shrewsbury, Shrops.
Abbey Galleries, Bath, Somerset.

SPECIALIST DEALERS

D. and B. Dickinson, Bath, Somerset.
E.P. Mallory and Son Ltd, Bath, Somerset.
Castle Antiques, Burnham-on-Sea, Somerset.
M.G. Welch Jeweller, Taunton, Somerset.
Winston Mac (Silversmith), Bury St. Edmunds,
 Suffolk.
A. Abbott Antiques, Ipswich, Suffolk.
Temptations, Ashtead, Surrey.
Scotts of Dorking, Dorking, Surrey.
Temptations, Antique Jewellery & Silver,
 Dorking, Surrey.
Cry for the Moon, Guildford, Surrey.
Glydon and Guess Ltd, Kingston-upon-Thames,
 Surrey.
Horton, Richmond, Surrey.
Lionel Jacobs, Richmond, Surrey.
S. Warrender and Co, Sutton, Surrey.
Church House Antiques, Weybridge, Surrey.
Not Just Silver, Weybridge, Surrey.
Harry Diamond and Son, Brighton, Sussex East.
Paul Goble Jewellers, Brighton, Sussex East.
Douglas Hall Ltd, Brighton, Sussex East.
Hallmark Jewellers, Brighton, Sussex East.
Harry Mason, Brighton, Sussex East.
S.L. Simmons, Brighton, Sussex East.
W. Bruford, Eastbourne, Sussex East.
Trade Wind, Rottingdean, Sussex East.
Aarquebus Antiques, St. Leonards-on-Sea,
 Sussex East.
Peter Hancock Antiques, Chichester, Sussex West.
Rathbone Law, Chichester, Sussex West.
Nicholas Shaw Antiques, Petworth, Sussex West.
Sovereign Antiques, Gateshead, Tyne and Wear.
A.C. Silver, Jesmond, Tyne and Wear.
Davidson's The Jewellers Ltd, Newcastle-upon-
 Tyne, Tyne and Wear.
Intercoin, Newcastle-upon-Tyne, Tyne and Wear.
Coleshill Antiques and Interiors Ltd, Coleshill,
 Warks.
Howards Jewellers, Stratford-upon-Avon, Warks.
Russell Lane Antiques, Warwick, Warks.
Peter Clark Antiques, Birmingham, West Mids.
Maurice Fellows, Birmingham, West Mids.
Rex Johnson and Sons, Birmingham, West Mids.
Piccadilly Jewellers, Birmingham, West Mids.
Cross Keys Jewellers, Devizes, Wilts.
Howards of Broadway, Broadway, Worcs.
Magpie Jewellers and Antiques and Magpie
 Arms & Armour, Evesham, Worcs.
B.B.M. Coins., Kidderminster, Worcs.
Lower House Fine Antiques, Redditch, Worcs.
Bygones by the Cathedral, Worcester, Worcs.
Karen Guest Antiques, Beverley, Yorks. East.
Karen Guest Antiques, Driffield, Yorks. East.
Lesley Berry Antiques, Flamborough, Yorks.
 East.
Carlton Hollis Ltd, Harrogate, Yorks. North.
Ogden of Harrogate Ltd, Harrogate, Yorks.
 North.

Mary Milnthorpe and Daughters Antique Shop,
 Settle, Yorks. North.
Barbara Cattle, York, Yorks. North.
Golden Memories of York, York, Yorks. North.
Geoff Neary (incorporating Fillans Antiques
 Ltd) , Huddersfield, Yorks. West.
Jack Shaw and Co, Ilkley, Yorks. West.
Aladdin's Cave, Leeds, Yorks. West.
N. St. J. Paint & Sons Ltd, St Peter Port,
 Guernsey, C.I.
St. James's Gallery Ltd, St. Peter Port,
 Guernsey, C.I.
A. & R. Ritchie, St. Helier, Jersey, C.I.
Roberts Antiques, St Helier, Jersey, C.I.
The Country Antiques, Antrim, Co. Antrim, N.
 Ireland.
Dunluce Antiques, Bushmills, Co. Antrim, N.
 Ireland.
Brian R. Bolt Antiques, Portballintrae, Co.
 Antrim, N. Ireland.
Cookstown Antiques, Cookstown, Co. Tyrone,
 N. Ireland.
McCalls (Aberdeen), Aberdeen, Scotland.
McCalls Limited, Aberdeen, Scotland.
Treasures of Ballater, Ballater, Scotland.
Joseph Bonnar, Jewellers, Edinburgh, Scotland.
Bow-well Antiques, Edinburgh, Scotland.
Goodwin's Antiques Ltd, Edinburgh, Scotland.
Royal Mile Curios, Edinburgh, Scotland.
John Whyte, Edinburgh, Scotland.
Cathedral Antiques, Fortrose, Scotland.
A.D. Hamilton and Co, Glasgow, Scotland.
Jeremy Sniders Antiques, Glasgow, Scotland.
Tim Wright Antiques, Glasgow, Scotland.
Michael Young Antiques at Glencarse,
 Glencarse, Scotland.
Kilmacolm Antiques Ltd, Kilmacolm, Scotland.
Quarrelwood Art & Antiques Ltd, Kirkmahoe,
 Scotland.
County Antiques, Linlithgow, Scotland.
Mir Russki, Linlithgow, Scotland.
Harper-James, Montrose, Scotland.
Hardie Antiques, Perth, Scotland.
TheDavid Brown (St. Andrews) Gallery, St.
 Andrews, Scotland.
Abbey Antiques, Stirling, Scotland.
Hazel of Brecon, Brecon, Wales.
Silvertime, Brecon, Wales.
Audrey Bull, Carmarthen, Wales.
Gold and Silver Shop, Gorseinon, Wales.
Cartrefle Antiques, Mathry, Wales.
Audrey Bull, Tenby, Wales.

Sporting Items & Memorabilia
Holland & Holland, London W1.
Sean Arnold Sporting Antiques, London W2.
Below Stairs of Hungerford, Hungerford, Berks.
Sir William Bentley Billiards (Antique Billiard
 Table Specialist Company), Hungerford, Berks.

Beer Collectables, Beer, Devon.
Yesterday Tackle and Books, Bournemouth, Dorset.
John Burton Natural Craft Taxidermy, Ebrington, Glos.
Hamilton Billiards & Games Co., Knebworth, Herts.
Sporting Antiques, Tunbridge Wells, Kent.
The Spinning Wheel Antiques, Southport, Merseyside.
Golfark International, Rothbury, Northumbs.
Manfred Schotten Antiques, Burford, Oxon.
Quillon Antiques of Tetsworth, Tetsworth, Oxon.
Billiard Room Antiques, Chilcompton, Somerset.
Academy Billiard Company, West Byfleet, Surrey.
Griffin & Mace Antiques, Lewes, Sussex East.
Burman Antiques, Stratford-upon-Avon, Warks.
Grant Books, Droitwich, Worcs.
Dunkeld Antiques, Dunkeld, Scotland.
The David Brown (St. Andrews) Gallery, St. Andrews, Scotland.
Old Troon Sporting Antiques, Troon, Scotland.

Sporting Paintings & Prints
Swan Fine Art, London N1.
Ackermann & Johnson, London SW1.
Frost and Reed Ltd (Est. 1808), London SW1.
Paul Mason Gallery, London SW1.
The O'Shea Gallery, London SW1.
Tryon Gallery (incorporating Malcolm Innes), London SW1.
Old Church Galleries, London SW3.
Richard Green, London W1.
Holland & Holland, London W1.
Frank T. Sabin Ltd, London W1.
Connaught Galleries, London W2.
Iona Antiques, London W8.
Grosvenor Prints, London WC2.
Coltsfoot Gallery, Leominster, Herefs.
G. and D.I. Marrin and Sons, Folkestone, Kent.
Sporting Antiques, Tunbridge Wells, Kent.
Paul Hopwell Antiques, West Haddon, Northants.
Sally Mitchell's Gallery, Tuxford, Notts.
H.C. Dickins, Bloxham, Oxon.
Quillon Antiques of Tetsworth, Tetsworth, Oxon.
Julian Armytage, Crewkerne, Somerset.
The Falcon Gallery, Wortham, Suffolk.
Julia Holmes Antique Maps and Prints, South Harting, Sussex West.
Anthony Woodd Gallery, Edinburgh, Scotland.

Stamps
Argyll Etkin Gallery, London W1.
Michael Coins, London W8.
Stanley Gibbons, London WC2.
Avalon Post Card and Stamp Shop, Chester, Cheshire.

Penrith Coin and Stamp Centre, Penrith, Cumbria.
Jeremy's (Oxford Stamp Centre), Oxford, Oxon.
Bath Stamp and Coin Shop, Bath, Somerset.
Corbitt Stamps Ltd, Newcastle-upon-Tyne, Tyne and Wear.
J. Smith, York, Yorks. North.
Edinburgh Coin Shop, Edinburgh, Scotland.
Glance Back Bookshop, Chepstow, Wales.

Tapestries, Textiles & Needlework
The Textile Company, London N1.
Alexander Juran and Co, London N4.
Joseph Lavian, London N4.
Gallery of Antique Costume and Textiles, London NW8.
Coats Oriental Carpets, London SE5.
S. Franses Ltd, London SW1.
Joss Graham, London SW1.
Keshishian, London SW1.
Peta Smyth - Antique Textiles, London SW1.
The Dining Room Shop, London SW13.
Tobias and The Angel, London SW13.
Joanna Booth, London SW3.
Orientalist, London SW3.
Robert Stephenson, London SW3.
Antiques and Things, London SW4.
Perez Antique Carpets Gallery, London SW6.
Atlantic Bay Carpets Gallery, London SW7.
John Eskenazi Ltd, London W1.
C. John (Rare Rugs) Ltd, London W1.
Pelham Galleries Ltd, London W1.
Linda Wrigglesworth Ltd, London W1.
A. Zadah, London W1.
Sheila Cook, London W11.
Jonathan Horne, London W8.
Storm Fine Arts Ltd, Great Shelford, Cambs.
Martin and Dorothy Harper Antiques, Bakewell, Derbys.
The House that Moved, Exeter, Devon.
The Honiton Lace Shop, Honiton, Devon.
Georgina Ryder, Frampton, Dorset.
Robson's Antiques, Barnard Castle, Durham.
Maureen Morris, Saffron Walden, Essex.
Catherine Shinn Decorative Textiles, Cheltenham, Glos.
Anthony Hazledine, Fairford, Glos.
Huntington Antiques Ltd, Stow-on-the-Wold, Glos.
Meg Andrews, Harpenden, Herts.
Farmhouse Antiques, Bolton-by-Bowland, Lancs.
Past Caring Vintage Clothing, Holt, Norfolk
Country and Eastern Ltd., Norwich, Norfolk.
Witney Antiques, Witney, Oxon.
Antique Textiles & Lighting, Bath, Somerset.
Ann King, Bath, Somerset.
Susannah, Bath, Somerset.
Winder's Fine Art and Antiques, Newcastle-under-Lyme, Staffs.

Sarah Meysey-Thompson Antiques,
Woodbridge, Suffolk.
Patrick and Gillian Morley Antiques, Warwick,
Warks.
Avon Antiques, Bradford-on-Avon, Wilts.
Penny Farthing Antiques, North Cave, Yorks.
East.
London House Oriental Rugs and Carpets,
Boston Spa, Yorks. West.
Echoes, Todmorden, Yorks. West.
Hand in Hand, Coldstream, Scotland.
Gladrags, Edinburgh, Scotland.
Circa Vintage, Glasgow, Scotland.

Taxidermy
Get Stuffed, London N1.
Below Stairs of Hungerford, Hungerford, Berks.
Yesterday Tackle and Books, Bournemouth,
Dorset.
John Burton Natural Craft Taxidermy,
Ebrington, Glos.
Heads 'n' Tails, Wiveliscombe, Somerset.
The Enchanted Aviary, Bury St. Edmunds,
Suffolk.
A.F.J. Turner Antiques, East Molesey, Surrey.
Hawkins & Hawkins, Edinburgh, Scotland.

Tools - including Needlework & Sewing
Woodville Antiques, Hamstreet, Kent.
Norton Antiques, Twyford, Norfolk.
Ark Antiques, Bishop's Castle, Shrops.
Peppers Period Pieces, Wattisfield, Suffolk.
Trinders' Fine Tools, Clare, Suffolk.
Roy Arnold, Needham Market, Suffolk.
The Tool Shop, Needham Market, Suffolk.

Toys - see Dolls

Trade Dealers - see Shipping Goods

Treen
Eldridge London, London EC1.
Halcyon Days, London EC3.
Robert Young Antiques, London SW11.
Halcyon Days, London W1.
Phoenix Antiques, Fordham, Cambs.
A.P. and M.A. Haylett, Outwell, Cambs.
Baggott Church Street Ltd, Stow-on-the-Wold,
Glos.
Huntington Antiques Ltd, Stow-on-the-Wold, Glos.
Peter Norden Antiques, Tetbury, Glos.
Prichard Antiques, Winchcombe, Glos.
Millers of Chelsea Antiques Ltd, Ringwood,
Hants.
Brian and Caroline Craik Ltd, Bath, Somerset.
Peppers Period Pieces, Wattisfield, Suffolk.
J. Du Cros Antiques, Petworth, Sussex West.
Moxhams Antiques, Bradford-on-Avon, Wilts.
Paul Martin Antiques, Marlborough, Wilts.

Annmarie Turner Antiques, Marlborough, Wilts.
Stephen Cook Antiques, Broadway, Worcs.
Fenwick and Fenwick Antiques, Broadway, Worcs.
Michael Green Pine & Country Antiques,
Harrogate, Yorks. North.
Shieling Antiques, Harrogate, Yorks. North.
Brian R. Bolt Antiques, Portballintrae, Co.
Antrim, N. Ireland.
Islwyn Watkins, Knighton, Wales.

Vintage Cars - see Cars & Carriages

Watercolours
Gladwell and Company, London EC4.
Finchley Fine Art Galleries, London N12.
Lauri Stewart - Fine Art, London N2.
The Totteridge Gallery, London N20.
Angela Hone Watercolours, London NW1.
Newhart (Pictures) Ltd, London NW3.
Gallery Kaleidoscope incorporating Scope
Antiques, London NW6.
The Greenwich Gallery, London SE10.
Ackermann & Johnson, London SW1.
Chris Beetles Ltd, London SW1.
Miles Wynn Cato, London SW1.
Douwes Fine Art Ltd, London SW1.
Frost and Reed Ltd (Est. 1808), London SW1.
Martyn Gregory Gallery, London SW1.
Messums, London SW1.
Moreton Street Gallery, London SW1.
Oakham Gallery, London SW1.
Old Maps and Prints, London SW1.
Paisnel Gallery, London SW1.
Michael Parkin Fine Art Ltd, London SW1.
Bill Thomson - Albany Gallery, London SW1.
Waterman Fine Art Ltd, London SW1.
Langton Street Gallery, London SW10.
Park Walk Gallery, London SW10.
Regent House Gallery, London SW11.
John Spink, London SW13.
The David Curzon Gallery, London SW19.
Campbell's of Walton Street, London SW3.
Gallery Lingard, London SW3.
Stephanie Hoppen Ltd, London SW3.
20th Century Gallery, London SW6.
Agnew's, London W1.
Victor Arwas Gallery - Editions Graphiques
Gallery Ltd, London W1.
Andrew Clayton-Payne Ltd, London W1.
Connaught Brown plc, London W1.
Dover Street Gallery, London W1.
The Fine Art Society plc, London W1.
Maas Gallery, London W1.
Mallett and Son (Antiques) Ltd, London W1.
Mallett Gallery, London W1.
John Mitchell and Son, London W1.
Piccadilly Gallery, London W1.
Royal Exchange Art Gallery at Cork St., London
W1.

Shapero Gallery, London W1

Stephen Somerville (W.A.) Ltd, London W1.

Waterhouse and Dodd, London W1.

Crawley and Asquith Ltd, London W10.

Charles Daggett Gallery, London W11.

Milne and Moller, London W11.

Justin F. Skrebowski Prints, London W11.

Ealing Gallery, London W5.

Pawsey and Payne, London W8.

Simon Spero, London W8.

Beryl Kendall, The English Watercolour Gallery, London W9.

Abbott and Holder, London WC1.

Michael Finney Antique Prints and Books, London WC1.

David Ball Antiques, Leighton Buzzard, Beds.

Foye Gallery, Luton, Beds.

Graham Gallery, Burghfield Common, Berks.

J. Manley, Windsor and Eton, Berks.

Grosvenor House Interiors, Beaconsfield, Bucks.

Windmill Fine Art, High Wycombe, Bucks.

Penn Barn, Penn, Bucks.

Cambridge Fine Art Ltd, Cambridge, Cambs.

Storm Fine Arts Ltd, Great Shelford, Cambs.

Baron Fine Art, Chester, Cheshire.

Harper Fine Paintings, Poynton, Cheshire.

Copperhouse Gallery - W. Dyer & Sons, Hayle, Cornwall.

Tony Sanders Penzance Gallery and Antiques, Penzance, Cornwall.

St. Breock Gallery, Wadebridge, Cornwall.

Peter Haworth, Beetham, Cumbria.

Kenneth Upchurch, Ashbourne, Derbys.

Medina Gallery, Barnstaple, Devon.

J. Collins and Son, Bideford, Devon.

Cooper Gallery, Bideford, Devon.

Godolphin Antiques, Chagford, Devon.

Chantry Bookshop and Gallery, Dartmouth, Devon.

Mill Gallery, Ermington, Devon.

Honiton Fine Art, Honiton, Devon.

Skeaping Gallery, Lydford, Devon.

Michael Wood Fine Art, Plymouth, Devon.

Hampshire Gallery, Bournemouth, Dorset.

The Swan Gallery, Sherborne, Dorset.

Margaret Bedi Antiques & Fine Art, Billingham, Durham.

T.B. and R. Jordan (Fine Paintings), Stockton-on-Tees, Durham.

Brandler Galleries, Brentwood, Essex.

Neil Graham Gallery, Brentwood, Essex.

S. Bond and Son, Colchester, Essex.

Newport Gallery, Newport, Essex.

Barling Fine Porcelain Ltd, Wickham Bishops, Essex.

Cleeve Picture Framing, Bishops Cleeve, Glos.

The Priory Gallery, Bishops Cleeve, Glos.

Alexander Gallery, Bristol, Glos.

The Loquens Gallery, Cheltenham, Glos.

Manor House Gallery, Cheltenham, Glos.

School House Antiques, Chipping Campden, Glos.

The Roger Widdas Gallery, Moreton-in-Marsh, Glos.

Nina Zborowska, Painswick, Glos.

The Fosse Gallery, Stow-on-the-Wold, Glos.

Kenulf Fine Arts, Stow-on-the-Wold, Glos.

Roger Lamb Antiques & Works of Art, Stow-on-the-Wold, Glos.

Styles of Stow, Stow-on-the-Wold, Glos.

The Titian Gallery, Stow-on-the-Wold, Glos.

Tetbury Gallery, Tetbury, Glos.

Laurence Oxley, Alresford, Hants.

J. Morton Lee, Hayling Island, Hants.

Century Fine Arts, Lymington, Hants.

The Petersfield Bookshop, Petersfield, Hants.

The Wykeham Gallery, Stockbridge, Hants.

Bell Fine Art, Winchester, Hants.

Lacewing Fine Art Gallery, Winchester, Hants.

Coltsfoot Gallery, Leominster, Herefs.

Linden House Antiques, Leominster, Herefs.

The Shanklin Gallery, Shanklin, Isle of Wight.

Cooper Fine Arts Ltd, Brasted, Kent.

Cranbrook Gallery, Cranbrook, Kent.

Francis Iles, Rochester, Kent.

Langley Galleries, Rochester, Kent.

Sundridge Gallery, Sundridge, Kent.

Redleaf Gallery, Tunbridge Wells, Kent.

Apollo Antique Galleries, Westerham, Kent.

Old Corner House Antiques, Wittersham, Kent.

Fulda Gallery Ltd, Manchester, Lancs.

P. Stanworth (Fine Arts), Market Bosworth, Leics.

Graftons of Market Harborough, Market Harborough, Leics.

The Boydell Galleries, Liverpool, Merseyside.

Crome Gallery and Frame Shop, Norwich, Norfolk.

The Fairhurst Gallery, Norwich, Norfolk.

Mandell's Gallery, Norwich, Norfolk.

The Westcliffe Gallery, Sheringham, Norfolk.

Staithe Lodge Gallery, Swafield, Norfolk.

Norton Antiques, Twyford, Norfolk.

Coughton Galleries Ltd, Arthingworth, Northants.

Right Angle, Brackley, Northants.

Castle Ashby Gallery, Castle Ashby, Northants.

Dragon Antiques, Kettering, Northants.

Anthony Mitchell Fine Paintings, Nottingham, Notts.

John Harrison Fine Art, Aston Tirrold, Oxon.

H.C. Dickins, Bloxham, Oxon.

The Burford Gallery, Burford, Oxon.

Horseshoe Antiques and Gallery, Burford, Oxon.

The Stone Gallery, Burford, Oxon.

Wren Gallery, Burford, Oxon.

The Barry Keene Gallery, Henley-on-Thames, Oxon.

SPECIALIST DEALERS

The Old House Gallery, Oakham, Rutland.
Marc Oxley Fine Art, Uppingham, Rutland.
John Boulton Fine Art, Broseley, Shrops.
Adam Gallery Ltd, Bath, Somerset.
Trimbridge Galleries, Bath, Somerset.
Sadler Street Gallery, Wells, Somerset.
England's Gallery, Leek, Staffs.
Thompson's Gallery, Aldeburgh, Suffolk.
J. and J. Baker, Lavenham, Suffolk.
Peasenhall Art and Antiques Gallery, Peasenhall, Suffolk.
The Falcon Gallery, Wortham, Suffolk.
Hampton Court Palace Antiques, East Molesey, Surrey.
Glencorse Antiques, Kingston-upon-Thames, Surrey.
Limpsfield Watercolours, Limpsfield, Surrey.
Bourne Gallery Ltd, Reigate, Surrey.
The Gallery, Reigate, Surrey.
Roland Goslett Gallery, Richmond, Surrey.
Marryat, Richmond, Surrey.
Palmer Galleries, Richmond, Surrey.
Sage Antiques and Interiors, Ripley, Surrey.
John Day of Eastbourne Fine Art, Eastbourne, Sussex East.
Nicholas Bowlby, Poundgate, Sussex East.
Faringdon Gallery, Arundel, Sussex West.
Chichester Gallery, Chichester, Sussex West.
The Canon Gallery, Petworth, Sussex West.
Wilsons Antiques, Worthing, Sussex West.
Anna Harrison Fine Antiques, Gosforth, Tyne and Wear.
MacDonald Fine Art, Gosforth, Tyne and Wear.
Arden Gallery, Henley-in-Arden, Warks.
Fine-Lines (Fine Art), Shipston-on-Stour, Warks.
The Windmill Gallery, Birmingham, West Mids.
Oldswinford Gallery, Stourbridge, West Mids.
Driffold Gallery, Sutton Coldfield, West Mids.
Richard Hagen, Broadway, Worcs.
Haynes Fine Art of Broadway, Broadway, Worcs.
John Noott Galleries, Broadway, Worcs.
The Highway Gallery, Upton-upon-Severn, Worcs.
James H. Starkey Galleries, Beverley, Yorks. East.
W. Greenwood (Fine Art), Burneston, Yorks. North.
Garth Antiques, Harrogate, Yorks. North.

McTague of Harrogate, Harrogate, Yorks. North.
Walker Galleries Ltd, Harrogate, Yorks. North.
E. Stacy-Marks Limited, Helmsley, Yorks. North.
Rose Fine Art and Antiques, Stillington, Yorks. North.
Kirkgate Fine Art & Conservation, Thirsk, Yorks. North.
Garth Antiques, Whixley, Yorks. North.
Coulter Galleries, York, Yorks. North.
Huddersfield Picture Framing Co, Huddersfield, Yorks. West.
Robin Taylor Fine Arts, Wakefield, Yorks. West.
Beverley J. Pyke - Fine British Watercolours, Alderney, C.I.
C.I Galleries Ltd, St. Peter Port, Guernsey, C.I.
Falle Fine Art Limited, St Helier, Jersey, C.I.
The Bell Gallery, Belfast, Co. Antrim, N. Ireland.
Phyllis Arnold Gallery Antiques, Greyabbey, Co. Down, N. Ireland.
The Rendezvous Gallery, Aberdeen, Scotland.
Nigel Stacy-Marks Ltd, Auchterarder, Scotland.
The McEwan Gallery, Ballater, Scotland.
Calton Gallery, Edinburgh, Scotland.
Anthony Woodd Gallery, Edinburgh, Scotland.
Young Antiques, Edinburgh, Scotland.
The Roger Billcliffe Fine Art, Glasgow, Scotland.
Ewan Mundy Fine Art Ltd, Glasgow, Scotland.
Inchmartine Fine Art, Inchture, Scotland.
Mainhill Gallery, Jedburgh, Scotland.
Newburgh Antiques, Newburgh, Scotland.
Kirk Ports Gallery, North Berwick, Scotland.
Nigel Stacy-Marks Ltd, Perth, Scotland.
St. Andrews Fine Art, St. Andrews, Scotland.
David Windsor Gallery, Bangor, Wales.
Michael Webb Fine Art, Bodorgan (Anglesey), Wales.
Rowles Fine Art, Welshpool, Wales.

Wholesale Dealers - see Shipping Goods

Wine Related Items
Christopher Sykes Antiques, Woburn, Beds.
Neil Willcox & Mark Nightingale, Penry, Cornwall.
Malt House Antiques, Stow-on-the-Wold, Glos.
Robin Butler, Clare, Suffolk.
Marston House, Petworth, Sussex West.

Dealers' Index

In order to facilitate reference both the names of individuals and their business name are indexed separately. Thus A E Jones and C Smith of High Street Antiques will be indexed under:

Jones, A E, Town, County.
Smith, C, Town, County.
High Street Antiques, Town, County.

Barn Antiques, Nantwich, Cheshire.
Barn at Bislington, The, Bilsington, Kent.
Barn Book Supply, The, Salisbury, Wilts.
Barn Court Antiques, Crafts & Tearoom, Templeton, Wales.
Barn Full of Brass Beds, A, Conisholme, Lincs.
Barn, The, Petersfield, Hants.
Barnard, Mrs J.P., Ilminster, Somerset.
Barnes Antiques & Interiors, Jane, Honiton, Devon.
Barnes Jewellers, Bond Street Silver Galleries, London W1.
Barnes Richard, Talbot Walk Antique Centre, Ripley, Surrey.
Barnes, Charlotte, Grays Antique Markets, London W1.
Barnes, H. and V., Penkridge, Staffs.
Barnes, J.A.C. and S.J., Honiton, Devon.
Barnes, Mandy, Jubilee Hall Antiques Centre, Lechlade, Glos.
Barnes, R.A., Bicester, Oxon.
Barnet, Mrs V., Chichester, Sussex West.
Barnet-Cattanach, Borehamwood, Herts.
Barnett Antiques, Roger, Windsor and Eton, Berks.
Barnett R .K., Almshouses Arcade, Chichester, Sussex West.
Barnett, R.G. and D.C., Dunham-on-Trent, Notts.
Barnicott, R.W. and J.A., Cowbridge, Wales.
Barnt Green Antiques, Barnt Green, Worcs.
Barntiques, Colchester, Essex.
Barometer Shop, Leominster, Herefs.
Barometer World Ltd, Merton, Devon.
Baron Art, Holt, Norfolk.
Baron Fine Art, Chester, Cheshire.
Baron, Anthony R., Holt, Norfolk.
Baron, S. and R., Chester, Cheshire.
Barr, R.W., Westerham, Kent.
Barr, S.M and R.W., Westerham, Kent.
Barratt, Mike and Jane, Warrington, Cheshire.
Barrett, Mark and Iryna, Coggeshall, Essex.
Barrett, P., Weymouth, Dorset.
Barrett, S.M., Seaford, Sussex East.
Barrie, K., London NW6.
Barrington, D. and G., London N1.
Barrington, David, Brasted, Kent.
Barrington-Doulby, Edward, Barnard Castle, Durham.
Barrows, N., J.S. and M.J., Ollerton, Notts.
Barrs, Darren, Sudbury, Suffolk.
Barry's Antiques, Great Yarmouth, Norfolk.
Barry, Sean, Cuckfield, Sussex West.
Barter Books, Alnwick, Northumbs.
Bartlett Street Antiques Centre, Bath, Somerset.
Bartlett, Nigel A., London SW1.
Bartley, Miles, Hastings, Sussex East.
Bartman, F., London SW1.
Basey, S., Bristol, Glos.
Baskerville Antiques, Petworth, Sussex West.
Baskerville Bindings, Holt, Norfolk.
Baskerville Books, Wadhurst, Sussex East.
Baskerville, A. and B., Petworth, Sussex West.
Bass, B., Cheltenham, Glos.
Bass, V.E., Market Deeping, Lincs.
Bassett, M. and G., Ashbourne, Derbys.
Bastians, Maurice, Windsor and Eton, Berks.
Bateman Antiques, J. and R., Chalford, Glos.
Bateman, Jo and Jim, Woodstock, Oxon.
Bates and Sons Ltd., Eric, Hoveton, Norfolk.
Bates and, Paulette, Grays Antique

Markets, London W1.
Bates, Eric, Graham and James, Hoveton, Norfolk.
Bates, Nick, Tunbridge Wells, Kent.
Bates, Steve, Penrith, Cumbria.
Bates, T. and P., Tavistock, Devon.
Bates, V., London W11.
Bath Antiques Market Ltd, London SE1.
Bath Antiques Market Ltd, London W11.
Bath Antiques Market Ltd, Taunton, Somerset.
Bath Galleries, Bath, Somerset.
Bath Saturday Antiques Market, Bath, Somerset.
Bath Stamp and Coin Shop, Bath, Somerset.
Bathurst, Timothy, London SW1.
Batstone Antiques inc. Rose Uniacke Interiors, Hilary, London SW1.
Battams, Glenys, Porlock, Somerset.
Batten's Jewellers, Bridport, Dorset.
Batten, Nigel and Gill, Tenby, Wales.
Batten, R. and G., Bridport, Dorset.
Battlesbridge Antique Centre, Battlesbridge, Essex.
Battye, Stephen P. and C.J., Batley, Yorks. West.
Baumkotter Gallery, London W8.
Baumkotter, Mrs L., London W8.
Bawden Keith and Lin, Jubilee Hall Antiques Centre, Lechlade, Glos.
Baxter and Sons, H.C., London SW16.
Baxter CBE, Ian, Callington, Cornwall.
Baxter, Patricia, The Mall Antiques Arcade, Lower Mall, London N1.
Baxter, Paul, Birmingham, West Mids.
Baxter, T.J., J. and G.J., London SW16.
Bay Tree Antiques, Wilton, Wilts.
Bayley, C., London W14.
Baylis Country Chairs, Chris, Woodstock, Oxon.
Bayliss Antiques, Ludlow, Shrops.
Bayliss, D., A.B. and N., Ludlow, Shrops.
Bayney, Don, Grays Antique Markets, London W1.
Baynton-Williams, Arundel, Sussex West.
Baynton-Williams, R.H. and S.C., Arundel, Sussex West.
Bayntun, George, Bath, Somerset.
Bayntun-Coward, C.A.W., Bath, Somerset.
Bayntun-Coward, E.W.G., Bath, Somerset.
Bazaar, The, Whitby, Yorks. North.
Beach Antiques, Clevedon, Somerset.
Beagle Antiques, The Swan at Tetsworth, Oxon.
Bear Steps Antiques, Shrewsbury, Shrops.
Beardall Antiques, Clive, Maldon, Essex.
Beardsell, Elaine V., Holmfirth, Yorks. West.
Beare Ltd, J. & A., London W1.
Bearly Trading of London, London SE20.
Beasley, P.T. and R., Farningham, Kent.
Beasley, P.T., Farningham, Kent.
Beau Nash Antiques, Tunbridge Wells, Kent.
Beauty & The Beast, Antiquarius, London SW3.
Beaver Coin Room, London SW5.
Beazor and Sons Ltd, John, Cambridge, Cambs.
Bebb Fine Art, Ludlow, Shrops.
Bebb, R. and L., Kidwelly, Wales.
Bebb, Richard, Kidwelly, Wales.
Bebb, Roger, Ludlow, Shrops.
Bebes et Jouets, Edinburgh, Scotland.
Beck, B., Preston, Lancs.
Beck, Irene M., Lockerbie, Scotland.
Beck, J.A., Long Sutton, Lincs.
Beck, Peter, Salisbury, Wilts.
Beckenham Antiques & Collectors' Market, Beckenham, Kent.
Becker, A.G., M.S. and J.A.,

Attleborough, Norfolk.
Becker, Susan, Walton-on-Thames, Surrey.
Beckett, J., Wimborne Minster, Dorset.
Beckman Antiques, Patricia, London NW3.
Beckman, Patricia and Peter, London NW3.
Beckwith and Son, Hertford, Herts.
Bed Bazaar, Framlingham, Suffolk.
Bedale, David, Mobberley, Cheshire.
Bedford Antiques, Bridport, Dorset.
Bedford, P.E.L., Bridport, Dorset.
Bedi Antiques & Fine Art, Margaret, Billingham, Durham.
Bedi, M., Ginnel Antiques Centre, The, Harrogate, Yorks North.
Bedi, Margaret, Red House Antiques Centre, York, Yorks. North.
Bednarz, C.J., London N9
Bedsteads, Bath, Somerset.
Bedwell, Sylvia, Grays Antique Markets, London W1.
Bee, Linda, Grays Antique Markets, London W1.
Beech House, Sheffield, Yorks. South.
Beech, Garland, London SW11.
Beech, J.M. and A.J., Sheffield, Yorks. South.
Beech, R. and K., Ashbourne, Derbys.
Beecham, Chris, Diss, Norfolk.
Beedham Antiques Ltd, Hungerford, Berks.
Beedle, D.W., Sheffield, Yorks. South.
Beehive, Petts Wood, Kent.
Beeney, Martin, Arundel, Sussex West.
Beer Collectables, Beer, Devon.
Beer, John, London NW8.
Bees Antiques, Woodstock, Oxon.
Beesley, Mike, Leckhampstead, Berks.
Beet, Brian, Bond Street Silver Galleries, London W1.
Beetholme-Smith, Patrick and Maggie, Tetbury, Glos.
Beetles Ltd, Chris, London SW1.
Begley-Gray, Margaret, Newark, Notts.
Behind the Boxes - Art Deco, London SE26.
Belcher Antiques, Robert, Droitwich, Worcs.
Belcher, David, Chipping Norton, Oxon.
Belcher, Robert & Wendy, Droitwich, Worcs.
Belgrave Antique Centre, Darwen, Lancs.
Belgrave Carpet Gallery Ltd, London SW1.
Bell Antiques, Grimsby, Lincs.
Bell Antiques, J. and H., Castletown, Isle of Man.
Bell Antiques, Romsey, Hants.
Bell Antiques, Twyford, Berks.
Bell Fine Art, Winchester, Hants.
Bell Gallery, The, Belfast, Co. Antrim, N. Ireland.
Bell House Antiques, Cambridge, Glos.
Bell Passage Antiques, Wickwar, Glos.
Bell, Aline, Petworth, Sussex West.
Bell, E., Cockermouth, Cumbria.
Bell, J.N., Belfast, Co. Antrim, N. Ireland.
Bell, John, Jesmond, Tyne and Wear.
Bell, L.E., Winchester, Hants.
Bell, Mrs J., Alston, Cumbria.
Bell, R. and N., York, Yorks. North.
Bell, Roy and Pat, Southport, Merseyside.
Bellinger Antiques, C., Barnet, Herts.
Bellis, Michael J., Holt, Norfolk.
Bellord, E., London SW1.
Belmonts, London Silver Vaults, London WC2.
Below Stairs of Hungerford, Hungerford, Berks.
Belsten, R., Stiffkey, Norfolk.

Brittons - Watches and Antiques, Clitheroe, Lancs.
Broad, Anthony, Tunbridge Wells, Kent.
Broad, S., Eastbourne, Sussex East.
Broadbelt, P.F., Harrogate, Yorks. North.
Broadfoot, Tony, Brighton, Sussex East.
Broadhurst and Co Ltd, C.K., Southport, Merseyside.
Broadley, E. and D., Kirk Deighton, Yorks. North.
Broadstairs Antiques and Collectables, Broadstairs, Kent.
Broadway Clocks, Durham House Antiques Centre, Stow-on-the-Wold, Glos.
Broadway Dolls and Bears, Broadway, Worcs.
Brobbin, L.M. and H.C., Whaley Bridge, Derbys.
Brocante Antiques Centre, Marlborough, Wilts.
Brocante, Weybridge, Surrey.
Brooke, Nigel, Alfies, London NW8.
Brooke, S.T., Wroxham, Norfolk.
Brooke, T.C.S., Wroxham, Norfolk.
Brookes-Smith Antiques, Forest Row, Sussex East.
Brookes-Smith, Richard and Kate, Forest Row, Sussex East.
Brooks, D., Chippenham, Wilts.
Brooks, Naneen and Peter, Alfies, London NW8.
Brookstone, M. and J., London SW1.
Broome, P., Barnstaple, Devon.
Broomfield, Jim, Brackley, Northants.
Broomfield, P.L., Wincanton, Somerset.
Broughton Books, Edinburgh, Scotland.
Broughton, Ian, Alfies, London NW8.
Brower Antiques, David, London W8.
Browgate Antiques, Baildon, Yorks. West.
Brown & Kingston, Antiquarius, London SW3.
Brown Antiques, P.J., Haslingden, Lancs.
Brown Ltd, I. and J.L., Hereford, Herefs.
Brown Ltd, I. and J.L., London SW6.
Brown's Antique Furniture, The Furniture Cave, London SW10.
Brown's Antiques & Collectables, Middleton-in-Teesdale, Durham.
Brown's Clocks, Glasgow, Scotland.
Brown, A., London W1.
Brown, A.J., The Swan at Tetsworth, Oxon.
Brown, Alasdair, London SW6.
Brown, G.D. and S.T., Poole, Dorset.
Brown, Gordon and Anne, Glasgow, Scotland.
Brown, J.M., Auchterarder, Scotland.
Brown, Jenny, Hastings Antique Centre, St. Leonards-on-Sea, E. Sussex.
Brown, John and Val, Middleton-in-Teesdale, Durham.
Brown, M., Woodbridge, Suffolk.
Brown, Millicent, Chipping Sodbury, Glos.
Brown, Mr and Mrs D.R., St. Andrews, Scotland.
Brown, P., Burford, Oxon.
Brown, Philip, Stow-on-the-Wold, Glos.
Brown, R. and J., Beaumaris (Anglesey), Wales.
Brown, Richard, Harrogate, Yorks. North.
Brown, Robert, Holywood, Co. Down, N. Ireland.
Brown, S., Grays Antique Markets, London W1.
Brown, S., London N1.
Brown (St. Andrews) Gallery, The David, St. Andrews, Scotland.
Brown, T.D., Edinburgh, Scotland.
Brown, Tom and Alice, Launceston, Cornwall.
Brown, V., The Mall Antiques Arcade,

Lower Mall, London N1.
Browne, E.A., Bournemouth, Dorset.
Brownlow Antiques Centre, Faldingworth, Lincs.
Brownrigg, Petworth, Sussex West.
Browns' of West Wycombe, High Wycombe, Bucks.
Browse and Darby Ltd, London W1.
Broxup, David, Cottered, Herts.
Bruce, Diana, Jedburgh, Scotland.
Bruce, F., Strathblane, Scotland.
Bruce, J., Aberdeen, Scotland.
Bruce, Mrs J., Bideford, Devon.
Bruce, W.F., Lewes, Sussex East.
Bruford and Heming, Bond Street Silver Galleries, London W1.
Bruford, W., Eastbourne, Sussex East.
Brun Lea Antiques (J. Waite Ltd), Burnley, Lancs.
Brun Lea Antiques, Burnley, Lancs.
Brunning, M. and J., Redbourn, Herts.
Bruno Antiques, Hastings Antique Centre, St. Leonards-on-Sea, E. Sussex.
Bruno, Bernie, Alfies, London NW8.
Brunsveld, S., Lymm, Cheshire.
Brunswick Antiques, Penrith, Cumbria.
Brunt, Iain M., London SW11.
Brunton, Laurie, Nettlebed, Oxon.
Bruschweiler (Antiques) Ltd, F.G., Rayleigh, Essex.
Bruton Gallery, Holmfirth, Yorks. West.
Bryan, Douglas and Catherine, Cranbrook, Kent.
Bryan, Douglas, Cranbrook, Kent.
Bryan, Ian, London Silver Vaults, London WC2.
Bryan, Louise, London W1.
Bryan, Tina, Wymondham, Leics.
Bryan-Peach Antiques, N., Wymeswold, Leics.
Bryant, D., Lostwithiel, Cornwall.
Bryant, E.H., Epsom, Surrey.
Bryant, Mrs Frances, Sherborne, Dorset.
Bryars, Tim, London W1.
Brynin, Peter, Brighton, Sussex East.
Buchan, K.S., Leigh-on-Sea, Essex.
Buchanan Antiques J., McBains Antiques, Exeter, Devon.
Buchinger, T., Antiquarius, London SW3.
Buck Antiques, Christopher, Sandgate, Kent.
Buck House Antique Centre, Beaconsfield, Bucks.
Buck, Christopher and Jane, Sandgate, Kent.
Buck, W.F.A., Stockbury, Kent.
Buckie, Mrs R.D., Swaffham, Norfolk.
Buckies, Cambridge, Cambs.
Buckingham Antiques Centre, Buckingham, Bucks.
Buckingham's, Cadnam, Hants.
Buckler, Robin and Sue, Thornton-le-Dale, Yorks. North.
Buckley Antique Exports, Dave, Nottingham, Notts.
Buckley Antiques Exports, W., Congleton, Cheshire.
Buckley, W., Stoke-on-Trent, Staffs.
Buddell, Philip and Linda, Tresillian, Cornwall.
Bulka, Lynn, London Silver Vaults, London WC2.
Bull (Antiques) Ltd JB Silverware, John, London W1.
Bull and Son (Cirencester) Ltd, Walter, Cirencester, Glos.
Bull, Audrey, Carmarthen, Wales.
Bull, Audrey, Tenby, Wales.
Bull, Jonathan and Jane, Tenby, Wales.
Bullock, Gabrielle Doherty, Worcester, Worcs.
Bullock, Gabrielle, Worcester, Worcs.
Bumbles, Ashtead, Surrey.
Bundock, N., Reepham, Norfolk.

Bunker, Gary, Mildenhall, Suffolk.
Bunn, R.J. and E.R., Evesham, Worcs.
Bunting Antiques, Peter, Bakewell, Derbys.
Burbidge Antiques M., McBains Antiques, Exeter, Devon.
Burden Ltd, Clive A., Rickmansworth, Herts.
Burden, Philip D., Rickmansworth, Herts.
Burdett, Raymond, Bournemouth, Dorset.
Burfield, P., Lake, Isle of Wight.
Burford Antique Centre, Burford, Oxon.
Burford Gallery, The, Burford, Oxon.
Burgate Antique Centre, Canterbury, Kent.
Burgess - Horologist, Derek J., Parkstone, Dorset.
Burgess Farm Antiques, Winchester, Hants.
Burgess, Murray Ginnel Antiques Centre, The, Harrogate, Yorks North.
Burke-White, Linda, Petworth, Sussex West.
Burlington Designs, Angel Arcade, London N1.
Burlington Paintings Ltd, London W1.
Burman Antiques, Stratford-upon-Avon, Warks.
Burman Holtom, J. and J., Stratford-upon-Avon, Warks.
Burman, C. & L., London W1.
Burne (Antique Glass) Ltd, W.G.T., London SW20.
Burne, Mrs G. and A.T., London SW20.
Burnell, F., London NW9.
Burness Antiques and Scientific Instruments, Victor, London SE1.
Burness, V.G., London SE1.
Burnett, CMBHI, C.A., Northleach, Glos.
Burnett, David and Sally, Ryde, Isle of Wight.
Burnham Model & Collectors Shop, Burnham-on-Sea, Somerset.
Burning Embers, Aberdeen, Scotland.
Burniston, Lucy, London W1.
Burns and Graham, Winchester, Hants.
Burns, G.H., Stamford, Lincs.
Burrell, V.S., Abinger Hammer, Surrey.
Burroughs, Hilary, Farnham, Surrey.
Burrows, David E., Osgathorpe, Leics.
Burrows, Raul, Solihull, West Mids.
Bursill, P. and Mrs M., Aberdeen, Scotland.
Burslem Antiques & Collectables, Stoke-on-Trent, Staffs.
Burton Antique Clocks, Ian, Auchterarder, Scotland.
Burton Antiques, Burton-upon-Trent, Staffs.
Burton Natural Craft Taxidermy, John, Ebrington, Glos.
Burton, D., Christchurch, Dorset.
Burton, J., Dorchester, Dorset.
Burton-Garbett, A., Morden, Surrey.
Bush - Antique & Decorative Furniture, Robert, London SE1.
Bush and Partners, A.E., Attleborough, Norfolk.
Bush Antiques, Saffron Walden, Essex.
Bush House, Corringham, Essex.
Bush, Anthony, Redbourn, Herts.
Bushey Antiques Centre, Bushey, Herts.
Bushwood Antiques, Redbourn, Herts.
Butcher, F.L. and N.E., Sherborne, Dorset.
Butchoff Antiques, London W8.
Butchoff, Ian, London W8.
Butler and Wilson, London SW3.
Butler's Furniture Galleries, Glasgow, Scotland.
Butler, Adrian, Hadlow Down, Sussex East.
Butler, Laurence, Glasgow, Scotland.
Butler, Rita, Pangbourne, Berks.
Butler, Robin, Clare, Suffolk.

Butler, Roderick and Valentine, Honiton, Devon.
Butler, Roderick, Honiton, Devon.
Butt Antiques, Anthony, Baldock, Herts.
Butt, Mrs G., Cheltenham, Glos.
Butterworth, Adrian, London W8.
Butterworth, Brian, Knutsford, Cheshire.
Butterworth, John, Potterspury, Northants.
Buttigieg, Mrs Joyce M., London SE25.
Buttigieg, Pat, Angel Arcade, London N1.
Button Queen Ltd., The, London W1.
Button, K., Bungay, Suffolk.
Buxcey, Paul and Jeri, Marple Bridge, Cheshire.
By George! Antiques Centre, St. Albans, Herts.
Byatte, Ann, Stoke-on-Trent, Staffs.
Byethorpe Furniture, Barlow, Derbys.
Bygones by the Cathedral, Worcester, Worcs.
Bygones of Worcester, Worcester, Worcs.
Bygones Reclamation, Canterbury, Kent.
Bygones, Angmering, Sussex West.
Bygones, Burford, Oxon.
Bygones, Huntly, Scotland.
Bygones, Red House Antiques Centre, York, Yorks. North.
Byles and Optimum Brasses, Robert, Bampton, Devon.
Byles, Robert and Rachel, Bampton, Devon.
Byrne, A., Londonderry, Co. Londonderry, N. Ireland.

C

C & S Antiques, Honiton, Devon.
C.A.R.S. (Classic Automobilia & Regalia Specialists), Brighton, Sussex East.
Cabello, John, Plymouth, Devon.
Caboodle, Edinburgh, Scotland.
Cacrodain, Martin, London SW1
Caedmon House, Whitby, Yorks. North.
Caelt Gallery, London W11.
Cafferella, Vincenzo, Alfies, London NW8.
Cain, Liz, Williton, Somerset.
Cain, R.J., Henley-on-Thames, Oxon.
Cairncross and Sons, Filey, Yorks. North.
Cairncross, G., Filey, Yorks. North.
Cairns, J., Glasgow, Scotland.
Cairns, John and Tina, Moira, Co. Armagh, N. Ireland.
Caistor Antiques, Caistor, Lincs.
Calder, Simon and Eileen, Ullapool, Scotland.
Caldwell, Ian, Walton-on-the-Hill and Tadworth, Surrey.
Caldwell, Peter, Ampthill, Beds.
Cale, Kathryn, Windsor and Eton, Berks.
Caledonian Antiques, Bristol, Glos.
Caley, J. and M., Totnes, Devon.
Calgie, John, Jubilee Hall Antiques Centre, Lechlade, Glos.
Calleja, L., Ledbury, Herefs.
Callen, Pat, Swansea, Wales.
Callie's Curiosity Shop, Maindee, Wales.
Callingham Antiques, Northchapel, Sussex West.
Calne Antiques, Calne, Wilts.
Calton Gallery, Edinburgh, Scotland.
Calverley Antiques, Tunbridge Wells, Kent.
Camberwell Architectural Salvage & Antiques, London SE5.
Cambridge Fine Art Ltd, Cambridge, Cambs.
Cambridge Fine Art, Chappells Antiques Centre, Bakewell, Derbys.
Cambridge Pine, Bottisham, Cambs.
Camden Books, Bath, Somerset.
Camden Passage Antiques Market and Pierrepont Arcade Antiques Centre, London N1.

Cameo Antiques, Chester, Cheshire.
Camerer Cuss and Co, London SW1.
Cameron, Jasmine, Antiquarius, London SW3
Cameron, K. and E., Edinburgh, Scotland.
Cameron, Kate, Edinburgh, Scotland.
Cameron, Sheila, Alfies, London NW8.
Camilla's Bookshop, Eastbourne, Sussex East.
Campbell & Sons, A. K., Kirkcaldy, Scotland.
Campbell Antiques, Peter, Atworth, Wilts.
Campbell Gallery, The Lucy B., London W8.
Campbell Wilson, Brighton, Sussex East.
Campbell's of Walton Street, London SW3.
Campbell, Andrew, Jesmond, Tyne and Wear.
Campbell, F.D., Kelvedon, Essex.
Campbell, Iain, Widnes, Cheshire.
Campbell, Meg, Southampton, Hants.
Campbell, Mrs S., Colchester, Essex.
Campbell, P.R., Atworth, Wilts.
Campbell, S., Stirling, Scotland.
Campbell, William, Alfies, London NW8.
Campden Country Pine Antiques, Winchcombe, Glos.
Campion, R.J., London SW6.
Campsie Antiques, Lennoxtown, Scotland.
Candle Lane Books, Shrewsbury, Shrops.
Candlin, Z., London N1.
Candlin, Z., London SW3.
Canetti, A., Antiquarius, London SW3.
Cannell Antiques, M.D., Raveningham, Norfolk.
Cannon Antiques, Elizabeth, Colchester, Essex.
Cannon Militaria, Durrington, Wilts.
Cannonbury, Southwold, Suffolk.
Canon Gallery, The, Petworth, Sussex West.
Canon Gate Bookshop, Chichester, Sussex West.
Canterbury Antiques, Canterbury, Kent.
Canterbury Bookshop, The, Canterbury, Kent.
Capel Mawr Collectors Centre, Criccieth, Wales.
Capon, Patric, Bromley, Kent.
Cardiff Antiques Centre, Cardiff, Wales.
Cardiff Reclamation, Cardiff, Wales.
Cardingmill Antiques, Church Stretton, Shrops.
Caris, Gordon, Alnwick, Northumbs.
Caris, Gordon, Hexham, Northumbs.
Carleton Gallery, Birmingham, West Mids.
Carlisle Antiques Centre, Carlisle, Cumbria.
Carlton Antiques, Great Malvern, Worcs.
Carlton Clocks, Amersham, Bucks.
Carlton Davidson Antiques, London SW10.
Carlton-Smith, John, London SW1.
Carnegie Paintings & Clocks, Yealmpton, Devon.
Carnegie, Chris, Yealmpton, Devon.
Carney, A., Elstead, Surrey.
Carningli Centre, The, Newport, Wales.
Carpenter, John, Llanelli, Wales.
Carpenter, Rosemary, Truro, Cornwall.
Carr Antiques, Harold J., Washington, Tyne and Wear.
Carr, Mrs Dianne M., Coggeshall, Essex.
Carr, R.G., Salisbury, Wilts.
Carr, Ronald, Salisbury, Wilts.
Carrasco, Marylise, London SW1.
Carrick's Antiques and Shipping, S., Gainsborough, Lincs.
Carrington and Co. Ltd, London W1.

Carrington House, Llanrwst, Wales.
Carroll, M. and A., Halifax, Yorks. West.
Carroll, Paul, London SW4.
Carroll, Vivian, Antiquarius, London SW3.
Carruthers, C.J., Carlisle, Cumbria.
Carruthers, J., St. Andrews, Scotland.
Carruthers, L., Buxton, Derbys.
Carshalton Antique Galleries, Carshalton, Surrey.
Carter Antiques, Mark, Fairford, Glos.
Carter, A., Poole, Dorset.
Carter, D., London W11.
Carter, Mark and Karen, Fairford, Glos.
Carter, Mike, Chichester, Sussex West.
Carter, Neil, Olney, Bucks.
Carter, Nick, Edinburgh, Scotland.
Cartmell, T., Tring, Herts.
Cartrefle Antiques, Mathry, Wales.
Cartwright, Mia, Alfies, London NW8.
Casey Antiques, William J., Warwick, Warks.
Casey, Ann, The Swan at Tetsworth, Oxon.
Casey, William and Pat, Warwick, Warks.
Casimir Ltd, Jack, London W11.
Caslake, J., Sevenoaks, Kent.
Casque and Gauntlet Militaria, Farnham, Surrey.
Cass Interiors, Maria, Nayland, Suffolk.
Cassidy (Books), P.J., Holbeach, Lincs.
Cassidy's Antiques, Warminster, Wilts.
Cassidy, M., Warminster, Wilts.
Castaside, Alfies, London NW8.
Castle Antiques Centre, Middleham, Yorks. North.
Castle Antiques Centre, Westerham, Kent.
Castle Antiques Ltd, Deddington, Oxon.
Castle Antiques, Burnham-on-Sea, Somerset.
Castle Antiques, Deganwy, Wales.
Castle Antiques, Downham Market, Norfolk.
Castle Antiques, Nottingham, Notts.
Castle Antiques, Orford, Suffolk.
Castle Antiques, Warwick, Warks.
Castle Ashby Gallery, Castle Ashby, Northants.
Castle Bookshop, Colchester, Essex.
Castle Close Antiques, Dornoch, Scotland.
Castle Galleries, Salisbury, Wilts.
Castle Gate Antiques Centre, Newark, Notts.
Castle Hill Books, Kington, Herefs.
Castle Reclamation, Martock, Somerset.
Caswell, Mrs P., Woking, Surrey.
Cat in the Window, Keswick, Cumbria.
Cater, Patricia, Stow-on-the-Wold, Glos.
Cathay Antiques, Nottingham, Notts.
Cathedral Antiques, Fortrose, Scotland.
Cathedral Jewellers, Manchester, Lancs.
Cato, Lennox and Susan, Edenbridge, Kent.
Cato, Lennox, Edenbridge, Kent.
Cato, Miles Wynn, London SW1.
Cato, Miles Wynn, Tywyn, Wales.
Catt, C., Talbot Walk Antique Centre, Ripley, Surrey.
Cattle, Barbara, York, Yorks. North.
Caudwell, Doreen, Antiques at Heritage, Woodstock, Oxon.
Cavanagh, D., Edinburgh, Scotland.
Cave and Sons Ltd, R.G., Ludlow, Shrops.
Cave, F. and C.H., Northampton, Northants.
Cave, Mrs M.C., R.G., J.R. and T.G., Ludlow, Shrops.
Cavendish Antiques & Collectors Centre, York, Yorks. North.
Cavendish Antiques, Rupert, London SW6.
Cavendish Fine Arts, Sonning-on-Thames, Berks.

Cavendish Rose Antiques, Cavendish, Suffolk.
Caversham Antiques, The Swan at Tetsworth, Oxon.
Cavey, Christopher, Grays Antique Markets, London W1.
Cawood Antiques, Cawood, Yorks. North.
Cawson, Peter, St. Leonards-on-Sea, Sussex East.
Cayley, John, London SW15.
Cedar Antiques Centre Ltd, Hartley Wintney, Hants.
Cedar Antiques Limited, Hartley Wintney, Hants.
Cedarstar Ltd, Wantage, Oxon.
Cekay, Grays Antique Markets, London W1.
Cellar Antiques, Hawes, Yorks. North.
Central Gallery (Portobello), London W11.
Century Fine Arts, Lymington, Hants.
Ceres Antiques, Ceres, Scotland.
Cerne Antiques, Cerne Abbas, Dorset.
CG's Curiosity Shop, Cockermouth, Cumbria.
Chacewater Antiques, Chacewater, Cornwall.
Chaffer, John, The Swan at Tetsworth, Oxon.
Chair Set - Antiques, The, Woodstock, Oxon.
Chalk, M., Horncastle, Lincs.
Chalon Antiques, Nick, Chard, Somerset.
Chalon, Jake, Chard, Somerset.
Chambers Fine Antiques, Ronald G., Petworth, Sussex West.
Chambers, Graham H., Lancaster, Lancs.
Chambers, Julian and Linda, Elham, Kent.
Chambers, Ronald G., Petworth, Sussex West.
Champion, Miss A., Redruth, Cornwall.
Champkins, Paul, London W1.
Chan, Linda, Alfies, London NW8.
Chancery Antiques, The Mall Antiques Arcade, London N1.
C.I Galleries Ltd, St. Peter Port, Guernsey, C.I.
Chantry Bookshop and Gallery, Dartmouth, Devon.
Chantziaras, Panagiotis, London W1.
Chapel Antiques Centre, Barmouth, Wales.
Chapel Antiques Centre, Sheffield, Yorks. South.
Chapel Antiques, Nantwich, Cheshire.
Chapel Emporium Antique Centre, The, Long Sutton, Lincs.
Chapel House Fireplaces, Holmfirth, Yorks. West.
Chapel Place Antiques, Tunbridge Wells, Kent.
Chapel Street Antiques Arcade, Penzance, Cornwall.
Chapel Walk Antique Centre, Leominster, Herefs.
Chapman Antiques and Restoration, Peter, London N1.
Chapman, Giles, Haverfordwest, Wales.
Chapman, H., London SW6.
Chapman, I. and J., Whixley, Yorks. North.
Chapman, Ida, Lamb Arcade, Wallingford, Oxon
Chapman, J. and I., Harrogate, Yorks. North.
Chapman, J.W. & A.A., Skenfrith, Wales.
Chapman, M.C., Finedon, Northants.
Chapman, P.J. and Z.A., London N1.
Chappell's Antiques & Fine Art, Chappells Antiques Centre, Bakewell, Derbys.
Chappells Antiques Centre, Bakewell, Derbys.
Chapter & Verse Booksellers, Rye, Sussex East.
Chapter House Books, Sherborne, Dorset.
Chapter One, London N1.
Chard Antique Centre, Chard, Somerset.
Chard Coins, Blackpool, Lancs.
Charles Antiques, Whitwick, Leics.
Charlesworth's Snuff Box, Benny, Great Harwood, Lancs.
Charlesworth, J., London W9.
Charlton House Antiques, London N1.
Charman, G., Birmingham, West Mids.
Charnwood Antiques and Arcane Antiques Centre, Sawbridgeworth, Herts.
Charpentier, Maggie, London SW10.
Chart House, The, Shenfield, Essex.
Chateaubriand Antiques Centre, Burwash, Sussex East.
Chatfield-Johnson, Peter, Penzance, Cornwall.
Chatterton, Jocelyn, Grays Antique Markets, London W1.
Chaucer Bookshop, Canterbury, Kent.
Chaucer Fine Arts Ltd, London N4.
Chavasse, T. and B., Pulborough, Sussex West.
Chawner, John, Birchington, Kent.
Checkley, Alan and Marjory, Chester, Cheshire.
Checkley, Mr and Mrs L., Grantham, Lincs.
Chelminski, Hilary, London SW6.
Chelminski, London SW6.
Chelsea Antique Mirrors, London SW1.
Chelsea Antiques Rug Gallery, Antiquarius, London SW3.
Chelsea Clocks & Antiques, London W11
Chelsea Military Antiques, Antiquarius, London SW3.
Cheltenham Antique Market, Cheltenham, Glos.
Cheneviere Fine Arts, Antoine, London W1.
Cheney Antiques, Robert, Finedon, Northants.
Cherkas, Ian, Amersham, Bucks.
Cherry Antiques, Hemel Hempstead, Herts.
Cherry, C., Monkton, Devon.
Chertsey Antiques, Chertsey, Surrey.
Cherub Antiques, Carshalton, Surrey.
Cherub Antiques, Skipton, Yorks. North.
Cheshire Brick and Slate Co, Tarvin Sands, Cheshire.
Chesney's Antique Fireplace Warehouse, London N19.
Chess Antiques, Chesham, Bucks.
Chest of Drawers, London N1.
Chest of Drawers, The, Tetbury, Glos.
Chesterfield Antiques, Birmingham, West Mids.
Chesters, Y., Mathry, Wales.
Cheung, K.S., Bath, Somerset.
Chevertons of Edenbridge Ltd, Edenbridge, Kent.
Chew, J.E., Ginnel Antiques Centre, The, Harrogate, Yorks North.
Chew, J.E., Red House Antiques Centre, York, Yorks. North.
Cheyne House, Rye, Sussex East.
Chez Chalon, Chard, Somerset.
Chichester Antiques Centre, Chichester, Sussex West.
Chichester Gallery, Chichester, Sussex West.
Chidwick, Gerald, Bampton, Devon.
Child, J.C. and E.A., Morchard Bishop, Devon.
Child, John and Angela, Wimborne Minster, Dorset.
Child, P., London N1.
Childs, Graham and Wendy, Ipswich, Suffolk.
Childs, Wendy, Ipswich, Suffolk.
Chilton Antiques and Interiors, Juliet, Shrewsbury, Shrops.
China Locker, The, Lamberhurst, Kent.
Chipping Norton Antique Centre, Chipping Norton, Oxon.
Chislehurst Antiques, Chislehurst, Kent.
Chiswick Fireplace Co., The, London W4.
Chloe Antiques, Worthing, Sussex West.
Choice Antiques, Warminster, Wilts.
Chorley-Burdett Antiques, Bournemouth, Dorset.
Chris's Crackers, Carhampton, Somerset.
Christchurch Carpets, Christchurch, Dorset.
Christian, Ann and Peter, Blackpool, Lancs.
Christie Antiques, Robert, Carrickfergus, Co. Antrim, N. Ireland.
Christie, G. A., Fochabers, Scotland.
Christophe, J., London W1.
Christopher's Antiques, Farnham, Surrey.
Christophers, W.J., Canterbury, Kent.
Chua, Myrna, London SW15.
Chugg Antiques, Keith, Swansea, Wales.
Chugg, Helen, Barnstaple, Devon.
Church House Antiques, Weybridge, Surrey.
Church Street Antiques Centre, Stow-on-the-Wold, Glos.
Church Street Antiques, Altrincham, Cheshire.
Church Street Antiques, London NW8.
Church Street Antiques, Wells-next-the-Sea, Norfolk.
Church Street Centre, Woodbridge, Suffolk.
Church Stretton Books, Church Stretton, Shrops.
Church-Hill Antiques Centre, Lewes, Sussex East.
Churchgate Antiques, Empingham, Rutland.
Churchill Clocks, Midhurst, Sussex West.
Churchod, Mrs R., Rolvenden, Kent.
Churt Curiosity Shop, Churt, Surrey.
Ciancimino Ltd, London SW1.
Cider House Galleries Ltd, Bletchingley, Surrey.
Cider Press Antiques Centre, Taunton, Somerset.
Cinema Bookshop, London WC1.
Circa 1900, Liverpool, Merseyside.
Circa Vintage, Glasgow, Scotland.
Cirencester Arcade, Cirencester, Glos.
Cirjanic, Mara, Birmingham, West Mids.
City Antiques Ltd, Rochester, Kent.
City Clocks, London EC1.
City Pride Ltd, Canterbury, Kent.
Clare Antique Warehouse, Clare, Suffolk.
Clare, J. and A., Tunbridge Wells, Kent.
Clare, M., Stretton, Cheshire.
Claremont Antiques, Tunbridge Wells, Kent.
Clarence House Antiques, Watchet, Somerset.
Clarendon Books, Leicester, Leics.
Clark & Co, Jonathan, London SW10.
Clark Antiques, Annarella, Stow-on-the-Wold, Glos.
Clark Antiques, Peter, Birmingham, West Mids.
Clark Galleries, Towcester, Northants.
Clark Gallery - Scotland's Map Heritage Centre, The Carson, Edinburgh, Scotland.
Clark, A. and S.D., Towcester, Northants.
Clark, A. Carson, Edinburgh, Scotland.
Clark, A., London SE9.
Clark, David, Brampton, Cambs.
Clark, Diana, Antiques at Heritage, Woodstock, Oxon.
Clark, John, Brighton, Sussex East.
Clark, Michael, Topsham, Devon.

Clark, R. J., Pittenweem, Scotland.
Clark, Roger, Stow-on-the-Wold, Glos.
Clarke Antiques Ltd, Christopher, Stow-on-the-Wold, Glos.
Clarke Antiques Simon, Durham House Antiques Centre, Stow-on-the-Wold, Glos.
Clarke, I.D., D.S. and S.F., Stow-on-the-Wold, Glos.
Clarke, Janet, Freshford, Somerset.
Clarke, Norman D.J., Taunton, Somerset.
Clarke, R.A., Oakham, Rutland.
Clarke, Roger S., Petworth, Sussex West.
Clarke, Roger, Tutbury, Staffs.
Clarke-Hall Ltd, J., Deal, Kent.
Classic Bindings, London SW1.
Classic Rocking Horses, Thirsk, Yorks. North.
Clay, John, London SW6.
Clayton Jewellery & Antiques, Tim, King's Lynn, Norfolk.
Clayton, Teresa, Grays Antique Markets, London W1.
Clayton, Tim and Sue, King's Lynn, Norfolk.
Clayton-Payne Ltd, Andrew, London W1.
Cleeve Antiques, Bristol, Glos.
Cleeve Picture Framing, Bishops Cleeve, Glos.
Clegg, John, Ludlow, Shrops.
Clegg, William, Huntercombe, Oxon.
Clements, K. R., London W1.
Clements, V. and R., Plumley, Cheshire.
Cliffe Antiques Centre, Lewes, Sussex East.
Clifford and Son Ltd, T.J., Bath, Somerset.
Clifford, K., Lyneham, Wilts.
Clock Clinic Ltd, The, London SW15.
Clock House Antiques, Keighley, Yorks. West.
Clock House, Leavenheath, Suffolk.
Clock Inn, The, Ginnel Antiques Centre, The, Harrogate, Yorks North.
Clock Shop - Philip Setterfield of St. Albans, The, St. Albans, Herts.
Clock Shop Weybridge, The, Weybridge, Surrey.
Clock Shop, The, Hurstpierpoint, Sussex West.
Clock Shop, The, Winchcombe, Glos.
Clock Showrooms, The, Canonbie, Scotland.
Clock Workshop (Winchester)., The, Winchester, Hants.
Clock Workshop, The, Caversham, Berks.
Clocks in the Peak, Chappells Antiques Centre, Bakewell, Derbys.
Clockwise, Emsworth, Hants.
Cloisters Antique & Collectors Fair, Norwich, Norfolk.
Cloisters Antiques, Ely, Cambs.
Clola Antiques Centre, Clola by Mintlaw, Scotland.
Close Jewellery Restoration, R., Bond Street Silver Galleries, London W1.
Close, Gillian, Seapatrick, Co. Down, N. Ireland.
Clubb, A., Twickenham, Middx.
Cluzan, M., Framlingham, Suffolk.
Clydach Antiques, Swansea, Wales.
Clyde Antiques, Patrington, Yorks. East.
Coach House Antiques Centre, Canterbury, Kent.
Coach House Antiques Ltd, Stanley, Scotland.
Coach House Antiques, Hastings, Sussex East.
Coach House Antiques, The, Gomshall, Surrey.
Coach House Antiques, Whitby, Yorks. North.
Coach House, The, London W11.
Coakley-Webb, P., London N1.

Coats Oriental Carpets, London SE5.
Coats, A., London SE5.
Cobbled Yard, The, London N16
Coblands Farm Antiques, Depden, Suffolk.
Cobra and Bellamy, London SW1.
Cobweb Antiques, Cullompton, Devon.
Cobweb Books, Thornton-le-Dale, Yorks. North.
Cobwebs of Lockerbie Ltd, Lockerbie, Scotland.
Cobwebs, London SE9.
Cobwebs, Southampton, Hants.
Cochraneand Leigh Warren Antiques, Fergus, London SW6.
Cockaday, Dean, Diss, Norfolk.
Cockburn, F.J., Northwich, Cheshire.
Cockermouth Antiques Market, Cockermouth, Cumbria.
Cockermouth Antiques, Cockermouth, Cumbria.
Cocking D., Ginnel Antiques Centre, The, Harrogate, Yorks North.
Cockman, N., Ross-on-Wye, Herefs.
Cockram, Mrs A., Lincoln, Lincs.
Cockram, T.A.M., Cowes, Isle of Wight.
Cockrell Antiques, Surbiton, Surrey.
Cockrell, Sheila and Peter, Surbiton, Surrey.
Cockton, Mrs L., London SE26.
Cocoa, Cheltenham, Glos.
Coffey, Norman and Margaret, Louth, Lincs.
Cohen & Cohen, London W8.
Cohen Numismatics, Philip, London WC2.
Cohen, A., Antiquarius, London SW3.
Cohen, Ewa and Michael, London W8.
Cohen, Jeffrey S., Reigate, Surrey.
Cohn, George and Peter, London WC1.
Cohu Antiques, Stephen, St Ouen, Jersey, C.I.
Coin and Jewellery Shop, The, Accrington, Lancs.
Coinage Hall Antiques Centre, The, Truro, Cornwall.
Coldstream Antiques, Coldstream, Scotland.
Cole, J., London N1.
Colefax & John Fowler, Sibyl, London W1.
Coleman Antiques Robin, Piccadilly Antiques, Batheaston, Somerset.
Coleman Antiques, Simon, London SW13.
Coleman, G.D. and G.E., London W8.
Coleman, Garrick D., London W11.
Coleman, Garrick D., London W8.
Coleman, M.L., Maidenhead, Berks.
Coles, D.A., Clevedon, Somerset.
Coles, Gail and Zachary, Blackburn, Lancs.
Coles, Graham, Newport, Wales.
Coles, Lorna, Tetbury, Glos.
Coles, Richard, London SW3.
Coleshill Antiques and Interiors Ltd, Coleshill, Warks.
Coll, Mrs P., Long Melford, Suffolk.
Collard, B., Totnes, Devon.
Collards Books, Totnes, Devon.
Collectables, Honiton, Devon.
Collectables, Kingston-on-Spey, Scotland.
Collection Antiques, Grays Antique Markets, London W1.
Collector Limited, The, London N11.
Collector's Corner, Truro, Cornwall.
Collector, The, Barnard Castle, Durham.
Collector, The, Clevedon, Somerset.
Collectors Centre - Antique City, London E17.
Collectors Centre, The, St Peter Port, Guernsey, C.I.
Collectors Choice, Modbury, Devon.
Collectors Corner, Almshouses Arcade,

Chichester, Sussex West.,
Collectors Corner, Carshalton, Surrey.
Collectors Corner, Northallerton, Yorks. North.
Collectors Old Toy Shop and Antiques, Halifax, Yorks. West.
Collectors Shop, The, Edinburgh, Scotland.
Collectors World, Cromer, Norfolk.
Collectors World, Nottingham, Notts.
Collectors' Paradise, Leigh-on-Sea, Essex.
Collectors' Place, Shrewsbury, Shrops.
Colledge, John and Margaret, Hatton, Warks.
Collet, David, Brampton, Cambs.
Collett, J., Chipping Campden, Glos.
Collicott, R., Honiton, Devon.
Collie, Mr. and Mrs James, Uppingham, Rutland.
Collier, Mark, Fordingbridge, Hants.
Collier, Mrs D.E., Sheringham, Norfolk.
Collinge Antiques, Llandudno Junction, Wales.
Collinge, Nicky, Llandudno Junction, Wales.
Collingridge Antiques Ltd, Peter, Angel Arcade, London N1.
Collingridge Jeremy, Tudor House, Stow-on-the-Wold, Glos.
Collingridge Peter, Tudor House, Stow-on-the-Wold, Glos.
Collingridge, Peter, Stow-on-the-Wold, Glos.
Collings, B.L., Cambridge, Cambs.
Collins and Hastie Ltd, London SW10.
Collins and Son, J., Bideford, Devon.
Collins Antiques (F.G. and C. Collins Ltd.), Wheathampstead, Herts.
Collins Antiques, Frank, Mendlesham Green, Suffolk.
Collins, A. Lamb Arcade, Wallingford, Oxon.
Collins, B.L., London Silver Vaults, London WC2.
Collins, Barry, London Silver Vaults, London WC2.
Collins, Diana, London SW10.
Collins, Edwin, Leominster, Herefs.
Collins, J., Llanrwst, Wales.
Collins, Len and Mary, Barkham, Berks.
Collins, Olivia Howard, Grays Antique Markets, London W1.
Collins, S.J. and M.C., Wheathampstead, Herts.
Collins, Tracey, Horncastle, Lincs.
Colliton Antique Centre, Dorchester, Dorset.
Collyer Antiques, Jean, Boughton, Kent.
Collyer, Bryan, Durham House Antiques Centre, Stow-on-the-Wold, Glos.
Collyer, Mrs J.B., Boughton, Kent.
Collyer, R., Birmingham, West Mids.
Colnaghi & Co Ltd, P. and D., London W1.
Colonial Times, Cross in Hand, Sussex East.
Colquhoun, Wayne, Liverpool, Merseyside.
Colt, R., Farnham, Surrey.
Coltishall Antiques Centre, Coltishall, Norfolk.
Colton Antiques, Kelvedon, Essex.
Colton, Gary, Kelvedon, Essex.
Coltsfoot Gallery, Leominster, Herefs.
Colyer, J.M., Wallasey, Merseyside.
Colystock Antiques, Stockland, Devon.
Colyton Antiques Centre, Colyton, Devon.
Comben, Chris, Rait Village Antiques Centre, Scotland.
Comberton Antiques, Comberton, Cambs.
Complete Automobilist, The, Bourne, Lincs.

Cradlewell Antiques, Jesmond, Tyne and Wear.
Crafts Nouveau, London N10
Craiglea Clocks, Edinburgh, Scotland.
Craik Ltd, Brian and Caroline, Bath, Somerset.
Craik, Angie, Haywards Heath, Sussex West.
Cranbrook Gallery, Cranbrook, Kent.
Cranford Galleries, Knutsford, Cheshire.
Cranglegate Antiques, Swaffham, Norfolk.
Cranston, Enid, Melrose, Scotland.
Crapper & Co, Thomas, Stratford-upon-Avon, Warks.
Craven Gallery, London W2.
Craven, H., Eversley, Hants.
Crawford, Alastair, London SW1.
Crawford, M., London N1.
Crawford, M., London SW3.
Crawforth Andrew, Jubilee Hall Antiques Centre, Lechlade, Glos.
Crawley and Asquith Ltd, London W10.
Crawley, Mrs M., Chislehurst, Kent.
Crawley, R.A. and I.D., Watlington, Oxon.
Crawshaw, Humphrey and Elsa, Lichfield, Staffs.
Creamer, C. and L., Emsworth, Hants.
Creaton, I., St. Helier, Jersey, C.I.
Cree, G.W., Market Deeping, Lincs.
Creek Antiques, London SE10.
Creese-Parsons, S.H., Bath, Somerset.
Cremer-Price, T., Plymouth, Devon.
Cremyll Antiques, Cremyll, Cornwall.
Crest Collectables, Eastbourne, Sussex East.
Crested China Co, The, Driffield, Yorks. East.
Crewe-Read, D., London SW6.
Crewkerne Antique Centre, Crewkerne, Somerset.
Criccieth Gallery, Criccieth, Wales.
Crick Chandeliers, Mrs. M.E., London W8.
Cringle, M. and A., Burnham Market, Norfolk.
Cripps, Lilian, Penrith, Cumbria.
Crispin Antiques, Madeline, London NW1.
Critchlow, Nigel, Shardlow, Derbys.
Crocket, Sue, Brockenhurst, Hants.
Crockwell Antiques, Durham House Antiques Centre, Stow-on-the-Wold, Glos.
Crofts, Mrs Pat L., Wisbech, Cambs.
Crofts, Peter A., Wisbech, Cambs.
Cromarty Antiques, Cromarty, Scotland.
Crome Gallery and Frame Shop, Norwich, Norfolk.
Cromwell House Antique Centre, Battlesbridge Antique Centre, Essex
Cronan Ltd, Sandra, London W1.
Crook, Sandra, Stockport, Cheshire.
Crook, W.V. and A., Kidderminster, Worcs.
Crooked Window, The, Dunster, Somerset.
Cross - Fine Paintings, Edward, Weybridge, Surrey.
Cross Antiques, Watlington, Oxon.
Cross Hayes Antiques, Chippenham, Wilts.
Cross Keys Jewellers, Devizes, Wilts.
Cross's Curios, Birmingham, West Mids.
Cross, Anthony, London SE10.
Cross, B. J., Kendal, Cumbria.
Cross, John and Valerie, Birmingham, West Mids.
Crossley, Peter and Mary, Haslingden, Lancs.
Crossroads Antiques, Prestwick, Scotland.
Crouchman, C.C., Shenfield, Essex.
Crowder P., Talbot Walk Antique Centre, Ripley, Surrey.
Crown Arcade, London W11.
Crown Silver, London Silver Vaults, London WC2.
Crowson, Julie, Wainfleet, Lincs.
Crowston, M., Earl Shilton, Leics.
Crowther, D.J., Hartlepool, Durham.
Crowther, Mrs V., London SW4.
Crozier, G.R., Bishop's Stortford, Herts.
Crozier, Richard J., Beccles, Suffolk.
Cruck House Antiques, Much Wenlock, Shrops.
Cruz, Mary, Bath, Somerset.
Cry for the Moon, Guildford, Surrey.
Csaky's Antiques, Hook, Hants.
Cuchet, Melanie, London SW1.
Cudlipp, Jane, Bungay, Suffolk.
Cufflink Shop, The, Antiquarius, London SW3.
Cullen, A. and R.S., Hemel Hempstead, Herts.
Cullen, James, Ripley, Derbys.
Cullompton Antiques, Cullompton, Devon.
Cullompton Old Tannery Antiques, Cullompton, Devon.
Cullup, S. and K., The Swan at Tetsworth, Oxon.
Cumbley, G.R., King's Lynn, Norfolk.
Cumbria Architectural Salvage, Raughton Head, Cumbria.
Cumbrian Antiques Centre, The, Brampton, Cumbria.
Cumming, A. & Y., Lewes, Sussex East.
Cumming, R.L., Grimsby, Lincs.
Cummins, Cornelius, Bristol, Glos.
Cunningham, J.R., Kilmarnock, Scotland.
Cupboard Antiques, The, Amersham, Bucks.
Curá Antiques, London W11.
Curio City., Southend- on- Sea, Essex.
Curio Corner, Tynemouth, Tyne and Wear.
Curios of Chale, Chale, Isle of Wight.
Curiosity Shop, The, South Shields, Tyne and Wear.
Curiosity Shop, The, St. Sampson, Guernsey, C.I.
Curry, Peter, Finchingfield, Essex.
Curtis Antiques, Long Melford, Suffolk.
Curtis, P., London SW3.
Curzon Gallery, The David, London SW19.
Cusack, T., Barnstaple, Devon.
Cushion Corner, Alfies, London NW8.
Cwmgwili Mill, Carmarthen, Wales.
Cyrlin, Philip, Bond Street Antiques Centre, London W1.
Czerek, John, Dundee, Scotland.

D

D & J Lines Antiques, Wychbold, Worcs.
D & T Architectural Salvage, Birkenhead, Merseyside.
D'Ardenne, P.J., Branksome, Dorset.
D'Eyncourt, Chertsey, Surrey.
D'Oyly, N.H., Saffron Walden, Essex.
D.M. Restorations, Weston-Super-Mare, Somerset.
Da Capo Antiques, Edinburgh, Scotland.
Da Silva, Vera, Alfies, London NW8.
Dade, Clifford and Roger, Thames Ditton, Surrey.
Daggett Gallery, Charles, London W11.
Daggett, Caroline, London W11.
Daggett, Charles and Caroline, London W11.
Dahling Antiques, Oscar, Croydon, Surrey.
Dahling, Oscar, Croydon, Surrey.
Dahmen, K., London W11
Dairy House Antiques, Semley, Wilts.
Dale House Antiques, Moreton-in-Marsh, Glos.
Dale Ltd, Peter, London SW1.
Dale, Joan, Ilchester, Somerset.
Dale, John, London W11.
Dale, Sharon, Grays Antique Markets, London W1.
Daleside Antiques, Markington, Yorks. North.
Daltrey, Jonathan, The Mall Antiques Arcade, London N1.
Daly, M. and S., Wadebridge, Cornwall.
Dampier, Mrs J., Bexley, Kent.
Dams, Tim, Shifnal, Shrops.
Danbury Antiques, Danbury, Essex.
Dance, T.A.B., Martock, Somerset.
Dando, A.P. and J.M., Bradford-on-Avon, Wilts.
Dando, Andrew, Bradford-on-Avon, Wilts.
Daniel Charles Antiques, Ashbourne, Derbys.
Daniel, Anjula, Brighton, Sussex East.
Daniel, Francoise, Antiques at Heritage, Woodstock, Oxon.
Daniel, Francoise, Jubilee Hall Antiques Centre, Lechlade, Glos.
Daniell, J., Upton-upon-Severn, Worcs.
Daniels, Mrs Gina, Brighton, Sussex East.
Daniels, P., London Silver Vaults, London WC2.
Dann Antiques Ltd, Melksham, Wilts.
Dann, M., Hatherleigh, Devon.
Daphne's Antiques, Penzance, Cornwall.
Darby, W., Framlingham, Suffolk.
Darley, Mike, Coltishall, Norfolk.
Dartmoor Bookshop, Ashburton, Devon.
Daszewski, A.A.W., East Grinstead, Sussex West.
Davey, Alison, Woodseaves, Staffs.
Davey, Mrs P., Blandford Forum, Dorset.
David's, Brampton, Cambs.
David, G., Cambridge, Cambs.
David, P., Aberystwyth, Wales.
Davidson and Morgan, London NW8
Davidson Antiques, Carlton, London N1.
Davidson's The Jewellers Ltd, Newcastle-upon-Tyne, Tyne and Wear.
Davidson, Anthony and Helen, Newcastle-upon-Tyne, Tyne and Wear.
Davidson, Edward, London NW8
Davidson, Michael, London W11.
Davie, Janet, Pershore, Worcs.
Davies & Son Antiques, Edmund, Whalley, Lancs.
Davies Antiques, London SW8.
Davies Gallery, The John, Stow-on-the-Wold, Glos.
Davies John, Piccadilly Antiques, Batheaston, Somerset.
Davies Oriental Art, Barry, London W1.
Davies, E. and P., Whalley, Lancs.
Davies, Elinor, Penzance, Cornwall.
Davies, G., Cockermouth, Cumbria.
Davies, G.D., South Shields, Tyne and Wear.
Davies, H., Coxley, Somerset.
Davies, H.Q.V., London SW8.
Davies, L., Botley, Hants.
Davies, Mr and Mrs, Chertsey, Surrey.
Davies, Mrs J., Rochester, Kent.
Davies, P.A., Tunbridge Wells, Kent.
Davies, P.H., London SW6.
Davies, R.E., Fishguard, Wales.
Davies, W.H., Murton, Wales.
Davis (Works of Art) Ltd, Kenneth, London SW1.
Davis Antiquarian Horologist, Roger A., Great Bookham, Surrey.
Davis Ltd, A. B., London W1.
Davis Ltd, Reginald, Oxford, Oxon.
Davis, Amanda, Brighton, Sussex East.
Davis, Andrew and Glynis, Kew Green, Surrey.
Davis, Andrew, Kew Green, Surrey.
Davis, Jesse, Antiquarius, London SW3.

Hamilton, M. & J., London Silver Vaults, London WC2.
Hamilton, Nikki, Long Melford, Suffolk.
Hamilton, S., Brockenhurst, Hants.
Hamlyn Lodge, Ollerton, Notts.
Hammond Antiques, Jeffery, Leominster, Herefs.
Hammond, D. and R., Buxton, Derbys.
Hammond, G.and M., Chipping Campden, Glos.
Hammond, J. and E., Leominster, Herefs.
Hampden Trading Company, The, Great Missenden, Bucks.
Hampshire Gallery, Bournemouth, Dorset.
Hampshires of Dorking, Dorking, Surrey.
Hampstead Antique and Craft Emporium, London NW3.
Hampton Court Emporium, East Molesey, Surrey.
Hampton Court Palace Antiques, East Molesey, Surrey.
Hampton Gallery, Tetbury, Glos.
Hampton, G., Christchurch, Dorset.
Hamptons, Christchurch, Dorset.
Han Classical Chinese Furniture, Bath, Somerset.
Hancock Antiques, Peter, Chichester, Sussex West.
Hancock, Mike, Needham Market, Suffolk.
Hancocks and Co, London W1.
Hand in Hand, Coldstream, Scotland.
Hand, Mrs Ruth, Coldstream, Scotland.
Hanham, William, London W1.
Hanlon, W. and J., Menston, Yorks. West.
Hannam, Nick, London SW4.
Hannen, P.A., London W1.
Hanover Antiques & Collectables, Scarborough, Yorks. North.
Hansen Chard Antiques, Pershore, Worcs.
Hansford at No 2 Antiques & Period Design, Lincoln, Lincs.
Hanshan Tang Books, London SW15.
Hansord & Son, David J., Lincoln, Lincs.
Hansord, David, John and Anne, Lincoln, Lincs.
Harby, Diane, Grays Antique Markets, London W1.
Harcourt Antiques, London W1.
Harcourt, P., London W1.
Hardie Antiques, Perth, Scotland.
Hardie, Ross, Chipping Campden, Glos.
Hardie, T.G., Perth, Scotland.
Hardie, Tim, Edinburgh, Scotland.
Harding's World of Mechanical Music, Keith, Northleach, Glos.
Harding, B. and Mrs J., Duffield, Derbys.
Harding, FBHI, K., Northleach, Glos.
Harding, John, Topsham, Devon.
Harding, Mrs Janet, Depden, Suffolk.
Harding, N.J., Tunbridge Wells, Kent.
Harding, R., London W1.
Hardinge, Hugh, Cambridge, Cambs.
Hardman, Laurens R., Southport, Merseyside.
Hardwick, Trevor and Linda, Rotherham, Yorks. South.
Hardy and Co, James, London SW3.
Hardy Antiques Ltd, James, Barnard Castle, Durham.
Hardy Country, Melbury Osmond, Dorset.
Hardy Pine and Country Furniture, Joyce, Hacheston, Suffolk.
Hardy, A., London W1.
Hardy, Alan, Barnard Castle, Durham.
Hardy, Stuart, Salisbury, Wilts.
Hare, Allan G., Cirencester, Glos.
Hares, Cirencester, Glos.
Harkin, D., London NW10.
Harkins Oriental Art, Brian, London SW1.
Harkness, C. S., Edinburgh, Scotland.
Harkness, N. and E., Bournemouth, Dorset.

Harlequin Antiques, Edinburgh, Scotland.
Harlequin Antiques, Grantham, Lincs.
Harlequin Antiques, Nottingham, Notts.
Harlequin Antiques, Porthcawl, Wales.
Harlequin Gallery and Golden Goose Globe Restorers, Lincoln, Lincs.
Harley Antiques, Christian Malford, Wilts.
Harley, Anthony, London SW6.
Harley, G.J., Christian Malford, Wilts.
Harman D., Talbot Walk Antique Centre, Ripley, Surrey.
Harman's Antiques, Dorking, Surrey.
Harman, Paul and Nicholas, Dorking, Surrey.
Harmandian, G., Bath, Somerset.
Harmer, Steve, Eye, Suffolk.
Harms, A., London N6.
Harness Antiques, Jack, Marlow, Bucks.
Harper Antiques, Martin and Dorothy, Bakewell, Derbys.
Harper Fine Paintings, Poynton, Cheshire.
Harper, D. A., Derby, Derbys.
Harper, David, Barnard Castle, Durham.
Harper, P.R., Poynton, Cheshire.
Harper-James, Montrose, Scotland.
Harpers Jewellers, York, Yorks. North.
Harpers, Red House Antiques Centre, York, Yorks. North.
Harpur Dearden, The Furniture Cave, London SW10.
Harriet Ann Sleigh Beds, Rolvenden, Kent.
Harrington Antiquarian Bookseller, Peter, London SW3.
Harrington, Adrian, London W8.
Harrington, Mrs M., London SW3.
Harris & Holt, Chester, Cheshire.
Harris (Jewellery) Ltd, Jonathan, London EC1.
Harris Antiques, Colin, Eversley, Hants.
Harris Antiques, Thaxted, Essex.
Harris Lindsay, London SW1.
Harris, A.R., Stourbridge, West Mids.
Harris, Anita, Jubilee Hall Antiques Centre, Lechlade, Glos.
Harris, E.C., D. I. and J., London EC1.
Harris, F.A.D. and B.D.A., Thaxted, Essex.
Harris, Ian, London SW1.
Harris, Jonathan, London SW1.
Harris, Martin, Grays Antique Markets, London W1.
Harris, S., Stockport, Cheshire.
Harris, Sandra, Chester, Cheshire.
Harris, Steve, Hawarden, Wales.
Harrison Fine Antiques, Anna, Gosforth, Tyne and Wear.
Harrison Fine Art, John, Aston Tirrold, Oxon.
Harrison Steen Ltd, Chorley, Lancs.
Harrison, Beryl and Brian, Durham House Antiques Centre, Stow-on-the-Wold, Glos.
Harrison, J., Newtonmore, Scotland.
Harrison, J.M.C., Aston Tirrold, Oxon.
Harrison, John, Chepstow, Wales.
Harrison, R., London W11.
Harrison, Richard, Grays Antique Markets, London W1.
Harrods Ltd, London SW1.
Harrop Fold Clocks (F. Robinson), Bolton-by-Bowland, Lancs.
Hart, Ann and Bernard, London NW3.
Hart, J.A. and N., Bletchingley, Surrey.
Hart, Mrs Elizabeth, Ceres, Scotland.
Hart, Rosemary, Angel Arcade, London N1.
Hart, Sylvia, Bournemouth, Dorset.
Hartles, B., Talbot Walk Antique Centre, Ripley, Surrey.
Hartley Antiques Ltd, J., Ripley, Surrey.
Hartley, Connie, Trawden, Lancs.
Hartley, Philip, Deal, Kent.

Hartnoll, Julian, London SW1.
Harvey & Co (Antiques) Ltd, W.R., Witney, Oxon.
Harvey and Gore, London SW1.
Harvey Antiques and Decoration, Patricia, London NW8.
Harvey Antiques, Kenneth, The Furniture Cave, London SW10.
Harvey, Helen, Ashburton, Devon.
Harvey, John, The Mall Antiques Arcade, London N1.
Harvey, Korin, Grays Antique Markets, London W1.
Harvey, Mrs Jacqui, Longhaven, Scotland.
Harvey-Jones, A., Woodbridge, Suffolk.
Harvey-Lee, Elizabeth, North Aston, Oxon.
Harwich Antiques Centre, Harwich, Essex.
Haslam and Whiteway, London W8.
Haslam, Katherine, Olney, Bucks.
Haslam-Hopwood, R.G.G., Wadebridge, Cornwall.
Haslemere Antique Market, Haslemere, Surrey.
Hassell, Geoff, Cheltenham, Glos.
Hastie, Caroline, London SW10.
Hastings Antique Centre, The, St. Leonards-on-Sea, Sussex East.
Hastings, Bill, Falkirk, Scotland.
Hastings-Spital, K., Bath, Somerset.
Hatch Rugs, Gideon, London SW11.
Hatchwell Antiques, Simon, The Furniture Cave, London SW10.
Hatherleigh Antiques, Hatherleigh, Devon.
Hatrell, Satoe, Grays Antique Markets, London W1.
Haughey Antiques, Kirkby Stephen, Cumbria.
Haughey, D.M., Kirkby Stephen, Cumbria.
Haughton Antiques, Brian, London W1.
Havard and Havard, Cowbridge, Wales.
Havard, Philip and Christine, Cowbridge, Wales.
Havard, T. and P., Harpole, Northants.
Havelocks, Harrogate, Yorks. North.
Haven Antiques, Wainfleet, Lincs.
Havenplan's Architectural Emporium, Killamarsh, Derbys.
Havlik, Jan, Bond Street Antiques Centre, London W1.
Haw, S., Haslemere, Surrey.
Hawkey, V., Grimsby, Lincs.
Hawkins & Hawkins, Edinburgh, Scotland.
Hawkins, B., London E11.
Hawkins, Emma H., Edinburgh, Scotland.
Hawkins, G. and J., Cambridge, Glos.
Hawkins, Mark and David, Brighton, Sussex East.
Hawkins, Mary-Louise, The Swan at Tetsworth, Oxon.
Hawkridge, Mrs M., Skipton, Yorks. North.
Hawley Antiques, Beverley, Yorks. East.
Haworth, Peter, Beetham, Cumbria.
Hawthorn Ltd, Gerard, London W1.
Hay Antique Market, Hay-on-Wye, Wales.
Haybarn and Bridgebarn Antique Centres, Battlesbridge Antique Centre, Essex
Haycraft, R., Lamb Arcade, Wallingford, Oxon
Haydock, Robin, Antiquarius, London SW3.
Haydon, Brian, Whitwick, Leics.
Haydon, Mrs Maureen, Chichester, Sussex West.
Hayes, Mrs Pat, Tunbridge Wells, Kent.

Jewel Antiques, Leek, Staffs.

Jewell Ltd, S. and H., London WC2.

Jezebel, Brighton, Sussex East.

Jillings Antiques - Distinctive Antique Clocks, Newent, Glos.

Jillings, Doro and John, Newent, Glos.

Joan's Antiques, Littlehampton, Sussex West.

Joel, Mrs J., Dorking, Surrey.

Joel, Mrs J., London SW6.

John (Rare Rugs) Ltd, C., London W1.

John Anthony Antiques, Bletchingley, Surrey.

John Lewis Partnership, London SW3.

John's Corner, Petworth, Sussex West.

Johns Ltd, Derek, London SW1.

Johns, T., Lytchett Minster, Dorset.

Johnson and Sons, Rex, Birmingham, West Mids.

Johnson Gibbs, Ilona, Stow-on-the-Wold, Glos.

Johnson Medals & Militaria, Steve, Newcastle-upon-Tyne, Tyne and Wear.

Johnson Walker & Tolhurst Ltd, London W1.

Johnson's, Leek, Staffs.

Johnson, D., Birmingham, West Mids.

Johnson, D.A., Kilmarnock, Scotland.

Johnson, Lucy, London SW11.

Johnson, M., Hainault, Essex.

Johnson, Mrs Sarah, St Mary, Jersey, C.I.

Johnson, P.M. and Mrs. J.H., Leek, Staffs.

Johnson, Peter, London SW1.

Johnson, Peter, Penzance, Cornwall.

Johnson, Quentin, Tenterden, Kent.

Johnson, R. and R., Birmingham, West Mids.

Johnson, Roger and Bridget, Henley-on-Thames, Oxon.

Johnston, L., Belfast, Co. Antrim, N. Ireland.

Johnston, Nigel, The Swan at Tetsworth, Oxon.

Johnstone, Patricia, Penzance, Cornwall.

Jones - The Silver Shop, Howard, London W8.

Jones Antique Lighting, London W11.

Jones Antiques, Christopher, Flore, Northants.

Jones Antiques, Christopher, London SW6.

Jones at PJ2, Peter, London SW3.

Jones Jeweller, Michael, Northampton, Northants.

Jones, Ashley, London WC1.

Jones, Danny, Barmouth, Wales.

Jones, David, Ludlow, Shrops.

Jones, G. Trefor, Alfies, London NW8.

Jones, G., Godalming, Surrey.

Jones, Gary, Leamington Spa, Warks.

Jones, Graham, Ripley, Surrey.

Jones, Graham, Talbot Walk Antique Centre, Ripley, Surrey.

Jones, I. and Mrs A. S., Shrewsbury, Shrops.

Jones, John and Christine, Sandbach, Cheshire.

Jones, Judy, London W11.

Jones, Keith, Shrewsbury, Shrops.

Jones, L., Ludlow, Shrops.

Jones, M.R.T. and J.A., Cromer, Norfolk.

Jones, Mr and Mrs P., Chepstow, Wales.

Jones, Mr., Antiquarius, London SW3.

Jones, P.W., Oakham, Rutland.

Jones, Paul, London WC2

Jones, Sally and Neil Brent, Sherborne, Dorset.

Jones-Fenleigh, Jennifer, Great Glen, Leics.

Jonkers Rare Books, Henley-on-Thames, Oxon.

Jonkers, Christiaan, Henley-on-Thames, Oxon.

Jordan (Fine Paintings), T.B. and R., Stockton-on-Tees, Durham.

Jordan, James A., Lichfield, Staffs.

Jordan, Robert A., Barnard Castle, Durham.

Joseph and Pearce Ltd, London EC1.

Joseph, John, Grays Antique Markets, London W1.

Josh Antiques, Debenham, Suffolk.

Journeyman Antiques Centre, East Molesey, Surrey.

Jowitt, C.S., Brasted, Kent.

Jubb Antiques, Margaret R., Bristol, Glos.

Jubilee Antiques, Tottenhill, Norfolk.

Jubilee Hall Antiques Centre, Lechlade, Glos.

Jubilee Photographica, London N1.

Judge, D., Emsworth, Hants.

Judge, S., Ginnel Antiques Centre, Harrogate, Yorks North.

Judith Charles Antiques & Collectables, Oswestry, Shrops.

Judson, Grays Antique Markets, London W1.

Jukes, Mr and Mrs G., St. Leonards-on-Sea, Sussex East.

Julian Alexander Antiques, London N20.

Julian Antiques, Hurstpierpoint, Sussex West.

Junk Box, The, London SE10.

Junk Shop, The, London SE10.

Junktion, New Bolingbroke, Lincs.

Juran and Co, Alexander, London N4.

Juro Antiques, Worcester, Worcs.

Jury, D., Bristol, Glos.

JUS Watches, Grays Antique Markets, London W1.

Just a Second, London SW18.

Just Desks, London NW8.

Just Glass, Alston, Cumbria.

K

K & M Antiques, Grays Antique Markets, London W1.

K D Antiques, Chester, Cheshire.

K. & Y. Oriental Antiques, Grays Antique Markets, London W1.

K.C. Antiques, Darwen, Lancs.

K.L.M. & Co. Antiques, Lepton, Yorks. West.

Kaae, Minoo & Andre, Grays Antique Markets, London W1.

Kaimes Smithy Antiques, Edinburgh, Scotland.

Kaizen International Ltd, Rochester, Kent.

Kallin, Lucy, London SW11.

Kalms, Stephen, London Silver Vaults, London WC2.

Kames Antiques & Jewellery, Brodick and Whiting Bay, Scotland.

Kaszewski, E., Cremyll, Cornwall.

Kate, Hemswell Cliff, Lincs.

Katharine House Gallery, Marlborough, Wilts.

Katta, Bond Street Antiques Centre, London W1.

Katz Ltd, Daniel, London W1.

Katz, G., Richmond, Surrey.

Kavanagh, Christine, Newark, Notts.

Kay, Barbara, Ashtead, Surrey.

Kay, S., Headley, Hants.

Kaye of Lyndhurst, Lita, Lyndhurst, Hants.

Kaye, N.J., Chester, Cheshire.

Kayes of Chester, Chester, Cheshire.

Kayll, James, London W1.

Kealey, David, Melton Mowbray, Leics.

Kear, P.W., Cranborne, Dorset.

Kearin, J. and J., White Colne, Essex.

Kearney & Sons, T.H., Belfast, Co. Antrim, N. Ireland.

Keats, Kate, Alfies, London NW8.

Keddie, Mrs A.C., East Grinstead, Sussex West.

Keeble Antiques, Sherborne, Dorset.

Keeble, C.P., Sherborne, Dorset.

Keeble, E.J., Fareham, Hants.

Keehan, Michael P., Brighton, Sussex East.

Keel Row Books, North Shields, Tyne and Wear.

Keene Gallery, The Barry, Henley-on-Thames, Oxon.

Keene, B.M. and J.S., Henley-on-Thames, Oxon.

Keepsakes, Innerleithen, Scotland.

Keil Ltd, H.W., Broadway, Worcs.

Keil Ltd, John, London SW3.

Kellam, Ian, Durham House Antiques Centre, Stow-on-the-Wold, Glos.

Kelleher, Michael, Antiquarius, London SW3.

Keller, Patricia, Saintfield, Co. Down, N. Ireland.

Keller, W.K., Sheffield, Yorks. South.

Kelly Antiques, Omagh, Co. Tyrone, N. Ireland.

Kelly Lighting, Sheffield, Yorks. South.

Kelly, Don, Antiquarius, London SW3.

Kelly, Frank R., Sheffield, Yorks. South.

Kelly, Louis, Omagh, Co. Tyrone, N. Ireland.

Kelsey, P., Bramley, Surrey.

Kembery Antique Clocks Ltd, Bath, Somerset.

Kembery, P. and E., Bath, Somerset.

Kemp Ltd, Melville, Nottingham, Notts.

Kemp, Chris and Ann, Bath, Somerset.

Kemp, Martin, London SE10.

Kemp, Norman, Old Bank Antiques Centre, Bath, Somerset.

Kemp, Peter, London W8.

Kemp, Valerie and Tony, Wrentham, Suffolk.

Kemp, W., Newport, Essex.

Kemps, Bristol, Glos.

Kendal Studios Antiques, Kendal, Cumbria.

Kendall, G., Ginnel Antiques Centre, Harrogate, Yorks North.

Kendall, The English Watercolour Gallery, Beryl, London W9.

Kendons, Ingatestone, Essex.

Kennaugh, P. and C., London SW10.

Kennedy Carpets, London N4.

Kennedy Wolfenden, Belfast, Co. Antrim, N. Ireland.

Kennedy Wolfenden, Portrush, Co. Antrim, N. Ireland.

Kennedy, Frank, Winchcombe, Glos.

Kennedy, Graham and Pippa, Truro, Cornwall.

Kennedy, Jane, Winchcombe, Glos.

Kennedy, K., London NW5.

Kennedy, M., London N4.

Kennedy, Robin, Richmond, Surrey.

Kensington Church Street Antiques Centre, London W8.

Kent & Sussex Gold Refiners, Tunbridge Wells, Kent.

Kent House Antiques, Haverfordwest, Wales.

Kent, G. and P., Marlborough, Wilts.

Kentdale Antiques, Tunbridge Wells, Kent.

Kenulf Fine Arts, Stow-on-the-Wold, Glos.

Kenyon, David S., Burnham Market, Norfolk.

Ker, David, London SW1.

Kern, R.A.B., London SW1.

Kern, Virginia, London SW3.

Kerr - Gatehouse Bookshop, Norman, Cartmel, Cumbria.

Kerr Antiques Ltd, Thomas, London SW10.

Rossi & Rossi Ltd, London W1.
Rossi, Anna Maria and Fabio, London W1.
Rossini, Paul, Porthcawl, Wales.
Rosson, J., London EC1.
Rostrum Antiques, South Petherton, Somerset.
Rota Ltd, Bertram, London WC2.
Rotchell, P., Godalming, Surrey.
Rote, R., The Mall Antiques Arcade, London N1.
Rothera, D., London N1.
Rotherfold Antiques, Totnes, Devon.
Rothman, J., Antiquarius, London SW3.
Rothwell and Dunworth, Dulverton, Somerset.
Rothwell, David, Bridlington, Yorks. East.
Rothwell, M., Dulverton, Somerset.
Rothwell, Mrs C., Dulverton, Somerset.
Roughshed, Petworth, Sussex West.
Round, S., Brighton, Sussex East.
Roundabout Antiques Centre, Haywards Heath, Sussex West.
Roundell, James, London SW1.
Rourke, J. Talbot Walk Antique Centre, Ripley, Surrey.
Rowan, Mrs Michelle, Antiquarius, London SW3.
Rowland Antiques, Michael, Stow-on-the-Wold, Glos.
Rowles Fine Art, Welshpool, Wales.
Rowles, Mark and Glenn, Welshpool, Wales.
Rowlett, A.H. and P.L., Lincoln, Lincs.
Rowlett, Nicola, Tunbridge Wells, Kent.
Rowletts of Lincoln, Lincoln, Lincs.
Royal Arcade Watch Shop, The, London W1.
Royal Exchange Art Gallery at Cork St., London W1.
Royal Mile Curios, Edinburgh, Scotland.
Royal Mile Gallery, Edinburgh, Scotland.
Royal Standard Antiques, Cowes, Isle of Wight.
Roylance, A., Bristol, Glos.
Rubin, A. and L.J., London W1.
Ruby Antiques Ltd, Penryn, Cornwall.
Rudder, G. and L., Talbot Walk Antique Centre, Ripley, Surrey.
Ruddy Antiques, Petworth, Sussex West.
Ruddy, Harry, Boscastle, Cornwall.
Ruddy, Robin and Paula, Petworth, Sussex West.
Rug Gallery, The, Leicester, Leics.
Rugeley Antique Centre, Brereton, Staffs.
Ruglen, L., Balfron, Scotland.
Rule, Sue, Windsor and Eton, Berks.
Rules Antiques, Windsor and Eton, Berks.
Rumble Antiques, Simon and Penny, Chittering, Cambs.
Rumford, L., Worcester, Worcs.
Rumours, The Mall Antiques Arcade, London N1.
Rundle, Andrew, St Peter Port, Guernsey, C.I.
Rundle, J., New Bolingbroke, Lincs.
Rushton - Early Oriental Art, Malcolm, London NW3.
Rushton, Dr Malcolm, London NW3.
Ruskin Decorative Arts, Stow-on-the-Wold, Glos.
Russell Antiquarian Prints, Sarah, Bath, Somerset.
Russell Rare Books, London SW3.
Russell, C., London SW3.
Russell, K., Berwick-upon-Tweed, Northumbs.
Russell, M. and J., Yazor, Herefs.
Russell-Davis, P.S., Norwich, Norfolk.
Rutherford Antiques, Marlene, Chesterfield, Derbys.
Rutherford, Rosamond, Victorian Village,

Glasgow, Scotland.
Rutland Antiques Centre, Uppingham, Rutland.
Rutter, A. and Mrs E., Menai Bridge, Wales.
Rutter, John and Kate, Walsall, West Mids.
Rutter, Susan, Caistor, Lincs.
Ruttleigh Antiques incorporating Crudwell Furniture, Philip A., Crudwell, Wilts.
Ryan-Wood Antiques, Liverpool, Merseyside.
Ryder, Georgina, Frampton, Dorset.
Rymer, Michael and Deborah, Seaton, Devon.

S

S. and G. Antiques, Kleanthous Antiques, London W11.
S.R. Furnishing and Antiques, Halesowen, West Mids.
S.W. Antiques, Pershore, Worcs.
Saalmans, J.A. and K.M., Grasmere, Cumbria.
Sabera Trading Co, London NW2.
Sabin Ltd, Frank T., London W1.
Sabin, John, London W1.
Sabine, B. and T., Honiton, Devon.
Sabine, T. and B., Honiton, Devon.
Saddle Room Antiques, The, Cookstown, Co.Tyrone, N. Ireland.
Sadler Street Gallery, Wells, Somerset.
Saffell, Michael and Jo, Bath, Somerset.
Saffer, J., York, Yorks. North.
Saffron Walden Antiques Centre, Saffron Walden, Essex.
Safi, Sabor, Grays Antique Markets, London W1.
Sage Antiques and Interiors, Ripley, Surrey.
Sage, H. and C., Ripley, Surrey.
Sainsburys of Bournemouth Ltd, Bournemouth, Dorset.
Saint Nicholas Galleries Ltd. (Antiques and Jewellery), Carlisle, Cumbria.
Saintfield Antiques & Fine Books, Saintfield, Co. Down, N. Ireland.
Sakhai, E. and H., London NW5.
Sakhai, E., H. and M., London SW3.
Sakhai, E., London W1.
Salim, Solomon, London N8.
Salisbury Antiques Warehouse Ltd, Salisbury, Wilts.
Salisbury, R.D.N., M.E. and J.W., Sidmouth, Devon.
Salmon, A., Oxford, Oxon.
Salt Antiques, N.P. and A., Sheffield, Yorks. South.
Salter Antiques, F.D., Clare, Suffolk.
Salter Antiques, Nicholas, London E4.
Salter, N., London E4.
Salter, Sherley, London E4.
Saltgate Antiques, Beccles, Suffolk.
Salusbury Antiques, Tom, Hitchin, Herts.
Samarkand Galleries, Edinburgh, Scotland.
Samarkand Galleries, Stow-on-the-Wold, Glos.
Sambourne House Antiques Ltd, Swindon, Wilts.
Samii, Hoshang, Alfies, London NW8.
Samiramis, Grays Antique Markets, London W1.
Samlesbury Hall Trust, Samlesbury, Lancs.
Samlesbury Hall, Samlesbury, Lancs.
Samne, H., London WC2.
Samovar Antiques, Hythe, Kent.
Sampson Antiques Ltd, Alistair, London W1.
Sampson Antiques, Anthony, Dulverton, Somerset.
Samuels Spencers Antiques and

Decorative Arts Emporium, Winchester, Hants.
San Domenico Stringed Instruments, Cardiff, Wales.
Sandberg Antiques, Patrick, London W8.
Sandberg, P.C.F., London W8.
Sandell, M.J., Carmarthen, Wales.
Sanders and Sons, Robin, Woodstock, Oxon.
Sanders of Oxford Ltd, Oxford, Oxon.
Sanders Penzance Gallery and Antiques, Tony, Penzance, Cornwall.
Sanders, A.F., Grimsby, Lincs.
Sandgate Antiques, Penrith, Cumbria.
Sandringham Antiques, Hull, Yorks. East.
Sands, J. and M.M., Stow-on-the-Wold, Glos.
Sandwich Fine Books, Sandwich, Kent.
Sandy's Antiques, Bournemouth, Dorset.
Sankey, Richard, Devizes, Wilts.
Sansom, K.W., Enderby, Leics.
Santos, London W8.
Saracen's Lantern, The, Canterbury, Kent.
Sargeant Antiques, Sevenoaks, Kent.
Sargeant, A.W. and K.M., Stansted, Essex.
Sargeant, D. and Miss A., Sevenoaks, Kent.
Satrapel, Grays Antique Markets, London W1.
Saunders Antiques, Charles, London SW3.
Saunders, E., Great Waltham, Essex.
Saunders, E.A. and J.M., Weedon, Northants.
Saunders, L. and S., Honiton, Devon.
Saunderson Antiques, Elaine, Dorking, Surrey.
Saunderson, Mrs E.C., Dorking, Surrey.
Savage, B., Wolverhampton, West Mids.
Savage, Ian, London N1.
Savery Antiques, Brighton, Sussex East.
Savery, A. and M., Brighton, Sussex East.
Sawers, Robert G., London W1.
Saxon Cross Antiques Emporium, Sandbach, Cheshire.
Sayers, Charlotte, Grays Antique Markets, London W1.
Sayers, D., Tetbury, Glos.
Scales, R., London SE26.
Scarisbrick and Bate Ltd, London W1.
Scarlett Antiques, Chappells Antiques Centre, Bakewell, Derbys.
Schell, Christine, London SW3.
Schlesinger, A.R., Bath, Somerset.
Schloss, E., Edgware, Middx.
Schmid, Andreas, Alfies, London NW8.
Scholz, K.V., Eastbourne, Sussex East.
Scholz, P., Long Melford, Suffolk.
Scholz, Patrick and Hans, Harwich, Essex.
School House Antiques, Chipping Campden, Glos.
Schotte Antiques, T., Southwold, Suffolk.
Schotte, T. and J., Southwold, Suffolk.
Schotten Antiques, Manfred, Burford, Oxon.
Schrager, H.J. and G.R., London W11.
Schredds of Portobello, London W11.
Schuster Gallery, The, Torquay, Devon.
Schwartz, N., London W5.
Schwarz, Pauline, Dorking, Surrey.
Schwetje, E., Red House Antiques Centre, York, Yorks. North.
Scobie, W.D.L., Wallasey, Merseyside.
Scott Antiques, Richard, Holt, Norfolk.
Scott Repair & Restoration, Mike, Salisbury, Wilts.
Scott, Chris, Sawbridgeworth, Herts.
Scott, Damian, Bond Street Silver Galleries, London W1
Scott, David, Geraldine, Jonathan and Benjamin, Salisbury, Wilts.

Simpkin, S., Orford, Suffolk.

Simply Antiques, Durham House Antiques Centre, Stow-on-the-Wold, Glos.

Simply Antiques, Moreton-in-Marsh, Glos.

Simply Oak, Biggleswade, Beds.

Simpson and Sons Jewellers (Oldham) Ltd, H.C., Oldham, Lancs.

Simpson, Angela, Lymington, Hants.

Simpson, Bev and Graham, Long Marston, Warks.

Simpson, D. M., Antiquarius, London SW3.

Simpson, Elizabeth, London Silver Vaults, London WC2.

Simpson, M.R., Fochabers, Scotland.

Simpson, Marianne, Fochabers, Scotland.

Simpsons - Mirrors & Carvings, Brentwood, Essex.

Sims, N., Stratford-upon-Avon, Warks.

Sims, Reed Ltd, London SW1.

Sims, T.J., Evesham, Worcs.

Sinai Antiques Ltd, London W8.

Sinai Ltd, E., London W8.

Sinai, M., London W1.

Sinclair Antiques, Castle Gate Antiques Centre, Newark, Notts.

Sinclair's, Stamford, Lincs.

Sinclair, Gloria, Alfies, London NW8.

Sinclair, J.S., Stamford, Lincs.

Sinclair, James, Kirkcaldy, Scotland.

Sinclair, K., London W11

Sinfield Gallery, Brian, Burford, Oxon.

Sinfield, S.E., Biggleswade, Beds.

Singleton Antiques, Skenfrith, Wales.

Singleton, A., Yoxford, Suffolk.

Sirett, G., Kleanthous Antiques, London W11.

Sirrs, Linda and John, Market Weighton, Yorks. East.

Sisson, Kim, Bungay, Suffolk.

Sitch and Co. Ltd., W., London W1.

Sitch, R., London W1.

Sitting Pretty Antiques, Sudbury, Suffolk.

Sitting Pretty, Great Glen, Leics.

Sixways Antique Centre, Cheltenham, Glos.

Sjovold, Audun, Brighton, Sussex East.

Skailes, Kate, Honiton, Devon.

Skea., R., Haddington, Scotland.

Skeaping Gallery, Lydford, Devon.

Skeel, K., London N1.

Skellgate Curios, Ripon, Yorks. North.

Skiba, J., Weedon, Northants.

Skilling, L., Walton-on-Thames, Surrey.

Skinner, A.P., Cross in Hand, Sussex East.

Skipper, G. and K., Bungay, Suffolk.

Skipton Antiques Centre, Skipton, Yorks. North.

Sklar, Robert, Olney, Bucks.

Skoob Russell Square, London WC1.

Skrebowski Prints, Justin F., London W11.

Slack FRSA & Shirley Warren, Raymond, Sanderstead, Surrey.

Slade Antiques, Michael, London N4

Slade, P.J., Bristol, Glos.

Sladmore Gallery of Sculpture, The, London W1.

Slater Antiques, Anderson, Settle, Yorks. North.

Slater, G., Walsden, Yorks. West.

Slater, K.C., Settle, Yorks. North.

Slater, N., Barnt Green, Worcs.

Sledge, H., Honiton, Devon.

Sleeping Beauty Antique Beds, Brighton, Sussex East.

Sloane, Peter, Grays Antique Markets, London W1.

Small Fish Antiques, Red House Antiques Centre, York, Yorks. North.

Smalley, Alex, Altrincham, Cheshire.

Smeeth, A.G., Leavenheath, Suffolk.

Smith (Antiques), P. J., Stewartstown, Co. Tyrone, N. Ireland.

Smith (Bookseller), Peter Bain, Cartmel, Cumbria.

Smith and Gerald Robinson Antiques, Colin, London W11.

Smith Antique Clocks, Allan, Swindon, Wilts.

Smith Antiques Ltd, Ken, Enderby, Leics.

Smith Antiques, David, Manton, Rutland.

Smith Antiques, Graham, Jesmond, Tyne and Wear.

Smith Antiques, Peter, Sunderland, Tyne and Wear.

Smith Books, Keith, Ledbury, Herefs.

Smith's (The Rink) Ltd, Harrogate, Yorks. North.

Smith, A.W.E. and Mrs J., Chard, Somerset.

Smith, Abigail, Alfies, London NW8.

Smith, Alan, Stow-on-the-Wold, Glos.

Smith, Angela, Poynton, Cheshire.

Smith, Anthony, London W1.

Smith, B. Roderick, Much Wenlock, Shrops.

Smith, B., Teynham, Kent. Wright, John, Lubenham, Leics.

Smith, D. A., Driffield, Yorks. East.

Smith, D.B., Chipping Campden, Glos.

Smith, D.K., London W1.

Smith, David, Alfies, London NW8.

Smith, Debbie and Mark, York, Yorks. North.

Smith, Dr A.J., London SW1

Smith, E.B. and E.M., Hungerford, Berks.

Smith, G.P., Hereford, Herefs.

Smith, Gordon M., Sherborne, Dorset.

Smith, H.W. and P.E., Leigh-on-Sea, Essex.

Smith, J. A., Edinburgh, Scotland.

Smith, J., York, Yorks. North.

Smith, Julian, Leicester, Leics.

Smith, L. Royden, Lichfield, Staffs.

Smith, L.K., Leiston, Suffolk.

Smith, Lewis, London WC2.

Smith, M.S. and D.J., York, Yorks. North.

Smith, Michelle, Hemel Hempstead, Herts.

Smith, Miriam and Brian, Tetbury, Glos.

Smith, Mr and Mrs W.A., Edinburgh, Scotland.

Smith, N., Wortham, Suffolk.

Smith, Nicola, Sawbridgeworth, Herts.

Smith, P., Lye, West Mids.

Smith, P.A., Whitby, Yorks. North.

Smith, Philip, Sleights, Yorks. North.

Smith, R. and J., Ramsey, Cambs.

Smith, R. Morley, Rottingdean, Sussex East.

Smith, T., Chalfont St. Giles, Bucks.

Smith, T.J., Tenterden, Kent.

Smith, Tim, Ludlow, Shrops.

Smith, Trak E. and Mrs, Nottingham, Notts.

Smyth - Antique Textiles, Peta, London SW1.

Smyth, John G. and Janet A., Kendal, Cumbria.

Smyth, S., Tynemouth, Tyne and Wear.

Snap Dragon, South Molton, Devon.

Snape Antiques and Collectors Centre, Snape, Suffolk.

Sneath, Pat, Grays Antique Markets, London W1.

Snell Antiques, Tim, Bath, Somerset.

Snelling, Tim, Norwich, Norfolk.

Sniders Antiques, Jeremy, Glasgow, Scotland.

Snodin, Julian Howard, Ashbourne, Derbys.

Snowden, Ruby, Red House Antiques Centre, York, Yorks. North.

Snowdonia Antiques, Llanrwst, Wales.

Sodbury Antiques, Chipping Sodbury, Glos.

Soleimani, Hadji, London W1.

Solemani Gallery, Grays Antique Markets, London W1.

Soler, Evelyne, London SW10.

Soleymani, R., London W1.

Solomon, London N8.

Solomons, Ralph and Nola, Bodmin, Cornwall.

Solopark Plc, Cambridge, Cambs.

Somers, Jeffrey, London WC1.

Somerset, B.V.M., Tonbridge, Kent.

Somerton Antiques Centre, Somerton, Somerset.

Somervale Antiques, Midsomer Norton, Somerset.

Somerville (W.A.) Ltd, Stephen, London W1.

Something Different, St Helen Auckland, Durham.

Something Old Something New, Bowness on Windermere, Cumbria.

Something Old, Something New, Brampton, Cumbria.

Somlo Antiques, London SW1.

Sommers, S., Bagshot, Surrey.

Somnez, N., Antiquarius, London SW3.

Soo San, London SW6

Sosna, Boris, Grays Antique Markets, London W1.

Soteriades, Angelo, London W11.

Sotheran Ltd, Henry, London W1.

Soton, P., South Molton, Devon.

Soucek, O., Lewes, Sussex East.

Soule, Michael, The Swan at Tetsworth, Oxon.

Source, Bath, Somerset.

South, Len and Jean, Great Harwood, Lancs.

Southdown Antiques, Lewes, Sussex East.

Southdown House Antiques, Brasted, Kent.

Southgate, Mrs Pam, Danbury, Essex.

Southport Antiques Centre, The, Southport, Merseyside.

Southwick Rare Art, David L.H., Kingswear, Devon.

Southworth, S. and R., Staunton Harold, Leics.

Souvenir Antiques, Carlisle, Cumbria.

Sovereign Antiques, Gateshead, Tyne and Wear.

Sovereign Furniture Gallery, The, Chesham, Bucks.

Soviet Carpet & Art Galleries, London NW2.

Spalding Antiques, Spalding, Lincs.

Sparks, Robert, Lyndhurst, Hants.

Sparks, Roderick, Swansea, Wales.

Sparks, Terry, Jubilee Hall Antiques Centre, Lechlade, Glos.

SPCK Bookshops, Winchester, Hants.

Specht, Dr H., London W1.

Spectrum, Grays Antique Markets, London W1.

Speelman Ltd, A. & J., London W1.

Speight, Connie, Alfies, London NW8.

Spelman, Ken, York, Yorks. North.

Spence Antiques, Gail, The Swan at Tetsworth, Oxon.

Spencer Antiques, Don, Warwick, Warks.

Spencer, A. and R., Leeds, Yorks. West.

Spencer, Charles, Hay-on-Wye, Wales.

Spencer-Brayn, N., Winchester, Hants.

Spero, Simon, London W8.

Sperr, J.R., London N6.

Spice, Hastings, Sussex East.

Spink and Son Ltd, London WC1.

Spink, John, London SW13.

Spinning Wheel Antiques, The, Southport, Merseyside.

Spongs Antiques Centre, Lindfield, Sussex West.

OF WHAT DOES YOUR STOCK CHIEFLY CONSIST?

(A) Please list in order of importance	(B) Approximate period or date of stock	(C) Indication of price range of stock eg £50-£100 or £5-£25
1. (Principal stock)		
2.		
3.		

IS PARKING *OUTSIDE* YOUR SHOP (BUSINESS) Easy (Yes or No)

TELEPHONE NUMBER Business ....

Home ....

(only if customers can ring for appointments outside business hours)

V.A.T. scheme operated – Standard/Special/Both ....

SERVICES OFFERED:

Valuations (Yes or No) ....

Restorations (Yes or No) ....

Type of work ....

Buying specific items at auction for a commission (Yes or No) ....

Type of item ....

FAIRS:

At which fairs (if any) do you normally exhibit? ....

....

....

CERTIFICATION:

The information given above is accurate and you may publish it in the Guide.
I understand that this entry is entirely free.

Signed .... Date ....

OF WHAT DOES YOUR STOCK CHIEFLY CONSIST?

(A) Please list in order of importance	(B) Approximate period or date of stock	(C) Indication of price range of stock eg £50-£100 or £5-£25
1. (Principal stock)		
2.		
3.		

IS PARKING *OUTSIDE* YOUR SHOP (BUSINESS) Easy (Yes or No)

TELEPHONE NUMBER Business ....

Home ....

(only if customers can ring for appointments outside business hours)

V.A.T. scheme operated – Standard/Special/Both ....

SERVICES OFFERED:

Valuations (Yes or No) ....

Restorations (Yes or No) ....

Type of work ....

Buying specific items at auction for a commission (Yes or No) ....

Type of item ....

FAIRS:
At which fairs (if any) do you normally exhibit? ....

....

....

CERTIFICATION:
The information given above is accurate and you may publish it in the Guide.
I understand that this entry is entirely free.

Signed .... Date ....

Unmistakably
FRANKLIN

Our door-to-door weekly service throughout Europe is well known and very reliable.

Visit our offices in three prime European locations.

Container and Airfreight Services Worldwide.

Alan Franklin Transport

ALAN FRANKLIN TRANSPORT
Continental Removals to and from the U.K.
SPECIALIST CARRIERS OF ANTIQUES AND FINE ARTS